POLYMER HANDBOOK

Polymer Handbook

Editors

J. BRANDRUP / E. H. IMMERGUT

with the collaboration of

H.-G. ELIAS

INTERSCIENCE PUBLISHERS

a division of John Wiley & Sons

NEW YORK • LONDON • SYDNEY

PREFACE

The reaction of most polymer scientists who were told of our endeavor to compile physical and chemical data of polymers was: "at last!" We hope that this Handbook will satisfy the need expressed by their reaction and that it will be a useful addition to the polymer literature.

All those working with polymers have experienced the frustration of searching for data in the rapidly expanding literature and know the difficulties involved in trying to locate particular constants. Our Handbook is an attempt to help them in the search for data and constants needed in theoretical and experimental polymer work.

This intention sets the frame for the content of the Handbook. First of all, only fundamental constants and parameters were compiled rather than data of interest to the polymer engineer or fabricator. Data of fundamental interest are interpreted as data which are either physical or chemical constants of the polymer molecule within reasonable or predictable limits, or are constants of existing physical laws describing the properties and the behavior of polymers. Constants which depend to a major extent on the particular processing conditions, or sample history, were not compiled as they be found in existing plastics handbooks and encyclopedias. Within these limits the selection of tables to be compiled was governed by two principles: sufficient data should exist to make a compilation worthwhile, and their scientific basis should be commonly accepted.

No critical evaluation of published values was attempted since this would have been an impossible undertaking within a reasonable time or with the manpower available for the task. Therefore, the authors of the individual tables were urged to list all data found in the literature except for values which, in their judgement, were obviously erroneous. The reader is requested to use the data with this restriction in mind and to consult the original literature references for details. Whereas a complete compilation of existing data was attempted, there will, no doubt, be some omissions. The users are asked to send to the editors any data they might be aware of but cannot find in the Handbook. This would help to make the Handbook a more reliable information source, and, therefore, an increasingly useful tool for polymer scientists. Suggestions and comments on the selection of tables are also welcomed, so that the next edition might be better tailored to the needs of the users.

The inclusion of the table on prices and practical processing data of commercial polymers may seem to be an inconsistency with the selection principles expressed earlier. But, we felt that a selected listing of such data would remind all of us that polymer "science is not a religion to be worshipped for its own sake. Science is not an ornament on society's chest. It must be woven into the fabric of life to help with the world needs." (W. J. Sparks - Presidential Address, American Chemical Society Meeting, Detroit, 1965.)

The editors would like to thank all contributors for their painstaking and time consuming efforts which have made the Polymer Handbook possible. We hope that their reward lies in the knowledge that they are making life easier for their fellow polymer scientists. The editors would also like to acknowledge the collaboration of H. G. Elias in this endeavor, and the criticism, advice and encouragement of H. N. Friedlander, L. H. Peebles, R. Buchdahl, J. J. Hermans, and P. J. Flory. Help in naming most polymers in a consistent and scientific manner was kindly given by R. B. Fox, R. L. Miller, J. K. Lawson and K. L. Loening. Thanks are due Mrs. N. Poston for typing the camera-copy manuscript in a highly conscientious and accurate fashion. Last, but not least, the editors express their appreciation to Chemstrand Research Center for constant encouragement and for generous support.

July, 1965   The Editors

CONTRIBUTORS

A. Abe
Polymer Research Institute,
Polytechnic Institute of Brooklyn,
Brooklyn, New York

New Address: Department of Chemistry,
Stanford University,
Stanford, California

G. Adank
Department of Industrial and Engineering Chemistry,
Swiss Federal Institute of Technology,
Zurich, Switzerland

S. L. Aggarwal
Research and Development Center,
The General Tire and Rubber Company,
Akron, Ohio

K. I. Beynon
Shell Research Limited,
Chester, England

C. Booth
Department of Chemistry,
University of Manchester,
Manchester, England

F. A. Bovey
Bell Telephone Laboratories,
Murray Hill, New Jersey

G. Brandrup
Research Triangle Institute,
Durham, North Carolina

New Address: Frankfurt/Main, Germany

J. Brandrup
Chemstrand Research Center,
Durham, North Carolina

New Address: Farbwerke Höchst,
Kunststoff-Laboratorium,
Frankfurt/Main, Germany

H. Burrell
Interchemical Corporation,
Clifton, New Jersey

Y. P. Castille
Research Triangle Institute,
Durham, North Carolina

New Address: DuPont Experimental Station,
Wilmington, Delaware

A. Chapiro
Laboratoire de Chimie des Radiations,
Bellevue, France

R. Chiang
Chemstrand Research Center,
Durham, North Carolina

J. V. Dawkins
Department of Chemistry,
Duke University,
Durham, North Carolina

Hj. Dietschy
Department of Industrial and Engineering Chemistry,
Swiss Federal Institute of Technology,
Zurich, Switzerland

H.-G. Elias
Department of Industrial and Engineering Chemistry,
Swiss Federal Institute of Technology,
Zurich, Switzerland

H. A. Ende
Chemstrand Research Center,
Durham, North Carolina

New Address: Monsanto International,
Hydrocarbon and Plastics Division,
St. Louis, Missouri

CONTRIBUTORS

O. Etter
      Department of Industrial and Engineering Chemistry,
      Swiss Federal Institute of Technology,
      Zurich, Switzerland

Y. L. Fan
      Polymer Research Institute,
      Polytechnic Institute of Brooklyn,
      Brooklyn, New York

H. Gerrens
      Kunststoff-Laboratorium,
      Badische Anilin und Soda-Fabrik,
      Ludwigshafen, Germany

M. Goodman
      Polymer Research Institute,
      Polytechnic Institute of Brooklyn,
      Brooklyn, New York

N. Grassie
      Department of Chemistry,
      The University,
      Glasgow, Scotland

U. Gruber
      Department of Industrial and Engineering Chemistry,
      Swiss Federal Institute of Technology,
      Zurich, Switzerland

G. M. Guzmán
      Departamento de Plásticos del Patronato
      "Juan de la Cierva" (C.S.I.C.),
      Madrid, Spain

F. W. Ibrahim
      Department of Industrial and Engineering Chemistry,
      Swiss Federal Institute of Technology,
      Zurich, Switzerland

B. Immergut
      Polytechnic Institute of Brooklyn,
      Brooklyn, New York

E. H. Immergut
      Interscience Publishers (John Wiley), New York
      and
      Polytechnic Institute of Brooklyn, Brooklyn, New York

K. J. Ivin
      Department of Physical Chemistry,
      University of Leeds,
      Leeds, England

M. Iwama
      Institute for Chemical Research,
      Kyoto University,
      Kyoto, Japan

M. N. Jones
      Department of Chemistry,
      University of Manchester,
      Manchester, England

K. Kamada
      Institute for Chemical Research,
      Kyoto University,
      Kyoto, Japan

G. J. Knight
      Royal Aircraft Establishment,
      Farnborough, Hants, England

W. R. Krigbaum
      Department of Chemistry,
      Duke University,
      Durham, North Carolina

M. Kurata
      Institute for Chemical Research,
      Kyoto University,
      Kyoto, Japan

W. A. Lee
      Royal Aircraft Establishment,
      Farnborough, Hants, England

CONTRIBUTORS

T. Lukanoff   Deutsche Akademie der Wissenschaften zu Berlin,
Institut für Faserstoff-Forschung,
Teltow-Seehof, Germany

H. F. Mark   Polymer Research Institute,
Polytechnic Institute of Brooklyn,
Brooklyn, New York

J. C. Masson   Chemstrand Research Center,
Durham, North Carolina

K. Meyersen   Mellon Institute,
Pittsburgh, Pennsylvania

R. L. Miller   Chemstrand Research Center,
Durham, North Carolina

L. H. Peebles, Jr.   Chemstrand Research Center,
Durham, North Carolina

B. Philipp   Deutsche Akademie der Wissenschaften zu Berlin,
Institut für Faserstoff-Forschung,
Teltow-Seehof, Germany

O. A. Pickett, Jr.   Chemstrand Research Center,
Durham, North Carolina

J. Powers,   Washington, D. C.

New Address: American Cyanamid Co.,
Stamford, Connecticut

J. Rehner, Jr.   Chemicals Research Division,
Esso Research and Engineering Company,
Linden, New Jersey

E. L. Ringwald   Chemstrand Research Center,
Durham, North Carolina

M. Rothe   Universität Mainz,
Organisch-Chemisches Institut,
Mainz, Germany

J. F. Rudd   Physical Research Laboratory,
Dow Chemical Company,
Midland, Michigan

E. G. Shafrin   U. S. Naval Research Laboratory,
Washington, D. C.

G. H. Stempel   Research and Development Center,
The General Tire and Rubber Company,
Akron, Ohio

V. N. Tsvetkov   Institute for Makromolecular Compounds,
Academy of Science U.S.S.R.,
Leningrad, U.S.S.R.

J. Ulbricht   Deutsche Akademie der Wissenschaften zu Berlin,
Institut für Faserstoff-Forschung,
Teltow-Seehof, Germany

New Address: Institut für Technologie der Hochpolymeren,
Technische Hochschule Merseburg,
Merseburg, Germany

CONTRIBUTORS

L. A. Wood

National Bureau of Standards,
Washington, D. C.

H. Yasuda

Cedar-Sinai Medical Center,
Eye Research Laboratory,
Los Angeles, California

L. J. Young

Plastics Department,
The Dow Chemical Company,
Midland, Michigan

TABLE OF CONTENTS

TABLE OF CONTENTS

I.
NOMENCLATURE RULES

I. NOMENCLATURE RULES

A Handbook should be usable effectively without an extensive introduction. However, an explaining word is necessary about the polymer nomenclature used. The correct naming of a compound is essential if the reader is to find the information wanted at the place he is looking for it. Unfortunately, no universally accepted set of rules for naming all classes of polymers exists, although several attempts have been made to achieve uniformity by proposing certain rules of polymer nomenclature (1,2,3,4). Even Chemical Abstracts gives rather scarce information for polymers in their latest publication on nomenclature (5).

This Handbook is not the place to create a new nomenclature for polymers, nevertheless we were forced to adopt certain rules for naming polymers in order to be able to list them in a relatively systematic manner. In doing so, our main principle was to make the information in this Handbook as easily accessible as possible. Since a stiff system of rules may easily act as a Procrustean bed, i.e. the information is stretched and bent to the need of the system instead of vice versa, no inflexible, absolutely consistent pattern was adopted. We preferred to compromise between consistency and easy accessibility by adopting certain commonly used nomenclature rules permitting a relatively consistent listing of polymers in the various tables. Therefore, we used common names, like poly(vinyl chloride), but not polychloroethamer; poly(6-amino-caproic acid), but not poly(hexahydro-2H-azepin-2-one), although sometimes, the reader must be prepared to look for more systematic names for the sake of consistency. In such cases, we have tried to refer the reader from the common to the more systematic name. Especially for some of the condensation polymers, more systematic names like poly(4,4'-isopropylidenediphenylene carbonate), instead of trade names like poly-carbonate from bisphenol A or Poly(4,4'-dihydroxydiphenyl-propane carbonate) were used. This is described in detail below.

Although the use of trade names was avoided wherever possible, it soon was realized that different tables sometimes required different names for the same polymer in order to reveal certain similarities. Therefore, naming procedures suggested in Reference 4 were applied in some of the tables (for example: Poly(hexamethylenediamine-co-adipic acid)). These deviations should be kept in mind when reading the following nomenclature rules:

1. The polymer was named according to its source, whenever it is derived from one single original or hypothetical monomer (e.g. poly(vinyl chloride) or poly(vinyl alcohol)), or when it is derived from two or more components which are built into the polymer in a random order. In the latter case the names of the monomers are separated by the suffix -co-. This rule applies to most polyolefins, vinyl polymers, acrylic polymers, most copolymers, and for certain condensation polymers (e.g. polyformaldehyde and not polyoxymethylene). This rule is used whether or not there is a gain or loss of atoms during polymerization, therefore we also write poly(6-aminocaproic acid). Thus, these names do not describe the real structure of the repeat unit of the polymer, but are synonymous for "polymers made from....", where it is irrelevant whether or not the polymer was really made from this mono-mer (4). Therefore, poly(6-aminocaproic acid) is used for polymers made from this monomer, and also for polymers made from ϵ-caprolactam. Occasionally, a common polymer may be synthesized from an unusual monomer. The common name was always used, unless it was important to stress the exact origin of the polymer. There-fore, poly(ethylene oxide) is used rather than poly(ethylene glycol), poly(ethylene chlorohydrin), or poly(bischloromethyl ether), as suggested in Reference 4.

2. The polymer was named according to its structure, whenever its repeating unit is composed of several monomeric components following each other in a regular fashion, such as is the case with most condensation polymers. This seems to be the commonly accepted practice with polymers such as poly(ethylene terephthalate) or poly-(hexamethylene adipamide). Using this rule, we have tried to name also more com-plicated structures in a consistent manner. The structural repeat unit was divided into its possible components and each monomeric part was essentially treated as a diradical. The names of these diradicals start from the center of the chemical unit, using Chemical Abstract names for the different parts, although exemptions may be found. For example,

would be named 4,4'-isopropylidenediphenylene

$-CH_2-CH_2-\bigcirc-CH_2-CH_2-$ would be named as p-phenylenediethylene

The names of the individual radicals are listed separately enclosed by parentheses and preceeded by the suffix poly. One of the radicals is chosen as the parent compound and connected with the name of the functional group, for instance, poly-(ethylene terephthalate) or poly(hexamethylene adipamide). Polyurethans were named as compositions of diols with diisocyanates, polyureas as compositions of diamines with diisocyanates. In the case of symmetrical functional groups such as oxides, sulfides, and amines, the radicals were listed alphabetically. Table I illustrates the principle:

Table I: System for Naming Polymers According to Their Structural Unit

Polymer Structure	Linking Radical	Parent Compound
polyester	diol	diacid
polyamide	diamine	diacid
polyurethan	diol	diisocyanate
polyurea	diamine	diisocyanate
polyoxide	alphabetical listing	
polysulfide	"	
polyamine	"	

3. <u>Copolymers</u> essentially were treated as under 1., i.e. the different components are separated by the suffix -co-. This system may also be found in certain tables for cocondensates, which otherwise are treated as under 2.. Components of <u>block-polymers</u> were separated by the symbol : and the components of <u>graftpolymers</u> by the symbol +.

4. The suffix <u>poly-</u> was separated from the name by parentheses whenever the name was composed of more than one word or rather long. Therefore polystyrene, but poly-(methyl methacrylate) and poly(tetrafluoroethylene).

5. Chemical Abstract rules were followed for naming <u>low molecular weight compounds</u> although, again, common names are more frequently found.

6. In extensive tabulations the polymers were subdivided into several classes and listed accordingly in order to improve accessibility. The subgroups vary from table to table according to the kind and the amount of information available. <u>Within each class, polymers are mostly listed alphabetically</u>, whereby derivatives are kept together, like polystyrene, poly(chlorostyrene), or different acrylic esters. A selected list of formulas and corresponding names follows this introduction to demonstrate the application of the nomenclature rules and to help in finding polymers in this Handbook.

Table II: Examples of Polymer Names

1. <u>Polymer Names Based on Source</u>.

<u>Olefin, Vinyl, and Acrylic Polymers</u>

$[-CH_2-CH_2-]_n$ polyethylene

$[-CH-CH_2-]_n$ poly(1-butene)
$\ \ CH_2-CH_3$

$[-CH-CH_2-]_n$ polyacrylonitrile
$\ \ CN$

$[-CH-CH_2-]_n$ poly(vinyl chloride)
$\ \ Cl$

$[-CH-CH_2-]_n$ poly(methyl acrylate)
$\ \ COOCH_3$

Polyamides*

$[-NH-CH_2-COO-]_n$ polyglycine

$[-NH-(CH_2)_2-COO-]_n$ poly(β-alanine) or poly(3-aminopropionic acid)

$[-NH-(CH_2)_3-COO-]_n$ poly(4-aminobutyric acid)

$[-NH-(CH_2)_4-COO-]_n$ poly(5-aminovaleric acid)

$[-NH-(CH_2)_5-COO-]_n$ poly(6-aminocaproic acid)

$[-NH-(CH_2)_6-COO-]_n$ poly(7-aminoenanthic acid)

$[-NH-(CH_2)_7-COO-]_n$ poly(8-aminocaprylic acid)

$[-NH-(CH_2)_8-COO-]_n$ poly(9-aminopelargonic acid)

$[-NH-(CH_2)_9-COO-]_n$ poly(10-aminocapric acid)

$[-NH-(CH_2)_{10}-COO-]_n$ poly(11-aminoundecanoic acid)

$[-NH-(CH_2)_{11}-COO-]_n$ poly(12-aminolauric acid)

Polyoxides

$[-CH_2-O-]_n$ polyformaldehyde

$[-CH_2-O-]_n$ polyacetaldehyde
  CH_3

$[-CH_2-CH_2-O-]_n$ poly(ethylene oxide)

$[-CH-CH_2-O-]_n$ poly(propylene oxide)
  CH_3

$[-CH_2-CH_2-CH_2-O-]_n$ poly(trimethylene oxide)

2. Polymer Names Based on Structure

  a. Linking Radicals (see Table I)

$-CH_2-CH_2-$ ethylene

$-CH_2-CH_2-CH_2-$ trimethylene

$-CH_2-CH_2-O-CH_2-CH_2-$ oxydiethylene

$-CH_2-CH_2-O-CH_2-CH_2-O-CH_2-CH_2-$ ethylenedioxy-diethylene

$-CH_2-CH_2-\overset{O}{\underset{O}{S}}-CH_2-CH_2-$ sulfonyldiethylene

$-CH_2-CH_2-CH_2-\overset{CH_3}{P}-CH_2-CH_2-CH_2-$ methylphosphinidene-ditrimethylene

$-CH_2-CH_2-\bigcirc-CH_2-CH_2-$ p-phenylenediethylene

$-CH_2-CH_2-\bigcirc-\bigcirc-CH_2-CH_2-$ 4,4'-biphenylenediethylene

$-\bigcirc-CH_2-\bigcirc-$ 4,4'-methylenediphenylene

$-\bigcirc-\underset{CH_3}{CH}-\bigcirc-$ 4,4'-ethylidenediphenylene

---

* Polyesters are treated similarly

$$\text{-}\overset{CH_3}{\underset{CH_3}{}}\text{-}$$

Structure	Name
phenylene-C(CH₃)₂-phenylene	4,4'-isopropylidenediphenylene
phenylene-CH((CH₂)₂-CH₃)-phenylene	4,4'-butylidenediphenylene
phenylene-C(CH₃)(CH₂-CH₃)-phenylene	4,4'-(2,2-butylidene)diphenylene
phenylene-O-phenylene	4,4'-oxydiphenylene
phenylene-SO₂-phenylene	4,4'-sulfonyldiphenylene

b. <u>Parent Compounds</u> (see Table I)

Structure	Name
-OOC-COO- (-NHOC-CONH-)	oxalate (oxamide)
-OOC-CH₂-COO-	malonate (malonamide)
-OOC-(CH₂)₂-COO-	succinate (succinamide)
-OOC-(CH₃)₃-COO-	glutarate (glutaramide)
-OOC-(CH₂)₄-COO-	adipate (adipamide)
-OOC-(CH₂)₅-COO-	pimelate (pimelamide)
-OOC-(CH₂)₆-COO-	suberate (suberamide)
-OOC-(CH₂)₇-COO-	azelaate (azelaamide)
-OOC-(CH₂)₈-COO-	sebacate (sebacamide)
-OOC-(CH₂)₉-COO-	nonanedioate (nonanediamide)
-OOC-CH₂-CH₂-O-CH₂-CH₂-COO-	oxydipropionate
-OOC-CH₂-phenylene-CH₂-COO-	p-phenylenediacetate
-OOC-(CH₂)₂-phenylene-(CH₂)₂-COO-	p-phenylenedipropionate
-OOC-phenylene-phenylene-COO-	4,4'-dibenzoate
-OOC-phenylene-CH₂-phenylene-COO-	4,4'-methylenedibenzoate
-OOC-phenylene-O-phenylene-COO-	4,4'-oxydibenzoate
-OOC-phenylene-SO₂-phenylene-COO-	4,4'-sulfonyldibenzoate
-OOC-CH₂-phenylene-O-phenylene-CH₂-COO-	4,4'-oxydiphenylenediacetate
-OOC-phenylene-O-CH₂-CH₂-O-phenylene-COO-	4,4'-(ethylenedioxy)dibenzoate
-OOC-CH₂-O-phenylene-O-CH₂-COO-	p-(phenylenedioxy)diacetate
-OOC-phenylene-O-CH₂-COO-	(p-carboxyphenoxy)acetate
OOC-CH₂-N(piperazine)N-CH₂-COO-	1,4-piperazinediacetate

c. Polymer Names

Polyesters*

$[-CH_2-CH_2-OOC\text{⬡}-COO-]_n$	poly(ethylene terephthalate)
$[-CH_2-CH_2-OOC\text{⬡}-\text{⬡}-COO-]_n$	poly(ethylene 4,4'-dibenzoate)
$[-CH_2-CH_2-OOC-CH_2-\text{⬡}-CH_2-COO-]_n$	poly(ethylene p-phenylenediacetate)

$$[-CH_2-CH_2-OOC-\text{⬡}-\overset{\overset{\displaystyle CH_3}{|}}{\underset{\underset{\displaystyle CH_3}{|}}{C}}-\text{⬡}-COO-]_n$$

poly(ethylene 4,4'-isopropylidene-dibenzoate)

$$[-CH_2-CH_2-OOC-\text{⬡}-\overset{\overset{\displaystyle O}{\uparrow}}{\underset{\underset{\displaystyle O}{\downarrow}}{S}}-\text{⬡}-COO-]_n$$

poly(ethylene 4,4'-sulfonyldibenzoate)

Polyurethans

$$\ce{[CH_2-CH_2-CH_2-O-\overset{\overset{\displaystyle O}{||}}{C}-NH-CH_2-CH_2-NH-\overset{\overset{\displaystyle O}{||}}{C}-O-]_n}$$ poly(trimethylene ethylene-urethan)

Polyoxides, Polysulfides, Polyamines

$[-(CH_2)_2-O-(CH_2)_3-]_n$	poly(ethylene trimethylene oxide)
$[-(CH_2)_2-S-(CH_2)_3-]_n$	poly(ethylene trimethylene sulfide)
$[-(CH_2)_2-NH-(CH_2)_3-]_n$	poly(ethylene trimethylene amine)

References

1. International Union of Pure and Applied Chemistry, "Report on Nomenclature in the Field of Macromolecules," J. Polymer Sci., 8, 257, (1952).
2. M. L. Huggins, G. Natta, V. Desreux, and H. Mark, "Report on Nomenclature Dealing with Steric Regularity in High Polymers," J. Polymer Sci., 56, 153 (1962).
3. M. L. Huggins, G. Natta, V. Desreux, and H. Mark, "Nomenklaturbericht über sterische Anordnung in Hochpolymeren," Makromol. Chem. 82, 1 (1965).
4. ACS Committee on Nomenclature of the Polymer Division, Newsletter, October, 1964.
5. "The Naming and Indexing of Chemical Compounds by Chemical Abstracts," Chem. Abstracts, 56, Subject Index A (1962).

* Polyamides are treated similarly

II.
POLYMERIZATION

DECOMPOSITION RATES OF ORGANIC FREE RADICAL INITIATORS

J. C. Masson

Chemstrand Research Center
Durham, North Carolina

Contents

A. INTRODUCTION

The decomposition of most organic free radical initiators follows first order kinetics. With some of the peroxide compounds, however, higher order decompositions are observed. Generally, the higher order reaction is caused by reaction of radicals with the peroxide (induced decomposition) and may be eliminated by 1.) extrapolation of rate data to zero concentration, 2.) addition of a monomer or other "radical trap".

Decomposition rate (k_d) data in these tables are reported for first order kinetics

$$-dI/dt = k_d I$$

where I = initiator concentration

and t = time

The decomposition rate constant k_d is related to half-life ($t_{1/2}$) by the following equation:

$$t_{1/2} = 0.693/k_d$$

Figure 1 relates k_d in sec^{-1} to half-life for the range of k_d found in the tables.

For some of the initiators listed, the enthalpy ($\Delta H^{\neq}$) is given (see notes) rather than the Arrhenius activation energy (E_a). The two quantities are related by the equation $E_a = \Delta H^{\neq} + RT$ where R is the gas constant (in kcal/mole-deg.) and T the absolute temperature (94). Assuming that k_d is linear with respect to 1/T and that the activation energy E_a and the decomposition rate constant k_d for one temperature are known, k_d for any temperature can be calculated from the following expression:

$$\log k_2 = \log k_1 - \frac{E_a(T_2-T_1)}{2.303 \ R \ (T_2T_1)}$$

Where given by the author, the overall equation for k_d in terms of the frequency factor (A) and activation energy (E_a) has been included. Thus, for any temperature (converted to °K) the k_d may be calculated:

$$k_d = A \ \exp[-E_a/RT]$$

The data have been arranged into six tables. Within each table, individual initiators are listed according to the following criteria:

    I.   Initiators

        a. according to increasing number of carbon atoms.
        b. for compounds containing equal number of carbons, alphabetically, neglecting trivial prefixes.

    II. For each initiator, solvents are listed alphabetically. Additives present in the vapor phase are in parenthesis.

    III. For a given solvent, all measurements reported by one investigator are listed in a series, with the activation energy listed opposite the lowest temperature. Series are ordered by the lowest temperature.

As Chemical Abstracts does not systematically list initiators under a general subject index, it was necessary to peruse specific journals for articles of interest. Other references were found from literature citations in the journals checked.

RELATIONSHIP OF HALF LIFE (t $_{1/2}$) TO RATE CONSTANT (k)

(Half Lives are to the Left of Each Vertical Line)

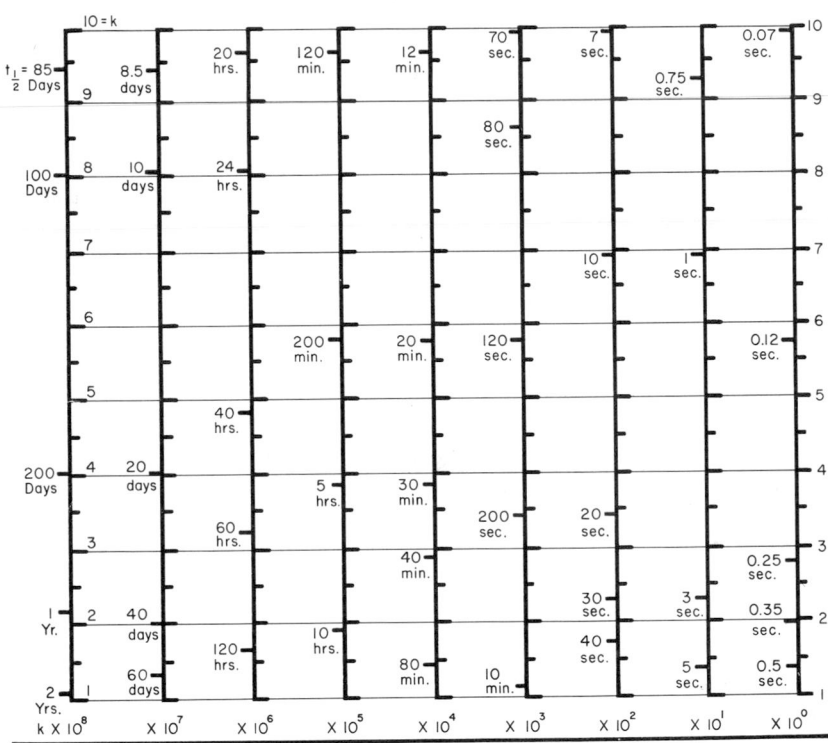

Number of C atoms	Initiator	Solvent	Temp. °C	k_d (sec^{-1})	E_a	Notes	Ref.
			1 - AZO-NITRILES				
5	2-Cyano-2-propyl-azo-formamide	chlorobenzene	100	1.5×10^{-5}			93
		toluene	100	2.1×10^{-5}	34.5		93
			110	6.8×10^{-5}			93
		xylene	100	2.1×10^{-5}	34.5		93
			120	2.4×10^{-4}			93
8	2,2'-Azo-bis-isobutyronitrile (2,2'-azo-bis-2-methylpropio-nitrile)	acetic acid	80	1.52×10^{-4}		a	62
			82	1.50×10^{-4}		a	2
		tert-amyl alcohol	80.2	1.40×10^{-4}			61
		aniline	80.2	1.68×10^{-4}			61
		benzene	40.0	5.44×10^{-7}	30.7	a, t_2	69
			45.2	1.12×10^{-6}		a, t_2	69
			50.0	2.64×10^{-6}		a, t_2	69
			55.0	5.19×10^{-6}		a, t_2	69
			60.5	1.15×10^{-5}		a, t_2	69
			69.5	3.78×10^{-5}		a, t_2	69
			40	4.83×10^{-7}	29.5		66
			50	2.035×10^{-6}			66
			60	8.45×10^{-6}			66
			70	3.166×10^{-5}			66
			78	8.023×10^{-5}			66
		benzene or toluene	37	2.83×10^{-7}	30.8		39
			43	7.35×10^{-7}			39
			50	2.16×10^{-6}			39
			60	9.15×10^{-6}			39
			100	1.52×10^{-3}			39
			T(°K)	$1.58 \times 10^{15} \exp[-30.8 \text{ kcal}/RT]$			39

Notes page II-52; References page II-53

Number of C atoms	Initiator	Solvent	Temp. °C	k_d (sec^{-1})	E_a	Notes	Ref.
		AZO-NITRILES (Cont'd.)					
8	2,2'-azo-bis-isobutyronitrile	n-butanol	82	1.55×10^{-4}		a	2
		isobutanol	82	1.66×10^{-4}		a	2
			80.2	$1.67\text{-}1.76 \times 10^{-4}$			61
		carbon tetrachloride	40	2.15×10^{-7}	30.7	a,t_2	69
			60	4.00×10^{-6}		a,t_2	69
			77	1.21×10^{-4}		a	62
		cyclohexanone	82	1.43×10^{-4}		a	2
		dodecanethiol	80	1.46×10^{-4}		a	62
		ethyl acetate	40	4.7×10^{-7}	30.7	a,t_2	69
			60	9.36×10^{-6}		a,t_2	69
		diethylene glycol monobutyl ether	66.82	2.442×10^{-5}			26
		N,N-dimethylaniline	66.82	3.483×10^{-5}			26
			72.27	6.914×10^{-5}			26
			80	1.83×10^{-4}		a	62
		1-nitrobutane	82	1.45×10^{-4}		a	2
		propylene carbonate	72.27	5.821×10^{-5}			26
		styrene	50	2.97×10^{-6}	30.5	a	132
			70	4.72×10^{-5}		a	132
			T(°K)	1.29×10^{15} exp $[-30.5$ kcal/RT$]$			132
		toluene	70	4.0×10^{-5}	29±2		47
			80.4	1.55×10^{-4}			47
			90.0	4.86×10^{-4}			47
			100.0	1.60×10^{-3}			47
			105.0	2.61×10^{-3}			47

Number of C atoms	Initiator	Solvent	Temp. °C	k_d (sec^{-1})	E_a	Notes	Ref.
			AZO-NITRILES (Cont'd.)				
8	2,2'-azo-bis-isobutyronitrile	toluene	69.8	3.8 × 10^{-5}	34±3		61
			80.2	1.72-1.60 × 10^{-4}			61
		xylene	80	1.53 × 10^{-4}	31.3	a	62
			80	1.50 × 10^{-4}		a, t$_4$	62
			82	1.45 × 10^{-5}		a	2
10	1,1'-azo-bis-1-cyclobutane-nitrile	mesitylene	130.4	5.20±.16 × 10^{-5}	32.1±1		101
		xylene	140.6	1.60±.03 × 10^{-4}			101
			120.4	2.05±.05 × 10^{-5}			101
	2,2'-azo-bis-2-methylbutyro-nitrile	toluene	69.8	2.3 × 10^{-5}	31±3		61
			80.2	8.4 -9.0 × 10^{-5}			61
12	4,4'-azo-bis-4-cyanopentanoic acid	xylene	80	9.97 × 10^{-5}	29.4	a	62
		water	80	8.97 × 10^{-5}	34.0	a	62
	1,1'-azo-bis-1-cyclopentane nitrile	toluene	80.3	7.45±.39 × 10^{-5}	33.8±.9		101
			89.2	2.43±.06 × 10^{-4}			101
			95.1	5.18±.11 × 10^{-4}			101
	2,2'-azo-bis-2-cyclopropyl-propionitrile (mp 64-65)	toluene	44.2	3.50±.011 × 10^{-5}	28±1	w	57
			49.5	7.53±.005 × 10^{-5}		w	57
			59.2	2.68±.05 × 10^{-4}		w	57
	2,2'-azo-bis-2-cyclopropyl-propionitrile (mp 76-77)	toluene	44.2	3.90±.03 × 10^{-5}	26±1	w	57
			49.5	8.17 × 10^{-5}		w	57
			59.3	2.46±.02 × 10^{-4}		w	57
	2,2'-azo-bis-2,3-dimethyl-butyronitrile	toluene	69.8	2.6 × 10^{-5}	32±4		61
			80.2	1.02 × 10^{-4}			61
	2,2'-azo-bis-2-methylvalero-nitrile	toluene	69.8	4.2 × 10^{-5}	33±4		61

AZO-NITRILES (Cont'd.)

Number of C atoms	Initiator	Solvent	Temp.°C	k_d (sec^{-1})	E_a	Notes	Ref.
12	2,2'-azo-bis-2-methylvalero-nitrile	toluene	80.2	1.65-1.74 $\times$ 10^{-4}			61
14	2,2'-azo-bis-2-cyclobutyl-propionitrile (mp 38-42)	toluene	80.5	1.51 $\times$ 10^{-4}		w	104
	2,2'-azo-bis-2-cyclobutyl-propionitrile (mp 81.5-82.5)	toluene	80.5	1.51 $\times$ 10^{-4}		w	104
	1,1'-azo-bis-1-cyclohexane nitrile	toluene	80.3	6.5 $\times$ 10^{-6}	29.0		101
			95.2	5.44 $\times$ 10^{-5}			101
			102.4	1.26 $\times$ 10^{-4}			101
	2,2'-azo-bis-2,3,3-trimethyl-butyronitrile (mp 114-16)	toluene	79.9	7.42 $\times$ 10^{-5}	35±1	w	57
			89.0	2.59 $\times$ 10^{-4}		w	57
	2,2'-azo-bis-2,3,3-trimethyl-butyronitrile (mp 116-18)	toluene	79.9	1.05 $\times$ 10^{-4}	30±2	w	57
			88.9	3.09 $\times$ 10^{-4}			57
	2,2'-azo-bis-2-methylhexylo-nitrile	toluene	80.2	1.58 $\times$ 10^{-4}		w	61
	2,2'-azo-bis-2,4-dimethyl-valeronitrile	toluene	69.8	1.98 $\times$ 10^{-4}	29±4		61
			80.2	7.1 $\times$ 10^{-4}			61
	2,2'-azo-bis-2,4-dimethyl-valeronitrile (mp 56-57)	toluene	59.7	8.05 $\times$ 10^{-5}	29±2	w	57
			69.9	2.89 $\times$ 10^{-4}		w	57
	2,2'-azo-bis-2,4-dimethyl-valeronitrile (mp 74-76)	toluene	69.8	1.98 $\times$ 10^{-4}	29±2	w	57
	2,2'-azo-bis-2-isopropyl-butyronitrile	toluene	80.2	7.1 $\times$ 10^{-4}		w	57
			80.5	1.01± .05 $\times$ 10^{-4}			50

AZO-NITRILES (Cont'd.)

Number of C atoms	Initiator	Solvent	Temp. °C	k_d (sec^{-1})	E_a	Notes	Ref.
16	1,1'-azo-bis-1-cycloheptane nitrile	acetic acid	69.5	3.28×10^{-4}			101
		toluene	48.9	$2.69 \pm .05 \times 10^{-5}$	$27.5 \pm .9$		101
			58.9	$9.72 \pm .12 \times 10^{-5}$			101
			67.3	$2.69 \pm .12 \times 10^{-4}$			101
	2,2'-azo-bis-2-methylheptylo-nitrile	toluene	80.0	$1.63 \pm .1 \times 10^{-4}$			50
	1,1'-azo-bis-1-(2-methyl-cyclohexane)nitrile	xylene	80.0	1.78×10^{-4}	30.2	a	62
		toluene	80.2	$7.43 \pm .18 \times 10^{-6}$			101
	1,1'-azo-bis-1-cyclohexane-carbonitrile	xylene	80	4.7×10^{-6}	39.9	a	62
	2,2'-azo-bis-2-cyclopentyl-propionitrile (mp 72.2-74.5)	toluene	80.5	1.31×10^{-4}		w	104
	2,2'-azo-bis-2-cyclopentyl-propionitrile (mp 96.3-97.6)	toluene	80.5	1.30×10^{-4}		w	104
	2,2'-azo-bis-2,4,4-trimethyl-valeronitrile (mp 67.5-69)	toluene	40	$1.175 \pm .01 \times 10^{-4}$	27 ± 1.5	w	50
			50	$4.45 \pm .14 \times 10^{-4}$		w	50
	2,2'-azo-bis-2,4,4-trimethyl-valeronitrile (mp 94.5-95.5)	toluene	40	$6.95 \pm .1 \times 10^{-5}$	29 ± 1.5	w	50
			50	$2.89 \pm .14 \times 10^{-4}$		w	50
	2,2'-azo-bis-2-isopropyl-3-methylbutyronitrile	toluene	80.5	$1.325 \pm .035 \times 10^{-4}$			50
18	2,2'-azo-bis-2-cyclohexyl-propionitrile	toluene	80.2	8.3×10^{-6}			61
			80.5	2.27×10^{-4}			104
	1,1'-azo-bis-1-cyclooctane nitrile	toluene	36.6	$5.35 \pm .08 \times 10^{-5}$	$25.9 \pm .9$		101
			45.4	$1.45 \pm .05 \times 10^{-4}$			101

Notes page II-52; References page II-53

Number of C atoms	Initiator	Solvent	Temp. °C	k_d (sec^{-1})	E_a	Notes	Ref.
		AZO-NITRILES (Cont'd.)					
18	1,1'-azo-bis-1-cyclooctane nitrile	toluene	49.7	$2.60 \pm .08 \times 10^{-4}$			101
20	2,2'-azo-bis-2-benzyl-propionitrile	toluene	80	1.16×10^{-4}			54
	2,2'-azo-bis-2-isobutyl-4-methylvaleronitrile	toluene	60.1	$3.78 \pm .18 \times 10^{-4}$			50
			80.5	5.28×10^{-3}			50
	2,2'-azo-bis-2-(4-chloro-benzyl)propionitrile	toluene	80	8.8×10^{-5}			54
	2,2'-azo-bis-2-(4-nitro-benzyl)propionitrile	toluene	80	1.00×10^{-4}			54
22	1,1'-azo-bis-1-cyclodecane nitrile	toluene	50.8	$5.40 \pm .11 \times 10^{-5}$			101
			60.2	$1.70 \pm .03 \times 10^{-4}$			101
			69.5	$5.69 \pm .02 \times 10^{-4}$			101

2 - MISCELLANEOUS AZO DERIVATIVES

Number of C atoms	Initiator	Solvent	Temp. °C	k_d (sec⁻¹)	E_a	Notes	Ref.
6	2,2'-azo-bis-propane	vapor	250	7.67×10^{-3}	40.9	a	110
			260	1.67×10^{-2}		a	110
			270	3.55×10^{-2}		a	110
			280	6.52×10^{-2}		a	110
			290	1.28×10^{-1}		a	110
	triazobenzene	nitrobenzene	105	3.5×10^{-7}	33.5		45
			115	1.20×10^{-6}			45
			130	6.25×10^{-6}			45
			145	2.50×10^{-5}			45
		tetralin	105	4.0×10^{-7}	32.5		45
			115	1.34×10^{-6}			45
			130	6.01×10^{-6}			45
			145	2.47×10^{-5}			45
8	azo-bis-isobutyramidine	DMSO (dimethyl sulfoxide)	70	3.68×10^{-6}			21
	azo-bis-isobutyramidine·2HCl	water	70	1.52×10^{-4}			21
	azo-bis-isobutyramidine·2HNO₃	DMSO-cumene	60	4.86×10^{-5}			21
			70	1.53×10^{-4}			21
10	2,2'-azo-bis-methyl-2-methyl-propionate	xylene	80	1.09×10^{-4}	35.8	a	62
12	azo-bis-(N,N'-dimethyleneiso-butyramidine)·2HNO₃	DMSO	60	2.06×10^{-4}			21
			70	6.64×10^{-4}			21
			75	1.08×10^{-3}			21
		DMSO-cumene	70	6.97×10^{-4}			21
		DMSO-tetralin	60	2.13×10^{-4}			21

MISCELLANEOUS AZO DERIVATIVES (Cont'd.)

Number of C atoms	Initiator	Solvent	Temp. °C	k_d (sec^{-1})	E_a	Notes	Ref.
12	azo-bis-(N,N'-dimethyleneiso-butyramidine)	DMSO	80	1.79×10^{-4}			21
		DMSO-cumene	75	8.04×10^{-5}			21
			80	1.39×10^{-4}			21
			85	2.6×10^{-4}			21
		DMSO-tetralin	60	1.09×10^{-5}			21
	azo-bis-(1-carbomethoxy-3-methylpropane)	benzene	36	3.05×10^{-7}			68
			45	1.31×10^{-6}			68
			55	4.54×10^{-6}			68
			65	1.82×10^{-5}			68
		carbon tetrachloride	45	7.18×10^{-7}			68
			55	3.79×10^{-6}			68
			65	1.02×10^{-5}			68
16	1,1'-azo-bis-1-phenylethane	dodecane	97.3	3.175×10^{-5}			26
		ethylbenzene, toluene	100.4	$5.45 \pm .05 \times 10^{-5}$	$32.6 \pm .5$		107, 98
			110.3	$1.69 \pm .01 \times 10^{-4}$			107, 98
		N-methyl-N-benzylaniline	97.3	4.135×10^{-5}			26
		N-methylpropionamide	97.3	3.688×10^{-5}			26
		diphenylmethane	97.3	3.995×10^{-5}			26
		propylene carbonate	97.3	3.294×10^{-5}			26
17	3,7-diphenyl-1,2-diaza-1-cycloheptene	xylene	80	4.26×10^{-4}		a	44
			100.2	3.94×10^{-3}		a	44

MISCELLANEOUS AZO DERIVATIVES (Cont'd.)

Number of C atoms	Initiator	Solvent	Temp. °C	k_d (sec^{-1})	E_a	Notes	Ref.
18	1,1'-azo-bis-1-(4-methoxyphenyl)-ethane	ethylbenzene	100.4	7.15 ± .1 × 10^{-5}	35.8±1.0		98
			110.3	2.48 ± .05 × 10^{-4}			98
	1,1'-azo-bis-1-phenylpropane	ethylbenzene	100.4	2.35 ± .1 × 10^{-5}	32.3±2.8		98
			110.3	7.2 ± .2 × 10^{-5}			98
	1,1'-azo-bis-1-(4-tolyl)ethane	ethylbenzene	100.4	5.9 ± .2 × 10^{-5}	32.9±1.8		98
			110.3	1.85 ± .05 × 10^{-4}			98
19	phenyl-azo-diphenylmethane	decalin	124.5	3.44 × 10^{-5}	34.0±1.3		46
			144.5	2.69 × 10^{-4}			46
22	1,1'-azo-bis-1-phenyl-3-methylbutane	ethylbenzene	100.4	7.6 ± .05 × 10^{-5}	33.3±1.0		98
			110.3	2.42 ± .04 × 10^{-4}			98
25	phenyl-azo-triphenylmethane	acetic acid	43.30	5.7 × 10^{-5}	28		52
			64.00	8.4 × 10^{-4}			52
		anisole	25.0	2.53 × 10^{-6}	28.8±.2	b,h	103
			50.2	1.31 × 10^{-4}		b	103
			74.7	3.03 × 10^{-3}		b	103
			25.0	3.0 × 10^{-6}	28.28±.30		114
			74.5	2.9 × 10^{-3}			114
			80.1	6.8 × 10^{-3}			114
			85.9	1.1 × 10^{-2}			114
		benzene	25.0	4.29 × 10^{-6}	26.8±1	b,h	103
			49.6	1.24 × 10^{-4}			103
			74.7	3.12 × 10^{-3}		b	103
		benzonitrile	25.0	2.62 × 10^{-6}	29.0±.3	b,h	103
			50.3	1.56 × 10^{-4}		b	103
			74.7	3.14 × 10^{-3}			103

Notes page II-52; References page II-53

MISCELLANEOUS AZO DERIVATIVES (Cont'd.)

Number of C atoms	Initiator	Solvent	Temp. °C	k_d (sec^{-1})	E_a	Notes	Ref.
25	phenyl-azo-triphenylmethane	chlorobenzene	25.0	3.77×10^{-6}	28.3±1	b,h	103
			49.6	1.67×10^{-4}		b	103
			74.7	3.93×10^{-3}		b	103
		cyclohexane	25.0	4.22×10^{-6}	24.5±1	h	103
			49.6	9.90×10^{-5}		b	103
			74.7	1.75×10^{-3}		b	103
		diethyl malonate	25.1	3.1×10^{-6}	27.86±15		114
			74.5	2.8×10^{-3}			114
			80.1	5.9×10^{-3}			114
			85.9	1.0×10^{-2}			114
		nitrobenzene	25.0	2.6×10^{-6}	28.38±.25		114
			74.5	3.0×10^{-3}			114
			80.1	5.8×10^{-3}			114
			85.9	9.8×10^{-3}			114
		pyridine	53.35	1.74×10^{-4}	31		52
			64.00	8.0×10^{-4}			52
		toluene	43.8	6.3×10^{-5}	27.6		42
			53.8	2.4×10^{-4}			42
			45.45	$8.48 \pm .11 \times 10^{-5}$	29.3±.3		75
			55.55	3.51×10^{-4}			75
			43.30	6.0×10^{-5}	27		52
			53.35	2.25×10^{-4}			52
			53.3	2.25×10^{-4}	27.0±1.0		46
	3-bromophenyl-azo-triphenyl-methane	toluene	53.8	1.14×10^{-4}	29.9		42
			64.0	4.58×10^{-4}			42

MISCELLANEOUS AZO DERIVATIVES (Cont'd.)

Number of C atoms	Initiator	Solvent	Temp. °C	k_d (sec^{-1})	E_a	Notes	Ref.
25	4-bromophenyl-azo-triphenyl-methane	toluene	53.35	1.05×10^{-4}	28		52
			64.30	4.28×10^{-4}			52
	4-hydroxyphenyl-azo-triphenyl-methane	acetic acid	54.00	1.42×10^{-4}	32		52
			64.00	6.2×10^{-4}			52
		pyridine	54.00	1.52×10^{-4}	32±2		52
			64.00	6.7×10^{-4}			52
		toluene	54.00	1.70×10^{-4}	29		52
			64.00	6.4×10^{-4}			52
	2-nitrophenyl-azo-9-phenyl-fluorene	toluene	45.45	1.01×10^{-4}	28.6±.3		75
			55.55	$3.71 \pm .04 \times 10^{-4}$			75
	4-nitrophenyl-azo-9-phenyl-fluorene	toluene	45.45	$2.06 \pm .02 \times 10^{-4}$	26.7±.3		75
			55.55	$7.53 \pm .02 \times 10^{-4}$			75
	2,4-dinitrophenyl-azo-9-phenylfluorene	toluene	55.55	$2.06 \pm .01 \times 10^{-4}$	28.5±.3		75
			64.94	$6.92 \pm .04 \times 10^{-4}$			75
	2-nitrophenyl-azo-triphenyl-methane	toluene	64.94	$1.46 \pm .01 \times 10^{-4}$	29.6±.5		75
			75.06	$5.26 \pm .08 \times 10^{-4}$			75
	3-nitrophenyl-azo-triphenyl-methane	toluene	53.8	5.8×10^{-5}	26.5		42
			64.0	1.99×10^{-4}			42
	4-nitrophenyl-azo-triphenyl-methane	toluene	64.94	$2.58 \pm .04 \times 10^{-4}$	29.4±.4		75
			75.06	$9.19 \pm .04 \times 10^{-4}$			75
			33.35	5.7×10^{-5}	27		52
			54.30	2.25×10^{-4}			52
	2,4-dinitrophenyl-azo-tri-phenylmethane	toluene	75.06	$1.90 \pm .02 \times 10^{-4}$	29.3±.4		75
			84.98	$6.13 \pm .03 \times 10^{-4}$			75

Notes page II-52; References page II-53

Number of C atoms	Initiator	Solvent	Temp. °C	k_d (sec^{-1})	E_a	Notes	Ref.
		MISCELLANEOUS AZO DERIVATIVES (Cont'd.)					
26	azo-bis-diphenylmethane	toluene	64.0	3.40 x 10^{-4}	26.6±1.3		46,107
			54.0	1.01 x 10^{-4}			107
	4-methoxyphenyl-azo-tri-phenylmethane	toluene	54.00	2.13 x 10^{-4}	28		52
			64.00	7.6 x 10^{-4}			52
	3-tolyl-azo-triphenylmethane	toluene	43.8	7.4 ± .2 x 10^{-5}	27.2±1.5		42
			53.8	2.77 ± .1 x 10^{-4}			42
	4-tolyl-azo-triphenylmethane	toluene	43.30	6.9 ± .1 x 10^{-5}	24±1.		52
			53.35	2.25 ± .05 x 10^{-4}			52
27	4-acetaminophenyl-azo-tri-phenylmethane	toluene	54.00	1.46 x 10^{-4}	30		52
			64.00	5.9 x 10^{-4}			52
40	3,10,13,20-tetraphenyl-1,2,11,12-tetraaza-1,11-cycloeicosadiene	xylene	110	7.20 ± .35 x 10^{-5}	34.8±.4		38
			120	2.30 ± .09 x 10^{-4}			38
			130	6.90 ± .15 x 10^{-4}			38
44	3,12,15,24-tetraphenyl-1,2,13,14-tetraaza-1,13-cyclotetracosadiene	xylene	110.8	8.9 x 10^{-5}	30.2		48
			119.8	2.2 x 10^{-4}			48
			110	7.63 ± .4 x 10^{-5}			38
			120	2.46 ± .12 x 10^{-4}	34.4±.3		38
			130	7.12 ± .22 x 10^{-4}			38
48	3,14,17,28-tetraphenyl-1,2,15,16-tetraaza-1,15-cyclooctacosadiene	xylene	110	9.9 ± .01 x 10^{-5}	33.7±.1		38
			120	2.99 ± .02 x 10^{-4}			38
			130	8.15 ± .08 x 10^{-4}			38

3 - ALKYL PEROXIDES

Number of C atoms	Initiator	Solvent	Temp. °C	k_d (sec⁻¹)	E_a	Notes	Ref.
2	methyl peroxide	vapor	T(°K)	1.6×10^{15} exp[$-35.3\pm2.5/RT$]			72
4	ethyl peroxide	styrene	60	1.2×10^{-9}	35.2		92
		vapor	140.2	1.75×10^{-4}	31.5	a	127
			147.8	3.60×10^{-4}		a	127
			160.0	1.08×10^{-3}		a	127
			175.5	3.78×10^{-3}		a	127
			184.5	7.16×10^{-3}		a	127
		vapor (toluene)	200	3.58×10^{-2}	31.7		87
			210	6.76×10^{-2}			87
			218	1.47×10^{-1}			87
			226	2.23×10^{-1}			87
			234	3.86×10^{-1}			87
			245	6.43×10^{-1}			87
6	propyl peroxide	vapor	146.5	2.50×10^{-4}	31.6	a	128
			155.3	6.00×10^{-4}		a	128
			166.8	1.95×10^{-3}		a	128
			175.4	4.10×10^{-3}		a	128
8	isopropyl peroxide	styrene	50	$6. \times 10^{-10}$	37		92
	tert-butyl peroxide	benzene	30	7.81×10^{-8}	34	m_2,y	129
			130	2.48 -3.04×10^{-5}		m_2,y	129
			100	8.8×10^{-7}	35.1	a	126
			115	5.66×10^{-6}		a	126
			130	3.00×10^{-5}		a	126
			120	1.39×10^{-5}		z_1	33
			120	7.6×10^{-6}		z_{880}	33
			120	7.5×10^{-6}		z_{1650}	33

Number of C atoms	Initiator	Solvent	Temp. °C	k_d (sec^{-1})	E_a	Notes	Ref.
		ALKYL PEROXIDES (Cont'd.)					
8	tert-butyl peroxide	benzene	120	3.7 × 10^{-6}		z_{3550}	33
		tri-n-butylamine	125	1.7 ± .3 × 10^{-5}			64
			135	4.2 ± .4 × 10^{-5}			64
			145	1.60 ± .21 × 10^{-4}			64
			T(°K)	2.8 × 10^{14}	exp [-35.0 kcal/RT]		123
		tert-butylbenzene	125	1.5 ± .2 × 10^{-5}			64
			135	5.0 ± .3 × 10^{-5}			64
			145	1.51 ± .22 × 10^{-4}			64
			T(°K)	2.8 × 10^{14}	exp[-35.0 kcal/RT]		123
		carbon tetra- chloride	120	9 × 10^{-6}		z_1	33
			120	2.4 × 10^{-6}		z_{1970}	33
			120	2.3 × 10^{-6}		z_{2950}	33
			120	8.6 × 10^{-7}		z_{5625}	33
		cumene	125	1.6 ± .1 × 10^{-5}			64
			135	5.2 ± .3 × 10^{-5}			64
			145	1.56 ± .13 × 10^{-4}			64
			T(°K)	2.8 × 10^{14}	exp[-35.0 kcal/RT]		123
		cyclohexene	120	8.3 × 10^{-6}		z_1	33
			120	6.2 × 10^{-6}		z_{1300}	33
			120	3.77 × 10^{-6}		z_{2950}	33
			120	2.65 × 10^{-6}		z_{5840}	33
		methyl methacrylate	T(°K)	2.8 × 10^{14}	exp[-35.0 kcal/RT]		123
		styrene	T(°K)	2.8 × 10^{14}	exp[-35.0 kcal/RT]		123
		toluene	120	1.34 × 10^{-5}		z_1	33
			120	9.5 × 10^{-6}		z_{2040}	33

ALKYL PEROXIDES (Cont.'d.)

Number of C atoms	Initiator	Solvent	Temp.°C	k_d (sec^{-1})	E_a	Notes	Ref.
8	tert-butyl peroxide	toluene	120	8.0×10^{-6}		z_{2900}	33
			120	5.7×10^{-6}		z_{5270}	33
		vapor	125	1.1×10^{-5}			64
			135	3.6×10^{-5}			64
			145	1.15×10^{-4}			64
			129.6	1.64×10^{-5}			86
			141.0	6.28×10^{-5}			86
			152.5	2.25×10^{-4}			85
			166.8	8.92×10^{-4}			86
			130	1.82×10^{-5}	38	a	96
			140	5.75×10^{-5}		a	96
			150	1.75×10^{-4}		a	96
			160	4.88×10^{-4}		a	96
			170	1.35×10^{-3}		a	96
			129	1.97×10^{-5}			88
			138	4.3×10^{-5}			88
			149	1.30×10^{-4}			88
			152	1.62×10^{-4}			88
			159.7	6.0×10^{-5}	$39.1 \pm .5$		63
			147.2	1.43×10^{-4}			63
			154.6	3.22×10^{-4}			63
			159.8	5.53×10^{-4}			63
			$T(°K)$	$3.2 \times 10^{16} \exp[-39.1 \text{ kcal}/RT]$			63
			145	1.3×10^{-4}	38.6		125
			$T(°K)$	$1.9 \times 10^{16} \exp[-38.6 \text{ kcal}/RT]$			125
			149.5	$1.79 \pm .06 \times 10^{-4}$	37.4	i_{28-132}	83

Notes page I-52; References page II-53

Number of C atoms	Initiator	Solvent	Temp. °C	k_d (sec^{-1})	E_a	Notes	Ref.
		ALKYL PEROXIDES (Cont'd.)					
8	tert-butyl peroxide	vapor	160	4.00×10^{-4}	37	a,i$_2$	117
		vapor	160	4.53×10^{-4}		a,i$_{25}$	117
		vapor	160	4.83×10^{-4}		a,i$_{75}$	117
		vapor (He)	280	7.7	37	i$_8$	111
			290	1.51×10^{1}		i$_8$	111
			300	2.77×10^{1}		i$_8$	111
			310	4.87×10^{1}		i$_8$	111
			320	8.34×10^{1}		i$_8$	111
			330	1.38×10^{2}		i$_8$	111
			340	2.13×10^{2}		i$_8$	111
			350	3.22×10^{2}		i$_8$	111
		vapor (acetone)	145	1.3×10^{-4}	39.5		125
			T(°K)	5.9×10^{16} exp$[-39.5$ kcal/RT$]$			125
		vapor (carbon tetrachloride)	150	8.58×10^{-4}		1	130
		vapor (chloroform)	150	1.167×10^{-3}		1	130
		vapor (dichlorodi-fluoromethane)	150	2.00×10^{-4}		1	130
		vapor (trichloro-fluoromethane)	150	$>5.90 \times 10^{-4}$			130
		vapor (trichloro-ethylene)	150	2.35×10^{-3}		1	130
		vapor (methylene chloride)	150	1.017×10^{-3}		1	130
		vapor (3-pentanone)	145	1.5×10^{-4}	39.5		125
			T(°K)	6.8×10^{16} exp$[-39.5$ kcal/RT$]$			125

Number of C atoms	Initiator	Solvent	Temp.°C	k_d (sec^{-1})	E_a	Notes	Ref.
		ALKYL PEROXIDES (Cont'd.)					
8	tert-butyl peroxide	vapor(silicon tetrafluoride)	160	1.05×10^{-3}	27	a,i$_2$	117
			160	1.25×10^{-3}		a,i$_{25}$	117
			160	1.27×10^{-3}		a,i$_{75}$	117
		vapor (toluene)	148	9.0×10^{-5}			88
			158	2.5×10^{-4}			88
	butyl peroxide	styrene	60	3.3×10^{-9}	34		92
	1-hydroxybutyl-n-butyl peroxide	α-methylstyrene	79.4	1.7×10^{-5}	24.6		32
			99.4	1.06×10^{-4}			32
			109.9	2.9×10^{-4}			32
	1-hydroxyisobutyl-isobutyl peroxide	α-methylstyrene	79.4	3.7×10^{-5}	20.0	c	32
			99.4	2.0×10^{-4}		c	32
			109.9	4.8×10^{-4}		c	32
	1-hydroxyisobutyl-1-d-isobutyl-1,1-d$_2$-peroxide	α-methylstyrene	99.5	6.9×10^{-5}	21.4		25
			109.8	1.8×10^{-4}			25
			122.0	4.2×10^{-4}			25
10	tert-amyl peroxide	vapor	132.2	7.2×10^{-5}	37-41	i$_{150-70}$	63
			-36.7	1.15×10^{-4}		i$_{150-70}$	63
			142.2	2.16×10^{-4}		i$_{150-70}$	63
			149.2	4.8×10^{-4}		i$_{70-150}$	63
			136.7	1.34×10^{-4}		i$_{330-60}$	63
			142.2	2.41×10^{-4}		i$_{330-60}$	63
			149.7	5.61×10^{-4}		i$_{330-60}$	63
13	tert-butyl-α-cumyl peroxide	tert-butylbenzene	138	1.48×10^{-4}		a	80
			158	9.62×10^{-4}		a	80

ALKYL PEROXIDES (Cont'd.)

Number of C atom	Initiator	Solvent	Temp. °C	k_d (sec^{-1})	E_a	Notes	Ref.
13	tert-butyl-α-cumyl peroxide	cumene	138	1.44×10^{-4}		a	80
			158	8.88×10^{-4}		a	80
		dodecane	128	4.44×10^{-5}	35	a	80
			138	1.39×10^{-4}		a	80
			148	3.21×10^{-4}		a	80
			158	8.88×10^{-4}		a	80
16	2,5-dimethyl-2,5-di(tert-butyl-peroxy)hexane	benzene	115	1.15×10^{-5}	39.9	a	126
			130	6.86×10^{-5}		a	126
			145	4.75×10^{-4}		a	126
	2,5-dimethyl-2,5-di(tert-butyl-peroxy)-3-hexyne	benzene	115	3.91×10^{-6}	37.5	a	126
			130	2.35×10^{-5}		a	126
			145	1.14×10^{-4}		a	126
			160	6.17×10^{-4}		a	126
17	n-butyl-4,4-bis(tert-butylperoxy)-valerate	dodecane	100	5.83×10^{-6}		a	8
			115	3.53×10^{-5}		a	8
			130	2.91×10^{-4}		a	8
18	cumyl peroxide	benzene	115	1.56×10^{-5}	40.7	a	126
			130	1.05×10^{-4}		a	126
			145	6.86×10^{-4}		a	126
		tert-butylbenzene	158	1.72×10^{-3}		a	80
		cumene	T(°K)	$4.31 \times 10^{14} \exp[-34.5 \text{ kcal/RT}]$			67
			138	2.57×10^{-4}		a	80
			158	1.52×10^{-3}		a	80

Number of C atoms	Initiator	Solvent	Temp. °C	k_d (sec^{-1})	E_a	Notes	Ref.
		ALKYL PEROXIDES (Cont'd.)					
18	cumyl peroxide	dodecane	128	8.75×10^{-5}		a	80
			138	2.31×10^{-4}		a	80
			148	5.37×10^{-4}		a	80
			158	1.83×10^{-3}		a	80
		diisopropylcarbinol	138	3.16×10^{-4}		a	80

Notes page II-52; References page II-53

Number of C atoms	Initiator	Solvent	Temp. °C	k_d (sec⁻¹)	E_a	Notes	Ref.
		4 - ACYL PEROXIDES					
4	acetyl peroxide	acetic acid	55.2	2.8×10^{-6}	30.2	d,e	106
			64.9	9.9×10^{-6}		d,e	106
			75.2	3.75×10^{-5}		d,e	106
			85.2	1.30×10^{-4}		d,e	106
		benzene	73.2	2.62×10^{-5}		a	100
			35	9.5×10^{-7}			68
			55	3.14×10^{-6}			68
			65	1.27×10^{-5}			68
			50	1.22×10^{-6}	32.5	a	126
			70	2.39×10^{-5}		a	126
			85	1.73×10^{-4}		a	126
			70	2.38×10^{-5}		a	16
			60.3	5.0×10^{-6}			4
			80	8.7×10^{-5}			20
			55.2	2.6×10^{-6}	32.3	c,e	106
			64.9	1.07×10^{-5}		c,e	106
			75.2	4.65×10^{-5}		c,e	106
			85.2	1.62×10^{-4}		c,e	106
		n-butanol	60.3	3.4×10^{-5}			4
		sec-butanol	60.3	3×10^{-5}			4
		tert-butanol	60.3	3.1×10^{-6}	32		4
			80.3	4.9×10^{-5}			4
		carbon tetrachloride	26	1.08×10^{-7}			68
			46	4.84×10^{-7}			68
			65	2.11×10^{-6}			68
			80	5.5×10^{-5}			20

ACYL PEROXIDES (Cont'd.)

Number of C atoms	Initiator	Solvent	Temp. °C	k_d (sec^{-1})	E_a	Notes	Ref.
4	acetyl peroxide	chloroform	80.3	~5			4
		cyclohexane	55.2	2.1×10^{-6}	31.4	c,e	106
			64.9	8.3×10^{-6}		c,e	106
			75.2	3.60×10^{-5}		c,e	106
			85.2	1.27×10^{-4}		c,e	105
		cyclohexene	60	4.5×10^{-6}	31.9		20
			70	1.77×10^{-5}			20
			80	7.0×10^{-5}			20
			90	2.28×10^{-4}			20
			100	7.61×10^{-4}			20
		cyclopentene	70	1.60×10^{-5}	32.8		20
			83	7.0×10^{-5}			20
			90	2.55×10^{-4}			20
			100	7.25×10^{-4}			20
		cumene	80	7.6×10^{-5}			20
		n-dodecane	60	2.3×10^{-6}			70
		ethanol	60.3	1.01×10^{-4}	31		4
			80.3	1.40×10^{-3}			4
		n-hexane	50	3.4×10^{-6}			70
		1-hexene	70	2.35×10^{-5}	31.7		20
			80	8.7×10^{-5}			20
			90	3.05×10^{-4}			20
			100	9.83×10^{-4}			20
		2-methyl-1-pentene	80	9.0×10^{-5}	30.3		20
			90	3.12×10^{-4}			20
			100	9.8×10^{-4}			20

Notes page II-52; References page II-53

ACYL PEROXIDES (Cont'd.)

Number of C atoms	Initiator	Solvent	Temp.°C	k_d (sec^{-1})	E_a	Notes	Ref.
4	acetyl peroxide	n-octadecane	60	1.9 x 10^{-6}			70
		n-octane	60	2.9 x 10^{-6}			70
		isooctane	60	2.9 x 10^{-6}			70
			55.2	2.35 x 10^{-6}	32.2	c,e	106
			64.9	9.4 x 10^{-6}		c,e	106
			75.2	4.03 x 10^{-5}		c,e	106
			85.2	1.49 x 10^{-4}		c,e	106
		1-pentene	70	2.45 x 10^{-5}			20
			80	9.4 x 10^{-5}			20
			90	3.22 x 10^{-4}			20
		propionic acid	64.9	1.4 x 10^{-5}			106
			85.2	1.66 x 10^{-4}		d,e	106
		n-tetradecane	60	2.0 x 10^{-6}			70
		toluene	60.3	5 x 10^{-6}	31		4
			55.2	2.7 x 10^{-6}	32.0	c,e	106
			64.9	1.14 x 10^{-5}		c,e	106
			75.2	4.70 x 10^{-5}		c,e	106
			85.2	1.59 x 10^{-4}		c,e	106
			73.2	3.06 x 10^{-5}	33.0	a	100
			85.5	1.72 x 10^{-4}		a	100
			80	7.33 x 10^{-5}	31	a	113
			87.3	1.80 x 10^{-4}		a	113
		vapor (toluene)	88.0	3.12 x 10^{-4}	29.5±.2	a	105
			134.7	3.1 x 10^{-2}			105
			150.7	1.18 x 10^{-1}			105

ACYL PEROXIDES (Cont'd.)

Number of C atoms	Initiator	Solvent	Temp. °C	k_d (sec^{-1})	E_a	Notes	Ref.
4	acetyl peroxide	vapor (toluene)	161.7	2.77×10^{-1}			105
			170.7	6.10×10^{-1}			105
			184.2	1.76			105
6	propionyl peroxide	acetic acid	65.0	3.8×10^{-5}	29.4	c,e	51
			85.0	4.3×10^{-4}		c,e	51
		acetic anhydride	65.0	3.5×10^{-5}	30.8	d,e	51
			85.0	4.5×10^{-4}		c,e	51
		benzene	65.0	1.88×10^{-5}	30.9	c,e	51
			85.0	2.40×10^{-4}		c,e	51
			50	2.72×10^{-6}	30.5	a	126
			70	4.30×10^{-5}		a	126
			85	2.89×10^{-4}		a	126
		benzonitrile	65.0	3.9×10^{-5}	31.2	d,e	51
			85.0	5.1×10^{-4}		d,e	51
		dioxane	65.0	4.5×10^{-5}	27.9	c,e	51
			85.0	4.5×10^{-4}		c,e	51
		n-hexane	65.0	1.50×10^{-5}	29.6		51
			85.0	1.72×10^{-4}			51
		isooctane	65.0	9.8×10^{-6}	31.2	c,e	51
			86.5	1.44×10^{-4}		c,e	51
		nitrobenzene	65.0	3.7×10^{-5}	28.9	c,e	51
			85.0	4.1×10^{-4}			51
		toluene	65.0	1.87×10^{-5}	31.1		51
			85.0	2.54×10^{-4}			51

Notes page II-52; References page II-53

ACYL PEROXIDES (Cont'd.)

Number of C atoms	Initiator	Solvent	Temp.°C	k_d (sec^{-1})	E_a	Notes	Ref.
6	propionyl peroxide	vapor	65.0	1.0×10^{-5}	30.0		51
			85.0	1.6×10^{-4}			51
			99.4	8×10^{-4}	30.0		85
			134.4	2.6×10^{-2}			85
			152.2	1.22×10^{-1}			85
			176.4	8.0×10^{-1}			85
			190.9	2.33			85
			T(°K)				
		vapor	56	2.5×10^{14} exp[-30.0 kcal/RT]			85
	2-iodopropionyl peroxide	acetone	62.5	2.19×10^{-4}		s	77
		benzene	62.5	2.40 -2.81×10^{-4}		s	77
			62.5	7.12×10^{-4}		n,s	77
			62.5	$2.36 \pm .07 \times 10^{-4}$	26	p	77
		n-butyl vinyl ether	62.5	2.47×10^{-4}		s	77
		cyclohexene	62.5	2.7×10^{-4}		s	77
		95% ethanol	62.5	4.0×10^{-4}		s	77
8	butyryl peroxide	acetic acid	65.0	4.7×10^{-5}	29.9	c,e	51
			85.0	5.6×10^{-4}		c,e	51
		acetic anhydride	65.0	4.3×10^{-5}		c,e	51
			85.0	5.5×10^{-4}		c,e	51
		benzene	65.0	2.24×10^{-5}	31.4	d,e	51
			85.0	3.02×10^{-4}		c,e	51
		benzonitrile	65.0	4.3×10^{-5}	31.4	d,e	51
			85.0	5.8×10^{-4}		c,e	51
		dioxane	65.0	4.6×10^{-5}	27.8	c,e	51
			85.0	4.6×10^{-4}		c,e	51

ACYL PEROXIDES (Cont'd.)

Number of C atoms	Initiator	Solvent	Temp. °C	k_d (sec^{-1})	E_a	Notes	Ref.
8	butyryl peroxide	hexane	65.0	1.14×10^{-5}	31.4	c,e	51
			85.0	1.53×10^{-4}		c,e	51
		isooctane	65.0	1.11×10^{-5}	31.9	c,e	51
			85.0	1.56×10^{-4}		c,e	51
		toluene	65.0	2.14×10^{-5}	31.2	d,e	51
			85.0	2.87×10^{-4}		c,e	51
		vapor	65.0	1.6×10^{-5}	29.6		51
			85.0	2.0×10^{-4}			51
			96.7	8.6×10^{-4}	29.6		85
			127.4	1.5×10^{-2}			85
			158.9	3.0×10^{-1}			85
			178.9	1.27			85
			T(°K)	$1.9 \times 10^{14} \exp[-29.6 \text{ kcal}/RT]$			85
	isobutyryl peroxide	isooctane	25	$3.35 \pm .03 \times 10^{-6}$	27.3		84
			35	$1.54 \pm .02 \times 10^{-5}$			84
			45	$6.14 \pm .02 \times 10^{-5}$			84
			55	2.26×10^{-4}			34
			T(°K)	$2.8 \times 10^{14} \exp[-27.3 \text{ kcal}/RT]$			34
	cyclopropane formyl peroxide	carbon tetra-chloride	64.5	4.4×10^{-6}			34
			70.4	9.3×10^{-6}			34
			77.8	2.31×10^{-5}			34
	succinoyl peroxide	acetone	70	2.80×10^{-5}	23.8	a	126
			85	1.21×10^{-4}		a	126
			100	4.36×10^{-4}		a	126

Notes page II-52; References page II-53

Number of C atoms	Initiator	Solvent	Temp.°C	k_d (sec^{-1})	E_a	Notes	Ref.
		ACYL PEROXIDES (Cont'd.)					
10	cyclobutane formyl peroxide	carbon tetra-chloride	65	5.15×10^{-5}			34
			70	$8.95, 6.63 \times 10^{-5}$			34
			75	1.41×10^{-4}			34
	cyclopropane acetyl peroxide	carbon tetra-chloride	14	9.45×10^{-5}			34
			25	$9.75, 10.57 \times 10^{-4}$			34
			44.5	$5.01 \pm .23 \times 10^{-5}$	24.3		24
			56.5	$2.64 \pm .01 \times 10^{-4}$			24
			44.5	$6.5 -8.0 \times 10^{-4}$		n	24
12	cyclobutane acetyl peroxide	carbon tetra-chloride	65	1.37×10^{-5}			34
			70	$2.13, 3.08 \times 10^{-5}$			34
			75	3.83×10^{-5}			34
	cyclopentane formyl peroxide	carbon tetra-chloride	40	1.50×10^{-5}			34
			45	2.55×10^{-5}			34
			50	4.96×10^{-5}			34
			55	$8.17, 7.85 \times 10^{-5}$			34
14	benzoyl peroxide	acetic acid	75	7.53×10^{-5}		a,r	74
		acetone	50	2.25×10^{-6}	26.6	a	126
			70	2.63×10^{-5}		a	126
			85	1.34×10^{-4}		a	126
			100	5.83×10^{-4}		a	126
		acetonitrile	70	1.76×10^{-5}		t_1	124
		acetophenone	70	1.15×10^{-5}	30.2	a	5
			80	4.32×10^{-5}		a	5
			94.5	2.30×10^{-4}		a	5

ACYL PEROXIDES (Cont'd.)

Number of C atoms	Initiator	Solvent	Temp.°C	k_d (sec^{-1})	E_a	Notes	Ref.
14	benzoyl peroxide	allyl alcohol	80	3.80×10^{-4}		a,r	74
		anisole	30	1.42×10^{-7}		a	109
		benzaldehyde	80	5.50×10^{-5}		a,r	74
			90	1.71×10^{-4}		a,r	74
		benzene	30	4.80×10^{-8}	27.8	a	109
			55	1.14×10^{-6}		a,r	74
			60	2.76×10^{-6}		a,r	74
			60	2.0×10^{-6}	29.7	m$_2$	14
			80	2.5×10^{-5}		m$_2$	14
			80	4.8×10^{-5}		a	20
			66	7.72×10^{-6}	31.0	a	131
			72.5	1.87×10^{-5}		a	131
			78	3.77×10^{-5}		a	131
			70	1.17×10^{-5}	32	a	73
			75	2.62×10^{-5}		a	73
			80	4.39×10^{-5}		a	73
			50.8	4.28×10^{-7}	29.6	a,t$_2$	69
			54.9	8.53×10^{-7}		a,t$_2$	69
			60.9	1.66×10^{-6}		a,t$_2$	69
			65.6	3.22×10^{-6}		a,t$_2$	69
			71.0	5.94×10^{-6}		a,t$_2$	69
			75.8	1.19×10^{-5}		a,t$_2$	69
			70	1.48×10^{-5}		a	126
			85	8.94×10^{-5}		a	126
			100	4.95×10^{-4}		a	126
			70	1.03×10^{-5}		a,m$_2$	16

Notes page II-52; References page II-53

ACYL PEROXIDES (Cont'd.)

Number of C atoms	Initiator	Solvent	Temp. °C	k_d (sec^{-1})	E_a	Notes	Ref.
14	benzoyl peroxide	benzene	70	1.18×10^{-5}		t_1	124
			75	1.48×10^{-5}	30.6		12
			75	1.66×10^{-5}	29.7	m_3	12
			85	4.7×10^{-5}			12
			85	5.5×10^{-5}		m_3	12
			100	2.28×10^{-4}			12
			100	2.56×10^{-4}		m_3	12
			79	2.58×10^{-5}		a,t_6	120
			80	3.35×10^{-5}		a	7
		benzyl alcohol	80	4.44×10^{-4}		a,r	74
		butanol	80	6.06×10^{-4}		a,r	74
		butanone	80	4.64×10^{-5}		a,r	74
		carbon tetrachloride	75	1.07×10^{-5}		a,r	74
			79	1.69×10^{-5}		t_6,a	121
		chlorobenzene	80	4.64×10^{-5}		a,r	74
			70	1.35×10^{-5}		t_1	124
		chloroform	30	5.47×10^{-8}		a	109
		cumene	80	3.69×10^{-5}		a,r	74
			85	6.39×10^{-5}		a,r	74
			90	1.19×10^{-4}		a,r	74
			30	7.30×10^{-8}		a	109
			45	1.85×10^{-7}			67
			60	1.45×10^{-6}			67
			80	1.70×10^{-5}			67
			T(°K)	$1.20 \times 10^{13} \exp[-28.8 \text{ kcal}/RT]$	28.8		67
			100	2.5×10^{-4}		a,t_7	122

Number of C atoms	Initiator	Solvent	Temp.°C	k_d (sec^{-1})	E_a	Notes	Ref.
		ACYL PEROXIDES (Cont'd.)					
14	benzoyl peroxide	cyclohexane	80	7.72×10^{-5}		a,r	74
		decalin	80	2.26×10^{-4}		a,r	74
		dioxane	80	6.72×10^{-4}		a,r	74
			80	4.20×10^{-4}		a,r	6
			70	1.30×10^{-5}		t_1	124
		ethylbenzene	75	1.81×10^{-5}		a,r	74
			80	3.33×10^{-5}		a,r	74
			85	5.56×10^{-5}		a,r	74
			90	1.01×10^{-4}		a,r	74
			30	3.61×10^{-8}		a	109
		90% formic acid	80	6.94×10^{-4}		a,r	74
		n-heptane	80	3.11×10^{-5}		a,r	74
		methyl acetate	49.2	6.28×10^{-7}	29.6	a,t_2	69
			53.9	1.0×10^{-6}		a,t_2	69
		methylcyclohexane	80	5.25×10^{-5}		a,r	74
		4-methyl-2-pentanone	80	4.28×10^{-5}		a,r	74
		nitrobenzene	80	4.58×10^{-5}		a,r	74
			30	6.61×10^{-8}	28.1	a	109
		n-pentanol	30	1.48×10^{-4}		a,r	74
		phenol	30	6.25×10^{-4}		a,r	74
		propionic acid	80	3.19×10^{-5}		a,r	74
		styrene	34.8	3.89×10^{-8}		a	10
			49.4	5.28×10^{-7}		a	10
			61.0	2.58×10^{-6}		a	10
			74.8	1.83×10^{-5}		a	10
			100.0	4.58×10^{-4}		a	10

Notes page II-52; References page II-53

ACYL PEROXIDES (Cont'd.)

Number of C rates	Initiator	Solvent	Temp.°C	k_d (sec^{-1})	E_a	Notes	Ref.
14	benzoyl peroxide	polystyrene	56.4	3.8×10^{-7}		a	17
			64.6	1.47×10^{-6}		a	17
			76.7	9.27×10^{-6}		a	17
			83.4	2.50×10^{-5}		a	17
			98.5	1.41×10^{-4}		a	17
			70.9	2.86×10^{-6}		a	15
			80.1	1.11×10^{-5}		a	15
			89.5	3.33×10^{-5}		a	15
		tetralin	80	3.72×10^{-5}		a,r	74
		toluene	30	4.94×10^{-8}	28.8	a	109
			49.0	6.0×10^{-7}	29.6	a,t$_2$	69
			55.1	1.31×10^{-6}		a,t$_2$	69
			60.2	2.83×10^{-6}		a,t$_2$	69
			65.1	5.69×10^{-6}		a,t$_2$	69
			70.3	1.10×10^{-5}		a,t$_2$	69
		poly(vinyl chloride)	64.6	6.3×10^{-7}		a	17
			76.7	5.11×10^{-6}		a	17
			83.4	1.44×10^{-5}		a	17
			98.5	9.33×10^{-5}		a	17
	3-bromobenzoyl peroxide	benzene	60	1.1×10^{-6}			116
			80	1.22×10^{-5}			116
			80	2.60×10^{-5}		a	7
	4-bromobenzoyl peroxide	dioxane	80	2.57×10^{-5}		a,m$_1$	6
		dioxane	80	3.23×10^{-2}		a,m$_1$	6
	2-chlorobenzoyl peroxide	acetophenone	80	3.88×10^{-4}	29.4	a	5
		benzene	80	3.12×10^{-4}		a	7

ACYL PEROXIDES (Cont'd.)

Number of C atoms	Initiator	Solvent	Temp.°C	k_d (sec^{-1})	E_a	Notes	Ref.
14	3-chlorobenzoyl peroxide	acetophenone	80	2.85×10^{-5}	30.7	a	5
		dioxane	80	2.63×10^{-5}		a,m$_1$	6
	4-chlorobenzoyl peroxide	acetophenone	80	3.83×10^{-5}	30.4	a	5
		benzene	30	2.17×10^{-5}		a	7
			50	6.2×10^{-7}	30.8	a	126
			85	6.64×10^{-5}		a	126
			100	3.86×10^{-4}		a	126
		dioxane	80	3.62×10^{-5}		a,m$_1$	6
		styrene	34.8	8.3×10^{-8}		a	10
			49.4	8.3×10^{-7}		a	10
			61.0	3.33×10^{-6}		a	10
			74.8	2.22×10^{-5}		a	10
			100.0	4.17×10^{-4}		a	10
	2,4-dichlorobenzoyl peroxide	benzene	70	9.70×10^{-5}		a,j	16
			70	1.24×10^{-4}		a,k	16
			50	1.08×10^{-5}	28.1	a	126
			70	1.37×10^{-4}		a	126
			85	7.69×10^{-4}		a	126
		styrene	34.8	3.88×10^{-6}		a	10
			49.4	2.39×10^{-5}		a	10
			61.0	7.78×10^{-5}		a	10
			74.8	2.78×10^{-4}		a	10
			100.0	4.17×10^{-3}		a	10
	cyclohexane formyl peroxide	carbon tetra-chloride	35	2.37×10^{-5}			34
			40	$5.22, 5.29 \times 10^{-5}$			34
			45	9.67×10^{-5}			34

ACYL PEROXIDES (Cont'd.)

Number of C atoms	Initiator	Solvent	Temp. °C	k_d (sec^{-1})	E_a	Notes	Ref.
14	cyclopentane acetyl peroxide	carbon tetrachloride	65	1.48×10^{-5}			34
			70	3.20×10^{-5}			34
			75	4.97×10^{-5}			34
	heptanoyl peroxide	toluene	77	1.24×10^{-4}		a	19
	6-heptenoyl peroxide	toluene	70	5.33×10^{-5}		a,k	19
			70	5.01×10^{-5}		a,j	19
			77	1.07×10^{-4}		a,j	19
			85	2.88×10^{-4}		a,k	19
	2-iodobenzoyl peroxide	chloroform	22	1.86×10^{-3}			82
	2-iodobenzoyl-4-nitrobenzoyl peroxide	acetone	25	3.0×10^{-4}			78
		acetonitrile	25	2.1×10^{-4}			78
		benzene	25	5.7×10^{-5}			78
		carbon tetrachloride	25	3.4×10^{-5}			78
		chloroform	25	2.8×10^{-4}			78
		nitrobenzene	25	6.2×10^{-4}			78
	2-nitrobenzoyl peroxide	acetophenone	59.3	5.80×10^{-5}	28.6	a	5
			80	1.34×10^{-3}		a	5
		methyl iodide	24.95	1.78×10^{-5}	19.4	h	82
			45.05	1.50×10^{-4}			82
	3-nitrobenzoyl peroxide	acetophenone	80	3.80×10^{-5}	30.2	a	5
	4-nitrobenzoyl peroxide	acetophenone	80	4.33×10^{-5}	30.3	a	5
	3,5-dinitrobenzoyl peroxide	acetophenone	80	1.87×10^{-5}	31.2	a	5
15	3-cyanobenzoyl-benzoyl peroxide	dioxane	80	2.73×10^{-2}		a,m$_l$	6
	3-methoxybenzoyl-benzoyl peroxide	dioxane	80	4.82×10^{-2}		a,m$_l$	6
	4-methoxybenzoyl-benzoyl peroxide	dioxane	80	7.57×10^{-5}		a,m$_l$	6

Number of C atoms	Initiator	Solvent	Temp.°C	k_d (sec^{-1})	E_a	Notes	Ref.
		ACYL PEROXIDES (Cont'd.)					
15	4-methoxybenzoyl-3-bromobenzoyl peroxide	dioxane	80	4.43×10^{-2}		a, m_1	6
	4-methoxybenzoyl-3,5-dinitro-benzoyl peroxide	benzene	51	1.02×10^{-5}			108
		nitrobenzene	51	9.61×10^{-4}			108
			51	1.67×10^{-3}		t_5	108
	4-methoxybenzoyl-4-nitrobenzoyl peroxide	benzene	70	2.08×10^{-5}		a	89
16	3,5-dibromo-4-methoxybenzoyl peroxide	benzene	70	8.03×10^{-5}		a, v	89
			60	9.5×10^{-7}			95
			60	6.1×10^{-7}			116
			80	9.4×10^{-6}			116
	caprylyl peroxide	benzene	50	3.44×10^{-6}	30.8	a	126
			70	5.78×10^{-5}		a	126
			85	3.78×10^{-4}		a	126
		mineral oil	$T(°K)$	9.8×10^{15} exp$[-33.49\pm1.17$ kcal/RT$]$			1
	3-cyanobenzoyl peroxide	dioxane	30	1.70×10^{-2}		a, m_1	6
	4-cyanobenzoyl peroxide	acetophenone	80	2.43×10^{-5}		a	5
		dioxane	80	2.03×10^{-5}		a, m_1	6
	cycloheptane formyl peroxide	carbon tetra-chloride	35	7.85×10^{-5}			34
			40	$1.63 , 1.34 \times 10^{-5}$			34
			45	2.02×10^{-4}			34
	cyclohexane acetyl peroxide	carbon tetra-chloride	65	1.27×10^{-5}			34
			70	2.76×10^{-5}			34
			75	3.61×10^{-5}			34

Notes page II-52; References page II-53

ACYL PEROXIDES (Cont'd.)

Number of C atoms	Initiator	Solvent	Temp.°C	k_d (sec^{-1})	E_a	Notes	Ref.
16	cyclohexane acetyl peroxide	carbon tetrachloride	54.4	$3.1 \pm .1 \times 10^{-6}$			24
			64.3	$1.19 \pm .05 \times 10^{-5}$			24
			71.8	$2.95 \pm .11 \times 10^{-5}$			24
	2-ethyl-4-methyl-2-pentenoyl peroxide	mineral oil	T(°K)	7.1×10^{16}	$\exp[-33.09\pm3.03 \text{ kcal/RT}]$		1
	2-ethylhexanoyl peroxide	mineral oil	T(°K)	1.2×10^{14}	$\exp[-25.43\pm1.32 \text{ kcal/RT}]$		1
	2-ethyl-2-hexenoyl peroxide	mineral oil	T(°K)	1.6×10^{16}	$\exp[-32.58\pm2.06 \text{ kcal/RT}]$		1
	2-iodophenylacetyl peroxide	acetone	0	2.60×10^{-5}		o	79
		chloroform	0	3.98×10^{-5}		c,e,q	79
		toluene	0	1.3×10^{-5}		q	79
	2-methoxybenzoyl peroxide	acetophenone	50	6.0×10^{-5}	27.2	a	5
		acetophenone	80	2.15×10^{-3}		a	5
	3-methoxybenzoyl peroxide	acetophenone	80	6.42×10^{-5}	28.9	a	5
		dioxane	80	5.75×10^{-5}		a,m$_1$	6
	4-methoxybenzoyl peroxide	acetophenone	80	1.56×10^{-4}	28.7	a	6
		dioxane	80	1.18×10^{-4}		a,m$_1$	6
	2-methylbenzoyl peroxide	acetophenone	70	9.02×10^{-5}	30.2	a	5
	3-methylbenzoyl peroxide	acetophenone	80	4.70×10^{-5}	30.2	a	5
		dioxane	80	4.40×10^{-5}		a,m$_1$	6
	4-methylbenzoyl peroxide	acetophenone	80	5.92×10^{-5}	29.9	a	5
		dioxane	80	6.13×10^{-5}		a,m$_1$	6
	endo-norbornane-2-carbonyl peroxide	carbon tetrachloride	44.5	$6.1 \pm .2 \times 10^{-6}$		j	23
			53.9	$2.83 \pm .17 \times 10^{-5}$		j	23
			65.9	$1.25 \pm .07 \times 10^{-4}$		j	23
			44.5	$9.1 \pm 1.3 \times 10^{-6}$		j,m$_2$	23

Number of C atoms	Initiator	Solvent	Temp. °C	k_d (sec^{-1})	E_a	Notes	Ref.
			ACYL PEROXIDES (Cont'd)				
16	endo-norbornane-2-carbonyl peroxide	carbon tetrachloride	53.9	$4.33 \pm .13 \times 10^{-5}$		j,m$_2$	23
			65.9	$1.28 \pm .18 \times 10^{-4}$		j,m$_2$	23
	exo-norbornane-2-carbonyl peroxide	carbon tetrachloride	44.5	$4.68 \pm 1 \times 10^{-5}$		j	23
			53.9	$2.05 \pm .13 \times 10^{-4}$		j	23
			65.9	$8.18 \pm .77 \times 10^{-4}$		j	23
			44.5	$7.2 \pm .6 \times 10^{-5}$		j,m$_2$	23
			53.9	$1.60 \pm .3 \times 10^{-4}$		j,m$_2$	23
			65.9	$8.48 \pm .17 \times 10^{-4}$		j,m$_2$	23
	endo-norbornene-5-carbonyl peroxide	carbon tetrachloride	44.5	$6.30 \pm .27 \times 10^{-5}$		j	23
			53.9	$1.21 \pm .07 \times 10^{-4}$		j	23
			65.9	$7.18 \pm .55 \times 10^{-4}$		j	23
			44.5	$2.22 \pm .10 \times 10^{-5}$		j,m$_2$	23
			53.9	$4.52 \pm .28 \times 10^{-5}$		j,m$_2$	23
			65.9	$2.37 \pm .02 \times 10^{-4}$		j,m$_2$	23
	exo-norbornene-5-carbonyl peroxide	carbon tetrachloride	44.5	$6.58 \pm .52 \times 10^{-5}$		j	23
			53.9	$1.21 \pm .12 \times 10^{-4}$		j	23
			65.9	$8.42 \pm .17 \times 10^{-4}$		j	23
			44.5	$2.58 \pm .15 \times 10^{-5}$		j,m$_2$	23
			53.9	$1.20 \pm .05 \times 10^{-4}$		j,m$_2$	23
			65.9	$7.10 \pm .32 \times 10^{-4}$		j,m$_2$	23
	phenylacetyl peroxide	toluene	0	2.50×10^{-5}	23	f,u	59
			18	3.34×10^{-4}		f,u	59

Notes page II-52; References page II-53

Number of C atoms	Initiator	Solvent	Temp.°C	k_d (sec^{-1})	E_a	Notes	Ref.
				ACYL PEROXIDES (Cont'd.)			
16	triptoyl peroxide	benzene	80	1.42×10^{-4}			102
18	apocamphoyl peroxide	benzene	80	2.3×10^{-4}			102
	nonanoyl peroxide	mineral oil	T(°K)	8.4×10^{14} exp[-30.38 ± 1.39 kcal/RT]			1
	2-nonenoyl peroxide	mineral oil	T(°K)	1.6×10^{15} exp[-30.79 ± 2.35 kcal/RT]			1
	3-nonenoyl peroxide	mineral oil	T(°K)	3.7×10^{14} exp[-25.81 ± 3.40 kcal/RT]			1
20	decanoyl peroxide	benzene	60	1.53×10^{-5}	30.4	a	126
			70	5.67×10^{-5}		a	126
			85	3.80×10^{-4}		a	126
	4-ethyl-2-octenoyl peroxide	mineral oil	T(°K)	2.7×10^{15} exp[-31.52 ± 1.44 kcal/RT]			1
	4-tert-butylbenzoyl peroxide	mineral oil	T(°K)	8.2×10^{14} exp[-30.46 ± 3.7 kcal/RT]			1
22		dioxane	80	6.08×10^{-2}		a,m$_1$	6
	cis-4-tert-butylcyclohexane formyl peroxide	carbon tetrachloride	40.0	$8.65 \pm .35 \times 10^{-5}$	18.2±6	h	35
			45.45	$1.32 \pm .04 \times 10^{-4}$			35
			50.7	$2.35 \pm .05 \times 10^{-4}$			35
	trans-4-tert-butylcyclohexane formyl peroxide	carbon tetrachloride	40.0	$4.25 \pm .23 \times 10^{-5}$	19.5±.9	h	35
			44.7	$7.10 \pm .38 \times 10^{-5}$			35
			48.9	$1.14 \pm .04 \times 10^{-4}$			35
	4-benzylidenebutyryl peroxide	acetophenone	50	7.92×10^{-5}			133
			55	1.45×10^{-4}			133
			65	4.13×10^{-4}			133
			T(°K)	1.07×10^{12} exp[-23.8 kcal/RT]	23.8		133
			55	1.38×10^{-4}	23.6	m$_2$	133
			65	4.02×10^{-4}		m$_2$	133
			T(°K)	7.14×10^{11} exp[-23.6 kcal/RT]		m$_2$	133

ACYL PEROXIDES (Cont'd.)

Number of C atoms	Initiator	Solvent	Temp. °C	k_d (sec^{-1})	E_a	Notes	Ref.
22	4-benzylidenebutyryl peroxide	carbon tetrachloride	60	3.47×10^{-5}	26.9	m_2	133
			70	1.06×10^{-4}		m_2	133
			T(°K)	1.42×10^{13} exp[-26.9 kcal/RT]		m_2	133
		nitrobenzene	60	3.33×10^{-4}			133
		propylene carbonate	40	7.36×10^{-5}	21.4		133
			50	2.13×10^{-4}			133
			T(°K)	5.93×10^{10} exp[-21.4 kcal/RT]		m_2	133
			50	2.08×10^{-4}			133
	5-phenylvaleryl peroxide	toluene	70	1.64×10^{-4}			133
		acetophenone	77	2.37×10^{-4}			133
		carbon tetrachloride	70	2.76×10^{-5}	31.1	m_2	133
			77	7.19×10^{-5}		m_2	133
			85	1.87×10^{-4}		m_2	133
			T(°K)	1.76×10^{15} exp[-31.1 kcal/RT]		m_2	133
		propylene carbonate	60	4.41×10^{-5}		m_2	133
			60	2.80×10^{-5}			133
24	lauroyl peroxide	benzene	30	2.56×10^{-7}		a	99
			40	4.91×10^{-7}			68
			50	2.19×10^{-6}			68
			60	9.17×10^{-6}			68
			70	2.86×10^{-5}			68
			60	1.51×10^{-5}	30.4	a	126
			70	5.58×10^{-5}		a	126
			85	3.75×10^{-4}		a	126
			70	4.23×10^{-5}		a,j	16

Notes page II-52; References page II-53

Number of C atoms	Initiator	Solvent	Temp.°C	k_d (sec^{-1})	E_a	Notes	Ref.
		ACYL PEROXIDES (Cont'd.)					
24	lauroyl peroxide	carbon tetra-chloride	40	2.91×10^{-7}			68
			50	1.15×10^{-6}			68
			60	4.75×10^{-6}			68
			70	1.87×10^{-5}			68
		ethyl acetate	40	6.03×10^{-7}			68
			50	2.70×10^{-6}			68
			61	1.05×10^{-5}			68
			70	3.99×10^{-5}			68
		ethyl ether	30	1.97×10^{-6}		a	99
		styrene	34.8	2.06×10^{-7}		a	10
			49.4	2.25×10^{-6}		a	10
			61.0	1.42×10^{-5}		a	10
			74.8	1.00×10^{-4}		a	10
			100.0	2.39×10^{-3}		a	10
		mineral oil	T(°K)	$2.2 \times 10^{16} \exp[-32.95 \pm 1.13 \text{ kcal/RT}]$		a	1
26	2-phenoxybenzoyl peroxide	acetophenone	65	8.18×10^{-5}	29.0	a	5
28	myristoyl peroxide	benzene	70	3.38×10^{-5}		a	16
36	menthylphthaloyl peroxide	dioxane	55	1.15×10^{-4}			65

Number of C atoms	Initiator	Solvent	Temp.°C	k_d (sec^{-1})	E_a	Notes	Ref.
		5 - HYDROPEROXIDES AND KETONE PEROXIDES					
4	tert-butyl hydroperoxide	benzene	154.5	4.29×10^{-6}	40.8	h	76
			161.7	9.27×10^{-6}			76
			169.3	2.0×10^{-5}			76
			174.6	4.0×10^{-5}			76
		dodecane	86.1	1.32×10^{-6}	30.7	b	41
			98.5	5.55×10^{-6}		b	41
		n-octane	149.8	8×10^{-6}	$39.0\pm.6$	f	118
			159.9	2.5×10^{-5}		f	118
			169.6	6.9×10^{-5}		f	118
			179.6	1.82×10^{-5}		f	118
	methyl ethyl ketone peroxides	ethyl acetate	70	1.28×10^{-6}			13
6	cyclohexyl hydroperoxide	benzene	70	0			91
		benzene/styrene 50/50	70	1.27×10^{-3}		a	91
		cyclohexane	130	2.33×10^{-3}		a	91
			140	1.15×10^{-2}		a	91
			150	3.20×10^{-2}		a	91
		benzene	80	reaction order varies from 1.5 to 2.0			119
		cyclohexane	80				119
		cyclohexene	80				119
		dimethylheptadiene	80				119
		1-octene	80				119
9	cumene hydroperoxide	mesitylene	130		23.6 ± 2		58
		styrene			24.2 ± 3		58
10	pinane hydroperoxide	benzene	130	7.08×10^{-6}	29.6	a	18
			145	2.72×10^{-5}		a	18
			160	9.17×10^{-5}		a	18

Notes page II-52; References page II-53

Number of C atoms	Initiator	Solvent	Temp. °C	k_d (sec^{-1})	E_a	Notes	Ref.
		HYDROPEROXIDES AND KETONE PEROXIDES (Cont'd.)					
10	1-phenyl-2-methylpropyl-1-hydroperoxide	benzene	133.8	3.18×10^{-6}	29.2	h	76
			143.9	8.95×10^{-6}			76
			153.9	2.0×10^{-5}			76
			163.7	4.03×10^{-5}			76
			174	9.77×10^{-5}			76
	1-phenyl-2-methylpropyl-2-hydroperoxide	benzene	144.2	5.04×10^{-6}	30	h	76
			154.5	1.21×10^{-5}			76
			165.6	2.92×10^{-5}			76
			176.0	6.97×10^{-5}			76
	tetralin hydroperoxide	polybutene	170	2.17×10^{-3}	18.7	t_3	71
		n-butyl stearate	170	1.47×10^{-4}	30.0	t_3	71
		2-ethyl-1-hexene	130	1.08×10^{-4}	19.8	e,t_3	71
			170	1.26×10^{-3}		t_3	71
		1-hexadecene	170	7.92×10^{-4}	28.0	t_3	71
		mineral oil	135.6	4.2×10^{-5}	31.4	t_3	71
			150.6	1.00×10^{-4}		e,t_3	71
			170	4.82×10^{-4}		t_3	71
		n-octadecane	170	2.54×10^{-4}	28.5	t_3	71
		isooctane	170	1.31×10^{-4}		t_3	71
		octyl ether	170	1.45×10^{-3}	29.0	t_3	71
		polypropylene	170	2.50×10^{-3}		t_3	71
		n-tetradecane	170	2.32×10^{-4}		t_3	71
		tetralin	T(°K)	$2.27 \times 10^{9} \exp[-24.4 \text{ kcal/RT}]$			112
		2,2,4-trimethyl-1-pentene	170	1.67×10^{-3}		t_3	71

6 - PERESTERS AND PEROXY CARBONATES

Number of C atoms	Initiator	Solvent	Temp. °C	k_d (sec^{-1})	E_a	Notes	Ref.
6	tert-butyl peracetate	benzene	85	2.18 × 10^{-6}	36.3	a	126
			100	1.54 × 10^{-5}		a	126
			115	1.02 × 10^{-4}		a	126
			130	5.69 × 10^{-4}		a	126
		chlorobenzene	60	2.31 × 10^{-8}	38	a,h	31
	tert-butyl trichloroperacetate	chlorobenzene	60	1.19 × 10^{-5}	30.1	a,h	81
			66.8	2.75 × 10^{-5}	30.3	h	28
			77.0	1.00 × 10^{-4}			28
	diethyl peroxydicarbonate	tert-butanol	45	1.25 × 10^{-5}	32-33	c	18
			55	5.7 × 10^{-5}		c	18
		2,2'-oxydiethylene bis(allyl carbonate)	40	6.94 × 10^{-6}	30.4	a	90
			50	2.86 × 10^{-5}		a	90
			60	1.28 × 10^{-4}		a	90
8	tert-butyl perisobutyrate	benzene	78	3.77 × 10^{-5}	33.6	a	37
			70	6.69 × 10^{-5}		a	126
			85	5.33 × 10^{-5}		a	126
			100	3.50 × 10^{-4}		a	126
		bulk	70	4.12 × 10^{-5}		a	37
	tert-butylperoxyisopropyl carbonate	benzene	90	6.64 × 10^{-6}		a	9
			100	2.21 × 10^{-5}		a	9
			110	6.87 × 10^{-5}		a	9
	ethyl tert-butyl peroxalate	benzene	45	4.48 × 10^{-5}	26.9	c,h	31
			55	1.63 × 10^{-4}		c	31
			65	5.93 × 10^{-4}		c	31

Notes page II-52; References page II-53

PERESTERS AND PEROXY CARBONATES (Cont'd.)

Number of C atoms	Initiator	Solvent	Temp. °C	k_d (sec^{-1})	E_a	Notes	Ref.
8	diisopropyl peroxydicarbonate	benzene	54.0	5.0×10^{-5}		m_2	60
		ethylbenzene	54.3	4.5×10^{-5}			60
			54.3	5.2×10^{-5}		m_2	60
		2,2'-oxydiethylene bis(allyl carbonate)	40	6.39×10^{-6}	28.1	a	90
			50	2.28×10^{-5}		a	90
			60	9.44×10^{-5}		a	90
		toluene	50	3.03×10^{-5}		a	90
9	tert-butyl perpivalate	benzene	50	9.77×10^{-6}	28.6	a	126
			70	1.24×10^{-4}		a	126
			85	7.64×10^{-4}		a	126
		chlorobenzene	58.6	3.35×10^{-5}	30.0	h	28
			64.3	7.01×10^{-5}			28
			74.8	2.79×10^{-4}			28
	di-(tert-butylperoxy)-carbonate	chlorobenzene	60	3.85×10^{-5}	30.6	a,h	81
			99.95	6.72×10^{-5}	31.8		27
			110.1	2.13×10^{-4}			27
			120.1	6.05×10^{-4}			27
		1,2-dichlorobenzene	120.1	5.98×10^{-4}			27
		cumene	99.95	6.72×10^{-5}			27
		isopropyl ether	99.95	2.76×10^{-4}			27
10	di(tert-butylperoxy)-oxalate	benzene	35.0	6.77×10^{-5}	25.5	c,h	30
			45.0	2.61×10^{-4}		c	30
			55.0	9.3×10^{-4}		c	30
	bis(2-nitro-2-methylpropyl)-peroxydicarbonate	toluene	50	2.22×10^{-5}		a	90

Number of C atoms	Initiator	Solvent	Temp. °C	k_d (sec^{-1})	E_a	Notes	Ref.
		PERESTERS AND PEROXY CARBONATES (Cont'd.)					
11	tert-butyl perbenzoate	acetic acid	100.0	3.83 x 10^{-5}	31.1	a	56
			110.0	1.14 x 10^{-4}		a	56
		benzene	100	1.07 x 10^{-5}	34.7	a	126
			115	6.22 x 10^{-5}		a	126
			130	3.50 x 10^{-4}		a	126
			110.0	3.50 x 10^{-5}	34.5	a	56
			119.4	1.04 x 10^{-4}		a	56
			130.0	3.30 x 10^{-4}		a	56
		bromobenzene	119.4	1.32 x 10^{-4}		a	56
		n-butanol	90.0	9.27 x 10^{-5}	28.8	a	56
			100.0	2.70 x 10^{-4}		a	56
		n-butyl acetate	110.0	1.06 x 10^{-4}	29.5	a	56
			119.4	2.67 x 10^{-4}		a	56
			110.0	3.61 x 10^{-5}	35.5	a,m$_2$	56
			119.4	1.10 x 10^{-4}		a,m$_2$	56
		tert-butylbenzene	119.4	1.03 x 10^{-4}		a	56
		n-butyl ether	100.0	7.80 x 10^{-5}	23.7	a	56
			110.0	1.80 x 10^{-4}		a	56
		chlorobenzene	110.0	3.83 x 10^{-5}	33.9	a	56
			119.4	1.11 x 10^{-4}		a	56
			120	1.31 x 10^{-4}		m$_2$	22
			135	6.74 x 10^{-4}		m$_2$	22
			150	3.12 x 10^{-3}		m$_2$	22
		4-chlorotoluene	110.0	3.25 x 10^{-5}	34.5	c	55
			119.4	9.80 x 10^{-5}		c	55
			130.0	3.05 x 10^{-4}		c	55

PERESTERS AND PEROXY CARBONATES (Cont'd.)

Number of C atoms	Initiator	Solvent	Temp. °C	k_d (sec^{-1})	E_a	Notes	Ref.
11	tert-butyl perbenzoate	4-chlorotoluene	60	3.85×10^{-7}	33.5	a,h	81
		ethylbenzene	119.4	1.07×10^{-4}		a	56
		methyl benzoate	119.4	7.80×10^{-5}		a	56
		phenyl ether	100.0	6.94×10^{-6}	37.5±.7	a	53
			110.1	2.28×10^{-5}		a	53
			120.2	9.00×10^{-5}		a	53
			130.9	2.92×10^{-4}		a	53
		xylene	119.4	1.09×10^{-4}	33.8	a	56
			130.0	3.42×10^{-4}		a	56
	tert-butyl-N-(4-bromophenyl-peroxy) carbamate	toluene	70.8	3.32×10^{-5}	30.5	h	36
			79.8	1.04×10^{-4}			36
			84.0	1.75×10^{-4}			36
			96.0	7.70×10^{-4}			36
	tert-butyl-4-chloroperbenzoate	phenyl ether	100.0	3.89×10^{-6}	39.3±.7	a	53
			110.1	1.85×10^{-5}		a	53
			120.2	6.39×10^{-5}		a	53
			130.9	2.42×10^{-4}		a	53
	tert-butyl-N-(2-chlorophenyl-peroxy) carbamate	toluene	87.0	3.5×10^{-5}	37.6	h	36
			95.5	1.48×10^{-4}			36
			103.3	3.3×10^{-4}			36
	tert-butyl-N-(3-chlorophenyl-peroxy) carbamate	toluene	78.0	2.6×10^{-5}	27.6	h	36
			87.0	7.8×10^{-5}			36
			96.6	2.03×10^{-5}			36
			102.7	4.62×10^{-4}			36

PERESTERS AND PEROXY CARBONATES (Cont'd.)

Number of C atoms	Initiator	Solvent	Temp.°C	k_d (sec^{-1})	E_a	Notes	Ref.
11	tert-butyl-N-(4-chlorophenyl-peroxy) carbamate	toluene	73.0	5.57×10^{-5}	28.6	h	36
			78.5	1.42×10^{-4}			36
			87.0	2.75×10^{-4}			35
			92.5	5.37×10^{-4}			36
	tert-butyl-N-(2,5-dichlorophenyl-peroxy) carbamate	toluene	88.0	2.75×10^{-5}	30.8	h	36
			95.0	5.58×10^{-5}			36
			103.3	1.48×10^{-4}			36
			114.5	4.82×10^{-4}			36
	tert-butyl 2-iodoperbenzoate	chlorobenzene	85.0	$4.02 \pm .04 \times 10^{-5}$			134
			102.4	$2.58 \pm .02 \times 10^{-4}$			134
			118.8	$1.32 \pm .02 \times 10^{-3}$			134
	tert-butyl 4-nitroperbenzoate	phenyl ether	110.1	7.56×10^{-6}	$41.3 \pm .7$		53
			120.2	3.19×10^{-5}			53
			150.9	1.11×10^{-4}			53
			141.5	3.92×10^{-4}			53
	tert-butyl-N-(3-nitrophenyl-peroxy) carbamate	toluene	78.0	8.4×10^{-6}	31.8	h	36
			38.7	2.43×10^{-5}			36
			98.0	1.01×10^{-4}			36
			106.0	2.36×10^{-4}			36
	tert-butyl-N-(4-nitrophenyl-peroxy) carbamate	toluene	73.0	6.4×10^{-6}	27.2	h	36
			87.0	3.11×10^{-5}			36
			98.0	8.75×10^{-5}			36
			106.0	2.38×10^{-4}			36

PERESTERS AND PEROXY CARBONATES (Cont'd.)

Number of C atoms	Initiator	Solvent	Temp. °C	k_d (sec^{-1})	E_a	Notes	Ref.
11	tert-butyl-N-(phenylperoxy) carbamate	toluene	51.2	3.4×10^{-6}	33.4	h	36
			67.7	2.31×10^{-5}			36
			77.7	1.15×10^{-4}			36
			90.7	6.41×10^{-4}			36
		chlorobenzene	T(°K)	1.51×10^{16} exp[-32.5 kcal/RT]			40
12	tert-butyl 4-methoxyperbenzoate	phenyl ether	100.0	1.07×10^{-5}	35.8±.7	a	53
			110.1	4.17×10^{-5}		a	53
			120.2	1.28×10^{-4}		a	53
			130.9	4.28×10^{-4}		a	53
	tert-butyl 4-methylperbenzoate	phenyl ether	100.0	9.42×10^{-6}	36.1±.7	a	53
			110.1	3.19×10^{-5}		a	53
			120.2	1.06×10^{-4}		a	53
			130.9	3.25×10^{-4}		a	53
	tert-butyl 2-methylsulfonyl-perbenzoate	chlorobenzene	105	6.68×10^{-6}			22
			120	5.57×10^{-5}			22
			135	2.76×10^{-4}			22
			150.6	2.05×10^{-3}			22
	tert-butyl 2-(methylthio)-perbenzoate	chlorobenzene	60	8.08×10^{-4}	22.7	a,h	97
			39.4	2.59×10^{-5}		b	134
			50.1	$2.42 \pm .04 \times 10^{-4}$		c	134
			50.2	$1.88 \pm .01 \times 10^{-4}$		m$_2$	134
			69.8	$1.96 \pm .03 \times 10^{-3}$			134
	tert-butyl 4-(methylthio)-perbenzoate	chlorobenzene	120.4	$1.75 \pm .05 \times 10^{-4}$			134

Number of C atoms	Initiator	Solvent	Temp.°C	k_d (sec⁻¹)	E_a	Notes	Ref.
		PERESTERS AND PEROXY CARBONATES (Cont'd.)					
12	tert-butyl phenylperacetate	chlorobenzene	60	6.79×10^{-6}	28.7	a,h	81
			77.0	6.85×10^{-5}	28.1	h	28
			88.6	2.45×10^{-4}		m_2	28
	tert-butyl-N-(3-tolylperoxy) carbamate	toluene	64.0	4.58×10^{-5}	24.6	h	36
			70.7	9.17×10^{-5}			36
			78.0	2.03×10^{-4}			36
			88.5	5.78×10^{-4}			36
13	benzyl (tert-butylperoxy) oxalate	benzene	45	3.65×10^{-5}	26.6	c,h	31
			55	1.33×10^{-4}		c	31
			65	4.69×10^{-4}		c	31
	4-nitrobenzyl (tert-butylperoxy) oxalate	benzene	45	1.30×10^{-5}	27.9	c,h	31
			55	4.89×10^{-5}		c	31
			65	1.89×10^{-4}		c	31
14	tert-butyl 2-phenyl-3-perbutenoate	chlorobenzene	60	2.9×10^{-3}	23.0	c,h	81
	tert-butyl 4-phenyl-3-perbutenoate	chlorobenzene	60	1.15×10^{-4}	23.5	c,h,g	81
	tert-butyl phenyldimethyl- peracetate	chlorobenzene	60	9.6×10^{-4}	26.1	c,h	81
	4-methoxybenzyl (tert-butylperoxy) oxalate	benzene	45	6.69×10^{-5}	26.2	c,h	31
			55	2.48×10^{-4}		c	31
			65	8.27×10^{-4}		c	31
15	tert-butyl 4-tert-butylperbenzoate	chlorobenzene	100.1	$3.81^* \pm .02 \times 10^{-5}$			134
			119.8	$4.50 \pm .09 \times 10^{-4}$			134
			135.9	$2.38 \pm .03 \times 10^{-3}$			134

Number of C atoms	Initiator	Solvent	Temp. °C	k_d (sec^{-1})	E_a	Notes	Ref.
	PERESTERS AND PEROXY CARBONATES (Cont'd.)						
16	dibenzyl peroxydicarbonate	toluene	50	2.92×10^{-5}		a	90
	di-tert-butyl perphthalate	benzene	100	1.08×10^{-5}	37.7	a	126
			115	7.83×10^{-5}		a	126
			130	4.80×10^{-4}		a	126
	cumyl N-phenylperoxy carbamate	xylene	$T(^\circ K)$	1.26×10^{14} exp$[-28.1$ kcal$/RT]$			40
17	tert-butyl 2-(phenylthio)-perbenzoate	acetone	25	1.89×10^{-5}		m_2	22
			40	1.22×10^{-4}		m_2	22
		acetonitrile	25	1.01×10^{-4}		m_2	22
			40	5.44×10^{-4}		m_2	22
		tert-butanol	25	5.26×10^{-5}		m_2	22
			40	3.24×10^{-4}		m_2	22
		chlorobenzene	39.3	4.98×10^{-5}		b	134
			53.8	$5.23 \pm .06 \times 10^{-4}$			134
			53.8	$4.58 \pm .07 \times 10^{-4}$			134
			70.0	$2.62 \pm .04 \times 10^{-3}$			134
			25	1.76×10^{-5}		m_2	22
			40	1.03×10^{-4}		m_2	22
		cyclohexane	25	9.8×10^{-7}		m_2	22
			40	6.9×10^{-6}		m_2	22
		DMSO	25	1.11×10^{-4}		m_2	22
			40	6.02×10^{-4}		m_2	22
		ethanol	25	2.31×10^{-4}		m_2	22
			40	1.65×10^{-3}		m_2	22
		methanol	25	8.21×10^{-4}		m_2	22
			40	4.75×10^{-3}		m_2	22

PERESTERS AND PEROXY CARBONATES (Cont'd.)

Number of C atoms	Initiator	Solvent	Temp. °C	k_d (sec^{-1})	E_a	Notes	Ref.
17	tert-butyl 2-(phenylthic)-perbenzoate	isopropanol	25	1.33×10^{-4}		m_2	22
			40	7.25×10^{-4}		m_2	22
	tert-butyl dibenzothiophene-4-percarboxylate	chlorobenzene	105	2.79×10^{-5}	30.6	h	22
			119.4	1.29×10^{-4}			22
			135.1	6.07×10^{-4}			22
18	tert-butyl diphenylperacetate	chlorobenzene	60	4.44×10^{-4}	24.3	a,h	81
	tert-butyl thioxanthone-4-percarboxylate	chlorobenzene	120	1.89×10^{-4}	37.4	h,m_2	22
			135	1.15×10^{-3}		m_2	22
19	tert-butyl diphenylmethylperacetate	chlorobenzene	60	1.9×10^{-3}	24.7	a,h	81
22	2,5-dimethylhexyl 2,5-di(peroxy-benzoate)	benzene	130	1.87×10^{-5}	36.8	a	126
			115	1.25×10^{-4}		a	126
			130	7.14×10^{-4}		a	126

C. Notes

a k_d converted to $\sec^{-1}$ from author's units

b k_d values for several concentrations averaged

c k_d increases with increasing initiator concentration

d k_d decreases with increasing initiator concentration

e k_d listed is for lowest initiator concentration

f k_d is extrapolated value for zero initiator concentration

g k_d has been corrected for induced decomposition

h $\Delta H^{\neq}$ not E_a

i pressure (subscript gives mm Hg)

j iodometric analysis

k infrared analysis

l k_d is limiting value with respect to additive concentration

m_1 3,4-dichlorostyrene added to minimize induced decomposition

m_2 styrene added to minimize induced decomposition

m_3 methyl methacrylate added to minimize induced decomposition

n trichloroacetic acid added

o addition of trichloroacetic acid did not affect k_d

p degassed; the rate is independent of concentration

q addition of trichloroacetic acid increased k_d several fold

r not inhibited, but initiator concentration low enough (.01-.09 molar) so that higher order decomposition is unimportant

s solvent not degassed

t_1 2,6-di-tert-butylphenol added to inhibit induced decomposition

t_2 α,α-diphenyl β-picryl hydrazyl added to inhibit induced decomposition

t_3 phenyl α-naphthylamine added to inhibit induced decomposition

t_4 tetrachloroquinone added to inhibit induced decomposition

t_5 1,3,5-trinitrobenzene to inhibit induced decomposition

t_6 I_2 added to inhibit induced decomposition

t_7 O_2 added to inhibit induced decomposition

u in absence of oxygen

v acetic acid added

w stereoisomers

y from initiation rate data

z pressure (subscript in kg/cm^2)

1. J. E. Guillet, T. R. Walker, M. F. Meyer, J. P. Hawk, and E. B. Towne, Ind. Eng. Chem., Prod. Res. Develop., 3, 257 (1964).
2. L. M. Arnett, J. Am. Chem. Soc., 74, 2027 (1952).
3. L. M. Arnett and J. H Peterson, J. Am. Chem. Soc., 74, 2031 (1952).
4. W. M. Thomas and M. T. O'Shaughnessy, J. Polymer Sci., 11, 455 (1953).
5. A. T. Blomquist and A. J. Buselli, J. Am. Chem. Soc., 73, 3883 (1951).
6. C. G. Swain, J T. Clarke, and W. H. Stockmeyer, J. Am. Chem. Soc., 72, 5426 (1950).
7. D. J. Brown, J. Am. Chem. Soc., 70, 1208 (1948).
8. S. W. Butaka, L. L. Zabrocki, M. F. McLaughlin, J. R. Kolcznski, and O. L. Mageli, Ind. Eng. Chem., Prod. Res. Develop., 3, 261 (1964).
9. W. A. Strong, Ind. Eng. Chem., Prod. Res. Develop., 3, 264 (1964).
10. L. E. Redington, J. Polymer Sci., 3, 503 (1948).
11. B. Baysal and A. V. Tobolsky, J. Polymer Sci., 8, 529 (1952).
12. A. Conix and G. Smets, J. Polymer Sci., 10, 525 (1953).
13. M. R. Gopalan and M. Santhappa, J. Polymer Sci., 25, 333 (1957).
14. J. C. Bevington and J. Toole, J. Polymer Sci., 28, 413 (1958).
15. H. C. Haas, J. Polymer Sci., 39, 493 (1959).
16. A. T. Lowell and J. R. Price, J. Polymer Sci., 43, 1 (1960).
17. H. C. Haas, J. Polymer, Sci., 55, 33 (1961).
18. D. F. Doehnert and O. L. Mageli, Mod. Plastics, 36, No. 6, 142 (1959).
19. R. C. Lamb, P. W. Ayers, and M. K. Toney, J. Am. Chem. Soc., 85, 3483 (1963).
20. H. J. Shine, J. A. Waters, and D. M. Hoffman, J. Am. Chem. Soc., 85, 3613 (1963).
21. G. S. Hammond and R. C. Neuman, Jr., J. Am. Chem. Soc., 85, 1501 (1963).
22. D. L. Tuleen, W. G. Bentrude, and J. C. Martin, J. Am. Chem. Soc., 85, 1938 (1963).
23. H. Hart and F. J. Chloupek, J. Am. Chem. Soc., 85, 1155 (1963).
24. H. Hart and R. A. Cipriani, J. Am. Chem. Soc., 84, 3697 (1962).
25. L. J. Durham and H. S. Mosher, J. Am. Chem. Soc., 84, 2811 (1962).
26. R. C. Petersen, J. H. Markgraf, and S. D. Ross, J. Am. Chem. Soc., 83, 3819 (1961).
27. M. M. Martin, J. Am. Chem. Soc., 83, 2869 (1961).
28. P. D. Bartlett and D. M. Simons, J. Am. Chem. Soc., 82, 1753 (1960).
30. P. D. Bartlett, E. P. Benzing, and R. E. Pincock, J. Am. Chem. Soc., 82, 1762 (1960).
31. P. D. Bartlett and R. E. Pincock, J. Am. Chem. Soc., 82, 1769 (1960).
32. L. J. Durham, and H. S. Mosher, J. Am. Chem. Soc., 82, 4537 (1960).
33. C. Walling and G. Metzger, J. Am. Chem. Soc., 81, 5365 (1959).
34. H. Hart and D. P. Wyman, J. Am. Chem. Soc., 81, 4891 (1959).
35. H. H. Lau and H. Hart, J. Am. Chem. Soc., 81, 4897 (1959).
36. E. L. O'Brien, F. M. Beringer, and R. B. Mesrobian, J. Am. Chem. Soc., 81, 1506 (1959).
37. N. A. Milas and A. Golubovic, J. Am. Chem. Soc., 80, 5994 (1958).
38. C. G. Overberger, I. Tashlick, M. Bernstein, and R. G. Hiskey, J. Am. Chem. Soc., 80, 6556 (1958).
39. J. P. Van Hook and A. V. Tobolsky, J. Am. Chem. Soc., 80, 779 (1958).
40. E. L. O'Brien, F. M. Berringer, and R. B. Mesrobian, J. Am. Chem. Soc., 79, 6238 (1957).
41. B. K. Morse, J. Am. Chem. Soc., 79, 3375 (1957).
42. S. Solomon, C. H. Wang, and S. G. Cohen, J. Am. Chem. Soc., 79, 4104 (1957).
43. C. Walling and J. Pellon, J. Am. Chem. Soc., 79, 4786 (1957).
44. C. G. Overberger, J. G. Lombardino, I. Tashlick, and R. G. Hiskey, J. Am. Chem. Soc., 79, 2662 (1957).
45. K. E. Russel, J. Am. Chem. Soc., 77, 3487 (1955).
46. S. G. Cohen and C. H. Wang, J. Am. Chem. Soc., 77, 3628 (1955).
47. M. Talât-Erben and S. Bywater, J. Am. Chem. Soc., 77, 3712 (1955).
48. C. G. Overberger and M. Lapkin, J. Am. Chem. Soc., 77, 4651 (1955).
49. G. S. Hammond, J. N. Sen, and C. E. Boozer, J. Am. Chem. Soc., 77, 3244 (1955).
50. C. G. Overberger, W. F. Hale, M. B. Berenbaum, and A. B. Finestone, J. Am. Chem. Soc., 76, 6185 (1954).
51. J. Smid, A. Rembaum, and M. Szwarc, J. Am. Chem. Soc., 78, 3315 (1956).
52. S. G. Cohen and C. H. Wang, J. Am. Chem. Soc., 75, 5504 (1953).
53. A. T. Blomquist and I. A. Berstein, J. Am. Chem. Soc., 73, 5546 (1951).
54. C. G. Overberger and H. Biletch, J. Am. Chem. Soc., 73, 4880 (1951).
55. A. T. Blomquist and A. F. Ferris, J. Am. Chem. Soc., 73, 3408 (1951).
56. A. T. Blomquist and A. F. Ferris, J. Am. Chem. Soc., 73, 3412 (1951).
57. C. G. Overberger and M. B. Berenbaum, J. Am. Chem. Soc., 73, 2618 (1951).
58. V. Stannett and R. B. Mesrobian, J. Am. Chem. Soc., 72, 4125 (1950).
59. P. D. Bartlett and J. E. Leffler, J. Am. Chem. Soc., 72, 3030 (1950).
60. S. G. Cohen and D. B. Sparrow, J. Am. Chem. Soc., 72, 611 (1950).

61. C. G. Overberger, M. T. O'Shaughnessy, and H. Shalit, J. Am. Chem. Soc., 71, 2661 (1949).
62. F. M. Lewis and M. S. Matheson, J. Am. Chem. Soc., 71, 747 (1949).
63. J. H. Raley, F. F. Rust, and W. E. Vaughan, J. Am. Chem. Soc., 70, 88 (1948).
64. J. H. Raley, F. F. Rust, and W. E. Vaughan, J. Am. Chem. Soc., 70, 1336 (1948).
65. C. S. Marvel, R. L. Frank, and E. Prill, J. Am. Chem. Soc., 65, 1647 (1943).
66. C. E. H. Bawn and D. Verdin, Trans. Faraday Soc., 56, 815 (1960).
67. H. C. Bailey and G. W. Godin, Trans. Faraday Soc., 52, 68 (1956).
68. C. E. H. Bawn and R. G. Halford, Trans. Faraday Soc., 51, 780 (1955).
69. C. E. H. Bawn and S. F. Mellish, Trans. Faraday Soc., 47, 1216 (1951).
70. W. Braun, L. Rajbenbach, and F. R. Eirich, J. Phys. Chem., 66, 1591 (1962).
71. J. R. Thomas and O. L. Harle, J. Phys. Chem., 63, 1027 (1959).
72. P. L. Hanst and J. G. Calvert, J. Phys. Chem., 63, 104 (1959).
73. B. Barnett and W. E. Vaughan, J. Phys. Chem., 51, 926 (1947).
74. B. Barnett and W. E. Vaughan, J. Phys. Chem., 51, 942 (1947).
75. S. G. Cohen, F. Cohen, and C. H. Wang, J. Org. Chem., 28, 1479 (1963).
76. R. R. Hiatt and W. M. J. Strachan, J. Org. Chem., 28, 1893 (1963).
77. J. E. Leffler and J. S. West, J. Org. Chem., 27, 4191 (1962).
78. W. Honsberg and J. E. Leffler, J. Org. Chem., 26, 733 (1961).
79. J. E. Leffler and A. F. Wilson, J. Org. Chem., 25, 424 (1960).
80. M. S. Kharasch, A. Fono, and W. Nudenberg, J. Org. Chem., 16, 105 (1951).
81. P. D. Bartlett and R. R. Hiatt, J. Am. Chem. Soc., 80, 1398 (1958).
82. J. E. Leffler, R. D. Faulkner, and C. C. Petropoulos, J. Am. Chem. Soc., 80, 5435 (1958).
83. L. Batt and S. W. Benson, J. Chem. Phys., 36, 895 (1962).
84. J. Smid and M. Szwarc, J. Chem. Phys., 29, 432 (1958).
85. A. Rembaum and M. Szwarc, J. Chem. Phys., 23, 909 (1955).
86. R. K. Brinton and D. H. Volman, J. Chem. Phys., 20, 25 (1952).
87. R. E. Rebbert and K. J. Laidler, J. Chem. Phys., 20, 574 (1952).
88. J. Murawski, J. S. Roberts, and M. Szwarc, J. Chem. Phys., 19, 698 (1951).
89. J. E. Leffler, J. Am. Chem. Soc., 72, 67 (1950).
90. F. Strain, W. E. Bissinger, W. R. Dial, H. Rudoff, B. J. DeWitt, H. C. Stevens, and J. H. Langston, J. Am. Chem. Soc., 72, 1254 (1950).
91. A. Farkas and E. Passaglia, J. Am. Chem. Soc., 72, 3333 (1950).
92. W. A. Pryor, D. M. Huston, T. R. Fiske, T. L. Pickering, and E. Ciuffarin, J. Am. Chem. Soc., 86, 4237 (1964).
93. J. C. Bevington and A. Wahid, Polymer, 4, 129 (1963).
94. A. A. Frost and R. G. Pearson, "Kinetics and Mechanism," Wiley, New York (1953) p. 97.
95. J. C. Bevington and T. D. Lewis, Polymer, 1, 1 (1960).
96. F. W. Birss, C. J. Danby, and C. Hinshelwood, Proc. Roy. Soc. (London), A, 239, 154 (1957).
97. J. C. Martin and W. G. Bentrude, Chem. Ind. (London), 1959, 192.
98. S. G. Cohen, S. J. Groszos, and D. B. Sparrow, J. Am. Chem. Soc., 72, 3947 (1950).
99. W. E. Cass, J. Am. Chem. Soc., 72, 4915 (1950).
100. S. D. Ross and M. A. Fineman, J. Am. Chem. Soc., 73, 2176 (1951).
101. C. G. Overberger, H. Biletch, A. B. Finestone, J. Lilker, and J. Herbert, J. Am. Chem. Soc., 75, 2078 (1953).
102. P. D. Bartlett and F. D. Greene, J. Am. Chem. Soc., 76, 1088 (1954).
103. M. G. Alder and J. E. Leffler, J. Am. Chem. Soc., 76, 1425 (1954).
104. C. G. Overberger and A. Lebovits, J. Am. Chem. Soc., 76, 2722 (1954).
105. A. Rembaum and M. Szwarc, J. Am. Chem. Soc., 76, 5975 (1954).
106. M. Levy, M. Steinberg, and M. Szwarc, J. Am. Chem. Soc., 76, 5978 (1954).
107. S. G. Cohen and C. H. Wang, J. Am. Chem. Soc., 77, 2457 (1955).
108. J. E. Leffler and C. C. Petropoulos, J. Am. Chem. Soc., 79, 3068 (1957).
109. W. E. Cass, J. Am. Chem. Soc., 68, 1976 (1946).
110. H. C. Ramsperger, J. Am. Chem. Soc., 50, 714 (1928).
111. F. P. Lossing and A. W. Tickner, J. Chem. Phys., 20, 907 (1952).
112. A. Robertson and W. A. Waters, J. Chem. Soc., 1948, 1578.
113. O. J. Walker and G. L. E. Wild, J. Chem. Soc., 1937, 1132.
114. J. E. Leffler and R. A. Hubbard, II, J. Org. Chem., 19, 1089 (1954).
115. P. D. Bartlett and K. Nozaki, J. Polymer Sci., 3, 216 (1948).
116. J. C. Bevington, J. Toole, and L. Trossarelli, Makromol. Chem., 32, 57 (1959).
117. A. N. Bose and C. Hinshelwood, Proc. Roy. Soc. (London), A, 249, 173 (1959).
118. E. R. Bell, J. H. Raley, F. F. Rust, F. H. Seubold, and W. E. Vaughan, Discussions Faraday Soc., 10, 242 (1951).
119. L. Bateman, H. Hughes, and A. L. Morris, Discussions Faraday Soc., 14, 190 (1953).

120. G. S. Hammond, J. Am. Chem. Soc., 72, 3737 (1950).
121. G. S. Hammond and L. M. Soffer, J. Am. Chem. Soc., 72, 4711 (1950).
122. G. A. Russell, J. Am. Chem. Soc., 78, 1044 (1956).
123. J. A. Offenbach and A. V. Tobolsky, J. Am. Chem. Soc., 79, 278 (1957).
124. G. S. Hammond and U. S. Nandi, J. Am. Chem. Soc., 83, 1213 (1961).
125. G. O. Pritchard, H. O. Pritchard, and A. F. Trotman-Dickenson, J. Chem. Soc., 1954, 1425.
126. O. L. Mageli, S. D. Butaka, and D. J. Bolton, Wallace & Tiernan, Lucidol Division, Bulletin 30.30, "Evaluation of Organic Peroxides from Half-Life Data."
127. E. J. Harris and A. C. Egerton, Proc. Roy. Soc., (London), A 168, 1 (1938).
128. E. J. Harris, Proc. Roy. Soc., (London), A 173, 126 (1939).
129. J. K. Allen and J. C. Bevington, Proc. Roy. Soc., (London), A 262, 271 (1961).
130. G. Archer and C. Hinshelwood, Proc. Roy. Soc., (London), A 261, 293 (1961).
131. J. H. McClure, R. E. Robertson, and A. C. Cuthbertson, Can. J. Res., B20, 103 (1942).
132. J. W. Breitenbach and A. Schindler, Monatsh. Chem., 83, 724 (1952).
133. R. C. Lamb, F. F. Rogers, G. D. Dean, and F. W. Voight, J. Am. Chem. Soc., 84, 2635 (1962).
134. W. G. Bentrude and J. C. Martin, J. Am. Chem. Soc., 84, 1561 (1962).

PROPAGATION AND TERMINATION CONSTANTS IN FREE RADICAL POLYMERIZATION

J. Ulbricht

Deutsche Akademie der Wissenschaften zu Berlin
Institut für Faserstoff-Forschung
Teltow-Seehof, Germany*

The propagation constant k_p is the rate constant of the reaction of a polymer radical P· with a monomer molecule M:

$$P_n^· + M \xrightarrow{k_p} P_{n+1}^·$$

The termination constant k_t is the rate constant of the reaction between two polymer radicals:

$$P_n^· + P_m^· \xrightarrow{k_t} polymer$$

The rate of termination R_t is defined by the relation:

$$R_t = -d[P·]/dt = k_t[P·]^2$$

The determination of k_p and k_t requires in the simplest case the determination of the average life time τ of the growing free radicals:

$$\tau = [P·]/R_i$$

where R_i is the rate of initiation.

The value of τ is usually obtained by measuring either the acceleration or the deceleration (decay period) of the rate of photo polymerization. While intermittent illumination in the rotating sector technique integrates over a large number of these periods (method A in table), non-steady state measurements determine only one single period (method B). In the latter approach, various experimental methods have been used: highly sensitive dilatometers (B1), dielectric constant measurements (B2), interferometry (B3), thermocouple (B4) and thermistor (B5) methods and viscosity determinations (B6). Details of theory and of experimental techniques may be found in references (1,2,3).

Methods A and B yield the average lifetime τ of radicals. Since τ is also given by:

$$\tau = k_p[M]/k_t R_p$$

where R_p is the rate of propagation, the ratio k_p/k_t is obtained. The evaluation of the individual rate constant k_p and k_t involves the independent determination of a second value usually the ratio $k_p/(k_t)^{\frac{1}{2}}$ or R_i measured under steady state conditions of polymerization. These values have not been determined with sufficient accuracy in many cases owing to the lack of knowledge about several characteristics of the polymerization process: for instance, the mechanism of termination, the exact molecular weight average, the initiator efficiency, the mechanism of inhibition, etc. Therefore, several authors have recalculated some of the earlier data in order to overcome these shortcomings (method C). Emulsion polymerization offers the possibility to determine the absolute propagation rate constant k_p using the Smith-Ewart Theory (9) (method D).

The following tables contain all data as they were found in the literature in the order of their publication without correction. The results regarded as most reliable by recent workers (using method C) are indicated in every case. Some authors state for the same constant two values, one of which is put in brackets without valuation. All data refer to low conversion.

* Present address: Institut für Chemie und Technologie der Hochpolymeren, Technische Hochschule für Chemie, Leuna-Merseburg, Germany

Propagation and Termination Constants in Free Radical Polymerization

Monomer	k_p (1/mole·sec)	$k_t \cdot 10^{-6}$ (1/mole·sec)	$k_p/k_t \cdot 10^6$	T°C	Method	Remarks	References
Acrylic acid, butyl ester	13	0.018	-	25	A		17
	14.5	0.018	-	35	A		17
	-	-	820(680)	15	B2		26
	-	-	59	25	B4		37
	-	-	1250	30	B1		58
	-	-	1410	30	B1	solvent: benzene	58
	-	-	833	30	B1	solvent: ethyl acrylate	58
	-	-	840	30	B1	solvent: n-butyl propionate	58
-- , methyl ester	2100	330	-	25	B4		63
	1580	55	28	25	A		23
	720	4.3	-	30	A		25
	2090	9.5	-	60	A		25
	1300	75	17	15	A	from unpublished results of Ross and Melville	26
	880	260	3.4	15	A	from unpublished results of Matheson	26
	-	-	12(10)	15	B2		26
	580	6.5	-	25	B1		56
	1000	3.55	283	50	A		57
Acrylamide	18000±1500	14.5±2.0	-	25	A	solvent: water	52
Acrylonitrile	24	23	-	-	-		41
	3000-5000	-	-	0	D		50
	20000	-	-	40	D		50
	1960	782	-	60	A	solvent: dimethyl-formamide	51
	127	12.2	10.4	25	B4		54

Monomer	k_p (1/mole·sec)	$k_t \cdot 10^{-6}$ (1/mole·sec)	$k_p/k_t \cdot 10^6$	T°C	Method	Remarks	References
Acrylonitrile (Cont'd.)	14500	2000	-	25	A	in water	60
	23000	2800	-	15	A	" "	61
	28000	3700	-	25	A	" "	61
	32500	4400	-	30	A	" "	61
	-	-	3.4	25	A	solvent: dimethylformamide	62
	52	5	-	25	B4		69
	1910	290	-	25	A	solvent: dimethyl sulfoxide	73
	11600	19000	-	60	A	" "	73
	178	24.9	-	0	A	solvent: dimethylformamide	76
	382±230	47.6±22	-	25.0	A	" "	76
	660	86.5	-	66.0	A	" "	76
	51	1.8	29	25	B4,B5	" "	79
Butadiene	8.4	-	-	10	D		28
Ethylene	470±30	1050±50	-	83	A	solvent: benzene	59
	18.6	455±50	0.041	-20,01	A		71
	242	540	-	83	C	using results of ref. 59	71
Isoprene	2.8	-	-	5	D		29
Methacrylic acid,							
-- , n-butyl ester	369	10.2	-	30	A		31
-- , tert-butyl ester	350	14	-	25	A		65
-- , methyl ester	-	-	7.73	5	A		11
	143	12.2	-	30	A		11
	-	-	16.06	50	A		11
	367	18.7	-	60	A		11
	41.6	2.69	-	0	B6	assuming biradical initiation	13
	310±20	66±4	-	23.6	A		16
	410±50	68±12	-	35.9	A		15

References page II-64

Monomer	k_p (1/mole·sec)	$k_t \cdot 10^{-6}$ (1/mole·sec)	$k_p/k_t \cdot 10^6$	T°C	Method	Remarks	References
Methacrylic acid (Cont'd.) -- , methyl ester	580±60	69±10	-	50.5	A		16
	248	22.7	10.9	30	A		18
	-	-	6.75	15	B3		27
	-	-	9.8	15	B4		37
	-	-	13.6	30	B4		37
	512.6	46.6	-	25	A		38
	128	8.44	15.2	22	B1		39
	573	2.0	-	60	C	termination by combinat. using results of ref. 11 and 35	40
	573	11.9	-	60	C	termination by disprop. using results of 11 and 35	40
	-	-	7.41	30	B5		44
	-	-	8.08	35	B5		44
	-	-	8.92	40	B5		44
	-	-	14	30	A		45
	-	-	19	50	A		45
	404	17.6	23	40	B1	solvent: ethyl acetate	58
	-	-	40	30	B1	solvent: ethyl acetate	58
	-	-	14	30	B1	solvent: diethyl ether	58
	-	-	46	30	B1		58
	106	5.7	-	32	B4		64
	384	44	8.7	22.5	B4		66
	251	21	-	30	C	using results of ref. 11	68
	322	22.5	-	40	C	" " " "	68
	410	24	-	50	C	" " " "	68
	515	25.5	-	60	C	" " " "	68

Monomer	k_p (1/mole·sec)	$k_t \cdot 10^{-6}$ (1/mole·sec)	$k_p/k_t \cdot 10^6$	T°C	Method	Remarks	References
Methacrylic acid (Cont'd.)							
-- , methyl ester	640	27.5	-	70	C	using results of ref. 11	68
	300	30.5	-	80	C	" " " "	68
	224	-	-	45	D		72
-- , n-propyl ester	467	45.1	-	30	A		32
Methacrylamide	800	16.5	-	25	A	solvent: water	77
Methacrylonitrile	~21	~27	-	30	-		33
	-	-	1.04	20	A		46
	26	2?	-	25	A		46
	-	-	1.51	30	A		46
Styrene	390	-	-	50	D		8
	6.91	1.83	-	0	B6		10
	18.7	2.79	-	25	B6		10
	51.9	10.5	4.93	30	A		20
	29.2	5.55	-	15	B1		21
	39.5	5.96	-	25	B1		21
	13.2	33.2	-	0	A		24
	-	-	0.538	10	A		24
	44	47.5	-	25	A		24
	55	50.5	1.089	30	A		24
	123	-	1.895	50	A		24
	176	72	-	60	A		24
	-	-	0.65(0.68)	15	B2		26
	-	-	2.0	15	B3		27
	22	-	-	5	D		29
	139	-	-	40	D		29
	24	14	-	20	A	from copolymerization data with sulfur dioxide	30
	-	-	0.55	20	A		34

References page II-64

Monomer	k_p (1/mole·sec)	$k_t \cdot 10^{-6}$ (1/mole·sec)	$k_p/k_t \cdot 10^6$	T°C	Method	Remarks	References
Styrene (Cont'd.)	-	-	2.36	30	A		34
	-	-	2.06;2.28	30	B5		44
	-	-	2.50	35	B5		44
	-	-	2.77	40	B5		44
	72.5	66.5	-	30	A		47
	63	-	-	35	D		48
	96	-	-	40	D		48
	151	-	-	45	D		48
	223	-	-	50	D		48
	270	-	-	55	D		48
	376	-	-	60	D		48
	40±20	80±40	0.5	15	A	dimension of k_p and k_t: kg/mole·sec	53
	209	115	-	50	C	using results of ref. 24	67
	164	-	-	45	D		72
	206	-	-	50	D		72
	106	108	-	30	A		74
	51.0	-	-	30.5	D		78
	120.5	-	-	40.5	D		78
	300.3(291.0)	-	-	50.2	D		78
	357.9	-	-	70.9	D		78
-- , p-chloro-	150	77	-	30	A		75
-- , p-cyano-	219	35	-	30	A	solvent: dimethylacetamide	75
-- , p-methoxy-	2.92	1.06	-	0	B6		14
	71	33	-	30	A		74
-- , o-methyl-	60	-	-	50	D		78
-- , p-methyl-	84	66	-	30	A		74
	140	-	-	50	D		78

Monomer	k_p (1/mole·sec)	$k_t \cdot 10^{-6}$ (1/mole·sec)	$k_p/k_t \cdot 10^6$	T°C	Method	Remarks	References
Vinyl acetate	586(556)	3040(2860)	-	15.9	A		4
	1100	80	-	25	A		5
	670	250	-	15.9	A		6
	700	2600	-	15.9	A	solvent: n-hexane	7
	1012	58.8	17.2	25	A		12
	2640	116.8	22.6	50	A		12
	2000	220	-	-15	B6		15
	2800	220	-	0	B6		15
	1000	59	-	25	A		19
	-	-	3.1(3.5)	15	B2		26
	-	-	20	15	B3		27
	-	-	26	16	B4		37
	895	24	37.2	25	B4	at 4% conversion	42
	-	-	12.1	30	B5		44
	-	-	13.4	35	B5		44
	-	-	14.4	40	B5		44
	559	51.8	10.8	20	B5		49
	910(680)	57(36)	16(19)	15	B1		55
	9500-19000	380-760	-	60	C	using results of ref. 12 and 19	70
Vinyl chloride	6200	1100	-	25	A	solvent: tetrahydrofuran	36
	11000	2100	-	50	A	"	36
	11000	2100	71	25	A		62
Vinylidene chloride	2.3	0.023	-	15	A		22
	8.6	0.175	-	25	A		22
	36.8	1.80	-	35	A		22
4-Vinylpyridine	12	3	-	25	B6		43
	-	-	19	25	B5		79
5-Vinylpyridine, 2-methyl-	47	3.5	13.4	25	B5		79

References page II-64

REFERENCES

1. G. M. Burnett, "Mechanism of Polymer Reactions," Interscience Publishers, New York, 1954, p. 187-222.
2. A. Weissberger, "Technique of Organic Chemistry," Vol. VIII, Investigation of Rates and Mechanisms of Reactions, Interscience Publishers, New York, 1953.
3. C. H. Bamford, W. G. Barb, A. D. Jenkins and P. F. Onyon, "The Kinetics of Vinyl Polymerization by Radical Mechanisms" Butterworths Scientific Publications, London, 1958.
4. G. M. Burnett and H. W. Melville, Nature $\underline{156}$, 661 (1945).
5. C. G. Swain and P. D. Bartlett, J. Amer. Chem. Soc. $\underline{68}$, 2381 (1946).
6. G. M. Burnett and H. W. Melville, Proc. Roy. Soc. (London) A $\underline{189}$, 456 (1947).
7. G. M. Burnett and H. W. Melville, Proc. Roy. Soc. (London) A $\underline{189}$, 494 (1947).
8. W. V. Smith, J. Amer. Chem. Soc. 70, 3695 (1948).
9. W. V. Smith and R. H. Ewart, J. Chem. Phys. $\underline{16}$, 592 (1948).
10. C. H. Bamford and M. J. S. Dewar, Proc. Roy. Soc. (London) A $\underline{192}$, 308 (1948).
11. M. S. Matheson, E. E. Auer, E. B. Bevilacqua and E. J. Hart, J. Amer. Chem. Soc. $\underline{71}$, 497 (1949).
12. M. S. Matheson, E. E. Auer, E. B. Bevilacqua and E. J. Hart, J. Amer. Chem. Soc. $\underline{71}$, 2610 (1949).
13. C. H. Bamford and M. J. S. Dewar, Proc. Roy. Soc. (London)A $\underline{197}$, 356 (1949).
14. D. W. E. Axford, Proc. Roy. Soc. (London) A $\underline{197}$, 374 (1949).
15. G. Dixon-Lewis, Proc. Roy. Soc. (London) A $\underline{198}$, 510 (1949).
16. M. H. Mackay and H. W. Melville, Trans. Faraday Soc. $\underline{45}$, 323 (1949).
17. H. W. Melville and A. F. Bickel, Trans. Faraday Soc. $\underline{45}$, 1049 (1949).
18. L. Valentine, Thesis, Aberdeen 1949, through ref. 39.
19. H. Kwart, H. S. Broadbent and P. D. Bartlett, J. Amer. Chem. Soc. $\underline{72}$, 1060 (1950).
20. H. W. Melville and L. Valentine, Trans. Faraday Soc. $\underline{46}$, 210 (1950).
21. G. M. Burnett, Trans. Faraday Soc. $\underline{46}$, 772 (1950).
22. J. D. Burnett and H. W. Melville, Trans. Faraday Soc. $\underline{46}$, 976 (1950).
23. 　　　　 Ross, Thesis, Aberdeen 1950, through ref. 31.
24. M. S. Matheson, E. E. Auer, E. B. Bevilacqua and E. J. Hart, J. Amer. Chem. Soc. $\underline{73}$, 1700 (1951).
25. M. S. Matheson, E. E. Auer, E. B. Bevilacqua and E. J. Hart, J. Amer. Chem. Soc. $\underline{73}$, 5395 (1951).
26. T. G. Majury and H. W. Melville, Proc. Roy. Soc. (London) A $\underline{205}$, 496 (1951).
27. N Grassie and H. W. Melville, Proc. Roy. Soc. (London) A $\underline{207}$, 285 (1951).
28. M. Morton, P. P. Salatiello, and H. Landfield, J. Polymer Sci. $\underline{8}$, 215 (1952).
29. M. Morton, M. P. Salatiello, and H. Landfield, J. Polymer Sci. $\underline{8}$, 279 (1952).
30. W. G. Barb, Proc. Roy. Soc. (London) A $\underline{212}$, 177 (1952).
31. G. M. Burnett, P. Evans and H. W. Melville, Trans. Faraday Soc. $\underline{49}$, 1096 (1953).
32. G. M. Burnett, P. Evans and H. W. Melville, Trans. Faraday Soc. $\underline{49}$, 1105 (1953).
33. P. J. Flory, "Principles of Polymer Chemistry," Cornell University Press, New York 1953, p. 158.
34. S. Fujii, Bull. Chem. Soc. Japan $\underline{27}$, 216 (1954).
35. J. C. Bevington, H. W. Melville and R. P. Taylor, J. Polymer Sci. $\underline{14}$, 463 (1954).
36. G. M. Burnett and W. W. Wright, Proc. Roy. Soc. (London) A $\underline{211}$, 41 (1954).
37. W. J. Bengough and H. W. Melville, Proc. Roy. Soc. (London) A $\underline{225}$, 330 (1954).
38. B. R. Chinmayanandam and H. W. Melville, Trans. Faraday Soc. $\underline{50}$, 73 (1954).
39. G. M. Burnett, "Mechanism of Polymer Reactions," Interscience Publishers, New York, 1954, p. 230, 233.
40. J. L. O'Brien and F. Gormick, J. Amer. Chem. Soc. $\underline{77}$, 4757 (1955).
41. J. Durup and M. Magat, J. Polymer Sci. $\underline{18}$, 586 (1955).
42. W. J. Bengough and H. W. Melville, Proc. Roy. Soc. (London) A $\underline{230}$, 429 (1955).
43. P. F. Onyon, Trans. Faraday Soc. $\underline{51}$, 400 (1955).
44. H. Miyama, Bull. Chem. Soc. Japan $\underline{29}$, 711, 715 (1956).
45. S. Fujii, S. Tanaka, and S. Sutani, J. Polymer Sci. $\underline{20}$, 586 (1956).
46. N. Grassie and E. Vance, Trans. Faraday Soc. $\underline{52}$, 727 (1956).
47. E. A. Nicholson and R. G. W. Norrish, Discussions Faraday Soc. $\underline{22}$, 104 (1956).
48. E. Bartholome, H. Gerrens, R. Herbeck and H. Weitz, Z. Elektrochem. $\underline{60}$, 334 (1956).
49. H. Miyama, Bull. Chem. Soc. Japan $\underline{29}$, 720 (1956), $\underline{30}$, 10 (1957).
50. W. M. Thomas and R. L. Webb, J. Polymer Sci. $\underline{25}$, 124 (1957).
51. C. H. Bamford, A. D. Jenkins and R. Johnston, Proc. Roy. Soc. (London) A $\underline{241}$, 364 (1957).
52. F. S. Dainton and M. Tordoff, Trans. Faraday Soc. $\underline{53}$, 499 (1957).
53. K. Ueberreiter and G. Sorge, Z. Phys. Chem. (Frankfurt) $\underline{13}$, 158 (1957).
54. W. J. Bengough, J. Polymer Sci. $\underline{28}$, 475 (1958).
55. W. J. Bengough, Trans. Faraday Soc. $\underline{54}$, 868 (1958).
56. W. J. Bengough and A. C. K. Smith, Trans. Faraday Soc. $\underline{54}$, 1553 (1958).
57. Z. A. Sinitsyna and Kh. S. Bagdasaryan, Zh. Fiz. Khim. $\underline{32}$, 1319 (1958).

58. S. W. Benson and A. M. North, J. Amer. Chem. Soc. 81, 1339 (1959).
59. Z. Laita and Z. Machacek, J. Polymer Sci. 38, 459 (1959).
60. F. S. Dainton and D. C. L. James, J. Polymer Sci. 39, 299 (1959).
61. F. S. Dainton and R. S. Eaton, J. Polymer Sci. 39, 313 (1959).
62. W. J. Bengough, S. A. McIntosh and R. A. M. Thomson, Nature 184, 266 (1959).
63. W. J. Bengough and H. W. Melville, Proc. Roy. Soc. (London) A 249, 445 (1959).
64. W. J. Bengough and H. W. Melville, Proc. Roy. Soc. (London) A 249, 455 (1959).
65. D. H. Grant and N. Grassie, Trans. Faraday Soc. 55, 1042 (1959).
66. P. Hyden and H. W. Melville, J. Polymer Sci. 43, 201 (1960).
67. G. Henrici-Olive and S. Olive, Makromol Chem. 37, 71 (1960).
68. G. V. Schulz, G. Henrici-Olive and S. Olive, Z. Phys. Chem. (Frankfurt) 27, 1
     (1960).
69. W. J. Bengough, Proc. Roy. Soc. (London) A 260, 205 (1961).
70. G. V. Schulz and D. J. Stein, Makromol. Chem. 52, 1 (1962).
71. W. Rabel and K. Ueberreiter, Ber. Bunsenges. 67, 710 (1963).
72. H. Gerrens, Ber. Bunsenges. 67, 741 (1963).
73. E. F. T. White and M. J. Zissell, J. Polymer Sci. A 1, 2189 (1963).
74. M. Kinoshita and M. Imoto, Kobunshi Kagaku 20, 231 (1963).
75. M. Kinoshita, Kobunshi Kagaku 20, 237 (1963).
76. N. Colebourne, E. Collinson, D. J. Currie and F. S. Dainton, Trans. Faraday Soc.
     59, 1357 (1963).
77. F. S. Dainton and W. D. Sisley, Trans. Faraday Soc. 59, 1369 (1963).
78. K. P. Paoletti and F. W. Billmeyer, Jr., J. Polymer Sci. A 2, 2049 (1964).
79. A. F. Revzin and Kh. S. Bagdasaryan, Zh. Fiz. Khim. 38, 1020 (1964).

ACTIVATION ENERGY OF PROPAGATION AND TERMINATION
IN FREE RADICAL POLYMERIZATION

J. Ulbricht

Deutsche Akademie der Wissenschaften zu Berlin
Institut für Faserstoff-Forschung
Teltow-Seehof, Germany*

Determination of the temperature coefficient of the rate constant k yields the activation energy E of the reaction. This is commonly expressed by the Arrhenius equation:

$$k = A \exp(-E/RT)$$

where A is the frequency factor of the reaction, R the gas constant, and T the absolute temperature. The measurement of the rate constant of the propagation reaction k_p, or of the rate constant of the termination reaction k_t, at different temperatures allows the determination of the activation energy of propagation E_p, or of the activation energy of termination E_t, respectively.

Monomer	E_p (kcal/mole)	E_t (kcal/mole)	Remarks	Ref.
Acetylene	5.1	-	in gas phase	21
Acrylic acid, butyl ester	2.1	0		8
	12.5	17.6	at 20% conversion	26
-- , methyl ester	7.1	5.3		12
	4.7	~0		23
Acrylonitrile	4.1	5.4	solvent: water	25
	3.88	3.70	solvent: dimethyl-formamide	32
	6.4	~0	" "	35
Butadiene	2.6	-	in gas phase	13
	9.3	-	in emulsion	14
	5.8,5.0	-	in gas phase (1)(2)	16
	4.9	-	" " "	21
Ethylene	8.2	-	" " "	21
	4.4	0.3	calculated using results of ref. 24	31
Isoprene	9.8	-	in emulsion	15
Methacrylamide	3.7	4.0	solvent: water	33
Methacrylic acid, tert-butyl ester	4.4	1.1		27

* Present address: Institut für Chemie und Technologie der Hochpolymeren
Technische Hochschule für Chemie, Leuna-Merseburg, Germany

Monomer	E_p (kcal/mole)	E_t (kcal/mole)	Remarks	Ref.
Methacrylic acid, methyl ester	6.31	2.84		4
	4.4	0		7
	5.8	0.5		28
	5.0±0.2	4.0±0.5	termination by disproportionation	30
	5.0±0.2	0±0.5	termination by combination	30
Methacrylonitrile	11.5	5.0		20
Propene	5.6	-	in gas phase	21
Styrene	11.7	-	in emulsion	2
	6.5±1	2.8±1		3
	6.3	1.9		10
	7.76	2.37		11
	7.4,8.4	-	in emulsion (3)(4)	15
	13.0,14.1	-	" "	19
	5.9	0.5		29
	17.6	-	in emulsion	34
-- , o-methyl-	13.9	-	" "	34
-- , p-methyl-	7.7	-	" "	34
-- , m : p-(60:40)methyl-	13.4	-	" "	34
Vinyl acetate	4.4	0		1
	7.32	5.24		5
	3.2	0		6
	4.2	<1		18
	4.2	0		22
	9.4±0.8	-		36
Vinyl chloride	3.7	4.2		17
Vinylidene chloride	25	40	solvent: hexane	9

NOTES

1. Initiation by di-tert-butyl peroxide and UV-light
2. Initiation by acetone and UV-light
3. Initiation by persulfate
4. Initiation by cumene hydroperoxide and triethylenetetramine

REFERENCES

1. G. M. Burnett and H. W. Melville; Nature 156, 661 (1945).
2. W. V. Smith, J. Amer. Chem. Soc. 70, 3695 (1948).
3. C. H. Bamford and M. J. S. Dewar, Proc. Roy. Soc. (London) A 192, 309 (1948).
4. M. S. Matheson, E. E. Auer, E. B. Bevilacqua and E. J. Hart, J. Amer. Chem. Soc. 71, 497 (1949).
5. M. S. Matheson, E. E. Auer, E. B. Bevilacqua and E. J. Hart, J. Amer. Chem. Soc. 71, 2610 (1949).
6. G. Dixon-Lewis, Proc. Roy. Soc. (London) A 198, 510 (1949).
7. M. H. Mackay and H. W. Melville; Trans. Faraday Soc. 45, 323 (1949).
8. H. W. Melville and A. F. Brickel, Trans. Faraday Soc. 45, 1049 (1949).
9. J. D. Burnett and H. W. Melville, Trans. Faraday Soc. 46, 976 (1950).
10. G. M. Burnett, Trans. Faraday Soc. 47, 772 (1950).
11. M. S. Matheson, E. E. Auer, E. B. Bevilacqua and E. J. Hart, J. Amer. Chem. Soc. 73, 1700 (1951).
12. M. S. Matheson, E. E. Auer, E. B. Bevilacqua and E. J. Hart, J. Amer. Chem. Soc. 73, 5395 (1951).
13. D. H. Volman, J. Chem. Phys. 19, 668 (1951).
14. M. Morton, P. P. Salatiello and H. Landfield, J. Polymer Sci. 8, 215 (1952).
15. M. Morton, P. P. Salatiello and H. Landfield, J. Polymer Sci. 8, 279 (1952).
16. D. H. Volman, and W. M. Graven, J. Amer. Chem. Soc. 75, 3111 (1953).
17. G. M. Burnett and W. W. Wright, Proc. Roy. Soc. (London) A 221, 41 (1954).
18. W. J. Bengough and H. W. Melville, Proc. Roy. Soc. (London) A 230, 429 (1955).
19. E. Bartholome, H. Gerrens, R. Herbeck and H. Weitz, Z. Elektrochem. 60, 334 (1956).
20. N. Grassie, E. Vance, Trans. Faraday Soc. 52, 727 (1956).
21. L. C. Landers and D. H. Volman, J. Amer. Chem. Soc. 79, 2996 (1957).
22. W. J. Bengough, Trans. Faraday Soc. 54, 868 (1958).
23. Z. A. Sinitsyna and Kh. S. Bagdasaryan, Zh. Fiz. Khim. 32, 1319 (1958).
24. Z. Laita and Z. Machacek, J. Polymer Sci. 38, 459 (1959).
25. F. S. Dainton and R. S. Eaton, J. Polymer Sci. 39, 313 (1959).
26. W. J. Bengough and H. W. Melville, Proc. Roy. Soc. (London) A 249, 445 (1959).
27. D. H. Grant and N. Grassie, Trans. Faraday Soc. 55, 1042 (1959).
28. P. Hyden and H. Melville, J. Polymer Sci. 43, 201 (1960).
29. G. Henrici-Olive and S. Olive, Makromol. Chem. 37, /1 (1960).
30. G. V. Schulz, G. Henrici-Olive and S. Olive, Z. Physik. Chem. (Frankfurt), 27, 1 (1960).
31. W. Rabel and K. Ueberreiter, Ber. Bunsenges. 67, 710 (1963).
32. N. Colebourne, E. Collinson, D. J. Currie and F. S. Dainton, Trans. Faraday Soc. 59, 1357 (1963).
33. F. S. Dainton and W. D. Sisley, Trans. Faraday Soc. 59, 1369 (1963).
34. K. P. Paoletti and F. W. Billmeyer, Jr., J. Polymer Sci. A 2, 2049 (1964).
35. A. F. Revzin and Kh. S. Bagdasaryan; Zh. Fiz. Khim. 38, 1020 (1964).
36. T. A. Berezsnich-Földes and F. Tüdős, Vysokomolekul. Soedin. 6, 1529 (1964).

INHIBITORS AND INHIBITION CONSTANTS IN FREE RADICAL POLYMERIZATION

J. Ulbricht

Deutsche Akademie der Wissenschaften zu Berlin
Institut für Faserstoff-Forschung
Teltow-Seehof, Germany*

The inhibition constant k_z is the rate constant of the reaction of a polymer radical P· with an inhibitor molecule Z:

$$P\cdot + Z \xrightarrow{\ k_z\ } X$$

X may represent unreactive or reactive products which can terminate or partially re-generate polymer chains as well as cause copolymerization of Z with the monomer M. The reaction of the inhibitor reduces more or less the overall rate of the polymerization.

The determination of the inhibition constant requires an exact kinetical analysis of each separate process, which has not been carried out in most cases. Generally only the ratio k_z/k_p is obtained, where k_p is the rate constant of the propagation reaction:

$$P\cdot + M \xrightarrow{\ k_p\ } P\cdot$$

Inhibitor	Monomer	Temp. °C	k_z/k_p	k_z (1/mole·sec)	Ref.
Acetophenone	methyl acrylate	50	-	<0.25	10
	vinyl acetate	50	0.0091	16	11,13
Aniline	methyl acrylate	50	0.0001	<0.1	10,13
	vinyl acetate	50	0.015	26	11,13
-- , o-nitro-	methyl acrylate	50	0.00341	-	10
-- , m-nitro-	" "	50	0.00421	4.21	10,13
-- , p-nitro-	" "	50	0.00267	2.67	10,13
	vinyl acetate	50	4.97	8500	11,13
Anisol					
-- , m-nitro-	methyl acrylate	50	0.00727	7.2	10,13
-- , p-nitro-	styrene	50	0.035	-	15
-- , 1,3,5-trinitro-	styrene	50	20.3	-	14
Anthracene	acrylonitrile	50	2.67	2670	12
	methyl acrylate	50	0.098	100	10
	vinyl acetate	50	20.9	36000	11,13
Benzene					
-- , bromo-	vinyl acetate	50	0.0019	3.3	11,13
-- , diazoamino-	methyl acrylate	50	0.00419	-	10

* Present address : Institut für Chemie und Technologie der Hochpolymeren
Technische Hochschule für Chemie, Leuna-Merseburg, Germany

Inhibitor	Monomer	Temp. °C	k_z/k_p	k_z (1/mole·sec)	Ref.
Benzene (Cont'd.)					
-- , o-dinitro-	methyl acrylate	50	0.018	-	10
	styrene	50	2.82	-	15
	vinyl acetate	45	96	-	1,2
-- , m-dinitro-	methyl acrylate	44.1	-	58	6
		50	0.0309	30.9	10,13
	methyl methacrylate	44.1	0.0048	2.2	4
	styrene	50	5.17	-	15
	vinyl acetate	45	105	-	1,2
		50	66.0	113000	11,13
-- , p-dinitro-	styrene	50	13.52	-	15
	vinyl acetate	45	267	-	1,2
		50	68.5	116000	11,13
-- , nitro-	methyl acrylate	50	0.00464	4.64	10,13
	styrene	50	0.326	-	15
	vinyl acetate	45	19	-	1
	" "	50	11.2	19300	11,13
-- , nitro-d_5-	methyl acrylate	50	0.00468	-	10
-- , p-nitro-chloro-	styrene	50	0.364	-	15
-- , 1,3,5-trinitro-	methyl acrylate	50	0.204	204	10,13
	styrene	50	64.2	-	14
	vinyl acetate	45	890	-	2
	" "	50	404	760000	11,13
Benzoic acid					
-- , p-nitro-	methyl acrylate	50	0.0107	10.7	10,13
	vinyl acetate	50	24.9	43000	11,13
-- , - , ethyl ester	styrene	50	1.68	-	15
-- , 1,3,5-trinitro-, ethyl ester	styrene	50	57.2	-	14
Benzonitrile	methyl acrylate	50	-	<0.1	13
	vinyl acetate	50	0.0041	7.1	11,13
Benzophenone	methyl acrylate	50	-	<0.15	13
	vinyl acetate	50	0.030	50	11,13
p-Benzoquinone	allyl acetate	80	50	-	3
	acrylonitrile	50	0.91	910	12
	methyl acrylate	44.1	-	1200	6
	methyl methacrylate	44.1	5.5	2400	4
		60	4.5	-	5
	styrene	50	518±25	-	16
		60	227	-	5
		90	560	-	3
p-Benzoquinone					
-- , chloro-	styrene	50	720±70	-	16
-- , 2,5-dichloro-	methyl acrylate	44.1	-	10200	6

References page II-75

Inhibitor	Monomer	Temp. °C	k_z/k_p	k_z (1/mole·sec)	Ref.
p-Benzoquinone (Cont'd.)					
-- , 2,5-dichloro-	methyl methacrylate	44.1	-	5500	6
	styrene	50	>0.0002	-	18
-- , 2,6-dichloro-	methyl acrylate	44.1	-	16700	6
	methyl methacrylate	44.1	-	16500	6
	styrene	50	$>10^{-4}$	-	18
-- , 2,3-dimethyl-	styrene	50	120±20	-	16
-- , 2,5-dimethyl-	styrene	40	106	-	17
(Phlorone)	styrene	50	82±10	-	16
	styrene	60	61	-	17
	styrene	90	43	-	3
-- , methoxy-	styrene	50	193±10	-	16
-- , methyl-	styrene	50	266±15	-	16
-- , tetrabromo- (Bromanil)	styrene	50	618±10	-	18
-- , tetrachloro- (Chloranil)	methyl acrylate	44.1	-	2000	6
	methyl methacrylate	44.1	0.26	120	4
	styrene	50	2040	-	18
-- , tetraiodo- (Iodanil)	styrene	50	2740±30	-	18
-- , tetramethyl-	allyl acetate	80	4.1	-	3
(Duroquinone)	styrene	90	0.68	-	3
-- , trichloro-	styrene	50	$>10^4$	-	18
-- , trimethyl-	styrene	50	25±5	-	16
Benzoyl chloride	methyl acrylate	50	-	<0.15	13
	vinyl acetate	50	0.037	64	11,13
Diphenyl	methyl acrylate	50	-	<0.2	13
	vinyl acetate	50	0.027	46	11,13
-- , nitro-	methyl acrylate	50	0.00604	-	10
Diphenylamine	vinyl acetate	50	0.014	24	11,13
Diphenylpicrylhydrazyl	methyl methacrylate	44.1	2000	-	4
Durene, dinitro-	vinyl acetate	45	1.3	-	1
Ferric chloride in N,N-dimethylformamide	acrylonitrile	60	3.33	6500	9
	methacrylonitrile	60	3.08	620	9
	methyl acrylate	60	-	6800	9
	methyl methacrylate	60	-	5000	9
	styrene	60	536	94000	9
	vinyl acetate	60	-	2350000	9
Fluorene	methyl acrylate	50	0.00602	-	10
Furfurylidene malononitrile	methyl acrylate	44.1	-	2900	6
	methyl methacrylate	44.1	1.2	550	4

Inhibitor	Monomer	Temp. °C	k_z/k_p	k_z (1/mole·sec)	Ref.
Methane, triphenyl-	methyl acrylate	50	0.00283	-	10
$(C_6H_5)_3 CH_{o,3} D_{o,7}$	methyl acrylate	50	0.00144	-	10
Naphthalene	methyl acrylate	50	-	<0.2	13
	vinyl acetate	50	0.144	25.5	11,13
-- , 1,5-dinitro-	methyl acrylate	50	0.0151	-	10
α-Naphthol	methyl acrylate	50	0.00496	-	10
-- , 2-nitro-	methyl acrylate	50	0.0111	-	10
β-Naphthol					
-- , 1-nitro-	methyl acrylate	50	0.0154	-	10
Oxygen	methyl methacrylate	50	33000	10^7	7
	styrene	50	14600	10^6-10^7	8
Phenanthrene	methyl acrylate	50	0.0026	2.6	10,13
	vinyl acetate	50	0.57	98.0	11,13
Phenol	methyl acrylate	50	0.0002	<0.2	10,13
	vinyl acetate	50	0.012	21	11,13
-- , 2,4-dinitro-	methyl acrylate	50	0.0649	-	10
-- , o-nitro-	methyl acrylate	50	0.0108	-	10
-- , m-nitro-	methyl acrylate	50	0.00562	5.62	10,13
-- , p-nitro-	methyl acrylate	50	0.00426	4.26	10,13
	vinyl acetate	50	9.07	15500	11,13
Picramide	styrene	50	11.8	-	14
Picric acid	methyl acrylate	50	0.319	-	10
	styrene	50	211	-	14
Picryl chloride	styrene	50	58.5	-	14
Stilbene	methyl acrylate	50	0.00196	-	10
Sulfur	methyl acrylate	44.1	-	1100	6
	methyl methacrylate	44.1	0.075	40	4
	vinyl acetate	45	470	-	2
Toluene	vinyl acetate	50	0.0012	2.1	11,13
-- , p-bromo-	vinyl acetate	50	0.0021	3.6	11,13
-- , 2,4-dinitro-	methyl acrylate	50	0.0188	-	10
	styrene	50	1.543	-	15
-- , o-nitro-	methyl acrylate	50	0.00323	-	10
	styrene	50	0.055	-	15
-- , m-nitro-	methyl acrylate	50	0.00412	4.12	10,13
-- , p-nitro-	methyl acrylate	50	0.00486	4.86	10,13
	styrene	50	0.203	-	15
	vinyl acetate	45	20	-	1
		50	10.8	18600	10,13
-- , 1,3,5-trinitro-	methyl acrylate	44.1	-	105	6
		50	0.0596	-	10
	methyl methacrylate	44.1	0.05	23	4
	styrene	50	14.6	-	14
	vinyl acetate	45	890	-	2
Tolunitrile	vinyl acetate	50	0.0039	6.7	11,13
p-Xylene	vinyl acetate	50	0.0015	2.6	11,13

REFERENCES

1. P. D. Bartlett and H. Kwart, J. Amer. Chem. Soc. 72, 1051 (1950).
2. P. D. Bartlett and H. Kwart, J. Amer. Chem. Soc. 74, 3969 (1952).
3. P. J. Flory, "Principles of Polymer Chemistry," Cornell University Press, New York (1953), p. 172.
4. J. L. Kice, J. Amer. Chem. Soc. 76, 6274 (1954).
5. J. C. Bevington, N. A. Chanem and H. W. Melville, J. Chem. Soc. (London) 1955, 2822.
6. J. L. Kice, J. Polymer Sci. 19, 123 (1956).
7. G. V. Schulz and G. Henrici, Makromol. Chem. 18/19, 437 (1956).
8. G. Henrici-Olive and S. Olive, Makromol. Chem. 24, 64 (1957).
9. C. H. Bamford, A. D. Jenkins and R. Johnston, Proc. Roy. Soc. (London) A 239, 214 (1957); J. Polymer Sci. 29, 355 (1958).
10. Z. A. Sinytsina and Kh. S. Bagdasaryan, Zh. Fiz. Khim. 32, 2663 (1958).
11. Z. A. Sinytsina and Kh. S. Bagdasaryan, Zh. Fiz. Khim. 34, 1110 (1960).
12. Z. A. Sinytsina and Kh. S. Bagdasaryan, Zh. Fiz. Khim. 34, 2736 (1960).
13. Kh. S. Bagdasaryan and Z. A. Sinytsina, J. Polymer Sci. 52, 31 (1961).
14. F. Tüdös, J. Kende and M. Azori, J. Polymer Sci. 53, 17 (1961), A1 1369 (1963).
15. F. Tüdös, J. Kende and M. Azori, Vysokomolekul. Soedin. 4, 1262 (1962).
16. F. Tüdös and L. Simandi, Vysokomolekul. Soedin. 4, 1271 (1962).
17. F. Tüdös and L. Simandi, Vysokomolekul. Soedin. 4, 1425 (1962).
18. F. Tüdös, L. Simandi and M. Azori, Vysokomolekul. Soedin. 4, 1431 (1962).

TRANSFER CONSTANTS TO MONOMER, POLYMER, CATALYST AND
SOLVENT IN FREE RADICAL POLYMERIZATION

L. J. Young
The Dow Chemical Company
Midland, Michigan

G. Brandrup
Research Triangle Institute
Durham, North Carolina

J. Brandrup
Chemstrand Research Center
Durham, North Carolina

Contents

A. INTRODUCTION

The transfer reaction in radical polymerization describes a process in which further growth of the individual polymer molecule is prevented but which does not interfere with the kinetic chain. The polymer radical reacts with an atom from another molecule (monomer, solvent, catalyst, etc.) forming dead polymer and a new radical.

$$P \cdot + RS \rightarrow PR + S \cdot$$

This new radical can continue the kinetic chain. If the activity of the latter radical is similar to that of the former, the transfer process will have no influence upon the overall polymerization kinetics, but the molecular weight of the polymer produced will be less than it would be without this transfer reaction. In other words, a single kinetic chain produces several polymer molecules with the aid of the transfer reaction.

The quantitative treatment of this transfer process defines a dimensionless transfer constant C as the ratio of the rate of the transfer reaction to the rate of propagation and is determined by the following expression (reference 84):

$$\frac{1}{\overline{P}_n} = \frac{1}{\overline{P}_{n,o}} + C_X \frac{[X]}{[M]}$$

$\overline{P}_n$ = number average molecular weight obtained in the presence of transfer agent X.

$\overline{P}_{n,o}$ = number average molecular weight obtained in the absence of transfer agent X.

C_X = transfer constant to transfer agent X.

[M] = monomer concentration

[X] = transfer agent concentration.

This expression is limited to cases, where $\dfrac{1}{\overline{P}_{n,o}}$ is a constant.

This holds only under certain conditions, for instance, if the rate of propagation is dependent on the square root of the monomer concentration (97).

A more general equation is given by the following (reference 97):

$$\frac{1}{\overline{P}_n} = A \frac{R_p}{[M]^2} + \Sigma\, C_X \frac{[X]}{[M]}$$

Where $A = \dfrac{k_{t,k} + 2k_{t,d}}{2k_p^2}$

and $\Sigma\, C_X \dfrac{[X]}{[M]} = C_M + C_I \dfrac{[I]}{[M]} + C_S \dfrac{[S]}{[M]} + C_P \dfrac{[P]}{[M]} + \ldots$

R_p = overall rate of polymerization

$k_{t,d}$ = constant of termination by disproportionation

$k_{t,k}$ = constant of termination by combination

k_p = propagation constant

[M] = concentration of monomer

[I] = concentration of catalyst

[S] = concentration of solvent

[P] = concentration of polymer

C_M = transfer constant to monomer $(k_{tr,M}/k_p)$

C_I = transfer constant to catalyst $(k_{tr,I}/k_p)$

C_S = transfer constant to solvent $(k_{tr,S}/k_p)$

C_P = transfer constant to polymer $(k_{tr,P}/k_p)$

The transfer constant is obtained by measuring the number average molecular weight of the polymer at different concentrations of the transfer agent X, all other variables being kept constant. The first part of the right side of this equation is calculated first and used with its numerical value. The slope of the plot ΣC_X [X]/[M] against [X]/[M] yields the transfer constant. Details of this evaluation can be found in the article of G. Henrici-Olivé and S. Olivé (97).

The transfer constant of a very reactive molecule can also be determined from the rate of disappearance of transfer agent and monomer.

$$\frac{d\ln[X]}{d\ln[M]} = C_X$$

The tables contain all data found in the literature. Some data (indicated by the letters j, s, or t) have to be used with caution especially if the correct molecular weight average has not been used, or if possible retardation of the polymerization rate has not been taken into account. Whereever possible, these errors have been mentioned. Unless otherwise noted, constants are assumed to have been determined in bulk, using azo-type initiators.

Remarks page II-134; References page II-135

B. Transfer Constants to Monomers

Monomer	T°C	$C_M \cdot 10^4$	Remarks	References
Acrylamide	25	0.2	e	67
	60	0.6	e	67
Acrylonitrile	20	0.18	e	204
	25	0.105		192
	30	1.5	f(DMSO)	128
	40	0.17		192
	50	0.050	f(ZC)	281
		0.27	f(MPC)	261
		8.2	f(SO_2)	253
	60	0.26		63
		0.3		14
Allyl acetate	80	1/6		20
		700		18
Allyl chloride	80	1600		18
Bornyl methacrylate	60	2.85		106
p-Bromostyrene	50	23		124
Butyl methacrylate	60	0.14		179
N,N-Dimethylacrylamide	50	1.5		183
Ethyl 2-chloroacrylate	60	3.0		234
Ethylene	50-70	5	x(1470)	147
	83	5.0	d,x	134
		5.32	d,x	135
Ethyl methacrylate	45	0.248	cc	125
	60	0.259	cc	125
	80	0.456	cc	125
	90	0.442	cc	125
p-Iodostyrene	50	1.9	f(B)	38
Isobornyl methacrylate	60	1.85		106
Isobutyl methacrylate	35	0.189	dd	125
	50	0.179	dd	125
	60	0.14		179
		0.165	f(B)	179
		0.224	dd	125
	80	0.301	dd	125
	100	0.382	dd	125
Maleic anhydride	75	750	c	114
Methacrylonitrile	25	2.08	z	82
	60	5.81	z	82
	70	8.00	z	82
	80	10.05	z	82
p-Methoxystyrene	0	0.198		6
	60	0.74		35
Methyl acrylate	55	0.275	c,aa	149
	60	0.036	b,aa	149
		0.325	c,aa	149
	65	0.10	c,aa	149
		0.11	c,f(EA)	81
		0.11	c,aa	149
		0.37	c,aa	149

Monomer	T°C	$C_M \cdot 10^4$	Remarks	References
Methyl acrylate (Cont'd.)	70	0.01	c,f(EA)	220
		0.072	b,aa	149
		0.16	c,aa	149
		0.18	c,aa	149
		0.405	c,aa	149
	75	0.224	c,aa	149
		0.25	c,aa	149
		0.25	c,f(EA)	81
3-Methyl-3-buten-2-one	80	4.00	c	57
Methyl methacrylate	0	0.128		46
		0.148		9
	30	0.117		46
		0.260	d	152
	50	0.10	f(B)	99,225
		0.15		97
		0.477	d	152
		0.85		46
	60	0.07		185
		0.10		25,197,216
		0.103	c	215
		0.18		97
	65	0.20		81
	70	0.17	c,f(EA)	81
		0.23		97
		0.29	c,f(Tol)	81
		0.30		81
		0.45		68
		0.807	d	152
	75	0.27	c,f(EA)	81
		0.33	c	81
		0.60	c,f(EMK)	81
		0.70	c,f(B)	81
	80	0.25		97
		0.40		81
	90	0.10		99
	100	0.38		97
	120	0.58		97
Styrene	0	~0	bb	251
		0.108		8,46
	25	0.279		46,166
		0.358		8
	27	0.31	a	97
	30	0.2	bb	217,251
		0.32		166
	45	0.3	bb	251
	50	0.35	h	266,267
		0.40	f(B)	225,217
		0.50	c,h	267
		0.6	c	97
		0.62	a,k	97
		0.65	b,c,h	267
		0.78	a	98
	60	0.6		25,112,151
		0.6	c	97,162
		0.6	bb	217,251
		0.79	a	97
		0.85	a,f	97
		1.1		35
	67.8	1.0		25
	70	0	c,f(EA)	81
		0.6	bb	251
		0.6		68
		0.8	b,h	267

Remarks page II-134; References page II-135

Monomer	T°C	$C_M \cdot 10^4$	Remarks	References
Styrene (Cont'd.)	70	0.96		45
		1.16	a	97
		1.35	a	97
		2.0	c,f(B)	81
	75	0	c,f(EA)	81
		1.6	c	81
		5.0	c,f(B)	81
		5.00	c,f(EMK)	81
	80	0.7		66
		0.75	bb	251
		1.00		217
	80.3	4.0		25
	90	0.85	bb	251
		1.25	c,f	97
		1.47	a	97
		1.79	a	97
	99	1.5		66
	100	1.72	a	97
		1.8	a,f	97
		1.83	a	97
	110	2.80	a	97
	117	1.40		217
	132	2.45	a	97
		3.0	a,f	97
		3.4	a	97
		5.33	a	97
Vinyl acetate	0	0.90	i(65)	58
	20	0.94		226
	25	1.3	i(132)	58
		1.45	i(132)	58
		2.4	d	132
		10.7		46
	40	1.29		5
		1.32		226
	50	1.29		5
		4.55	c	47
		20		153
	60	1.75		5
		1.91		226
		1.93		240
		2.0		156
		2.1	i(241)	97
		2.4		199
		2.5	c	58
		2.5		110
		2.6		110
		2.8	c	53
	70	2.4		278
		2.9	i(278)	58
Vinyl benzoate	60	6.0		219,270
	80	7.0		17
	95	2.0		219
		4.0		143
Vinyl butyrate	50	26.7		47
	80	22.3		130
Vinyl chloride	30	6.25	1	39
	40	50		167
	50	6.4	f(BA)	262
		7.8	f(BC)	262
		8.5		262
		13.5	1	39

Monomer	T°C	$C_M \cdot 10^4$	Remarks	References
Vinyl chloride (Cont'd.)	60	10.8	f(BA)	262
		12.3		262
		12.8	f(BC)	262
	70	23.8	1	39
Vinyl decanoate	50	45.5		47
Vinyl hexanoate	80	36		130
Vinyl isobutyrate	80	46		130
Vinyl 4-methylvalerate	80	24.8		130
Vinyl laurate	50	45.5		47
1-Vinylnaphthalene	50	290.		145
	60	310		145
	70	300		145
Vinyl propionate	50	48.9		47
4-Vinylpyridine	25	6.7		191
N-Vinylpyrrolidone	20	4.0		39
Vinyl salicylate	70	80.		93
Vinyl stearate	50	69.8		47
N-Vinylurethan	60	0.25		77

C. Transfer Constants to Polymers

Polymer	T°C	$C_p \cdot 10^4$	Remarks	References
Acrylonitrile				
Polyacrylonitrile	50	4.7	f(MPC)	261
	60	3.5	m	90
Poly(methyl methacrylate)	60	0.2	o	16
		240	n(-NHBu)	16
		900	n(-NEt$_2$)	16
		1270	n	16
Poly(sarcosine)	60	400		14
Cellulose	60	1.0	m,o	252
		11	m,n(-CH$_2$OH)	252
		20	m,n(-CHO)	252
1,3-Butadiene				
Poly(1,3-butadiene)	50	11		94
Butyl Methacrylate				
Poly(methyl methacrylate)	60	7700	n(-OC(:0)CH$_2$SH)	78

Remarks page II-134; References page II-135

Polymer	T°C	$C_p \cdot 10^4$	Remarks	References
		N,N-Dimethylacrylamide		
Poly(N,N-dimethylacrylamide)	50	0.61		183
		Ethyl Acrylate		
Poly(methyl methacrylate)	60	12800	$n(-OC(:0)CH_2SH)$	78
		Lauryl Methacrylate		
Poly(methyl methacrylate)	60	12800	$n(-OC(:0)CH_2SH)$	78
		Methyl Acrylate		
Poly(methyl acrylate)	60	0.5	m	142
		1.0	m	69
Poly(methyl methacrylate)	60	18000	$n(-OC(:0)CH_2SH)$	78
		Methyl Methacrylate		
Polyethylene	50	0.6		139
Poly(methyl methacrylate)	50	0.22	o	99
		1.5	o	224
		1.5	o	225
		350	n	224
		360	n	225
		1000	n	99
	60	0.1		69
		1.5	o	224
		2.1		177
		360	n	224
	80	2.48		177
	90	0.22	o	99
		1000	n	99
Polypropylene	50	1.0		139
Polystyrene	50	0.75		100
	60	2.20		177
	80	2.95		177
Poly(vinyl acetate)	60	2.0		178
	80	2.8		178
Poly(vinyl chloride)	--	11		168
Rubber, natural	50	10.9		174
		11.0	c	174
		Styrene		
Poly(ethyleneglycol), dodecyl ether	60	20		189
Poly(methyl methacrylate)	50	<0.3	o	224
		0.4	o	225
		1100	n	224
		1140	n	225
	60	16.4	$n(-CBr_3)$	42
		17.5	$n(-CBr_3^-)$	42
		57000	$n(-C(OH)HCH_2SH)$	78
		320000	$n(-OC(:0)CH_2^-SH)$	78
	80	3.74		177
	100	6.04		177

Polymer	T °C	$C_p \cdot 10^4$	Remarks	References
		Styrene (Cont'd.)		
Poly(pentaerythritol dibromide adipate)	60	4.05	m	223
Polypropylene	130	0.30		137
Polystyrene	50	1.9		96,100
		4.5		225
		14.0		225
		16.6		115
	55	15		116
	60	0.8	m	69
		1.9		48
		3.1		69
		15.4	n($-CBr_3$)	42
		15.8	n($-CBr_3$)	42
		16.6		115
	90	5.8		225
	100	2.0	o	187
	110	9.2		116
		10.8		115
	130	1.8		28
	154	1.5		28
Poly(vinyl acetate)	100	6.6		178
	130	9.2		178
Poly(vinyl chloride)	--	160		168
Poly(2-vinylpyridine)	50	8-10		190
		Vinyl Acetate		
Poly(ethyleneglycol)	60	17	o	188
	40		n	188
Poly(ethyleneglycol), dodecyl ether	60	10	n(dodecyl)	188
	40		n(C_2H_4OH)	188
		750		182
Poly(methyl methacrylate)	60	21		178
	75	26		178
Polystyrene	40	12		178
	60	15		178
	75	19		178
Poly(vinyl acetate)	-15	0.36		65
	0	0.5		65
		1.7		242
	11	2	p	97
	21	4	p	97
	31	16	p	97
	40	11.2		5
		30.9		28
		32.0		178
	50	3		28
		10.2		5
	60	1.4		110,111
		1.8		240
		1.9		226
		2.5		227
		3.0		108
		4.0		69
		6.8		5

Remarks page II-134; References page II-135

Polymer	T °C	$C_p \cdot 10^4$	Remarks	References
	Vinyl Acetate (Cont'd.)			
Poly(vinyl acetate) (Cont'd.)	60	8.0		69
		47.0		178
	60-70	3.5		242
	70	2	q	278
		4	p	278
Poly(vinyl acetate-co-vinyl chloride)	60	0.21	VCl-part	109
		3.0	VOAc-part	109
	Vinyl Chloride			
Poly(vinyl chloride)	50	5	m	141
	Vinyl Hexanoate			
Poly(ethyleneglycol), dodecyl ether	60	780		189
	N Vinylpyrrolidone			
Dextran	50	5		231
		5.87		133

D. Transfer Constants to Catalysts

Catalyst	T °C	C_I	Remarks	References
	Acrylamide			
Bisulfite ion	75	0.17	$f(H_2O)$	244
	Acrylonitrile			
Isobutyronitrile				
-- , 2,2'-azobis-	50	0	$f(SO_2)$	253
	60	0		63
	Ethylene			
Azoethane				
-- , 1,1-dimethyl-	83	0.5	d,x	134
		0.51	d,x	135
	Maleic Anhydride			
Peroxide				
-- , benzoyl	75	2.63		114
	Methacrylonitrile			
Isobutyronitrile				
-- , 2,2'-azobis-	60	0		82

Catalyst	T°C	C_I	Remarks	References

Methyl Acrylate

Catalyst	T°C	C_I	Remarks	References
Hydroperoxide				
-- , tert-butyl	60	0.01		149
	70	0.0266		149
Peroxide				
-- , benzoyl	55	0.0143		149
	60	0.0246		149
	65	0.0375		149
	70	∼0.01	c,f(EA)	220
		0.05		149
-- , 2-butanone	65	0.05		149
		0.05	f(EA)	81
	70	0.077		149
	75	0.113		149
		0.113	f(EA)	81
-- , tert-butyl	65	0.00047		149
	70	0.00082		149
	75	0.00111		149

3-Methyl-3-buten-2-one

Catalyst	T°C	C_I	Remarks	References
Peroxide				
-- , benzoyl	80	0.0509		57

Methyl Methacrylate

Catalyst	T°C	C_I	Remarks	References
Butyronitrile				
-- , 2-ethyl-				
-- , - , 2,2'-azobis-	60	0		216
-- , 2-methyl-				
-- , - , 2,2'-azobis-	60	0		216
-- , 2,3,3-trimethyl-				
-- , - , 2,2'-azobis-	60	0		216
Cyclohexanecarbonitrile,				
-- , 1,1'-azodi-	60	0		216
Hydroperoxide				
-- , tert-butyl	60	1.27		25
-- , α,α-dimethylbenzyl	60	0.33		25
Isobutyronitrile				
-- 2,2'-azobis-	50	∼0	f(B)	225
	60	0	f(EA)	25,197,216
Peroxide				
-- , p-anisoyl	60	0.037		215
-- , benzoyl	50	0.01		97
	60	∼0		25
		0.02	i(25)	97
-- , - , m-chloro-	60	0.003		215
-- , - , o-chloro-	60	0.019		215
		0.35	f(EA)	197
		0.8	i(197)	97

Remarks page II-134; References page II-135

Catalyst	T°C	C_I	Remarks	References

Methyl Methacrylate (Cont'd.)

Peroxide (Cont'd.)
-- , benzoyl

Catalyst	T°C	C_I	Remarks	References
-- , - , p-chloro-	60	0.009		215
-- , - , m-nitro-	60	0.012		215
-- , - , p-nitro-	60	0.144		215
-- , 2-butanone	65	0.0025	f(B)	81
		0.00698		81
	70	0.0033	f(Tol)	81
		0.0033	f(FA)	81
		0.0040	f(EMK)	81
		0.0092		81
	75	0.00553	f(EMK)	81
		0.00667	f(B)	81
		0.0071	f(EA)	81
		0.0089		81
	80	0.0111	f(Tol)	81
		0.0128		81
-- , cinnamoyl	60	0.009		215
-- , hydrogen	60	0.046	f(EMK)	197
-- , palmitoyl	60	∼0		215
		0.16	i(215)	97
-- , o-toluoyl	60	0.046		215
		0.06	i(215)	97

Valeronitrile
-- , 2-methyl-

Catalyst	T°C	C_I	Remarks	References
-- , - , 2,2'-azobis-	60	0		216

Styrene

Formamide
-- , 2-cyano-2-propylazo-

Catalyst	T°C	C_I	Remarks	References
-- , 2-cyano-2-propylazo-	100	0.17		32

Hydroperoxide
-- , tert-butyl

Catalyst	T°C	C_I	Remarks	References
-- , tert-butyl	60	0.035		112
	70	0.051	h	267
		0.060		274
		0.063	f(DCB)	275
		0.064		275
		0.066	f(B,CB)	275
	80	0.0033		264
-- , α,α-dimethylbenzyl	40	0.052	h	267
(Cumene hydroperoxide)	50	0.069	h	267
	60	0.063		112
	70	0.082	h	267
		0.10		274
-- , - , p-isopropyl-	70	0.033	h	267
-- , 1-menth-8-yl	50	0.048	h	267
-- , pinanyl	70	0.026	h	267

Isobutyronitrile
-- , 2,2'-azobis-

Catalyst	T°C	C_I	Remarks	References
-- , 2,2'-azobis-	50	0	h	267
		∼0	f(B)	225
	60	0		217
		0		112

Catalyst	T°C	C_I	Remarks	References

Styrene (Cont'd.)

Peroxide

Catalyst	T°C	C_I	Remarks	References
-- , acetyl	70	0		59,146
-- , anisoyl	70	0.074		59
-- , benzoyl	22	~0.1	d	43
	50	0.13		39
	60	0.048		112
		0.055		162
	70	0		146
		0.075		59
		0.12		45
		0.18		39,43
	80	0.13		39,43
-- , - , p-acetoxy-	70	0.187		59
-- , - , m-bromo-	70	0.465		59
-- , - , o-bromo-	50	1.0		39,43
	70	2.17		59
-- , - , p-bromo-	70	0.193		59
-- , - , p-tert-butyl-	70	0		59
-- , - , m-chloro-	70	0.346		59
-- , - , o-chloro-	22	~2.0	d	43
	70	1.91		59
-- , - , p-chloro-	70	0.216		146
-- , - , p-cyano-	70	0.804		59
-- , - , 2,4-dichloro-	60	2.9		146
	70	2.6		146
-- , - , m-fluoro-	70	0.246		59
-- , - , o-fluoro-	70	0.40		59
-- , - , p-fluoro-	70	0.219		59
-- , - , m-iodo-	70	0.262		59
-- , - , p-iodo-	70	0.293		59
-- , - , p-methoxycarbonyloxy-	70	0.208		59
-- , - , m-nitro-	70	6.2		59
-- , - , p-nitro-	70	7.4		59
-- , 2-butanone	50	0.46	h	267
	70	0.0667	f(B)	81
		0.1250	f(EA)	81
		0.1670	f(EMK)	81
	75	0.1250	f(B)	81
		0.1670	f(EA)	81
		0.2000	f(EMK)	81
		0.243		81
-- , tert-butoxymaleoyl	70	1.52		59

Catalyst	T °C	C_I	Remarks	References

Styrene (Cont'd.)

Peroxide (Cont'd.)

Catalyst	T °C	C_I	Remarks	References
-- , tert-butoxyphthaloyl	70	0.018		59
-- , butyl	60	0.00076	f(DX)	207
		0.00092	f(B)	207
	80	0.0029	f(DX)	207
-- , sec-butyl	60	0.0004	f(B)	206
	80	0.0021	f(B)	206
-- , tert-butyl	60	0.000234	f(DX)	208
		0.0003		208
		0.0006	f(B,Hep)	208
		0.00086		205
		0.0013		209
	70	0.039	f(B)	275
	80	0.0022	f(B)	208
		0.0033		264
-- , butyroyl	70	0.018		59
-- , cinnamoyl	70	1.10		59
-- , crotonoyl	70	0.146		59
-- , cyclohexanone	60	0.062		24
-- , α,α-dimethylbenzyl	50	0.01	h	267
-- , ethyl	60	0.00066	f(B)	206
	80	0.0024	f(B)	206
-- , furoyl	70	0.23		59
-- , hexanoyl	70	0.166		59
-- , hydroxyheptyl	50	<0.005	h	267
-- , isopropyl	60	0.0003	f(B)	206
	80	0.0015	f(B)	206
-- , lauroyl	70	0		146
		0.024		59
	84	0		146
-- , myristoyl	70	0		146
		0.116		59
-- , 2-naphthoyl	70	0.178		59
-- , octanoyl	70	0		146
		0.098		59
-- , oleoyl	70	0.154		59
-- , palmitoyl	70	0.142		59
-- , 2,4-pentadienoyl				
-- , - , 5-phenyl-	70	5.24		59
-- , propyl	60	0.00084		210
-- , sorboyl	70	1.19		59

Catalyst	T°C	C_I	Remarks	References

Styrene (Cont'd.)

Catalyst	T°C	C_I	Remarks	References
Peroxide (Cont'd.)				
-- , stearoyl	70	0.154		59
-- , 2-thenoyl	50	0.23		43
	70	0.38		43
-- , o-toluoyl	70	0.175		59
-- , p-toluoyl	50	0.17		43
	70	0.003		59
		0.19		43
-- , 9-undecenoyl	70	0.065		59

Vinyl Acetate

Catalyst	T°C	C_I	Remarks	References
Peroxide				
-- , benzoyl	60	0.09		156
		0.15		53
-- , - , m-bromo-	60	0.24		53
		0.6	i(53)	97
-- , - , o-bromo-	60	0.25		53
		3.5	i(53)	97
-- , - , p-bromo-	60	0.17		53
-- , - , o-chloro-	60	0.17	i(53)	97
-- , lauroyl	60	0.10		53
-- , palmitoyl	60	0.10		53
		0.17	i(53)	97

Vinyl benzoate

Catalyst	T°C	C_I	Remarks	References
Isobutyronitrile				
-- , 2,2'-azobis-	80	0		17
Peroxide				
-- , benzoyl	80	0.0527		17

Remarks page II-134; References page II-135

E. Transfer Constants to Solvents and Additives

Solvent	T°C	$c_S \cdot 10^4$	Remarks	References
Acrylamide				
Isopropyl alcohol	50	19	$f(H_2O)$	245
	80	7.2	$f(H_2O)$,t	245
Propionamide	25	220	e	67
	60	64	e	67
Acrylonitrile				
Acetamide				
-- , N,N-dimethyl-	50	4.945		260
		5.05		129
Acetic acid				
-- , ethyl ester	60	2.54	g	63
Acetone	60	1.13	g	63
Acetonitrile	60	2.0	f(SN)	58
Aluminum				
-- , hydrodiisobutyl	60	3940	f(DMF)	104
-- , triethyl	60	590	f(DMF)	104
Aniline	40	32.0	f(B),g	155
	50	44.0	f(B),g	155
		9600	$f(SO_2)$,g,j	154,155
	60	12200	$f(SO_2)$,g,j	155
-- , N,N-diethyl-	40	215	f(B),g	155
		58100	$f(SO_2)$,g,j	155
	50	359	f(B),g	155
		93800	$f(SO_2)$,g,j	154,155
	60	547	f(B),g	155
		143200	$f(SO_2)$,g,j	155
-- , N,N-dimethyl-	40	605	f(B),g	155
		11900	$f(SO_2)$,g,j	155
	50	708	f(B),g	155
		1040		105
		15400	$f(SO_2)$,g,j	154,155
		870	j	15
		964	f(B),g	155
		21800	$f(SO_2)$,g,j	155
Anthracene	50	18000		7
Arabinose	60	13.0	f(DMSO)	252
Benzene	60	2.46	g	63
-- , bromo-	60	1.36	g,t	63
-- , tert-butyl-	60	1.93	g	63
-- , chloro-	60	0.79	g,t	63
-- , ethyl-	60	35.73	g	63
-- , iodo-	60	5.19	g,t	63

Solvent	T°C	$c_S \cdot 10^4$	Remarks	References

Acrylonitrile (Cont'd.)

Solvent	T°C	$c_S \cdot 10^4$	Remarks	References
Benzoic acid				
-- , vinyl ester	65	1400		91
p-Benzoquinone	50	13000		7
Borane, tributyl-	60	6470	f(DMF)	104
2-Butanone	60	6.43	g	63
-- , 3-methyl-	60	21.08	g	63
Butyl alcohol	60	15.42	g	63
sec-Butyl alcohol	60	97.55	g	63
tert-Butyl alcohol	60	0.44	g	63
Butyric acid				
-- , 4-hydroxy, γ-lactone	50	0.658		260
		0.74		259
Cadmium, dibutyl-	60	55000	f(DMF)	104
Carbonic acid				
-- , cyclic ethylene ester	50	0.073		198
		0.33		129
		0.39		259
		0.474		260
		0.5		279
		1.0		247
	60	0.128		198
Carbon tetrabromide	60	500		11
		1900	f(DMF),j	15
Carbon tetrachloride	60	0.85	g	64
Chloroform	60	5.64	g	63
Copper(II) chloride ion, $(CuCl)^+$	35	180000	v(0.01)	277
		190000	v(0.1)	277
		320000	v(1.0)	277
Copper(II) sulfate	35	1900	$f(H_2O)$,j	277
		2800	j,w(0.0001)	277
		3000	j,v(0.01)	277
		10700	j,w(0.001)	277
		13500	j,v(0.1)	277
		39300	j,w(0.01)	277
		136000	j,v(1.0)	277
		210000	j,w(0.1)	277
Cumene	60	41.41	g	63
Cyclohexane	60	2.06	g	63
-- , methyl-	60	2.31	g	63
Diphenylamine-t	60	700	f(DMF)	41
Erythritol	60	12.8	f(DMSO)	252
Ethane				
-- , 1,2-dichloro-	60	1.47	g	63
-- 1,1,2,2-tetrachloro-	60	3.11	g	63

Remarks page II-134; References page II-135

Solvent	T°C	$c_S \cdot 10^4$	Remarks	References

Acrylonitrile (Cont'd.)

Solvent	T°C	$c_S \cdot 10^4$	Remarks	References
Ethane (Cont'd.)				
-- , 1,1,1-trichloro-	60	1.25	g	63
-- , 1,1,2-trichloro-	60	1.68	g	63
Ether				
-- , dodecyl vinyl	50	4.95	c	1
Ethylene carbonate - see Carbonic acid				
-- , cyclic ethylene ester				
Formamide				
-- , N,N-dimethyl-	50	1.0		239
		2.70		259
		2.78		129
		2.83		260
		10		247
	60	2.412		239
		4.494		13
		5.0	f(SN)	58
Glucose	60	6.9	f(DMSO)	252
α,D-Glucoside				
-- , methyl-	60	20	f(DMF)	148
-- , - , 6-deoxy-6-iodo-	60	50	f(DMF)	148
-- , - , 6-deoxy-6-mercapto-	60	1300	f(DMF)	148
-- , - , 6-deoxy-6-phthalimido-	60	50	f(DMF)	148
-- , - , 2,3-di-O-benzyl-	60	90	f(DMF)	148
-- , - , 2,3,4,6-tetra-O-acetyl-	60	30	f(DMF)	148
-- , - , 6-O-(p-toluenesulfonyl)-	60	10	f(DMF)	148
-- , - , 6-O-triphenylmethyl-	60	80	f(DMF)	148
β,D-Glucoside				
-- , methyl-	60	20	f(DMF)	148
-- , - , 6-deoxy-6-dipropylamino-	60	1100	f(DMF)	148
Glutaronitrile				
-- , 2,4-dimethyl-	50	0.6	f(MPC)	261
Glyceraldehyde	60	32.1	f(DMSO)	252
Glycerol	60	23.5	f(DMSO)	252
2,4,6-Heptanetricarbonitrile	50	1.0	f(MPC)	261
Indium, triethyl-	60	2220	f(DMF)	104
Iron(III) chloride	60	33300	f(DMF)	10
Isobutyl alcohol	60	24.06	g	63
Isobutyronitrile	50	1.3	f(MPC)	261
	60	1.8	i(90)	261
		3.5		90
		4.0	f(SN)	58

Solvent	T°C	$c_S \cdot 10^4$	Remarks	References
Acrylonitrile (Cont'd.)				
Lead, tetraethyl-	60	243	f(DMF)	104
Magnesium perchlorate	50	<0.05		261
Mercury, diethyl-	60	72.2	f(DMF)	104
Methane				
-- , dichloro-	60	3.06	g	63
-- , nitro-	60	6.0	f(SN)	58
2,6-Octadiene				
-- , 2,6-dimethyl-	60	450		3
2-Pentanone				
-- , 4-methyl-	60	11.79	g	63
Piperidine				
-- , N-ethyl-	60	3300	j	15
-- , N-methyl-	60	2300	j	15
Silane, tetraethyl-	60	21.0	f(DMF)	104
Sorbitol	60	6.1	f(DMSO)	252
Stilbene, tributyl-	60	111000	f(DMF)	104
Succinonitrile	60	0.6		58
Sulfoxide, dimethyl	30	0.47		128
	50	0.11		279
		0.29		129
		0.795		260
Sulfur dioxide	50	0		253
Tin, tetrabutyl-	60	80.8	f(DMF)	104
Toluene	50	1.153	g	239
	60	2.632	g	239
		3.2		12
		5.83	g	15,63
o-Toluidine				
-- , N,N-dimethyl-	40	272	f(B),g	155
	50	334	f(B),g	155
		30200	f(SO$_2$),g,j	154,155
	60	463	f(B),g	155
Tributylamine	60	6700	j	15
Triethylamine	60	1700	u	11
		1900		11
		3800		13
		5900	f(DMF),j	15
		6600	j	15
Trimethylamine	60	790	j	15
Tripropylamine	60	4280	f(DMF)	104
		10500	j	15
Zinc, diethyl-	50	16000	f(DMF)	104

Solvent	T°C	$c_S \cdot 10^4$	Remarks	References
Acrylonitrile (Cont'd.)				
Zinc chloride	50	0.006	$f(H_2O)$	281
Allyl Acetate				
Benzene	80	21.0		184
p-Benzoquinone	80	520000	j	18
-- , 2,3,5,6-tetrachloro-	80	1600000	j	18
-- , 2,3,5,6-tetramethyl-	80	41400	j	18
-- , 2,3,5-trichloro-	80	550000	j	18
Carbon tetrachloride	100	20000	c	140
Allyl Chloride				
Carbon tetrachloride	100	4800	c	140
Hydrogen chloride	80	18000	$r(C_1)$	161
		54000	$r(C_2^1)$	161
Butyl acrylate				
Aniline				
-- , N,N-dimethyl-	50	380		105
Butyl Methacrylate				
Benzene	60	0.158		179
p-Chlorostyrene				
Benzaldehyde	100	1.9	a	203
-- , p-chloro-	100	9.7	a	203
Carbon tetrabromide	60	52000	f(B)	70
Ethyl Acrylate				
Acetic acid				
-- , ethyl ester	60	0.69	c	89
Acetone	60	0.27	c	89
Benzene	60	0.27	c	88
		0.45	c	89
2-Butanone	60	0.151	c	89
Carbon tetrachloride	70	1.13	c	89
Chloroform	60	0.89	c	89
	70	1.57	c	89
Cyclohexane	60	0.61	c	89
Methanol	60	0.32	c	89
Toluene	70	1.84	c	89

Solvent	T°C	$C_S \cdot 10^4$	Remarks	References
Ethylene				
Benzene	20	0.629	e,x	95
	50-70	18	x(1470)	147
	83	20	d	134
		21	d,x	135
	130	9.4	c,x(20000)	175
-- , ethyl-	130	480	c,x(20000)	34
		560	c,x(20000)	34
Benzene-d_6	130	5.6	c,x(20000)	175
1-Butene	130	330	c,x(20000)	34
		470	c,x(20000)	34
Carbon tetrachloride	20	215	e,x	95
	70	7000	c,x(5000)	144
		32000	c	140
Chloroform	28	2100	e,r(C_1),x	165
		13000	e,r(C_2),x	165
		15000	e,r(C_3),x	165
	70	8000	c,x(5000)	144
		30000	c	140
	100	1500	e,r(C_1),x	165
		5400	e,r(C_2),x	165
		4500	e,r(C_3),x	165
Ethane				
-- , chloro-	70	120	c,x(5000)	144
-- , 1,1-dichloro-	70	1500	c,x(5000)	144
-- , 1,1,1-trichloro-	70	500	c,x(5000)	144
Ethyl alcohol	20	5.71	e,x	95
	125-35	~190	c,x(250)	263
Heptane	50-70	90	x(1470)	147
Isopropyl alcohol	125-35	~570	c,x(200)	263
Methane				
-- , chloro-	70	4	c,x(5000)	144
-- , dichloro-	70	700	c,x(5000)	144
1-Octene	130	360	c,x(20000)	34
Propane				
-- , 2-chloro-	70	250	c,x(5000)	144
-- , 2-chloro-2-methyl-	70	40	c,x(5000)	144
1-Propene	130	110	c,x(20000)	34
		150	c,x(20000)	34
Toluene	130	130	c,x(20000)	34
Water	20	1.71	e,x	95

Remarks page II-134; References page II-135

Solvent	T°C	$c_S \cdot 10^4$	Remarks	References
Ethyl Methacrylate				
Acetic acid	80	0.095	t	56
-- , ethyl ester	80	0.919		56
Acetone	80	0.102		56
Acetophenone	80	0.281		56
Benzene	80	0.081		56
-- , chloro-	80	0.436		56
-- , ethyl-	80	1.428		56
2-Butanone	80	0.252		56
Butyl alcohol	80	0.454		56
sec-Butyl alcohol	80	1.604		56
tert-Butyl alcohol	80	0.417		56
Carbon tetrachloride	80	0.901		56
		5.640	c	119
Chloroform	80	0.703		56
		2.360	c	119
Cumene	80	2.067		56
Cyclohexane	80	0.928		56
Ethane				
-- , 1,2-dichloro-	80	1.821	c	119
-- , 1,1,2,2-tetrachloro-	80	0.311		56
		1.820	c	119
-- , 1,1,1-trichloro-	80	0.536		56
Ethyl alcohol	80	0.429		56
Heptane	80	0.865		56
2-Heptanone	80	0.702		56
Isobutyl alcohol	80	0.445		56
2,4-Pentanedione	80	0.236		56
Toluene	80	0.436		56
Hexadecyl Methacrylate				
Carbon tetrachloride	70	0.983	c	92
Cumene	70	2.05	c	92
1-Hexene				
Cyclohexanol	125-35	390	c	263
Ethyl alcohol	30-35	170	d	263

Solvent	T°C	$C_S \cdot 10^4$	Remarks	References
p-Iodostyrene				
Benzene	50	0.2		38
Isobutyl Methacrylate				
Benzene	60	0.165		179
Carbon tetrachloride	80	1.971	c	119
Chloroform	80	1.110	c	119
Ethane				
-- , 1,2-dichloro-	80	0.510	c	119
-- , 1,1,2,2-tetrachloro-	80	0.510	c	119
Methacrylonitrile				
Carbon tetrabromide	100	900	a,f(DMF)	70
	120	1000	a,f(DMF)	70
Iron(III) chloride	60	30800	f(DMF)	10
Toluene	60	0.996		12
Methyl Acrylate				
Acetone	80	0.622		230
		1.1	c	72
Acetophenone	50	<2.5		7
Aluminum, triethyl-	60	480	f(B),t	104
Aniline	50	<1.0		7
-- , m-nitro-	50	42.1		7
-- , p-nitro-	50	26.7		7
Anisole				
-- , m-nitro-	50	72.7		7
Anthracene	50	1000		7
Benzene	80	0.326		230
		0.45	c	72
-- , chloro-	80	0.52	c	72
		0.986		230
-- , o-dichloro-	80	0.71	c	72
-- , m-dinitro-	50	309		7
-- , ethyl-	80	6.056		230
-- , nitro-	50	46.4		7
-- , 1,3,5-trinitro-	50	2040		7
Benzoic acid				
-- , p-nitro-	50	107		7
Benzonitrile	50	<1.0		7
Benzophenone	50	<1.5		7

Solvent	T °C	$c_S \cdot 10^4$	Remarks	References
		Methyl Acrylate (Cont'd.)		
p-Benzoquinone	50	8100		7
Benzoyl chloride	50	<1.5		7
Biphenyl	50	<2.0		7
2-Butanone	80	3.238		230
		3.61	c	72
Butyl alcohol	80	2.747		230
sec-Butyl alcohol	80	14.14		230
tert-Butyl alcohol	80	0.389		230
Carbon tetrabromide	40	3500	f(B)	70
	50	3500	f(B)	70
	60	4100	f(B)	70
Carbon tetrachloride	80	1.25	c	72
		1.266	c	119
		1.323		230
		1.55		119
Chloroform	80	2.100		119
		2.144		230
		2.333	c	119
		2.5	c	72
Cumene	80	6.966		230
		16.2	c	72
Cyclohexane	80	0.027		230
		1.2	c	72
Cyclohexanone	80	5.5	c	72
Diphenylamine-t	60	300	f(B)	31
Ethane -- , 1,2-dichloro-	80	0.82	c	119
		1.00		119
-- , 1,1,2,2-tetrachloro-	80	0.932		230
		1.55		119
		1.561	c	119
-- , 1,1,1-trichloro-	80	0.574		230
Glutaric acid -- , 2,4-dimethyl-				
-- , - , dimethyl ester	60	0.45		142
2,4,6-Heptanetricarboxylic acid -- , trimethyl ester	60	0.54		142
Isobutyl alcohol	80	2.496		230
Isobutyric acid -- , methyl ester	60	1.4		142
Napthalene	50	<2.0		7
2,6-Octadiene -- , 2,6-dimethyl-	60	42		222

Solvent	T°C	$C_S \cdot 10^4$	Remarks	References
Methyl Acrylate (Cont'd.)				
Phenanthrene	50	26		7
Phenol	50	<2.0		7
-- , m-nitro-	50	56.2		7
-- , p-nitro-	50	42.6		7
Phosphine, tributyl-	60	1890	f(B)	104
Silane, tetraethyl-	60	33.1	f(B)	104
Toluene	60	2.7		12,15
	80	1.775		230
		2.7	c	72
-- , m-nitro-	50	41.2		7
-- , p-nitro-	50	48.6		7
Triethylamine	60	400		15
Tripropylamine	60	470	f(B)	104
3-Methyl-3-buten-2-one				
Benzene	80	2.489	c	57
-- , ethyl-	80	6.934	c	57
Cyclohexane				
-- , methyl-	80	0.500	c	57
Toluene	80	3.282	c	57
Methyl Methacrylate				
Acetaldehyde	60	6.5		58
Acetic acid	80	0.24	a	22
-- , ethyl ester	60	0.100	c	215
		0.13	a	215,197
		0.132	c	215
		0.134		197
		0.155		197
		0.156	c	197
		0.46	i(197)	97
	70	0.55	c	81
	75	0.83	c	81
	80	0.240	a	22
-- , 1,1-dimethyl-2,2,2-trinitro- ethyl ester	45	520		71
Acetone	60	0.195		54
	80	0.275		54
		0.225	a	22
Aluminum				
-- , hydrodiisobutyl-	60	3600	t	104
-- , triethyl-	60	1240		104
Aniline				
-- , N,N-dimethyl-	50	30.4	h	280
		430		105
	70	10.8		181

Remarks page II-134; References page II-135

Solvent	T°C	$C_S \cdot 10^4$	Remarks	References
Methyl Methacrylate (Cont'd.)				
Aniline (Cont'd.)				
-- , N,N-divinyl-	60	340		55
Anthracene	50	0		7
Benzaldehyde	60	2.5		58
Benzene	50	0.036		99,225
	52	0.027		54
	60	0.040		54
		0.83	c	117
	75	0.33	c	81
	80	0.075	a	22
		0.24	i(22)	97
		0.080		54
	90	0.036		99
-- , tert-butyl-	80	0.260	a	22
-- , chloro-	60	0.074		54
	80	0.200	a	22
		0.207		54
-- , m-dinitro-	50	52		7
-- , ethyl-	52	0.501		54
	60	0.766		54
	80	1.311		54
		1.350	a	22
		2.1	i(22)	97
p-Benzoquinone	44.1	55000		126
	50	57000		7
	60	45000		27
-- , 2,3,5,6-tetrachloro-	44.1	2600		126
Borane, tributyl-	60	7.45		104
Butane				
-- , 1-chloro-	80	1.20	a	22
-- , 1,1,1-trinitro-	45	8300		71
2-Butanone	60	0.45	c	197
	70	0.56	c	81
	75	0.83	c	81
	80	0.70	a	22
1-Butene	40	3.1		195
	50	5.1		195
2-Butene				
-- , cis-	40	3.2		195
	50	4.9		195
-- , trans-	40	3.0		195
	50	5.2		195
Butylamine, N-nitro-	45	0		71
Butyl ether	60	0.8		58
Butyl alcohol	80	0.25	a	22

Solvent	T°C	$C_S \cdot 10^4$	Remarks	References
Methyl Methacrylate (Cont'd.)				
sec-Butyl alcohol	80	0.85	a	22
tert-Butyl alcohol	60	0.085		54
	80	0.100	a	22
		0.152		54
Carbon tetrabromide	60	2700	f(B)	70
	80	3300	f(B)	70
	100	4600	f(B)	70
Carbon tetrachloride	60	0.925		54
		2.40	c	117
		5		58
	80	2.393	a	22
		2.421		54
		3.3	i(22)	97
Chloroform	60	0.454		54
		1.77	c	117
	80	1.129		54
		1.400	a	22
		1.9	i(22)	97
Cumene	60	1.9		4
	80	1.9	a	22
		2.4	i(22)	97
Cyclohexane	60	12		58
	80	0.10	a	22
-- , methyl-	80	0.195	a	22
p-Dioxane	80	0.222	a	22
Diphenylamine	44.1	~0		126
Diphenylamine-t	60	0.3	f(B)	31
Ethane				
-- , 1,2-dichloro-	60	0.35		54
	80	0.756		54
-- , nitro-	45	2.0		71
-- , 1,1,2,2-tetrachloro-	60	0.155		54
	80	0.200	a	22
		0.235		54
-- , 1,1,1-trichloro-	80	0.600	a	22
-- , 1,1,1-trinitro-	45	1400		71
Heptane	50	1.8		136
Hydrazyl, 2,2-diphenyl-1-picryl-	44.1	20000000		126
Hydroquinone	45	7.0		21
	131	100	a	273
Indium, triethyl-	60	332		104
Isobutyl alcohol	60	0.10		54
	80	0.229		54
		0.250	a	22

Remarks page II-134; References page II-135

Solvent	T °C	$c_S \cdot 10^4$	Remarks	References
Methyl Methacrylate (Cont'd.)				
Isobutyric acid	80	0.900	a	22
-- , methyl ester	60	0.26		186
Isopropyl alcohol	60	0.583		54
	80	1.907		54
Lead, tetraethyl-	60	3.14	t	104
Malononitrile				
-- , furfurylidene-	44.1	12000		126
Mercury, diethyl-	60	0.898		104
Methane				
-- , bromotrichloro-	30	830	d,r(C_3)	213
		45000	d,r(C_4^-)	213
		12000	d	213
-- , bromotrinitro-	45	10000		71
-- , dichloro-	60	0.100		54
	80	0.217		54
-- , nitro-	60	2.0		58
-- , trinitro-	45	5400		71
-- , triphenyl-	60	4.0		29
1-Naphthol	45	<5.0		21
2,6-Octadiene				
-- , 2,6-dimethyl-	60	6.7		222
		8.0		4
Pentane				
-- , 2,2,4-trimethyl-	50	1.2		136
2-Pentanone				
-- , 4,4-dimethyl-5,5,5-trinitro-	45	400		71
-- , 4-methyl-	80	0.700	a	22
3-Pentanone	60	0.833		54
	80	1.729		54
		1.775	a	22
		2.7	i(22)	97
Phenol				
-- , 4-methoxy-	45	<5.0		21
-- , 2,3,4,6-tetramethyl-	45	11.0		21
Phosphine				
-- , octyl-	60	23000		200
-- , phenyl-	60	161000	t	200
-- , tributyl-	60	30.6		104
Piperidine				
-- , 1-nitroso-	45	8.2		71

Solvent	T °C	$c_S \cdot 10^4$	Remarks	References

Methyl Methacrylate (Cont'd.)

Solvent	T °C	$c_S \cdot 10^4$	Remarks	References
Propane				
-- , 1,2-dichloro-	80	0.675	a	22
-- , 1,1-dinitro-	45	68		71
-- , 2,2-dinitro-	45	15		71
-- , 1-nitro-	45	5		71
1-Propene				
-- , 2-methyl-	40	2.5		195
	50	4.4		195
Propionic acid				
-- , 2,2,2-trinitroethyl ester	45	3000		71
Propionitrile				
-- , 3-phosphino-	60	14000		200
-- , 3,3'-phosphinylidenedi-	60	13000		200
Pyrocatechol	45	<5		21
-- , 4-tert-butyl-	45	9		21
Pyrogallol	45	26		21
Silane, tetraethyl-	60	5.75		104
Stibine, tributyl-	60	<1.0		104
Tin, tetrabutyl-	60	1.32		104
Toluene	52	0.084		54
	60	0.170		12,54
		0.190	c	215
		0.202	c	23,215,216
		0.250	c	215
		0.26		186
		0.400	c	215
	70	0.567	c	81
	80	0.292	c	23
		0.303		54
		0.52	i(22)	97
		0.525	a	22
		0.91	c	81
-- , α-chloro-	60	4.17	c	117
-- , p-nitro-	44.1	∿0		126
-- , 2,4,6-trinitro-	44.1	500		126
Tributylamine	70	25.7		181
Triethylamine	60	8.3	j	15
		1900		16
Tripropylamine	60	14.6		104
Water	60	0		180

2-Methyl-1-propene

Solvent	T °C	$c_S \cdot 10^4$	Remarks	References
Carbon tetrachloride	100	170000	c	140

Remarks page II-134; References page II-135

Solvent	T °C	$C_s \cdot 10^4$	Remarks	References
1-Octene				
Butyl alcohol	117-18	270	c	263
sec-Butyl alcohol	117-18	520	c	263
Ethyl alcohol	115-18	230	c	263
Isopropyl alcohol	30-5	630	d	263
	120-5	520	c	263
Methanol	116-20	110	c	263
1-Propene				
Carbon tetrachloride	100	50000-100000	c	140
Chloroform	100	10300	c	140
Styrene				
Acetaldehyde	60	8.5		58
Acetamide				
-- , N,N-dimethyl-	50	0.743		260
	60	4.6		74
Acetic acid	60	2.0	c	264
-- , ethyl ester	70	5.5	c	81
	75	6.67	c	81
-- , bromo-	60	430		73
	68	300		101
-- , chloro-	68	200		101
-- , - , methyl ester	60	0.3	a	85
	100	0.75	a	85
-- , dibromo-				
-- , - , ethyl ester	90	2700	c	42
-- , dichloro-				
-- , - , ethyl ester	60	1.3	a	85
-- , iodo-	68	8000		101
-- , phenyl-	60	6.0	a	85
-- , tribromo-	90	24000	c	42
-- , - , ethyl ester	90	105000	c	42
-- , trichloro-	60	66.0	a	85
-- , - , ethyl ester	60	65.0	a	85
	90	90	c	42
	100	145.0	a	85
Acetic anhydride	60	0.7	a	85
Acetone	60	<0.5	a	85
		4.1	c	118

Solvent	T°C	$c_S \cdot 10^4$	Remarks	References
		Styrene (Cont'd.)		
Acetone (Cont'd.)				
-- , oxime	60	2.2	a	85
Acetonitrile	60	0.44	a	85
Acetyl bromide	60	8600	t	73
Acetyl chloride				
-- , chloro-	60	3300		73
Allyl alcohol	60	1.5	a	85
Aluminum				
-- , hydrodiisobutyl-	100	269000		104
		280000	a	103
-- , triethoxy-	100	<0.1	a	103,104
-- , triethyl-	100	80500		104
		170000	a	103
-- , triisobutoxy-	100	<1.0	a	103
-- , triisobutyl-	110	285000	a	103
Aniline	50	20	f(B)	102
	60	2.0	a	85
-- , N,N-dimethyl-	50	12	f(B)	102
		53		105
-- , N,N-divinyl-	60	130		55
-- , N-methyl-	50	13	f(B)	102
-- , 2,4,6-trinitro-	50	118000		256,258
Anisole,				
-- , 2,4,6-trinitro-	50	203000		256,258
Anthracene				
-- , dihydro-	50	610	d	182
Benzaldehyde	60	5.5		58
	100	2.6	a	203
-- , p-chloro-	100	5.6	a	203
Benzene	50	0.01		225
	60	0.018	a	84
		0.023		52
		0.028	c	171
		0.04	a,i(84)	97
		1.92	h	282
	70	5.50	c	81
	75	6.67	c	81
	80	0.061	i(84)	121
		0.121	c	171
		0.156		184
	100	0.184	a	84
		0.23	a,i(84)	97
		0.31	a	158
		0.42	a	158

Solvent	T°C	$C_S \cdot 10^4$	Remarks	References
Styrene (Cont'd.)				
Benzene (Cont'd.)	132	0.81	a	158
		0.89	a	84
		1.5	a,i(84)	97
-- , bromo-	60	1.78	c	118
	155	3	a	160
-- , sec-butyl-	60	6.22	h	282
-- , tert-butyl-	60	0.04	a,i(84)	97
		0.06	a	84
	80	0.193	i(84)	121
	100	0.55	a	84
-- , chloro-	60	0.133	c	171
		1.50	c	118
	80	0.235	c	171
		0.874	i(84)	121
	100	0.54	a	158
	140	0.6		39
-- , - , 2,4,6-trinitro-	50	585000		256,258
-- , 1,2-dibromoethyl-	60	1950		73
-- , p-dibutyl-	60	7.02	h	282
-- , p-di-sec-butyl-	60	10.70	h	282
-- , p-di-tert-butyl-	60	0.87	h	282
-- , m-dichloro-	140	0.2		39
		1.4		45
-- , o-dichloro-	60	3.4	c	118
-- , p-dichloro-	60	2.6	c	118
-- , diethyl (mixture)	100	3.35	a	158
		6.33	a	158
	132	5.13	a	158
-- , ethyl-	60	0.67	a	84
		0.70		52
		0.710	c	171
		0.83	a,i(84)	97
		2.7	c	254
	80	1.07	i(84)	121
		1.113	c	171
	100	1.38	a	158
		1.62	a	84
		2.2	a,i(84)	97
		2.33	a	158
	132	2.31	a	158
		2.9	a	84
		4.9	a,i(84)	97
-- , sec-hexyl-	60	12.76	h	282
-- , isopropyl- (see Cumene)				
-- , sec-pentyl-	60	9.43	h	282
-- , tri-sec-butyl-	60	13.30	h	282

Solvent	T°C	$c_S \cdot 10^4$	Remarks	References

Styrene (Cont'd.)

Solvent	T°C	$c_S \cdot 10^4$	Remarks	References
Benzene (Cont'd.)				
-- , 1,3,5-trinitro-	40	948000		257
	50	643000		256,257,258
	60	351000		257
Benzoic acid				
-- , 2,4,6-trinitro-				
-- , - , ethyl ester	50	572000		256,258
Benzoin	60	40	a	85
p-Benzoquinone	60	2270000		27
	80	5660000	j	18
-- , 2,5-dimethyl-	80	430000	j	18
-- , 2-methyl-	80	2100000	j	18
-- , 2,3,5,6-tetrachloro-	80	9500000	j	18
-- , 2,3,5,6-tetramethyl-	80	6700	j	18
-- , 2,3,5-trimethyl-	80	260000	j	18
Bibenzyl				
-- , α,α'-dibromo-	60	3020		73
Borane				
-- , tributoxy-	100	<0.1		104
-- , tributyl-	100	34.8		104
Butane				
-- , 1-bromo-	60	0.06	a	85
	100	0.35	a	85
-- , 1-chloro-	60	0.04	a	85
	100	0.37	a	85
-- , 2-chloro-	60	1.2	a,t	85
	100	0.3	a	85
-- , 2,2-dimethyl-	60	0.43		209
-- , 1-iodo-	60	1.85	a	85
	100	5.5	a	85
2-Butanone	60	4.98	c	118
	70	8.60	c	81
	75	12.00	c	81
1-Butene	100	2.6	a	249
-- , 2-methyl-	100	3.1	a	249
-- , 3-methyl-	100	6.9	a	249
2-Butene	100	2.0	a	249
-- , 1,4-dichloro-	80	51	c	73
-- , 2,3-dimethyl-	100	5.4	a	249
-- , 2-methyl-	100	2.9	a	249

Remarks page II-134; References page II-135

Solvent	T°C	$C_S \cdot 10^4$	Remarks	References
		Styrene (Cont'd.)		
Butyl alcohol	60	0.06	a	85
		1.6	a,c	221,264
tert-Butyl alcohol	60	6.65	a	264
	100	0.55	a	176
	130	1.0	a	176
Butylamine	60	0.5	a	85
tert-Butyl ether	60	2.6	c,f(B)	206
	80	1.0	c,f(B)	206
Butyraldehyde	60	5.7	a	85
	100	11.0	a	85
Butyric acid -- , 4-hydroxy-				
-- , - , γ-lactone	50	0.409		260
Cadmium, dibutyl-	100	1170		104
Carbon tetrabromide	40	18000	f(B)	70
	60	17800	c	42
		136000	a	85
		22000	f(B)	70
		25000	f(AN)	70
	70	18000		41
	80	23000	f(B)	70
	90	25100	c	42
	100	23500	a	85
Carbon tetrachloride	60	84	c,x(56000)	276
		87	c	73,118
		90	c,x(28400)	276
		92	a	85,86,140
		98	c	276
		110		151
		122	a,y	75
		148	y	76
	76	18	c	159
		117	a	159
	80	133	i(84)	121
	100	185	a	85,86
	132	304	a	86
	140	300		39
Chloroform	60	0.5	a	85,140
		0.566	c	171
		3.40	c	118
	68	4.0		101
	80	0.50	i(84)	121
		0.916	c	171
m-Cresol	50	11		169,170
o-Cresol	50	33		169,170
	60	43		79
p-Cresol	50	22.1		169,170
	60	39		79
-- , α-phenyl-	60	<5		79

Solvent	T°C	$C_S \cdot 10^4$	Remarks	References
Styrene (Cont'd.)				
Cumene	60	0.8		4
		0.82	a	84
		1.04	a,i(84)	97
	80	1.31	i(84)	121
	100	2.00	a	84
		2.90	a,i(84)	97
Cyclohexane	60	0.024	a	84
		0.031		52
		0.04	a,i(84)	97
		0.063	c	171
	80	0.066	i(84)	121
		0.083	c	171
		0.156		184
	100	0.16	a	84
		0.23	a,i(84)	97
		0.31	a	158
	132	0.81	a	158
		0.87	a	84
		1.5	a,i(84)	97
Cyclohexanone	60	7.90	c	118
Cyclohexene	80	0.083	c	171
Cyclopentanone	60	3.30	c	118
p-Dioxane	60	0	a,t	85
		2.28	c	1
		2.75	c	118
	100	0.8		148
Diphenylamine-t	60	0.9	f(B)	31
Ethane				
-- , 1,2-dibromo-	60	0.988	c	171
	80	1.914	c	171
-- , 1,2-dichloro-	60	0.333	c	171
		4.12	c	118
	70	1.1		45
	80	1.137	c	171
		9.8	c	73
	100	3.84	a	158
-- , pentaphenyl-	60	20000	a	84
-- , 1,1,2,2-tetrachloro-	100	10.8	a	158
Ethanehexacarboxylic acid				
-- , hexaethyl ester	50	<50		61
Ether				
-- , benzyl methyl	68	6.0		101
-- , p-bromobenzyl methyl	68	6.0		101
-- , p-chlorobenzyl methyl	68	4.0		101
-- , p-cyanobenzyl methyl	68	20.0		101
-- , dodecyl vinyl	60	3.32	c	1
		4.11	c	1

Remarks page II-134; References page II-135

Solvent	T°C	$C_S \cdot 10^4$	Remarks	References

Styrene (Cont'd.)

Solvent	T°C	$C_S \cdot 10^4$	Remarks	References
Ethyl ether	60	5.64	c	1
Fluorene	60	75.0	a	84
	100	124.0	a	84
Formamide				
-- , N,N-dimethyl-	50	0.869		260
	60	4.0		74
	100	1.08		172
α,ᴅ-Glucoside				
-- , methyl-				
-- , - , 6-deoxy-6-mercapto-	100	55000		148
-- , - , di-O-benzyl-	100	62		148
-- , - , 2,3,4,6-tetra-O-acetyl-	100	2.0		148
-- , - , 6-O-(p-toluenesulfonyl)-	100	2.0		148
-- , - , 2,3,4-tri-O-acetyl-6-deoxy-6-iodo-	100	50		148
-- , - , 6-O-triphenylmethyl-	100	21		148
β,ᴅ-Glucoside				
-- , methyl-				
-- , - , 6-deoxy-6-dipropylamino-	100	22		148
Heptane	60	0.42	a	84
	100	0.95	a	84
1-Heptene	100	2.7	a	249
2-Heptene	100	3.2	a	249
Hexane	100	0.9	a	249
1-Hexene	100	2.5	a	249
2-Hexene	100	3.6	a	249
Hydrogen chloride	100	∼0		161
Hydroquinone	60	3.6	a	85
Indium, triethyl-	100	17600		104
Iron(III) chloride	60	5360000		10
Isobutyl alcohol	60	0.17	a	264
Isobutyl alcohol-d	100	2.9	a	176
	130	7.8	a	176
Isobutyric acid	60	2.5	c	264
		4.6	a	264
Isobutyronitrile	100	2.7	a	176
	130	3.5	a	176

Solvent	T°C	$C_S \cdot 10^4$	Remarks	References
Styrene (Cont'd.)				
Isopropyl alcohol	100	1.7	a	176
	130	2.7	a	176
Isopropyl alcohol-d	100	1.6	a	176
Isopropyl-1-d alcohol-d	100	0.78	a	176
Lead, tetraethyl-	100	1.24		104
Malonic acid				
-- , diethyl ester	60	0.47	a	85
-- , bromo-				
-- , - , diethyl ester	60	700	a	85
	100	1200	a	85
-- , dibromo-				
-- , - , diethyl ester	60	12000	a	85
-- , dichloro-				
-- , - , diethyl ester	60	30.0	a	85
	100	62.0	a	85
Mercury, diethyl-	100	0.335		104
Methane				
-- , bis(2-chloroethoxy)-	80	6.0	c	73
-- , bromotrichloro-	30	76000	d,r(C_2)	214
		77000	d,r(C_2)	127
		2400000	d,r(C_3)	214
		2780000	d,r(C_3)	127
	80	9450	i(84)	121
-- , dibromo-	60	110		73
-- , dichloro-	60	0.15	a	85
	80	9.5	c	73
	100	11.8	a	85
-- , diiodo-	60	710		73
-- , diphenyl-	60	2.3	a	84
	100	4.2	a	84
-- , nitro-	60	10		58
-- , triphenyl-	60	3.5	a	84
	80	6.0		29
	100	8.0	a	84
Naphthalene	60	11		145
-- , decahydro-	60	0.4	a	84
-- , 2-isopropenyl-	80	56		66
		70		66
	99	69		66
		86		66
-- , 2-methoxy-	60	<5.0		79
1-Naphthol	60	480	j	33,79
-- , 2,4-dichloro-	60	490	j	79

Solvent	T °C	$c_S \cdot 10^4$	Remarks	References
	Styrene (Cont'd.)			
1-Naphthol-d	60	75		33,79
2-Naphthol	60	77		80
2,6-Octadiene				
-- , 2,6-dimethyl-	60	2.0	c	4,222
2-Octene	100	2.8	a	249
Pentane				
-- , 1-chloro-	60	0.49	a	85
-- , 2,2,4-trimethyl-	100	<10	a	103
3-Pentanone	60	2.6	a	264
1-Pentene	100	2.3	a	249
2-Pentene	100	4.2	a	249
-- , 2-methyl-	100	6.3	a	249
-- , 4-methyl-	100	6.9	a	249
Phenol	50	8.1		169,170
	60	14		80
-- , p-benzyloxy-	60	290	j	33,79
-- , p-tert-butyl-	60	26		79
-- , o-chloro-	60	6.0		80
-- , p-chloro-	60	-11		79
-- , 2,6-di-tert-butyl-	60	49		79
-- , 2,6-diisopropyl-	60	310	j	79
-- , p-fluoro-	60	54		79
-- , m-methoxy-	60	<5		79
-- , o-methoxy-	60	43		80
-- , p-methoxy-	60	260	j	79
-- , o-phenyl-	60	<5		79
-- , 2,3,4,6-tetramethyl-	60	580	j	33,79
-- , 2,4,6-trinitro-	50	2110000		256
Phenol-d				
-- , p-benzyloxy-	60	10		33
-- , 2,3,4,6-tetramethyl-	60	20		33
Phosphine				
-- , dibutyl-	100	20800		201
-- , diethyl-	100	13500		201
-- , octyl-	60	36000	a	200

Solvent	T°C	$C_S \cdot 10^4$	Remarks	References
Styrene (Cont'd.)				
Phosphine (Cont'd.)				
-- , phenyl-	60	439000	a,t	200
-- , tributyl-	100	24.4		104
Phosphoric acid				
-- , tributyl ester	100	<0.1		104
Piperidine	60	1.0	a	85
Propane				
-- , 1-chloro-2-methyl-	60	1.4	a	85
	100	3.0	a	85
-- , 1,1,1,3-tetrabromo-3-phenyl-	90	36500	c	42
-- , 1,1,1-tribromo-	90	24100	c	42
1,3-Propanediol				
-- , 2,2-bis(bromomethyl)-				
-- , - , diacetate	60	40500		223
1,3-Propanedione				
-- , 1,3-diphenyl-	60	7.0	a	85
1-Propene				
-- , 3-chloro-2-methyl-	60	24.0	a	85
-- , 2-methyl-	100	1.7	a	249
Propionic acid	60	0.05	a	85
		4.3	c	264
		4.5		221
		4.65	a	264
Propionitrile				
-- , 3-phosphino-	60	50000	a	200
-- , 3,3'-phosphinylidenedi-	60	50000	a	200
2-Propyn-1-ol	60	7.0	a	85
Pyridine	60	0.6	a	85
Pyrocatechol	60	1340	j	33,79
-- , p-tert-butyl-	60	3600	j	33,79
Pyrocatechol-d	60	260		33
-- , p-tert-butyl-	60	370		33
Pyrogallol	60	10400	j	33,79
Pyrogallol-d	60	1600		33
Silane				
-- , tetraethyl-	100	8.12		104
-- , triethyl-	70	33.4		62
	80	36.8		62
-- , triphenyl-	70	2.44		62
	80	1.3		62

Remarks page II-134; References page II-135

Solvent	T °C	$C_S \cdot 10^4$	Remarks	References
	Styrene (Cont'd.)			
Stibine, tributyl-	100	58.0		104
Stilbene, dibromo-	60	3020	a	73
Styrene, α-bromo-	70	10000		113
-- , β-bromo-	70	2000		113
-- , dibromo-	60	1950		73
-- , α-methyl-	74	95		235
	80	3.2		66
		4.9		66
	99	5.6		66
		8.5		66
Succinonitrile				
-- , tetraphenyl-	50	28000		61
Sulfoxide, dimethyl-	50	0.548		260
Tin, tetrabutyl-	100	3.71		104
Toluene	60	0.105	c	171
		0.121		12,15,52
		0.125	a	84
		0.134		51
		0.16	a,i(84)	97
		0.21		217
		1.10	c	254
		2.05		254
	80	0.15	c	264
		0.298	i(84)	121
		0.3	c	264
		0.308	c	171
		0.310		49,50
		0.313		51,184
	100	0.53	a	158
		0.55	c	264
		0.645	a	84
		0.72	a	158
		0.8	a,i(84)	97
	132	1.12	a	158
-- , o-chloro-	70	0.62		45
	140	1.8		45
-- , α-chloro-	60	1.56	a	85
-- , α,α-dichloro-	60	50.0	a	85
-- , α,α,α-trichloro·	60	57.5	a	85
-- , 2,4,6-trinitro-	50	146000		256,258
p-Toluidine	50	78	f(B)	102
-- , N,N-dimethyl-	50	16	f(B)	102
-- , N-methyl-	50	11	f(B)	102
s-Triazine, trimethyl-	60	0.468		60

Solvent	T°C	$C_S \cdot 10^4$	Remarks	References

Styrene (Cont'd.)

Solvent	T°C	$C_S \cdot 10^4$	Remarks	References
Triethylamine	60	1.4	x(64600)	255
		3.0	x(26600)	255
		7.1		15
		7.5		254,255
Tripropylamine	100	24.2		104
p-Xylene				
-- , α,α'-dibromo-	60	150		73
2,6-Xylenol	60	110		79
Zinc, diethyl-	100	3660		104

Vinyl Acetate

Solvent	T°C	$C_S \cdot 10^4$	Remarks	References
Acetaldehyde	30	400		238
	45	530	j	58
	60	0.72		173
		200	i(157)	97
		220		157
		570	f(B)	58
		660	j	58
	75	700	j	58
-- , acetal				
-- , - , diacetate	60	40		58
Acetamide				
-- , N-butyl-	60	40		58
Acetic acid	60	1.0	i(196)	97
		1.13		196
		10	f(B)	58
-- , allyl ester	60	85	f(B)	58
		94	j	58
-- , benzyl ester	60	80	f(B),j	58
-- , butyl ester	50	13.2		138
-- , sec-butyl ester	50	4.4		138
	60	8.0		58
-- , tert-butyl ester	50	1.5		138
	60	6.2		157
-- , ethyl ester	20	1.52		226
	40	2.11		226
	50	2.9		138
		12	c	47
	60	1.07		196
		1.25	c	53
		2.6		97,157
		2.96		226
		3.3		58
	70	7.8	c	269
-- , isobutyl ester	50	9.1		138
-- , isopropyl ester	50	3.5		138
	60	3.1		97,157
		8.0		58
	67.5	9.0	j	58
	75	10	j	58

Solvent	T°C	$c_S \cdot 10^4$	Remarks	References

Vinyl Acetate (Cont'd.)

Solvent	T°C	$c_S \cdot 10^4$	Remarks	References
Acetic acid (Cont'd.)				
-- , methyl ester	60	1.56		97,156
		1.6		97,157
		2.5		58
-- , pentyl ester	70	7.2	c	269
	75	87.0	c	120
-- , propyl ester	50	6.2		138
	60	3.4		97,157
-- , 1,3,3,3-tetrachloropropyl ester	70	423.2	c	268
-- , bromo-	60	489	c,j	265
	70	4450	c	268
-- , chloro-	70	2550	c	268
-- , cyano-				
-- , - , methyl ester	60	5000	j	58
-- , dichloro-				
-- , - , ethyl ester	60	210		58
-- , phenyl-	60	400	j	58
-- , trichloro-	70	1445	c	268
-- , - , ethyl ester	60	4400		58
-- , trifluoro-				
-- , - , ethyl ester	50	30	c	47
Acetic anhydride	60	8.0		58
Acetoacetic acid				
-- , ethyl ester	70	80.4	c	269
Acetone	60	1.5		58
		11.70		196
		12.0		97
	70	25.6	c	269
	75	42	c	120
Acetonitrile	60	10		58
-- , phenyl-	60	2100	j	58
Acetophenone	50	91.5		7
	60	100	j	58
	70	62.0	c	269
Aniline	50	149		7
		210	f(B)	102
-- , N,N-dimethyl-	50	260	f(B)	102
-- , N-methyl-	50	360	f(B)	102
-- , p-nitro-	50	48600		7

Solvent	T°C	$c_S \cdot 10^4$	Remarks	References
Vinyl Acetate (Cont'd.)				
m-Anisaldehyde	60	2500	j	58
o-Anisaldehyde	60	420	j	58
p-Anisaldehyde	60	370	j	58
Anisole	50	10	f(B),j	58
Anthracene	50	205700		7
Benzaldehyde	60	230	j	97,246
		460	f(B)	58
		540	j	58
	70	421	c,j	269
	75	600	j	58
-- , m-chloro-	60	860	j	58
-- , o-chloro-	60	390	j	58
-- , p-chloro-	60	340	j	58
-- , m-cyano-	60	1070	j	58
-- , p-cyano-	60	610	j	58
-- , p-isopropyl-	60	540	j	58
Benzene	60	1.07		178
		1.2	j	58
		1.2		199
		2.4	c	53
		2.96		196
		20		199
	70	5.27	c	269
	75	1.40		178
		1.4	j	58
		3.6	c	120
-- , bromo-	50	18.9		7
	70	134.2	c	268
	75	25.2	c	120
-- , tert-butyl-	60	3.61		196
-- , chloro-	60	8.35		196
		80	j	58
	70	2.61	c	268
	75	12.7	c	120
-- , o-dichloro-	75	42	c	120
-- , p-dichloro-	70	11.8	c	268
-- , m-dinitro-	45	1050000	c,j	19
	50	645700		7
-- , o-dinitro-	45	960000	c,j	19
-- , p-dinitro-	45	2670000	c,j	19
	50	662800		7
-- , ethyl-	60	55.15		196
		100	j	58
-- , isopropyl- (See Cumene)				

Remarks page II-134; References page II-135

Solvent	T °C	$c_S \cdot 10^4$	Remarks	References

Vinyl Acetate (Cont'd.)

Solvent	T °C	$c_S \cdot 10^4$	Remarks	References
Benzene (Cont'd.)				
-- , nitro-	50	110300		7
-- , 1,3,5-trinitro-	45	8900000	c,j	19
	50	4342800		7
Benzoic acid	60	50	j	58
-- , ethyl ester	60	26	j	58
-- , p-nitro-	50	245700		7
Benzoic anhydride	60	130	j	58
Benzoin	60	800	j	58
Benzonitrile	50	40.6		7
Benzophenone	50	286		7
p-Benzoquinone				
-- , 2,3,5,6-tetramethyl-	45	950000	j	18
Benzoyl chloride	50	366		7
	70	300	c	268
Benzyl alcohol	70	556	c	269
Biphenyl	50	263		7
	60	6.4		87
Borane, tributyl-	10	9000		123
Butane				
-- , 1-bromo-	60	50		58
	70	1100	c	268
-- , 1-chloro-	60	10		58
-- , 1-iodo-	60	800		58
2,3-Butanedione	60	670	f(B),j	58
2-Butanone	60	73.80		196
	70	63.6	c	269
	75	165	c	120
-- , 3-methyl-	60	118.16		196
1-Buten-3-yne	60	~0	j	157
Butyl alcohol	60	20.0	i(196)	97
		20.39		196
	70	29.1	c	269
sec-Butyl alcohol	60	31.74		196
	70	6.21	c	269
	75	95.0		120
tert-Butyl alcohol	60	0.46		196
		0.5	i(196)	97
		1.3		58
	70	12.1	c,j	269
Butyl ether	60	76		58

Solvent	T°C	$C_S \cdot 10^4$	Remarks	References

Vinyl Acetate (Cont'd.)

Solvent	T°C	$C_S \cdot 10^4$	Remarks	References
3-Butyn-2-ol				
-- , 2-methyl-	60	400	j	58
Butyraldehyde	60	650		157,246
		1000		58
	70	388	c	269
Butyric acid				
-- , ethyl ester	50	45	c	47
-- , methyl ester	60	18		97,157
		19		58
Carbon tetrabromide	60	7390000	f(B)	70,97
	70	28740	c	268
Carbon tetrachloride	0	1500		238
	20	4700	e	211
	45	7600	j	58
	60	7300	f(B)	58
		9600	j	58
		10000		140
	70	2023	c	268
	75	10500	j	58
Chloral	60	5000		58
	70	4927	c	268
Chloral hydrate	70	4312	c	268
Chloroform	--	100		237
	30	140		238
	60	125.18		196
		130	i(196)	97
		150	j	58
		160		140
		170	f(B)	58
	70	554	c	268
Crotonaldehyde	60	1800	j	246
Cumene	60	89.9		196
		100		4,58
	70	139	c	269
	75	356	c	120
Cyclohexane	60	6.59		196
		7.0	i(196)	97
		100	f(B)	58
-- , methyl-	60	11.75		196
		24		58
1,3-Cyclohexanedione				
-- , 5,5-dimethyl-	70	5580	c	269
Cyclohexanol	70	127	c	269
Cyclohexanone	60	180	f(B)	58
	75	670	c	120
Cyclohexene	60	620	j	58
		1600	f(B)	58
	75	770	j	58

Remarks page II-134; References page II-135

Solvent	T°C	$c_S \cdot 10^4$	Remarks	References
Vinyl Acetate (Cont'd.)				
Diethyleneglycol	70	85.3	c	269
p-Dioxane	60	20	f(B)	58
	70	49.1	c	269
Diphenylamine	50	138		7
	60	240		31
Diphenylamine-d	60	170		31
Diphenylamine-t	60	230		31
Ethane				
-- , 1,1-dibromo-	60	1100		58
-- , 1,2-dibromo-	70	134	c	268
-- , 1,1-dichloro-	60	65		58
-- , 1,2-dichloro-	60	5		58
		7	i(196)	97
		7.18		196
	70	10.2	c	268
-- , hexachloro-	70	1210	c	268
-- , pentachloro-	70	1348	c	268
-- , 1,1,2,2-tetrabromo-	60	6000		58
-- , 1,1,2,2-tetrachloro-	60	107.03		196
		160		58
	70	67.72	c	268
-- , 1,1,1-trichloro-	60	71.11		196
-- , 1,1,2-trichloro-	60	35.98		196
1,1-Ethanediol				
-- , diacetate	60	40		58
Ether				
-- , benzyl methyl	60	280	f(B),j	58
-- , bis(2-chloroethyl)	70	245	c	268
-- , dodecyl vinyl	60	57.2	c	1
		73.5	c	1
Ethyl alcohol	60	25	f(B)	58
	70	26.3	c	269
Ethylene				
-- , tetrabromo-	70	2800	c	268
-- , tetrachloro-	70	465	c	268
-- , tribromo-	70	34720	c	268
-- , trichloro-	70	3810	c	268
Ethyleneglycol	70	83.0	c,j	269
Ethyl ether	60	45.3	c	1

Solvent	T °C	$c_S \cdot 10^4$	Remarks	References
Vinyl Acetate (Cont'd.)				
Fluorene	60	4700	j	58
	70	3610	c,j	269
-- , 9-phenyl-	70	16240	c	269
Formamide				
-- , N,N-dimethyl-	60	50		58
Formic acid				
-- , ethyl ester	50	22	c	47
-- , methyl ester	60	3		58
2-Furaldehyde	60	15000	j	58
Furfuryl alcohol	70	2520	c,j	269
Glycolic acid				
-- , methyl ester	60	300		58
Heptane	50	17.0		138
1,5-Hexadien-3-yne	60	∼0		157
Hexanoic acid				
-- , 2-ethyl-				
-- , - , ethyl ester	50	65	c	47
Isobutyl alcohol	60	21.75		196
	70	32.4	c	269
Isobutyric acid	60	5.02		196
-- , ethyl ester	50	160	c	47
-- , methyl ester	60	58		97,157
		86		58
Isobutyronitrile	60	100		58
Isopropyl alcohol	70	44.6	c	269
Lactic acid				
-- , ethyl ester	60	700		58
-- , methyl ester	60	640		58
Lauric acid				
-- , ethyl ester	50	105	c	47
Malonic acid				
-- , dimethyl ester	60	17		58
p-Mentha-1,8-diene	60	1900	j	58
Methane				
-- , bromotrichloro-	25	>>10000	d,t	26
	60	6000	c	26
		>400000	c	26
	70	6303	c	268
-- , dichloro-	60	4		58
-- , iodo-	70	1230	c	268

Solvent	T °C	$c_S \cdot 10^4$	Remarks	References
Vinyl Acetate (Cont'd.)				
Methane (Cont'd.)				
-- , nitro-	60	2300	f(B),j	58
	75	2600	j	58
-- , tribromo-	70	34760	c	268
-- , triphenyl-	60	700		30
Methanol	10	3.4		122
	60	2.26		97,156
		4.3		218
		6.0		58
	70	5.5		218
		9.0		2
		10.0		2
		10.5		2
Naphthalene	50	1457		7
	70	1715	c,j	269
-- , decahydro-	60	48		58
Nonanoic acid				
-- , ethyl ester	50	80	c	47
2,6-Octadiene				
-- , 2,6-dimethyl-	60	430		222
		700		4
Octanoic acid				
-- , ethyl ester	50	70	c	47
Oleic acid				
-- , methyl ester	60	1000	j	58
Orthoformic acid				
-- , trimethyl ester	--	7.6		237
	30	8.0		238
Oxalic acid				
-- , diethyl ester	60	4.0		58
-- , dimethyl ester	60	1.0		58
		2.0		97,157
Paraldehyde	70	136	c	269
Pelargonic acid (see Nonanoic acid)				
Pentane				
-- , 2,2,4-trimethyl-	50	8.0		138
2,4-Pentanedione	60	10		58
2-Pentanone				
-- , 4-methyl-	60	34.52		196
3-Pentanone	60	10.0	i(196)	97
		114.39		196
Pentyl alcohol	75	56	c	120
Phenanthrene	50	5600		7
	70	3380	c,j	269

Solvent	T°C	$c_S \cdot 10^4$	Remarks	References
		Vinyl Acetate (Cont'd.)		
Phenol	50	120		7
	60	600	j	58
-- , p-nitro-	50	88600		7
Propane				
-- , 2-bromo-2-methyl-	60	150		58
-- , 2-chloro-2-methyl-	60	26		58
1-Propene				
-- , 3-chloro-	60	3100		58
-- , 3-chloro-2-methyl-	60	400	j	58
Propionaldehyde	60	950	j	58
		1000	f(B)	58
	70	457	c	269
Propionic acid				
-- , ethyl ester	50	40	c	47
-- , methyl ester	60	23		157
Salicylic acid	70	296	c	269
Stearic acid				
-- , ethyl ester	50	140	c	47
m-Tolualdehyde	60	570	j	58
p-Tolualdehyde	60	440	j	58
Toluene	50	12.0		7
		14.9	s	248
		100	c	47
		123		47
	60	17.8	s	248
		20.75	c	53
		20.89		12,40,196
		21.6		248
		34	j	58
		35	f(B)	58
	70	21.1	s	248
		21.8	c	269
		29.2		248
	75	66	c	120
	80	91.6		184
-- , bromo-	50	20.6		7
-- , α-chloro-	60	450	j	58
	70	584	c	268
	75	118	c	120
-- , o-chloro-	70	92.86	c	268
-- , p-chloro-	70	195	c	268
-- , α-cyano- (see acetonitrile, phenyl-)				
-- , p-nitro-	50	106300		7

Remarks page II-134; References page II-135

Solvent	T °C	$c_S \cdot 10^4$	Remarks	References
Vinyl Acetate (Cont'd.)				
p-Toluidine	50	750	f(B)	102
-- , N,N-dimethyl-	50	380	f(B)	102
-- , N-methyl-	50	830	f(B)	102
Toluonitrile	50	38.3		7
Triethylamine	50	360	f(B)	102
	60	370	j	15,97
Veratraldehyde	60	550	j	58
Xylene	50	14.9		7
	70	278	c	269
	75	166	c	120
Vinyl Benzoate				
Benzene	60	1.5		270
	80	0.4		17
Benzoic acid				
-- , isopropyl ester	60	1.0		270
2-Butanone	80	29.0		17
Carbon tetrachloride	80	730		17
Chloroform	80	105		17
Cyclohexane	80	2.3		17
Vinyl Butyrate				
Benzene	80	3.28		131
Vinyl Chloride				
Acetaldehyde	50	110		107
Aniline				
-- , N,N-dimethyl-	50	2700		105
Carbon tetrabromide	50	~500000		44
Ether				
-- , dodecyl vinyl	50	156		1
Furan				
-- , tetrahydro-	40	30		167
	50	24		107
Heptane				
-- , 2,4,6-trichloro-	50	5		141
Pentane				
-- , 2,4-dichloro-	50	5		141
Vinyl Hexanoate				
Benzene	80	4.9		131
Vinyl Isobutyrate				
Benzene	80	4.49		131

Solvent	T°C	$C_S \cdot 10^4$	Remarks	References
	Vinyl 4-Methylvalerate			
Benzene	80	6.2		131
	1-Vinylnaphthalene			
Naphthalene	60	30-50		145
	Vinyl Nonanoate			
Toluene	50	11.1	s	248
	60	13.9	s	248
	70	15.2	s	248
	Vinyl Stearate			
Toluene	50	20.7	s	248
	60	20.9	s	248
	70	21.6	s	248
	N-Vinylurethan			
Acetone	60	8.5		77
Benzene	60	1.25		77

F. Transfer Constants to Sulfur Compounds

Modifier	T°C	C_x	Remarks	References
	1,3-Butadiene			
1-Butanethiol				
-- , 1,1,3,3-tetramethyl-	5	5.3	h	163
	50	3.7	h	163
1-Octanethiol	5	21.8	h	163
	50	16.0	h	163
		19.0	h	164
-- , 1,1,3,3,5,5,7,7-octamethyl-	50	3.0	h	163
1-Tetradecanethiol	50	19.5	h	163
	1,3-Butadiene/styrene			
1-Hexanethiol				
-- , 1,1,3,3,5,5-hexamethyl-	5	2.7-4.7	h	36
		4.1	h	36,37
	Methyl Acrylate			
1-Butanethiol	30	1.53	a	272
	60	1.69	a	46,272
Ethanethiol	50	0.78	$r(C_1)$	228
		1.79	$r(C_2^1)$	228
		5.00	$r(C_3^2)$	228
		1.57		228

Remarks page II-134; References page II-135

Modifier	T°C	C_x	Remarks	References

Methyl Methacrylate

Modifier	T°C	C_x	Remarks	References
Acetic acid				
-- , dithiodi-				
-- , - , diethyl ester	60	0.00065		58
-- , mercapto-				
-- , - , butyl ester	50	0.60		97
-- , - , ethyl ester	60	0.63		185
Acetophenone				
-- , 3'-mercapto-	45	4.2		21
-- , 4'-mercapto-	45	2.6		21
Anisole				
-- , p,p'-dithiodi-	50	0.0044		193
	60	0.0052		193
Benzenethiol	45	4.7		21
	60	2.7		185
-- , 3-bromo-	45	3.8		21
-- , 4-bromo-	45	5.6		21
-- , 3-chloro-	45	3.5		21
-- , 4-chloro-	45	4.6		21
1-Butanethiol	60	0.66		185
		0.67	a	46,272
Disulfide				
-- , bis(p-bromophenyl)	50	0.0046		193
	60	0.0098		193
-- , bis(p-chlorophenyl)	50	0.0072		193
	60	0.0117		193
-- , bis(dimethylthiocarbamoyl)	70	0.0115		68
-- , bis(o-nitrophenyl)	50	0.0176		193
	60	0.0508		193
-- , bis(p-nitrophenyl)	50	0.0127		193
	60	0.0193		193
Ethanol				
-- , 2-mercapto-	60	0.62		185
Ethyl disulfide	60	0.00013		212
2-Naphthalenethiol	45	1.3		21
	60	3.1		185
1-Pentanethiol	50	0.8	h	236
Phenyl disulfide	50	0.0038		193
	60	0.0007		212
		0.0085		193
2-Propanethiol	60	0.38		185
-- , 2-methyl-	60	0.18		185

Modifier	T°C	C_x	Remarks	References

Methyl Methacrylate (Cont'd.)

Modifier	T°C	C_x	Remarks	References
Sulfur	44.1	0.075		126
m-Toluenethiol	45	4.7		21
p-Toluenethiol	45	7.4		21
p-Tolyl disulfide	50	0.0031		193
	60	0.0044		193

Styrene

Modifier	T°C	C_x	Remarks	References
Acetic acid				
-- , dithiodi-	50	<0.005		202
	99	0.2		64
-- , - , diethyl ester	60	0.015		58
-- , - , dimethyl ester	99	0.1		64
-- , mercapto-	99	>14.0	j,s	64
-- , - , butyl ester	50	26.0	a	98
-- , - , ethyl ester	60	58.0	a	83
-- , - , methyl ester	60	0.63		221
	99	27.6		64
-- , phenyl-				
-- , - , p,p'-dithiodi-	50	0.24		61
-- , thio-	99	>14.7	j	64
Aniline				
-- , o,o'-dithiobis-	25	3.8		202
	50	3.0		202
		3.4		202
	75	3.0		202
-- , p,p'-dithiobis-	50	0.24		61
-- , N-dodecyl-				
-- , - , p,p'-dithiobis-	50	0.21		61
Anisole				
-- , o,o'-dithiobis-	50	3.0		61
-- , p,p'-dithiobis-	50	0.18		61
-- , p-mercaptomethyl-	99	26.0		64
-- , p-methyl-				
-- , - , α,α'-dithiobis-	99	0.021		64
Anthranilic acid				
-- , 4,4'-dithiobis-	50	3.0		61
Benzenethiol	99	0.08		64
-- , o-ethoxy-	99	25.1		64
-- , p-ethoxy-	99	0.13		64
2-Benzimidazolethiol	99	0.21		64

Modifier	T°C	C_x	Remarks	References

Styrene (Cont'd.)

Modifier	T°C	C_x	Remarks	References
Benzoic acid				
-- , o,o'-dithiodi-	50	0.01		61
-- , - , diethyl ester	50	<0.005		61
-- , - , dimethyl ester	99	0.2		64
-- , p,p'-dithiodi-	50	0.11		202
		0.17		61
-- , - , diethyl ester	50	0.11		61,202
-- , o-mercapto-	99	>14.7		64
-- , - , methyl ester	99	17.0		64
-- , thio-	99	6.23	j	64
Benzothiazole				
-- , 2,2'-dithiobis-	25	2.3		202
	50	2.1		202
		2.3		202
	75	2.4		202
	99	2.73		64
-- , 2,2'-thiobis-	50	<0.005		202
2-Benzothiazolethiol	50	0.03		202
	99	0.26		64
Benzoyl disulfide	50	<0.005		61
	60	0.0107		209
	99	0.11		64
Benzyl alcohol				
-- , o,o'-dithiobis-	50	0.58		61
-- , p,p'-dithiobis-	50	0.09		202
Benzyl diselenide	60	2.0	a	85
Benzyl disulfide	50	0.02		61
		0.03		202
	60	0.01	a	85
	99	0.011		64
1-Butanethiol	25	5.4	$d,r(C_1)$	233
		13.2	d	233
	60	21.0	a	271
		22.0	a	46,272
	70	15.0	a	271
	80	17.0	a	271
	99	15.4		64
-- , 1,1,3,3-tetramethyl-	5	5.5	h	163
		6.4	h	150
	50	4.3	h	163
1-Butanethiol-d	60	5.2	a	271
	70	4.0	a	271
	80	7.0	a	271
Butyl disulfide	60	0.0024		209
	99	0.0068		64
	150	0.022	a	250

Modifier	T°C	C_x	Remarks	References
	Styrene (Cont'd.)			
Butyl sulfide	60	0.0022		209
sec-Butyl disulfide	50	<0.005		61
tert-Butyl disulfide	50	<0.005		61
	60	0.00014		209
tert-Butyl sulfide	60	0.025		209
Carbanilic acid -- , p,p'-dithiodi-				
-- , - , diethyl ester	50	0.24		61
Carbonic acid -- , dithio-				
-- , - , S,S'-bis(carboxymethyl) ester	50	0.36		202
-- , trithio- -- , - , S,S'-bis(carboxymethyl) ester	50	0.21		202
Disulfide -- , bis(α-bromo-o-tolyl)	50	1.0		202
-- , bis(chlorobenzyl)	50	<0.005		202
-- , bis(2-chloroethyl)	50	0.01		202
-- , bis(α-chloro-o-tolyl)	50	1.3		202
-- , bis(2-ethylhexyl)	50	<0.005		202
-- , bis(N-ethyl-N-phenylthio- carbamoyl) [diphenyl diethyl thiuram disulfide]	60	1.75		194
-- , bis(1-methylheptyl)	99	0.0104		64
-- , bis(morpholinothiocarbonyl)	60	6.1		194
-- , bis(1-naphthylmethyl)	99	0.033		64
-- , bis(o-nitrophenyl)	50	--		61
-- , bis(1-phenylethyl)	50	<0.005		61
-- , bis(β-(2-pyridyl)ethyl)	50	0.03		202
-- , bis(2,3,5,6-tetramethylphenyl)	50	0.73		202
-- , bis(2,4,6-triisopropylphenyl)	50	0.12		61
1-Dodecanethiol	60	14.8	a	46,83
		19.0		40
	100	13.0		104
	110	26.0		104
Ethanethiol	50	17.1		229

Remarks page II-134; References page II-135

Modifier	T°C	C_x	Remarks	References

Styrene (Cont'd.)

Modifier	T°C	C_x	Remarks	References
Ethanol -- , 2,2'-dithiodi-	50	<0.005		202
-- , - , di(chloroacetate)	50	<0.005		202
Ether -- , ethyl 3-mercaptopropyl	60 100	21.0 14.1 13.7	a	46 83 46
Ethyl disulfide	99	0.0045		64
Formic acid, thio, dithiobis , -- , - , - , diethyl ester	60	0.724		194
-- , - , - , diisopropylester	50 99	5.3 7.5		202 64
-- , - , - , dimethyl ester	60 70	1.11 0.0136		194 68
1-Heptanethiol	99	15.1		64
1-Hexanethiol -- , 1,1,3,3,5,5-hexamethyl-	99 25 50 75	15.3 3.2 2.9 2.4		64 202 202 202
Hexyl disulfide	99	0.0104		64
Isobutyl disulfide	60	0.0020		209
Isopropyl disulfide	60	0.00066		209
Lauryl disulfide	60	0.00023	a	85
Lepidine -- , 2,2'-dithiodi-	50	0.04		61
Mesityl disulfide	50	0.69		61
Methyl disulfide	60	0.0094		209
Morpholine -- , 4,4'-dithiodi-	50	<0.005		202
1-Naphthalenemethanethiol	25 50 75 99	12.7 18.3 15.7 24.6		202 202 202 64
1-Naphthalenethiol	99	0.15		64
2-Naphthalenethiol	99	0.18		64
1-Naphthoyl disulfide	50	0.34		61
1-Naphthyl disulfide	99	1.57		64
2-Naphthyl disulfide	25 50 75 99	0.17 0.19 0.29 0.36		202 202 202 64

Modifier	T°C	C_x	Remarks	References
Styrene (Cont'd.)				
1-Octadecanethiol	99	14.7		64
Octadecyl disulfide	99	0.024		64
1-Octanethiol	5	19.3	h	232
		23.0	h	163
	50	19.0	h	163
-- , 1,1,3,3,5,5,7,7-octamethyl-	50	4.7	h	163
2-Octanethiol	99	3.2		64
1-Oxa-4,5-dithiacycloheptane	150	0.057	a	250
1-Pentanethiol	50	20.0	h	236
Phenetole				
-- , o,o'-dithiobis-	99	0.075		64
-- , p,p'-dithiobis-	99	0.33		64
Phenyl disulfide	50	0.06		202
	60	0.147		193
2-Propanethiol				
-- , 2-methyl-	50	4.0	h	236
	60	3.1	a	176
		3.7	a	46,83
		4.6		40
	100	1.8	a	176
		2.3	a	46,83
Propionic acid				
-- , 3,3'-dithiodi-				
-- , - , dipropyl ester	50	<0.005		202
-- , 3-mercapto-	50	6.0		202
Propyl disulfide	60	0.00234		209
Pyridine				
-- , 2,2'-dithiodi-	50	0.01		61
Quinoline				
-- , 2,2'-dithiodi-	50	0.05		61
Sulfide				
-- , ethyl 2,4-diphenylbutyl	50	30.0		229
-- , ethyl phenethyl	50	7.15		229
-- , hydrogen	70	5.0		97
1-Tetradecanethiol	50	19.0	h	163
p-Toluenethiol	99	0.07		64
α-Toluenethiol	99	25.5		64
o-Tolyl disulfide	25	0.22		202
	50	0.23		202
		0.28		202
	75	0.32		202

Remarks page II-134; References page II-135

Modifier	T°C	C_x	Remarks	References
	Styrene (Cont'd.)			
p-Tolyl disulfide	50	0.11		202
	99	0.15		64
2,6-Xylyl disulfide	50	0.69		202
	Vinyl Acetate			
Acetic acid				
-- , dithiodi-				
-- , - , diethyl ester	60	1.5		243
		1.41		58
Acetyl disulfide	60	0.29	j	58
1-Butanethiol	60	48.0		97,272
Butyl disulfide	60	1.0	j	58,243
Butyl sulfide	60	0.026	j	243
1-Oxa-4,5-dithiacycloheptane	60	0.25-2.5		243
Sulfur	45	470.0	j	19
α-Toluenethiol	70	0.885	c	269

G. Remarks

a. Thermal initiation

b. Hydroperoxide initiation

c. Peroxide initiation

d. Photoinitiation

e. γ-ray initiation

f. In solution of ( ); AN acetonitrile; B benzene; BA butyl acetate; BC butyl
    chloride; CB chlorobenzene; DCB o-dichlorobenzene; DMF dimethylformamide; DMSO
    dimethylsulfoxide; DX p-dioxane; EA ethyl acetate; EMK ethyl methyl ketone; Hep
    heptane; H_2O water; MPC magnesium perchlorate; SN succinonitrile; SO_2 sulfur
    dioxide; Tol toluene; ZC zinc chloride.

g. Heterogeneous polymerization

h. Emulsion polymerization

i. Recalculated data from Ref. ( )

j. Apparent transfer constant; polymerization retarded

k. Average value

l. $C_M = 125 \exp(-7300/RT)$

m. Estimated from model compounds

n. For end groups ( )

o. For middle groups ( )

p. For sidechain

q. For main chain

r. Telomerization (C_i; i = number of monomer units in transferring chain)

s. Calculated from viscosity average molecular weight

t. Uncertain

u. In the presence of 0.4 mol./l. $LiNO_3$

v. In the presence of ( ) mol./l. NaCl

w. In the presence of ( ) mol./l. NaBr

x. Under pressure of ( ) P.S.I.

y. Corrected for loss of low molecular weight polymer

z. $C_M = 3.0 \exp(-5673/RT)$

aa. $C_M = 0.4 \exp(-6219/RT)$

bb. $C_M = 0.2 \exp(-5400/RT)$

cc. $C_M = 6.44 \exp(-4120/RT)$

dd. $C_M = 4.77 \exp(-3540/RT)$

H. References

1. G. Akazome, S. Sakai, and K. Murai, Kogyo Kagaku Zasshi 63, 592 (1960); from CA 56, 4924f (1962).
2. L. Alexandru and M. Oprish, Polymer Sci. USSR 3, 99 (1962).
3. P. W. Allen and G. P. McSweeney, Trans. Faraday Soc. 54, 715 (1958).
4. P. W. Allen, F. M. Merrett, and J. Scanlan, Trans. Faraday Soc. 51, 95 (1955).
5. R. Autrata and J. Müller, Collection Czech. Chem. Commun. 24, 3442 (1959).
6. D. W. E. Axford, Proc. Roy. Soc. (London) A197, 374 (1949).
7. Kh. S. Bagdasar'ian, and Z. A. Sinitsina, J. Polymer Sci. 52, 31 (1961).
8. C. H. Bamford, and M. J. S. Dewar, Proc. Roy. Soc. (London) A192, 309 (1948).
9. C. H. Bamford and M. J. S. Dewar, Proc. Roy. Soc. (London) A197, 356 (1949).
10. C. H. Bamford, A. D. Jenkins, and R. Johnston, Proc. Roy. Soc. (London) A239, 214 (1957).
11. C. H. Bamford, A. D. Jenkins and R. Johnston, Proc. Roy. Soc. (London) A241, 364 (1957).
12. C. H. Bamford, A. D. Jenkins, and R. Johnston, Trans. Faraday Soc. 55, 418 (1959).
13. C. H. Bamford, A. D. Jenkins, R. Johnston, and E. F. T. White, Trans. Faraday Soc. 55, 168 (1959).
14. C. H. Bamford, A. D. Jenkins, and E. F. T. White, J. Polymer Sci. 34, 271 (1959).
15. C. H. Bamford and E. F. T. White, Trans. Faraday Soc. 52, 716 (1956).
16. C. H. Bamford and E. F. T. White, Trans. Faraday Soc. 54, 268 (1958).
17. S. Banerjee and M. S. Muthana, J. Polymer Sci. 37, 469 (1959).
18. P. D. Bartlett, G. S. Hammond, and H. Kwart, Discussions Faraday Soc. 2, 342 (1947).
19. P. D. Bartlett and H. Kwart, J. Am. Chem. Soc. 74, 3969 (1952).
20. P. D. Bartlett and F. A. Tate, J. Am. Chem. Soc. 75, 91 (1953).
21. S. C. Barton, R. A. Bird, and K. E. Russell, Can. J. Chem. 41, 2737 (1963).
22. S. Basu, J. N. Sen, and S. R. Palit, Proc. Roy. Soc. (London) A202, 485 (1950).
23. S. Basu, J. N. Sen, and S. R. Palit, Proc. Roy. Soc. (London) A214, 247 (1952).
24. B. Baysal, J. Polymer Sci. 33, 381 (1958).
25. B. Baysal and A. V. Tobolsky, J. Polymer Sci. 8, 529 (1952).
26. W. I. Bengough and R. A. M. Thomson, Trans. Faraday Soc. 56, 407 (1960).
27. J. C. Bevington, N. A. Ghanem and H. W. Melville, J. Chem. Soc. 1955, 2822.
28. J. C. Bevington, G. M. Guzman, and H. W. Melville, Proc. Roy. Soc. (London) A221, 437 (1954).
29. J. C. Bevington and H. G. Troth, Trans. Faraday Soc. 58, 2005 (1962).
30. J. C. Bevington and H. G. Troth, Trans. Faraday Soc. 59, 127 (1963).
31. J. C. Bevington and H. G. Troth, Trans. Faraday Soc. 59, 1348 (1963).
32. J. C. Bevington and A. Wahid, Polymer 3, 585 (1962).
33. R. A. Bird, G. A. Harpell and K. E. Russell, Can. J. Chem. 40, 701 (1962).
34. L. Boghetich, G. A. Mortimer, and G. W. Daues, J. Polymer Sci. 61, 3 (1962).
35. E. P. Bonsall, L. Valentine, and H. W. Melville, J. Polymer Sci. 7, 39 (1951).
36. C. Booth and L. R. Beason, J. Polymer Sci. 42, 93 (1960).
37. C. Booth, L. R. Beason, and J. T. Bailey, J. Appl. Polymer Sci. 5, 116 (1961).
38. D. Braun, T.-O. Ahn, and W. Kern, Makromol. Chem. 53, 154 (1962).
39. J. W. Breitenbach, Makromol. Chem. 8, 147 (1952).
40. J. W. Breitenbach, Z. Elektrochem. 60, 286 (1956).
41. J. W. Breitenbach and H. Karlinger, Monatsh. Chem. 82, 245 (1951).
42. J. W. Breitenbach, O. F. Olaj, and A. Schindler, Monatsh. Chem. 91, 205 (1960).
43. J. W. Breitenbach and A. Schindler, Monatsh. Chem. 83, 724 (1952).
44. J. W. Breitenbach and A. Schindler, Monatsh. Chem. 86, 437 (1955).
45. J. W. Breitenbach and A. Schindler, Monatsh. Chem. 88, 53 (1957).
46. G. M. Burnett, Quart. Revs. 4, 292 (1950).
47. A. J. Buselli, M. K. Lindemann, and C. E. Blades, J. Polymer Sci. 28, 485 (1958).
48. M. Cantow, G. Meyerhoff, and G. V. Schulz, Makromol. Chem. 49, 1 (1961).
49. R. N. Chadha and G. S. Misra, Indian J. Phys. 28, 37 (1954).
50. R. N. Chadha and G. S. Misra, Current Sci.(India) 23, 186 (1954).
51. R. N. Chadha and G. S. Misra, Makromol. Chem. 14, 97 (1954).
52. R. N. Chadha and G. S. Misra, Current Sci. (India) 24, 26 (1955).
53. R. N. Chadha and G. S. Misra, Trans. Faraday Soc. 54, 1227 (1958).
54. R. N. Chadha, J. S. Shukla, and G. S. Misra, Trans. Faraday Soc. 53, 240 (1957).
55. E. Y. C. Chang and C. C. Price, J. Am. Chem. Soc. 83, 4650 (1961).
56. S. R. Chatterjee, S. N. Khanna, and S. R. Palit, J. Indian Chem. Soc. 41, 622 (1964).
57. A. K. Chaudhuri, Makromol. Chem. 31, 214 (1959).
58. J. T. Clarke, R. O. Howard, and W. H. Stockmayer, Makromol. Chem. 44/46, 427 (1961).
59. W. Cooper, J. Chem. Soc. 1952, 2408.

60. A. T. Coscia, R. L. Kugel, and J. J. Pellon, J. Polymer Sci. 55, 303 (1961).
61. A. J. Costanza, R. J. Coleman, R. M. Pierson, C. S. Marvel, and C. King, J. Polymer Sci. 17, 319 (1955).
62. J. Curtice, H. Gilman, and G. S. Hammond, J. Am. Chem. Soc. 79, 4754 (1957).
63. S. K. Das, S. R. Chatterjee, and S. R. Palit, Proc. Roy. Soc. (London) A227, 252 (1955).
64. V. A. Dinaburg and A. A. Vansheidt, Zh. Obshch. Khim. 24, 840 (1954).
65. G. Dixon-Lewis, Proc. Roy. Soc. (London) A198, 510 (1949).
66. K. W. Doak, M. A. Deahl, and I. H. Christmas, Abstracts of 137th ACS Meeting in Cleveland, 1960.
67. T. A. Fadner, and H. Morawetz, J. Polymer Sci. 45, 475 (1960).
68. T. E. Ferington and A. V. Tobolsky, J. Am. Chem. Soc. 77, 4510 (1955).
69. T. G. Fox and S. Gratch, Ann. N. Y. Acad. Sci. 57, 367 (1953).
70. N. Fuhrman and R. B. Mesrobian, J. Am. Chem. Soc. 76, 3281 (1954).
71. T. R. Fukuto and J. P. Kispersky, U. S. Dep. Comm. Office Tech. Serv., P. B. Rept. 147, 271 (1953).
72. S. Gadkary and S. Kapur, Makromol. Chem. 17, 29 (1955).
73. J. A. Gannon, E. M. Fettes, and A. V. Tobolsky, J. Am. Chem. Soc. 74, 1854 (1952).
74. M. H. George, J. Polymer Sci. A2, 3169 (1964).
75. M. H. George and P. F. Onyon, Trans. Faraday Soc. 59, 134 (1963).
76. M. H. George and P. F. Onyon, Trans. Faraday Soc. 59, 1390 (1963).
77. L. Ghosez and G. Smets, J. Polymer Sci. 37, 445 (1959).
78. M. S. Gluckman, M. J. Kampf, J. L. O'Brien, T. G. Fox, and R. K. Graham, J. Polymer Sci. 37, 411 (1959).
79. M. P. Godsay, G. A. Harpell, and K. E. Russell, J. Polymer Sci. 57, 641 (1962).
80. M. P. Godsay, D. H. Lohmann, and K. E. Russell, Chem. Ind. (London) 1959, 1603.
81. M. R. Gopalan and M. Santhappa, J. Polymer Sci. 25, 333 (1957).
82. N. Grassie and E. Vance, Trans. Faraday Soc. 52, 727 (1956).
83. R. A. Gregg, D. M. Alderman, and F. R. Mayo, J. Am. Chem. Soc. 70, 3740 (1948).
84. R. A. Gregg and F. R. Mayo, Discussions Faraday Soc. 2, 328 (1947).
85. R. A. Gregg and F. R. Mayo, J. Am. Chem. Soc. 75, 3530 (1953).
86. R. A. Gregg and F. R. Mayo, J. Am. Chem. Soc. 70, 2373 (1948).
87. H. C. Haas and H. Husek, J. Polymer Sci. A2, 2297 (1964).
88. Y. Hachihama and H. Sumitomo, Technol. Rept. Osaka Univ. 5, 491 (1955); from CA 51, 8474b (1957).
89. Y. Hachihama and H. Sumitomo, Technol. Rept. Osaka Univ. 5, 497 (1955); from CA 51, 8474c (1957).
90. G. E. Ham, J. Polymer Sci. 21, 337 (1956).
91. G. E. Ham and E. L. Ringwald, J. Polymer Sci. 8, 91 (1952).
92. D. Hardy, K. Nytrai, N. Fedorova, and G. Kovacs, Polymer Sci. USSR 4, 584 (1963).
93. D. Hardy, V. Spiegel, and K. Nytrai, Polymer Sci. USSR 2, 528 (1961).
94. R. A. Hayes, J. Polymer Sci. 13, 583 (1954).
95. E. J. Henley and C. Chong, J. Polymer Sci. 36, 511 (1959).
96. G. Henrici-Olivé and S. Olivé, Makromol. Chem. 37, 71 (1960).
97. G. Henrici-Olivé and S. Olivé, Fortschr. Hochpolymer. Forsch. 2, 496 (1961).
98. G. Henrici-Olivé and S. Olivé, Makromol. Chem. 53, 122 (1962).
99. G. Henrici-Olivé, S. Olivé, and G. V. Schulz, Makromol. Chem. 23, 207 (1957).
100. G. Henrici-Olivé, S. Olivé, and G. V. Schulz, Z. Physik. Chem. (Frankfurt) 20, 176 (1959).
101. R. Hiddema, Proefschrift Rijks Universität Groningen, 1953, Ref. 16 in Ref. 40.
102. F. Hrabak and L. Jiresova, Collection Czech. Chem. Commun. 26, 1283 (1961).
103. T. Huff and E. Perry, J. Am. Chem. Soc. 82, 4277 (1960).
104. T. Huff and E. Perry, J. Polymer Sci. A1, 1553 (1963).
105. M. Imoto, T. Otsu, T. Ota, H. Takatsugi, and M. Matsuda, J. Polymer Sci. 22, 137 (1956).
106. M. Imoto, T. Otsu, K. Tsuda, and T. Ito, J. Polymer Sci. A2, 1407 (1964).
107. M. Imoto, K. Takemoto, and Y. Nakai, Makromol. Chem. 48, 80 (1961).
108. S. Imoto and T. Kominami, Kobunshi Kagaku 15, 60 (1958); from CA 53, 8690g (1959).
109. S. Imoto and T. Kominami, Kobunshi Kagaku 15, 279 (1958); from CA 54, 2803a (1960).
110. S. Imoto, J. Ukida, and T. Kominami, Kobunshi Kagaku 14, 127 (1957); from CA 52, 1670a (1958).
111. S. Imoto, J. Ukida, and T. Kominami, Kobunshi Kagaku 14, 384 (1957); from CA 52, 5024d (1958).
112. D. H. Johnson and A. V. Tobolsky, J. Am. Chem. Soc. 74, 938 (1952).
113. M. H. Jones, Can. J. Chem. 34, 108 (1956).
114. R. M. Joshi, Makromol. Chem. 53, 33 (1962).
115. H. Kaemmerer and F. Rocaboy, Compt. Rend. 256, 4440 (1963).
116. H. Kaemmerer and F. Rocaboy, Makromol. Chem. 72, 76 (1964).

117. S. L. Kapur, J. Sci. Ind. Res. (India) 10B, 186 (1951).
118. S. L. Kapur, J. Polymer Sci. 11, 399 (1953).
119. S. L. Kapur and S. D. Gadkary, J. Sci. Ind. Res. (India) 17B, 152 (1958).
120. S. L. Kapur and R. M. Joshi, J. Polymer Sci. 14, 489 (1954).
121. K. Katagiri, K. Uno, and S. Okamura, J. Polymer Sci. 17, 142 (1955).
122. H. Kawakami, N. Mori, K. Kawashima, and M. Sumi, Kogyo Kagaku Zasshi 66, 88 (1963).
123. H. Kawakami, N. Mori and M. Sumi, Kobunshi Kagaku 20, 408 (1963); from CA 61, 13422d (1964).
124. W. Kern and D. Braun, Makromol. Chem. 27, 23 (1958).
125. S. N. Khanna, S. R. Chatterjee, U. S. Nandi, and S. R. Palit, Trans. Faraday Soc. 58, 1827 (1962).
126. J. L. Kice, J. Am. Chem. Soc. 76, 6274 (1954).
127. W. J. Kirkham and J. C. Robb, Trans. Faraday Soc. 57, 1757 (1961).
128. H. Kitagawa, Kobunshi Kagaku 20, 5 (1963); Makromol. Chem. 64, 229 (1963).
129. H. Kiuchi and M. Watanabe, Kobunshi Kagaku 21, 37 (1964); from CA 61, 7107f (1964).
130. C. J. Kurian and M. S. Muthana, Makromol. Chem. 29, 1 (1959).
131. C. J. Kurian and M. S. Muthana, Makromol. Chem. 29, 19 (1959).
132. H. Kwart, H. S. Broadbent, and P. D. Bartlett, J. Am. Chem. Soc. 72, 1060 (1950).
133. K. S. Kwei and F. R. Eirich, J. Phys. Chem. 66, 828 (1962).
134. Z. Laita, J. Polymer Sci. 38, 247 (1959).
135. Z. Laita and Z. Machacek, J. Polymer Sci. 38, 459 (1959).
136. M. Lazar and J. Pavlinec, Chem. Zvesti 15, 428 (1961); from CA 55, 22896c (1961).
137. M. Lazar and J. Pavlinec, J. Polymer Sci. A2, 3197 (1964).
138. M. Lazar, J. Pavlinec, and Z. Manasek, Collection Czech. Chem. Commun. 26, 1380 (1961).
139. M. Lazar, R. Rado, and J. Pavlinec, J. Polymer Sci. 53, 163 (1961).
140. F. M. Lewis and F. R. Mayo, J. Am. Chem. Soc. 76, 457 (1954).
141. D. Lim and M. Kolinsky, J. Polymer Sci. 53, 173 (1961).
142. D. Lim and O. Wichterle, J. Polymer Sci. 29, 579 (1958).
143. M. Litt and V. Stannett, Makromol. Chem. 37, 19 (1960).
144. J. R. Little, L. W. Hartzel, F. O. Guenther, and F. R. Mayo, Private Communication to C. Walling, "Free Radicals in Solution," John Wiley and Sons, N. Y., 1957, p. 257.
145. S. Loshaek, E. Broderick, and P. Bernstein, J. Polymer Sci. 39, 223 (1959).
146. A. I. Lowell and J. R. Price, J. Polymer Sci. 43, 1 (1960).
147. S. G. Lyubetskii, B. A. Dolgoplosk and B. L. Erusalimskii, Polymer Sci. USSR 3, 164 (1962).
148. G. Machell and G. N. Richards, J. Chem. Soc. 1961, 3308.
149. V. Mahedevan and M. Santhappa, Makromol. Chem. 16, 119 (1955).
150. K. L. Mallik, Naturwissenschaften, 45, 385 (1958).
151. T. Manabe, T. Utsumi, and S. Okamura, J. Polymer Sci. 58, 121 (1962).
152. M. S. Matheson, E. E. Auer, E. B. Bevilacqua, and E. J. Hart, J. Am. Chem. Soc. 71, 497 (1949).
153. M. S. Matheson, E. E. Auer, E. B. Bevilacqua, and E. J. Hart, J. Am. Chem. Soc. 71, 2610 (1949).
154. M. Matsuda, S. Abe, and N. Tokura, J. Polymer Sci. A2, 3877 (1964).
155. M. Matsuda and N. Tokura, J. Polymer Sci. A2, 4281 (1964).
156. M. Matsumoto and M. Maeda, J. Polymer Sci. 17, 438 (1955).
157. M. Matsumoto, J. Ukida, G. Takayama, T. Eguchi, K. Mukumoto, K. Imai, Y. Kazusa, and M. Maeda, Makromol. Chem. 32, 13 (1959).
158. F. R. Mayo, J. Am. Chem. Soc. 65, 2324 (1943).
159. F. R. Mayo, J. Am. Chem. Soc. 70, 3689 (1948).
160. F. R. Mayo, J. Am. Chem. Soc. 75, 6133 (1953).
161. F. R. Mayo, J. Am. Chem. Soc. 76, 5392 (1954).
162. F. R. Mayo, R. A. Gregg, and M. S. Matheson, J. Am. Chem. Soc. 73, 1691 (1951).
163. E. J. Meehan, I. M. Kolthoff, and P. R. Sinha, J. Polymer Sci. 16, 471 (1955).
164. E. J. Meehan, I. M. Kolthoff, and P. R. Sinha, J. Polymer Sci. A2, 4911 (1964).
165. F. W. Mellows and M. Burton, J. Phys. Chem. 66, 2164 (1962).
166. H. W. Melville, and L. Valentine, Trans. Faraday Soc. 46, 210 (1950).
167. H. S. Mickley, A. S. Michaels, and A. L. Moore, J. Polymer Sci. 60, 121 (1962).
168. Y. Minoura, Y. Hayashi, and M. Imoto, Kobunshi Kagaku 15, 260 (1958); from CA 54, 2803f (1960).
169. Y. Minoura, N. Yasumoto, and T. Ishii, Kogyo Kagaku Zasshi 65, 1299 (1962); from CA 58, 1538d (1963).
170. Y. Minoura, N. Yasumoto, and T. Ishii, Makromol. Chem. 71, 159 (1964).
171. G. S. Misra and R. N. Chadha, Makromol. Chem. 23, 134 (1957).
172. G. S. Misra, R. C. Rastogi, and V. P. Gupta, Makromol. Chem. 50, 72 (1961).
173. T. Miyake and M. Matsumoto, Kogyo Kagaku Zasshi 62, 1101 (1959); from CA 57, 15342a (1962).

174. Y. Mori, K. Sato, and Y. Minoura, Kogyo Kagaku Zasshi 61, 462 (1958); from CA 55, 4021f (1961).
175. G. A. Mortimer and L. C. Arnold, J. Am. Chem. Soc. 84, 4986 (1962).
176. M. Morton, J. A. Cala, and I. Piirma, J. Am. Chem. Soc. 78, 5394 (1956).
177. M. Morton and I. Piirma, J. Am. Chem. Soc. 80, 5596 (1958).
178. M. Morton and I. Piirma, J. Polymer Sci. A1, 3043 (1963).
179. A. S. Nair and M. S. Muthana, Makromol. Chem. 47, 114,128 (1961).
180. U. S. Nandi, P. Ghosh, and S. R. Palit, Nature 195, 1197 (1962).
181. K. Noma, Y. Tajima, and M. Niwa, Sci. Eng. Rev. Doshisha Univ. 3, 91 (1962); from CA 59, 2955c (1963).
182. R. G. W. Norrish, and J. P. Simons, Proc. Roy. Soc. (London) A251, 4 (1959).
183. A. M. North and A. M. Scallan, Polymer 5, 447 (1964).
184. K. Nozaki, Discussions Faraday Soc. 2, 337 (1947).
185. J. L. O'Brien and F. Gornick, J. Am. Chem. Soc. 77, 4757 (1955).
186. J. L. O'Brien, J. R. Panchak, and T. G. Fox, Abstracts of 124th ACS Meeting in Chicago, 1953.
187. S. Okamura, and K. Katagiri, Makromol. Chem. 28, 177 (1958).
188. S. Okamura, K. Katagiri, and T. Motoyama, J. Polymer Sci. 43, 509 (1960).
189. S. Okamura and T. Motoyama, J. Polymer Sci. 58, 221 (1962).
190. S. Okamura and K. Takeya, Kobunshi Kagaku 15, 353 (1958); from CA 54, 8143 (1960)
191. P. F. Onyon, Trans. Faraday Soc. 51, 400 (1955).
192. P. F. Onyon, J. Polymer Sci. 22, 19 (1956).
193. T. Otsu, Y. Kinoshita, and M. Imoto, Makromol. Chem. 73, 225 (1964).
194. T. Otsu and K. Nayatani, Makromol. Chem. 27, 149 (1955).
195. T. Otsu, A. Shimizu, and M. Imoto, J. Polymer Sci. B2, 973 (1964).
196. S. R. Palit and S. K. Das, Proc. Roy. Soc. (London) A226, 82 (1954).
197. S. R. Palit, U. S. Nandi, and N. G. Saha, J. Polymer Sci. 14, 295 (1954).
198. L. H. Peebles, J. Polymer Sci. A3, 341 (1965).
199. L. H. Peebles, J. T. Clark, and W. H. Stockmayer, J. Am. Chem. Soc. 82, 4780 (1960).
200. J. J. Pellon, J. Polymer Sci. 43, 537 (1960).
201. E. Perry, J. Polymer Sci. 54, S 46 (1961).
202. R. Pierson, A. Costanza, and A. Weinstein, J. Polymer Sci. 17, 221 (1955).
203. G. Platau, F. R. Eirich, R. B. Mesrobian, and A. E. Woodward, J. Polymer Sci. 39, 357 (1959).
204. A. Prevot-Bernas and J. Sebban-Danon, J. Chim. Phys. 53, 418 (1956).
205. W. A. Pryor, J. Phys. Chem. 67, 519 (1963).
206. W. A. Pryor, D. M. Huston, T. R. Fiske, T. L. Pickering, and E. Ciuffarin, J. Am. Chem. Soc. 86, 4237 (1964).
207. W. A. Pryor and G. L. Kaplan, J. Am. Chem. Soc. 86, 4234 (1964).
208. W. A. Pryor, A. Lee, and C. E. Witt, J. Am. Chem. Soc. 86, 4229 (1964).
209. W. A. Pryor and T. L. Pickering, J. Am. Chem. Soc. 84, 2705 (1962).
210. W. A. Pryor and E. P. Pultinas, Jr., J. Am. Chem. Soc. 85, 133 (1963).
211. A. J. Restaino and W. N. Reed, J. Polymer Sci. 36, 499 (1959).
212. E. H. Riddle, "Monomeric Acrylic Esters," Reinhold Publishing Corp., N. Y., 1954, Ref. 14, p. 64.
213. J. C. Robb and E. Senogles, Trans. Faraday Soc. 58, 708 (1962).
214. J. C. Robb and D. Vofsi, Trans. Faraday Soc. 55, 558 (1959).
215. N. G. Saha, U. S. Nandi, and S. R. Palit, J. Chem. Soc. 1956, 427.
216. N. G. Saha, U. S. Nandi, and S. R. Palit, J. Chem. Soc. 1958, 7.
217. N. G. Saha, U. S. Nandi, and S. R. Palit, J. Chem. Soc. 1958, 12.
218. I. Sakurada, Y. Sakaguchi, and K. Hashimoto, Kobunshi Kagaku 19, 593 (1962); from CA 61, 16159d (1964).
219. G. F. Santee, R. H. Marchessault, H. G. Clark, J. J. Kearny, and V. Stannett, Makromol. Chem. 73, 177 (1964).
220. M. Santhappa and V. M. Iyer, Current Sci. (India) 24, 173 (1955).
221. M. Santhappa and V. S. Vaidhyanathan, Current Sci. (India) 23, 259 (1954).
222. J. Scanlan, Trans. Faraday Soc. 50, 756 (1954).
223. E. Schonfeld and I. Waltcher, J. Polymer Sci. 35, 536 (1959).
224. G. V. Schulz, G. Henrici, and S. Olive, J. Polymer Sci. 17, 45 (1955).
225. G. V. Schulz, G. Henrici, and S. Olive, Z. Elektrochem. 60, 296 (1956).
226. G. V. Schulz, and L. Roberts-Nowakowska, Makromol. Chem. 80, 36 (1964).
227. G. V. Schulz and D. J. Stein, Makromol. Chem. 52, 1 (1962).
228. G. P. Scott, C. C. Soong, W.-S. Huang, and J. L. Reynolds, J. Org. Chem. 29, 83 (1964).
229. G. P. Scott, and J. C. Wang, J. Org. Chem. 28, 1314 (1963).
230. J. N. Sen, U. S. Nandi, and S. R. Palit, J. Indian Chem. Soc. 40, 729 (1963).
231. K. P. Shen and F. R. Eirich, J. Polymer Sci. 53, 81 (1961).
232. P. R. Sinha and K. L. Mallik, J. Indian Chem. Soc. 34, 424 (1957).
233. C. Sivertz, J. Phys. Chem. 63, 34 (1959).

234. G. Smets, L. Convent, and X. Van der Borght, Makromol. Chem. 23, 162 (1957).
235. G. Smets and L. de Haes, Bull. Soc. Chim. Belges 59, 13 (1950).
236. W. V. Smith, J. Am. Chem. Soc. 68, 2059 (1964).
237. R. D. Spencer and M. B. Fulton, U. S. Dep. Comm., Office Tech. Serv., P. B. Rept. 144,900 (1961).
238. R. D. Spencer, M. B. Fulton, and B. H. Beggs, Abstracts of 137th ACS Meeting in Cleveland, 1960.
239. N. T. Srinivasan and M. Santhappa, Makromol. Chem. 26, 80 (1958).
240. D. J. Stein, Makromol. Chem. 76, 170 (1964).
241. D. J. Stein and G. V. Schulz, Makromol. Chem. 38, 248 (1960).
242. D. J. Stein and G. V. Schulz, Makromol. Chem. 52, 249 (1962).
243. W. H. Stockmayer, R. O. Howard, and J. T. Clarke, J. Am. Chem. Soc. 75, 1756 (1953).
244. T. J. Suen, Y. Jen, and J. V. Lockwood, J. Polymer Sci. 31, 481 (1958).
245. T. J. Suen, A. M. Schiller, and W. N. Russell, Advances in Chem. Series No. 34, "Polymerization and Polycondensation Processes," ACS, Wash., D.C., 1962, pp. 217-24.
246. G. Takayama, Kobunshi Kagaku 15, 89 (1958); from CA 53, 8689d (1959).
247. W. M. Thomas, E. H. Gleason, and J. J. Pellon, J. Polymer Sci. 17, 275 (1955).
248. C. F. Thompson, W. S. Port, and L. P. Witnauer, J. Am. Chem. Soc. 81, 2552 (1959).
249. A. P. Titov, and I. A. Livshits, Zh. Obshch. Khim. 29, 1605 (1959).
250. A. V. Tobolsky and B. Baysal, J. Am. Chem. Soc. 75, 1757 (1953).
251. A. V. Tobolsky and J. Offenbach, J. Polymer Sci. 16, 311 (1955).
252. T. Toda, J. Polymer Sci. 58, 411 (1962).
253. N. Tokura, M. Matsuda, and F. Yazaki, Makromol. Chem. 42, 108 (1960).
254. A. C. Toohey and K. E. Weale, Trans. Faraday Soc. 58, 2439 (1962).
255. A. C. Toohey and K. E. Weale, Trans. Faraday Soc. 58, 2446 (1962).
256. F. Tüdos, I. Kende, and M. Azori, J. Polymer Sci. 53, 17 (1961).
257. F. Tüdos, I. Kende, and M. Azori, J. Polymer Sci. A1, 1353 (1963).
258. F. Tüdos, I. Kende, and M. Azori, J. Polymer Sci. A1, 1369 (1963).
259. J. Ulbricht, Faserforsch. Textiltech. 10, 166 (1959).
260. J. Ulbricht, Faserforsch. Textiltech. 11, 62 (1960).
261. J. Ulbricht, Z. Phys. Chem. 221, 346 (1962).
262. T. Uno and K. Yoshida, Kobunshi Kagaku 15, 819 (1958); from CA 54, 20298d (1960).
263. W. H. Urry, F. W. Stacey, E. S. Huyser, and O. O. Juveland, J. Am. Chem. Soc. 76, 450 (1954).
264. V. S. Vaidhyanathan and M. Santhappa, Makromol. Chem. 16, 140 (1955).
265. R. L. Vale and W. G. P. Robertson, J. Polymer Sci. 33, 518 (1958).
266. B. M. E. Van Der Hoff, J. Polymer Sci. 44, 241 (1960).
267. B. M. E. Van Der Hoff, J. Polymer Sci. 48, 175 (1960).
268. A. A. Vansheidt and G. Khardi, Acta Chim. Acad. Sci. Hung. 20, 261 (1959); from CA 54, 6180b (1960).
269. A. A. Vansheidt and G. Khardi, Acta Chim. Acad. Sci. Hung. 20, 381 (1959); from CA 54, 11552f (1960).
270. M. Vrancken and G. Smets, Makromol. Chem. 30, 197 (1959).
271. L. A. Wall and D. W. Brown, J. Polymer Sci. 14, 513 (1954).
272. C. Walling, J. Am. Chem. Soc. 70, 2561 (1948).
273. C. Walling and E. R. Briggs, J. Am. Chem. Soc. 68, 1141 (1946).
274. C. Walling and Y. Chang, J. Am. Chem. Soc. 76, 4878 (1954).
275. C. Walling and L. Heaton, J. Am. Chem. Soc. 87, 38 (1965).
276. C. Walling and J. J. Pellon, J. Am. Chem. Soc. 79, 4776 (1957).
277. M. Watanabe and H. Kiuchi, J. Polymer Sci. 58, 103 (1962).
278. O. L. Wheeler, E. Lavin and R. N. Crozier, J. Polymer Sci. 9, 157 (1952).
279. E. F. T. White and M. J. Zissell, J. Polymer Sci. A1, 2189 (1963).
280. S. D. Yevstratova, M.F. Margaritova, and S. S. Medvedev, Polymer Sci. USSR 5, 681 (1964).
281. M. Yoshida and K. Tanouchi, Kobunshi Kagaku 20, 545 (1963); from Makromol. Chem. 71, 216 (1964).
282. M. G. Zimina and N. P. Apukhtina, Kolloidn. Zh. 21, 181 (1959).

COPOLYMERIZATION
REACTIVITY RATIOS * †

HERMAN MARK, B. IMMERGUT, AND E. H. IMMERGUT, *Polytechnic Institute of Brooklyn, Brooklyn, New York,* L. J. YOUNG, *The Dow Chemical Company, Midland, Michigan,* AND K. I. BEYNON, *Shell Research Limited, Chester, England*

When a monomer 1 is copolymerized with a monomer 2 the relationship between the composition of the copolymer and the composition of the monomer mixture is given by eq. (1)

$$\frac{dm_1}{dm_2} = \frac{M_1 (r_1 M_1 + M_2)}{M_2 (r_2 M_2 + M_1)} \tag{1}$$

where m_1 = the moles of monomer 1 entering the copolymer, m_2 = the moles of monomer 2 entering the copolymer, M_1 = the moles of monomer 1 in the monomer mixture, M_2 = the moles of monomer 2 in the monomer mixture, and r_1 and r_2 are the monomer reactivity ratios.

The monomer reactivity ratios r_1 and r_2, for any monomer pair are the ratios of the rate constants of different propagation reactions as defined by eqs. (2) to (7):

$$\sim M_1 \cdot + M_1 \rightarrow \sim M_1 M_1 \cdot \quad \text{Rate constant } k_{11} \tag{2}$$

$$\sim M_1 \cdot + M_2 \rightarrow \sim M_1 M_2 \cdot \quad \text{Rate constant } k_{12} \tag{3}$$

$$\sim M_2 \cdot + M_2 \rightarrow \sim M_2 M_2 \cdot \quad \text{Rate constant } k_{22} \tag{4}$$

$$\sim M_2 \cdot + M_1 \rightarrow \sim M_2 M_1 \cdot \quad \text{Rate constant } k_{21} \tag{5}$$

$$r_1 = k_{11}/k_{12} \tag{6}$$

$$r_2 = k_{22}/k_{21} \tag{7}$$

$\sim M \cdot$ represents a polymer chain ending in a radical derived from monomer M.

The values of r_1 and r_2 have been collected from the literature and are presented here together with references. Some of the original papers have not been examined and in these cases the reference to the original papers includes the reference in *Chemical Abstracts*. The values which have been obtained from *Chemical Abstracts* should be used with caution for it is sometimes difficult to determine to which of the two monomers the values of r_1 and r_2 refer.

Each monomer pair is listed under both monomers.

In cases (indicated by the symbol f) where the abstract did not give the reactivity ratios and the original journal was not readily available, we have decided that it would at least be of value to list these systems in this table.

The column "Remarks" is intended to indicate the conditions of copolymerization. Unless otherwise shown, a free-radical system was used.

---

* Reprinted from G. E. Ham, *Copolymerization*, Interscience Publishers, New York, 1964.
† See also the appendix of recent copolymerization parameters following this table.

Copolymerization Reactivity Ratios

M_1	r_1	M_2	r_2	T, °C.	Remarks	Ref.
Abityl acrylate	4.2 ± 0.2	Vinyl chloride	0.13 ± 0.01	60		187
Acenaphthylene	0.38 ± 0.04	n-Butyl vinyl ether	1.3 ± 0.3	30	d	268
	0.24 ± 0.04	n-Butyl vinyl ether	4.2 ± 0.8	0	d	268
	0.14 ± 0.03	n-Butyl vinyl ether	6.0 ± 1.0	-20	d	268
	0.04 ± 0.02	n-Butyl vinyl ether	~20	-78	d	268
	0.33	Styrene	3.81	90		306
α-Acetoxyacrylonitrile	7.4 ± 0.40	Acrylonitrile	0.09 ± 0.17	60		337
	0.20 ± 0.052	Styrene	0.19 ± 0.056	60		337
1-Acetoxy-1,3-butadiene	0.7	Acrylonitrile	0.0	70		105
	Large	Vinyl acetate	0.0	70		105
α-Acetoxystyrene	0.4 ± 0.05	Acrylonitrile	0.08 ± 0.01	75		53
p-Acetylaminostyrene	0.50 ± 0.05	Methyl methacrylate	0.30 ± 0.05	65		106
Aconitic acid	—	Butadiene	—	50	r	228
	—	Styrene	—	60	r	228
Acrolein	2.0 ± 0.05	Acrylamide	0.76 ± 0.02	20		269
	1.65 ± 0.1	Acrylamide	0.19 ± 0.02	50		148a
	1.09 ± 0.05	Acrylonitrile	0.77 ± 0.1	20		269
	1.60 ± 0.04	Acrylonitrile	0.52 ± 0.02	50		148a
	0.72 ± 0.06	Methacrylonitrile	1.20 ± 0.08	50		148a
	10.0	Methyl acrylate	0.2	20		269
	0.0 ± 0.05	Methyl acrylate	7.7 ± 0.2	20		148a
	0.2 ± 0.05	Methyl methacrylate	10.0 ± 0.2	20		269
	3.33 ± 0.1	Vinyl acetate	0.1 ± 0.05	20		269
Acrylamide	0.76 ± 0.02	Acrolein	2.0 ± 0.05	20		269
	0.19 ± 0.02	Acrolein	1.65 ± 0.1	50		148a

M₁	r_1	M₂	r_2	Temp.	Ref.
	0.60 ± 0.02	Acrylic acid	1.43 ± 0.03	25	42
	1.38	Acrylic acid	0.36	60	282
	1.357	Acrylonitrile	0.875	30	127
	1.30 ± 0.05	Methyl acrylate	0.05 ± 0.05	60	24a
	0.56 ± 0.09	2-Methyl-5-vinyl pyridine	0.01 ± 0.09	60	24a
	1.10 ± 0.05	Sodium acrylate (90%)	0.35 ± 0.03	60	42
	14.9	Sodium vinylsulfonate	0	50	46
	4.89 ± 0.08	Vinylidene chloride	0.15 ± 0.08	60	24a
	0.68	Vinyl isothiocyanate	0.47	h	337
	0.0	p-Vinyl phenyl boronic acid	1.0	60	239c
1-Acrylamide-1-deoxy-D-glucitol	0.206	Methyl methacrylate	4.22	50	325a
	0.056	Styrene	2.72	50	325a
	2.41	Vinyl acetate	0.18	50	325a
Acrylic acid	1.43 ± 0.03	Acrylamide	0.60 ± 0.02	25	42
	0.36	Acrylamide	1.38	60	282
	1.15	Acrylonitrile	0.35	50	132
	6.0 ± 2.0	Acrylonitrile	0.13 ± 0.02	80	337
	f	Acrylonitrile	f	50	5
	1.0	2-Chloroallyl acetate	0.0	100	147
	0.4 ± 0.05	N,N-Dimethylacrylamide	0.5 ± 0.1	75	263
	0.10 ± 0.02	Sodium styrene sulfonate	1.0 ± 0.2	70	101
	0.15	Styrene	0.25		242a

(continued)

(continued)

M_1	r_1	M_2	r_2	T, °C.	Remarks	Ref.
Acrylic acid	0.35	Styrene	0.22	70		99
	0.25 ± 0.02	Styrene	0.15 ± 0.01	60		53
	0.45 ± 0.1	Styrene	0.25 ± 0.05	80		337
	2	Vinyl acetate	0.1	70		18
	10 ± 1	Vinyl acetate	0.01 ± 0.003	70		42
	0.26 ± 0.06	Vinylidene cyanide	0.29 ± 0.08	50	t, see ref. 108	93
	1.3 ± 0.2	N-Vinylpyrrolidone	0.15 ± 0.1	75		317
Acrylonitrile	0.09 ± 0.17	α-Acetoxyacryloni-trile	7.4 ± 0.40	60		337
	0.0	1-Acetoxy-1,3-buta-diene	0.7	70		105
	0.08 ± 0.01	α-Acetoxystyrene	0.4 ± 0.05	75		53
	0.77 ± 0.1	Acrolein	1.09 ± 0.05	20		269
	0.52 ± 0.02	Acrolein	1.60 ± 0.04	50		148a
	0.875	Acrylamide	1.357	h		127
	0.35	Acrylic acid	1.15	50		132
	0.13 ± 0.02	Acrylic acid	6.0 ± 2.0	80		337
	f	Acrylic acid	f	50		5
	f	C_8–C_{16} Alkyl vinyl ethers	f	50		294
	3.96 ± 0.53	Allyl alcohol	0.11 ± 0.10	25		229
	0.03	Allyl Alcohol	1.99	RT		60a
	5.5	Allyl chloride	0	60		193
	3.0 ± 0.2	Allyl chloride	0.05 ± 0.01	60		53

1.7	Allyl triethoxy silane	0		50	296
14.5 ± 0.5	α-Angelolactone	0		h	138
113 ± 14	β-Angelolactone	0		h	138
0.67	Bicyclo[2.2.1]-2,5-hepta-diene	0.08		50	343a
0.014 ± 0.002	1,1-Bis(p-anisyl) ethylene	0		60	68
0.03	Butadiene	0.18		5	73
0.0 ± 0.04	Butadiene	0.35 ± 0.08		50	119
0.05 ± 0.01	Butadiene	0.35 ± 0.01		50	120
0.04 ± 0.01	Butadiene	0.40 ± 0.02		50	30
0.0	Butadiene	0.46 ± 0.03		50	321
0.25	Butadiene	0.33		60	194
0.02	Butadiene	0.28		5	73
10.0	2-Butenyl triethoxy silane	0		50	296
1.2 ± 0.1	Butyl acrylate	0.89 ± 0.08		60	291
1.52 ± 0.03	Butyl acrylate	0.75 ± 0.18		60	141
1.003 ± 0.012	Butyl acrylate	1.005 ± 0.005	a	60	211,212
1.0 ± 0.1	Butyl acrylate	1.2 ± 0.1		h	293a
1.0 ± 0.1	Butyl acrylate	0.9 ± 0.1		h	293a
0.31	Butyl methacrylate	1.08		60	215
0.14 ± 0.04	t-Butyl vinyl ether	0.0032 ± 0.0002		60	337
0.005 ± 0.011	2-Chloro-1,3-buta-diene	6.07 ± 0.53		50	120

(continued)

(continued)

M_1	r_1	M_2	r_2	T, °C.	Remarks	Ref.
Acrylonitrile	0.034 ± 0.0	2-Chloro-1,3-butadiene	6.93 ± 0.23	50		120
	0.045 ± 0.004	2-Chloro-1,3-butadiene	5.35 ± 0.20	60		65
	0.01 ± 0.01	2-Chloro-1,3-butadiene	6.07 ± 0.53	50		119
	0.024 ± 0.003	1,1-bis(p-Chlorophenyl) ethylene	0	60		68
	0.7	α-Chlorovinyl triethoxy silane	0	50		296
	21 ± 10	Crotonic acid	0	60	c	65
	f	N-Cyclohexyl methacrylamide	f	70		6
	12.0	Δ³-Cyclohexenyl triethoxy silane	0	50		296
	0.26 ± 0.02	2,5-Dichlorostyrene	0.09 ± 0.02	38.5		97
	0.22 ± 0.05	2,5-Dichlorostyrene	0.07 ± 0.05	67.5		97
	0.25 ± 0.11	2,5-Dichlorostyrene	0.07 ± 0.06	86.5		97
	0.59 ± 0.02	Diethylene glycol monovinyl ether	0.0021 ± 0.0004	50		337
	8	Diethyl fumarate	0	60	b,c	193
	12	Diethyl maleate	0	60	b,c	193
	0.22 ± 0.2	2,4-Dimethoxy-6-(β-itaconylhydrazino)-s-triazine	0.7 ± 0.5	60		61
	13.6 ± 1.0	Diphenylacetylene	0	60		66
	0.028 ± 0.003	1,1-Diphenylethylene	0	60		65,68
	0.42	N-N-Divinylaniline	0.003	60		51

	Monomer				
3.2 ± 0.5	Dodecyl acrylate	1.3 ± 0.1	60		291
1.17 ± 0.1	Ethyl acrylate	0.67 ± 0.02	50		43a
0.44	Ethyl acrylate	0.95	80		337
10.5 ± 1.5	Ethyl 2-ethoxy-acrylate	0.02 ± 0.02	80		250
0.17 ± 0.01	1-Ethyl-2-vinyl-acetylene	0.63 ± 0.4	60		248
0.7 = 0.2	Ethyl vinyl ether	0.03 ± 0.02	80		250,270
5.0	Ethyl vinyl ether	0	60	b,c	195
2.0	Ethyl vinyl oxalate	0.2	60		146a
0.02 ± 0.02	5-Ethyl-2-vinyl-pyridine	0.43 ± 0.05	60		139
0.07 ± 0.03	2-Fluorobutadiene	0.50 ± 0.10	50		227
1.01	Glycidyl acrylate	1.02	60		134
0.14 ± 0.001	Glycidyl methacrylate	1.32 ± 0.03	60		135
12.2 ± 2.4	1-Hexene	0	60		66
5.4 ± 0.3	1-Hexyne	0	60		66
1.1 ± 0.1	Hydronopyl acrylate	0.9 ± 0.1	60		187
0.03	Indene	0	h		337
1.8 ± 0.2	Isobutylene	0.02 ± 0.02	50		30
1.02	Isobutylene	0	60		223
0.21	Isobutyl methacrylate	1.04	60		215
0.03 ± 0.03	Isoprene	0.45 ± 0.05	50		119
0.05 ± 0.02	Isoprene	0.29 ± 0.02	50		120
0.33 ± 0.01	Isopropenyl acetylene	0.47 ± 0.01	60		248
0.24 ± 0.02	Isopropenyl iso-cyanate	0.10 ± 0.11	h		136
0.3	Isopropenyl methyl ketone	1.2	h		242a
0.05 ± 0.01	β-Isopropenyl naph-thalene	0.23 ± 0.02	99		67

(continued)

(continued)

M_1	r_1	M_2	r_2	T, °C.	Remarks	Ref.
Acrylonitrile	6	Maleic anhydride	0	60		193
	0.06	Methacrolein	2.0	70		105
	1.94	Methacrylic anhydride	0.21	60		31a
	0.32	Methacrylonitrile	2.68	60		223
	0.9 ± 0.05	Methacrylonitrile	0.50 ± 0.05	-50	PhMgBr catalyst	68a
	1.0 ± 0.1	Methacrylonitrile	0.05 ± 0.02	-50	NaNH$_2$ cat.	68a
	0.19 ± 0.04	Methacryloxymethyl-pentamethyldisiloxane	1.44 ± 0.15	50		202
	0.25	3-o-Methacryloyl-1,2,5,6-diiso-propylidene-D-glucofuranose	0	50		149
	0.25	Methacryloyl-D-glucose	0	50		149
	0.86 ± 0.05	Methyl acrylate	1.25 ± 0.15	30		341
	0.70 ± 0.20	Methyl acrylate	1.22 ± 0.20	20		339
	1.5 ± 0.1	Methyl acrylate	0.84 ± 0.05	50		187
	1.26 ± 0.1	Methyl acrylate	0.67 ± 0.1	60		24
	1.4 ± 0.1	Methyl acrylate	0.95 ± 0.05	60		291
	0.84	Methyl acrylate	0.83	65		223
	0.50 ± 0.47	Methyl acrylate	0.71 ± 0.012	80		142
	1.5 ± 0.5	Methyl bicyclo-(2,2,1)-2-heptene-5-carboxylate	0.2 ± 0.1	60		145
	2.0	Methyl-1-chloro-acrylate	0.15	60		335

r_1	M_2	r_2	Temp, °C	Conditions	Ref.
0.15 ± 15%	Methyl-1-chloro-acrylate	2.0 ± 15%	70		9
6 ± 2	Methyl cinnamate	0	60		65
7.52 ± 0.08	β-Methylene-β-propiolactone	0	h		138
0.36 ± 0.08	Methyl isopropenyl ketone	0.70 ± 0.14	80		337
0.12	Methyl methacrylate	1.34	26	n-Bu₃B no solvent	343
0.12	Methyl methacrylate	1.34	12	n-Bu₃B no solvent	343
0.15	Methyl methacrylate	1.45	−80	n-Bu₃B in toluene	343
0.12	Methyl methacrylate	1.34	−12	n-Bu₃B ethylene dichlor.	343
0.12	Methyl methacrylate	1.34	26	n-Bu₂BCl in no solvent	343
0.15	Methyl methacrylate	1.05	26	i-Bu₃Al no solvent	343
0.09	Methyl methacrylate	0.85	26	n-Bu₂Zn no solvent	343
0.03	Methyl methacrylate	1.20	26	Me₂Cd no solvent	343
7	Methyl methacrylate	0.40	−12	Et₂Be no solvent	343
10	Methyl methacrylate	0.30	−80	n-Bu₂Mg in THF	343
5	Methyl methacrylate	0.14	−12	Cp₂Mg no solvent	343
7	Methyl methacrylate	0.39	−8	n-BuLi no solvent	343
5	Methyl methacrylate	0.14	−12	n-BuNa no solvent	343
0.13 ± 0.05	Methyl methacrylate	1.16 ± 0.22	60	e	17
Large	Methyl methacrylate	Small	−55	e	86
0.100 ± 0.070	Methyl methacrylate	1.351 ± 0.133	40		143
0.150 ± 0.080	Methyl methacrylate	1.224 ± 0.100	80		143
0.160 ± 0.100	Methyl methacrylate	1.186 ± 0.120	100		143
7.9 ± 1.6	Methyl methacrylate	0.25 ± 0.25	−30	e	164

(continued)

(*continued*)

M_1	r_1	M_2	r_2	T, °C.	Remarks	Ref.
Acrylonitrile	Small	Methyl methacrylate	Large	20	d	164
	0.15 ± 0.03	Methyl methacrylate	1.65 ± 0.40	20	m	339
	0.15 ± 0.07	Methyl methacrylate	1.20 ± 0.14	60		169
	0.12	Methyl methacrylate	1.34	70	1 atmos.	47b
	0.37	Methyl methacrylate	1.46	70	100 atmos.	47b
	0.45	Methyl methacrylate	2.01	70	1000 atmos.	47b
	6.5 ± 0.5	Methyl methacrylate	0.02 ± 0.01	−78	PhMgBr cat. in ether	68a
	4.5 ± 0.5	Methyl methacrylate	0.07 ± 0.02	−50	PhMgBr cat. in ether	68a
	1.5 ± 0.1	Methyl methacrylate	0.10 ± 0.03	−15	PhMgBr cat. in ether	68a
	5.0 ± 0.5	Methyl methacrylate	0.03 ± 0.01	−78	PhMgBr cat. in toluene	68a
	3.0 ± 0.1	Methyl methacrylate	0.03 ± 0.01	−30	PhMgBr cat. in toluene	68a
	2.0 ± 0.2	Methyl methacrylate	0.06 ± 0.02	20	PhMgBr cat. in toluene	68a
	4.0 ± 0.5	Methyl methacrylate	0.02 ± 0.01	−78	PhMgI in toluene	68a
	1.3 ± 0.1	Methyl methacrylate	0.05 ± 0.02	−40	PhMgI in toluene	68a
	7.9 ± 1.6	Methyl methacrylate	0.25 ± 0.25	−50	NaNH$_2$	68a
	10	Methyl methacrylate	0.3	−80	nBu$_2$Mg	68a
	0.06 ± 0.02	α-Methylstyrene	0.1 ± 0.02	75	t, see refs. 107,111	81
	0.06 ± 0.05	o-Methylstyrene	0.33 ± 0.1	h		24
	0.07 ± 0.04	m-Methylstyrene	0.43 ± 0.1	h		24
	0.05 ± 0.02	p-Methylstyrene	0.33 ± 0.1	h		24
	0.61 ± 0.04	Methyl vinyl ketone	1.78 ± 0.22	60		171
	0.16 ± 0.003	2-Methyl-5-vinyl pyridine	0.27 ± 0.04	60		290

r_1	M_2	r_2	Temp, °C		Ref.
0.10 ± 0.05	2-Methyl-5-vinyl pyridine	1.10 ± 0.2	h		335
0.42	N-Methyl-N-vinyl-p-toluene sulfonamide	0	60		90,91
f	N-Naphthyl methacrylamide	f	70		6
f	N-p-Nitrophenyl methacrylamide	f	70		6
f	N-Phenylmethacrylamide	f	70		6
1.74 ± 0.04	Octadecyl acrylate	0.68 ± 0.18	60		141
f	Octadecyl acrylate	f	50		5
4.1 ± 0.8	Octadecyl acrylate	1.2 ± 0.1	60		291
1.93 ± 0.08	Octyl acrylate	0.83 ± 0.23	60		153
f	Octyl acrylate	f	50		5
0.26 ± 0.03	Phenylacetylene	0.33 ± 0.05	60		66
1.03 ± 0.2	Poly(1,3-butylene glycol fumarate)	1.12 ± 0.40	60		283c
0.07 ± 0.02	Potassium styrene sulfonate	1.5 ± 0.4	70	m	101
20.0	Propenyl triethoxy silane	0	50		296
0.95 ± 0.05	trans-1,2-bis-(2-Pyridyl)-ethylene	0.02 ± 0.05	50		190
0.21	Sodium acrylate	0.77	50	j	132
0.05 ± 0.02	Sodium styrene sulfonate	1.5 ± 0.2	40	m	101
0.04 ± 0.04	Styrene	0.41 ± 0.08	60		169

(continued)

(continued)

M_1	r_1	M_2	r_2	T, °C.	Remarks	Ref.
Acrylonitrile	0.03 ± 0.03	Styrene	0.41 ± 0.08	75		80
	0.07 ± 0.006	Styrene	0.37 ± 0.03	50		297
	0.05 ± 0.02	Styrene	0.37 ± 0.02	50		119
	0.04 ± 0.04	Styrene	0.40 ± 0.05	60		66
	0.03 ± 0.03	Styrene	0.52 ± 0.04	67–80		79
	0.05 ± 0.02	Styrene	0.38 ± 0.03	41.5	a	97
	0.02 ± 0.02	Styrene	0.45 ± 0.03	65		97
	0.02 ± 0.02	Styrene	0.47 ± 0.03	86.5		97
	—	Styrene	—	75		107
	0.02 ± 0.02	Styrene	0.3 ± 0.08	40		31
	0.06 ± 0.01	Styrene	0.39 ± 0.02	99		67
	0.00 ± 0.02	Styrene	0.33 ± 0.03	50		171
	33	Styrene	0.005	−78°	γ irradiation	203a
	20 ± 2	Styrene	0.02 ± 0.01	−70 to 0°	PhMgBr cat. in Et$_2$O/toluene	68a
	15 ± 1	Styrene	0.05 ± 0.02	−45	Cyclohexene soln.	68a
	470	Tetrachloroethylene	0	60	b,c	64
	f	N-p-tolylmethacrylamide	f	70		6
	67	Trichloroethylene	0	60	b,c	193
	12.2 ± 1.2	3,3,3-Trichloropropene	0.100 ± 0.015	60		65
	0.7	6-Triethoxy silyl bicyclo-(2,2,1)-2-heptene	0	60		65
	5.50 ± 0.50	Trimethyl aconitate	-0.10 ± 0.10	50		296
	$8.0 \pm 15\%$	(Trimethylsiloxy)-vinyldimethyl-silane	$0.1 \pm 15\%$	60		182
				50		241

r_1	Monomer	r_2	Temp.	Ref.
8.0 ± 15%	bis(Trimethylsiloxy)-vinylmethylsilane	0.1 ± 15%	50	241
4.05 ± 0.3	tris-(Trimethylsiloxy)-vinyl silane	0.1 ± 15%	50	241
6 ± 2	Vinyl acetate	0.061 ± 0.013	60	195,333
6.0 ± 15%	Vinyl acetate	0.02 ± 0.02	60	81
6.0	Vinyl acetate	0.07 ± 15%	70	9
3.88	Vinyl acetate	0.07	70	333
5.6 ± 0.5	Vinyl acetate	0.009	25	293
f	Vinyl acetate	0.03 ± 0.03	40	31
0.13 ± 0.01	Vinyl acetate	f	h	338
5.0 ± 0.05	Vinyl acetylene	0.60 ± 0.02	60	248
0.06	Vinyl benzoate	0.05 ± 0.05	75	53
1.1 ± 0.2	Vinyl benzyl chloride (60% meta, 40% para)	0.67	60	24a
e	Vinyl butyl sulfone	0.2 ± 0.1	-78	86
4.0 ± 0.3	Vinyl caproate	0.04 ± 0.03	60	29
4.0 ± 0.3	Vinyl caproate	0.04 ± 0.03	60	29
4.0 ± 0.3	Vinyl caprylate	0.04 ± 0.03	60	29
3.28 ± 0.06	Vinyl chloride	0.02 ± 0.02	60	171
2.8 ± 0.5	Vinyl chloride	0.04 ± 0.02	40	261
3.7	Vinyl chloride	0.074	50	52
3.6 ± 0.2	Vinyl chloride	0.052 ± 0.009	50	297
2.7 ± 0.7	Vinyl chloride	0.04 ± 0.03	60	31
0.34	Vinyl chloroacetate	0.09	80	337
0.25	Vinyl dichloroacetate	0.18	80	337

(continued)

(continued)

M₁	r₁	M₂	r₂	T, °C.	Remarks	Ref.
Acrylonitrile	4.0 ± 0.3	Vinyl esters of fatty acids in C₆–C₁₈ range	0.04 ± 0.03	60	k	29
	9.0	Vinyl ethyl diethoxy-silane	0	50		296
	12 ± 2	Vinyl-2-ethylhexano-ate	0.01 ± 0.01	30		53
	3.0 ± 0.05	Vinyl formate	0.04 ± 0.005	60		53
	0.04	Vinyl formate	3.0	h		242a
	0.91 ± 0.10	Vinylidene chloride	0.37 ± 0.10	60		169
	0.19 ± 0.03	Vinyl isocyanate	0.16 ± 0.06	60		137
	0.36	Vinyl isothiocyanate	1.4	h		337
	4.0 ± 0.3	Vinyl laurate	0.04 ± 0.03	60		29
	0.98 ± 0.2	Vinyl mesitylene	0.16 ± 0.02	138		63
	6.0	Vinyl methyl diethoxysilane	0	50		296
	4.0 ± 0.3	Vinyl myristate	0.04 ± 0.03	60		29
	3.57 ± 0.16	Vinyl nonanoate	0.059 ± 0.095	60		179
	4.20 ± 0.02	Vinyl octadecanoate	0.064 ± 0.005	60		179
	4.3	Vinyl octadecanoate	0.03	70		333
	4.0 ± 0.3	Vinyl palmitate	0.04 ± 0.03	60		29
	8.3	Vinyl phenyl diethoxysilane	0	50		296
	3.40 ± 0.04	Vinyl pinonate	0.143 ± 0.046	60		179
	0.113 ± 0.002	2-Vinylpyridine	0.47 ± 0.03	60		139
	0.086	2-Vinylpyridine	2.13	h	j	340
	0.05 ± 0.01	2-Vinylpyridine	21.9 ± 5.52	60		160,161

M_1	r_1	M_2	r_2	Temp.	Ref.
	f	2-Vinylpyridine	f	h	342
	0.113 ± 0.005	4-Vinylpyridine	0.41 ± 0.09	60	139
	1.06	N-Vinylpyridinium fluoroborate	0.20	60	70b
	4.0 ± 0.3	Vinyl stearate	0.04 ± 0.03	60	29
	0.54	N-Vinylsuccinimide	0.16	60	90
	5 ± 1	Vinyl triethoxysilane	0	60	271
	4.5	Vinyl triethoxysilane	0	50	296
	6.5	Vinyl tri-isopropoxy-silane	0	50	296
	6.0	Vinyl trimethoxy-silane	0	50	296
	3.9 ± 3	Vinyl trimethylsilane	0.07 ± 0.03	60	271
	1.82 ± 0.04	Vinyl undecenoate	0.0 ± 0.10	60	179
Acrylyl chloride	2.3	Methyl acrylate	0.345	45	282a
	1.51	Methyl methacrylate	0.48	45	282a
C_8–C_{16} Alkyl vinyl ethers	f	Acrylonitrile	f	50	294
	f	Maleic anhydride	f	50	5
C_8–C_{18} Alkyl vinyl ethers	f	Methyl acrylate	f	50	5
	f	Methyl methacrylate	f	50	5
	f	Styrene	f	50	5
	f	Vinyl acetate	f	50	5
	f	Vinyl chloride	f	50	5
	f	Vinylidene chloride	f	50	5
Allyl acetate	0	2-Chloroethyl acrylate	5.5 ± 1.0	60	171
	<0.0075	Maleic anhydride	<0.13	30	36
	0	Methyl acrylate	5	60	193

(continued)

(continued)

M_1	r_1	M_2	r_2	T, °C.	Remarks	Ref.
Allyl acetate	0	Methyl methacrylate	23	60		193
	0.00	Styrene	90 ± 10	60		193
	0.45 ± 0.15	Vinyl acetate	0.60 ± 0.15	60		171
	0.7	Vinyl acetate	1.0	60		264
	—	Vinyl chloride	1.2	40		193
	0	Vinyl chloride	1.16	40		208
	0	Vinylidene chloride	6.6	60		193
Allyl alcohol	0.11 ± 0.10	Acrylonitrile	3.96 ± 0.53	25		229
	1.99	Acrylonitrile	0.03	RT		60a
Allyl benzoate	2.5	Allyl chloride	1.25	60		264
Allyl chloride	0	Acrylonitrile	5.5	60		193
	0.05 ± 0.01	Acrylonitrile	3.0 ± 0.2	60		53
	1.25	Allyl benzoate	2.5	60		264
	0.058 ± 0.003	Benzyl acrylate	9.90 ± 0.14	60		144
	0.016 ± 0.018	Benzyl methacrylate	58.7 ± 4.1	60		144
	0.10 ± 0.170	n-Butyl acrylate	5.83 ± 1.32	60		144
	0.058 ± 0.024	n-Butyl methacrylate	46.3 ± 2.6	60		144
	0.48 ± 0.05	Ethyl acrylate	2.3	70		16
	0.084 ± 0.100	Ethyl acrylate	7.73 ± 0.35	60		144
	0.082 ± 0.083	Ethyl methacrylate	57.9 ± 15.0	60		144
	0.016 ± 0.030	2-Hydroxyethyl acrylate	8.85 ± 1.32	60		144
	0.033 ± 0.048	2-Hydroxy ethyl methacrylate	35.6 ± 1.7	60		144
	0.047 ± 0.056	Isobutyl methacrylate	45.5 ± 10.2	60		144
	−0.020 ± 0.100	Methyl acrylate	9.100 ± 0.930	30		143
	0.054 ± 0.039	Methyl acrylate	8.450 ± 0.370	60		143
	0.404 ± 0.073	Methyl acrylate	6.460 ± 0.570	90		143
	0.071 ± 0.011	Methyl acrylate	5.450 ± 0.070	120		143

M_1	r_1	M_2	r_2	Temp (°C)		Ref.
	0	Methyl methacrylate	50	60		193
	0.048 ± 0.038	Methyl methacrylate	48.1 ± 5.00	60		144
	0.091 ± 0.013	n-Propyl acrylate	7.56 ± 0.10	60		144
	0.067 ± 0.027	n-Propyl methacrylate	52.0 ± 3.2	60		144
	0.016 ± 0.016	Styrene	31.5 ± 4	70		14
	0.029 = 0.006	Styrene	36.8 ± 0.60	60		144
	0.75 ± 0.46	Vinyl acetate	0.34 ± 0.26	60		144
	0.67	Vinyl acetate	0.7	68		3
	f	Vinyl acetate	f	60		264, 273
	0.88 ± 0.470	Vinyl benzoate	0.46 ± 0.16	60		144
	1.15 ± 0.59	Vinyl butanoate	0.31 ± 0.35	60		144
	0	N-Vinyl carbazole	Very large	70		16
	1.52 = 0.130	Vinyl 2-ethyl-hexanoate	0.71 ± 0.18	60		144
	0.78 ± 0.100	Vinyl formate	0.57 ± 0.08	60		144
	0.26	Vinylidene chloride	3.8	68		3
	0	Vinylidene chloride	4.5	60		193
	1.62 ± 0.310	Vinyl pentanoate	0.59 ± 0.20	60		144
	0.68 ± 0.110	Vinyl propionate	0.62 ± 0.09	60		144
	1.62	Vinyl valerate	0.59	60		144
Allyl chloroacetate	0	Methyl methacrylate	50	75		55
Allyl diethyl phosphinate	0.15 ± 0.06	Poly(ethylene glycol fumarate)	1.73 ± 0.03	h	g	191
Allyl diethyl phosphinic acid	0.12 ± 0.008	Poly(1,3-butanediol-fumarate)	9.25 ± 3.00	h		192
	0.09 ± 0.05	Poly(ethylene glycol fumarate phosphinate)	2.07 ± 1.12	h		191

(continued)

(continued)

M_1	r_1	M_2	r_2	T, °C.	Remarks	Ref.
Allyl diethyl phosphonate	0.075 ± 0.075	Poly(1,3-butylene glycol fumarate)	10.00 ± 2.00	80		191
Allyl esters	f	Methyl methacrylate	f	h		273
Allyl ethyl hydrogen phosphite	0.035 ± 0.035	Poly(1,3-butylene glycol fumarate)	5.50 ± 2.50	80		191
Allyl laurate	0.8	Vinyl acetate	0.71	60		265
Allyl methacrylate	0.69 ± 0.02	Methyl methacrylate	0.87 ± 0.025	65		262
Allyl triethoxy silane	0	Acrylonitrile	1.7	50		296
	0	Vinyl chloride	2.0	50		296
n-Amyl methacrylate	0.51	Methacrylonitrile	0.55	80		49
n-Amyl vinyl ether	0	Poly(1,3-butanediol fumarate)	2.7 ± 0.7	60		283b
Anethole	18 ± 3	o-Chlorostyrene	0.03 ± 0.005	0	d	7
	0 ± 0.01	o-Chlorostyrene	22 ± 8	70		7
α-Angelolactone	0	Acrylonitrile	14.5 ± 0.5	h		138
β-Angelolactone	0	Acrylonitrile	113 ± 14	h		138
1,1-bis-(p-Anisyl) ethylene	0	Acrylonitrile	0.014 ± 0.002	60		68
	0	Methyl acrylate	0.049 ± 0.005	60		66
N-(p-Anisyl)-meth-acrylamide	0.57	Methyl methacrylate	0.14	70		240
Benzal acetophenone	0.03	Butadiene	0.78 ± 0.12	60		274
Benzene	0	Vinyl acetate	500 ± 100	60		239a
Benzyl acrylate	9.90 ± 0.14	Allyl chloride	0.058 ± 0.003	60		144
N-Benzylidene-4-methacryloxyaniline	0.25 ± 0.05	Styrene	0.24 ± 0.01	60		257

	r_1		r_2			Ref.
Benzyl methacrylate	58.7 ± 4.1	Allyl chloride	0.016 ± 0.018	60		144
Bicyclo[2.2.1]-2,5-heptadiene	0.08	Acrylonitrile	0.67	50		343a
	0.01	Ethyl acrylate	3.05	50		343a
	~0.00	Methyl methacrylate	10.0	50		343a
	0.35	Vinyl chloride	0.74	50		343a
	0.08	Vinylidene chloride	1.41	50		343a
m-Bromostyrene	1.17 ± 0.25	Methyl methacrylate	0.48 ± 0.02	60		323
	1.05 ± 0.21	Styrene	0.55 ± 0.03	60		323
p-Bromostyrene	1.0 ± 0.1	p-Chlorostyrene	1.0 ± 0.1	0	d	231
	2.2 ± 0.5	p-Chlorostyrene	0.35 ± 0.05	0		231
	1.10 ± 0.25	Methyl methacrylate	0.395 ± 0.02	60		323
	0.99 ± 0.07	Styrene	0.695 ± 0.02	60		323
	0.55 ± 0.1	Styrene	1.75 ± 0.01	40	e	279
	1.05 ± 0.05	Styrene	0.71 ± 0.02	60		148b
2-Bromovinyl ethyl ether	0	Methyl acrylate	31.5 ± 2.5	80		250
	0.02 ± 0.02	Styrene	37.5 ± 2.0	80		250
Butadiene	f	Aconitic acid	f	50	r	228
	0.35 ± 0.08	Acrylonitrile	0.0 ± 0.04	50		119
	0.35 ± 0.01	Acrylonitrile	0.05 ± 0.01	50	a	120
	0.40 ± 0.02	Acrylonitrile	0.04 ± 0.01	50		30
	0.46 ± 0.03	Acrylonitrile	0.0	50		321
	0.33	Acrylonitrile	0.25	60	a	194
	0.28	Acrylonitrile	0.02	5		73
	0.18	Acrylonitrile	0.03	5		73
	0.78 ± 0.12	Benzalacetophenone	0.03	60		274

(continued)

(continued)

M₁	r_1	M₂	r_2	T, °C.	Remarks	Ref.
Butadiene	0.99 ± 0.07	Butyl acrylate	0.08 ± 0.02	5	a	324
	0.78	2-Chlorobenzalaceto-phenone	−0.04	60	a	274
	0.78	2-Chlorobenzalaceto-phenone	−0.02	59		274
	0.059 ± 0.014	2-Chloro-1,3-buta-diene	3.41 ± 0.07	50		120
	0.0	2-Chloro-1,3-buta-diene	2.86	50	a	120
	1.07	p-Chlorostyrene	0.42	50	a	321
	0	1-Cyano-1,3-buta-diene	1.70	50	a	321
	0.65 ± 0.1	2,5-Dichlorostyrene	0.2 ± 0.04	70	a	12
	0.46 ± 0.01	2,5-Dichlorostyrene	0.46 ± 0.01	50	a	321
	2.13	Diethyl fumarate	0.25	h	o	177
	8.08	Diethyl maleate	0.11	h	o	177
	0.35	1,1-Dihydroperfluoro-butyl acrylate	0.07	50	a	267
	1.26	Dimethyl butadiene	0.78	−18	a	226
	0.85	2,3-Dimethyl-1,3-butadiene	0.63	5	a	94
	0.0106 ± 0.0175	Dimethyl dithiol-fumarate	−0.0014 ± 0.027	50		185
	2.02	Dinonyl fumarate	0.32	h	o	177
	5.36	Dinonyl maleate	0.12	h	o	177
	0.25	Ethyl-1-cyano-cinnamate	0	35	a,c	209

	Monomer		Temp.		Ref.
1.1	Hydronopyl acrylate	0.2	h		188
0.01 ± 0.01	Isobutylene	115 ± 15	−103		295
0.75	Isoprene	0.85	5	a	94
0.94	Isoprene	1.06	−18	a	226
3.38 ± 0.14	Isoprene	0.47 ± 0.03	50	e	253
1	Isoprene	1	−15	AlEt$_2$Cl–cobalt diacetyl acetonate	214
1	Isoprene	1	13	AlEt$_2$Cl–cobalt diacetyl acetonate	239
1	Isoprene	1	20	AlEt$_2$Cl–cobalt diacetyl acetonate	239
1	Isoprene	1	48	AlEt$_2$Cl–cobalt diacetyl acetonate	239
0.201	Methacrylic acid	0.526	50		87
0.36 ± 0.07	Methacrylonitrile	0.04 ± 0.04	5	a	65
0.76 ± 0.04	Methyl acrylate	0.05 ± 0.02	5	a	324
1.07 ± 0.12	Methyl-2-chloro-cinnamate	<0.03	60	a	274
1.20 ± 0.12	Methyl-2-chloro-cinnamate	<0.02	80		274
2.73 ± 0.3	Methyl-4-chloro-cinnamate	<0.05	80		274
0.75 ± 0.05	Methyl methacrylate	0.25 ± 0.03	90		171
0.53 ± 0.05	Methyl methacrylate	0.06 ± 0.03	5	a	324

(continued)

(continued)

M_1	r_1	M_2	r_2	T, °C	Remarks	Ref.
Butadiene	0.70	Methyl methacrylate	0.32	h		178
	1.6 ± 0.5	α-Methylstyrene	0.010 ± 0.01	12.8		78a
	0.35 ± 0.01	Methyl thiolacrylate	0.20 ± 0.05	70		181
	1.32 ± 0.01	2-Methyl-5-vinyl pyridine	0.72 ± 0.03	h		305
	0.76	Nonyl methacrylate	0.32	h		178
	1.39 ± 0.03	Styrene	0.78 ± 0.01	60		171
	1.48 ± 0.08	Styrene	0.23 ± 0.07	50		119
	1.4 ± 0.2	Styrene	0.5 ± 0.1	50	a	200
	1.8 ± 0.4	Styrene	0.6 ± 0.1	45	a	206
	1.40 ± 0.08	Styrene	0.38 ± 0.08	5	a	224
	1.38	Styrene	0.64	5	a	94, 225
	1.37	Styrene	0.38	18	a	94, 225
	1.83	Styrene	0.65	45	a	94, 225
	20	Styrene	0.05	50	e	158
	1.35 ± 0.12	Styrene	0.58 ± 0.15	50		120
	1.40	Styrene	0.44	5		224
	1.59 ± 0.05	Styrene	0.44 ± 0.03	50	a	120
	1.30 ± 0.1	Styrene	0.01 ± 0.01	43	a	30
	1.83 ± 0.32	Styrene	0.65 ± 0.16	45	a	206
	0.50	Styrene (50%)	0.68	25	s	242b
	0.65 ± 0.05	Triethyl aconitate	0.02 ± 0.01	50		228
	0.37 ± 0.03	Triethyl aconitate	0.00 ± 0.01	60		182
	0.40 ± 0.03	Trimethyl aconitate	0.00 ± 0.03	60		182
	8.8	Vinyl chloride	0.035	50		300
	5.0 ± 0.01	Vinyl formate	0.2 ± 0.05	120		308
	1.9 ± 0.2	Vinylidene chloride	<0.05	5	a	324

Monomer 1	r_1	Monomer 2	r_2	Temp. (°C)	Notes	Ref.
	25.3 ± 10.0	Vinyl nonanate	0.02 ± 0.02	60	d	179
	34.5 ± 6.0	Vinyl octadecanoate	0.034 ± 0.034	60	e	179
	37.8 ± 6.5	Vinyl pinonate	0.015 ± 0.015	60	e	179
	37.9 ± 4.0	Vinyl undecenoate	0.015 ± 0.015	60	d	179
1-Butene	0.15 ± 0.05	2-Butene	3.1 ± 0.7	-20 to -3		201
	0.019	Ethylene	29.5	h		217
	f	Propylene	ī	h		198
2-Butene	3.1 ± 0.7	1-Butene	0.15 ± 0.05	-20 to -3		201
2-Butenyl triethoxy silane	0	Acrylonitrile	10.0	50		296
	0	Vinyl chloride	0.4	50		296
Butyl acrylate	0.89 ± 0.08	Acrylonitrile	1.2 ± 0.1	60		291
	0.75 ± 0.18	Acrylonitrile	1.52 ± 0.03	60		141
	1.005 ± 0.005	Acrylonitrile	1.003 ± 0.012	60		211, 212
	1.2 ± 0.1	Acrylonitrile	1.0 ± 0.1	h	a	293a
	0.9 ± 0.1	Acrylonitrile	1.0 ± 0.1	h		293a
	0.08 ± 0.02	Butadiene	0.99 ± 0.07	5	a	324
	0.40	Dimethyl itaconate	0.94	h		54
	0.65 ± 0.07	Methyl vinyl ketone	1.6 ± 0.1	50		58
	0.15 ± 0.04	Styrene	0.48 ± 0.04	25		27
	0.15	Styrene	0.76	60	0.00 mole fraction benzene as solvent	43
	0.19	Styrene	0.68	60	0.60 mole fraction benzene as solvent	43
	0.19	Styrene	0.64	60	0.90 mole fraction benzene as solvent	43

(continued)

(continued)

M_1	r_1	M_2	r_2	T, °C.	Remarks	Ref.
Butyl acrylate	0.34	Styrene	1.03	60	0.975 mole fraction benzene as solvent (Benzene here enters into polymer)	43
	4.4	Vinyl chloride	0.07	45		301
	0.46 ± 0.13	Vinylidene chloride	0.84 ± 0.2	70		175
	0.83 ± 0.02	Vinylidene chloride	0.88 ± 0.10	50		141
	0.58 ± 0.03	Vinylidene chloride	0.87 ± 0.01	0		175
	0.83 ± 0.02	Vinylidene chloride	0.88 ± 0.10	h		141
	2.51 ± 0.05	2-Vinyl pyridine	0.097 ± 0.04	60		294
	0.46 ± 0.09	4-Vinyl pyridine	0.15 ± 0.09	60	a	88
n-Butyl acrylate	5.83 ± 1.32	Allyl chloride	0.10 ± 0.170	60		144
n-Butyl cinnamate	0.10	Styrene	0.87	80		337
n-Butyl crotonate	0	Vinylidene chloride	33	70		69
t-Butylethylene	0.0	Vinyl chloride	5 ± 15%	70		9
n-Butyl maleimide	0.12 ± 0.02	Methyl methacrylate	1.33 ± 0.03	50		56
	0.06 ± 0.02	Styrene	0.025 ± 0.025	50		56
Butyl methacrylate	1.08	Acrylonitrile	0.31	60		215
	f	Methyl-1-chloro-acrylate	f	60–80		286
	13.5	Vinyl chloride	0.05	45		302
n-Butyl methacrylate	46.3 ± 2.6	Allyl chloride	0.058 ± 0.024	60		144
	0.69	Methacrylonitrile	0.51	80		49
	0.67	Styrene	0.97	30		48
	0.64	Styrene	0.63	50		316
	0.64	Styrene	0.54	70		316

	r_1		r_2			
t-Butyl methacrylate	28.8	Vinyl acetate	0.023	60		215
	62.1 ± 3.8	Vinyl acetate	0.127 ± 0.015	60		205
	0.22	Vinylidene chloride	0.35	70		3
n-Butyl vinyl ether	0.70	Methacrylonitrile	0.37	80		49
	1.3 ± 0.3	Acenaphthylene	0.38 ± 0.04	30	d	268
	4.2 ± 0.8	Acenaphthylene	0.24 ± 0.04	0	d	268
	6.0 ± 1.0	Acenaphthylene	0.14 ± 0.03	−20	d	268
	~20	Acenaphthylene	0.04 ± 0.02	−78	d	268
	0.2 ± 0.1	Methyl methacrylate	1.6 ± 0.2	h		148c
	0	Poly(1,3-butanediol fumarate)	1.8 ± 0.5	60		283b
t-Butyl vinyl ether	62.1 ± 3.8	Vinyl acetate	0.127 ± 0.015	60		205
	0	N-Vinyl succinimide	15	69		90
Butyl vinylsulfonate	0.0032 ± 0.0002	Acrylonitrile	0.14 ± 0.04	60		337
	0.11 ± 0.03	Methyl acrylate	5.0 ± 1.5	70		233
	0.20 ± 0.05	Vinyl acetate	0.04 ± 0.01	70		233
		Vinyl acetate	$r_1 = r_2$	170		298
	0.30 ± 0.05	Vinyl chloride	0.35 ± 0.05	70		233
n-Butyl vinylsulfonate	0.13 ± 0.03	Styrene	2.5 ± 1.0	90		233
	0.065 ± 0.007	Vinylidene chloride	7.5 ± 0.6	80		233
2-Chloroallyl acetate	0.0	Acrylic acid	1.0	100		147
	0	Maleic anhydride	0	120	b	147
	0	Methyl acrylate	0.7	100	b	147
	0	Methyl methacrylate	1.0	50	b,c	147
	0	Styrene	4.10	50		147
	0	Vinyl chloride	0.70	100		147

(continued)

(*continued*)

M_1	r_1	M_2	r_2	T, °C.	Remarks	Ref.
2-Chloroallyl alcohol	0.0	Methacrylic acid	4.5	100		147
	0	Methyl methacrylate	4.4	100	b,c	147
	0	Styrene	12.5	40		147
	0.0	Methacrylic acid	4.0	100		147
	0.017 ± 0.003	Methyl methacrylate	5.5 ± 0.8	70		15
	0	Methyl methacrylate	0.5	40	b,c	147
	0.06 ± 15%	Styrene	5.0 ± 15%	70		15
	0	Styrene	2.5	40		147
2-Chloroallyl chloride	0	N-Vinyl carbazole	∞	70		10,16
2-Chlorobenzal aceto-phenone	−0.02	Butadiene	0.78	59		274
	−0.04	Butadiene	0.78	60	a	274
1-Chloro-1-bromo-ethylene	2.38 ± 0.06	Vinylidene chloride	0.83 ± 0.08	h	Photosensitized initiation	327
2-Chloro-1,3-buta-diene	6.07 ± 0.53	Acrylonitrile	0.005 ± 0.011	50		120
	6.93 ± 0.23	Acrylonitrile	0.034 ± 0.0	50	a	120
	5.35 ± 0.20	Acrylonitrile	0.045 ± 0.004	60		65
	6.07 ± 0.53	Acrylonitrile	0.01 ± 0.01	50		119
	3.41 ± 0.7	Butadiene	0.059 ± 0.015	50		119
	3.41 ± 0.07	Butadiene	0.059 ± 0.014	50		120
	2.86	Butadiene	0.0	50	a	120
	6.65 ± 0.37	Diethyl fumarate	0.027 ± 0.010	60		65,68
	3.17 ± 0.16	1,1-Diphenyl ethylene	0.00 ± 0.05	60		65,68
	3.70	Fluoroprene	0.22	h		154,252
	5.47	Hexachlorobutadiene	0.10	40		154

	5.52	Hexafluorobutadiene	0.1	40	a	154
	3.65 ± 0.11	Isoprene	0.133 ± 0.025	50		119
	2.82 ± 0.22	Isoprene	0.063 ± 0.051	50	a	120
	11.1 ± 1.5	Methyl acrylate	0.078 ± 0.010	60		65,68
	6.12 ± 0.2	Methyl methacrylate	0.080 ± 0.007	60		68
	7 ± 2	Styrene	0.05 ± 0.02	70		12
	5.22 ± 0.64	Styrene	0.00	50	a	120
	6.3 ± 0.1	Styrene	0.00	50		120
	0.24	Styrene	15.6	−18	d	84
	8.11 ± 0.34	Styrene	0.052 ± 0.01	60		65
	50	Vinyl acetate	0.01	65		314
	90	Vinyl butanoate	0.02	65		314
	15.0	Vinyl formate	−0.035	h		148c
	30	Vinyl formate	0.01	65		314
	0.016	Vinylidene cyanide	0.0048	40		93
	0.010	Vinylidene cyanide	0.0017	40		93
	~0	Vinylidene cyanide	0.20 ± 0.06	40		93
	0.164 ± 0.043	Vinyl isopropyl ether	11.45 ± 0.54	65		207
	70	Vinyl propionate	0.05	65		314
	5.19 ± 0.03	2-Vinyl pyridine	0.06 ± 0.01	60		160,161
	2.10 ± 0.13	2-Vinylquinoline	0.38 ± 0.03	60		160,161
2-Chloroethyl acrylate	5.5 ± 1.0	Allyl acetate	0	60		171
	4 ± 1	Methallyl acetate	0	60		171
	0.9 ± 0.1	Methyl acrylate	0.9 ± 0.1	60		171
	0.95 ± 0.03	Methyl acrylate	0.92 ± 0.05	60		66
	0.08 ± 0.01	Styrene	0.59 ± 0.03	60		65
	0.10 ± 0.01	Styrene	0.54 ± 0.01	60		171

(continued)

(*continued*)

M_1	r_1	M_2	r_2	T, °C.	Remarks	Ref.
β-Chloroethyl itaconate	0.10 ± 0.05	Methyl methacrylate	2.63 ± 0.2	50		213
2-Chloroethyl itaconate	0.5 ± 0.05	Styrene	0	50		213
α-Chloro-β-fluoro-styrene	0.55	Styrene	2.1	60		91a
Chloromethylstyrene	f	Styrene	f	h		70
1,1-bis-(p-Chloro-phenyl)-ethylene	0	Acrylonitrile	0.024 ± 0.003	60	c	68
	0	Methyl acrylate	0.092 ± 0.006	60	c	66
N(-p-Chlorophenyl)-methacrylamide	0.24	Methyl methacrylate	0.61	70		240
1-Chloro-1-propene	0.24	Vinyl chloride	1.13	50		300
2-Chloro-1-propene	0.58	Vinyl chloride	0.75	50		300
	0	Vinylidene cyanide	0.20	40		93
m-Chlorostyrene	0.91 ± 0.11	Methyl methacrylate	0.47 ± 0.075	60		323
	1.09 ± 0.23	Styrene	0.64 ± 0.05	60		323
	0.3 ± 0.05	Styrene	3.3 ± 0.4	0		231
o-Chlorostyrene	22 ± 8	Anethole	18 ± 3	0	$SnCl_4$	7
	0.03 ± 0.005	Anethole	0 ± 0.01	70	d	7
	$3.5 \pm 15\%$	Indene	0	70		9
	$0.12 \pm 15\%$	Methacrylic acid	$0.7 \pm 15\%$	70		9
	0.78	Methacrylonitrile	0.86	80		49
	1.37 ± 0.1	Methyl methacrylate	0.50 ± 0.03	60		322
	1.6 ± 0.07	Styrene	0.56 ± 0.03	60		322
p-Chlorostyrene	1.0 ± 0.1	p-Bromostyrene	1.0 ± 0.1	0	d	231
	0.35 ± 0.05	p-Bromostyrene	2.2 ± 0.5	0		231
	0.42	Butadiene	1.07	50	a	321

0.69	Dimethyl itaconate	0.15	h		54
0.88 ± 0.30	β-Ethyl styrene	0	0	d	238
0.29 ± 0.04	p-Ethyl styrene	4.1 ± 0.5	0	d	238
1.02	Isobutylene	1.01	0	AlBr₃ in hexane	236
0.15	Isobutylene	14.7	0	AlBr₃ in nitro-benzene	236
0.7	Isobutylene	22.5	0	AlBr₃ in nitro-methane	236
1.2	Isobutylene	8.6	0	SnCl₄ in nitro-benzene	236
0.45	Methacrylonitrile	0.73	80		337
0.38 ± 0.05	m-Methoxystyrene	2.6 ± 0.4	0	d	231
0.86 ± 0.08	p-Methoxystyrene	0.58 ± 0.03	60		323
0.89 ± 0.05	Methyl methacrylate	0.415 ± 0.02	60		323
0.8 ± 0.4	Methyl methacrylate	0.4 ± 0.2	30–40		186
1.48 ± 0.02	α-Methylstyrene	0.25 ± 0.05	74		281
0.12 ± 0.03	α-Methylstyrene	28 + 2	−78		281
0.35 ± 0.05	α-Methylstyrene	15 ± 1.5	0	d	231
0.35 ± 0.05	α-Methylstyrene	15.5 ± 1.5	0	d	232
f	α-Methylstyrene	f	h	e	284
1.0 ± 0.1	cis-β-Methylstyrene	0.32 ± 0.02	0	d	238
0.74 ± 0.06	trans-β-Methyl-styrene				238
1.15 ± 0.05	p-Methylstyrene	0.32 ± 0.04	0	d	323
0.22 ± 0.05	p-Methylstyrene	0.61 ± 0.03	60	d	231
0.25 ± 0.05	m-Nitrostyrene	4.5 ± 0.7	0		283
0.70 ± 0.08	p-Nitrostyrene	1.3 ± 0.1	75		323
		0.91 ± 0.37	60		

(continued)

(continued)

M_1	M_2	r_1	r_2	T, °C.	Remarks	Ref.
p-Chlorostyrene	β-n-Propylstyrene	—	—	0	Sufficient data for calc. given but r_1 and r_2 not quoted	238
	Styrene	1.025 ± 0.05	0.74 ± 0.025	60		170
	Styrene	1.042 ± 0.05	0.816 ± 0.03	131		170
	Styrene	0.35 ± 0.02	2.10 ± 0.2	0	In CCl_4–$PhNO_2$ with $SnCl_4$	232
	Styrene	0.30 ± 0.03	2.5 ± 0.4	0	In CCl_4 soln. with $SnCl_4$	231,232
	Styrene	0.45 ± 0.02	2.2 ± 0.2	0	$SnCl_4$ nitrobenzene	235
	Styrene	0.45 ± 0.02	2.2 ± 0.2	0	$TiCl_4$ nitrobenzene	235
	Styrene	0.36 ± 0.05	2.3 ± 0.4	0	$AlBr_3$ nitrobenzene CCl_4	235
	Styrene	0.45 ± 0.02	2.2 ± 0.2	0	$TiCl_4$ nitrobenzene CCl_4 (1:1)	235
	Styrene	0.34 ± 0.05	2.0 ± 0.2	0	$AlBr_3$ nitrobenzene–CCl_4 (1:1)	235
	Styrene	0.55 ± 0.05	1.7 ± 0.2	0	$SbCl_4$ nitrobenzene–CCl_4 (1:1)	235
	Styrene	0.43 ± 0.03	2.0 ± 0.1	0	$FeCl_3$ nitrobenzene–CCl_4 (1:1)	235
	Styrene	0.50 ± 0.05	2.0 ± 0.4	0	$TiCl_4$–CCl_3COOH (1:4)	235
	Styrene	0.40 ± 0.02	1.51 ± 0.03	0	$AlBr_3$–CCl_4	235

M_1	r_1	M_2	r_2		Temp. °C	Ref.
	0.5 ± 0.1	Styrene	2.2 ± 0.2	c	40	216,279
	f	Styrene	f		h	284
	0.35 ± 0.05	Styrene	2.7 ± 0.3	d	30	23
	1.032 ± 0.030	Styrene	0.742 ± 0.030		60	170
	10	Vinyl mesitylene	0.06		130	63
Chlorotrifluoro-ethylene	0.005	Methyl methacrylate	75.0		60	294
	0.001	Styrene	7.0		60	294
	1.0	Tetrafluoroethylene	1.0	a	60	72
	0.05	bis-(Trimethylsiloxy)-vinyl methylsilane	0.20		60	241
	0.05	tris-(Trimethyl-siloxy)-vinyl silane	0.20		60	241
	0.01	Vinyl acetate	0.6		60	294
	0.01	Vinyl chloride	2.53		60	155
	1.2	Vinyl fluoride	0.8	a,b	80	72
	0.02	Vinylidene chloride	17.14		60	59
4-Chloro-1-vinyl naphthalene	0.7 ± 0.2	Methyl methacrylate	0.7 ± 0.2		60	247
	0.8 ± 0.1	Styrene	0.85 ± 0.1		60	247
6-Chloro-2-vinyl naphthalene	1.6 ± 0.2	Methyl methacrylate	0.45 ± 0.05		60	247
	1.5 ± 0.2	Styrene	0.4 ± 0.1		60	247
α-Chlorovinyltri-ethoxy silane	0	Acrylonitrile	0.7		50	296
	0	Vinyl chloride	0.2		50	296
Cinnamonitrile	0.1 ± 0.1	Styrene	0.9 ± 0.2		90	41

(continued)

(*continued*)

M_1	r_1	M_2	r_2	T, °C.	Remarks	Ref.
3-Cinnamoyl pyridine	0.09 ± 0.10	Styrene	0.85 ± 0.05	50	p	189
Citraconic anhydride	0.01 ± 0.01	Styrene	0.15 ± 0.02	60		53
Coumarin	0	Vinylidene chloride	Very large	70		9
Crotonaldehyde	0	Vinylidene chloride	17	70		69
Crotonamide	2.0 ± 0.05	Vinyl acetate	0.01 ± 0.01	110		315
Crotonic acid	0	Acrylonitrile	21 ± 10	60	c	65
	0	Styrene	20	60		65
	0.01 ± 0.01	Vinyl acetate	0.33 ± 0.05	68		53
	0	Vinyl acetate	0.33	h		107
	0.01	Vinyl acetate	0.3	70		294
	f	Vinyl acetate	f	h		309
γ-Crotonolactone	0.065 ± 0.005	Vinylidene chloride	35 ± 5	60		53
	0	Styrene	8.5 ± 5.6	60		145
1-Cyano-1,3-butadiene	1.70	Butadiene	0	50	a	321
p-Cyanostyrene	1.41 ± 0.13	Methyl methacrylate	0.22 ± 0.02	60		323
	1.16 ± 0.13	Styrene	0.28 ± 0.025	60		323
Cyclic siloxanes $\overline{(CH_3)_2SiCH_2\text{-}}$ $\overline{CH_2(CH_3)_2SiO}$	8.11 ± 0.13	$((CH_3)_2SiO)_3$	0.146 ± 0.014	40	e	203
	0.56 ± 0.015	$\overline{(CH_3)_2SiCH_2CH_2\text{-}}$ $\overline{(C_6H_5)(CH_3)SiO}$	2.11 ± 0.04	25	e	203
	4.10 ± 0.77	$((CH_3)_2SiO)_3$	0.31 ± 0.07	100	e	203
	0.178 ± 0.012	$\overline{(CH_3)_2SiCH_2CH_2\text{-}}$ $\overline{(C_6H_5)_2SiO}$	5.66 ± 0.3	52	e	203

M_1	r_1	M_2	r_2	Temp.		Ref.
(CH₃)₂SiCH₂CH₂-(C₆H₅)(CH₃)SiO	0.58 ± 0.16	((C₆H₅)₂SiO)₃	1.47 ± 0.25	25	e	203
	0.33 ± 0.04	(C₆H₅)(CH₃)SiCH₂-CH₂(C₆H₅)(CH₃)SiO	2.23 ± 0.36	25	e	203
	0.172 ± 0.004	(C₆H₅)(CH₃)SiCH₂-CH₂(C₆H₅)₂SiO	2.84 ± 0.10	25	e	203
	0.091 ± 0.007	(C₆H₅)₂SiCH₂CH₂-(C₆H₅)₂SiO	11.3 ± 3.2	25	e	203
Δ²-Cyclohexenyl triethoxy silane	0	Acrylonitrile	12.0	50		296
	0	Vinyl chloride	0.4	50		296
N-Cyclohexyl methacrylamide	f	Acrylonitrile	f	70		6
Decyl methacrylate	12.8 ± 0.5	N-Vinyl oxazolidone	0.015 ± 0.05	50		40
1-Deoxy-1-methacrylamido-D-glucitol	0.005	Styrene	2.09	50		325a
	0.036	Methyl methacrylate	4.20	50		325a
	0.56	Vinyl acetate	0.16	50		325a
Diallyl butylphosphonate	0.091 ± 0.02	Dodecyl methacrylate	18.7 ± 0.11	80		36b
Diallyl germanium	f	Methyl methacrylate	f	h		157
	f	Styrene	f	h		157
Diallyl melamine	0	Methyl methacrylate	27.8 ± 3.2	60		259a
	0	Methyl methacrylate	28.9 ± 2.3	60		259a
	0	Styrene	102.3 ± 15.1	60		259a

(continued)

(*continued*)

M_1	r_1	M_2	r_2	T, °C.	Remarks	Ref.
Diallyl melamine	0	Styrene	103.0 ± 11.8	60		259a
	0.20 ± 0.03	Vinyl acetate	1.44 ± 0.28	60		259a
	0.19 ± 0.004	Vinyl acetate	1.41 ± 0.06	60		259a
Diallyl phenylphosphine oxide	−0.011 ± 0.013	Dodecyl methacrylate	18.1 ± 0.4	80		36c
	−0.013 ± 0.025	Dodecyl methacrylate	11.1 ± 0.4	120		36c
	−0.089 ± 0.022	Dodecyl methacrylate	5.6 ± 0.4	140		36c
Diallyl phenylphosphonate	0.072 ± 0.22	Dodecyl methacrylate	19.5 ± 1.8	80		36b
Diallyl phthalate	2.0	Vinyl acetate	0.72	h		287
	0.2	Vinylidene chloride	5.0	70		10
Diallyl silicon	f	Methyl methacrylate	f	h		157
	f	Styrene	f	h		157
Diallyl tin	f	Methyl methacrylate	f	h		157
	f	Styrene	f	h		157
4,6-Diamino-2-vinyl-s-triazine	1.2 ± 0.15	Methyl vinyl ketone	0.26 ± 0.04	60		237
Dibenzyl maleate	0.02 ± 0.01	Styrene	0.55 ± 0.2	70		266a
Di-n-butyl itaconate	1.1	Dimethyl itaconate	1.1	h		54
	6.3	Vinyl acetate	0.02	h		54
	0.4	Methyl methacrylate	0.8	h		54
Dibutyl maleate	0.00	Vinyl chloride	1.4	40		150
2,3-Dichloro-1,3-butadiene	4.5 ± 0.45	1,1-Diphenylethylene	0	60		65,68
	10.3 ± 1.5	Methyl methacrylate	0.073 ± 0.015	60		68
	10.8 ± 1.2	Styrene	0.041 ± 0.012	60		65
1,1-Dichloro-2,2-difluoroethylene	0	Styrene	1.6	45	a	199
	0 ± 15%	Vinyl acetate	0.6 ± 15%	70		9
cis-Dichloroethylene	0	Styrene	210 ± 15%	60	c	168

M_1	r_1	M_2	r_2		Temp.	Ref.
	0	Styrene	75 ± 25		68	13
	0	Styrene	47.5		90	45
	0	Styrene	56.1		50	45
	0	Styrene	72.5		90	45
	0.018 ± 0.003	Vinyl acetate	6.3 ± 0.2		60	168
	0	Vinyl acetate	2.8		68	13
	~0	Vinylidene cyanide	30		40	93
trans-Dichloroethylene	0	Styrene	25.9		90	45
	0	Styrene	37 ± 3	c	60	168
	0	Styrene	~10		68	13
	0	Styrene	44.4		50	45
	0	Styrene	44.9		50	45
	0	Styrene	29.8		90	45
	0	Vinyl acetate	0.85		68	13
	0.086 ± 0.01	Vinyl acetate	0.99 ± 0.02		60	168
	~0	Vinylidene cyanide	30		40	93
Di-β-chloroethyl itaconate	0.10 ± 0.05	Methyl methacrylate	2.63 ± 0.2		50	213
	0	Styrene	0.50 ± 0.05		50	213
2,5-Dichlorostyrene	0.09 ± 0.02	Acrylonitrile	0.26 ± 0.02		38.5	97
	0.07 ± 0.05	Acrylonitrile	0.22 ± 0.05		67.5	97
	0.07 ± 0.06	Acrylonitrile	0.25 ± 0.11		86.5	97
	0.2 ± 0.04	Butadiene	0.65 ± 0.1		70	12
	0.46 ± 0.01	Butadiene	0.46 ± 0.01	a	50	321
	1.55	2,5-Dimethylstyrene	0.27		70	105
	3.4 = 1.4	Methyl acrylate	0.15 ± 0.03		70	166
	4.27 ± 0.28	Methyl acrylate	0.25 ± 0.04		60	2
	2.25	Methyl methacrylate	0.44		68	3
	3	α-Methylstyrene	0.14		70	18
	2.0	Methyl vinyl ketone	0.5		70	8
	0.8	Styrene	0.2		70	20

(continued)

(continued)

M_1	r_1	M_2	r_2	T, °C.	Remarks	Ref.
2,5-Dichlorostyrene	0.34 ± 0.2	Styrene	14.8 ± 2	0	d	75
	2.2	Styrene	0.29	70		123
	1.8	Styrene	0.30	70		123
	2.2	Styrene	0.23	70		123
	1.9	Styrene	0.31	70		123
	0.25 ± 0.09	Styrene	0.18 ± 0.07	41.7		91
	0.08 ± 0.05	Styrene	0.32 ± 0.06	65		97
	0.05 ± 0.03	Styrene	0.40 ± 0.03	86.5		97
	—	Vinyl acetate	<0.04	70		123
	8 ± 0.5	N-Vinyl carbazole	0.016 ± 0.002	70		18
	8.0	N-Vinyl carbazole	0.016	h		19
	0.031	Vinylidene cyanide	0.0092	40	see ref. 108	93
Dichlorostyrene (mixed isomers)	0.9	2-Vinylpyridine	1.1	70		18
3,4-Dichlorostyrene	0.11 ± 0.07	2-Vinylpyridine	0.63 ± 0.07	60		294
	0.48 ± 0.08	Styrene	3.1 ± 0.1	0	d, $AlCl_3$	75a
	0.45 ± 0.10	Styrene	2.8 ± 0.2	0	d, $AlBr_3$	75a
	0.0 ± 0.2	Styrene	6.8 ± 0.8	0	d, $TiCl_4$	75a
	0.38 ± 0.20	Styrene	7.2 ± 0.5	0	d, BF_3	75a
	0.27 ± 0.07	Styrene	5.9 ± 0.2	0	d, $ZnCl_2$	75a
	0.10 ± 0.05	Styrene	4.2 ± 0.2	0	H_2SO_4	75a
	0.20 ± 0.15	Styrene	3.0 ± 0.5	0	$AlCl_3$	75a
	0.0 ± 0.2	Styrene	3.5 ± 0.5	0	$AlCl_3$	75a
Diethyl allyl phosphinic acid	0.09 ± 0.95	Poly-(ethylene glycol fumarate)	2.07 ± 1.12	h	q	191

Monomer 1	r_1	Monomer 2	r_2	Temp	Conditions	Ref.
Diethyl allylphosphonate	0.066 ± 0.06	Dodecyl methacrylate	52.5 ± 1.8	80		36b
	0.12 ± 0.008	Poly-(1,3-butylene glycol fumarate)	9.22 ± 3.00	h		192
Diethylaminoethyl methacrylate	0.90 ± 0.23	Methacrylic acid	0.98 ± 0.16	70	K$_2$SO$_4$ pH 1.2	22
	0.65 ± 0.03	Methacrylic acid	0.08 ± 0.015	70	K$_2$SO$_4$ pH 7.2	22
	0.65 ± 0.03	Sodium methacrylate	0.08 ± 0.015	70		22
Diethyl chloromaleate	0	Styrene	2.5	70		20
Diethylene glycol monovinyl ether	0.0021 ± 0.0004	Acrylonitrile	0.59 ± 0.02	60		337
Diethyl fumarate	0	Acrylonitrile	8	60	b,c	193
	0.25	Butadiene	2.13	h	o	177
	0.027 ± 0.010	2-Chloro-1,3-butadiene	6.65 ± 0.37	60		65,68
	0	Isobutylene	0.17	60	e	126
	0.070 ± 0.007	Styrene	0.30 ± 0.02	60		170
	0.0905 ± 0.007	Styrene	0.400 ± 0.02	131		180
	0.0697 ± 0.0041	Styrene	0.301 ± 0.024	60		170
	1.10 ± 0.10	3,3,3-Trichloropropene	1.46 ± 0.35	60		65
	0.444 ± 0.003	Vinyl acetate	0.011 ± 0.001	60		168
	0.47 ± 0.05	Vinyl chloride	0.12 ± 0.01	60		168
	0.046 ± 0.015	Vinylidene chloride	12.2 ± 2	60		64
Di-2-ethyl hexyl maleate	0	Vinyl chloride	0.42	68		3
Diethyl itaconate	5.65 ± 0.25	Vinyl chloride	0.06 ± 0.01	50		214
Diethyl maleate	0	Acrylonitrile	12	60	b,c	193
	0.11	Butadiene	8.08	h	o	177

(continued)

(*continued*)

M_1	r_1	M_2	r_2	T, °C.	Remarks	Ref.
Diethyl maleate	0	Methyl methacrylate	20	60	b,c	193
	0.0 ± 0.1	Styrene	5 ± 1.5	70		20
	0	Styrene	5.48 ± 0.56	131	c	170
	0.005 ± 0.01	Styrene	6.52 ± 0.50	60		170
	<0.01	Styrene	6.52 ± 0.05	60		170
	0.043 ± 0.005	Vinyl acetate	0.17 ± 0.01	60		168
	0	Vinyl chloride	0.8	h		149a
	0.0	Vinyl chloride	0.8	40		152
	0.009 ± 0.003	Vinyl chloride	0.77 ± 0.03	60	a	168
	0 ± 15%	Vinyl chloride	0.9 ± 15%	70		9
	—	Vinylidene chloride	12.5	60		3
	0.0 ± 0.04	Vinylidene chloride	40 ± 8	60		65
Diethyl vinyl phosphonate	0	Styrene	3.25	116		25
	0.06 ± 0.02	Styrene	8.87 ± 0.4	h		305a
2,4-Difluorostyrene	0.75	Styrene	1.05	60		91a
α,β-Difluorostyrene	0.04	Styrene	2.42	60		91a
β,β-Difluorostyrene	0	Styrene	10.4	60		91a
1,1-Dihydroperfluorobutyl acrylate	0.07	Butadiene	0.35	50	a	267
	0.25	Methyl methacrylate	1.4	50		267
	0.07	Styrene	0.33	50		267
N-(1,1-Dihydroperfluorobutyl)-N-ethyl acrylamide	0.89	Methyl methacrylate	0.77	66		156
Diisobutyl maleate	0.1	Vinyl chloride	0.65 ± 0.05	40		151
Diisopropyl itaconate	6.0 ± 0.5	Vinyl chloride	0.06 ± 0.01	50		214

Monomer 1	r_1	Monomer 2	r_2	Catalyst	Temp (°C)	Note	Ref.
Diisopropyl maleate	0.043	Vinyl acetate	0.17		60		323
	0.0075	Vinyl octadecanoate	0		70		333
Dimethallyl oxalate	0.16 ± 0.01	Vinylidene chloride	4.8 ± 0.2		40		47
2,4-Dimethoxy-6-(β-itaconylhydrazino)-s-triazine	0.22 ± 0.2	Acrylonitrile	0.7 ± 0.5		60		61
N,N-Dimethylacryl-amide	0.5 ± 0.1	Acrylic acid	0.4 ± 0.05		75		263
p-Dimethylamino-styrene	31 ± 19	α-Methylstyrene	0.035 ± 0.015	SnCl₄	5		231
	0.11 ± 0.02	Methyl methacrylate	0.205 ± 0.02		60		323
	0.84 ± 0.05	Styrene	1.015 ± 0.06		60		323
2-N,N-Dimethyl-amino-4-vinyl-pyridine	1.4 ± 0.1	Styrene	0.35 ± 0.02		60		237
Dimethyl butadiene	0.63	Butadiene	0.85		5	a	94
	0.78	Butadiene	1.26		−18	a	226
	0.84	Isoprene	1.18		−18	e	226
	—	Isoprene	17 ± 5		50	e	254
	0.92 ± 0.02	Styrene	0.42 ± 0.02		−18	a	226
Dimethyl dithiol-fumarate	0.0014 ± 0.027; 0.0163 ± 0.013	Butadiene	0.0106 ± 0.0175		50		185
Dimethyl fumarate	0.025 ± 0.015	Styrene	0.098 ± 0.013		50		185
	0.94	Styrene	0.21 ± 0.02		60		168
	0.15	Butyl acrylate	0.40		h		54
	1.1	p-Chlorostyrene	0.69		h		54
Dimethyl itaconate	0.28	Di-n-butyl itaconate	1.1		h		54
		Methacrylonitrile	1.26		h		54

(continued)

(*continued*)

M_1	r_1	M_2	r_2	T, °C.	Remarks	Ref.
Dimethyl itaconate	0.3	Methyl methacrylate	1.2 ± 1.3	h		54
	0.14	Styrene	0.48	h		54
Dimethyl maleate	5.0 ± 0.2	Vinyl chloride	0.053 ± 0.01	50		213
	0.03 ± 0.01	Styrene	8.5 ± 0.2	60		168
	0.028	Vinyl acetate	0.12	60		334
Dimethyl methacryl-iminodiacetate	0.013	Methyl methacrylate	16.67	70		240
2,5-Dimethylstyrene	0.27	2,5-Dichlorostyrene	1.55	70		105
2,4-Dimethyl-6-vinyl-s-triazine	1.75	Methyl methacrylate	0.37	60		58a
	0.92	Styrene	0.12	60		58a
Dinonyl fumarate	0.32	Butadiene	2.02	h	o	177
Dinonyl maleate	0.12	Butadiene	5.36	h	o	177
Dioctyl fumarate	0.041 ± 0.007	N-Vinylpyrrolidone	0.030 ± 0.033	76		145a
Dioctyl itaconate	7.0 ± 1.0	Vinyl chloride	0.06 ± 0.02	50		214
Dioctyl maleate	0	Vinyl chloride	0.5	68		3
1,3-Dioxolane	0.47 ± 0.15	1,3,5-Trioxane	1.36 ± 0.03	35		148a
Diphenylacetylene	0	Acrylonitrile	13.6 ± 1.0	60	c	66
	0	Methyl acrylate	55 ± 5	60	c	66
1,1-Diphenylethylene	0	Acrylonitrile	0.028 ± 0.003	60	c	65,68
	0.00 ± 0.05	2-Chloro-1,3-butadiene	3.17 ± 0.16	60		65,68
	0	2,3-Dichloro-1,3-butadiene	4.5 ± 0.45	60		65,68
		Methyl acrylate	0.102 ± 0.006	60	c	66
N-N-Divinylaniline	0.003	Acrylonitrile	0.42	60		51
	0.01	Methyl methacrylate	2.0	60		51

Monomer 1	r_1	Monomer 2	r_2	Temp.		Ref.
m-Divinylbenzene	0.05	p-Methylstyrene	11.8	60		51
	0.45	Styrene	13.0	60		51
	2.0	Vinyl acetate	0.1	60		51
Divinyl ether	0.60	Styrene	0.65	60	g	331
	0.006	Methyl methacrylate	10.0	60		51
	0.02	Styrene	40	60		51
Divinyl sulfide	0.13 ± 0.05	Methyl methacrylate	0.85 ± 0.05	60		272
	0.47 ± 0.05	Styrene	1.90 ± 0.1	60		272
Divinyl sulfone	0.045	Methyl methacrylate	8.5	60		51
	0.01	Styrene	1.3	60		51
Divinyl tartrate	0.04	Methyl methacrylate	0.97	60		276
1,4-Divinyl-2,3,5,6-tetrachlorobenzene	—	Styrene	2.62	49.2		259
Dodecyl acrylate	1.3 ± 0.1	Acrylonitrile	3.2 ± 0.5	60		291
Dodecyl methacrylate	52.5 ± 1.8	Diethyl allylphosphonate	0.066 ± 0.06	80		36b
	18.7 ± 0.11	Diallyl butylphosphonate	0.091 ± 0.02	80		36b
	18.1 ± 0.4	Diallyl phenylphosphine oxide	-0.011 ± 0.013	80		36c
	11.1 ± 0.4		-0.013 ± 0.025	120		36c
	5.6 ± 0.4		-0.039 ± 0.022	140		36c
	19.5 ± 1.8	Diallyl phenylphosphonate	0.072 ± 0.22	80		36b
Dodecyl vinyl ether	-0.046 ± 0.054	Maleic anhydride	0.045 ± 0.052	50		5
	0	Methyl methacrylate	large	h		5
	0.00 ± 0.2	Vinylidene chloride	1.30 ± 0.015	50		4

(continued)

(continued)

M_1	r_1	M_2	r_2	T, °C	Remarks	Ref.
Epichlorohydrin	1.8 ± 0.3	Propylene oxide	0.6 ± 0.05	h	d	128
Ethyl 1-acetoxy acrylate	1.0 ± 0.05	Ethyl acrylate	1.0 ± 0.1	60		307
	0.65 ± 0.05	Methyl methacrylate	1.65 ± 0.07	60		307
	0.20 ± 0.05	Styrene	0.57 ± 0.05	60		307
	5.4 ± 0.5	Vinyl acetate	0.08 ± 0.03	60		307
Ethyl acid fumarate	0.25 ± 0.10	Styrene	0.18 ± 0.1	60		151
Ethyl acid maleate	0.035 ± 0.01	Styrene	0.13 ± 0.01	60		168
Ethyl acrylate	0.95	Acrylonitrile	0.44	80		337
	0.67 ± 0.02	Acrylonitrile	1.17 ± 0.1	50		43a
	2.3	Allyl chloride	0.48 ± 0.05	70		16
	7.73 ± 0.35	Allyl chloride	0.084 ± 0.100	60		144
	3.05	Bicyclo[2.2.1]hepta-2,5-diene	0.01	50		343a
	1.0 ± 0.1	Ethyl 1-acetoxy acrylate	1.0 ± 0.05	60		307
	0.79 ± 0.11	Isopropenyl isocyanate	0.15 ± 0.07	h		136
	$0.15^{+0.23}_{-0.13}$	Methylstyrene, mixt. of o- and p-isomers (ca. 1:2)	0.48 ± 0.06	80		24a
	5.7	Sodium acrylate	1.5	50	j	133
	0.19	Styrene	0.79	50		316
	0.20	Styrene	0.80	70		316
	0.48	Styrene	0.80	80		337
	0.19 ± 0.06	2-Vinylpyridine	0.23 ± 0.05	75		317

Monomer 1	Monomer 2	r_1	r_2	Temp.	Conditions	Ref.
Ethyl-1-cyano-cinnamate	Butadiene	0	0.25	35	a,c	209
N-Ethyl-N,1,1-di-hydroperfluoro-butyl acrylamide	Methyl methacrylate	0.89	0.77	66	e	156
Ethylene	1-Butene	29.1	0.019	h	e	217
	Propylene	5.61	0.145	75	e, VCl_3–Al$(C_6H_{13})_3$	218
	Propylene	7.08 ± 0.20	0.088 ± 0.003	25	e, VCl_4–Al$(C_6H_{13})_3$	196
	Propylene	17.95 ± 0.27	0.065 ± 0.002	25	e, $VOCl_3$–Al$(C_6H_{13})_3$	197
	Propylene	17.8	0.065	25	e, $VOCl_3$–Al$(C_6H_{13})_3$	197
	Propylene	33.4	0.032	25	e, $TiCl_4$–Al$(C_6H_{13})_2$	220
	Propylene	15.7	0.110	75	e, $TiCl_3$–Al$(C_6H_{13})_3$	220
	Propylene	15.7	0.110	75	e, $TiCl_2$–Al$(C_6H_{13})_3$	220
	Propylene	15.0	0.04	−20	e, Vanadium triacetyl-acetonate–AlEt$_2$Cl	219
	Propylene	4.7 ± 0.6	0.21 ± 0.02	20–60	Vanadyl compounds (VOX$_n$) activated by excess aluminum alkyl halides	285a
	Propylene	23 ± 3	0.043 ± 0.006	30	Vanadyl compounds (VOX$_n$) activated by excess aluminum alkyl halides	285a
	Tetrafluoroethylene	0.15	0.85	80	a	131
	Vinyl iso-caproate	—	—	80	r_1, r_2 could not be found accurately	321

(continued)

(*continued*)

M₁	r_1	M₂	r_2	T, °C.	Remarks	Ref.
Ethylene glycol dichloroacrylate	0.1	Styrene	0.6	h		283c
Ethylene glycol dimethacrylate	0.65	Styrene	0.35	60	g	331
Ethyl 2-ethoxy-acrylate	0.02 ± 0.02	Acrylonitrile	10.5 ± 1.5	80		250
	~0	Styrene	23.5 ± 1	80		250
N-Ethyl methacryl-amide	0.11	Methyl methacrylate	1.75	70		240
Ethyl methacrylyl-aminoacetate	0.90	Methyl methacrylate	1.09	70		240
Ethyl methacrylate	57.9 ± 15.0	Allyl chloride	0.082 ± 0.083	60		144
	0.83	Methacrylonitrile	0.46	80		49
	f	Methyl-1-chloro-acrylate	f	60–80		286
	0.26	Styrene	0.67	50		316
	0.29	Styrene	0.65	70		316
	0.22	Vinylidene chloride	0.35	68		3
d-Ethyl 2-methyl-2-ethyl-1-butenoate	2.2 ± 0.4	Vinyl acetate	0.1 ± 0.1	60		288
dl-Ethyl 2-methyl-2-ethyl-1-butenoate	3.2 ± 0.50	Vinyl acetate	0.3 ± 0.2	60		288
β-Ethyl styrene	0	p-Chlorostyrene	0.88 ± 0.30	0		238
p-Ethyl styrene	4.1 ± 0.5	p-Chlorostyrene	0.29 ± 0.04	0	d	238
	1.0 ± 0.2	Styrene	1.0 ± 0.2	40	e	216
	1.05 ± 0.1	Styrene	0.95 ± 1	40	e	279
1-Ethyl-2 vinyl-acetylene	0.63 ± 0.4	Acrylonitrile	0.17 ± 0.01	60		248

Ethyl vinyl ether	0.03 ± 0.02	Acrylonitrile	0.7 ± 0.2	80		250,270
	0	Acrylonitrile	5.0	60	b,c	195
	0	Methyl acrylate	3.3	60	b,c	193
	0	Styrene	80 ± 40	80		250
	0	Styrene	90 ± 20	60		171
	0	Vinyl acetate	3.0 ± 0.1	60	c	195
	0	Vinylidene chloride	3.2	60	b,c	193
Ethyl vinyl oxalate	0.2	Acrylonitrile	2.0	60		146a
	0.1	Methyl methacrylate	6.0	60		146a
	0.1	Styrene	8.0	60		146a
	3.0	Vinyl acetate	0.3	60		146a
5-Ethyl-2-vinyl-pyridine	0.43 ± 0.05	Acrylonitrile	0.02 ± 0.02	60		139
	1.16 ± 0.08	Methyl acrylate	0.179 ± 0.006	60		289
	0.69 ± 0.03	Methyl methacrylate	0.395 ± 0.003	60		289
	1.2 ± 0.2	Styrene	0.79 ± 0.03	60		289
5-Ethyl-2-vinyl-pyridine-N-oxide	5.5 ± 0.5	Methyl methacrylate	0.11 ± 0.01	60	Bulk	292
	4.7 ± 0.6	Methyl methacrylate	0.12 ± 0.02	60	In solution	292
	2.6 ± 0.3	Styrene	0.10 ± 0.01	60		292
Ethyl vinyl sulfide	0.3 ± 0.1	Methyl methacrylate	2.7 ± 1.5	60		277
	0.25 ± 0.1	Styrene	6.0 ± 1.5	h		277
N-Ethyl-N'-vinylurea	0.015	Methyl methacrylate	1.8	75		116
	0.020	Styrene	20.0	75		116
	0.63	Vinyl acetate	0.45	75		116
2-Fluorobutadiene	0.59 ± 0.10	Acrylonitrile	0.07 ± 0.03	50		227
	2.05 ± 0.19	Isoprene	0.19 ± 0.10	50		226
	1.54 ± 0.08	Methyl methacrylate	0.64 ± 0.08	50		227
	1.71 ± 0.19	α-Methylstyrene	0.38 ± 0.11	50		227

(continued)

(continued)

M_1	r_1	M_2	r_2	T, °C.	Remarks	Ref.
2-Fluorobutadiene	1.61 ± 0.24	Styrene	0.16 ± 0.08	5		227
	1.55 ± 0.10	Styrene	0.50 ± 0.10	50		227
Fluoroprene	0.22	2-Chloro-1,3-buta-diene	3.70	h		154,252
	2.93	Hexafluorobutadiene	0.24	40		154
p-Fluorostyrene	0.7 ± 0.1	Styrene	1.5 ± 0.2	40	e	216
	0.60 ± 0.1	Styrene	1.5 ± 0.1	40	e	279
	0.9	Styrene	0.7	60		91a
β-Fluorostyrene	0.01	Styrene	5.95	60		91a
N-(m-Fluorosulfonyl phenyl) acrylamide	0.60	Methyl methacrylate	1.47	h		117a
N-(m-Fluorosulfonyl phenyl)methacryl-amide	0.24	Styrene	0.63	h		117a
	0.71	Methyl methacrylate	1.24	h		117a
p-Fluoro-α-trifluoro-methylstyrene	0	Styrene	0.56	60		91a
Fumaronitrile	0.01 ± 0.01	Methyl methacrylate	3.5 ± 0.5	79		244
	0.00	α-Methylstyrene	0.022 ± 0.005	60		83
	0	Styrene	0.3 ± 0.3	50–70	t, see refs. 35, 110	210
	0.00	Styrene	0.09 ± 0.005	79		83
	0.01 ± 0.01	Styrene	0.23 ± 0.01	60		244
	0	Styrene	0.19 ± 0.03	60		168
	0.00 ± 0.02	Styrene	0.30 ± 0.02	49.65		258
Fumaryl chloride	0.00	Styrene	0.04	27		105

M_1	r_1	M_2	r_2	Temp. (°C)	Notes	Ref.
	0.00	Vinyl acetate	0.14	70	r_1 appears to vary with comp. mixture	105
Glycidyl acrylate	1.02	Acrylonitrile	1.01	60		134
	0.17	Styrene	0.60	60		134
Glycidyl methacrylate	1.32 ± 0.03	Acrylonitrile	0.14 ± 0.001	60		135
	1.05	Methyl methacrylate	0.80	60		96
	0.53 ± 0.07	Styrene	0.44 ± 0.001	60		135
	0.63 ± 0.1	Styrene	0.34 ± 0.05	65		280
Heptyl methacrylate	60.4 ± 0.4	Vinyl acetate	0.271 ± 0.039	60		205
Hexachlorobutadiene	0.10	2-Chlorobutadiene	5.47 ± 0.05	40		154
	0	Styrene	Very large	70		9
Hexadecyl methacrylate	68.3 ± 3.2	Vinyl acetate	0.135 ± 0.055	60		205
Hexafluorobutadiene	0.1	2-Chloro-1,3-butadiene	5.52	40		154
	0.10	2-Chloro-1,3-butadiene	5.47	50		148c
	0.24	Fluoroprene	2.93	40		154
	0.78 ± 0.05	Isoprene	1.19 ± 0.12	40		154
1-Hexene	0	Acrylonitrile	12.2 ± 2.4	60	c	66
	0	Methyl acrylate	8.5 ± 2	60	c	66

(continued)

(continued)

M₁	r_1	M₂	r_2	T, °C.	Remarks	Ref.
n-Hexyl methacrylate	0.56	Methacrylonitrile	0.75	80		49
1-Hexyne	0	Acrylonitrile	5.4 ± 0.3	60	c	66
	0	Methyl acrylate	11.2 ± 2	60	c	66
4-Hydroabietyl alcohol	0	Vinylidene chloride	2.6	70		69
Hydronopyl acrylate	0.9 ± 0.1	Acrylonitrile	1.1 ± 0.1	60		187
	0.29 ± 0.1	Styrene	0.66 ± 0.1	50		187
	0.2	Butadiene	1.1	h		188
	4.3 ± 0.2	Vinyl chloride	0.14 ± 0.01	60		187
2-Hydroxy ethyl acrylate	8.85 ± 1.32	Allyl chloride	0.016 ± 0.030	60		144
2-Hydroxy ethyl methacrylate	35.6 ± 1.7	Allyl chloride	0.033 ± 0.048	60		144
Hydroxy methyl-croton amide	0.045 ± 0.1	Vinyl acetate	0.01 ± 0.01	110		315
Indene	0	Acrylonitrile	0.03	h		337
	0	o-Chlorostyrene	3.5 ± 15%	70		9
	0.33 ± 15%	Vinylidene chloride	0.4 ± 15%	70		9
p-Iodostyrene	0.95 ± 0.20	Methyl methacrylate	0.36 ± 0.03	60		323
	1.09 ± 0.30	Styrene	0.62 ± 0.05	60		323
	1.03 ± 0.05	Styrene	0.45 ± 0.02	50		43b
Isoamyl vinyl ether	0	Poly(1,3-butanediol fumarate)	3.8 ± 0.7	60		283b
Isobutylene	0.02 ± 0.02	Acrylonitrile	1.8 ± 0.2	50		30
	0	Acrylonitrile	1.02	60		223
	115 ± 15	Butadiene	0.01 ± 0.01	-103		295
	8.6	p-Chlorostyrene	1.2	0	SnCl₄ in nitrobenzene	236

1.01	p-Chlorostyrene	1.02	0	AlBr₃ in hexane	236
14.7	p-Chlorostyrene	0.15	0	AlBr₃ in nitrobenzene	236
22.5	p-Chlorostyrene	0.7	0	AlBr₃ in nitromethane	236
0.17	Diethyl fumarate	0	60	e	236
2.5 ± 0.5	Isoprene	0.4 ± 0.1	−103	d	126
2.27	Isoprene	0.44	−90	d	295
2.26	Isoprene	0.38	−95.6	d	242b
0.4	Isopropenyl benzyl chloride	1	−100	d	242b
f	α-Methylstyrene	f	−78	d	140
1.79 ± 0.02	Styrene	0.24 ± 0.02	−90	AlCl₃ (0.14 g./100 ml. MeCl) with laminar agitation	222
1.66 ± 0.02	Styrene	0.42 ± 0.02	−90	AlCl₃ (0.50 g./100 ml. MeCl) with laminar agitation	255
2.36 ± 0.06	Styrene	0.76 ± 0.13	−30	AlCl₃ (0.14 g./100 ml. MeCl) with laminar agitation	255
2.51 ± 0.05	Styrene	1.21 ± 0.06	−30	AlCl₃ (0.50 g./100 ml. MeCl) with laminar agitation	255

(continued)

(*continued*)

M_1	r_1	M_2	r_2	T, °C.	Remarks	Ref.
Isobutylene	9.02 ± 0.77	Styrene	1.99 ± 0.24	−91 to −94	AlCl$_3$ (0.02 g./100 ml. MeCl) with turbulent agitation	255
	1.60	Styrene	0.17	0	d	174
	f	Styrene	f	−78	d	222
	0.0	Tetrafluoroethylene	<0.3	80	a	131
	8.0	Vinyl acetylene	0.13	−100	d	62
	4.5 ± 1	Vinyl benzyl chloride	0.7 ± 0.1	−100	d	140
	0.08 ± 0.1	Vinyl chloride	2.05 ± 0.3	60		171
	0.03	Vinyl chloride	1.3	0		275
	0	Vinyl chloride	4.3	65	b,c	95
	0	Vinylidene chloride	1.5	60	b,c	193
	0.00176	Vinylidene cyanide	0.182	h		26
Isobutyl methacrylate	1.04	Acrylonitrile	0.21	60		215
	45.5 ± 10.2	Allyl chloride	0.047 ± 0.056	60		144
	0.67	Methacrylonitrile	0.73	80		337
	29.8	Vinyl acetate	0.025	60		215
Isobutyl vinyl ether	0	Poly(1,3-butanediol fumarate)	2.0 ± 0.7	60		283b
Isoprene	0.45 ± 0.05	Acrylonitrile	0.03 ± 0.03	50		119
	0.29 ± 0.02	Acrylonitrile	0.05 ± 0.02	50	a	120
	1	Butadiene	1	48	AlEt$_2$Cl–cobalt diacetyl acetonate	239
	1	Butadiene	1	20	AlEt$_2$Cl–cobalt diacetyl acetonate	239

r_1	M_1	M_2	r_2	T, °C	Catalyst / Conditions	Ref.
1	Butadiene		1	13	AlEt₂Cl–cobalt diacetyl acetonate	239
1	Butadiene		1	−15	AlEt₂Cl–cobalt diacetyl acetonate	214
0.47 ± 0.03		Butadiene	3.38 ± 0.14	50	e	253
1.06		Butadiene	0.94	−18		226
0.85		Butadiene	0.75	5	a	94
0.063 ± 0.051		2-Chloro-1,3-butadiene	2.82 ± 0.22	50		120
0.133 ± 0.025		2-Chloro-1,3-butadiene	3.65 ± 0.11	50	a	119
1.18		Dimethylbutadiene	0.84	−18		226
17 ± 5		2,3-Dimethylbutadiene	—	50	e	254
0.19 ± 0.10		2-Fluorobutadiene	2.05 ± 0.19	50		226
1.19 ± 0.12		Hexafluorobutadiene	0.78 ± 0.05	40		154
0.4 ± 0.1		Isobutylene	2.5 ± 0.5	−103	d	295
0.44		Isobutylene	2.27	−90	d	242b
0.38		Isobutylene	2.26	−95.6	d	242b
17 ± 5		Piperylene	—	50	e	254
0.50		Propylene	0.23	−78	d	129
2.05 ± 0.45		Styrene	1.38 ± 0.54	50		120
1.68 ± 0.00		Styrene	0.80 ± 0.00	50	a	120
9.5		Styrene	0.25	h	e, in toluene	285
1		Styrene	0.8	h	e, in toluene-amine mixture	285

(continued)

(*continued*)

M₁	r₁	M₂	r₂	T, °C.	Remarks	Ref.
Isoprene	1.30	Styrene	0.48	−18	a	94,226
	2.0	Styrene	0.4	h		344
	1.30 ± 0.02	Styrene	0.48 ± 0.01	−18		226
	1.98	Styrene	0.44	h		344
	0.59 ± 0.05	2-Vinylpyridine	0.47 ± 0.07	60		160,161
	1.88 ± 0.02	2-Vinyl quinoline	0.53 ± 0.01	60		160,161
	0.27	Styrene	2.2	75	e	342a
Isopropenyl acetate	0.032 ± 0.005	Maleic anhydride	0.002	75		328
	0.017	Methyl methacrylate	30	75		115
	1.0	Vinyl acetate	1.0	75		115
	0.25	Vinyl chloride	2.2	65		240
Isopropenyl acetylene	0.47 ± 0.01	Acrylonitrile	0.33 ± 0.01	60		248
	0.55 ± 0.1	2-Vinyl pyridine	1.65 ± 0.05	60		248
Isopropyl benzyl chloride	1	Isobutylene	0.4	−100	d	140
Isopropenyl isocy-anate	0.10 ± 0.11	Acrylonitrile	0.24 ± 0.02	h		136
	0.15 ± 0.07	Ethyl acrylate	0.79 ± 0.11	h		136
	0.11 ± 0.04	Methyl acrylate	0.60 ± 0.03	h		136
	0.08	Methyl acrylate	0.8	h		114
	0.14 ± 0.10	Methyl methacrylate	3.10 ± 0.29	h		136
	0.14	Styrene	7.0	60		114
	0.07	Styrene	8.12	h		136
	0.31 ± 0.02	Vinylidene chloride	0.85 ± 0.04	h		136
Isopropenyl methyl ketone	1.2	Acrylonitrile	0.3	h		242a
	4.5	Vinylidene chloride	0.15	h		242a
β-Isopropenyl naphthalene	0.23 ± 0.02	Acrylonitrile	0.05 ± 0.01	99		67

Monomer 1	r_1	Monomer 2	r_2	Temp	Notes	Ref.
Isopropyl meth-acrylate	0.00	Methyl methacrylate	0.45 ± 0.03	99	p	67
Isostilbene	0.92	Methacrylonitrile	0.43	80		49
Itaconic acid	0.07 ± 0.07	Maleic anhydride	0.08 ± 0.08	60		168
	0	Methyl methacrylate	1.14	90		74
	0	Methyl methacrylate	1.23	h		117a,122
Itaconic anhydride	0	Styrene	0.34	h		122
	0.2	Styrene	0.3	70		82
	0.60	Styrene	0.10	65		70a
Maleic anhydride	0	Acrylonitrile	6	60	b,c	193
	f	C₈–C₁₆ Alkyl vinyl ethers	f	50		5
	<0.13	Allyl acetate	<0.0075	30		36
	0.13	Allyl acetate	0.0075	38.5		36
	0	2-Chloroallyl acetate	0	120	b	147
	0.046 ± 0.052	Dodecyl vinyl ether	−0.046 ± 0.054	50		5
	0.002	Isopropenyl acetate	0.032 ± 0.005	75		328
	0.08 ± 0.08	Isostilbene	0.07 ± 0.07	60		168
	0	Methyl acrylate	2.5	60	b,c	193
	0.02	Methyl acrylate	2.8 ± 0.05	75		328
	0.02	Methyl methacrylate	6.7 ± 0.2	75		328
	0.03	Methyl methacrylate	3.5	60		37
	0.27 ± 0.03	α-Methylstyrene	0.005 ± 0.005	60		251a
	0.08 ± 0.03	α-Methylstyrene	0.038 ± 0.003	60		251a
	0.03 ± 0.03	Stilbene	0.03 ± 0.03	60		168
	0	Styrene	0.01	60	t, see ref. 35	193
	0	Styrene	0.042 ± 0.008	80		17
	0	Styrene	0.02	60		33

(continued)

(continued)

M_1	r_1	M_2	r_2	T, °C.	Remarks	Ref.
Maleic anhydride	0.01	Vinyl acetate	0.072 ± 0.04	h		130
	0.003	Vinyl acetate	0.055 ± 0.015	75		328
	0.008	Vinyl chloride	0.296 ± 0.07	75		328
	0	Vinylidene chloride	9	60	b,c	193
	~0	Vinylidene cyanide	45	50		93
Maleonitrile	0	Styrene	0.19 ± 0.01	60		168
Methacrolein	2.0	Acrylonitrile	0.06	70		105
Methacrylamide	0.22	Methacrylic acid	2.0	50		60
	0.3	Methacrylic acid	2.0	70		242
	0.30	Methacrylic acid	2.50	70		242
	0.22 ± 0.0	Methyl acrylate	2.0	65		59
	0.47 ± 0.04	Methyl methacrylate	1.5 ± 0.02	65		59
	0.49 ± 0.02	Methyl methacrylate	1.65 ± 0.05	70		59
Methacrylic acid	0.526	Butadiene	0.201	50	a	87
	4.5	2-Chloroallyl alcohol	0.0	100		147
	4.0	2-Chloroallyl chloride	0.0	100		147
	0.7 ± 15%	o-Chlorostyrene	0.12 ± 15%	70		9
	0.98 ± 0.16	Diethylaminoethyl methacrylate	0.90 ± 0.23	70	K_2SO_4 pH 1.2	22
	0.08 ± 0.015	Diethylaminoethyl methacrylate	0.65 ± 0.03	70	K_2SO_4 pH 7.2	22
	2.0	Methacrylamide	0.22	50		60
	2.0	Methacrylamide	0.3	70		242
	2.50	Methacrylamide	0.30	70		242
	1.63 ± 0.08	Methacrylonitrile	0.59 ± 0.08	80		49
	1.64 ± 0.05	Methacrylonitrile	0.62 ± 0.05	65		102
	0.7 ± 0.05	Styrene	0.15 ± 0.01	60		53
	20	Vinyl acetate	0.01	70		18
	3.0 ± 15%	Vinylidene chloride	0.15 ± 15%	70		9
	0.58 ± 0.05	2-Vinyl pyridine	1.55 ± 0.10	70		21

M₁	r_1	M₂	r_2	Temp.	Conditions	Ref.
Methacrylic anhydride	0.21	Acrylonitrile	1.94	60		31a
Methacrylonitrile	1.20 ± 0.08	Acrolein	0.72 ± 0.06	50		148a
	2.68	Acrylonitrile	0.32	60		223
	0.50 ± 0.05	Acrylonitrile	0.9 ± 0.05	−50	PhMgBr catalyst	68a
	0.05 ± 0.02	Acrylonitrile	1.0 = 0.1	−50	NaNH₂ cat.	68a
	0.55	n-Amyl methacrylate	0.51	80		49
	0.04 ± 0.04	Butadiene	0.36 ± 0.07	5	a	65
	0.51	n-Butyl methacrylate	0.69	80		49
	0.37	t-Butyl methacrylate	0.70	80		49
	0.86	o-Chlorostyrene	0.78	80		49
	0.73	p-Chlorostyrene	0.45	80		337
	1.26	Dimethyl itaconate	0.28	h		54
	0.46	Ethyl methacrylate	0.83	80		49
	0.75	n-Hexyl methacrylate	0.56	80		49
	0.73	Isobutyl methacrylate	0.67	80		337
	0.43	Isopropyl methacrylate	0.92	80		49
	0.59 ± 0.08	Methacrylic acid	1.63 ± 0.08	80		49
	0.62 ± 0.05	Methacrylic acid	1.64 ± 0.05	65		102
	0.70	Methyl methacrylate	0.74	80		49
	5.2 ± 1.0	Methyl methacrylate	0.67 ± 0.2	−55	e	85
	0.65 ± 0.06	Methyl methacrylate	0.67 ± 0.1	60		171
	0.80	Methyl methacrylate	0.68	80		337
	0.30 ± 0.05	Methyl methacrylate	2.0 ± 0.5	−78	PhMgBr cat.	68a
	0.05 ± 0.02	Methyl methacrylate	5.0 ± 0.5	−30	PhMgBr cat.	68a
	6.20 ± 1	Methyl methacrylate	0.67 ± 0.2	−50	NaNH₂	68a
	0.35 ± 0.02	α-Methylstyrene	0.12 ± 0.02	80		81
	0.21	α-Methylstyrene	0.15	80		337
	0.90	Octadecyl methacrylate	1.13	80		49

(continued)

(continued)

M₁	r₁	M₂	r₂	T, °C.	Remarks	Ref.
Methacrylonitrile	0.75	n-Octyl methacrylate	0.58	80		49
	0.29	n-Propyl methacrylate	0.79	80		49
	0.26 ± 0.05	Styrene	0.38 ± 0.05	80		49
	0.28	Styrene	0.43	80		337
	0.25 ± 0.02	Styrene	0.25 ± 0.02	80		81
	0.16 ± 0.06	Styrene	0.30 ± 0.10	60		171
	12.0 ± 1	Styrene	0.05 ± 0.02	−78 to −30	PhMgBr	68a
4-Methacryloxy-benzylidene aniline	12 ± 2	Vinyl acetate	0.01 ± 0.01	70		81
4-Methacryloxy-benzylidene-4'-chloroaniline	2.4 ± 0.5	Styrene	0.25 ± 0.03	60		257
Methacryloxymethyl-pentamethyldisil-oxane	5.4 ± 0.6	Styrene	0.18 ± 0.03	60		257
	1.44 ± 0.15	Acrylonitrile	0.19 ± 0.04	50		202
	1.13 ± 0.1	Methyl methacrylate	0.93 ± 0.1	50		202
	0.58 ± 0.02	Styrene	0.77 ± 0.02	50		202
	24 ± 5	Vinyl acetate	0.16 ± 0.16	50		137
N-Methacryloyl-ε-caprolactam	0	Styrene	1.0	70–80		326
3-o-Methacryloyl-1,2,5,6-diisopropyl-idene-D-gluco-furanose	0	Acrylonitrile	0.25	50		149

Monomer 1	Monomer 2	r_1	r_2	Temp	Conditions	Ref.
Methallyl acetate	2-Chloroethyl acrylate	0	4 ± 1	60		171
	Methyl methacrylate	0	10	60	b,c	193
	Styrene	0	71 ± 10	60		193
Methallyl chloride	Vinylidene chloride	0	2.4	60	b,c	193
	Methyl methacrylate	0	7.7	60	b,c	193
	Styrene	0	22	60		193
	Vinyl acetate	0	0.13	73–90		208
	Vinyl chloride	0	0.31	45		208
	Vinylidene chloride	0	1.1	60	b,c	193
p-Methoxy-α-methyl styrene	Vinyl-2-chloroethyl ether	1.1	0.42	RT	d, in benzene	180
	Vinyl-2-chloroethyl ether	1.3	0.73	RT	d, in nitrobenzene	180
m-Methoxystyrene	p-Chlorostyrene	2.6 ± 0.4	0.38 ± 0.05	0	d	231
	α-Methylstyrene	0.3 ± 1	5 ± 1	5	SnCl$_4$	231
	Styrene	1.1 ± 0.15	0.90 ± 0.15	0	SnCl$_4$	231
p-Methoxystyrene	p-Chlorostyrene	0.58 ± 0.03	0.86 ± 0.08	60		323
	Methyl methacrylate	0.32 ± 0.05	0.29 ± 0.03	60		323
	Methyl methacrylate	0.32	0.29	60		39
	α-Methylstyrene	15 ± 5	0.30 ± 0.1	5	SnCl$_4$	231
	p-Methylstyrene	1.54 ± 0.10	0.52 ± 0.06	0	d, (TiCl$_4$–φNO$_2$)	303
	p-Methylstyrene	3.7 ± 0.40	−0.03 ± 0.07	0	d, (TiCl$_4$–CCl$_4$)	303
	p-Methylstyrene	1.9 ± 0.3	0.14 ± 0.14	0	d, (SnCl$_4$–φNO$_2$–CCl$_4$)	303
	p-Methylstyrene	0.68 ± 0.06	2.2 ± 0.1	0	e, (Na in THF)	303
	p-Methylstyrene	0.72 ± 0.02	1.93 ± 0.03	0	e, (Li in THF)	303
	Styrene	100	0.01	0	SnCl$_4$	231
	Styrene	0.82 ± 0.07	1.16 ± 0.09	60		323
	Styrene	0.93	1.13	60		201a

(continued)

(*continued*)

M_1	r_1	M_2	r_2	T, °C.	Remarks	Ref.
p-Methoxystyrene	19 ± 3	Styrene	-0.04 ± 0.04	0	d, SnCl$_4$ in PhNO$_2$·CCl$_4$	303
	29 ± 5	Styrene	-0.02 ± 0.07	0	d, SnCl$_4$ in PhNO$_2$·CCl$_4$	303
	11 ± 1	Styrene	0.34 ± 0.05	0	d, AlCl$_3$·PhNO$_2$·CCl$_4$	303
	14 ± 3	Styrene	0.12 ± 0.07	0	d, TiCl$_4$·PhNO$_2$·CCl$_4$	303
	11.5 ± 0.7	Styrene	0.38 ± 0.04	0	d, TiCl$_4$·PhNO$_2$·CCl$_4$	303
	46 ± 3	Styrene	0.05 ± 0.04	0	d, TiCl$_4$-CCl$_4$	303
	31 ± 6	Styrene	0.00 ± 0.03	0	d	303
	35 ± 5	Styrene	-0.12 ± 0.012	0	d, TiCl$_4$-PhNO$_2$-CCl$_4$	303
	5.6 ± 0.08	Styrene	0.48 ± 0.08	0	d, TiCl$_4$-PhNO$_2$	303
	7.6	Styrene	0.22	0	d	303
	72	Styrene	0.01	0	TiCl$_4$-φCH$_3$	303
	12 ± 2	Styrene	-0.33 ± 0.03	0	d	303
	0.13 ± 0.02	Styrene	4.1 ± 0.5	0	e, Na in THF	303
	0.23 ± 0.02	Styrene	2.9 ± 0.2	0	e, Li in THF	303
	0.05 ± 0.02	Styrene	10.9 ± 0.8	0	e, BuLi	303

Monomer 1	r_1	Monomer 2	r_2	Temp (°C)	Notes	Ref.
Methyl acid maleate	0.035	Vinyl acetate	0.522	56		312a
Methyl acrylate	0.015 ± 0.01	Vinyl acetate	0.13 ± 0.03	75		334
	0.0 ± 0.007	Vinyl acetate	0.09 ± 0.005	60		334
	0.2	Acrolein	10.0	20	a	269
	7.7 ± 0.2	Acrolein	0.0 ± 0.05	20		148a
	0.05 ± 0.05	Acrylamide	1.30 ± 0.05	60		24a
	1.25 ± 0.15	Acrylonitrile	0.86 ± 0.05	30	m	341
	1.22 ± 0.20	Acrylonitrile	0.70 ± 0.20	20	m	339
	0.84 ± 0.05	Acrylonitrile	1.5 ± 0.1	50		187
	0.67 ± 0.1	Acrylonitrile	1.26 ± 0.1	60		24
	0.95 ± 0.05	Acrylonitrile	1.4 ± 0.1	60		291
	0.83	Acrylonitrile	0.84	65		223
	0.71 ± 0.012	Acrylonitrile	0.50 ± 0.47	80		142
	0.345	Acrylyl chloride	2.3	45		282a
	f	C_8–C_{18} Alkyl vinyl ethers	f			5
	5	Allyl acetate	0	50	b,c	193
	9.100 ± 0.930	Allyl chloride	-0.020 ± 0.100	60		143
	8.450 ± 0.370	Allyl chloride	0.054 ± 0.039	30		143
	6.460 ± 0.570	Allyl chloride	0.404 ± 0.073	60		143
	5.450 ± 0.070	Allyl chloride	0.071 ± 0.011	90		143
	0.049 ± 0.005	1,1-bis(p-Anisyl)-ethylene	0	120	c	66
	31.5 ± 2.5	2-Bromovinyl ethyl ether	0	60		250
	0.05 ± 0.02	Butadiene	0.76 ± 0.04	80	a	324
	5.0 ± 1.5	Butyl vinylsulfonate	0.11 ± 0.03	5		233
	0.7	2-Chloroallyl acetate	0	70	d	147

(continued)

(continued)

M_1	r_1	M_2	r_2	T, °C.	Remarks	Ref.
Methyl acrylate	0.078 ± 0.010	2-Chloro-1,3-buta-diene	11.1 ± 1.5	60		65,68
	0.9 ± 0.1	2-Chloroethyl acrylate	0.9 ± 0.1	60		171
	0.92 ± 0.05	2-Chloroethyl acrylate	0.95 ± 0.03	60		66
	0.092 ± 0.006	1,1-bis(p-Chloro-phenyl)-ethylene	0	60	c	66
	0.15 ± 0.03	2,5-Dichlorostyrene	3.4 ± 1.4	70		166
	0.25 ± 0.04	2,5-Dichlorostyrene	4.27 ± 0.28	60		2
	55 ± 5	Diphenylacetylene	0	60	c	66
	0.102 ± 0.006	1,1-Diphenylethylene	0	60	c	66
	3.3	Ethyl vinyl ether	0	60	b,c	193
	0.179 ± 0.006	5-Ethyl-2-vinyl-pyridine	1.16 ± 0.08	60		289
	8.5 ± 2	1-Hexene	0	60	c	66
	11.2 ± 2	1-Hexyne	0	60	c	66
	0.8	Isopropenyl isocy-anate	0.08	h		114
	0.60 ± 0.03	Isopropenyl iso-cyanate	0.11 ± 0.04	h		136
	2.5	Maleic anhydride	0	60	b,c	193
	2.8 ± 0.05	Maleic anhydride	0.02	75		328
	2.0	Methacrylamide	0.22 ± 0.0	65		59
	>1	Methyl methacrylate	<1	20	d	164
	4.5 ± 0.5	Methyl methacrylate	0.1 ± 0.1	-30	e	164
	1.5 ± 0.01	Methyl methacrylate	0.3 ± 0.005	65		59
	$0.15 {}^{+0.25}_{-0.14}$	Methylstyrene, mixture of o- and p-isomers (1:2)	0.59 ± 0.06	80		24a

r_1	M_2	r_2	Temp °C	Conditions	Ref.
0.172 ± 0.007	2-Methyl-5-vinyl pyridine	0.88 ± 0.10	60		290
0.35 ± 0.04	Methyl vinyl sulfide	0.05 ± 0.03	60		251
0.89	Pentachlorophenyl vinyl sulfide	0.25	80		124
0.62 ± 0.02	Phenylacetylene	0.27 ± 0.04	60		66
0.40	Phenyl vinyl sulfide	0.05 ± 0.02	60		249
0.18 ± 0.02	Styrene	0.75 ± 0.03	60		66,170
0.20 ± 0.05	Styrene	0.75 ± 0.1	70		20
0.15 ± 0.05	Styrene	0.7 ± 0.1	60		187
0.238 ± 0.02	Styrene	0.825 ± 0.0	131		170
0.4 ± 0.2	Styrene	2.2 ± 0.2	20	SnCl$_4$	164
0.4 ± 0.2	Styrene	$r_1 \ll r_2$	h	Cationic in ethylene chloride	121
0.4 ± 0.2	Styrene	2.2 ± 0.2	h	Cationic in benzene	121
0.14	m-Styrenesulfonyl fluoride	1.50	75		113
0.20	p-Styrenesulfonyl fluoride	4.0	75		113
200	Tetrachloroethylene	0	60	b,c	193
830	Tetrachloroethylene	0	60	b,c	65
33	Trichloroethylene	0	60	b,c	193
9	Vinyl acetate	0.1	60		333
9 ± 2.5	Vinyl acetate	0.1 ± 0.1	60		195
f	Vinyl acetate	f	h		336
0.50	N-Vinyl carbazole	0.050	75		112

(continued)

(*continued*)

M_1	r_1	M_2	r_2	T, °C.	Remarks	Ref.
Methyl acrylate	4	Vinyl chloride	0.06	45		301, 302
	5	Vinyl chloride	0	60		193
	4.4 ± 0.5	Vinyl chloride	0.12 ± 0.01	50		187
	9.0	Vinyl chloride	0.083	50		52
	f	Vinyl chloride	f	50		162
	1	Vinylidene chloride	1	60		193
	1	Vinylidene chloride	1	70		18
	0.84 ± 0.06	Vinylidene chloride	0.99 ± 0.10	60		68
	1.38 ± 0.27	Vinyl isocyanate	0.14 ± 1.0	60		137
	0.1	2-Vinylmercapto-benzothiazole	1.0	60		148
	5.8	Vinyl octadecanoate	0.03	70		333
	0.1 ± 0.03	2-Vinyl phenanthrene	2.0 ± 0.2	60		247
	0.8 ± 0.05	3-Vinyl phenanthrene	1.75 ± 0.25	60		247
	0.20 ± 0.09	2-Vinyl pyridine	2.03 ± 0.49	60		2
	0.168 ± 0.003	2-Vinyl pyridine	1.58 ± 0.05	60		289
	0.22 ± 0.01	4-Vinyl pyridine	1.7 ± 0.2	60		289
	1.5	N-Vinyl pyridinium fluoroborate	0.2	60		70b
	0.27 ± 0.16	N-Vinyl pyrrolidone	0.041 ± 0.024	60		337
	1.2	N-Vinyl succinimide	0.4	60		90
	3.69 ± 0.12	Vinyl undecenoate	0.031 ± 0.12	60		179
Methyl bicyclo-(2,2,1)-2-heptene-5-carboxylate	0.2 ± 0.1	Acrylonitrile	1.5 ± 0.5	60		145
	0.45 ± 0.07	Vinyl acetate	1.5 ± 0.24	60		145

Methyl-1-chloro-acrylate	0.15	Acrylonitrile	2.0	60		335
	2.0 ± 15%	Acrylonitrile	0.15 ± 15%	70		9
	i	Butyl methacrylate	f	60–80		286
	f	Ethyl methacrylate	f	60–80		286
	1.2 ± 15%	Methyl methacrylate	0.3 ± 15%	70		9
	f	Methyl methacrylate	f	h		286
	0.30	Styrene	0.25	70		80
	0.41 ± 0.14	Vinylidene cyanide	0.091 ± 0.05	50		93
Methyl 2-chloro-cinnamate	<0.03	Butadiene	1.07 ± 0.12	60		274
	<0.02	Butadiene	1.20 ± 0.12	80		274
Methyl-4-chloro-cinnamate	<0.05	Butadiene	2.73 ± 0.3	80		274
Methyl cinnamate	0	Acrylonitrile	6 ± 2	60		65
	0	Styrene	1.9 ± 0.2	60	c	65
2-Methyl-5-cinnamoylpyridine	−0.15 ± 0.2	Styrene	0.92 ± 0.08	50		189
β-Methylene-β-propiolactone	0	Acrylonitrile	7.52 ± 0.08	h	h	138
5-Methyl-1-hexene	4.00 ± 0.28	Styrene	0.591 ± 0.057	35	e	24b
Methyl isopropenyl ketone	0.70 ± 0.14	Acrylonitrile	0.36 ± 0.08	80		337
	1.7	β-Methylstyrene	0.03	h		337
	0.66	Styrene	0.32	80		337
	0.29 ± 0.06	Styrene	0.44 ± 0.10	80		337
	4.5 ± 0.1	Vinylidene chloride	0.15 ± 0.02	60	p	53

(continued)

(continued)

M_1	r_1	M_2	r_2	T, °C.	Remarks	Ref.
N-Methyl methacrylamide						
Methyl methacrylate	0.24	Methyl methacrylate	1.54	70		240
	0.30 ± 0.05	p-Acetyl amino-styrene	0.50 ± 0.05	65		106
	10.0 ± 0.2	Acrolein	0.2 ± 0.05	20	K persulfonate-AgNO$_3$	269
	4.22	1-Acrylamido-1-deoxy-D-glucitol	0.206	50		325a
	1.34	Acrylonitrile	0.12	26	n-Bu$_3$B no solvent	343
	1.34	Acrylonitrile	0.12	12	n-Bu$_3$B no solvent	343
	1.45	Acrylonitrile	0.15	−80	n-Bu$_3$B in toluene	343
	1.34	Acrylonitrile	0.12	−12	n-Bu$_3$B ethylene dichlor.	343
	1.34	Acrylonitrile	0.12	26	n-Bu$_2$BCl in no solvent	343
	1.05	Acrylonitrile	0.15	26	i-Bu$_3$Al no solvent	343
	0.85	Acrylonitrile	0.09	26	n-Bu$_2$Zn no solvent	343
	1.20	Acrylonitrile	0.03	26	Me$_2$Cd no solvent	343
	0.40	Acrylonitrile	7	−12	Et$_2$Be no solvent	343
	0.30	Acrylonitrile	10	−80	n-Bu$_2$Mg in THF	343
	0.14	Acrylonitrile	5	−12	Cp$_2$Mg no solvent	343
	0.39	Acrylonitrile	7	−8	n-BuLi no solvent	343
	0.14	Acrylonitrile	5	−12	n-BuNa no solvent	343
	1.16 ± 0.22	Acrylonitrile	0.13 ± 0.05	60	e	17
	Small	Acrylonitrile	Large	−55	e	86
	1.351 ± 0.133	Acrylonitrile	0.100 ± 0.070	40		143
	1.224 ± 0.100	Acrylonitrile	0.150 ± 0.080	80		143
	1.186 ± 0.120	Acrylonitrile	0.160 ± 0.100	100		143
	0.25 ± 0.25	Acrylonitrile	7.9 ± 1.6	−30	e	164
	Large	Acrylonitrile	Small	20	d	164
	1.65 ± 0.40	Acrylonitrile	0.15 ± 0.03	20	m	339

r_1	Monomer	r_2	Temp.	Conditions	Ref.
1.20 ± 0.14	Acrylonitrile	0.15 ± 0.07	60	1 atmos.	169
1.34	Acrylonitrile	0.12	70	100 atmos.	47b
1.46	Acrylonitrile	0.37	70	1000 atmos.	47b
2.01	Acrylonitrile	0.45	70		47b
0.02 ± 0.01	Acrylonitrile	6.5 ± 0.5	−78	PhMgBr cat. in ether	68a
0.07 ± 0.02	Acrylonitrile	4.5 ± 0.5	−50	PhMgBr cat. in ether	68a
0.10 ± 0.03	Acrylonitrile	1.5 ± 0.1	−15	PhMgBr cat. in ether	68a
0.03 ± 0.01	Acrylonitrile	5.0 ± 0.5	−78	PhMgBr cat. in toluene	68a
0.03 ± 0.01	Acrylonitrile	3.0 ± 0.1	−30	PhMgBr cat. in toluene	68a
0.06 ± 0.02	Acrylonitrile	2.0 ± 0.2	20	PhMgBr cat. in toluene	68a
0.02 ± 0.01	Acrylonitrile	4.0 ± 0.5	−78	PhMgI in toluene	68a
0.05 ± 0.02	Acrylonitrile	1.3 ± 0.1	−40	PhMgI in toluene	68a
0.25 ± 0.25	Acrylonitrile	7.9 ± 1.6	−50	NaNH$_2$	68a
0.3	Acrylonitrile	10	−80	nBu$_2$Mg	68a
0.48	Acrylyl chloride	1.51	45		282a
f	C$_8$–C$_{18}$ Alkyl vinyl ethers	f	50		5
23	Allyl acetate	0	60	b,c	198
50	Allyl chloride	0	60	b,c	193
48.1 ± 5.00	Allyl chloride	0.048 ± 0.038	60		144
50	Allyl chloroacetate	0	75	c	55
f	Allyl esters	f	h		273
0.87 ± 0.025	Allyl methacrylate	0.69 ± 0.02	65		262
0.14	N-(p-Anisyl)-methacrylamide	0.57	70		240
10.0	Bicyclo[2 2 1]-2,5-heptadiene	~0.00	50		343a

(continued)

(continued)

M_1	r_1	M_2	r_2	T, °C.	Remarks	Ref.
Methyl methacrylate	0.57 ± 0.07	2,5-Bis(trifluoro-methyl) styrene	1.35 ± 0.05	60		57
	0.48 ± 0.02	m-Bromostyrene	1.17 ± 0.25	60		323
	0.395 ± 0.02	p-Bromostyrene	1.10 ± 0.25	60		323
	0.25 ± 0.03	Butadiene	0.75 ± 0.05	90		171
	0.06 ± 0.03	Butadiene	0.53 ± 0.05	5	a	324
	0.32	Butadiene	0.70	h		178
	1.33 ± 0.03	N-Butyl maleimide	0.12 ± 0.02	50		56
	1.6 ± 0.2	n-Butyl vinyl ether	0.2 ± 0.1	h		148c
	1.0	2-Chloroallyl acetate	0	50	b,c	147
	4.4	2-Chloroallyl alcohol	0	100	b,c	147
	5.5 ± 0.8	2-Chloroallyl chloride	0.017 ± 0.003	70		15
	0.5	2-Chloroallyl chloride	0	40	b,c	147
	0.080 ± 0.007	2-Chloro-1,3-buta-diene	6.12 ± 0.2	60		68
	2.63 ± 0.2	β-Chloroethyl ita-conate	0.10 ± 0.05	50		213
	0.61	N-(p-Chlorophenyl)-methacrylamide	.24	70		240
	0.47 ± 0.075	m-Chlorostyrene	0.91 ± 0.11	60		323
	0.50 ± 0.03	o-Chlorostyrene	1.37 ± 0.1	60		322
	0.415 ± 0.02	p-Chlorostyrene	0.89 ± 0.05	60		323
	0.4 ± 0.2	p-Chlorostyrene	0.8 ± 0.4	30–40		186
	75.0	Chlorotrifluoro-ethylene	0.005	60		294
	0.7 ± 0.2	4-Chloro-1-vinyl naphthalene	0.7 ± 0.2	60		247
	0.45 ± 0.05	6-Chloro-2-vinyl naphthalene	1.6 ± 0.2	60		247
	0.22 ± 0.02	p-Cyanostyrene	1.41 ± 0.13	60		323

r_1	Monomer	r_2		Temp.	Ref.
4.20	1-Deoxy-1-methacryl-amido-D-glucitol	0.036		50	325a
f	Diallyl germanium	f		h	157
27.8 ± 3.2	Diallyl melamine	0		60	259a
28.9 ± 2.3	Diallyl melamine	0		60	259a
f	Diallyl silicon	f		h	157
f	Diallyl tin	f		h	157
0.8	Di-n-butyl itaconate	0.4		h	54
0.073 ± 0.015	2,3-Dichloro-1,3-butadiene	10.3 ± 1.5		60	68
2.63 ± 0.2	Di-β-chloroethyl itaconate	0.10 ± 0.05		50	213
0.44	2,5-Dichlorostyrene	2.25		68	3
20	Diethyl maleate	0	b,c	60	193
1.4	1,1-Dihydroperfluoro-butyl acrylate	0.25		50	267
0.77	N-(1,1-Dihydroperfluorobutyl)-N-ethyl acrylamide	0.89		66	156
0.205 ± 0.02	p-Dimethylamino-styrene	0.11 ± 0.02		60	323
1.2 ± 1.3	Dimethyl itaconate	0.3		h	54
16.67	Dimethyl meth-acrylamino-diacetate	0.013		70	240
0.37	2,4-Dimethyl-6-vinyl-s-triazine	1.75		60	58a
2.0	N,N-Divinylaniline	0.01		60	51
10.0	Divinyl ether	0.006		60	51
0.85 ± 0.05	Divinyl sulfide	0.13 ± 0.05		60	272
8.5	Divinyl sulfone	0.045		60	51
0.97	Divinyl tartrate	0.04		60	276
Large	Dodecyl vinyl ether	0		h	5

(continued)

(*continued*)

M_1	r_1	M_2	r_2	T, °C.	Remarks	Ref.
Methyl methacrylate	1.65 ± 0.07	Ethyl 1-acetoxy acrylate	0.65 ± 0.05	60		307
	0.77	N-Ethyl-N,1,1-di-hydroperfluoro-butylacrylamide	0.89	66		156
	1.75	N-Ethyl methacryl-amide	0.11	70		240
	1.09	Ethyl methacrylyl-aminoacetate	0.9	70		240
	6.0	Ethyl vinyl oxalate	0.1	60		146a
	0.395 ± 0.003	5-Ethyl-2-vinyl-pyridine	0.69 ± 0.03	60		289
	0.11 ± 0.01	5-Ethyl-2-vinyl-pyridine-N-oxide	5.5 ± 0.5	60	Bulk	292
	0.12 ± 0.02	5-Ethyl-2-vinyl-pyridine-N-oxide	4.7 ± 0.6	60	In solution	292
	1.8	N-Ethyl-N'-vinylurea	0.015	75		116
	2.7 ± 1.5	Ethyl vinyl sulfide	0.3 ± 0.1	60		277
	0.64 ± 0.08	2-Fluorobutadiene	1.54 ± 0.08	50		227
	1.47	N-(m-Fluorosulfonyl-phenyl)acrylamine	0.60	h		117a
	1.24	N-(m-Fluorosulfonyl-phenyl)methacryl-amide	0.71	h		117a
	3.5 ± 0.5	Fumaronitrile	0.01 ± 0.01	79		244
	0.80	Glycidyl meth-acrylate	1.05	60		96
	0.36 ± 0.03	p-Iodostyrene	0.95 ± 0.20	60		323
	30	Isopropenyl acetate	0.017	75		115
	3.10 ± 0.29	Isopropenyl iso-cyanate	0.14 ± 0.10	h		136

0.45 ± 0.03	β-Isopropenylnaphthalene	0.00	99	p	67
1.14	I-aconic acid	0	90		74
1.23	I-aconic acid	0	h		122
6.7 ± 0.2	Maleic anhydride	0.02	75		328
3.5	Maleic anhydride	0.03	60		37
1.5 ± 0.02	Methacrylamide	0.47 ± 0.04	65		59
1.65 ± 0.05	Methacrylamide	0.49 ± 0.02	70		59
0.74	Methacrylonitrile	0.70	80		49
0.67 ± 0.2	Methacrylonitrile	5.2 ± 1.0	−55	c	85
0.67 ± 0.1	Methacrylonitrile	0.65 ± 0.06	60		171
0.68	Methacrylonitrile	0.80	80		337
2.0 ± 0.5	Methacrylonitrile	0.30 ± 0.05	−78	PhMgBr cat.	68a
5.0 ± 0.5	Methacrylonitrile	0.05 ± 0.02	−30	PhMgBr cat.	68a
0.67 ± 0.2	Methacrylonitrile	6.20 ± 1	−50	NaNH₂	68a
0.93 ± 0.1	Methacryloxymethyl-pentamethyl disiloxane	1.13 ± 0.1	50		202
10	Methallyl acetate	0	60	b,c	193
7.7	Methallyl chloride	0	60	b,c	193
0.29 ± 0.03	t-Methoxystyrene	0.32 ± 0.05	60		323
0.29	t-Methoxystyrene	0.32	60		39
<1	Methyl acrylate	>1	20	d	164
0.1 ± 0.1	Methyl acrylate	4.5 ± 0.5	−30	e	164
0.3 ± 0.005	Methyl acrylate	1.5 ± 0.01	65		59
0.3 ± 15%	Methyl 1-chloroacrylate	1.2 ± 15%	70		9
f	Methyl 1-chloroacrylate	f	h		286
1.54	N-Methylmethacrylamide	0.24	70		240

(continued)

(continued)

M_1	r_1	M_2	r_2	T, °C.	Remarks	Ref.
Methyl methacrylate	0.50 ± 0.03	α-Methylstyrene	0.14 ± 0.01	60		322
	0.89 ± 0.03	α-Methylstyrene	-0.01 ± 0.01	99		67
	0.53 ± 0.025	m-Methylstyrene	0.49 ± 0.02	60		323
	0.405 ± 0.025	p-Methylstyrene	0.44 ± 0.02	60		323
	0.46 ± 0.02	2-Methyl-4-vinyl pyridine	0.61 ± 0.08	60		290
	14 ± 2	Methyl vinyl sulfone	0	60	c	65
	20 ± 10	Methyl vinyl sulfoxide	0	60		245
	4.68	N-Methyl-N-vinyl-p-toluene-sulfonamide	0	60		90,91
	0.35 ± 0.05	m-Nitrostyrene	0.85 ± 0.2	75		283
	Large	Octadecyl vinyl ether	0	50		5
	Large	Octyl vinyl ether	0	50		5
	4.0 ± 0.4	Pentachlorostyrene	0.35 ± 0.05	70		11
	0.54	N-Phenyl methacrylamide	0.46	70		240
	2.1 ± 0.3	Poly(1,3-butanediol fumarate)	0.5 ± 0.5	60		283c
	17.5 ± 7.5	Poly(ethylene glycol fumarate)	0.35 ± 0.35	60		100
	0.44 ± 0.02	Styrene	0.50 ± 0.02	35		320
	0.49 ± 0.03	Styrene	0.54 ± 0.03	99		67
		Styrene	$r_1 \ll r_2$	h	Cationic in ethylene chloride	121
	0.1 ± 0.05	Styrene	10.5 ± 0.2	h	Cationic in benzene	121
	0.46 ± 0.026	Styrene	0.52 ± 0.026	60		170
	0.536 ± 0.026	Styrene	0.590 ± 0.026	131		170

0.50 ± 0.02	Styrene	60	0.50 ± 0.02		169, 165
0.1 ± 0.05	Styrene	20	10.5 ± 0.2	SnCl$_4$	165
6.4 ± 0.05	Styrene	−30	0.12 ± 0.05	NaNH$_2$	164, 165
0.44 ± 0.02	Styrene	35	0.50 ± 0.02		319
0.49	Styrene	35	0.56	a	319
0.50 ± 0.02	Styrene	35	0.56 ± 0.02	a	320
0.422	Styrene	30	0.485		28
0.46	Styrene	60	0.48		330
0.55	Styrene	132	0.60		330
0.42 ± 0.1	Styrene	60	0.54 ± 0.04		251a
0.5 ± 0.04	Styrene	60	0.44 ± 0.08		251a
>1	Styrene	−50 to −20	0	PhMgBr in toluene	68a
>1	Styrene	−78	0	PhMg in ether/toluene	68a
25.0 ± 2	Styrene	−30	0.01 ± 0.01	PhMg in ether/toluene	68a
4.5 ± 1	Styrene	20	0.07 ± 0.02	PhMg in ether/toluene	68a
20.0 ± 2	Styrene	−78	0.02 ± 0.01	PhMgBr in ether	68a
14.0 ± 2	Styrene	−30	0.05 ± 0.02	PhMgBr in ether	68a
2.0 ± 0.3	Styrene	20	0.30 ± 0.05	PhMgBr in ether	68a
6.4 ± 0.1	Styrene	−50	0.12 ± 0.05	NaNH$_2$	68a
17.1	Styrene	30	0.31	e	89a
0.39	N-p-Tolylmethacrylamide	70	0.67		240
50.2 ± 7.5	Triallyl cyanurate	60	0		259a
46.3 ± 5.3	Triallyl cyanurate	60	0		259a
48.9 ± 7.3	Triallyl isocyanurate	60	0		259a
45.0 ± 5.1	Triallyl isocyanurate	60	0		259a
8.6	B-Triallyl-N-triphenylborazine	80	0		239b
100	Trichloroethylene	60	0	b,c	193

(continued)

(*continued*)

M₁	r₁	M₂	r₂	T, °C.	Remarks	Ref.
Methyl methacrylate	0.60 ± 0.10	3-Trifluoromethyl-styrene	0.98 ± 0.15	60		57
	0.70	B-Trivinyl-N-triphenyl-yl-borazine	0	80		239b
	20 ± 3	Vinyl acetate	0.015 ± 0.015	60		195
	22.21 ± 0.89	Vinyl acetate	0.072 ± 0.026	60		205
	3.2 ± 1.1	Vinyl acetate	0.4 ± 0.2	−30	e	164
	20 ± 2	Vinyl bromide	0.05 ± 0.015	28	p	38
	25 ± 2	Vinyl bromide	0.05 ± 0.01	0	U.V. initiation	38
	2.0	N-Vinyl carbazole	0.04	75		112
	2.0 ± 0.3	N-Vinyl carbazole	0.20 ± 0.03	70		15
	12.5	Vinyl chloride	0	60	b,c	193
	10	Vinyl chloride	0.1	68		3
	15	Vinyl chloride	0.02	45		302
	70	Vinylidene carbonate	0.005	70		118
	2.7 ± 1.5	Vinyl ethyl sulfide	0.3 ± 0.1	60		277
	1.8	1-Vinyl-3-ethyl urea	0.015	70		116
	2.53 ± 0.01	Vinylidene chloride	0.24 ± 0.03	60		169
	0.046	Vinylidene cyanide	0.031	50		93
	0.046	Vinylidene cyanide	0.031	h		76
	5.57 ± 0.33	Vinyl isocyanate	0.16 ± 0.08	60		137
	3.3	Vinyl isocyanate	0.01	h		325
	0.85 ± 0.03	Vinyl isothiocyanate	0.6 ± 0.02	60		127a
	1.6 ± 0.3	Vinyl mesitylene	0.05 ± 0.01	130		63
	1.4	Vinyl mesitylene	0.08	85		63
	0.4 ± 0.05	2-Vinyl naphthalene	1.0 ± 0.15	60		247
	6.00	N-Vinyloxazolidinone	0.03	75		117
	9.6 ± 0.2	N-Vinyloxazolidinone	0.035	50		40
	0.439 ± 0.002	2-Vinylpyridine	0.77 ± 0.02	60		289
	0.395 ± 0.025	2-Vinylpyridine	0.86 ± 0.06	60		322

Monomer 1	r_1	Monomer 2	r_2	T	Conditions	Ref.
	0.33 ± 15%	2-Vinylpyridine	0.70 ± 15%	70		9
	0.574 ± 0.004	4-Vinylpyridine	0.79 ± 0.05	60		289
	0.13 ± 0.03	2-Vinylpyridine-N-oxide	3.9 ± 0.8	60		292
	4.75	N-Vinylpyridinium fluoroborate	0.008	60		70b
	4.7 ± 0.5	N-Vinyl pyrrolidi-none	0.005 ± 0.05	50		40
	9.5	N-Vinyl succinimide	0.064	60		125
	Large	Vinyl sulfonic acid	0	70		105
Methylolcrotonamide	0.045 ± 0.1	Vinyl acetate	0.01 ± 0.01	110		315
α-Methyl-p-methyl styrene	0.54	Vinyl-2-chloro-ethyl ether	1.7	RT	d, in benzene	180
	0.51	Vinyl-2-chloro-ethyl ether	1.7	RT	d, in benzene	180
	0.64	Vinyl-2-chloro-ethyl ether	1.7	RT	d, in nitrobenzene	180
4-Methyl-1-pentene	3.67 ± 0.22	Styrene	0.89 ± 0.05	45	e	24b
Methylstyrene mixture of o- and p-isomers (ca. 1:2)	0.48 ± 0.06	Ethyl acrylate	0.15 +0.23/−0.13	80		24a
	0.59 ± 0.06	Methyl acrylate	0.15 +0.25/−0.14	80		24a
	0.49 ± 0.06	Octyl acrylate	0.16 +0.16/−0.10	80		24a
α-Methylstyrene	0.1 ± 0.02	Acrylonitrile	0.06 ± 0.02	75	t, see refs. 107, 111	81
	0.010 ± 0.01	Butadiene	1.6 ± 0.5	12.8		78a
	0.25 ± 0.05	p-Chlorostyrene	1.48 ± 0.02	74		281
	28 ± 2	p-Chlorostyrene	0.12 ± 0.03	−78	d	281
	15 ± 1.5	p-Chlorostyrene	0.35 ± 0.05	0	d	231
	15.5 ± 1.5	p-Chlorostyrene	0.35 ± 0.05	0	d	232

(continued)

(continued)

M_1	r_1	M_2	r_2	T, °C.	Remarks	Ref.
α-Methylstyrene	f	p-Chlorostyrene	f	h	e	284
	0.14	2,5-Dichlorostyrene	3	70		18
	0.035 ± 0.015	p-Dimethylamino-styrene	31 ± 19	5	SnCl₄	231
	0.38 ± 0.11	2-Fluorobutadiene	1.71 ± 0.19	50		227
	0.022 ± 0.005	Fumaronitrile	0.00	60		83
	f	Isobutylene	f	−78	d	222
	0.005 ± 0.005	Maleic anhydride	0.27 ± 0.03	60		251a
	0.038 ± 0.003	Maleic anhydride	0.08 ± 0.03	60		251a
	0.12 ± 0.02	Methacrylonitrile	0.35 ± 0.02	80		81
	0.15	Methacrylonitrile	0.21	80		337
	5 ± 1	m-Methoxystyrene	0.3 ± 1	5	SnCl₄	231
	0.30 ± 0.1	p-Methoxystyrene	15 ± 5	5	SnCl₄	231
	0.03	Methyl isopropenyl ketone	1.7	h		337
	0.14 ± 0.01	Methyl methacrylate	0.50 ± 0.03	60		322
	−0.01 ± 0.01	Methyl methacrylate	0.89 ± 0.03	99		67
	2.90	Styrene	0.05	0		174
	0.36	Styrene	1.18 ± 0.04	h	d	98
	0.38	Styrene	2.3			242a
	0.33 ± 0.05	Vinyl-2-chloroethyl ether	5.03 ± 0.06	30	d, in benzene	71,180
	0.34, 0.42	Vinyl-2-chloroethyl ether	2.6, 3.3	RT	d, in nitrobenzene	180
	0.33	Vinyl-2-chloroethyl ether	5.0	RT	SnCl₄ in benzene	24
	0.34	Vinyl-2-chloroethyl ether	2.6	RT	SnCl₄ in nitro-benzene	24

M_1		M_2		RT		Ref.
	0.42	Vinyl-2-chloroethyl ether	3.3	0	$SnCl_4$ in nitrobenzene	24
cis-β-Methylstyrene	0.32 ± 0.02	p-Chlorostyrene	1.0 ± 0.1	0	d	238
trans-β-Methylstyrene	0.32 ± 0.04	p-Chlorostyrene	0.74 ± 0.06	h	d	238
m-Methylstyrene	0.43 ± 0.1	Acrylonitrile	0.07 ± 0.04	60		24
	0.49 ± 0.02	Methyl methacrylate	0.53 ± 0.025	40		323
	0.5 ± 0.1	Styrene	2.0 ± 0.2	h	e	216,279
o-Methylstyrene	0.33 ± 0.1	Acrylonitrile	0.06 ± 0.05	40		24
	0.1 ± 0.1	Styrene	12.1 ± 1	h	e	279
p-Methylstyrene	0.33 ± 0.1	Acrylonitrile	0.05 ± 0.02	60		24
	0.61 ± 0.03	p-Chlorostyrene	1.15 ± 0.05	0		323
	4.5 ± 0.7	p-Chlorostyrene	0.22 ± 0.05	60	d	231
	11.8	N,N-Divinylaniline	0.05	0		51
	0.52 ± 0.06	p-Methoxystyrene	1.54 ± 0.10	60	d, ($TiCl_4$–ϕNO_2)	303
	−0.03 ± 0.07	p-Methoxystyrene	3.7 ± 0.40	0	d, ($TiCl_4$–CCl_4)	303
	0.14 ± 0.14	p-Methoxystyrene	1.9 ± 0.3	0	d, ($SnCl_4$–ϕNO_2–CCl_4)	303
	2.2 ± 0.1	p-Methoxystyrene	0.68 ± 0.06	0	e, (Na in THF)	303
	1.93 ± 0.03	p-Methoxystyrene	0.72 ± 0.02	0	e, (Li in THF)	303
	0.44 ± 0.02	Methyl methacrylate	0.405 ± 0.025	60		323
	1.15 ± 0.05	Styrene	0.82 ± 0.1	40	e	216
	1 ± 0.12	Styrene	1 ± 0.12	70	e	230
	1.15 ± 1.18	Styrene	0.90 ± 0.08	h	e	279
	0.96	Styrene	0.83	63		329
	3.6 ± 0.1	Styrene	0.54 ± 0.04	0	d, $TiCl_4$ in $PhCH_3$	303
	1.18 ± 0.08	Styrene	0.55 ± 0.06	−78	d, $TiCl_4$ in $PhCH_3$	303
	1.08 ± 0.14	Styrene	0.32 ± 0.10	0	d, $TiCl_4$ in CCl_4	303
	1.10 ± 0.05	Styrene	0.68 ± 0.04	0	d, $TiCl_4$ in $PhNO_2$	303
	1.18 ± 0.14	Styrene	0.48 ± 0.07	0	d, $SnCl_4$ in $PhNO_2$ and CCl_4	303

(continued)

(continued)

M_1	r_1	M_2	r_2	T, °C.	Remarks	Ref.
p-Methylstyrene	0.38 ± 0.09	Styrene	1.97 ± 0.10	0	e, Na in THF	303
	0.91 ± 0.11	Styrene	1.30 ± 0.15	0	e, Li in THF	303
	0.26 ± 0.03	Styrene	2.5 ± 0.1	0	e, BuLi in THF	303
Methyl thiolacrylate	0.20 ± 0.05	Butadiene	0.35 ± 0.01	70		181
Methyl vinyl ketone	1.78 ± 0.22	Acrylonitrile	0.61 ± 0.04	60		171
	1.6 ± 0.1	Butyl acrylate	0.65 ± 0.07	50		58
	0.26 ± 0.04	4,6-Diamino-2-vinyl-s-triazine	1.2 ± 0.15	60		237
	0.5	2,5-Dichlorostyrene	2.0	70		8
	0.35 ± 0.02	Styrene	0.29 ± 0.04	60		171
	7.00	Vinyl acetate	0.05	70		105
	8.3	Vinyl chloride	0.10	70		8
	1.8	Vinylidene chloride	0.55	70		8
2-Methyl-5-vinyl-pyridine	0.01 ± 0.09	Acrylamide	0.56 ± 0.09	60		24a
	0.27 ± 0.04	Acrylonitrile	0.116 ± 0.003	60		290
	1.10 ± 0.2	Acrylonitrile	0.10 ± 0.05	h		335
	0.72 ± 0.03	Butadiene	1.32 ± 0.01	h		305
	0.88 ± 0.10	Methyl acrylate	0.172 ± 0.007	60		290
	0.61 ± 0.08	Methyl methacrylate	0.46 ± 0.02	60		290
	2.9 ± 0.3	Styrene	0.5 ± 0.1	70	e, AlEt$_3$–TiCl$_4$	266
	0.68 ± 0.1	Styrene	0.6 ± 0.1	70		266
	2.9 ± 0.3	Styrene	0.3 ± 0.1	70	e, AlEt$_3$–TiCl$_4$	266
	0.91 ± 0.02	Styrene	0.812 ± 0.005	60		290
	1.19 ± 0.12	Styrene	0.88 ± 0.2	60		229a
Methyl vinyl sulfide	0.05 ± 0.03	Methyl acrylate	0.35 ± 0.04	60		251
	0.12 ± 0.05	Styrene	5.1 ± 1.0	60		251

M₁	r_1	M₂	r_2	Temp.		Ref.
Methyl vinyl sulfone	0.15	Styrene	4.5	60		249
	10.6 ± 1.2	Vinylene carbonate	0.50 ± 0.04	60		145
	0	Methyl methacrylate	14 ± 2	60	c	65
	0.01 ± 0.01	Styrene	2.0 ± 0.5	60		251
	0.01 ± 0.01	Styrene	3.3	60		249
	0.0 ± 0.02	Styrene	2.4 ± 0.10	60		65
	0.01	Styrene	1.40	60		251
	0.35	Vinyl acetate	0.29	60		251
	0.4 ± 0.08	Vinyl acetate	0.0 ± 0.01	60		65
Methyl vinyl sulfoxide	0	Methyl methacrylate	20 ± 10	60		245
	0.01 ± 0.01	Styrene	4.2 ± 0.2	60		245
N-Methyl-N-vinyl-p-toluene sulfonamide	0	Acrylonitrile	0.42	60		90,91
	0	Methyl methacrylate	4.68	60		90,91
	0	Styrene	12.3	60		90,91
Monoethyl fumarate	0.25 ± 0.10	Styrene	0.18 ± 0.1	60		168
Monoethyl maleate	0.035 ± 0.01	Styrene	0.13 ± 0.1	60		168
Monomethyl maleate	0.0 ± 0.007	Vinyl acetate	0.09 ± 0.005	60		334
	0.015 ± 0.01	Vinyl acetate	0.13 ± 0.03	75		334
	0.4747	Vinyl acetate	0.04681	56		311,312
	0.522	Vinyl acetate	0.0345	65		311
	0.99959	Vinyl acetate	0.1168	78		311
N-Naphthyl methacrylamide	f	Acrylonitrile	f	70		6
N-p-Nitrophenyl methacrylamide	f	Acrylonitrile	f	70		6
m-Nitrostyrene	1.3 ± 0.1	p-Chlorostyrene	0.25 ± 0.05	75		283
	0.85 ± 0.2	Methyl methacrylate	0.35 ± 0.05	75		283

(continued)

(continued)

M_1	r_1	M_2	r_2	T, °C.	Remarks	Ref.
m-Nitrostyrene	0.03 ± 0.03	Styrene	20 ± 4	0	SnCl$_4$	231
	0.85 ± 0.1	Styrene	0.45 ± 0.05	75	Corrected for m-nitrostyrene consumed in termination	283
p-Nitrostyrene	0.91 ± 0.37	p-Chlorostyrene	0.70 ± 0.08	60		323
	1.15 ± 0.20	Styrene	0.19 ± 0.02	60		323
Nonyl methacrylate	0.32	Butadiene	0.76	h		178
Octadecyl acrylate	0.68 ± 0.18	Acrylonitrile	1.74 ± 0.04	60		141
	f	Acrylonitrile	f	50		5
	1.2 ± 0.1	Acrylonitrile	4.1 ± 0.8	60		291
	1.01 ± 0.01	Vinylidene chloride	0.91 ± 0.05	60		141
Octadecyl methacrylate	1.13	Methacrylonitrile	0.90	80		49
Octadecyl vinyl ether	0	Methyl methacrylate	Large	50		5
	2.67 ± 0.06	Vinyl-2-chloroethyl ether	0.21 ± 0.06	30	d	71
Octyl acrylate	0.0 ± 0.3	Vinylidene chloride	1.50 ± 0.15	50		4
	0.83 ± 0.23	Acrylonitrile	1.93 ± 0.08	60		153
	f	Acrylonitrile	f	50		5
	$0.16 ^{+0.16}_{-0.10}$	Methylstyrene [mixture of o- and p-isomers (1:2)]	0.49 ± 0.06	80		24a

Monomer	r_1	Comonomer	r_2	Temp	Ref.
	4.8	Vinyl chloride	0.12	45	301
Octyl methacrylate	0.70 ± 0.01	Vinylidene chloride	0.87 ± 0.02	60	141
n-Octyl methacrylate	14.0	Vinyl chloride	0.04	45	302
Octyl vinyl ether	0.58	Methacrylonitrile	0.75	80	49
	0	Methyl methacrylate	Large	50	5
α-Oleostearic acid	0.0 ± 0.2	Vinylidene chloride	1.35 ± 0.15	50	4
	4	Styrene	0.46	h	260
Pentachlorophenyl vinyl sulfide	0.25	Methyl acrylate	0.89	80	124
	0.24	Vinyl sulfide styrene	3.9	80	124
Pentachlorostyrene	0.35 ± 0.05	Methyl methacrylate	4.0 ± 0.4	70	11
	0.10 ± 0.02	Styrene	1.31 ± 0.2	70	11
	5.3	Vinyl chloride	0.43	h	299
1-Pentene	—	Vinyl chloride	0.5	68	3
Phenylacetylene	0.33 ± 0.05	Acrylonitrile	0.26 ± 0.03	60	66
	0.27 ± 0.04	Methyl acrylate	0.62 ± 0.02	60	66
	1.4	Vinylidene chloride	0.1	60	65
	0.2 ± 0.05	2-Vinyl pyridine	4.0 ± 0.07	60	246
4-Phenyl-1,3-dioxane	0	1,3,5-Trioxane	9 ± 2	35	148a
N-Phenylmethacryl-amide	f	Acrylonitrile	f	70	6
	0.46	Methyl methacrylate	0.54	70	240
Phenyl vinyl sulfide	0.05 ± 0.02	Methyl acrylate	0.40	60	249
	0.15	Styrene	4.5	60	249
Phenyl vinyl sulfone	0.01 ± 0.01	Styrene	3.3	60	249
	0.35	Vinyl acetate	0.28	60	249
Piperylene	—	Isoprene	17 ± 5	50 e	254

(continued)

(continued)

M_1	r_1	M_2	r_2	T, °C.	Remarks	Ref.
Poly(1,3-butylene glycol fumarate)	1.12 ± 0.40	Acrylonitrile	1.03 ± 0.2	60		283c
	9.25 ± 3.00	Allyl diethylphosphinic acid	0.12 ± 0.008	h		192
	10.00 ± 2.00	Allyl diethylphosphonate	0.075 ± 0.075	80		191
	5.50 ± 2.50	Allyl ethyl hydrogen phosphite	0.035 ± 0.035	80		191
	0	n-Amyl vinyl ether	0	60		283b
	1.8 ± 0.5	n-Butyl vinyl ether	0	60		283b
	9.22 ± 3.00	Diethyl allylphosphonate	0.12 ± 0.008	h		192
	3.8 ± 0.7	Isoamyl vinyl ether	0	60		283b
	2.0 ± 0.7	Isobutyl vinyl ether	0	60		283b
	0.5 ± 0.5	Methyl methacrylate	2.1 ± 0.3	60		283c
	1.6 ± 0.5	n-Propyl vinyl ether	0	60		283b
	0.03 ± 0.03	Styrene	3.0 ± 0.4	60		304
	0.2 ± 0.2	Vinyl acetate	0.15 ± 0.07	60		283c
Poly(dimethylsiloxy ethylene fumarate)	0.6 ± 0.3	Styrene	0.03 ± 0.03	h		47a
Poly(ethylene glycol fumarate)	1.73 ± 0.03	Allyl diethyl phosphinate	0.15 ± 0.06	h	g	191
	2.07 ± 1.12	Diethyl allyl phosphinic acid	0.09 ± 0.95	h	g	191
	0.35 ± 0.35	Methyl methacrylate	17.5 ± 7.5	60		100
	0.2 ± 0.1	Vinyl acetate	0.020 ± 0.02	60		283c

Monomer 1	r_1	Monomer 2	r_2	Temp.	Catalyst/notes	Ref.
Poly(ethyleneglycol fumarate phosphinate)	2.07 ± 1.12	Allyl diethyl-phosphinic acid	0.09 ± 0.05	h		191
Potassium styrene sulfonate	1.5 ± 0.4	Acrylonitrile	0.07 ± 0.02	70	m	101
p-Potassium styrene-sulfonate	0.54	Styrene	−0.06	90		332
	0.93	Styrene	0.02	110		332
Potassium p-vinyl-benzenesulfonate	0.56	Styrene	0	90		332
	0.93	Styrene	0.02	110		332
Propenyl triethoxy silane	0	Acrylonitrile	20.0	50		296
	0	Vinyl chloride	8.0	50		296
n-Propyl acrylate	7.56 ± 0.10	Allyl chloride	0.091 ± 0.013	60		144
n-Propyl crotonate	0	Vinylidene chloride	20	70		69
	f	1-Butene	f	h		198
Propylene	0.145	Ethylene	5.61	75	e, VCl_3–$Al(C_6H_{13})_3$	218
	0.088 ± 0.003	Ethylene	7.08 ± 0.20	25	e, VCl_4–$Al(C_6H_{13})_3$	196
	0.065 ± 0.002	Ethylene	17.95 ± 0.27	25	e, $VOCl_3$–$Al(C_6H_{13})_3$	197
	0.065	Ethylene	17.8	25	e, $VOCl_3$–$Al(C_6H_{13})_3$	197

(continued)

(continued)

M_1	r_1	M_2	r_2	T, °C.	Remarks	Ref.
Propylene	0.032	Ethylene	33.4	25	e, $TiCl_4$,–$Al(C_6H_{13})_3$	220
	0.110	Ethylene	15.7	75	e, $TiCl_3$–$Al(C_6H_{13})_3$	220
	0.110	Ethylene	15.7	75	e, $TiCl_2$–$Al(C_6H_{13})_3$	220
	0.04	Ethylene	15.0	−20	e, Vanadium tri-acetyl ace-tonate–$AlEt_2Cl$	219
	0.25 ± 0.02	Ethylene	4.7 ± 0.6	20–60	Vanadyl com-pounds (VOX_n) activated by ex-cess aluminium alkyl halides	285a
	0.043 ± 0.006	Ethylene	23 ± 3	30	Vanadyl com-pounds (VOX_n) activated by excess aluminium alkyl halides	285a
	0.23	Isoprene	0.50	−78	d	129
	0.6 ± 0.05	Epichlorohydrin	1.8 ± 0.3	h	d	128
Propylene oxide	73.3 ± 7.4	Vinyl acetate	0.186 ± 0.038	60		205
Propyl methacrylate	52.0 ± 3.2	Allyl chloride	0.067 ± 0.027	60		144
n-Propyl meth-acrylate	0.79	Methacrylonitrile	0.29	80		49

				0	Sufficient data for calc. given but r_1 and r_2 not quoted	
β-n-Propyl styrene	—	p-Chlorostyrene	—			238
n-Propyl vinyl ether	0	Poly(1,3-butylene glycol fumarate)	1.6 ± 0.5	60		283b
3-Pyridalacetophenone	0.00 ± 0.25	Styrene	0.50 ± 0.10	60		189
trans-1,2-bis-(2-Pyridyl)-ethylene	0.02 ± 0.05	Acrylonitrile	0.95 ± 0.05	50		190
	0.17 ± 0.1	Styrene	1.85 ± 0.1	50		190
Sodium acrylate	0.35 ± 0.03	Acrylamide	1.10 ± 0.05	70		42
	0.77	Acrylonitrile	0.21	50	j	132
	1.5	Ethyl acrylate	5.7	50	j	133
	5.8	Sodium ethylene sulfonate	0	60		46
Sodium ethylene sulfonate	0.34 ± 0.23	Sodium styrene sulfonate	2.3 ± 1.2	40	m	101
	2	Vinyl acetate	0.01	60		42
Sodium methacrylate	0	Acrylamide	14.9	50		46
	0	Sodium acrylate	5.8	60		46
	0.08 ± 0.015	Diethylaminoethyl methacrylate	0.65 ± 0.03	70		22
Sodium styrene sulfonate	1.0 ± 0.2	Acrylic acid	0.10 ± 0.02	70		101
	1.5 ± 0.2	Acrylonitrile	0.05 ± 0.02	40	m	101
	2.3 ± 1.2	Sodium acrylate	0.34 ± 0.23	40	m	101
Stilbene	0.03 ± 0.03	Maleic anhydride	0.03 ± 0.03	60		168
	0	Styrene	11.2 ± 1.2	60	c	50

(continued)

(*continued*)

M_1	r_1	M_2	r_2	T, °C.	Remarks	Ref.
Styrene	3.81	Acenaphthylene	0.33	90		306
	0.19 ± 0.056	α-Acetoxyacrylonitrile	0.20 ± 0.052	60		337
	—	Aconitic acid	—	60	n	228
	2.72	1-Acrylamido-1-deoxy-D-glucitol	0.056	50		325a
	0.22	Acrylic acid	0.35	70		99
	0.15 ± 0.01	Acrylic acid	0.25 ± 0.02	60		53
	0.25 ± 0.05	Acrylic acid	0.45 ± 0.1	80		337
	0.25	Acrylic acid	0.15	h		242a
	0.41 ± 0.08	Acrylonitrile	0.04 ± 0.04	60		169
	0.41 ± 0.08	Acrylonitrile	0.03 ± 0.03	75		80
	0.37 ± 0.03	Acrylonitrile	0.07 ± 0.006	50		297
	0.37 ± 0.02	Acrylonitrile	0.05 ± 0.02	50		119
	0.40 ± 0.05	Acrylonitrile	0.04 ± 0.04	60		66
	0.52 ± 0.04	Acrylonitrile	0.03 ± 0.03	67–80	a	79
	0.38 ± 0.03	Acrylonitrile	0.05 ± 0.02	41.5		97
	0.45 ± 0.03	Acrylonitrile	0.02 ± 0.02	65		97
	0.47 ± 0.03	Acrylonitrile	0.02 ± 0.02	86.5		97
	—	Acrylonitrile	—	75	n	107
	0.3 ± 0.08	Acrylonitrile	0.02 ± 0.02	40	e	31
	0.39 ± 0.02	Acrylonitrile	0.06 ± 0.01	99		67
	0.33 ± 0.03	Acrylonitrile	0.00 ± 0.02	50	a	171
	f	C_8–C_{18} Alkyl vinyl ethers	f			5
	90 ± 10	Allyl acetate	0.00	50		193
	31.5 ± 4	Allyl chloride	0.016 ± 0.016	70		14

r_1	Monomer	r_2	Temp. (°C)	Note	Ref.
36.8 ± 0.60	Allyl chloride	0.029 ± 0.006	60		144
0.24 ± 0.01	N-Benzylidene-4-methacryloxyaniline				
0.55 ± 0.03	m-Bromostyrene	0.25 ± 0.05	60		257
0.695 ± 0.02	p-Bromostyrene	1.05 ± 0.21	60		323
0.71 ± 0.02	p-Bromostyrene	0.99 ± 0.07	60		323
1.75 ± 0.1	p-Bromostyrene	1.05 ± 0.05	60		148b
37.5 ± 2.0	2-Bromovinyl ethyl ether	0.55 ± 0.1	40	e	279
0.78 ± 0.01	Butadiene	0.02 ± 0.02	80		250
0.23 ± 0.07	Butadiene	1.39 ± 0.03	60		171
0.5 ± 0.1	Butadiene	1.48 ± 0.08	50		119
0.68	Butadiene	1.4 ± 0.2	50	a	200
0.6 ± 0.1	Butadiene	0.50	25	s	242b
0.64	Butadiene	1.8 ± 0.4	45	a	206
0.38	Butadiene	138	5	a	94,225
0.65	Butadiene	1.37	−18	a	94,225
	Butadiene	1.83	45		94,225
0.05	Butadiene	20	50	e	158
0.58 ± 0.15	Butadiene	1.35 ± 0.12	50		120
0.44	Butadiene	1.40	5		224
0.38 ± 0.03	Butadiene	1.40 ± 0.08	5	a	224
0.44 ± 0.03	Butadiene	1.59 ± 0.05	50		120
0.01 ± 0.01	Butadiene	1.30 ± 0.1	43	a	30
0.65 ± 0.16	Butadiene	1.83 ± 0.32	45	a	206
0.48 ± 0.04	Butyl acrylate	0.15 ± 0.04	25		27

(continued)

(continued)

M_1	r_1	M_2	r_2	T, °C.	Remarks	Ref.
Styrene	0.76	Butyl acrylate	0.15	60	0.00 mole-fraction benzene as solvent	53
	0.68	Butyl acrylate	0.19	60	0.60 mole-fraction benzene as solvent	43
	0.64	Butyl acrylate	0.19	60	0.90 mole-fraction benzene as solvent	43
	1.03	Butyl acrylate	0.34	60	0.975 mole-fraction benzene as solvent (benzene here enters into polymer)	43
	0.87	n-Butyl cinnamate	0.10	80		337
	0.025 ± 0.025	n-Butylmaleimide	0.06 ± 0.02	50		56
	0.97	n-Butyl methacrylate	0.67	30		48
	0.63	n-Butyl methacrylate	0.64	50		316
	0.54	n-Butyl methacrylate	0.64	70		316
	2.5 ± 1.0	n-Butyl vinyl sulfonate	0.13 ± 0.03	90		233
	4.10	2-Chloroallyl acetate	0	50		147
	12.5	2-Chloroallyl alcohol	0	40		147
	5.0 ± 15%	2-Chloroallyl chloride	0.06 ± 15%	70		15
	2.5	2-Chloroallyl chloride	0	40		147
	0.05 ± 0.02	2-Chloro-1,3-butadiene	7 ± 2	70		12

2-Chloro-1,3-butadiene	5.22 ± 0.64	0.00	50	a	120
2-Chloro-1,3-butadiene	6.3 ± 0.1	0.00	50		120
2-Chloro-1,3-butadiene	0.24	15.6	−18	d	84
2-Chloro-1,3-butadiene	8.11 ± 0.34	0.052 ± 0.01	60		65
2-Chloroethyl acrylate	0.08 ± 0.01	0.59 ± 0.03	60		65
2-Chloroethyl acrylate	0.10 ± 0.01	0.54 ± 0.01	60		171
2-Chloroethylitaconate	0.5 ± 0.05	0	50		213
α-Chloro-β-fluorostyrene	0.55	2.1	60		91a
Chloromethylstyrenes	f	f	h		70
m-Chlorostyrene	1.09 ± 0.23	0.64 ± 0.05	60		323
m-Chlorostyrene	0.3 ± 0.05	3.3 ± 0.4	0	SnCl$_4$	231
o-Chlorostyrene	1.6 ± 0.07	0.56 ± 0.03	60		322
p-Chlorostyrene	1.025 ± 0.05	0.74 ± 0.025	60		170
p-Chlorostyrene	1.042 ± 0.05	0.816 ± 0.03	131		170
p-Chlorostyrene	0.35 ± 0.02	2.10 ± 0.2	0	In CCl$_4$–PhNO$_2$ with SnCl$_4$	232
p-Chlorostyrene	0.30 ± 0.03	2.5 ± 0.4	0	In CCl$_4$ soln. with SnCl$_4$	231,232
p-Chlorostyrene	0.45 ± 0.02	2.2 ± 0.2	0	SnCl$_4$ nitrobenzene	235
p-Chlorostyrene	0.45 ± 0.02	2.2 ± 0.2	0	TiCl$_4$ nitrobenzene	235
p-Chlorostyrene	0.36 ± 0.05	2.3 ± 0.4	0	AlBr$_3$ nitrobenzene-CCl$_4$	235

(continued)

(*continued*)

M₁	r_1	M₂	r_2	T, °C.	Remarks	Ref.
Styrene	2.2 ± 0.2	p-Chlorostyrene	0.45 ± 0.02	0	TiCl$_4$ nitrobenzene–CCl$_4$ (1:1)	235
	2.0 ± 0.2	p-Chlorostyrene	0.34 ± 0.05	0	AlBr$_3$ nitrobenzene–CCl$_4$ (1:1)	235
	1.7 ± 0.2	p-Chlorostyrene	0.55 ± 0.05	0	SbCl$_5$ nitrobenzene–CCl$_4$ (1:1)	235
	2.0 ± 0.1	p-Chlorostyrene	0.43 ± 0.03	0	FeCl$_3$ nitrobenzene–CCl$_4$ (1:4)	235
	2.0 ± 0.4	p-Chlorostyrene	0.50 ± 0.05	0	TiCl$_4$–CCl$_3$COOH	235
	1.51 ± 0.03	p-Chlorostyrene	0.40 ± 0.02	0	AlBr$_3$–CCl$_4$	235
	2.2 ± 0.2	p-Chlorostyrene	0.5 ± 0.1	40	e	216,279
	f	p-Chlorostyrene	f	h	e	284
	2.7 ± 0.3	p-Chlorostyrene	0.35 ± 0.05	30	d	23
	0.742 ± 0.030	p-Chlorostyrene	1.032 ± 0.030	60		171
	7.0	Chlorotrifluoroethylene	0.001	60		294
	0.85 ± 0.1	4-Chloro-1-vinylnaphthalene	0.8 ± 0.1	60		247
	0.4 ± 0.1	6-Chloro-2-vinylnaphthalene	1.5 ± 0.2	60		247
	0.9 ± 0.2	Cinnamonitrile	0.1 ± 0.1	90		41
	0.85 ± 0.05	3-Cinnamoyl pyridine	0.09 ± 0.10	50	p	189
	0.15 ± 0.02	Citraconic anhydride	0.01 ± 0.01	60		53
	20	Crotonic acid	0	60		65
	8.5 ± 5.6	γ-Crotonolactone	0	60		145
	0.28 ± 0.025	p-Cyanostyrene	1.16 ± 0.13	60		323
	2.09	1-Deoxy-1-methacrylamido-D-glucitol	0.005	50		325a

r_1	Monomer	r_2	Temp		Ref.
f	Diallyl germanium	f	h		157
103.0 ± 11.8	Diallyl melamine	0	60		259a
102.3 ± 15.1	Diallyl melamine	0	60		259a
f	Diallyl silicon	f	h		157
f	Diallyl tin	f	h		157
0.55 ± 0.2	Dibenzyl maleate	0.02 ± 0.01	70		266a
0.041 ± 0.012	2,3-Dichloro-1,3-butadiene	10.8 ± 1.2	60		65
1.6	1,1-Dichloro-2,2-difluoroethylene	0	60		199
210 ± 15	cis-Dichloroethylene	0	45	a	168
75 ± 25	cis-Dichloroethylene	0	60	c	13
47.5	cis-Dichloroethylene	0	68		45
56.1	cis-Dichloroethylene	0	90		45
72.5	cis-Dichloroethylene	0	50		45
37 ± 3	trans-Dichloroethylene	0	90		168
~10	trans-Dichloroethylene	0	60	c	13
44.4	trans-Dichloroethylene	0	68		45
44.9	trans-Dichloroethylene	0	50		45
29.8	trans-Dichloroethylene	0	50		45
25.9	trans-Dichloroethylene	0	90		45
0.50 ± 0.05	Di-β-chloroethyl itaconate	0	90		213

| | | | | 50 | |

(continued)

(*continued*)

M₁	r_1	M₂	r_2	T, °C.	Remarks	Ref.
Styrene	0.2	2,5-Dichlorostyrene	0.8	70		20
	14.8 ± 2	2,5-Dichlorostyrene	0.34 ± 0.2	30	d	75
	0.29	2,5-Dichlorostyrene	2.2	70		123
	0.30	2,5-Dichlorostyrene	1.8	70		123
	0.23	2,5-Dichlorostyrene	2.2	70		123
	0.31	2,5-Dichlorostyrene	1.9	70		123
	0.18 ± 0.07	2,5-Dichlorostyrene	0.25 ± 0.09	41.5		91
	0.32 ± 0.06	2,5-Dichlorostyrene	0.08 ± 0.05	65		97
	0.40 ± 0.03	2,5-Dichlorostyrene	0.05 ± 0.03	86.5		97
	3.1 ± 0.1	3,4-Dichlorostyrene	0.48 ± 0.08	0	d, AlCl₃	75a
	2.8 ± 0.2	3,4-Dichlorostyrene	0.45 ± 0.10	0	d, AlBr₃	75a
	6.8 ± 0.8	3,4-Dichlorostyrene	0.0 ± 0.2	0	d, TiCl₄	75a
	7.2 ± 0.5	3,4-Dichlorostyrene	0.38 ± 0.20	0	d, BF₃	75a
	5.9 ± 0.2	3,4-Dichlorostyrene	0.27 ± 0.07	30	d, ZnCl₂	75a
	4.2 ± 0.2	3,4-Dichlorostyrene	0.10 ± 0.05	0	H₂SO₄	75a
	3.0 ± 0.5	3,4-Dichlorostyrene	0.20 ± 0.15	0	AlCl₃	75a
	3.5 ± 0.5	3,4-Dichlorostyrene	0.0 ± 0.2	0	AlCl₃	75a
	2.5	Diethyl chloromaleate	0	70		20
	0.30 ± 0.02	Diethyl fumarate	0.070 ± 0.007	60		170
	0.400 ± 0.02	Diethyl fumarate	0.0905 ± 0.007	131		170
	0.301 ± 0.024	Diethyl fumarate	0.0697 ± 0.0041	60		170
	5 ± 1.5	Diethyl maleate	0.0 ± 0.1	70		20
	6.52 ± 0.50	Diethyl maleate	0.005 ± 0.01	60		170
	5.48 ± 0.56	Diethyl maleate	0	131	c	170
	6.52 ± 0.05	Diethyl maleate	<0.01	60		171
	3.25	Diethyl vinyl phos-phonate	0	116		25

r₁	Monomer	r₂	T, °C		Ref.
8.87 ± 0.4	Diethyl vinyl phosphonate	0.06 ± 0.02	h		305a
1.05	2,4-Difluorostyrene	0.75	60		91a
2.42	α,β-Difluorostyrene	0.04	60		91a
10.4	β,β-Difluorostyrene	0	60		91a
0.33	1,1-Dihydroperfluorobutylacrylate	0.07	50		267
1.015 ± 0.06	p-(Dimethylamino)styrene	0.84 ± 0.05			323
0.35 ± 0.02	2-N,N-Dimethylamino-4-vinyl pyridine	1.4 ± 0.1	60		237
0.42 ± 0.02	Dimethylbutadiene	0.92 ± 0.02	60		226
0.098 ± 0.013	Dimethyl dithiolfumarate	0.0163 ± 0.013	-18	f	185
0.21 ± 0.02	Dimethyl fumarate	0.025 ± 0.015	50		168
0.48	Dimethyl itaconate	0.14	60		54
8.5 ± 0.2	Dimethyl maleate	0.03 ± 0.01	h		168
0.12	2,4-Dimethyl-6-vinyl-s-triazine	0.92	60		58a
13.0	N,N-Divinylaniline	0.45	60		51
0.65	m-Divinylbenzene	0.60	60		331
40	Divinyl ether	0.02	60		51
1.90 ± 0.1	Divinyl sulfide	0.41 ± 0.05	60		272
1.3	Divinyl sulfone	0.01	60		51
2.62	1,4-Divinyl-2,3,5,6-tetrachlorobenzene	—	49.2	g	259
0.57 ± 0.05	Ethyl 1-acetoxyacrylate	0.20 ± 0.05	60		307
0.18 ± 0.1	Ethyl acid fumarate	0.25 ± 0.10	60		151

(continued)

(continued)

M₁	r_1	M₂	r_2	T, °C.	Remarks	Ref.
Styrene	0.13 ± 0.01	Ethyl acid maleate	0.035 ± 0.01	60		168
	0.79	Ethyl acrylate	0.19	50		316
	0.80	Ethyl acrylate	0.20	70		316
	0.80	Ethyl acrylate	0.48	80		337
	0.6	Ethylene glycol di-chloroacrylate	0.1	h		283c
	0.35	Ethylene glycol di-methacrylate	0.65	60	g	331
	23.5 ± 1	Ethyl 2-ethoxy-acrylate	~ 0	80		250
	0.67	Ethyl methacrylate	0.26	50		316
	0.65	Ethyl methacrylate	0.29	70		316
	1.0 ± 0.2	p-Ethylstyrene	1.0 ± 0.2	40	e	216
	0.95 ± 1	p-Ethylstyrene	1.05 ± 0.1	40	e	279
	80 ± 40	Ethyl vinyl ether	0	80		250
	90 ± 20	Ethyl vinyl ether	0	60		171
	8.0	Ethyl vinyl oxalate	0.1	60		146a
	0.79 ± 0.03	5-Ethyl-2-vinyl py-ridine	1.2 ± 0.2	60		289
	0.10 ± 0.01	5-Ethyl-2-vinyl py-ridine-N-oxide	2.6 ± 0.3	60		292
	6.0 ± 1.5	Ethyl vinyl sulfide	0.25 ± 0.1	h		277
	20.0	N-Ethyl-N'-vinylurea	0.020	75		116
	0.16 ± 0.08	2-Fluorobutadiene	1.61 ± 0.24	5		227
	0.50 ± 0.10	2-Fluorobutadiene	1.55 ± 0.10	50	a	226
	5.95	β-Fluorostyrene	0.01	60		91a
	1.5 ± 0.2	p-Fluorostyrene	0.7 ± 0.1	40	e	216

1.5 ± 0.1	p-Fluorostyrene	0.60 ± 0.1	40	e	279
0.7	p-Fluorostyrene	0.9	60		91a
0.63	N-(m-Fluorosulfonyl-phenyl)acrylamide	0.24	h		117a
0.56	p-Fluoro-α-trifluoro-methylstyrene		60		91a
0.3 ± 0.3	Fumaronitrile	0	50–70	t, see refs. 35,110	210
0.09 ± 0.005	Fumaronitrile	0.00	79		83
0.23 ± 0.01	Fumaronitrile	0.01 ± 0.01	60		244
0.19 ± 0.03	Fumaronitrile	0	60		168
0.30 ± 0.02	Fumaronitrile	0.00 ± 0.02	49.65		258
0.04	Fumaryl chloride	0.00	27		105
0.60	Glycidyl acrylate	0.17	60		134
0.53 ± 0.07	Glycidyl methacrylate	0.44 ± 0.001	60		135
0.34 ± 0.05	Glycidyl methacrylate	0.63 ± 0.1	65		280
Very large	Hexachlorobutadiene	0	70		9
0.66 ± 0.1	Hydronopyl acrylate	0.29 ± 0.1	50		187
0.45 ± 0.02	p-Iodostyrene	1.03 ± 0.05	50		43b
0.62 ± 0.05	p-Iodostyrene	1.09 ± 0.30	60		323
0.24 ± 0.02	Isobutylene	1.79 ± 0.02	−90	AlCl₃ (0.14 g./100 ml. MeCl) with laminar agitation	255
0.42 ± 0.02	Isobutylene	1.66 ± 0.02	−90	AlCl₃ (0.50 g./100 ml. MeCl) with laminar agitation	255

(continued)

(*continued*)

M_1	r_1	M_2	r_2	T, °C.	Remarks	Ref.
Styrene	0.76 ± 0.13	Isobutylene	2.36 ± 0.06	-30	AlCl₃ (0.14 g./100 ml. MeCl) with laminar agitation	255
	1.21 ± 0.06	Isobutylene	2.51 ± 0.05	-30	AlCl₃ (0.50 g./100 ml. MeCl) with laminar agitation	255
	1.99 ± 0.24	Isobutylene	9.02 ± 0.77	-91 to -94	AlCl₃ (0.02 g./100 ml. MeCl) with turbulent agitation	255
	0.17	Isobutylene	1.60	0	d	174
	f	Isobutylene	f	-78	d	222
	1.38 ± 0.54	Isoprene	2.05 ± 0.45	50		120
	0.8 ± 0.00	Isoprene	1.68 ± 0.00	50	a	120
	0.25	Isoprene	9.5	h	e, in toluene	285
	0.8	Isoprene	1	h	e, in tolueneamine mixture	285
	0.48	Isoprene	1.30	-18	a	94, 226
	0.4	Isoprene	2.0	h		344
	0.44	Isoprene	1.98	h		344
	2.2	Isoprene	0.27	75	e	342a
	7.0	Isopropenylisocyanate	0.14	60		114
	8.12	Isopropenylisocyanate	0.07 ± 0.00	h		136
	0.3	Itaconic acid	0.2	70		82
	0.34	Itaconic acid	0	h		122

0.10	Itaconic anhydride	0.60	65		70a
0.01	Maleic anhydride	0	60	t, see ref. 35	193
0.042 ± 0.008	Maleic anhydride	0	80		17
0.02	Maleic anhydride	0	60		33
0.19 ± 0.01	Maleonitrile	0	60		168
0.15 ± 0.01	Methacrylic acid	0.7 ± 0.05	60		53
0.38 ± 0.05	Methacrylonitrile	0.26 ± 0.05	80		49
0.43	Methacrylonitrile	0.28	80		337
0.25 ± 0.02	Methacrylonitrile	0.25 ± 0.02	80		81
0.30 ± 0.10	Methacrylonitrile	0.16 ± 0.06	60		171
0.05 ± 0.02	Methacrylonitrile	12.0 ± 1	−78 to −30	PhMgBr	68a
0.25 = 0.03	4-Methacryloxybenzylidene aniline	2.4 ± 0.5	60		257
0.18 ± 0.03	4-Methacryloxybenzylidene-4'-chloroaniline	5.4 ± 0.6	60		257
0.77 ± 0.02	Methacryloxymethylpentamethyldisiloxane	0.58 ± 0.02	50		202
1.0	N-Methacryloyl-ε-caprolactam	0	70-80		326
71 ± 10	Methallyl acetate	0	60		193
22	Methallyl chloride	0	60		193
0.90 ± 0.15	m-Methoxystyrene	1.1 ± 0.15	0	SnCl4	231
0.01	p-Methoxystyrene	100	0	SnCl4	231

(continued)

(continued)

M_1	r_1	M_2	r_2	T, °C.	Remarks	Ref.
Styrene	1.16 ± 0.09	p-Methoxystyrene	0.82 ± 0.07	60		323
	1.13	p-Methoxystyrene	0.93	60		201a
	-0.04 ± 0.04	p-Methoxystyrene	19 ± 3	0	d, $SnCl_4$ in $PhNO_2 \cdot CCl_4$	303
	-0.02 ± 0.07	p-Methoxystyrene	29 ± 5	0	d, $SnCl_4$ in $PhNO_2 \cdot CCl_4$	303
	0.34 ± 0.05	p-Methoxystyrene	11 ± 1	0	d, $AlCl_3 \cdot PhNO_2 \cdot CCl_3$	303
	0.12 ± 0.07	p-Methoxystyrene	14 ± 3	0	d, $TiCl_4 \cdot PhNO_2 \cdot CCl_4$	303
	0.38 ± 0.04	p-Methoxystyrene	11.5 ± 0.7	0	d, $TiCl_4 \cdot PhNO_2 \cdot CCl_4$	303
	0.05 ± 0.04	p-Methoxystyrene	46 ± 3	0	d, $TiCl_4$–CCl_4	303
	0.00 ± 0.03	p-Methoxystyrene	31 ± 6	0	d	303
	-0.12 ± 0.12	p-Methoxystyrene	35 ± 5	0	d, $TiCl_4$–$PhNO_2$–CCl_4	303
	0.48 ± 0.08	p-Methoxystyrene	5.6 ± 0.08	0	d, $TiCl_4$–$PhNO_2$	303
	0.22	p-Methoxystyrene	7.6	0	d	303
	0.01	p-Methoxystyrene	72	0	$TiCl_4$–ϕCH_3	303
	-0.33 ± 0.03	p-Methoxystyrene	12 ± 2	0	d	303
	4.1 ± 0.5	p-Methoxystyrene	0.13 ± 0.02	0	e, Na in THF	303
	2.9 ± 0.2	p-Methoxystyrene	0.23 ± 0.02	0	e, Li in THF	303
	10.9 ± 0.8	p-Methoxystyrene	0.05 ± 0.02	0	e, BuLi	303
	0.75 ± 0.03	Methyl acrylate	0.18 ± 0.02	60		66,170
	0.75 ± 0.1	Methyl acrylate	0.20 ± 0.05	70		20
	0.7 ± 0.1	Methyl acrylate	0.15 ± 0.05	60		187
	0.825 ± 0.0	Methyl acrylate	0.238 ± 0.02	131		170

r_1	Monomer	r_2	Temp.	Catalyst	Ref.
2.2 ± 0.2	Methyl acrylate	0.4 ± 0.2	20	SnCl$_4$	164
	Methyl acrylate	$r_1 \gg r_2$	h	Cationic in ethylene chloride	121
2.2 ± 0.2	Methyl acrylate	0.4 ± 0.2	h	Cationic in benzene	121
0.25	Methyl 1-chloro-acrylate	0.30	70		80
1.9 ± 0.2	Methyl cinnamate	0	60	c	65
0.92 ± 0.08	2-Methyl-5-cinnamoyl-pyridine	−0.15 ± 0.2	50		189
0.591 ± 0.057	5-Methyl-1-hexene	4.00 ± 0.28	35	e	24b
0.32	Methyl isopropenyl ketone	0.66	80		337
0.44 ± 0.10	Methyl isopropenyl ketone	0.29 ± 0.06	80		337
0.50 ± 0.02	Methyl methacrylate	0.44 ± 0.02	35		320
0.54 ± 0.03	Methyl methacrylate	0.49 ± 0.03	99		67
	Methyl methacrylate	$r_1 \gg r_2$	h	Cationic in ethylene chloride	121
10.5 ± 0.2	Methyl methacrylate	0.1 ± 0.05	h	Cationic in benzene	121
0.52 ± 0.026	Methyl methacrylate	0.46 ± 0.026	60		170
0.590 ± 0.026	Methyl methacrylate	0.536 ± 0.026	131		170
0.50 ± 0.02	Methyl methacrylate	0.50 ± 0.02	60		169
10.5 ± 0.2	Methyl methacrylate	0.1 ± 0.05	20	SnCl$_4$	165
0.12 ± 0.05	Methyl methacrylate	6.4 ± 0.05	−30	NaNH$_2$	164,165
0.50 ± 0.02	Methyl methacrylate	0.44 ± 0.02	35		319
0.56	Methyl methacrylate	0.49	35	a	319

(continued)

(*continued*)

M_1	r_1	M_2	r_2	T, °C.	Remarks	Ref.
Styrene	0.56 ± 0.02	Methyl methacrylate	0.50 ± 0.02	35	a	320
	0.485	Methyl methacrylate	0.422	30		28
	0.48	Methyl methacrylate	0.46	60		330
	0.44 ± 0.08	Methyl methacrylate	0.5 ± 0.04	60		251a
	0.54 ± 0.04	Methyl methacrylate	0.42 ± 0.1	60		251a
	0.60	Methyl methacrylate	0.55	132		330
	0	Methyl methacrylate	>1	-50 to -20	PhMgBr in toluene	68a
			>1	-78	PhMg in ether/ toluene	68a
	0	Methyl methacrylate				
	0.01 ± 0.01	Methyl methacrylate	25.0 ± 2	-30	PhMg in ether/ toluene	68a
	0.07 ± 0.02	Methyl methacrylate	4.5 ± 1	20	PhMg in ether/ toluene	68a
	0.02 ± 0.01	Methyl methacrylate	20.0 ± 2	-78	PhMgBr in ether	68a
	0.05 ± 0.02	Methyl methacrylate	14.0 ± 2	-30	PhMgBr in ether	68a
	0.30 ± 0.05	Methyl methacrylate	2.0 ± 0.3	20	PhMgBr in ether	68a
	0.12 ± 0.05	Methyl methacrylate	6.4 ± 0.1	-50	$NaNH_2$	68a
	0.31	Methyl methacrylate	17.1	30		89a
	0.89 ± 0.05	4-Methyl-1-pentene	3.67 ± 0.22	45	e	24b
	0.05	α-Methylstyrene	2.90	0	e	174
	1.18 ± 0.04	α-Methylstyrene	0.36	h	d	98
	2.3	α-Methylstyrene	0.38	h		242a
	2.0 ± 0.2	m-Methylstyrene	0.5 ± 0.1	40		216,279
	12.1 ± 1	o-Methylstyrene	0.1 ± 0.1	40	e	279
	0.82 ± 0.1	p-Methylstyrene	1.15 ± 0.05	40	e	216
	1 ± 0.12	p-Methylstyrene	1 ± 0.12	70	e	230
	0.90 ± 0.08	p-Methylstyrene	1.15 ± 1.18	h	e	279
	0.83	p-Methylstyrene	0.96	63		329
	0.54 ± 0.04	p-Methylstyrene	3.6 ± 0.1	0	d, $TiCl_4$ in $PhCH_3$	303

			Temp (°C)	Conditions	Ref.
0.55 ± 0.06	p-Methylstyrene	1.18 ± 0.08	−78	d, TiCl$_4$ in PhCH$_3$	303
0.32 ± 0.10	p-Methylstyrene	1.08 ± 0.14	0	d, TiCl$_4$ in CCl$_4$	303
0.68 ± 0.04	p-Methylstyrene	1.10 ± 0.05	0	d, TiCl$_4$ in PhNO$_2$	303
0.48 ± 0.07	p-Methylstyrene	1.18 ± 0.18	0	d, SnCl$_4$ in PhNC$_2$ and CCl$_4$	303
1.97 ± 0.10	p-Methylstyrene	0.38 ± 0.09	0	e, Na in THF	303
1.30 ± 0.15	p-Methylstyrene	0.91 ± 0.11	0	e, Li in THF	303
2.5 ± 0.1	p-Methylstyrene	0.26 ± 0.03	0	e, BuLi in THF	303
0.29 ± 0.04	Methyl vinyl ketone	0.35 ± 0.02	60		171
0.5 ± 0.1	2-Methyl-5-vinylpyridine	2.9 ± 0.3	70	e, AlEt$_3$–TiCl$_4$	266
0.6 ± 0.1	2-Methyl-5-vinylpyridine	0.68 ± 0.1	70		266
0.3 ± 0.1	2-Methyl-5-vinylpyridine	2.9 ± 0.3	70	e, Na	266
0.812 ± 0.005	2-Methyl-5-vinylpyridine	0.91 ± 0.02	60		290
0.88 ± 0.2	2-Methyl-5-vinylpyridine	1.19 ± 0.12	60		229a
5.1 ± 1.0	Methyl vinyl sulfide	0.12 ± 0.05	60		251
4.5	Methyl vinyl sulfide	0.15	60		249
2.0 ± 0.5	Methyl vinyl sulfone	0.01 ± 0.01	60		251
3.3	Methyl vinyl sulfone	0.01 ± 0.01	60		249
2.4 ± 0.10	Methyl vinyl sulfone	0.0 ± 0.2	60		65
1.40	Methyl vinyl sulfone	0.01	60		251
4.2 ± 0.2	Methyl vinyl sulfoxide	0.01 ± 0.01	60		245
12.3	N-Methyl-N-vinyl-p-toluene sulfonamide	0	60		90, 91
0.18 ± 0.1	Monoethyl fumarate	0.25 ± 0.10	60		168
0.13 ± 0.01	Monoethyl maleate	0.035 ± 0.01	60		168
20 ± 4	m-Nitrostyrene	0.03 ± 0.03	0	SnCl$_4$	231

(continued)

(continued)

M_1	r_1	M_2	r_2	T, °C.	Remarks	Ref.
Styrene	0.45 ± 0.05	m-Nitrostyrene	0.85 ± 0.1	75	Corrected for m-nitrostyrene styrene con-sumed in ter-mination	283
	0.19 ± 0.02	p-Nitrostyrene	1.15 ± 0.20	60		323
	0.46	α-Oleostearic acid	4	h		260
	3.9	Pentachlorophenyl vinyl sulfide	0.24	80		124
	1.31 ± 0.2	Pentachlorostyrene	0.10 ± 0.02	70		11
	4.5	Phenyl vinyl sulfide	0.15	60		249
	3.3	Phenyl vinyl sulfone	0.01 ± 0.01	60		249
	3.0 ± 0.4	Poly(1,3-butylene glycol)-fumarate	0.03 ± 0.03	60		304
	0.03 ± 0.03	Poly(dimethyl siloxy ethylene fumarate)	0.6 ± 0.3	h		47a
	-0.06	p-Potassium styrene-sulfonate	0.54	90		332
	0.02	p-Potassium styrene-sulfonate	0.93	110		332
	0	Potassium p-vinyl-benzenesulfonate	0.56	90		332
	0.02	Potassium p-vinyl-benzenesulfonate	0.93	110		332
	0.50 ± 0.10	3-Pyridalaceto-phenone	0.00 ± 0.25	50		189

1.85 ± 0.1	trans-1,2-bis-(2-Pyridyl)-ethylene	0.17 ± 0.1	50		190
11.2 ± 1.2	Stilbene	0	60	c	50
0.8	m-Styrenesulfonyl fluoride	1.25	75		113
0.25	p-Styrenesulfonyl fluoride	1.30	75		113
0.24	p-Sulfonamido styrene	1.07	90	c	332
185 ± 20	Tetrachloroethylene	0	60		64
165	Tetrachloroethylene	0	50		45
208	Tetrachloroethylene	0	50		45
66.4	Tetrachloroethylene	0	90		45
129	Tetrachloroethylene	0	90		45
187	Tetrachloroethylene	0	90		45
80.7 ± 9.3	Triallyl cyanurate	0	60		259a
90.6 ± 13.2	Triallyl cyanurate	0	60		259a
87.6 ± 10.0	Triallyl isocyanurate	0	60		259a
90.1 ± 13.1	Triallyl isocyanurate	0	60		259a
42.9	B-Triallyl-N-triphenyl-borazine	0	80		239b
16 ± 2	Trichloroethylene	0.0	60		64
16.5	Trichloroethylene	0	50		45
17.1	Trichloroethylene	0	50		45
12.1	Trichloroethylene	0	90		45
12.7	Trichloroethylene	0	90		45
6.9 ± 0.2	3,3,3-Trichloropropene	0.0 ± 0.02	60		65
1.10 ± 0.10	Triethyl aconitate	−0.10 ± 0.10	60		182

(continued)

(*continued*)

M_1	r_1	M_2	r_2	T, °C.	Remarks	Ref.
Styrene	0.62	*m*-Trifluoromethyl-styrene	0.75	60		91a
	0.70 ± 0.05	3-Trifluoromethyl-styrene	1.05 ± 0.05	60		57
	0.45 ± 0.05	2,5-bis(Trifluoro-methyl)styrene	1.15 ± 0.08	60	a	57
	0.66	α,β,β-Trifluorostyrene	0.07	50		172
	3.5	α,β,β-Trifluorostyrene	0.15	60		91a
	0.71 ± 0.02	*p*-Trimethoxysilyl-styrene	1.4 ± 0.1	70.3		167
	1.10 ± 0.01	Trimethyl aconitate	0.00 ± 0.01	60		182
	$60 \pm 15\%$	(Trimethylsiloxy)-vinyl dimethyl silane	$0.1 \pm 15\%$	50		241
	$60 \pm 15\%$	bis-(Trimethylsiloxy)-vinyl methyl silane	$0.1 \pm 15\%$	50		241
	1.0 ± 0.2	*p*-Trimethylsilyl-styrene	1.0 ± 0.2	70.3		167
	$60 \pm 15\%$	tris-(Trimethylsil-oxy)-vinylsilane	$0.1 \pm 15\%$	50		241
	0.4 ± 0.3	1,3,5-Trioxane	1.23 ± 0.10	25	Determined for $[M_1]:[M_2]$ from 64:1 to 8:1	148a
	0.26	*B*-Trivinyl-*N*-triphenylborazine	0	80		239b
	2.64 ± 0.35	Vinyl acetate	0.30 ± 0.15	h	Cationic in eth-ylene chloride	121

6.1 ± 0.8	Vinyl acetate	0.18 ± 0.08	h	Cationic in nitrobenzene	121
55 ± 10	Vinyl acetate	0.01 ± 0.01	60		195
8.25 ± 0.05	Vinyl acetate	0.015 ± 0.015	20	$SnCl_4$	164,165
0.01 ± 0.01	Vinyl acetate	0.1 ± 0.1	−30	$NaNH_2$	164,165
f	Vinyl acetate	f	h	d	121
38	Vinyl benzoate	0.05	80		34
0.72	Vinyl benzyl chloride 60% *meta*, 40% *para*	1.08	60		24a
20–25	Vinyl bromide	<0.05	0	U.V. irradiation	38
18 ± 2	Vinyl bromide	0.06 ± 0.015	280	p	38
5.5 ± 15%	N-Vinyl carbazole	0.012 ± 15%	70		15
5.7	N-Vinyl carbazole	0.035	75		112
5.7	Vinyl chloride	0.035	75		112
17 ± 3	Vinyl chloride	0.02	60		64
35	Vinyl chloride	0.067	50		52,242a
35	Vinyl chloride	0.077	50	a	52
—	Vinyl chloride	—	h	r	109
12.4	Vinyl chloride	0.045	h		299
45	Vinyl chloroacetate	0.03	80		337
20	Vinyl dichloroacetate	0.28	80		337
6.0 ± 1.5	Vinyl ethyl sulfide	0.25 ± 0.1	60		277
20	1-Vinyl-3-ethyl urea	0.020	70		116
1.85 ± 0.05	Vinylidene chloride	0.085 ± 0.010	60		64
2.1 ± 0.2	Vinylidene chloride	0.145 ± 0.009	50		297
2.0 ± 0.1	Vinylidene chloride	0.14 ± 0.05	60		169
0	Vinylidene chloride	0.046	h		204
0.0054	Vinylidene chloride	0.001	45		93
0	Vinylidene cyanide	0.0459	h		204

(continued)

(continued)

M₁	r₁	M₂	r₂	T, °C.	Remarks	Ref.
Styrene	0.005	Vinylidene cyanide	0.001	45		93
	50	Vinyl isobutyl ether	0.01	h		242a
	8.13 ± 0.04	Vinyl isocyanate	0.08 ± 0.04	60		137
	6.9	Vinyl isocyanate	0.1	h		325
	6.9 ± 0.5	Vinyl isocyanate	0.1 ± 0.05	60		127a
	0.8	Vinyl isothiocyanate	0.5	h		337
	0.65 ± 0.02	Vinyl isothiocyanate	0.37 ± 0.02	60		127a
	100	Vinyl methyl ether	0.01	h		242a
	0.67 ± 0.03	1-Vinyl naphthalene	1.35 ± 0.15	60		173
	3.3 ± 0.5	1-Vinyl naphthalene	0.35 ± 0.2	40	e	279
	0.5 ± 0.1	2-Vinyl naphthalene	1.4 ± 0.1	60		247
	49.5 ± 15	Vinyl nonanoate	0.01 ± 0.01	60		179
	68 ± 30	Vinyl octadecanate	0.01 ± 0.01	60		179
	30 ± 0.5	N-Vinyl oxazolidinone	0.05 ± 0.05	50		40
	8.73	Vinyl perfluoro-butyrate	0.017	h		337
	0.9	m-Vinylphenol	1.21	60		39
	1.04 ± 0.06	1-p-Vinyl phenyl disiloxane	1.2 ± 0.4	80		127a
	1.11 ± 0.01	1-p-Vinyl phenyl pentasiloxane	1.2 ± 0.1	80		127a
	1.15 ± 0.05	1-p-Vinyl phenyl tetrasiloxane	1.1 ± 0.3	80		127a
	0.90 ± 0.03	1-p-Vinyl phenyl trisiloxane	1.2 ± 0.2	80		127a
	65 ± 17	Vinyl pinonate	0.01 ± 0.01	60		179
	0.56 ± 0.02	2-Vinylpyridine	0.9 ± 0.2	60		289

M_1	r_1	M_2	r_2	Temp.	Ref.
Styrene oxide	0.55	2-Vinylpyridine	1.14	60	237
	0.55 ± 0.025	2-Vinylpyridine	1.135 ± 0.05	60	322
	0.55 ± 0.03	2-Vinylpyridine	1.81 ± 0.05	60	160, 161
	0.62 ± 0.02	4-Vinylpyridine	0.52 ± 0.06	80	89
	0.54 ± 0.03	4-Vinylpyridine	0.7 ± 0.1	60	289
	0.11 ± 0.01	2-Vinylpyridine-N-oxide	2.1 ± 0.6	60	292
	0.17 ± 0.02	4-Vinylpyrimidine	1.2 ± 0.1	60	237
	15.7 ± 0.5	N-Vinyl pyrrolidone	0.045 ± 0.05	50	40
	9.0	N-Vinyl pyrrolidone	0.11	80	337
	0.49 ± 0.14	2-Vinylquinoline	2.09 ± 0.55	60	160, 161
	7.0	N-Vinylsuccinimide	0.09	60	90
	10.5	N-Vinylsuccinimide	0.07	60	125
	0.35 ± 0.025	2-Vinylthiophene	3.10 ± 0.45	60	322
	22 ± 5	Vinyl trimethoxysilane	0	60	271
	22 ± 5	Vinyl trimethoxy-siane	0	60	271
	26 ± 8	Vinyl trimethoxy-siane	0	60	271
	29 ± 9	Vinyl undecenoate	0.02 ± 0.02	60	179
	0	1,3,5-Trioxane	2.7 ± 0.3	35	148a
m-Styrenesulfonyl fluoride	1.50	Methyl acrylate	0.14	75	113
	1.25	Styrene	0.8	75	113
p-Styrenesulfonyl fluoride	4.0	Methyl acrylate	0.20	75	113
	1.30	Styrene	0.25	75	113

(continued)

(continued)

M_1	r_1	M_2	r_2	T, °C.	Remarks	Ref.
p-Sulfonamido styrene	1.07	Styrene	0.24	90		332
Tetrachloroethylene	0	Acrylonitrile	470	60	b,c	64
	0	Methyl acrylate	200	60	b,c	193
	0	Methyl acrylate	830	60	b,c	65
	0	Styrene	208	50		45
	0	Styrene	66.4	90		45
	0	Styrene	129	90		45
	0	Styrene	187	90		45
	0	Styrene	185 ± 20	60	c	64
	0	Styrene	165	50		45
	0	Vinyl acetate	6.8 ± 0.5	60		64
	0	Vinyl acetate	5	68		3
Tetrafluoroethylene	1.0	Chlorotrifluoroethylene	1.0	60	a	72
	0.85	Ethylene	0.15	80	a	131
	<0.3	Isobutylene	0.0	80	a	131
N-p-Tolylmethacrylamide	f	Acrylonitrile	f	70		6
	0.67	Methyl methacrylate	0.39	70		240
Triallyl cyanurate	0	Methyl methacrylate	50.2 ± 7.5	60		259a
	0	Methyl methacrylate	46.3 ± 5.3	60		259a
	0	Styrene	90.6 ± 13.2	60		259a
	0	Styrene	80.7 ± 9.3	60		259a
	0.62 ± 0.05	Vinyl acetate	0.71 ± 0.02	60		259a
	0.52 ± 0.07	Vinyl acetate	0.77 ± 0.15	60		259a
Triallyl isocyanurate	0	Methyl methacrylate	48.9 ± 7.3	60		259a
	0	Methyl methacrylate	45.0 ± 5.1	60		259a

	r_1		r_2		Temp.	Notes	Ref.
	0	Styrene	90.1 ± 13.1		60		259a
	0	Styrene	87.6 ± 10.0		60		259a
	0.75 ± 0.06	Vinyl acetate	0.91 ± 0.03		60		259a
	0.70 ± 0.09	Vinyl acetate	0.95 ± 0.18		60		259a
B-Triallyl-N-triphenylborazine	0	Methyl methacrylate	8.6		80		239b
	0	Styrene	42.9		80		239b
Trichloroethylene	0	Acrylonitrile	67		60	b,c	193
	0	Methyl acrylate	33		60	b,c	193
	0	Methyl methacrylate	100		60	b,c	193
	0.0	Styrene	16 ± 2		60		64
	0	Styrene	16.5		50		45
	0	Styrene	17.1		50		45
	0	Styrene	12.1		90		45
	0	Styrene	12.7		90		45
	0.01 ± 0.01	Vinyl acetate	0.66 ± 0.04		60		195
	0	Vinyl acetate	0.67		68		13
3,3,3-Trichloropropene	0.100 ± 0.015	Acrylonitrile	12.2 ± 1.2		60		65
	1.46 ± 0.35	Diethyl fumarate	1.10 ± 0.10		60		65
3,3,3-Trichloropropene	0.0 ± 0.02	Styrene	6.9 ± 0.2		60		65
	0.19 ± 0.03	Vinyl acetate	0.19 ± 0.04		60		65
6-Triethoxy silyl bicyclo-(2,2,1)-2-heptene	0	Acrylonitrile	0.7		50		296
	0	Vinyl chloride	1.6		50		296

(continued)

(*continued*)

M_1	r_1	M_2	r_2	T, °C.	Remarks	Ref.
Triethyl aconitate	0.00 ± 0.01	Butadiene	0.37 ± 0.03	60		182
	0.02 ± 0.01	Butadiene	0.65 ± 0.05	50		228
	-0.10 ± 0.10	Styrene	1.10 ± 0.10	60		182
N,N,N-Triethyl-N-[2-(methacryloxy)-ethyl] ammonium iodide	0.61 ± 0.09	4-Vinylpyridine	0.30 ± 0.02	60		234
m-Trifluoromethyl-styrene	0.75	Styrene	0.62	60		91a
3-Trifluoromethyl-styrene	0.98 ± 0.15	Methyl methacrylate	0.60 ± 0.10	60		57
	1.05 ± 0.05	Styrene	0.70 ± 0.05	60		57
2,5-bis-(Trifluoro-methyl) styrene	1.35 ± 0.05	Methyl methacrylate	0.57 ± 0.07	60		57
	1.15 ± 0.08	Styrene	0.45 ± 0.05	60		57
α,β,β-Trifluorostyrene	0.07	Styrene	0.66	50	a	172
	0.15	Styrene	3.5	60		91a
p-Trimethoxysilyl-styrene	1.4 ± 0.1	Styrene	0.71 ± 0.02	70.3		167
Trimethyl aconitate	-0.10 ± 0.10	Acrylonitrile	5.50 ± 0.50	60		182
	0.00 ± 0.03	Butadiene	0.40 ± 0.03	60		182
	0.00 ± 0.01	Styrene	1.10 ± 0.01	60		182
$trans$-Trimethyl aco-nitate	0.00 ± 0.50	Vinyl chloride	0.15 ± 0.10	60		182
	0.01 ± 0.1	Vinylidene chloride	54 ± 5	60		184

M1	M2	r1	r2	Temp. °C		Refs.
(Trimethylsiloxy)-vinyl-dimethyl-silane	Acrylonitrile	0.1 ± 15%	8.0 ± 15%	50		241
	Styrene	0.1 ± 15%	60 ± 15%	50		241
	Vinyl acetate	0.01 ± 15%	0.99 ± 15%	70		241
bis-(Trimethylsiloxy)-vinylmethylsilane	Acrylonitrile	0.1 ± 15%	8.0 ± 15%	50		241
	Styrene	0.1 ± 15%	60 ± 15%	50		241
	Vinyl acetate	0.01 ± 15%	0.99 ± 15%	70		241
	Vinyl chloride	0.50 ± 15%	0.90 ± 15%	50		241
	Chloro trifluoro-ethylene	0.20	0.05	60		241
tris-(Trimethylsiloxy)-vinyl silane	Acrylonitrile	0.1 ± 15%	8.0 ± 15%	50		241
	Chloro trifluoro-ethylene	0.20	0.05	60		241
	Styrene	0.1 ± 15%	60 ± 15%	50		241
	Vinyl acetate	0.01 ± 15%	0.99 ± 15%	70		241
	Vinyl chloride	0.50	0.90	50		241
	N-Vinyl pyrrolidone	0.1 ± 15%	4.0 ± 15%	125		241
p-Trimethylsilyl styrene	Styrene	1.0 ± 0.2	1.0 ± 0.2	70.3		167
1,3,5-Trioxane	1,3-Dioxolane	1.36 ± 0.03	0.47 ± 0.015	35		148a
	4-Phenyl-1,3-dioxane	9 ± 2	0	35		148a
	Styrene	1.23 ± 0.10	0.4 ± 0.3	25	Determined for [M1]:[M2] from 64:1 to 8:1	148a
	Styrene oxide	2.7 ± 0.3	0	35		148a

(continued)

(*continued*)

M₁	r₁	M₂	r₂	T, °C.	Remarks	Ref.
B-Trivinyl-N-triphenyl borazine	0	Methyl methacrylate	0.70	80		239b
	0	Styrene	0.26	80		239b
	0	Vinyl acetate	0	80		239b
Vinyl acetate	0.0	1-Acetoxy-1,3-butadiene	Large	70		105
	0.1 ± 0.05	Acrolein	3.33 ± 0.1	20	a	269
	0.18	1-Acrylamido-1-deoxy-D-glucitol	2.41	50		325a
	0.1	Acrylic acid	2	70		18
	0.01 ± 0.003	Acrylic acid	10 ± 1	70		42
	0.061 ± 0.013	Acrylonitrile	4.05 ± 0.3	60		195, 333
	0.02 ± 0.02	Acrylonitrile	6 ± 2	60		81
	0.07 ± 15%	Acrylonitrile	6.0 ± 15%	70		9
	0.07	Acrylonitrile	6.0	70		333
	0.009	Acrylonitrile	3.88	25		293
	0.03 ± 0.03	Acrylonitrile	5.6 ± 0.5	40	e	31
	f	Acrylonitrile	f	h		338
	f	C₈–C₁₈ Alkyl vinyl ethers	f	50		5
	0.60 ± 0.15	Allyl acetate	0.45 ± 0.15	60		171
	1.0	Allyl acetate	0.7	60		264
	0.34 ± 0.26	Allyl chloride	0.75 ± 0.46	60		144
	0.7	Allyl chloride	0.67	68		3
	f	Allyl chloride	f	60		273, 264
	0.71	Allyl laurate	0.8	60		265
	500 ± 100	Benzene	0	60		239a

r_1	Monomer	r_2	Temp	Ref.
0.023	n-Butyl methacrylate	28.8	60	215
0.127 ± 0.015	n-Butyl methacrylate	62.1 ± 3.8	60	205
0.127 ± 0.015	n-Butyl vinyl ether	62.1 ± 3.8	60	205
0.04 ± 0.01	Butyl vinyl sulfonate	0.20 ± 0.05	70	233
0.01	Butyl vinyl sulfonate	$r_1 = r_2$	170	298
0.6	2-Chloro-1,3-buta-diene	50	65	314
0.33 ± 0.05	Chlorotrifluoro-ethylene	0.01	60	294
0.33	Crotonic acid	0.01 ± 0.01	68	53
0.3	Crotonic acid	0	h	107
f	Crotonic acid	0.01	70	294
0.01 ± 0.01	Crotonic acid	f	h	309
0.16	Crotonamide	2.0 ± 0.05	110	315
1.41 ± 0.06	1,-Deoxy-1-meth-acrylamido-D-glucitol	0.56	50	325a
1.44 ± 0.28	Diallyl melamine	0.19 ± 0.004	60	259
0.72	Diallyl melamine	0.20 ± 0.03	60	259
0.02	Diallyl phthalate	2.0	h	287
0.6 ± 15%	Di-n-butyl itaconate	6.3	h	54
6.3 ± 0.2	1,1-Dichloro-2-2-difluoroethylene	0 ± 15%	70	9
2.8	cis-Dichloroethylene	0.018 ± 0.003	60	168
0.85	cis-Dichloroethylene	0	68	13
0.99 ± 0.02	trans-Dichloro-ethylene	0	68	13
<0.04	trans-Dichloro-ethylene	0.086 ± 0.01	60	168
	2,5-Dichlorostyrene	—	70	123

(continued)

(continued)

M_1	r_1	M_2	r_2	T, °C.	Remarks	Ref.
Vinyl acetate	0.011 ± 0.001	Diethyl fumarate	0.444 ± 0.003	60		168
	0.17 ± 0.01	Diethyl maleate	0.043 ± 0.005	60		168
	0.17	Diisopropyl maleate	0.043	60		323
	0.12	Dimethyl maleate	0.028	60		334
	0.1	N,N-Divinylaniline	2.0	60		51
	0.08 ± 0.03	Ethyl 1-acetoxy-acrylate	5.4 ± 0.5	60		307
	0.3 ± 0.2	dl-Ethyl 2-methyl-2-ethyl-1-butenoate	3.2 ± 0.50	60		288
	0.1 ± 0.1	d-Ethyl 2-methyl-2-ethyl-1-butenoate	2.2 ± 0.4	60		288
	3.0 ± 0.1	Ethyl vinyl ether	0	60		195
	0.3	Ethyl vinyl oxalate	3.0	60	c	146a
	0.45	N-Ethyl-N'-vinylurea	0.63	75		116
	0.14	Fumaryl chloride	0.00	70	r_1 appears to vary with comp. mixture	105
	0.271 ± 0.039	Heptyl methacrylate	60.4 ± 0.4	60		205
	0.135 ± 0.055	Hexadecyl methacrylate	68.3 ± 3.2	60		205
	0.01 ± 0.01	Hydroxy methyl-crotonamide	0.045 ± 0.1	110		315
	0.025	Isobutyl methacrylate	29.8	60		215
	1.0	Isopropenyl acetate	1.0	75		115
	0.072 ± 0.04	Maleic anhydride	0.01	h		130
	0.055 ± 0.015	Maleic anhydride	0.003	75		328
	0.01	Methacrylic acid	20	70		18
	0.01 ± 0.01	Methacrylonitrile	12 ± 2	70		81

r_1	M_2	r_2	Temp		Ref.
0.16 ± 0.16	Methacryloxymethyl-pentamethyldisiloxane	24 ± 5	50		137
0.13	Methallyl chloride	0	73–90		208
0.522	Methyl acid maleate	0.035	56		312a
0.09 ± 0.005	Methyl acid maleate	0.0 ± 0.007	60		334
0.13 ± 0.03	Methyl acid maleate	0.015 ± 0.01	75		334
0.1	Methyl acrylate	9	60		333
0.1 ± 0.1	Methyl acrylate	9 ± 2.5	60		195
f	Methyl acrylate	f	h		336
1.5 ± 0.24	Methyl bicyclo(2,2,1)-2-heptene-5-carboxylate	0.45 ± 0.07	60		145
0.015 ± 0.015	Methyl methacrylate	20 ± 3	60		195
0.072 ± 0.026	Methyl methacrylate	22.21 ± 0.89	60		205
0.4 ± 0.2	Methyl methacrylate	3.2 ± 1.1	–30	e	164
0.01 ± 0.01	Methylolcrotonamide	0.045 ± 0.1	110		315
0.05	Methyl vinyl ketone	7.00	70		105
0.29	Methyl vinyl sulfone	0.35	60		251
0.0 ± 0.01	Methyl vinyl sulfone	0.4 ± 0.08	60		65
0.09 ± 0.005	Monomethyl maleate	0.0 ± 0.007	60		334
0.13 ± 0.03	Monomethyl maleate	0.015 ± 0.01	75		334
0.04681	Monomethyl maleate	0.4747	56		311,312
0.0345	Monomethyl maleate	0.522	65		311
0.1168	Monomethyl maleate	0.99959	78		311
0.28	Phenyl vinyl sulfone	0.35	60		249
0.15 ± 0.07	Poly(1,3-butylene glycol fumarate)	0.2 ± 0.2	60		283c

(continued)

(*continued*)

M_1		r_1	M_2	r_2	T, °C.	Remarks	Ref.
Vinyl acetate		0.020 ± 0.02	Poly(ethylene glycol fumarate)	0.2 ± 0.1	60		283c
		0.186 ± 0.038	Propyl methacrylate	73.3 ± 7.4	60		205
		0.01	Sodium acrylate	2	60		42
		0.30 ± 0.15	Styrene	2.64 ± 0.35	h	Cationic in ethylene chloride	121
		0.18 ± 0.08	Styrene	6.1 ± 0.8	h	Cationic in nitrobenzene	121
		0.01 ± 0.01	Styrene	55 ± 10	60		195
		0.015 ± 0.015	Styrene	8.25 ± 0.05	20	$SnCl_4$	164,165
		0.1 ± 0.1	Styrene	0.01 ± 0.01	-30	$NaNH_2$	164,165
		f	Styrene	f	h	d	121
		6.8 ± 0.5	Tetrachloroethylene	0	60		64
		5	Tetrachloroethylene	0	68		3
		0.71 ± 0.02	Triallyl cyanurate	0.62 ± 0.05	60		259a
		0.77 ± 0.15	Triallyl cyanurate	0.52 ± 0.07	60		259a
		0.91 ± 0.03	Triallyl isocyanurate	0.75 ± 0.06	60		259a
		0.95 ± 0.18	Triallyl isocyanurate	0.70 ± 0.09	60		259a
		0.66 ± 0.04	Trichloroethylene	0.01 ± 0.01	60		195
		0.67	Trichloroethylene	0	68		13
		0.19 ± 0.04	3,3,3-Trichloropropane	0.19 ± 0.03	60		65
		$0.99 \pm 15\%$	Trimethylsiloxyvinyl-dimethylsilane	$0.01 \pm 15\%$	70		241
		$0.99 \pm 15\%$	bis-Trimethylsiloxy-vinylmethylsilane	$0.01 \pm 15\%$	70		241

r_1	M_2	r_2	Temp.	Notes	Ref.
$0.99 \pm 15\%$	tris-(Trimethylsiloxy)-vinylsilane	$0.01 \pm 15\%$	70		241
0	B-Trivinyl-N-triphenyl borazine	0			239b
0.35 ± 0.09	Vinyl benzoate	0.99 ± 0.13	80		318
0.7	Vinyl benzoate	1.5	60		34
0.35 ± 0.09	Vinyl bromide	4.5 ± 1.2	80		95
0.126 ± 0.32	N-Vinyl carbazole	2.68 ± 0.10	60		310,313
0.152 ± 0.018	N-Vinyl carbazole	3.02 ± 0.24	65		310,313
0.3	Vinyl chloride	2.1	100		3
0.6 ± 0.2	Vinyl chloride	1.8 ± 0.6	68		183,242a
0.23 ± 0.02	Vinyl chloride	1.68 ± 0.08	40		195
0.65 ± 0.04	Vinyl chloride	1.35 ± 0.05	60		153
0.033	Vinyl chloride	3.74	-32	e	32
0.73	Vinyl chloroacetate	1.20	60		78
3.0	Vinylene carbonate	0.27	70		118
3.71	Vinylene carbonate	0.0579	55		176
4.00	Vinylene carbonate	0.015	70		104
7.3 ± 0.7	Vinylene carbonate	0.13 ± 0.1	60		145
0.45	1-Vinyl-3-ethyl urea	0.63	70		116
0.1	Vinylidene chloride	6	68		3
0.0 ± 0.03	Vinylidene chloride	3.6 ± 0.5	60		64
0.0054	Vinylidene cyanide	0.11	45		93
0.67	Vinyl isocaproate	1.14	80		163
1.4	Vinyl laurate	0.7	60		265
0.90	Vinyl octadecanoate	0.73	70		333
0.97	Vinyl octadecanoate	1.00	50	M_2 impure	1
0.60	N-Vinyl oxazolidinone	1.50	75		117

(continued)

(continued)

M_1	r_1	M_2	r_2	T, °C.	Remarks	Ref.
Vinyl acetate	0.52 ± 0.08	N-Vinyl oxazolidinone	1.90 ± 0.10	50		40
	1.15 ± 0.13	Vinyl palmitate	0.78 ± 1.0	70–73	r_1 and r_2 cal. from polymer analysis	243
	0.84 ± 0.10	Vinyl palmitate	0.66 ± 0.07	70–73	r_1 and r_2 cal. from residual monomer analysis	243
	0.3	2-Vinylpyridine	10	h		221
	0	2-Vinylpyridine	30 ± 15	70		9
	0.205 ± 0.015	N-Vinylpyrrolidone	3.30 ± 0.15	50		40
	0.38	N-Vinylpyrrolidone	0.44	h		44
	0.38	N-Vinylpyrrolidone	0.44	70		118
	0.237 ± 0.037	N-Vinylpyrrolidone	2.28 ± 0.19	76		145a
	0.18	N-Vinyl succinimide	6.1	60		125
	0.6	Vinyl trifluoroacetate	0.32	60		103
	0.33	N-Vinyl urethane	0.33	65		92
Vinyl acetylene	0.60 ± 0.02	Acrylonitrile	0.13 ± 0.01	60		248
	0.13	Isobutylene	8.0	−100	d	62
Vinyl benzoate	0.05 ± 0.05	Acrylonitrile	5.0 ± 0.05	75		53
	0.46 ± 0.16	Allyl chloride	0.88 ± 0.470	60		144
	0.05	Styrene	38	80		34
	0.99 ± 0.13	Vinyl acetate	0.35 ± 0.09	60		318
	1.5	Vinyl acetate	0.7	80		34
	0.5	Vinyl chloride	1.7	40	a	153
	0.28	Vinyl chloride	0.72	45		302
	0.1 ± 0.02	Vinylidene chloride	7.0 ± 1	50	p	53,242a
	0.008	Vinylidene cyanide	0.10	43		93
	0.44 ± 0.09	N-Vinyl pyrrolidinone	2.45 ± 0.1	60		318

Monomer 1	Monomer 2	r_1	r_2	Temp (°C)	Conditions	Ref.
Vinyl benzyl chloride 60% *meta*, 40% *para*	Acrylonitrile	0.67	0.06	60		24a
	Isobutylene	0.7 ± 0.1	4.5 ± 1	−100	d	140
	Styrene	1.08	0.72	60		24a
Vinyl bromide	Methyl methacrylate	0.05 ± 0.015	20 ± 2	28	p	38
	Methyl methacrylate	0.05 ± 0.01	25 ± 2	0	U.V. initiation	38
	Styrene	<0.05	20–25	0	U.V. irradiation	38
	Styrene	0.06 ± 0.015	18 ± 2	280	p	38
Vinyl butanoate	Vinyl acetate	4.5 ± 1.2	0.35 ± 0.09	60		95
	Allyl chloride	0.31 ± 0.35	1.15 ± 0.59	60		144
	2-Chloro-1,3-butadiene	0.02	90	65		314
	N-Vinyl carbazole	0.059 ± 0.020	1.28 ± 0.06	100		310,313
Vinyl butyl sulfone	Vinyl chloride	0.65 ± 0.04	1.35 ± 0.05	50		256
Vinyl caprate	Acrylonitrile	0.2 ± 0.1	1.1 ± 0.2	−78	e	86
	Acrylonitrile	0.04 ± 0.03	4.0 ± 0.3	60		29
	Vinyl chloride	0.2	4.7	40		153
Vinyl caproate	Acrylonitrile	0.04 ± 0.03	4.0 ± 0.3	60		29
	Vinyl chloride	0.1	1.8	40		153
	Vinyl chloride	0.65 ± 0.04	1.35 ± 0.05	40	a	153
Vinyl caprylate	Acrylonitrile	0.04 ± 0.03	4.0 ± 0.3	60		29
	Vinyl chloride	0.2	3.2	86	a	153
N-Vinyl carbazole	Allyl chloride	Very large	0	70		16
	2-Chloroallyl chloride	Very large		70		10,16
	2,5-Dichlorostyrene	0.016 ± 0.002	8 ± 0.5	h		18
	2,5-Dichlorostyrene	0.016	8.0	75		19
	Methyl acrylate	0.050	0.50	70		112
	Methyl methacrylate	0.20 ± 0.03	2.0 ± 0.3	75		15
	Methyl methacrylate	0.04	2.0			112

(continued)

(*continued*)

M_1	r_1	M_2	r_2	T, °C.	Remarks	Ref.
N-Vinyl carbazole	$0.012 \pm 15\%$	Styrene	$5.5 \pm 15\%$	70		15
	0.035	Styrene	5.7	75		112
	2.68 ± 0.10	Vinyl acetate	0.126 ± 0.32	65		310,313
	3.02 ± 0.24	Vinyl acetate	0.152 ± 0.018	100		310,313
	1.28 ± 0.06	Vinyl butanoate	0.059 ± 0.020	100		310,313
	3.7	Vinylidene chloride	0.020	h		112
	4.22 ± 0.16	Vinyl formate	0.196 ± 0.004	100		310,313
	1.68 ± 0.140	Vinyl propionate	0.076 ± 0.018	100		310,313
Vinyl chloride	0.13 ± 0.01	Abityl acrylate	4.2 ± 0.2	60		187
	0.02 ± 0.02	Acrylonitrile	3.28 ± 0.06	60		171
	0.04 ± 0.02	Acrylonitrile	2.8 ± 0.5	40		261
	0.074	Acrylonitrile	3.7	50		52
	0.052 ± 0.009	Acrylonitrile	3.6 ± 0.2	50		297
	0.04 ± 0.03	Acrylonitrile	2.7 ± 0.7	60	e	31
	f	C_8-C_{18} Alkyl vinyl ethers	f	50		5
	1.2	Allyl acetate	—	40		193
	1.16	Allyl acetate	0	40		208
	2.0	Allyl triethoxy silane	0	50		296
	0.74	Bicyclo[2.2.1]-2,5-heptadiene	0.35	50		343a
	1.41	Bicyclo[2.2.1]-2,5-heptadiene	0.08	50		343a
	0.035	Butadiene	8.8	50		300
	0.4	2-Butenyl triethoxy silane	0	50		296

	Monomer				Ref.
0.07	Butyl acrylate	4.4		45	301
5 ± 15%	t-Butylethylene	0.0		70	9
0.05	Butyl methacrylate	13.5		45	302
0.35 ± 0.05	Butyl vinyl sulfonate	0.30 ± 0.05		70	233
0.70	2-Chloroallyl acetate	0		100	147
1.13	1-Chloro-1-propene	0.24		50	300
0.75	2-Chloro-1-propene	0.58		50	300
2.53	Chlorotrifluoro-ethylene	0.01		60	155
0.2	α-Chlorovinyltri-ethoxysilane	0		50	296
0.4	Δ³-Cyclohexenyltri-ethoxysilane	0		50	296
1.4	Dibutyl maleate	0.0		40	150
0.65 ± 0.05	Diisobutyl maleate	0.1		40	151
0.12 ± 0.01	Diethyl fumarate	0.47 ± 0.05		60	168
0.42	Di-2-ethylhexyl maleate	0		68	3
0.06 ± 0.01	Diethyl itaconate	5.65 ± 0.25		50	214
0.8	Diethyl maleate	0.0	a	40	149a,152
0.77 ± 0.03	Diethyl maleate	0.009 ± 0.003		60	168
0.9 ± 15%	Diethyl maleate	0 ± 15%		70	9
0.06 ± 0.01	Diisopropyl itaconate	6.0 ± 0.5		50	214
0.053 ± 0.01	Dimethyl itaconate	5.0 ± 0.2		50	213
0.06 ± 0.02	Dioctyl itaconate	7.0 ± 1.0		50	214
0.5	Dioctyl maleate	0		68	3
0.14 ± 0.01	Hydronopyl acrylate	4.3 ± 0.2		60	187
2.05 ± 0.3	Isobutylene	0.08 ± 0.1		60	171
1.3	Isobutylene	0.03		0	275

(continued)

(continued)

M_1	r_1	M_2	r_2	T, °C.	Remarks	Ref.
Vinyl chloride	4.3	Isobutylene	0	65	b,c	95
	2.2	Isopropenyl acetate	0.25	65		240
	0.296 ± 0.07	Maleic anhydride	0.008	75		328
	0.31	Methallyl chloride	0	45		208
	f	Methyl acrylate	f	50		162
	0.06	Methyl acrylate	4	45		301,302
	0	Methyl acrylate	5	60		193
	0.12 ± 0.01	Methyl acrylate	4.4 ± 0.5	50		187
	0.083	Methyl acrylate	9.0	50		52
	0	Methyl methacrylate	12.5	60	b,c	193
	0.1	Methyl methacrylate	10	68		3
	0.02	Methyl methacrylate	15	45		302
	0.10	Methyl vinyl ketone	8.3	70		8
	0.12	Octyl acrylate	4.8	45		301
	0.04	Octyl methacrylate	14.0	45		302
	0.43	Pentachlorostyrene	5.3	h		299
	0.5	1-Pentene	—	68		3
	8.0	Propenyl triethoxy silane	0	50		296
	0.035	Styrene	5.7	75		112
	0.02	Styrene	17 ± 3	60		64
	0.067	Styrene	35	50		52,242a
	0.077	Styrene	35	50	a	52
	—	Styrene	—	h	n	109
	0.045	Styrene	12.4	h		299
	1.6	6-Triethoxysilyl bicyclo[2,2,1]-2-heptene	0	50		296

r_1	M_2	r_2	Temp		Ref.
0.15 ± 0.10	trans-Trimethyl aconitate	0.00 ± 0.50	60		182
0.90 ± 15%	bis-(Trimethylsiloxy)-vinyl-methyl silane	0.50 ± 15%	50		241
0.90	tris-(Trimethylsiloxy)-vinyl silane	0.50	50		241
2.1	Vinyl acetate	0.3	68		3
1.8 ± 0.6	Vinyl acetate	0.6 ± 0.2	40		183, 242a
1.68 ± 0.08	Vinyl acetate	0.23 ± 0.02	60		195
1.35 ± 0.05	Vinyl acetate	0.65 ± 0.04	40		153
3.74	Vinyl acetate	0.033	−32	e	32
1.7	Vinyl benzoate	0.5	40	a	153
0.72	Vinyl benzoate	0.28	45		302
1.35 ± 0.05	Vinyl butanoate	0.65 ± 0.04	40		256
2.0 ± 0.2	Vinyl isobutyl ether	0.02 ± 0.01	50		53
4.7	Vinyl caprate	0.2	40		153
1.8	Vinyl caproate	0.1	40	a	153
1.35 ± 0.05	Vinyl caproate	0.65 ± 0.04	40		153
3.2	Vinyl caprylate	0.2	86	a	153
5.2	Vinylene carbonate	0.09	80		118
1.0	Vinyl ethyl diethoxy silane	0	50		296
0.3	Vinylidene chloride	3.2	60		193
0.5	Vinylidene chloride	7.5	47		36a
0.23	Vinylidene chloride	3.15	55		73a
0.14	Vinylidene chloride	Large	68		3
0.2	Vinylidene chloride	4.5	50		300
0.2 ± 0.2	Vinylidene chloride	1.8 ± 0.5	45		256
0.017 ± 0.01	Vinylidene cyanide	0.54 ± 0.2	50		93

(continued)

(*continued*)

M₁	r_1	M₂	r_2	T, °C.	Remarks	Ref.
Vinyl chloride	0.0093	Vinylidene cyanide	0.72	h		77
	2.0	Vinyl isobutyl ether	0.02	h		242a
	7.4	Vinyl laurate	0.2	h	a	153
	1.40 ± 0.004	Vinyl levulinate	0.419 ± 0.002	60	a	179
	1.0	Vinyl methyl diethoxy silane	0	50		296
	1.16 ± 0.06	Vinyl nonanoate	0.282 ± 0.35	60		179
	0.745 ± 0.026	Vinyl octadecanoate	0.290 ± 0.025	60		179
	0.84 ± 0.02	N-Vinyl oxazolidinone	0.35 ± 0.02	50		40
	0.60	N-Vinyl oxazolidinone	1.50	h		117
	0.7	Vinyl phenyl diethoxy silane	0	50		296
	1.458 ± 0.04	Vinyl pinonate	0.446 ± 0.028	60		179
	1.35 ± 0.05	Vinyl propionate	0.65 ± 0.04	40		153
	0.53	N-Vinyl pyrrolidone	0.38	h		44
	0.38	N-Vinyl pyrrolidone	0.53	h		44
	0.9	Vinyl triethoxy silane	0	50		296
	0.8	Vinyl trimethoxy silane	0	50		296
	0.8	Vinyl triisopropoxy silane	0	50		296
	1.06 ± 0.05	Vinyl undecenoate	0.358 ± 0.065	60		179
Vinyl chloroacetate	0.09	Acrylonitrile	0.34	80		337
	0.03	Styrene	45	80		337
	1.20	Vinyl acetate	0.73	60		78
	<0.004	Vinylidene cyanide	0.13 ± 0.05	40		93
Vinyl-2-chloroethyl ether	0.42	p-Methoxy-α-methyl styrene	1.1	RT	d, in benzene	180

M1	r1	M2	r2	Temp	Notes	Ref
	0.73	p-Methoxy-α-methyl styrene	1.3	RT	d, in nitrobenzene	180
	1.7	α-Methyl-p-methyl styrene	0.54	RT	d, in benzene	180
	1.7	α-Methyl-p-methyl styrene	0.51	RT	d, in benzene	180
	1.7	α-Methyl-p-methyl styrene	0.64	RT	d, in nitrobenzene	180
	5.03 ± 0.66	α-Methylstyrene	0.33 ± 0.05	30	d, in benzene	71, 180
	2.6, 3.3	α-Methylstyrene	0.34, 0.42	RT	d, in nitrobenzene	180
	5.0	α-Methylstyrene	0.33	RT	SnCl$_4$ in benzene	24
	2.6	α-Methylstyrene	0.34	RT	SnCl$_4$ in nitrobenzene	24
Vinyl-2-chloroethyl ether	3.3	α-Methylstyrene	0.42	RT	SnCl$_4$ in nitrobenzene	24
	0.21 ± 0.06	Octadecyl vinyl ether	2.67 ± 0.06	30	d	71
	0.34 ± 0.14	Vinyl isobutyl ether	2.03 ± 0.55	30	d	71
Vinyl cyclohexene	0	Vinylidene chloride	1.8	70		69
Vinyl dichloroacetate	0.18	Acrylonitrile	0.25	80		337
	0.28	Styrene	20	80		337
Vinylene carbonate	0.005	Methyl methacrylate	70	70		118
	0.50 ± 0.04	Methyl vinyl sulfide	10.6 ± 1.2	60		145
	0.27	Vinyl acetate	3.0	70		118
	0.0579	Vinyl acetate	3.71	55		176
	0.015	Vinyl acetate	4.00	70		104
	0.13 ± 0.1	Vinyl acetate	7.3 ± 0.7	60		145
	0.09	Vinyl chloride	5.2	80		118

(continued)

(continued)

M_1	r_1	M_2	r_2	T, °C.	Remarks	Ref.
Vinylene carbonate	0.4	N-Vinylpyrrolidone	0.7	60		118
	0.04 ± 0.01	Vinyl thioacetate	12.9 ± 1.1	60		234
Vinyl esters of fatty acids in C_6-C_{18} range	0.04 ± 0.03	Acrylonitrile	4.0 ± 0.3	60	k	29
1-Vinyl-2-ethyl acetylene	0.6 ± 1	2-Vinylpyridine	1.5 ± 0.5	60		248
Vinyl ethyl diethoxy-silane	0	Acrylonitrile	9.0	50		296
	0	Vinyl chloride	1.0	50		296
Vinyl 2-ethyl hexanoate	0.01 ± 0.01	Acrylonitrile	12 ± 2	30		53
	0.71 ± 0.18	Allyl chloride	1.52 ± 0.130	60		144
Vinyl ethyl sulfide	0.3 ± 0.1	Methyl methacrylate	2.7 ± 1.5	60		277
	0.25 ± 0.1	Styrene	6.0 ± 1.5	60		277
1-Vinyl-3-ethyl urea	0.015	Methyl methacrylate	1.8	70		116
	0.020	Styrene	20	70		116
	0.63	Vinyl acetate	0.45	70		116
Vinyl fluoride	0.8	Chloro trifluoro-ethylene	1.2	80	a,b	72
Vinyl formate	0.04 ± 0.005	Acrylonitrile	3.0 ± 0.05	60		53
	3.0	Acrylonitrile	0.40	h		242a
	0.57 ± 0.08	Allylchloride	0.78 ± 0.100	60		144
	0.2 ± 0.05	Butadiene	5.0 ± 0.01	120		308
	0.01	2-Chloro-1,3-butadiene	30	65		314
	−0.035	2-Chloro-1,3-butadiene	15 0	h		148c

Monomer 1	Monomer 2	r₁	r₂	Temp.	Notes	Ref.
2-Vinyl furan	N-Vinyl carbazole	0.196 ± 0.004	4.22 ± 0.16	100		310,313
Vinylidene bromide	Vinylidene chloride	0.15 ± 0.014	11.7 ± 0.07	h	Photosensitized initiator	146
Vinylidene chloride	Vinylidene chloride	1.90 ± 0.11	1.04 ± 0.10	h		327
Vinylidene chloride	Acrylamide	0.15 ± 0.08	4.89 ± 0.08	60		24a
	Acrylonitrile	0.37 ± 0.10	0.91 ± 0.10	60		169
	C₈–C₁₈ Alkyl vinyl ethers	f	f	50		5
	Allyl acetate	6.6	0	60	b,c	193
	Allyl chloride	3.8	0.26	68		3
	Allyl chloride	4.5	0	60	c	193
	Butadiene	<0.05	1.0 ± 0.2	5	a	324
	Butyl acrylate	0.84 ± 0.2	0.46 ± 0.13	70		175
	Butyl acrylate	0.87 ± 0.01	0.58 ± 0.03	0		175
	Butyl acrylate	0.88 ± 0.10	0.83 ± 0.02	h	a	141
	n-Butyl crotonate	33	0	70		69
	n-Butyl methacrylate	0.35	0.22	70		3
	n-Butyl vinyl-sulfonate	7.5 ± 0.6	0.065 ± 0.007	80		233
	1-Chloro-1-bromo-ethylene	0.83 ± 0.08	2.38 ± 0.06	h	Photosensitized initiation	327
	Chlorotrifluoro-ethylene	17.14	0.02	60		59
	Coumarin	Very large	0	70		9
	Crotonaldehyde	17	0	70		69
	Crotonic acid	35 ± 5	0.065 ± 0.005	60		53
	Diallyl phthalate	5.0	0.2	70		10
	Diethyl fumarate	12.2 ± 2	0.046 ± 0.015	60		64
	Diethyl maleate	12.5	—	60		3

(continued)

(continued)

M_1	r_1	M_2	r_2	T, °C.	Remarks	Ref.
Vinylidene chloride	40 ± 8	Diethyl maleate	0.0 ± 0.04	60		65
	4.8 ± 0.2	Dimethallyl oxalate	0.16 ± 0.01	40		47
	1.30 ± 0.015	Dodecyl vinyl ether	0.00 ± 0.2	50		4
	0.35	Ethyl methacrylate	0.22	68		3
	3.2	Ethyl vinyl ether	0	60	b,c	193
	2.6	4-Hydroabietyl alcohol	0			69
	$0.4 \pm 15\%$	Indene	$0.33 \pm 15\%$	70		9
	1.5	Isobutylene	0	70	b,c	193
	0.85 ± 0.04	Isopropenyl iso-cyanate	0.31 ± 0.02	60		136
	0.15	Isopropenyl methyl ketone	4.5	h		242a
	9	Maleic anhydride	0	h		193
	$0.15 \pm 15\%$	Methacrylic acid	$3.0 \pm 15\%$	70		9
	2.4	Methallyl acetate	0	60	b,c	193
	1.1	Methallyl chloride	0	60	b,c	193
	1	Methyl acrylate	1	60		193
	1	Methyl acrylate	1	70		18
	0.99 ± 0.10	Methyl acrylate	0.84 ± 0.06	60		68
	0.15 ± 0.02	Methyl isopropenyl ketone	4.5 ± 0.1	60	p	53
	0.24 ± 0.03	Methyl methacrylate	2.53 ± 0.01	60		169
	0.55	Methyl vinyl ketone	1.8	70		8
	0.91 ± 0.05	Octadecyl acrylate	1.01 ± 0.01	60		141
	1.50 ± 0.15	Octadecyl vinyl ether	0.0 ± 0.3	50		4
	0.87 ± 0.02	Octyl acrylate	0.70 ± 0.01	60		141

1.35 ± 0.15	Octyl vinyl ether	0.0 ± 0.2	50		4
0.1	Phenyl acetylene	1.4	60		65
20	n-Propyl crotonate	0	70		69
0.085 ± 0.010	Styrene	1.85 ± 0.05	60		64
0.145 ± 0.009	Styrene	2.1 ± 0.2	50		297
0.14 ± 0.05	Styrene	2.0 ± 0.1	60		169
0.046	Styrene	0	h		204
0.001	Styrene	0.0054	45		93
54 ± 5	trans-Trimethyl aconitate	0.01 ± 0.1	60		184
6	Vinyl acetate	0.1	68		3
3.6 ± 0.5	Vinyl acetate	0.0 ± 0.03	60		64
7.0 ± 1	Vinyl benzoate	0.1 ± 0.02	50	p	53, 242a
0.020	N-Vinyl carbazole	3.7	h		112
3.2	Vinyl chloride	0.3	60		193
Large	Vinyl chloride	0.14	68		3
4.5	Vinyl chloride	0.2	50		300
3.15	Vinyl chloride	0.23	55		73a
1.8 ± 0.5	Vinyl chloride	0.2 ± 0.2	45		256
7.5	Vinyl chloride	0.5	47		36a
1.8	Vinyl cyclohexene	0	70		69
11.7 ± 0.07	2-Vinyl furan	0.15 ± 0.014	h		146
1.04 ± 0.10	Vinylidene bromide	1.90 ± 0.11	h	Photosensitized initiator	327
0.012	Vinylidene cyanide	0.049	22	t, see ref. 108	93
1.46 ± 0.28	Vinyl isocyanate	0.33 ± 0.18	60		137
4.08 ± 0.20	Vinyl nonanoate	0.0 ± 0.01	60		179
3.80 ± 0.05	Vinyl octadecanoate	0.075 ± 0.025	60		179

(continued)

(*continued*)

M_1	r_1	M_2	r_2	T, °C.	Remarks	Ref.
Vinylidene chloride	1.35	N-Vinyl-2-oxazolidinone	0.08	75		117
	3.00 ± 0.18	Vinyl pinonate	0.03 ± 0.028	60		179
	1.44	N-Vinyl succinimide	0.32	60		125
	2.58 ± 0.09	Vinyl undecenoate	0.054 ± 0.30	60		179
Vinylidene cyanide	0.29 ± 0.08	Acrylic acid	0.26 ± 0.06	50	t, see ref. 108	93
	0.0048	2-Chlorobutadiene	0.016	40		93
	0.0017	2-Chlorobutadiene	0.010	40		93
	0.20 ± 0.06	2-Chlorobutadiene	~0	40		93
	0.20	2-Chloro-1-propene	0	40		93
	30	cis-Dichloroethylene	~0	40		93
	30	trans-Dichloroethylene	~0	40		93
	0.0092	2,5-Dichlorostyrene	0.031	40	t, see ref. 108	93
	0.182	Isobutylene	0.00176	h		26
	45	Maleic anhydride	~0	50		93
	0.091 ± 0.05	Methyl 1-chloroacrylate	0.41 ± 0.14	50		93
	0.031	Methyl methacrylate	0.046	50		93
	0.031	Methyl methacrylate	0.046	h		76
	0.0459	Styrene	0	h		204
	0.001	Styrene	0.005	45		93
	0.11	Vinyl acetate	0.0054	45		93

M_1	r_1	M_2	r_2	Temp., °C		Ref.
	0.10	Vinyl benzoate	0.008	43		93
	0.54 ± 0.2	Vinyl chloride	0.017 ± 0.01	50		93
	0.72	Vinyl chloride	0.0093	h		77
	0.13 ± 0.05	Vinyl chloroacetate	<0.004	40		93
	0.049	Vinylidene chloride	0.012	22		93
Vinyl isobutyl ether	0.01	Styrene	50	h	t, see ref. 108	242a
	0.02 ± 0.01	Vinyl chloride	2.0 ± 0.2	50		53, 242a
	2.03 ± 0.55	Vinyl-2-chloro-ethyl ether	0.34 ± 0.14	30	d	71
Vinyl isocaproate	—	Ethylene	—	80	r_1, r_2 could not be found accurately	321
	1.14	Vinyl acetate	0.67	80		163
	0.16 ± 0.06	Acrylonitrile	0.19 ± 0.03	60		137
	0.14 ± 1.0	Methyl acrylate	1.38 ± 0.27	60		137
	0.16 ± 0.08	Methyl methacrylate	5.57 ± 0.33	60		137
Vinyl isocyanate	0.01	Methyl methacrylate	3.3	h		325
	0.01 ± 0.02	Methyl methacrylate	3.3 ± 0.2	60		127a
	0.08 ± 0.04	Methyl methacrylate	8.13 ± 0.04	60		137
	0.1	Styrene	6.9	h		325
	0.1 ± 0.05	Styrene	6.9 ± 0.5	60		127a
	0.33 ± 0.18	Vinylidene chloride	1.46 ± 0.28	60		137
Vinyl isopropyl ether	11.45 ± 0.54	2-Chloro-1,3-butadiene	0.164 ± 0.043	65		207
	0.47	Acrylamide	0.68	h		337
	1.4	Acrylonitrile	0.36	h		337
Vinyl isothiocyanate	0.6 ± 0.02	Methyl methacrylate	0.85 ± 0.03	60		127a
	0.5	Styrene	0.8	h		337
	0.37 ± 0.02	Styrene	0.65 ± 0.02	60		127a

(continued)

(continued)

M_1	r_1	M_2	r_2	T, °C.	Remarks	Ref.
Vinyl laurate	0.04 ± 0.03	Acrylonitrile	4.0 ± 0.3	60		29
	0.7	Vinyl acetate	1.4	60		265
	0.2	Vinyl chloride	7.4	h	a	153
Vinyl levulinate	0.419 ± 0.002	Vinyl chloride	1.40 ± 0.004	60	a	179
2-Vinylmercapto-benzothiazole	1.0	Methyl acrylate	0.1	60		148
Vinyl mesitylene	0.16 ± 0.02	Acrylonitrile	0.98 ± 0.2	138		63
	0.06	p-Chlorostyrene	10	130		63
	0.05 ± 0.01	Methyl methacrylate	1.6 ± 0.3	130		63
	0.08	Methyl methacrylate	1.4	85		63
Vinyl methyl di-ethoxysilane	0	Acrylonitrile	6.0	50		296
	0	Vinyl chloride	1.0	50		296
Vinyl methyl ether	0.01	Styrene	100	h		242a
Vinyl myristate	0.04 ± 0.03	Acrylonitrile	4.0 ± 0.3	60		29
1-Vinyl naphthalene	1.35 ± 0.15	Styrene	0.67 ± 0.03	60		173
	0.35 ± 0.2	Styrene	3.3 ± 0.5	40		279
2-Vinyl naphthalene	1.0 ± 0.15	Methyl methacrylate	0.4 ± 0.05	60	e	247
	1.4 ± 0.1	Styrene	0.5 ± 0.1	60		247
Vinyl nonanoate	0.059 ± 0.095	Acrylonitrile	3.57 ± 0.16	60		179
	0.02 ± 0.02	Butadiene	26.3 ± 10.0	60		179
	0.01 ± 0.01	Styrene	49.5 ± 15	60		179
	0.282 ± 0.35	Vinyl chloride	1.16 ± 0.06	60		179
	0.0 ± 0.01	Vinylidene chloride	4.08 ± 0.20	60		179
Vinyl octadecanoate	0.064 ± 0.005	Acrylonitrile	4.20 ± 0.02	60		179
	0.03	Acrylonitrile	4.3	70		333
	0.034 ± 0.034	Butadiene	34.5 ± 6.0	60		179

M1	r_1	M2	r_2	Temp	Notes	Ref
	0	Diisopropyl maleate	0.0075	70		333
	0.03	Methyl acrylate	5.8	70		333
	0.01 ± 0.01	Styrene	68 ± 30	60		179
	0.73	Vinyl acetate	0.90	70		333
	1.00	Vinyl acetate	0.97	50	M2 impure	1
	0.290 ± 0.025	Vinyl chloride	0.745 ± 0.026	60		179
	0.075 ± 0.025	Vinylidene chloride	3.80 ± 0.05	60		179
N-Vinyl oxazolidone	0.015 ± 0.05	Decyl methacrylate	12.8 ± 0.5	50		40
N-Vinyl oxazolidinone	0.03	Methyl methacrylate	6.00	75		117
	0.035	Methyl methacrylate	9.6 ± 0.2	50		40
	0.05 ± 0.05	Styrene	30 ± 0.5	50		40
	1.50	Vinyl acetate	0.60	75		117
	1.90 ± 0.10	Vinyl acetate	0.52 ± 0.08	50		40
	0.35 ± 0.02	Vinyl chloride	0.84 ± 0.02	50		40
	1.50	Vinyl chloride	0.60	h		117
	0.08	Vinylidene chloride	1.35	75		117
Vinyl palmitate	0.04 ± 0.03	Acrylonitrile	4.0 ± 0.3	60		29
	0.78 ± 1.0	Vinyl acetate	1.15 ± 0.13	70–73	r_1 and r_2 cal. from polymer analysis	
	0.66 ± 0.07	Vinyl acetate	0.84 ± 0.10	70–73	r_1 and r_2 cal. from residual monomer analysis	243
Vinyl pentanoate	0.59 ± 0.20	Allyl chloride	1.62 ± 0.310	60		243
Vinyl perfluoro-butyrate	0.017	Styrene	8.73	h		144
2-Vinyl phenanthrene	2.0 ± 0.2	Methyl acrylate	0.1 ± 0.03	60		337
3-Vinyl phenanthrene	1.75 ± 0.25	Methyl acrylate	0.8 ± 0.05	60		247
m-Vinyl phenol	1.21	Styrene	0.9	60		247
						39

(continued)

(continued)

M_1	r_1	M_2	r_2	T, °C.	Remarks	Ref.
Vinyl phenyl boronic acid	1.0	Acrylamide	0.0	60		239c
Vinyl phenyl di-ethoxysilane	0	Acrylonitrile	8.3	50		296
	0	Vinyl chloride	0.7	50		296
1-p-Vinyl phenyl disiloxane	1.2 ± 0.4	Styrene	1.04 ± 0.06	80		127a
1-p-Vinyl phenyl pentasiloxane	1.2 ± 0.1	Styrene	1.11 ± 0.01	80		127a
1-p-Vinyl phenyl tetrasiloxane	1.1 ± 0.3	Styrene	1.15 ± 0.05	80		127a
1-p-Vinyl phenyl trisiloxane	1.2 ± 0.2	Styrene	0.90 ± 0.03	80		127a
Vinyl pinonate	0.143 ± 0.046	Acrylonitrile	3.40 ± 0.04	60		179
	0.015 ± 0.015	Butadiene	37.8 ± 6.5	60		179
	0.01 ± 0.01	Styrene	65 ± 17	60		179
	0.446 ± 0.028	Vinyl chloride	1.458 ± 0.04	60		179
	0.03 ± 0.028	Vinylidene chloride	3.00 ± 0.18	60		179
Vinyl propionate	0.62 ± 0.09	Allyl chloride	0.68 ± 0.110	60		144
	0.05	2-Chloro-1,3-buta-diene	70	65		314
	0.076 ± 0.018	N-Vinyl carbazole	1.68 ± 0.140	100		310,313
	0.65 ± 0.04	Vinyl chloride	1.35 ± 0.05	40		153
2-Vinylpyridine	0.47 ± 0.03	Acrylonitrile	0.113 ± 0.002	60		139
	2.13	Acrylonitrile	0.086	h	j	340
	21.9 ± 5.52	Acrylonitrile	0.05 ± 0.01	60		160,161
	f	Acrylonitrile	f	h		342

2-Vinylpyridine	0.097 ± 0.04	Butyl acrylate	2.51 ± 0.05	60	294
	0.06 ± 0.01	2-Chloro-1,3-butadiene	5.19 ± 0.03	60	160,161
	0.63 ± 0.07	Dichlorostyrene (mixed isomers)	0.11 ± 0.07	60	2
	1.1	2,5-Dichlorostyrene	0.9	70	18
	0.23 ± 0.05	Ethyl acrylate	0.19 ± 0.06	75	317
	0.47 ± 0.07	Isoprene	0.59 ± 0.05	60	160,161
	1.65 ± 0.05	Isopropenyl acetylene	0.55 ± 0.01	60	248
	1.55 ± 0.10	Methacrylic acid	0.58 ± 0.05	70	21
	2.03 ± 0.49	Methyl acrylate	0.20 ± 0.09	60	2
	1.58 ± 0.05	Methyl acrylate	0.168 ± 0.003	60	289
	0.77 ± 0.02	Methyl methacrylate	0.439 ± 0.002	60	289
	0.86 ± 0.06	Methyl methacrylate	0.395 ± 0.025	60	322
	0.70 ± 15%	Methyl methacrylate	0.33 ± 15%	70	9
	4.0 ± 0.07	Phenylacetylene	0.2 ± 0.05	60	246
	0.9 ± 0.2	Styrene	0.56 ± 0.02	60	289
	1.14	Styrene	0.55	60	237
	1.135 ± 0.08	Styrene	0.55 ± 0.025	60	322
	1.81 ± 0.05	Styrene	0.55 ± 0.03	60	160,161
	10	Vinyl acetate	0.3	h	221
	30 ± 15	Vinyl acetate	0	70	9
	1.5 ± 0.5	1-Vinyl-2-ethyl acetylene	0.6 ± 1	60	248
4-Vinylpyridine	0.41 ± 0.09	Acrylonitrile	0.113 ± 0.005	60	139
	5.15 ± 0.09	Butyl acrylate	0.46 ± 0.09	60	88
	1.7 ± 0.2	Methyl acrylate	0.22 ± 0.01	60	289
	0.79 ± 0.05	Methyl methacrylate	0.574 ± 0.004	60	289
	0.52 ± 0.06	Styrene	0.62 ± 0.02	80	89

(continued)

(continued)

M_1	r_1	M_2	r_2	T, °C.	Remarks	Ref.
4-Vinylpyridine	0.7 ± 0.1	Styrene	0.54 ± 0.03	60		289
	0.30 ± 0.02	N,N,N-Triethyl-1-N-[2-(methacryloxy)-ethyl]-ammonium iodide	0.61 ± 0.09	60		234
2-Vinylpyridine-N-oxide	3.9 ± 0.8	Methyl methacrylate	0.13 ± 0.03	60		292
	2.1 ± 0.6	Styrene	0.11 ± 0.01	60		292
N-Vinylpyridinium fluoroborate	0.20	Acrylonitrile	1.06	60		70b
	0.2	Methyl acrylate	1.5	60		70b
	0.008	Methyl methacrylate	4.75	60		70b
4-Vinylpyrimidine	1.2 ± 0.1	Styrene	0.17 ± 0.02	60		237
N-Vinylpyrrolidone	0.15 ± 0.1	Acrylic acid	1.3 ± 0.2	75		317
	0.030 ± 0.033	Dioctyl fumarate	0.041 ± 0.007	76		145a
	0.041 ± 0.024	Methyl acrylate	0.27 ± 0.16	60		337
	0.005 ± 0.05	Methyl methacrylate	4.7 ± 0.5	50		40
	0.045 ± 0.05	Styrene	15.7 ± 0.5	50		40
	0.11	Styrene	9.0	80		337
	4.0 ± 15%	tris-(Trimethylsiloxy)vinylsilane	0.1 ± 15%	125		241
	3.30 ± 0.15	Vinyl acetate	0.205 ± 0.015	50		40
	0.44	Vinyl acetate	0.38	h		44
	0.44	Vinyl acetate	0.38	70		118
	2.28 ± 0.19	Vinyl acetate	0.237 ± 0.037	76		145a
	2.45 ± 0.1	Vinyl benzoate	0.44 ± 0.09	60		318
	0.38	Vinyl chloride	0.53	h		44

Monomer 1	r1	Monomer 2	r2	Temp	Ref
2-Vinylquinoline	0.7	Vinylene carbonate	0.4	60	118
	2	N-Vinyl urethane	0.42	65	92
	0.38 ± 0.03	2-Chloro-1,3-butadiene	2.10 ± 0.13	60	160,161
	0.53 ± 0.01	Isoprene	1.88 ± 0.02	60	160,161
	2.09 ± 0.55	Styrene	0.49 ± 0.14	60	160,161
Vinyl stearate	0.04 ± 0.03	Acrylonitrile	4.0 ± 0.3	60	29
N-Vinylsuccinimide	0.16	Acrylonitrile	0.54	60	90
	15	n-Butyl vinyl ether	0	60	90
	0.4	Methyl acrylate	1.2	60	90
	0.064	Methyl methacrylate	9.5	60	125
	0.09	Styrene	7.0	60	90
	0.07	Styrene	10.5	60	125
	6.1	Vinyl acetate	0.18	60	125
	0.32	Vinylidene chloride	1.44	60	125
Vinyl sulfonic acid	0	Methyl methacrylate	Large	70	105
Vinyl thioacetate	12.9 ± 1.1	Vinylene carbonate	0.04 ± 0.01	60	234
2-Vinylthiophene	3.10 ± 0.45	Styrene	0.35 ± 0.025	60	322
Vinyl triethoxysilane	0	Acrylonitrile	5 ± 1	60	271
	0	Acrylonitrile	4.5	50	296
	0	Vinyl chloride	0.9	50	296
Vinyl trifluoroacetate	0.32	Vinyl acetate	0.6	60	103
Vinyl triisopropoxy-silane	0	Acrylonitrile	6.5	50	296
	0	Vinyl chloride	0.8	50	296
Vinyl trimethoxy-silane	0	Acrylonitrile	6.0	50	296
	0	Styrene	22 ± 5	60	271
	0	Vinyl chloride	0.8	50	296

(continued)

(*continued*)

M_1	r_1	M_2	r_2	T, °C.	Remarks	Ref.
Vinyl trimethoxy-silane	0.07 ± 0.03	Acrylonitrile	3.9 ± 3	60		271
Vinyl trimethylsilane	0	Styrene	26 ± 8	60		271
Vinyl undecenoate	0.0 ± 0.10	Acrylonitrile	1.82 ± 0.04	60		179
	0.015 ± 0.015	Butadiene	37.9 ± 4.0	60		179
	0.031 ± 0.12	Methyl acrylate	3.69 ± 0.12	60		179
	0.02 ± 0.02	Styrene	29 ± 9	60		179
	0.358 ± 0.065	Vinyl chloride	1.06 ± 0.05	60		179
	0.054 ± 0.30	Vinylidene chloride	2.58 ± 0.09	60		179
N-Vinyl urethane	0.33	Vinyl acetate	0.33	65		92
	0.42	N-Vinyl pyrrolidone	2	65		92
Vinyl valerate	0.59	Allyl chloride	1.62	60		144

[a] Emulsion system.
[b] Value from single experiment.
[c] r_2 value assumed.
[d] Friedel–Crafts system.
[e] Anionic or Ziegler catalysts.
[f] r_1 and r_2 not quoted in the abstract from which the information is taken.
[g] r_1 is monomer reactivity ratio (mrr) of styrene relative to vinyl group in divinyl benzene and r_2 is mrr of vinyl group in DVB relative to styrene.
[h] No temperature quoted in abstract.
[i] In the presence of H_2O_2 and $NaNO_2$ in water.
[j] In water in the presence of ammonium persulfate.
[k] Values are independent of chain length of the ester.
[l] Dye sensitized polymerization.

[m] Redox system.
[n] Penultimate group effect considered. See original paper for values of reactivity ratios.
[o] r_1 and r_2 calculated by the method of Gundin [*Chem. Abstr.* **42**, 5115c (1948)].
[p] Thermal initiation.
[q] M_1 and M_2 are named differently in the two literature sources quoted.
[r] r_1 and r_2 may not be calculated due to effect not only of penultimate unit but units even further removed from chain end.
[s] At lower styrene r_1 and r_2 increase. Mechanism unknown.
[t] A penultimate group effect operates.

References

1. Adicoff, A., and A. Buselli, *J. Polymer Sci.* **21**, 340 (1956).
2. Aggarwal, S. L., and F. A. Long, *J. Polymer Sci.*, **11**, 127 (1953).
3. Agron, P., T. Alfrey, Jr., J. Bohrer, H. Haas, and H. Wechsler, *J. Polymer Sci.* **3**, 157 (1948).
4. Akazome, G., S. Sakai, Y. Choshi, and K. Murai, *Chem. High Polymers* (*Tokyo*) **17**, 558 (1960).
4a. Akazome, G., S. Sakai, Y. Choshi, and K. Murai, *Kobunshi Kagaku* **17**, 627 (1960) through *Makromol. Chem.* **42**, 174 (1960).
5. Akazome, G., S. Sakai, and K. Murai, *Kobunshi Kagaku* **17**, 449 (1960).
5a. Akazome, G., S. Sakai, and K. Murai, *Kobunshi Kagaku* **17**, 618 (1960); through *Makromol. Chem.* **42**, 174 (1960).
6. Akiyoshi, S., C. Aşo, and K. Sadakata, *Kogyo Kagaku Zasshi* **60**, 1081 (1957); *Chem. Abstr.* **53**, 10836h (1959).
7. Alfrey, T., Jr., L. Arond, and C. G. Overberger, *J. Polymer Sci.* **4**, 539 (1949).
8. Alfrey, T., Jr., L. Arond, and C. G. Overberger, quoted in ref. 10, p. 35.
9. Alfrey, T., Jr., J. Bohrer, H. Haas, and C. Lewis, *J. Polymer Sci.* **5**, 719 (1950).
10. Alfrey, T., Jr., J. Bohrer, and H. Mark, *Copolymerization*, High Polymer Series; Vol. VIII, Interscience, New York, 1952, p. 40.
11. Alfrey, T., Jr., and W. H. Ebelke, *J. Am. Chem. Soc.* **71**, 3235 (1949).
12. Alfrey, T., Jr., A. I. Goldberg, and W. P. Hohenstein, *J. Am. Chem. Soc.* **68**, 2464 (1946).
13. Alfrey, T., Jr., and S. Greenberg, *J. Polymer Sci.* **3**, 297 (1948).
14. Alfrey, T., Jr., and J. G. Harrison, Jr., *J. Am. Chem. Soc.* **68**, 299 (1946).
15. Alfrey, T., Jr., and S. L. Kapur, *J. Polymer Sci.* **4**, 215 (1949).
16. Alfrey, T., Jr., and S. L. Kapur, quoted in ref. 10, p. 33, 39.
17. Alfrey, T., Jr., and E. Lavin, *J. Am. Chem. Soc.* **67**, 2044 (1945).
18. Alfrey, T., Jr., and B. Magel, quoted in ref. 10.
19. Alfrey, T., Jr., and B. Magel, quoted by R. Hart, *Makromol. Chem.* **47**, 143 (1960).
20. Alfrey, T., Jr., E. Merz, and H. Mark, *J. Polymer Sci.* **1**, 37 (1946).
21. Alfrey, T., Jr., and H. Morawetz, *J. Am. Chem. Soc.* **74**, 436 (1952).
22. Alfrey, T., Jr., C. G. Overberger, and S. H. Pinner, *J. Am. Chem. Soc.* **75**, 4221 (1953).
23. Alfrey, T., Jr., and H. Wechsler, *J. Am. Chem. Soc.* **70**, 4266 (1948).
24. American Cyanamid Company, *The Chemistry of Acrylonitrile*, 2nd ed., 1960, p. 34.
24a. American Cyanamid Company, private communication.
24b. Anderson, I. H., G. M. Burnett, and P. J. Tait, *J. Polymer Sci.* **56**, 391 (1962).
25. Arcus, C. L., and R. J. S. Matthews, *J. Chem. Soc.* **1956**, 4607.
26. Ardis, A., Can. Patent 516,315 (1955).

27. Arlman, E. J., and H. W. Melville, *Proc. Roy. Soc. (London)* **A203**, 301 (1950).

28. Arlman, E. J., H. W. Melville, and L. Valentine, *Rec. Trav. Chim.* **68**, 945, (1949).

29. Asahara, T., and K. Mitsuhashi, *Yukagaku* **6**, 331 (1957); *Chem. Abstr.* **54**, 20303*f* (1960).

30. Ashikari, N., *Bull. Chem. Soc. Japan* **32**, 1060 (1959).

31. Ashik ari, N., and A. Nishimura, *J. Polymer Sci.* **31**, 250 (1958).

31a. Aso, C., *Kogyo Kagaku Zasshi* **63**, 363 (1960); through *Resins, Rubbers, Plastics*, **14**, 867 (1960).

32. Baker, W. P., *J. Polymer Sci.* **42**, 578 (1960).

33. Bamford, C. H., and W. G. Barb, *Discussions Faraday Soc.* **14**, 208 (1953).

34. Banerjee, S., and M. S. Muthana, *J. Polymer Sci.* **35**, 292 (1959).

35. Barb, W. G., *J. Polymer Sci.* **11**, 117 (1953).

36. Bartlett, P. D., and K. Nozaki, *J. Am. Chem. Soc.* **68**, 1495 (1946).

36a. Bengough, W. I., and R. G. W. Norrish, *Proc. Roy. Soc. (London)* **A218** 155 (1953).

36b. Beynon, K. I., *J. Polymer Sci.* **A1**, 3343 (1963).

36c. Beynon, K. I., *J. Polymer Sci.* **A1**, 3357 (1963).

37. Blackley, D. C., and H. W. Melville, *Makromol. Chem.* **18**, 16 (1956).

38. Blauer, G., and L. Goldstein, *J. Polymer Sci.* **25**, 19 (1957).

39. Bonsall, E. P., L. Valentine, and H. W. Melville, *Trans. Faraday Soc.* **48**, 763 (1952).

40. Bork, J. F., and L. E. Coleman, *J. Polymer Sci.* **43**, 413 (1960)

41. Borrows, E. T., R. N. Haward, J. Porges, and J. Street, *J. Appl. Chem. (London)* **5**, 379 (1955).

42. Bourdais, J., *Bull. Soc. Chim. France* **1955**, 485.

43. Bradbury, J. H., and H. W. Melville, *Proc. Roy. Soc. (London)* **A222**, 456 (1954).

43a. Brandrup, J., *Faserforsch. Textiltech.* **12**, 135 (1961).

43b. Braun, D., T. Ahn, and W. Kern, *Makromol. Chem.* **53**, 154 (1962).

44. Breitenbach, J. W., and H. Edelhauser, *Ric. Sci.* **25**, 242 (1955).

45. Breitenbach, J. W., A. Schindler, and C. Pflug, *Monatsh. Chem.* **81**, 21 (1950); *Chem. Abstr.* **44**, 8693*i* (1950).

46. Breslow, D. S., and A. Kutner, *J. Polymer Sci.* **27**, 295 (1958).

47. Britton, E. C., C. W. Davis, and F. L. Taylor, U. S. Patent 2,160,940 (1939), calc. by F. R. Mayo and C. Walling, ref. 194, assuming only one dimethylal group reacts.

47a. Bulatov, M. A., and S. S. Spasskii, *Vysokomolekul. Soedin.* **2**, 658 (1960); through *J. Polymer Sci.* **47**, 544 (1960).

47b. Burkhart, R. D., and N. L. Zutty, *J. Polymer Sci.* **57**, 783 (1962).

48. Burnett, G. M., P. Evans, and H. W. Melville, *Trans. Faraday Soc.*, **49**, 1096 (1953).

49. Cameron, G. G., D. H. Grant, N. Grassie, J. E. Lamb, and I. C. McNeill, *J. Polymer Sci.* **36**, 173 (1959).

50. Cameron, G. G., and N. Grassie, *Makromol. Chem.* **51**, 130 (1962).

51. Chang, E. Y. C., and C. C. Price, *J. Am. Chem. Soc.* **83**, 4650 (1961).

52. Chapin, E. C., G. E. Ham, and R. G. Fordyce, *J. Am. Chem. Soc.* **70**, 538 (1948).
53. Chapin, E. C., G. E. Ham, and C. L. Mills, *J. Polymer Sci.* **4**, 597 (1949); erratum: *J. Polymer Sci.* **55**, S6 (1961).
54. Chas. Pfizer and Co., *Product News*, quoted by L. J. Young, ref. 337.
55. Cohen, S. G., and D. B. Sparrow, *J. Polymer Sci.* **3**, 693 (1948).
56. Coleman, L. E., Jr., and J. A. Conrady, *J. Polymer Sci.* **38**, 241 (1959).
57. Coleman, L. E., Jr., and W. S. Durrell, *J. Org. Chem.* **23**, 1211 (1958).
58. Cooper, W., and E. Catterall, *Can. J. Chem.* **34**, 387 (1956).
58a. Coscia, A. T., R. L. Kugel, and J. Pellon, *J. Polymer Sci.* **55**, 303 (1961).
59. Crauwels, K , and G. Smets, *Bull. Soc. Chim. Belges* **59**, 443 (1950).
60. Crauwels, K., and G. Smets, *Bull. Soc. Chim. Belges* **59**, 182 (1950).
60a. Csuros, Z., M. Gara, and I. Gyukovics, *Acta. Chim. Acad. Sci. Hung.* **29**, 207 (1961); *Chem. Abstr.* **56**, 10385e (1962).
61. D'Alelio, G. F., and L. X. Mallavarapu, *Makromol. Chem.* **37**, 25 (1960).
62. Denoon, C. E., U. S. Patent 2,384,731 (1945), calc. by F. R. Mayo and C. Walling, ref. 194.
63. De Pauw, A., and G. Smets, *Bull. Soc. Chim. Belges* **59**, 629 (1950).
64. Doak, K. W., *J. Am. Chem. Soc.* **70**, 1525 (1948).
65. Doak, K. W., quoted in ref. 194.
66. Doak, K. W., *J. Am. Chem. Soc.* **72**, 4681 (1950).
67. Doak, K. W., M. A. Deahl, and I. H. Christmas, 137th ACS Meeting, Cleveland, Ohio, Abstr. Papers, Vol. 1, No. 1, 151 (April 1960).
68. Doak, K. W., and D. L. Dineen, *J. Am. Chem. Soc.* **73**, 1084 (1951).
68a. Dawans, F., and G. Smets, *Makromol. Chem.* **59**, 163 (1963).
69. Dolgin, G., and P. Gordon, quoted in ref. 10, p. 40.
70. Dokukina, A. F., Z. A. Smirnova, and M. M. Koton, *Vysokomolekul. Soedin.* **2**, 1247 (1960).
70a. Drougas, J., and R. L. Guile, *J. Polymer Sci.* **55**, 297 (1961).
70b. Duling, I. N., and C. C. Price, *J. Am. Chem. Soc.* **84**, 578 (1962).
71. Dunphy, J. F., and C. S. Marvel, *J. Polymer Sci.* **47**, 1 (1960).
72. DuPont Co., British Patent 593,605 (1947), calc. by F. R. Mayo and C. Walling, ref. 194.
73. Embree, W. H., J. M. Mitchell, and H. L. Williams, *Can. J. Chem.* **29**, 253 (1951).
73a. Enomoto, S., *J. Polymer Sci.* **55**, 95 (1961).
74. Exner, J., and M. Bohdanecky, *Chem. Listy* **48**, 483 (1954); *Chem. Abstr.* **48**, 8583g (1954).
75. Florin, R. E., *J. Am. Chem. Soc.* **71**, 1867 (1949).
75a. Florin, R. E., *J. Am. Chem. Soc.* **73**, 4468 (1951).
76. Folt, V. L., Canadian Patent 509,259 (1955).
77. Folt, V. L., Canadian Patent 510,354 (1955).
78. Fordham, J. W. L., G. H. McCain, and L. E. Alexander, *J. Polymer Sci.* **39**, 335 (1959).
78a. Fordham, J. W. L., and H. L. Williams, *J. Phys. Chem.* **57**, 346 (1953).
79. Fordyce, R. G., *J. Am. Chem. Soc.* **69**, 1903 (1947).
80. Fordyce, R. G., and E. C. Chapin, *J. Am. Chem. Soc.* **69**, 581 (1947).

81. Fordyce, R. G., E. C. Chapin, and G. E. Ham, *J. Am. Chem. Soc.* **70**, 2489 (1948).

82. Fordyce, R. G., and G. E. Ham, *J. Am. Chem. Soc.* **69**, 695 (1947).

83. Fordyce, R. G., and G. E. Ham, *J. Am. Chem. Soc.* **73**, 1186 (1951).

84. Foster, F. C., *J. Polymer Sci.* **5**, 369 (1950).

85. Foster, F. C., *J. Am. Chem. Soc.* **72**, 1370 (1950).

86. Foster, F. C., *J. Am. Chem. Soc.* **72**, 2299 (1952).

87. Frank, C. E., G. Kraus, and A. J. Haefner, *Ind. Eng. Chem.* **44**, 1600 (1952).

88. Funt, B. L., and E. A. Ogryzlo, *J. Polymer Sci.* **25**, 279 (1957).

89. Fuoss, R. M., and G. I. Cathers, *J. Polymer Sci.* **4**, 97 (1949).

89a. Furukawa, J., T. Tsuruta, S. Inoue, A. Kawasaki, and N. Kawabata, *J. Polymer Sci.* **35**, 269 (1959).

90. Furukawa, J., T. Tsuruta, N. Yamamoto, and H. Fukutani, *J. Polymer Sci.* **37**, 215 (1959).

91. Furukawa, J., T. Tsuruta, and N. Yameda, *Kogyo Kagaku Zasshi* **61**, 734 (1958).

91a. Gantmakher, A. R., Yu. L. Spirin, and S. S. Medvedev, *Vysokomolekul. Soedin.* **1**, 1526 (1959); through *Chem. Zentr.* **132**, 10581 (1961).

92. Ghosez, L., and G. Smets, *J. Polymer Sci.* **35**, 215 (1959).

93. Gilbert, H., et al., *J. Am. Chem. Soc.* **78**, 1669 (1956).

94. Gilbert, R. D., and H. L. Williams, *J. Am. Chem. Soc.* **74**, 4114 (1952).

95. Gleason, A. H., U. S. Patent 2,379,292 (1945), calc. by F. R. Mayo and C. Walling, ref. 194.

96. Gluckman, M. S., M. J. Kampf, J. L. O'Brien, T. G Fox, and R. K. Graham, *J. Polymer Sci.* **37**, 411 (1959).

97. Goldfinger, G., and M. Steidiltz, *J. Polymer Sci.* **3**, 786 (1948).

98. Golubeva, A. V., N. F. Usmanova, and A. A. Vansheidt, *J. Polymer Sci.* **52**, 63 (1961).

99. Goodstein, M., quoted in ref. 10, p. 35.

100. Gordon, M., B. M. Grieveson, and I. D. McMillan, *J. Polymer Sci.* **18**, 497 (1955).

101. Grabief, C. E., and D. L. Decker, *J. Polymer Sci.* **59**, 425 (1962).

102. Grassie, N., and I. C. McNeill, *J. Polymer Sci.* **27**, 207 (1958).

103. Haas, H. C., E. S. Emerson, and N. W. Schuler, *J. Polymer Sci.* **22**, 291 (1956).

104. Haas, H. C., and N. W. Schuler, *J. Polymer Sci.* **31**, 237 (1958).

105. Haas, H. C., and M. S. Simon, *J. Polymer Sci.* **9**, 309 (1952).

106. Hahn, W., and A. Fischer, *Makromol. Chem.* **21**, 77 (1956).

107. Ham, G. E., *J. Polymer Sci.* **24**, 87 (1954).

108. Ham, G. E., *J. Polymer Sci.* **24**, 349 (1957).

109. Ham, G. E., *J. Polymer Sci.* **38**, 543 (1959).

110. Ham, G. E., *J. Polymer Sci.* **45**, 177 (1960).

111. Ham, G. E., *J. Polymer Sci.* **45**, 183 (1960).

112. Hart, R., *Makromol. Chem.* **47**, 143 (1961).

113. Hart, R., *Makromol. Chem.* **49**, 33 (1961).

114. Hart, R., and A. E. van Dormael, *Bull. Soc. Chim. Belges* **65**, 571 (1956).

115. Hart, R., and G. Smets, *J. Polymer Sci.* **5**, 55 (1950).

116. Hart, R., and D. Timmerman, *Bull. Soc. Chim. Belges* **67**, 123 (1958).

117. Hart, R , and D. Timmerman, *Makromol. Chem.* **31**, 223 (1959).

117a. Hart, R., and D. Timmerman, *J. Polymer Sci.* **48**, 151 (1960).

118. Hayashi, K., and G. Smets, *J. Polymer Sci.* **27**, 275 (1958).

119. Henery-Logan, K. R., and R. V. V. Nicholls, quoted in ref. 279a.

120. Henery-Logan, K. R., and R. V. V. Nicholls, quoted in ref. 194.

121. Higashimura, T., and S. Okamura, *Chem. High Polymers (Tokyo)* **17**, 635 (1960); *Chem. Abstr.* **55**, 21654e (1961).

122. Higuchi, T., and H. Imoto, *Kogyo Kagaku Zasshi* **61**, 1053 (1958).

123. Hess, R., quoted in ref. 10, pp. 36, 37.

124. Holly, E. D., *J. Polymer Sci.* **36**, 329 (1959).

124a. Holly, E. D., unpublished data.

124b. Holly, E. D., and W. R. Nummy, unpublished data.

125. Hopff, H., and P. Schlumbom, *Makromol. Chem.* **43**, 173 (1961).

126. Hopff, H., and D. Sterck, *Makromol. Chem.* **48**, 50 (1961).

127. Hunyar, A., and H. Reichert, *Faserforsch. Textiltech.* **5**, 204 (1954); *Chem. Abstr.* **48**, 11106d (1954).

127a. Husemann, E., University of Freiburg i. Br. Germany, private communication. See also G. Greber and E. Reese, *Makromol. Chem.* **55**, 96 (1962).

128. Ichida, S., *Bull. Chem. Soc. Japan* **33**, 731 (1960).

129. Immergut, E. H., G. Kollmann, and A. Malatesta, *Makromol. Chem.* **41**, 15 (1960).

130. Imoto, E., and H. Horiuchi, *Kobunshi Kagaku* **8**, 463 (1951); *Chem. Abstr.* **47**, 9664a (1953).

131. Imperial Chemical Industries Ltd., British Patent 594,249 (1947), calc. by F. R. Mayo and C. Walling, ref. 194.

132. Ito, H., and S. Suzuki, *Kogyo Kagaku Zasshi* **58**, 627 (1955); *Chem. Abstr.* **50**, 7501e (1956).

133. Ito, H., and S. Suzuki, *Kogyo Kagaku Zasshi* **60**, 341 (1957); *Chem. Abstr.* **53**, 5732f (1959).

134. Iwakura, Y., T. Kurosaki, and N. Nakabayashi, *Makromol. Chem.* **46**, 570 (1961).

135. Iwakura, Y., and K. Matsuzaki, *Chem. High Polymers (Tokyo)* **17**, 187 (1960).

136. Iwakura, Y., M. Sato, T. Tamikado, and S. Mimashi, *Kobunshi Kagaku* **13**, 125 (1956); *Chem. Abstr.* **51**, 4045d (1957).

137. Iwakura, Y., M. Sato, T. Tamikado, and T. Mizoguchi, *Kobunshi Kagaku* **13**, 390 (1956); *Chem. Abstr.* **51**, 18694b (1957).

138. Iwakura, Y., T. Tamikado, Y. Fujimoto, S. Ikegami, and M. Maruyama, *Kobunshi Kagaku* **15**, 469 (1958); *Chem. Abstr.* **54**, 11155a (1960).

139. Iwakura, Y., T. Tamikado, M. Yamaguchi, and K. Takei, *J. Polymer Sci.* **39**, 203 (1959).

139a. Johnson, W. A., and L. J. Young, unpublished data.

140. Jones, G. D., J. R. Runyonrana, and J. Ong, *Ind. Eng. Chem.* **53**, 297 (1961).

141. Jordan, E. F., K. M. Doughty, and W. S. Port, *J. Appl. Polymer Sci.* **4**, 203 (1960).

142. Joshi, R. M., and S. L. Kapur, *J. Polymer Sci.* **14**, 508 (1954).

143. Joshi, R. M., and S. L. Kapur, *J. Sci. Ind. Res. (India)* **16B**, 379 (1957); *Chem. Abstr.* **52**, 5029a (1958).

144. Joshi, R. M., and S. L. Kapur, *J. Sci. Ind. Res. (India)* **16B**, 441, 1957; *Chem. Abstr.* **52**, 5105h (1958).

145. Judge, J. M., and C. C. Price, *J. Polymer Sci.* **41**, 435 (1959).

145a. Kahn, D. J., and H. H. Horowitz, *J. Polymer Sci.* **54**, 363 (1961).

146. Kamenar, S., et al., *Chem. Zvesti* **14**, 581 (1960); *Chem. Abstr.* **55**, 15450i (1961).

146a. Kawabata, N., T. Tsuruta, and J. Furukawa, *Makromol. Chem.* **48**, 106 (1961).

147. Kenyon, W. O., and J. H. van Campen, U. S. Patent 2,419,221 (1947), calc. by F. R. Mayo and C. Walling, ref. 194.

148. Kern, R. J., *J. Polymer Sci.* **43**, 549 (1960).

148a. Kern, W., University of Mainz, Germany, private communication.

148b. Kern, W., and D. Braun, *Makromol. Chemie* **27**, 23 (1958).

148c. Khomutov, A. M., *Izv. Acad. Nauk SSSR Otd. Khim. Nauk*, **1961**, 352; English transl., p. 324.

149. Kimura, T., and M. Imoto, *Makromol. Chem.* **50**, 155 (1961).

149a. Kimura, T., and K. Yoshida, *Kagaku To Kogyo (Osaka)* **27**, 288 (1953); through *Chem. Abstr.* **49**, 12034a (1955).

150. Kimura, T., and K. Yoshida, *Kagaku To Kogyo (Osaka)* **28**, 158 (1954); *Chem. Abstr.* **49**, 12873b (1955).

151. Kimura, T., and K. Yoshida, *Kagaku To Kogyo (Osaka)* **29**, 43, 288 (1955); *Chem. Abstr.* **49**, 13688g (1955).

152. Kimura, T., and K. Yoshida, *Kagaku To Kogyo (Osaka)* **29**, 288 (1955).

153. Kimura, T., and K. Yoshida, *Kagaku To Kogyo (Osaka)* **32**, 223, 341 (1958); *Chem. Abstr.* **53**, 4806g (1959).

154. Klebanskii, A. L., and O. A. Timofeev, *Zh. Prikl. Khim.*, **32**, 2294 (1959); *Chem. Abstr.* **54**, 8587a (1960); *J. Polymer Sci.* **52**, 23 (1961).

154a. Klebanskii, A. L., and O. A. Timofeev, *Zh. Obshch. Khim.* **30**, 60 (1960); English transl. p. 62.

155. Kliman, N., and M. Lazar, *Chem. Prumysl* **9**, 668 (1959); *Chem. Abstr.* **54**, 10390d (1960).

156. Knobloch, F. W., *J. Polymer Sci.* **25**, 453 (1957).

157. Kolesnikov, G. S., et al., *Vysokomolekul. Soedin.* **2**, 567 (1960).

158. Korotkov, A. A., and N. N. Chesnokova, *Vysokomolekul. Soedin.* **2**, 365 (1960); *Chem. Abstr.* **54**, 20302e (1960).

159. Korotkov, A. A., S. P. Mitsengendler, and K. M. Aleev, *Vysokomolekul. Soedin.* **2**, 1811 (1960); *Chem. Abstr.* **55**, 26518i (1961).

160. Koton, M. M., *J. Polymer Sci.* **30**, 331 (1958).

161. Koton, M. M., *Inst. Akad. Nauk Latv. SSR Riga* **119** (1957); *Chem. Abstr.* **55**, 16546g (1961).

162. Kubouchi, Y., T. Yamamoto, and Y. Sono, *J. Chem. Soc. Japan (Ind. Chem. Sect.)* **57**, 316, 678 (1954); *Chem. Abstr.* **49**, 4324g (1955).

163. Kurian, C. J., and M. S. Muthana, *Makromol. Chem.* **29**, 26 (1959).
164. Landler, Y., *J. Polymer Sci.* **8**, 63 (1952).
165. Landler, Y., *Compt. Rend.* **230**, 539 (1950).
166. Leonard, F., W. P. Hohenstein, and E. Merz, *J. Am. Chem. Soc.* **70**, 1283 (1948).
167. Lewis, C. W., and D. W. Lewis, *J. Polymer Sci.* **36**, 325 (1959).
168. Lewis, F. M., and F. R. Mayo, *J. Am. Chem. Soc.* **70**, 1533 (1948).
169. Lewis, F. M., F. R. Mayo, and W. F. Hulse, *J. Am. Chem. Soc.* **67**, 1701 (1945).
170. Lewis, F. M., C. Walling, W. Cummings, E. R. Briggs, and F. R. Mayo, *J. Am. Chem. Soc.* **70**, 1519 (1948).
171. Lewis, F. M., C. Walling, W. Cummings, E. R. Briggs, and W. J. Wenisch, *J. Am. Chem. Soc.* **70**, 1527 (1948).
172. Livingston, D. I., P. M. Kamath, and R. S. Corley, *J. Polymer Sci.* **20**, 485 (1956).
173. Loshaek, S., and E. Broderick, *J. Polymer Sci.* **39**, 241 (1959).
173a. Lowry, G. G., and W. K. Carrington, unpublished data.
174. Lyudvig, E. B., A. R. Gantmakher, and S. S. Medvedev, *Vysokomolekul. Soedin.* **1**, 1333 (1959); *Chem. Abstr.* **54**, 14767h (1960).
175. Machacek, Z., *Chem. Listy* **48**, 477 (1954); *Chem. Abstr.* **48**, 8583e (1954).
176. Marder, H. L., and C. Schuerch, *J. Polymer Sci.* **44**, 129 (1960).
177. Margaritova, M. F., and G. D. Berezhnov, *Tr. Mosk. Inst. Tonkoi Khim. Tekhnol.* **4**, 46 (1953); *Chem. Abstr.* **50**, 1361f (1956).
178. Margaritova, M. F., and V. A. Raiskaya, *Tr. Mosk. Inst. Tonkoi Khim. Tekhnol.* **4**, 37 (1953); *Chem. Abstr.* **49**, 14372h (1955).
179. Marvel, C. S., and W. G. DePierri, *J. Polymer Sci.* **27**, 39 (1958).
180. Marvel, C. S., and J. F. Dunphy, *J. Org. Chem.* **25**, 2209 (1960).
181. Marvel, C. S., S. L. Jacobs, W. K. Taft, and B. G. Labbe, *J. Polymer Sci.* **19**, 59 (1956).
182. Marvel, C. S., J. W. Johnson, J. P. Economy, G. P. Scott, W. K. Taft, and B. G. Labbe, *J. Polymer Sci.* **20**, 437 (1956).
183. Marvel, C. S., G. D. Jones, T. W. Mastin, and G. L. Schertz, *J. Am. Chem. Soc.* **64**, 2356 (1942).
184. Marvel, C. S., and E. B. Mano, *J. Polymer Sci.* **31**, 165 (1958).
185. Marvel, C. S., and J. F. Porter, *J. Org. Chem.* **24**, 137 (1959).
186. Marvel, C. S., and G. L. Schertz, *J. Am. Chem. Soc.* **65**, 2054 (1943); **66**, 2135 (1944).
187. Marvel, C. S., and R. Schwen, *J. Am. Chem. Soc.* **79**, 6003 (1957).
188. Marvel, C. S., R. Schwen, R. W. Hobson, and R. J. Coleman, *J. Polymer Sci.* **33**, 27 (1958).
189. Marvel, C. S., V. Sziraky, and J. P. Economy, *J. Org. Chem.* **21**, 1314 (1956).
190. Marvel, C. S., A. T. Tweedie, and J. P. Economy, *J. Org. Chem.* **21**, 1420 (1956).
191. Mat'kova, M. E., and S. S. Spasskii, *Vysokomolekul. Soedin.* **2**, 879 (1960); *Chem. Abstr.* **55**, 7898i (1961).
192. Mat'kova, M. E., and S. S. Spasskii, *Vysokomolekul. Soedin.* **3**, 93 (1961); *Chem. Abstr.* **31**, 26518d (1961).

193. Mayo, F. R., F. M. Lewis, and C. Walling, *J. Am. Chem. Soc.* **70**, 1529 (1948).

194. Mayo, F. R., and C. Walling, *Chem. Rev.* **46**, 191 (1950).

195. Mayo, F. R., C. Walling, F. M. Lewis, and W. F. Hulse, *J. Am Chem. Soc.* **70**, 1523 (1948).

196. Mazzanti, G., A. Valvassori, and G. Pajaro, *Chim. Ind.* (*Milan*) **39**, 825 (1957).

197. Mazzanti, G., A. Valvassori, and G. Pajaro, *Chim. Ind.* (*Milan*) **39**, 743 (1957).

198. Mazzanti, G., A. Valvassori, G. Sartori, and G. Pajaro, *Chim. Ind.* (*Milan*) **42**, 468 (1960).

199. McBee, E. T., H. M. Hill, and G. B. Bachman, *Ind. Eng. Chem.* **41**, 70 (1949).

200. Meehan, E. J., *J. Polymer Sci.* **1**, 318 (1946).

201. Meier, R. L., *J. Chem. Soc.* **1950**, 3656.

201a. Melville, H. W., and L. Valentine, *Trans. Faraday Soc.* **51**, 1474 (1955).

202. Merker, R. L., and M. J. Scott, *J. Polymer Sci.* **25**, 115 (1957).

203. Merker, R. L., and M. J. Scott, *J. Polymer Sci.* **43**, 297 (1960).

203a. Mezhirova, L. P., A. P. Sheinker, and A. D. Abkin, *Vysokomolekul. Soedin.* **3**, 99 (1961).

204. Miller, F., Canadian Patent 516,532 (1955).

205. Min (Szu-Kwei) and Chen Ho Chu, *Hua Hsueh Hsueh Pao* **23**, 262 (1957); *Chem. Abstr.* **52**, 19232 (1958).

206. Mitchell, J. M., and H. L. Williams, *Can. J. Research* **27**, 35 (1949).

207. Mitsengendler, S. P., V. N. Krasulina, and L. B. Trukhmanova, *Izv. Akad. Nauk SSSR Otd. Khim. Nauk* **1956**, 1120; *Chem. Abstr.* **51**, 3178d (1957).

208. Moffett, E. W., and R. E. Smith, U. S. Patent 2,356,871 (1944), values calc. by F. R. Mayo and C. Walling, ref. 194.

209. Mowry, D. T., U. S. Patent 2,398,321 (1946), values calc. by F. R. Mayo and C. Walling, ref. 194.

210. Mowry, D. T., U. S. Patent 2,417,607 (1947), values calc. by F. R. Mayo and C. Walling, ref. 194.

211. Müller, J., *Chem. Listy* **48**, 1593 (1954); *Chem. Abstr.* **49**, 5077d (1955).

212. Müller, J., *Collection Czech. Commun.* **20**, 241 (1955); *Chem. Abstr.* **49**, 11318d (1955).

213. Nagai, S., T. Uno, and K. Yoshida, *Kobunshi Kagaku* **15**, 550 (1958); *Chem. Abstr.* **54**, 11558b (1960).

214. Nagai, S., and K. Yoshida, *Kobunshi Kagaku* **17**, 77 (1960); *Chem. Abstr.* **55**, 14973g (1961).

215. Nair, A. S., and M. S. Kuthana, *Makromol. Chem.* **47**, 138 (1961).

216. Natta, G., F. Danusso, and D. Sianesi, *Makromol. Chem.* **30**, 238 (1959).

217. Natta, G., G. Mazzanti, A. Valvassori, and G. Pajaro, *Chim. Ind.* (*Milan*) **41**, 764 (1959).

218. Natta, G., G. Mazzanti, A. Valvassori, and G. Sartori, *Chim. Ind.* (*Milan*) **40**, 717 (1958).

219. Natta, G., G. Mazzanti, A. Valvassori, G. Sartori, and D. Fiumani, *J. Polymer Sci.* **51**, 411 (1961).

220. Natta, G., A. Valvassori, G. Mazzanti, and G. Sartori, *Chim. Ind. (Milan)* **40**, 896 (1958).

220a. Nowak, R. M., and P. L. Brissette, unpublished data.

221. Okamura, S., and K. Uno, *Kobunshi Kagaku* **8**, 467 (1951); *Chem. Abstr.* **47**, 9663*h* (1953).

222. Okamura, S., and T. Higashimura, *Kobunshi Kagaku* **18**, 389 (1961); *Chem. Abstr.* **55**, 24099*i* (1961).

223. Okamura, S., and T. Yamashita, *J. Soc. Textile Cellulose Ind. Japan* **9**, 446 (1953); *Chem. Abstr.* **48**, 1010*c* (1954).

224. Orr, R. J., *Polymer* **2**, 79 (1961), calc. from data of J. Furukawa.

225. Orr, R. J., and H. L. Williams, *Can. J. Chem.* **29**, 270 (1951).

226. Orr, R. J., and H. L. Williams, *Can. J. Chem.* **30**, 108 (1952).

227. Orr, R. J., and H. L. Williams, *Can. J. Chem.* **33**, 1328 (1955).

228. Orr, R. J., and H. L. Williams, *J. Polymer Sci.* **32**, 89 (1958).

229. Oster, G., and Y. Mizutani, *J. Polymer Sci.* **22**, 173 (1956).

229a. Ostroverkhov, V. G., I. S. Vakarchuk, and V. G. Sinyavskii, *Vysokomolekul. Soedin.* **3**, 1197 (1961); through *Chem. Abstr.* **56**, 8921*d* (1962).

230. Overberger, C. G., and F. Ang, *J. Am. Chem. Soc.* **82**, 929 (1960).

231. Overberger, C. G., L. H. Arnold, D. Tanner, J. J. Taylor, and T. Alfrey, Jr., *J. Am. Chem. Soc.* **74**, 4848 (1952).

232. Overberger, C. G., L. H. Arnold, and J. J. Taylor, *J. Am. Chem. Soc.* **73**, 5541 (1951).

233. Overberger, C. G., D. E. Baldwin, and H. P. Gregor, *J. Am. Chem. Soc.* **72**, 4864 (1950).

234. Overberger, C. G., H. Biletch, and R. G. Nickerson, *J. Polymer Sci.* **27**, 381 (1958).

235. Overberger, C. G., R. J. Ehrig, and D. Tanner, *J. Am. Chem. Soc.* **76**, 772 (1954).

236. Overberger, C. G., and V. J. Kamath, *J. Am. Chem. Soc.* **81**, 2910 (1959).

237. Overberger, C. G., and F. W. Michelotti, *J. Am. Chem. Soc.* **80**, 988 (1958).

238. Overberger, C. G., D. Tanner, and E. M. Pearce, *J. Am. Chem. Soc.* **80**, 4566 (1958).

239. Pasquon, I., et al., *Chim. Ind. (Milan)* **43**, 509 (1961).

239a. Peebles, L. H., J. T. Clark, and W. H. Stockmayer, *J. Am. Chem. Soc.* **82**, 4780 (1960).

239b. Pellon, J., W. G. Deichert, and W. M. Thomas, *J. Polymer Sci.* **55**, 153 (1961).

239c. Pellon, J., L. H. Schwind, M. J. Guinard, and W. M. Thomas, *J. Polymer Sci.* **55**, 161 (1961).

240. Petrova, G. A., G. A. Shtraikhman, and A. A. Vansheidt, *Zh. Fiz. Khim.* **33**, 1246 (1959); *Chem. Abstr.* **54**, 8613*g* (1960).

241. Pike, R. M., and D. L. Bailey, *J. Polymer Sci.* **22**, 55 (1956).

242. Pinner, S. H., *J. Polymer Sci.* **10**, 379 (1953).

242a. Platzer, Monsanto Chemical Company, private communication, based on unpublished results by E. C. Chapin, P. C. Hamm, and R. G. Fordyce.

242b. Polymer Corporation Ltd., Sarnia, Canada, private communication.

243. Port, W. S., E. F. Jordan, J. E. Hansen, and D. Swern, *J. Polymer Sci.* 9, 493 (1952).
244. Price, C. C., and R. D. Gilbert, *J. Polymer Sci.* 8, 580 (1952).
245. Price, C. C., and R. D. Gilbert, *J. Am. Chem. Soc.* 74, 2073 (1952).
246. Price, C. C., and C. E. Greene, *J. Polymer Sci.* 6, 111 (1951).
247. Price, C. C., B. D. Halpern, and S. T. Voong, *J. Polymer Sci.* 11, 575 (1953).
248. Price, C. C., and T. F. McKeon, 41, 445 (1959).
249. Price, C. C., and H. Morita, *J. Am. Chem. Soc.* 75, 4747 (1953).
250. Price, C. C., and T. C. Schwan, *J. Polymer Sci.* 16, 577 (1955).
251. Price, C. C., and J. Zomlefer, *J. Am. Chem. Soc.* 72, 14 (1950).
251a. Price, C. C., and J. G. Walsh, *J. Polymer Sci.* 6, 239 (1951).
252. Rakityanskii, N. V., and R. L. Rabinovich, Report of the All Union Scientific Institute of Synthetic Rubber, 1951.
253. Rakova, G. V., and A. A. Korotkov, *Dokl. Akad. Nauk SSSR* 119, 982 (1958); *Chem. Abstr.* 53, 4809i (1959).
254. Rakova, G. V., A. A. Korotkov, and Tszun Chan-Li, *Dokl. Akad. Nauk SSSR* 126, 582 (1959); *Chem. Abstr.* 53, 19425c (1959).
255. Rehner, J., R. L. Zapp, and W. J. Sparks, *J. Polymer Sci.* 11, 21 (1953).
256. Reinhardt, R. C., *Ind. Eng. Chem.* 35, 422 (1943), calc. by F. R. Mayo and C. Walling, ref. 194.
257. Ringsdorf, H., and G. Greber, *Makromol. Chem.* 31, 27 (1959).
257a. Roche, A. F., and G. Corey, unpublished data.
258. Rodriguez, L., *Makromol. Chem.* 12, 110 (1954).
259. Ross, S. D., M. Markarian, H. H. Young, Jr., and M. Nazzewski, *J. Am. Chem. Soc.* 72, 1133 (1950).
259a. Roth, R. W., and R. F. Church, *J. Polymer Sci.* 55, 41 (1961).
260. Rozovskaya, N. N., and A. D. Abkin, *Lakokrasochnye Materialy i ikh Primenenie* 1, 9 (1961); *Chem. Abstr.* 55, 20500c (1961).
261. Rugeley, E. W., T. A. Field, Jr., and G. H. Fremon, *Ind. Eng. Chem.* 40, 1724 (1948).
262. Rutovskii, B. N., and A. M. Shur, *Zh. Prikl. Khim.* 24, 1173 (1951).
263. Saini, G., G. Polla-Mattiot, and M. Meirone, *J. Polymer Sci.* 50, S13 (1961).
264. Sakurada, I., and G. Takahashi, *Kobunshi Kagaku* 11, 286 (1954); *Chem. Abstr.* 50, 602a (1956).
265. Sakurada, I., G. Takahashi, and H. Mata, *Kobunshi Kagaku* 12, 362 (1955); *Chem. Zentr.* 131, 7869 (1960).
266. Sakurada, I., *Chem. High Polymers (Tokyo)* 18, 496 (1961); *Abstr., Makromol. Chem.* 49, 252 (1961).
266a. Sakurai, F., and C. Huang, *Kogyo Kagaku Zasshi* 61, 1629 (1958); through *Chem. Abstr.* 55, 27964d (1961).
267. Sandberg, C. L., and F. A. Bovey, *J. Polymer Sci.* 15, 553 (1955).
268. Saotome, K., and M. Imoto, *Kobunshi Kagaku* 15, 368 (1958); *J. Polymer Sci.* 31, 208 (1958).
269. Schulz, R. C., H. Cherdron, and W. Kern, *Makromol. Chem.* 28, 197 (1958).
270. Schwan, T. C., and C. C. Price, *Proc. Indiana Acad. Sci.* 63, 103 (1953).
271. Scott, C. E., and C. C. Price, *J. Am. Chem. Soc.* 81, 2670 (1959).

272. Scott, C. E., and C. C. Price, *J. Am. Chem. Soc.* **81**, 2672 (1959).
273. Senda, H., and R. Oda, *Chem. High Polymers (Tokyo)* **7**, 150 (1951); *Chem. Abstr.* **47**, 345c (1953).
274. Scott, G. P., *J. Org. Chem.* **20**, 736 (1955).
275. Sheinker, A. P., M. K. Yakovleva, B. V. Kristal'nyi, and A. D. Abkin, *Dokl. Akad. Nauk SSSR* **124**, 632 (1959); *Resins, Rubbers, Plastics* **13**, 659 (1959).
276. Shostakovskii, M. F., A. M. Khomutov, and A. P. Alimov, *Izv. Akad. Nauk SSSR, Otd. Khim. Nauk* **1961**, 706; *Chem. Abstr.* **55**, 27021 (1961).
277. Shostakovskii, M. F., E. N. Prilezhaeva, and J. M. Karavaeva, *Vysokomolekul. Soedin.* **1**, 781 (1959); *J. Polymer Sci.* **40**, 598 (1959); *Chem. Abstr.* **54**, 14893h (1960).
278. Shtraĭkhman, G. A., A. A. Vansheĭdt, and G. A. Petrova, *Zh. Fiz. Khim.* **32**, 512 (1958); *Chem. Abstr.* **52**, 14299a (1958).
279. Sianesi, D., G. Pajaro, and F. Danusso, *Chim. Ind. (Milan)* **41**, 1176 (1959).
279a. Simha, R., and L. A. Wall, *J. Res. Natl. Bur. Std.* **41**, 521 (1948).
280. Simms, J. A., *J. Appl. Polymer Sci.* **5**, 58 (1961).
281. Smets, G., and L. de Haes, *Bull. Soc. Chim. Belges* **59**, 13 (1950).
282. Smets, G., and A. M. Hesbain, *J. Polymer Sci.* **40**, 217 (1959).
282a. Smets, G., A. Poot, and G. L. Duncan, *J. Polymer Sci.* **54**, 65 (1961).
283. Smets, G., and A. Reckers, *Rec. Trav. Chim.* **68**, 983 (1949).
283a. Spassakii, S. S., and A. I. Tavasov, *Zhur. Obshchei Khim.* **30**, 257 (1960); Engl. translation, p. 275.
283b. Spasskii, S. S., A. V. Tokarev, S. A. Mikhailova, T. V. Molchanova, and M. E. Mat'kova, *Zhur. Obshchei Khim.* **30**, 250 (1960), Engl. translation, p. 268.
284. Spirin, Yu. L., A. R. Gantmakher, and S. S. Medvedev, *Dokl. Akad. Nauk SSSR* **128**, 1232 (1959); *Chem. Abstr.* **55**, 26518e.
285. Spirin, Yu. L., D. K. Polyakov, A. R. Gantmakher, and S. S. Medvedev, *Vysokomolekul. Soedin.* **2**, 1082 (1960).
285a. Spurlin, H. M., Hercules Powder Co., private communication.
286. Suzuki, S., and H. Tatemichi, *J. Chem. Soc. Japan (Ind. Chem. Sect.)* **56**, 870 (1953); *Chem. Abstr.* **48**, 14288 (1954).
287. Takashi, G., *Kobunshi Kagaku* **14**, 151 (1957); *Chem. Abstr.* **52**, 1670c (1948).
288. Takebayashi, M., and Y. Ito, *Bull. Chem. Soc., Japan* **29**, 287 (1956).
289. Tamikado, T., *J. Polymer Sci.* **43**, 489 (1960).
290. Tamikado, T., *Makromol. Chem.* **38**, 85 (1960).
291. Tamikado, T., and Y. Iwakura, *J. Polymer Sci.* **36**, 529 (1959).
292. Tamikado, T., T. Sakai, and K. Sagisaka, *Makromol. Chem.* **50**, 244 (1961).
293. Taniyama, M., and G. Oster, *Bull. Chem. Soc. Japan* **30**, 856 (1957).
293a. Tatemichi, H., and S. Suzuki, *Kogyo Kagaku Zasshi* **63**, 1843 (1960); *Chem. Abstr.* **56**, 13084 (1962).
294. Thomas, W. M., and M. T. O'Shaughnessy, *J. Polymer Sci.* **11**, 455 (1953).
295. Thomas, R. M., and W. J. Sparks, U. S. Patent 2,356,128 (1944), calc. by F. R. Mayo and C. Walling, ref. 194.

296. Thompson, B. R., *J. Polymer Sci.* **19**, 373 (1956).
297. Thompson, B. R., and R. H. Raines, *J. Polymer Sci.* **41**, 265 (1959).
298. Tichy, J. R., *J. Polymer Sci.* **33**, 353 (1958).
299. Tkachenko, G. V., V. S. Etlis, L. V. Stupen, and L. P. Kofman, *Zh. Fiz. Khim.* **33**, 25 (1959); *Chem. Abstr.* **54**, 11557e (1960).
300. Tkachenko, G. V., P. H. Khomikovskii, A. D. Abkin, and S. S. Medvedev, *Zh. Fiz. Khim.* **31**, 242 (1957).
301. Tkachenko, G. V., L. V. Stupen, L. P. Kofman, and L. Z. Frolova, *Zh. Fiz. Khim.* **31**, 2676, 1957; *Chem. Abstr.* **52**, 8614d (1958).
302. Tkachenko, G. V., L. V. Stupen, L. P. Kofman, and L. A. Karacheva, *Zh. Fiz. Khim.* **32**, 2492 (1958).
303. Tobolsky, A. V., and R. J. Boudreau, *J. Polymer Sci.* **51**, S53 (1961).
304. Tokarev, A. V., and S. S. Spasskii, *Zh. Fiz. Khim.* **33**, 554 (1959); *Chem. Abstr.* **53**, 20900i (1959).
305. Tsailingol'd, V. L., M. I. Farberov, and G. A. Burgova, *Vysokomolekul. Soedin.* **1**, 415 (1959); *Chem. Abstr.* **54**, 5157c (1960).
305a. Tsuda, T., and Y. Yamashita, *Kogyo Kagaku Zasshi* **65**, 811 (1962).
306. Ueberreiter, K., and W. Krull, *Z. Physik. Chem.* (*Frankfurt*) **12**, 303 (1957).
307. Unruh, C. C., and T. M. Laakso, *J. Polymer Sci.* **33**, 87 (1958); *Ind. Eng. Chem.* **50**, 1124 (1958).
308. Ushakov, S. N., and S. S. Ivanov, *Izv. Akad. Nauk SSSR Otd. Khim. Nauk* **1957**, 1465.
309. Ushakov, S. N., and E. M. Lavrent'eva, *Zh. Prikl. Khim.* **31**, 1686 (1958); *Chem. Abstr.* **53**, 4811a (1959).
310. Ushakov, S. N., and A. F. Nikolaev, *Izv. Akad. Nauk SSSR Otd. Khim. Nauk* **1956**, 83; *Chem. Abstr.* **50**, 13867 (1956).
311. Ushakov, S. N., S. P. Mitsengendler, and B. M. Polyatskina, *Zh. Prikl. Khim.* **24**, 289 (1951); *Chem. Abstr.* **47**, 7820d (1953) and *Chem. Abstr.* **46**, 774c (1952).
312. Ushakov, S. N., S. P. Mitsengendler, and B. M. Polyatskina, *Zh. Prikl. Khim.* **23**, 512 (1950); *Chem. Abstr.* **46**, 8893a (1952).
312a. Ushakov, S. N., S. P. Mitsengendler, and B. M. Polyatskina, *Khim. i Fiz. Khim. Vysokomolekul. Soedin. Dokl. k Konf. po Vysokomolekul. Soedin.*, *7-ya Konf.* **1952**, 59; *Chem. Abstr.* **47**, 7820 (1953).
313. Ushakov, S. N., and A. F. Nikolaev, *Bull. Acad. Sci. USSR Div. Chem. Sci.* (*English Transl.*) **1**, 79 (1956).
314. Ushakov, S. N., and L. B. Trukhmanova, *Izv. Akad. Nauk SSSR Otd. Khim. Nauk* **1957**, 980; *Chem. Abstr.* **52**, 4237i (1958).
315. Ushakov, S. N., and L. B. Trukhmanova, *Vysokomolekul. Soedin.* **1**, 1754, (1959); *Chem. Abstr.* **54**, 20302h (1960).
316. Vanderhoff, J. W., in E. H. Riddle, *Monomeric Acrylic Esters*, Reinhold, New York, 1954, p. 94, ref. 154.
317. van Paesschen, G., and G. Smets, *Bull. Soc. Chim. Belges* **64**, 173 (1955).
318. Vrancken, M., and G. Smets, *Makromol. Chem.* **30**, 197 (1959).
319. Wall, F. T., quoted by F. R. Mayo and C. Walling, ref. 194.
320. Wall, F. T., R. E. Florin, and C. J. Delbecq, *J. Am. Chem. Soc.* **72**, 4769 (1950).

321. Wall, F. T., R. W. Powers, G. D. Sands, and G. S. Stent, *J. Am. Chem. Soc.* **70**, 1031 (1948).
322. Walling, C., E. R. Briggs, and K. B. Wolfstirn, *J. Am. Chem. Soc.* **70**, 1543 (1948).
323. Walling, C., E. R. Briggs, K. B. Wolfstirn, and F. R. Mayo, *J. Am. Chem. Soc.* **70**, 1537 (1948).
324. Walling, C., and J. A. Davidson, *J. Am. Chem. Soc.* **73**, 5736 (1951).
325. Welzel, G., and G. Greber, *Makromol. Chem.* **31**, 230 (1959).
325a. Whistler, R. L., and J. L. Goatley, *J. Polymer Sci.* **50**, 127 (1961).
326. Wichterle, O., and V. Gregor, *J. Polymer Sci.* **34**, 309 (1959).
327. Wichterle, O., and J. Zelinka, *Chem. Listy* **51**, 2146 (1957); *Chem. Abstr.* **52**, 3395 (1958).
328. de Wilde, M. C., and G. Smets, *J. Polymer Sci.* **5**, 253 (1950).
329. Wiley, R. H., and B. Davis, *J. Polymer Sci.* **46**, 423 (1960).
330. Wiley, R. H., and E. E. Sale, *J. Polymer Sci.* **42**, 479 (1960).
331. Wiley, R. H., and E. E. Sale, *J. Polymer Sci.* **42**, 491 (1960).
332. Wiley, R. H., and W. A. Trinler, *J. Polymer Sci.* **28**, 163 (1958).
333. Witnauer, L. P., N. Watkins, and W. S. Port, *J. Polymer Sci.* **20**, 213 (1956).
334. Yamada, M., and I. Takase, *Chem. High Polymers (Tokyo)* **18**, 85 (1961); *Chem. Abstr.* **55**, 24100d (1961).
335. Yamamoto, T., *Kogyo Kagaku Zasshi* **62**, 476 (1959).
336. Yoshida, M., and I. Sakurada, *Chem. High Polymers (Tokyo)* **7**, 334 (1950).
337. Young, L. J., unpublished data, quoted in *J. Polymer Sci.* **54**, 411 (1961).
338. Yuguchi, S., H. Kiuchi, and M. Watanabe, *Chem. High Polymers (Tokyo)* **18**, 510 (1961); *Makromol. Chem.* **49**, 252 (1961).
339. Yuguchi, S., and M. Watanabe, *Kobunshi Kagaku* **15**, 129 (1958).
340. Yuguchi, S., and M. Watanabe, *Chem. High Polymers (Tokyo)* **18**, 386 (1961); *Makromol. Chem.* **49**, 243 (1961).
341. Yuguchi, S., and M. Watanabe, *Chem. High Polymers (Tokyo)* **18**, 613 (1961); *Abstr., Makromol. Chem.* **51**, 246 (1962).
342. Zharkova, M. A., and G. I. Kudryavtsev, *Khim. Volokna* **3**, 15 (1960); *Chem. Abstr.* **54**, 23419h (1960).
342a. Zabolotskaya, E. V., V. A. Khodzhemijov, A. R. Gantmakher, and S. S. Medvedev, *Bull. Acad. Sci. USSR* **140**, 964 (1961).
343. Zutty, N. L., and F. J. Welch, *J. Polymer Sci.* **43**, 447 (1960).
343a. Zutty, N. L., Union Carbide Chemicals Company, private communication.
344. Zverev, M. P., and M. F. Margaritova, *Ukr. Khim. Zh.* **24**, 626 (1958); *Chem. Abstr.* **53**, 10823f (1959).

COPOLYMERIZATION REACTIVITY RATIOS (APPENDIX)

Lewis J. Young

The Dow Chemical Company
Plastics Department Research Laboratory
Midland, Michigan

This Appendix contains reactivity ratios collected in the time interval between the preparation of the preceding table and the end of 1964.

In order to permit direct reproduction of the original table, the new values were not integrated into the main table. This will be done in subsequent editions of the Handbook.

For explanations of symbols and abbreviations used in the Appendix, see the last page of the main table.

M_1	r_1	M_2	r_2	$T, °C$	Remarks	Ref.
Acenaphthylene	64	Vinyl chloride	0.001	-		75
Acetaldehyde	0.6 ± 0.1	Chloroacetaldehyde	0.28 ± 0.05	-78	AlEt$_3$	80
Acetonitrile	0 ± 0.02	Epichlorohydrin	4.2 ± 0.4	70	d	48
Acrolein	1.69 ± 0.1	Acrylamide	0.21 ± 0.02	50	Homogeneous	153
	2.0 ± 0.05	Acrylamide	0.76 ± 0.02	50	Heterogeneous	153
	1.60 ± 0.04	Acrylonitrile	0.52 ± 0.02	50	Homogeneous	153
	1.09 ± 0.05	Acrylonitrile	0.77 ± 0.1	50	Heterogeneous	153
	0.72 ± 0.06	Methacrylonitrile	1.20 ± 0.08	50	Homogeneous	153
	0	Methyl acrylate	7.7 ± 0.2	50	Heterogeneous	153
	3.3 ± 0.1	Vinyl acetate	0.1 ± 0.05	50	Heterogeneous	153
	4.0	2-Vinylpyridine	0	50	Homogeneous	153
Acrylamide	0.21 ± 0.02	Acrolein	1.69 ± 0.1	50	Homogeneous	153
	0.76 ± 0.02	Acrolein	2.0 ± 0.05	50	Heterogeneous	153
	0.19	1,2-Dimethyl-5-vinylpyridinium methyl sulfate	2.7	48		159
	0.74 ± 0.11	Methacrylamide	1.1 ± 0.20	25	Photoinitiated	41
	2.9 ± 0.4	N-Methylolacrylamide	0.9 ± 0.2			90
	0 ± 0.1	Vinyl bromide	70 ±16	50	Heterogeneous	181
Acrylic acid	0.58	n-Butyl acrylate	1.07	50		138
	0.29	n-Butyl methacrylate	3.67	50		138
	0.9 ± 0.1	Ethyl ethacrylate	0.45 ± 0.05	80		162
	5.55	Vinyl N,N-diethylcarbamate	0.09	80	62	
Acrylic anhydride	0.9	Methacrylonitrile	0.4	35		161
	0.1	Styrene	0.17	35		161
Acrylonitrile	0.52 ± 0.02	Acrolein	1.60 ± 0.04	50	Homogeneous	153
	0.77 ± 0.1	Acrolein	1.09 ± 0.05	50	Heterogeneous	153
	8.2	Allyl acetate	0.0	50	γ-rays	180
	5.5	Allyl alcohol	0.1	50	γ-rays	180

M_1	r_1	M_2	r_2	T, °C	Remarks	Ref.
Acrylonitrile	3.61 ± 0.087	N-Allylstearamide	0.118 ± 0.084	80		85
	1.490	Benzyl acrylate	0.631	25	γ-rays	16
	1.055	Benzyl methacrylate	1.15	25	γ-rays	16
	0.67	Bicyclo(2.2.1)-hepta-2,5-diene	0.08	50		191
	0.65 ± 0.02	Bicyclo(2.2.1)-hepta-2,5-diene	0.47 ± 0.08	60		55
	0.06	1,3-Butadiene	0.1	40		152
	0.02	1,3-Butadiene	0.3	40		152
	1.0	1-Butene:SO₂	0.8	-78		64
	1.0 ± 0.1	n-Butyl acrylate	1.2 ± 0.1		emulsion	177
	1.0 ± 0.1	n-Butyl acrylate	0.9 ± 0.1		solution	177
	0.026 ± 0.014	1,3-Cyclohexadiene	0.20 ± 0.01	60		55
	3.67	4-Cyclopenten-1,3-dione	0.21	60		63
	0.938	Divinyl ether	0.024	50		18
	0.82 ± 0.05	n-Dodecyl vinyl ether	0.0 ± 0.2	50		5
	7.0	Ethylene	0	20	γ-rays	61
	0.22 ± 0.01	Ethyleneglycol dimethacrylate	1.24 ± 0.10			14
	1.4	Glycidyl bicyclo(2.2.1)-hept-5-en-2-carboxylate	0	100		78
	1.5	Glycidyl 2-methyl-bicyclo-(2.2.1)-hept-5-en-2-carboxylate	0	100		78
	18.4	Glycidyl 1-methyl-3-cyclohexen-1-carboxylate	0.02	100		78
	0.25	Itaconic acid	1.57	5C		124
	0.15 ± 0.04	Methacrolein	1.7 ± 0.3	3C		101
	0.9 ± 0.05	Methacrylonitrile	0.50 ± 0.05	-5C	PhMgBr/toluene	44
	1.0 ± 0.1	Methacrylonitrile	0.05 ± 0.02	-50	NaNH₂	44
	0.25	Methacryloyl-D-glucose	0	50		96
	0.527	N-Methylcitraconimide	0.604	60		10

M_1	r_1	M_2	r_2	T, °C	Remarks	Ref.
Acrylonitrile	0.9	Methyl methacrylate	0.32	-60	NaNH$_2$	13
	0.01	Methyl methacrylate	0.13	-78	γ-rays	167
	0.10	Methyl methacrylate	1.30	-20 to -52	γ-rays	167
	7.0	Methyl methacrylate	0.05	-78	e	118
	0.12	Methyl methacrylate	1.34	90	1 atm.	192
	0.37	Methyl methacrylate	1.46	90	100 atm.	192
	0.45	Methyl methacrylate	2.01	90	1000 atm.	192
	0.09 ± 0.05	Methyl methacrylate	1.01 ± 0.07		Liq. SO$_2$	115
	6.5 ± 0.5	Methyl methacrylate	0.02 ± 0.01	-78	PhMgBr/tol.	44
	4.5 ± 0.5	Methyl methacrylate	0.07 ± 0.02	-50	PhMgBr/tol.	44
	1.5 ± 0.1	Methyl methacrylate	0.10 ± 0.03	-15	PhMgBr/tol.	44
	5.0 ± 0.5	Methyl methacrylate	0.03 ± 0.01	-78	PhMgBr/tol.	44
	3.0 ± 0.1	Methyl methacrylate	0.03 ± 0.01	-30	PhMgBr/tol.	44
	2.0 ± 0.2	Methyl methacrylate	0.06 ± 0.02	20	PhMgBr/tol.	44
	4.0 ± 0.5	Methyl methacrylate	0.02 ± 0.01	-78	PhMgI/tol.	44
	1.3 ± 0.1	Methyl methacrylate	0.05 ± 0.02	-40	PhMgI/tol.	44
	0.7 ± 0.1	N-Methylolacrylamide	1.2 ± 0.1			89
	0.08 ± 0.03	α-Methylstyrene	0.25 ± 0.06		Liq. SO$_2$	115
	0.15	2-Methyl-5-vinylpyridinium HCl	2.3			50
	0.90	2-Nitrobutyl acrylate	1.58	70		175
	1.10 ± 0.035	N-n-Octadecylacrylamide	1.44 ± 0.019	60		85
	0.85 ± 0.05	n-Octadecyl vinyl ether	0.0 ± 0.2	50		5
	0.81 ± 0.05	n-Octyl vinyl ether	0.0 ± 0.2	50		5
	1.116	1,4-Pentadiene	<0.01	50		18
	0.43	Potassium itaconate	0.10	50		124
	0.8	Propylene	0.1		e	93
	4.94 ± 0.06	Sodium allylsulfonate	0.07 ± 0.06	30	m	120

M_1	r_1	M_2	r_2	T, °C	Remarks	Ref.
Acrylonitrile	0.69 ± 0.05	Sodium allylsulfonate	0.18 ± 0.05	60		120
	0.05 ± 0.01	p-Sodium styrenesulfonate	1.40 ± 0.04	45	pH 7.0	82
	0.17	Styrene	0.09	40		152
	0.07	Styrene	0.37	90	1 atm.	192
	0.13	Styrene	0.43	90	100 atm.	192
	0.14	Styrene	0.55	90	1000 atm.	192
	33.0	Styrene	0.005	-78	e	117
	33	Styrene	0.005	-78	e	2
	0.03	Styrene	0.36	20		36
	20 ± 2	Styrene	0.02 ± 0.01	-70 to 0	PhMgBr/tol.	44
	15 ± 1	Styrene	0.05 ± 0.02	-45	PhMgBr/tol.	44
	0	Styrene	0	-78	γ-rays	163
	0.28	Styrene	0	-20	γ-rays	168
	0.03	Styrene	0.33	0 to 15	γ-rays	168
	0.10 ± 0.02	p-Styrenesulfonic acid	1.20 ± 0.10	45	pH 3.0	82
	0.20	trans-2,3,4,5-tetrachlorchexa-1,3,5-triene	4.05	70		7
	0.689	Tetrahydrofurfuryl acrylate	0.665	70		129
	1.577	Tetrahydrofuryl acrylate	0.91	25	γ-rays	6
	0.477	Tetrahydrofuryl methacrylate	1.01	25	γ-rays	16
	4.2	Vinyl acetate	0.05	50		46,47
	0.066 ± 0.004	N-Vinyl glycidylurethan	1.5 ± 0.5	60		79
	0.585	Vinylidene chloride	0.390	32.8		112
	1.20	Vinylidene chloride	0.49	45		137
	2.96 ± 0.12	Vinyl 9(10)-ketostearate	0.0 ± 0.091	60		113
	3.11 ± 0.05	Vinyl 12-ketostearate	0.0 ± 0.02	60		113
	1.5	Vinylsulfonic acid	0.15			107

M_1	r_1	M_2	r_2	T, °C	Remarks	Ref.
Allyl acetate	0.0	Acrylonitrile	8.2		γ-rays	180
Allyl alcohol	0.1	Acrylonitrile	5.5		γ-rays	180
Allyl chloride	–	Methyl acrylate	22 ± 4	60		150
	–	Methyl methacrylate	56	60		150
	–	Styrene	30	60		150
	–	Vinyl acetate	1.30	60		150
Allyl glycidyl ether	0.035	Methyl methacrylate	40.7	70		165
N-Allylstearamide	0.118 ± 0.084	Acrylonitrile	3.61 ± 0.087	80		85
	0.532 ± 0.012	Vinyl acetate	0.740 ± 0.087	70		85
	0 ± 0.136	Vinylidene chloride	5.23 ± 0.067	80		85
m-Aminophenyl vinyl ether	0.75 ± 0.05	Methyl methacrylate	0.07 ± 0.02	60		158
Atroponitrile	0.7	Styrene	0.02	80		104
Benzonitrile	0 ± 0.02	Epichlorohydrin	2.8 ± 0.2	70	d	48
Benzyl acrylate	0.631	Acrylonitrile	1.490	25	γ-rays	16
Benzylidenemalononitrile	0	Styrene	0.125	80	t	104
Benzyl methacrylate	1.15	Acrylonitrile	1.055	25	γ-rays	16
Bicyclo(2.2.1)hepta-2,5-diene	0.08	Acrylonitrile	0.67	50		191
	0.47 ± 0.08	Acrylonitrile	0.65 ± 0.02	60		55
	0.01	p-Chlorostyrene	85	60		139
	0.01	Ethyl acrylate	3.05	50		191
	0	Methyl methacrylate	10.0	50		191
	1.28	Vinyl acetate	0.82	60		139
	0.35	Vinyl chloride	0.74	50		191
	0.08	Vinylidene chloride	1.41	50		191
Bis(β-chloroethyl) vinyl-phosphonate	0.1 ± 0.075	Methacrylic acid	1.7 ± 0.5			133
	0.2 ± 0.2	Styrene	2.2 ± 0.4			133

M_1	r_1	M_2	r_2	T, °C	Remarks	Ref.
3,3-Bis(chloromethyl) oxetane	1.5	1,3-Dioxolane	0.65	0	d	81
	16 ± 3	β-Propiolactone	0.05 ± 0.05	-50	$BF_3 \cdot Et_2O$	174
	30 ± 10	β-Propiolactone	0.04 ± 0.04	-50	$AlEt_3 \cdot H_2O/CH_2Cl_2$	174
	38 ± 3	β-Propiolactone	0.06 ± 0.05	0	$BF_3 \cdot Et_2O$	174
	30 ± 10	β-Propiolactone	0.1 ± 0.1	0	$AlEt_3 \cdot H_2O/CH_2Cl_2$	174
	3.5	β-Propiolactone	0.05	0	$AlEt_3 \cdot H_2O/Hexane$	174
	0.82 ± 0.05	Tetrahydrofuran	1.00 ± 0.05	0	d	151
Bis(triethyleneglycol)-phthalate dimethacrylate	0.75	Styrene	0.15	0	$TiCl_4/EtCl$	111
1,4-Bis(4-vinylphenyl)-butane	0.78	Styrene	1.13	61		190
1,2-Bis(4-vinylphenyl)-ethane	0.87	Styrene	1.05	61		190
Bis(4-vinylphenyl)ether	1.06	Styrene	0.94	61		190
Bis(4-vinylphenyl)methane	0.93	Styrene	1.01	61		190
1,3-Bis(4-vinylphenyl)-propane	0.89	Styrene	1.11	61		190
Bis(4-vinylphenyl)sulfide	1.50	Styrene	0.60	61		190
Bornyl methacrylate	0.44	Styrene	0.49	60		74
	12.5	Vinyl chloride	0.06	60		74
4-(β-Bromoethyl)styrene	0.75 ± 0.01	Styrene	0.85 ± 0.01	50		28
p-Bromostyrene	0.4 ± 0.1	Styrene	0.8 ± 0.3	-20 to 10	BF_3/SO_2	178
1,3-Butadiene	0.3 ± 0.2	Styrene	1.8 ± 0.6	-15 to 10	$BF_3/SO_2/CCl_4$	178
	0.1	Acrylonitrile	0.06	4C		152
	0.3	Acrylonitrile	0.02	40		152
	3.6	Isoprene	0.11		$BuLi \cdot Et_3N$	30,32
	4.5	Isoprene	0.13		$BuLi \cdot THF$	30,32

M_1	r_1	M_2	r_2	T, °C	Remarks	Ref.
1,3-Butadiene	1.0 ± 0.05	Isoprene	1.0 ± 0.05	30	e	31,32
	2.3 ± 0.1	Isoprene	1.15 ± 0.05	30	e	31,32
	0.12	Isoprene	3.4		EtAlCl$_2$·HCl	32
	0.99	Isoprene	1.37		e	57
	0.92	Isoprene	1.25		e	57
	1.15	Isoprene	0.59		e	57
	3.0	Styrene	0.06	29	e	121
	7.0	Styrene	-0.1	30	e	108
1-Butene	0.019	Ethylene	29.60	0 to 75	e	125
	0.043	Ethylene	26.96	0 to 75	e	125
	-	Ethylene	3.25 ± 0.38	130 to 220	25,000 psi	23
	0.16	Ethylene	3.6	60	10 cm. press.	51
	8.5	3-Methyl-1-butene	0.013		e	94
	0.227	Propylene	4.39	0 to 75	e	125
	0.252	Propylene	4.04	0 to 75	e	125
1-Butene: SO$_2$	0.8	Acrylonitrile	1.0	-78		64
n-Butyl acrylate	1.07	Acrylic acid	0.58	50		138
	1.2 ± 0.1	Acrylonitrile	1.0 ± 0.1		emulsion	177
	0.9 ± 0.1	Acrylonitrile	1.0 ± 0.1		solution	177
	0.3	n-Butyl methacrylate	2.2	50		138
	11.9 ± 2.5	Ethylene	0.03 ± 0.01	70	1000 atm.	34
	0.35	Methacrylic acid	1.31	50		138
	0.87 ± 0.05	N-Methylolacrylamide	0.61 ± 0.17			88

M₁	r₁	M₂	r₂	T, °C	Remarks	Ref.
n-Butyl methacrylate	3.67	Acrylic acid	0.29	50		138
	2.2	n-Butyl acrylate	0.3	50		138
	1.20	Methacrylic acid	0.75	50		138
n-Butyl vinyl ether	0.2 ± 0.05	Vinyl acetate	0.71 ± 0.1	-		95
	0.5 ± 0.02	Vinyl chloroacetate	1.0 ± 0.02	-		95
	0.46	Vinyl chloroacetate	1.01	60		157
	0.82	β-Vinyloxyethyl methacrylate	0.004	26	Al₂(SO₄)₃/H₂SO₄	109
γ-Butyrolactone	0.36 ± 0.10	β-Propiolactone	18 ± 2	0	AlEt₃·H₂O Na	172
ε-Caprolactam	0.75	α-Pyrrolidone	5.0	90		97
Carbon monoxide	0	Ethylene	0.045	20	γ-rays; 680 atm.	40
	0	Ethylene	0.147	120-30	850-1000 atm.	40
	0	Ethylene	0.500	135	136 atm.	40
	0	Ethylene	0.16 ± 0.02	70		25
Δ³-Carene	0.33 ± 0.05	Vinyl acetate	0.24 ± 0.05	60		119
	0.22	Methyl methacrylate	3.58	h		145
Chloroacetaldehyde	0.28 ± 0.05	Acetaldehyde	0.6 ± 0.1	-78	AlEt₃	80
α-Chloroacrylonitrile	0.08 ± 0.02	Styrene	0.1 ± 0.03	80		29
2-Chloro-1,3-butadiene	2.7 ± 0.2	Methacrylic acid	0.15 ± 0.05	40	a	184
	3.6 ± 0.2	Methyl isopropenyl ketone	0.1 ± 0.05	40	a	184
	0.065 ± 0.01	Styrene	16.0 ± 0.05	0	d	135
	0.04 ± 0.01	Styrene	6.9 ± 0.5	0	d	135
	0.06 ± 0.01	Styrene	12.8 ± 0.3	0	d	135
	0.15 ± 0.05	Styrene	33.0 ± 0.5	0	d	135
	3.6 ± 0.17	trans-2,3,4,5-tetrachloro-1,3,5-hexatriene	0.2 ± 0.07	70		106
3-Chloro-α,β-difluoro-4-methylstyrene	0.294	Styrene	2.157	60		52
β-Chloro-α,β-difluoro-styrene	0.402	Styrene	2.099	60		52

M_1	r_1	M_2	r_2	T,°C	Remarks	Ref.
2-Chloroethyl vinyl ether	0.70 ± 0.05	Isobutyl vinyl ether	1.90 ± 0.05	25	d	53
	0.5	Isobutyl vinyl ether	2.0	30	d	91
	2	p-Methoxystyrene	11	30	d	91
	2.0 ± 0.2	α-Methylstyrene	0.75 ± 0.07	-30	$BF_3 \cdot 2HOAc$	33
	3.9 ± 0.15	α-Methylstyrene	0.48 ± 0.04	0	$BF_3 \cdot 2HOAc$	33
	4.5 ± 0.5	α-Methylstyrene	0.07 ± 0.01	25	$BF_3 \cdot 2HOAc$	33
	45	p-Methylstyrene	5	30	d	91
	8.0 ± 1.0	Styrene	0.06 ± 0.02	-30	Fullers earth	33
	16.0 ± 1.5	Styrene	0.04 ± 0.01	-30	$BF_3 \cdot Et_2O$	33
	30.5 ± 8.0	Styrene	0.12 ± 0.05	-30	$BF_3 \cdot 2HOAc$	33
	12.0 ± 1.0	Styrene	0.06 ± 0.02	25	$HgCl_2$	33
	24.0 ± 3.0	Styrene	0.11 ± 0.04	25	$BF_3 \cdot Et_2O$	33
	24.0 ± 2.0	Styrene	0.08 ± 0.03	25	$BF_3 \cdot 2HOAc$	33
	51.0 ±15	Styrene	0 ± 0.01	25	$BF_3 \cdot 2HOAc$	33
	36	Styrene	3	30	d	91
4-(Chloromethyl dimethyl silyl)styrene	0.86 ± 0.03	Styrene	0.69 ± 0.03	80		60
4-Chloromethyl-1,3-dioxolane	0.15	1,3-dioxolane	1.8	0	d	81
ω-Chloromethyl-ω'(4-vinyl-phenyl)hexamethyltri-siloxane	0.97 ± 0.10	Styrene	1.02 ± 0.04	80		60
ω-Chloromethyl-ω'(4-vinyl-phenyl)octamethyltetra-siloxane	1.08 ± 0.08	Styrene	0.98 ± 0.04	80		60
ω-Chloromethyl-ω'(4-vinyl-phenyl)tetramethyldi-siloxane	1.08 ± 0.16	Styrene	1.01 ± 0.08	80		60
p-Chlorostyrene	85	Bicyclo(2.2.1)hepta-2,5-diene	0.01	60		139

M_1	r_1	M_2	r_2	T, °C	Remarks	Ref.
p-Chlorostyrene	2.8 ± 0.03	Isobutylene	12.2 ± 1.0	0	d	135
	1.25 ± 0.1	Isobutylene	3.6 ± 0.2	0	d	135
	1.04	Isobutylene	1.1	0	d	135
	0.99 ± 0.10	Isobutylene	1.14 ± 0.10	0	d	135
	0.89	Isobutylene	2.80	0	d	135
	0.53 ± 0.04	Isobutylene	14.9 ± 0.2	0	d	135
	0.73 ± 0.05	Isobutylene	22.2 ± 0.5	0	d	135
	0.75	Isobutylene	18.0	0	d	135
	0.19	p-Methylstyrene	6.5	30	d	91
	0.45	Styrene	2.5	30	d	91
Cinnamic acid	0	Styrene	1.85 ± 0.03	60		17
Cinnamonitrile	0	Styrene	2.2	80	t	104
Crotononitrile	0	Styrene	20.0 ± 0.5	50	n	84
α-(2-Cyanoethyl)-acrylonitrile	1.24 ± 0.76	Methyl vinyl ketone	5.05 ± 0.95			176
	0.25 ± 0.15	Styrene	0.85 ± 0.06			176
1,3-Cyclohexadiene	0.20 ± 0.01	Acrylonitrile	0.026 ± 0.014	60		55
	0.6 ± 0.05	Isoprene	0.4 ± 0.03	0	TiCl$_4$/tol.	43
	0.2 ± 0.05	Isoprene	1.5 ± 0.1	30	BuLi/Heptane	43
	0.6 ± 0.05	Isoprene	0.4 ± 0.05	30	LiAlH$_4$/TiCl$_4$	43
4-Cyclopenten-1,3-dione	0.21	Acrylonitrile	3.57	60		63
	0.083	Methyl methacrylate	7.4	65		63
Deuteromethyl acrylate	0.42 ± 0.06	Methyl methacrylate	2.2 ± 0.4	130		155
Deuteromethyl methacrylate	2.3 ± 0.5	Methyl acrylate	0.50 ± 0.08	130		155
Diallyl n-butylphosphonate	0.091 ± 0.04	n-Lauryl methacrylate	18.7 ± 0.2	80		20
Diallyl phenyl phosphine oxide	-0.011 ± 0.013	n-Lauryl methacrylate	18.1 ± 0.4	80	t	21
	-0.013 ± 0.025	n-Lauryl methacrylate	11.1 ± 0.4	110	t	21
	-0.089 ± 0.022	n-Lauryl methacrylate	5.59 ± 0.24	140	t	21

References page II-336

COPOLYMERIZATION PARAMETER

M_1	r_1	M_2	r_2	T, °C	Remarks	Ref.
Diallyl phenylphosphonate	0.072 ± 0.44	n-Lauryl methacrylate	19.5 ± 3.6	80		20
Di-n-Amyl itaconate	0.52 ± 0.02	Styrene	0.34 ± 0.02	60		26
N,N-Di-n-butylacrylamide	0.42 ± 0.04	Methyl methacrylate	1.85 ± 0.05	50		24
	0.32 ± 0.02	Styrene	1.65 ± 0.03	50		24
Di-n-butyl itaconate	0.38 ± 0.02	Styrene	0.40 ± 0.05	60		26
Di-n-butyl vinylphosphonate	0.3	Styrene	5.4	60		99
1,3-Dichloro-2-butene	4.8 ± 0.9	Vinyl acetate	0.0	50		49
2,5-Dichlorostyrene	1.77	Styrene	0.38	70		186
Diethyl allylphosphonate	0.066 ± 0.12	n-Lauryl methacrylate	52.5 ± 3.6	80		20
Diethyl itaconate	0.33 ± 0.03	Styrene	0.30 ± 0.02	60		26
Diethylphosphonoethyl acrylate	0.15 ± 0.03	Methyl methacrylate	2.02 ± 0.05	65		136
Diethylphosphonomethyl acrylate	0.29 ± 0.05	Methyl acrylate	0.88 ± 0.09	75		136
	0.27 ± 0.01	Methyl methacrylate	1.88 ± 0.03	75		136
Diethylphosphonomethyl methacrylate	0.50 ± 0.03	Methyl methacrylate	1.43 ± 0.05	68		136
N-Diethyl-O-vinyl carbamate	0.03 ± 0.01	Styrene	32 ± 5	66		143
	0.25 ± 0.08	Vinyl acetate	1.8 ± 0.4	66		143
N-Diethyl-S-vinyl monothiol-carbamate	0.14 ± 0.03	Styrene	4.4 ± 0.6	66		143
	1.5 ± 0.3	Vinyl acetate	0.16 ± 0.08	66		143
Diethyl vinylphosphonate	0.06 ± 0.02	Styrene	8.87 ± 0.14			179
	0	Styrene	4.1	60		109
α-Difluoromethylstyrene	1.313	Styrene	0.54	60		52
2,5-Difluorostyrene	2.195	Styrene	0.044	60		52
Diglycidyl 1,2-dimethyl-3-cyclohexen-1,5-dicarboxylate	0	Styrene	17.2	100		78

M_1	r_1	M_2	r_2	T,°C	Remarks	Ref.
Diisobutyl vinyl phosphine oxide	0	Methyl methacrylate	30 ± 10	60		141
	0	Styrene	17 ± 5	60		141
Diisobutyl vinylphosphonate	0.5	Styrene	4.4	60		99
Diisopropyl vinylphosphonate	0	Styrene	2.39	60		99
2 5-Dimethoxystyrene	0.72 ± 0.04	Methyl methacrylate	0.25 ± 0.01	70		87
	1.13 ± 0.13	Styrene	0.77 ± 0.07	70		87
N,N-Dimethylacrylamide	0.45 ± 0.08	Methyl methacrylate	1.8 ± 0.18	50		132
	0.23 ± 0.13	Styrene	1.23 ± 0.43	50		132
p-Dimethylaminostyrene	0.62	Styrene	0.89			189
	1.0	α-Methylstyrene	1.0		cationic polymerization	193
Dimethyl itaconate	0.25 ± 0.02	Styrene	0.32 ± 0.02	60		26
N-(1,1-Dimethyl-3-oxobutyl)-acrylamide	0.57 ± 0.03	Methyl methacrylate	1.68 ± 0.06	60		39
2,5-Dimethylstyrene	0.49 ± 0.06	Styrene	1.77 ± 0.08	60		39
	0.20	3-Methyl-α,β,β-trifluoro-styrene	0.50	60		52
	0.44	4-Methyl-α,β,β-trifluoro-styrene	0.7	60		52
	0.32	α,β,β-Trifluorostyrene	0.67	60		52
Dimethyl vinylphosphonate	0.4	Styrene	4.61	60		99
1,2-Dimethyl-5-vinyl-pyridinium methyl sulfate	2.7	Acrylamide	0.19	48		159
	1.2	Methacrylamide	0.14	48		159
	0.60	Methacrylic acid	0.58	50		159
	1.8	Methyl methacrylate	0.12	50		159
Di-n-Octyl itaconate	0.60 ± 0.02	Styrene	0.35 ± 0.03	60		26
1,3-Dioxolane	0.65	3,3-Bis(chloromethyl)oxetane	1.5	0	d	81
	1.8	4-Chloromethyl-1,3-dioxolane	0.15	0	d	81

M_1	r_1	M_2	r_2	T, °C	Remarks	Ref.
Dipentene	0.30	Methyl methacrylate	2.35	h		145
Diphenyl 4-vinylphenyl phosphine	0.91 ± 0.12	Methyl methacrylate	0.32 ± 0.02	60		142
	1.43 ± 0.25	Styrene	0.52 ± 0.05	60		142
Diphenyl 4-vinylphenyl phosphine oxide	1.46 ± 0.10	Methyl methacrylate	0.38 ± 0.02	60		142
	1.40 ± 0.15	Styrene	0.42 ± 0.02	60		142
Diphenyl 4-vinylphenyl phosphine sulfide	1.22 ± 0.34	Methyl methacrylate	0.29 ± 0.01	60		142
	1.49 ± 0.33	Styrene	0.43 ± 0.05	60		142
Diphenyl vinyl phosphine	0	Methyl methacrylate	5.1 ± 0.2	60		141
	0	Styrene	7 ± 1	60		141
Diphenyl vinyl phosphine oxide	0	Methyl methacrylate	11 ± 4	60		141
Diphenyl vinyl phosphine sulfide	0	Styrene	5 ± 1	60		141
	0	Methyl methacrylate	13 ± 3	60		141
Diphenyl vinylphosphonate	0	Styrene	2.1 ± 0.3	60		141
	0	Styrene	2.03	60		99
Di-n-propyl itaconate	0.41 ± 0.04	Styrene	0.25 ± 0.03	60		26
Di-n-propyl vinylphosphonate	0.9	Styrene	4.24	60		99
Divinyl acetal	0.99 ± 0.08	Vinyl acetate	1.005 ± 0.08	60		114
m-Divinylbenzene	0.60	Styrene	0.65	61		190
o-Divinylbenzene	1.0	Styrene	0.92	80		188
p-Divinylbenzene	0.5	Styrene	0.14	80		188
Divinyl n-butyral	1.06 ± 0.01	Vinyl acetate	1.005 ± 0.015	60		114
Divinyl ether	0.024	Acrylonitrile	0.938	50		18
Divinyl formal	1.005 ± 0.105	Vinyl acetate	1.012 ± 0.107	60		114
Divinyl isoamylal	0.987 ± 0.057	Vinyl acetate	1.04 ± 0.08	60		114

M_1	r_1	M_2	r_2	T,°C	Remarks	Ref.
Divinyl isobutyral	0.985 ± 0.05	Vinyl acetate	1.002 ± 0.047	60		114
n-Dodecyl vinyl ether	0.0 ± 0.2	Acrylonitrile	0.82 ± 0.05	50		5
	0.0 ± 0.05	Styrene	56 ± 5	70		6
	0.0 ± 0.05	Styrene	27 ± 2	100		6
	0 ± 0.23	Vinyl acetate	3.67 ± 0.45	50		4
	0.15 ± 0.2	Vinyl chloride	1.93 ± 0.15	50		3
α-Eleostearic acid	4	Styrene	0.46	h		146
Epichlorohydrin	4.2 ± 0.4	Acetonitrile	0 ± 0.02	70	d	48
	2.8 ± 0.2	Benzonitrile	0 ± 0.02	70	d	48
	0.06	Tetrahydrofuran	3.9	0	d	81
Ethyl acrylate	3.05	Bicyclo(2.2.1)hepta-2,5-diene	0.01	50		191
	1.4 ± 0.2	N-Methylolacrylamide	1.4 ± 0.2			89
	0.07	2-Vinylthianthrene	0.314	60		67
Ethyl benzylidene-cyanoacetate	0	Styrene	0.3	80	t	104
Ethyl cinnamate	0.05	Styrene	2.7 ± 0.3	75		144
Ethylene	0	Acrylonitrile	7.0	20	γ-rays	61
	3.25 ± 0.38	1-Butene	- -	130-220	25,000 psi	23
	3.6	1-Butene	0.16	0-75	10 cm. press.	51
	29.60	1-Butene	0.019	0-75	e	125
	26.96	1-Butene	0.043	0-75	e	125
	0.03 ± 0.01	n-Butyl acrylate	11.9 ± 2.5	70	1000 atm.	34
	0.045	Carbon monoxide	0	20	γ-ray/680 atm.	40
	0.16 ± 0.02	Carbon monoxide	0	70		25
	0.147	Carbon monoxide	0	120-30	1000 atm.	40
	0.500	Carbon monoxide	0	135	136 atm.	40
	3.66 ± 0.15	1-Octene	- -	130-220	25,000 psi	23
	3.43 ± 0.15	Propylene	- -	130-220	25,000 psi	23

References page II-336

M_1	r_1	M_2	r_2	T, °C	Remarks	Ref.
Ethylene	0.9 ± 0.1	Propylene	1.9 ± 0.2	120	e	56
	17.95	Propylene	0.065	0-75	e	125
	7.08	Propylene	0.088	0-75	e	125
	5.61	Propylene	0.145	0-75	e	125
	33.36	Propylene	0.032	0-75	e	125
	15.72	Propylene	0.11	0-75	e	125
	15.72	Propylene	0.11	0-75	e	125
	1.07 ± 0.06	Vinyl acetate	1.08 ± 0.19	90	1000 atm.	34
	0.20 ± 0.02	Vinyl chloride	1.85 ± 0.2	70	300 atm.	54
	0.24 ± 0.07	Vinyl chloride	3.60 ± 0.30	90	1000 atm.	34
	4.39 ± 0.77	Vinyl fluoride	0.16 ± 0.05	160	1000 atm.	34
Ethyleneglycol dimethacrylate	1.24 ± 0.10	Acrylonitrile	0.22 ± 0.01			14
	0.65	Styrene	0.40	61		190
N,N-Ethylene-N'-iso-propenylurea	0.01 ± 0.03	Styrene	15.7 ± 0.8	60		79
Ethylene oxide	0.08	Tetrahydrofuran	2.2	0	d	81
	0.08	Tetrahydrofuran	2.2	0	d	123
N,N-Ethylene-N'-vinylurea	0.08 ± 0.04	Methyl methacrylate	1.70 ± 0.10	60		79
	0.05 ± 0.04	Styrene	14.5 ± 0.9	60		79
Ethyl ethacrylate	0.45 ± 0.05	Acrylic acid	0.9 ± 0.1	80		162
Ethyl glycidyl ether	0.75	Styrene	0	50		83
S-Ethyl-N-methyl-N-vinyl monothiolcarbamate	0.025 ± 0.01	Styrene	13.0 ± 3.0	66	d	143
Ethyl vinyl ether	1.3 ± 0.2	Vinyl acetate	0.6 ± 0.1	66		143
	0.26	Vinyl chloroacetate	0.98	60		157
4-Fluoro-4'-vinylbiphenyl	0.88 ± 0.07	Styrene	0.50 ± 0.15	70		22
Glycidyl acetate	0.25	Tetrahydrofuran	2.5	0	d	134

M_1	r_1	M_2	r_2	T, °C	Remarks	Ref.
Glycidyl bicyclo-(2.2.1)hept-5-en-2-carboxylate	0.25	Tetrahydrofuran	2.5	0	d	134
	0	Acrylonitrile	1.4	100		78
Glycidyl methacrylate	0.94	Methyl methacrylate	0.75	80		166
	0.55 ± 0.002	Styrene	0.45 ± 0.001	60		163
	0.544 ± 0.004	Styrene	0.441 ± 0.007	60		164
	0.60	Styrene	0.50	120		164
	0.25	Tetrahydrofuran	2.5	0	d	134
	8.84	Vinyl chloride	0.04			75
Glycidyl 2-methylbicyclo-(2.2.1)hept-5-en-2-carboxylate	0	Acrylonitrile	1.5	100		78
Glycidyl 1-methyl-3-cyclohexen-1-carboxylate	0.02	Acrylonitrile	18.4	100		78
	0	Styrene	21.0	100		78
Glycidyl methyl ether	1.03	Isobutyl vinyl ether	7.3	50	d	83
	1.8	Styrene	0	50	d	83
	4.9	Styrene	0	50	d	83
Glycidyl n-propyl ether	0.01 ± 0.13	Methyl methacrylate	14.4 ± 2.4	70		77
Glycidyl vinylsulfonate	0.03 ± 0.08	Styrene	1.19 ± 0.11	70		77
Isobornyl methacrylate	0.32	Styrene	0.70	60		74
	10.0	Vinyl chloride	0.12	60		74
Isobutylene	12.2 ± 1.0	p-Chlorostyrene	2.8 ± 0.03	0	d	135
	8.6 ± 0.20	p-Chlorostyrene	1.25 ± 0.1	0	d	135
	1.1	p-Chlorostyrene	1.04	0	d	135
	1.14 ± 0.10	p-Chlorostyrene	0.99 ± 0.10	0	d	135
	2.80	p-Chlorostyrene	0.89	0	d	135
	14.9 ± 0.2	p-Chlorostyrene	0.53 ± 0.04	0	d	135
	22.2 ± 0.5	p-Chlorostyrene	0.73 ± 0.05	0	d	135

References page II-336

COPOLYMERIZATION PARAMETER

M_1	r_1	M_2	r_2	T, °C	Remarks	Ref.
Isobutylene	18.0	p-Chlorostyrene	0.75	0	d	135
	3.5	Styrene	0.33	-78	d	1
	3.1	Styrene	1.1	-78	d	71
	3.0	Styrene	0.6	-103	d	196
	2.2	Styrene	1.1	-78	d	71
	1.5	Styrene	1.0	-78	d	71
	0.8	Styrene	0.5	-78	d	71
	1.9	Styrene	0.6	-78	d	71
	0.5	Styrene	3.7	0	γ-rays	140
	3.3	Styrene	0.2	0	γ-ray/ZnO	140
	0	Tetrafluoroethylene	0	-78	γ-rays	169
Isobutyl vinyl ether	1.90 ± 0.05	2-Chloroethyl vinyl ether	0.70 ± 0.05	25	d	53
	2.0	2-Chloroethyl vinyl ether	0.5	30	d	91
	7.3	Glycidyl methyl ether	1.03	50	d	83
Isoprene	0.11	1,3-Butadiene	3.6		$BuLi/Et_3N$	30,32
	0.13	1,3-Butadiene	4.5		BuLi/THF	30,32
	1.0 ± 0.05	1,3-Butadiene	1.0 ± 0.05	30	e	31,32
	1.15 ± 0.05	1,3-Butadiene	2.3 ± 0.1	30	e	31,32
	3.4	1,3-Butadiene	0.12		$EtAlCl_2 \cdot HCl$	32
	1.37	1,3-Butadiene	0.99		e	57
	1.25	1,3-Butadiene	0.92		e	57
	0.59	1,3-Butadiene	1.15		e	57
	0.4 ± 0.05	1,3-Cyclohexadiene	0.6 ± 0.05	0	$TiCl_4/tol.$	43
	1.5 ± 0.1	1,3-Cyclohexadiene	0.2 ± 0.05	30	BuLi/heptane	43
	0.4 ± 0.05	1,3-Cyclohexadiene	0.6 ± 0.05	30	$LiAlH_4/TiCl_4$	43
	0.1	Styrene	0.8	0 to -30	$SnCl_4/C_2H_5Cl$	195
	7.0 ± 0.6	Styrene	0.14 ± 0.02	30	e	103

M_1	r_1	M_2	r_2	T, °C	Remarks	Ref.
Isoprene	1.92	Styrene	0.50	100		187
	1.92	Styrene	0.54	80		187
	1.18	Styrene	0.66	22	γ-rays	187
	5.89	Styrene	0.03	30	BuLi	187
	0.58 ± 0.02	trans-2,3,4,5-tetrachloro-1,3,5-hexatriene	1.58 ± 0.1	70		106
Isopropenyl acetate	0.5	Styrene	2.6	30	d	69
N-Isopropenyl glycidylurethan	0.12	Methyl methacrylate	1.70	60		79
p-Isopropylstyrene	0.54 ± 0.01	Styrene	1.11 ± 0.01	50		28
Itaconic acid	1.57	Acrylonitrile	0.25	50		124
n-Lauryl methacrylate	18.7 ± 0.2	Diallyl n-butylphosphonate	0.091 ± 0.04	80		20
	18.1 ± 0.4	Diallyl phenyl phosphine oxide	-0.011 ± 0.013	80	t	21
	11.1 ± 0.4	Diallyl phenyl phosphine oxide	-0.013 ± 0.025	110	t	21
	5.59 ± 0.24	Diallyl phenyl phosphine oxide	-0.089 ± 0.022	140	t	21
	19.5 ± 3.5	Diallyl phenyl phosphonate	0.072 ± 0.44	80		20
	52.5 ± 3.5	Diethyl allyl phosphonate	0.066 ± 0.12	80		20
Linoleic acid	0.29	Styrene	7.16	150		156
Maleic anhydride	-0.18 ± 0.28	Methyl methacrylate	4.63 ± 1.14	30		131
	0 ± 0.002	Styrene	0.097 ± 0.002	50		68
	0.015	Styrene	0.040	50		130
	0	Styrene	0.019	50		10
	0	Vinyl N,N-diethylcarbamate	0.035	80		62
Maleimide	0.17	Methyl methacrylate	2.50	75		183
	0.1	Styrene	0.1	75		183
	0.48	Vinylidene chloride	0.71	75		183

References page II-336

M_1	r_1	M_2	r_2	T, °C	Remarks	Ref.
Methacrolein	1.7 ± 0.3	Acrylonitrile	0.15 ± 0.04	30		101
	1.78 ± 0.06	Methacrylonitrile	0.40 ± 0.04	50	Homogeneous	153
	1.1 ± 0.20	Acrylamide	0.74 ± 0.11	25	Photoinitiated	41
	0.14	1,2-Dimethyl-5-vinylpyridinium methyl sulfate	1.2	48		159
Methacrylic acid	0.49 ± 0.02	Methyl methacrylate	1.65 ± 0.05	70		122
	1.7 ± 0.5	Bis(β-chloroethyl)vinyl phosphonate	0.1 ± 0.075			133
	1.31	n-Butyl acrylate	0.35	50		138
	0.75	n-Butyl methacrylate	1.20	50		138
	0.15 ± 0.05	2-Chloro-1,3-butadiene	2.7 ± 0.2	40	a	184
	0.58	1,2-Dimethyl-5-vinylpyridinium methyl sulfate	0.60	50		159
	1.55 ± 0.06	Methyl methacrylate	0.55 ± 0.02	45		148
	0.68 ± 0.05	Methyl methacrylate	0.98 ± 0.04	45	DMF	148
	0.66 ± 0.08	Styrene	0.2 ± 0.02	45		148
	0.45 ± 0.06	Styrene	0.53 ± 0.02	45	DMF	148
	0 ± 0.1	Vinyl bromide	90 ±15	50		181
	0.44 ± 0.02	2-Vinylpyridine	1.38 ± 0.04	h		147
Methacrylic anhydride	1.6	Methacrylonitrile	0.27	36.6		161
	0.26	Styrene	0.12	36.6		161
Methacrylonitrile	1.20 ± 0.08	Acrolein	0.72 ± 0.06	50	Homogeneous	153
	0.4	Acrylic anhydride	0.9	35		161
	0.50 ± 0.05	Acrylonitrile	0.9 ± 0.05	-50	PhMgBr/tol.	44
	0.05 ± 0.02	Acrylonitrile	1.0 ± 0.1	-50	NaNH$_2$	44
	0.40 ± 0.04	Methacrolein	1.78 ± 0.06	50	Homogeneous	153
	0.27	Methacrylic anhydride	1.6	36.6		161
	0.30 ± 0.05	Methyl methacrylate	2.0 ± 0.5	-78	PhMgBr/Et$_2$O	44

M_1	r_1	M_2	r_2	T, °C	Remarks	Ref.
Methacrylonitrile	0.05 ± 0.02	Methyl methacrylate	5.0 ± 0.5	-30	PhMgBr/Et$_2$O	44
	12.0 ± 1.0	Styrene	0.05 ± 0.02	-78 to -30	PhMgBr/Et$_2$O	44
Methacryloyl-D-glucose	4.6 ± 0.4	Vinyl cinnamate	0.15 ± 0.06	70		144
	0	Acrylonitrile	0.25	50		96
Methacrylyl triethyl germanium	0.93 ± 0.08	Styrene	1.05 ± 0.02	60		98
o-Methoxystyrene	0.35 ± 0.03	p-Methoxystyrene	2.9 ± 0.7	30	d	72
	0.35 ± 0.09	p-Methoxystyrene	3.9 ± 0.1	-20	d	72
	0.45 ± 0.05	p-Methoxystyrene	6.4 ± 0.4	-50	d	72
	3.9 ± 0.7	Styrene	0.2 ± 0.02	30	d	72
	3.6 ± 0.8	Styrene	0.11 ± 0.04	-20	d	72
p-Methoxystyrene	11	2-Chloroethyl vinyl ether	2	30	d	91
	2.9 ± 0.7	o-Methoxystyrene	0.35 ± 0.03	30	d	72
	3.9 ± 0.1	o-Methoxystyrene	0.35 ± 0.09	-20	d	72
	6.4 ± 0.4	o-Methoxystyrene	0.45 ± 0.05	-50	d	72
	4.3	p-Methylstyrene	0.30	30	d	91
	1.50 ± 0.22	Styrene	0.70 ± 0.10	25	γ-rays	35
	0.045	Styrene	19	25	e	154
	0.79	Styrene	1.05	-		189
	38	Styrene	0.5	30	d	72
Methyl acrylate	7.7 ± 0.2	Acrolein	0	50	Heterogeneous	153
	22 ± 4	Allyl chloride	-	60		150
	0.50 ± 0.08	Deuteromethyl methacrylate	2.3 ± 0.5	130		155
	0.88 ± 0.09	Diethylphosphonomethyl acrylate	0.29 ± 0.05	75		136
	0.504	Methyl methacrylate	1.91	130		155
	1.3 ± 0.2	N-Methylolacrylamide	1.9 ± 0.7			88

References page II-336

COPOLYMERIZATION PARAMETER

M_1	r_1	M_2	r_2	T, °C	Remarks	Ref.
Methyl acrylate	0.13	Styrene	0.30 to 1.50	0	$r_2 \propto [SO_2]$	116
	0.18 ± 0.03	Styrene	0.75 ± 0.11	25	γ-rays	35
	0.27 ± 0.04	trans-2,3,4,5-tetrachlorohexa-1,3,5-triene	3.17 ± 0.27			8
	8.87 ± 0.07	Tetravinyl silane	0.133 ± 0.006	h		160
	4.45	Vinyl N,N-diethylcarbamate	0.01	80		62
	0.46	Vinylhydroquinone dibenzoate	0.75	78		86
	38	Vinylidene chloride	0.005	50	e	102
Methyl α-benzylacrylate	0.17 ± 0.03	Styrene	0.59 ± 0.05	65		38
3-Methyl-1-butene	0.013	1-Butene	8.5	60	e	94
Methyl α-n-butylacrylate	0.20 ± 0.05	Styrene	0.80 ± 0.05	65		38
Methyl α-sec-butylacrylate	0	Styrene	2.25 ± 0.05	65		38
N-Methylcitraconimide	0.604	Acrylonitrile	0.527	60		110
	0.15	Methyl methacrylate	3.24	70		110
	0.24	Styrene	0.153	70		110
	0.256	2-Vinylnaphthalene	0.187	70		110
Methyl α-cyclohexylacrylate	0	Styrene	1.65 0.05	65		38
Methyl ethacrylate	0.1	Methyl methacrylate	2.03	30,60		19
	0.96	Methyl methacrylate	1.16	30	Na	19
5-Methyl-1-hexene	0.21 ± 0.02	Styrene	0.82 ± 0.08	65		38
	4.00 ± 0.28	Styrene	0.591 ± 0.057	35	e	9
Methyl α-isobutylacrylate	0.20 ± 0.0	Styrene	0.96 ± 0.05	65		38
Methyl isopropenyl ketone	0.1 ± 0.05	2-Chloro-1,3-butadiene	3.6 ± 0.2	40	a	184
Methyl α-isopropylacrylate	0	Styrene	1.85 ± 0.07	65		38
N-Methylmethacrylamide	0.24 ± 0.02	Methyl methacrylate	1.54 ± 0.05	70		122
Methyl methacrylate	0.02 ± 0.01	Acrylonitrile	6.5 ± 0.5	-78	PhMgBr/tol.	44
	0.07 ± 0.02	Acrylonitrile	4.5 ± 0.5	-50	PhMgBr/tol.	44
	0.10 ± 0.03	Acrylonitrile	1.5 ± 0.1	-15	PhMgBr/tol.	44

M_1	r_1	M_2	r_2	T, °C	Remarks	Ref.
Methyl methacrylate	0.03 ± 0.01	Acrylonitrile	5.0 ± 0.5	-78	PhMgBr/tol.	44
	0.03 ± 0.01	Acrylonitrile	3.0 ± 0.1	-30	PhMgBr/tol.	44
	0.06 ± 0.02	Acrylonitrile	2.0 ± 0.2	20	PhMgBr/tol.	44
	0.02 ± 0.01	Acrylonitrile	4.0 ± 0.5	-78	PhMgI/tol.	44
	0.05 ± 0.02	Acrylonitrile	1.3 ± 0.1	-40	PhMgI/tol.	44
	1.01 ± 0.07	Acrylonitrile	0.09 ± 0.05		Liq. SO_2	115
	0.05	Acrylonitrile	7.0	-78	e	118
	1.34	Acrylonitrile	0.12	90	1 atm.	192
	1.45	Acrylonitrile	0.37	90	100 atm.	192
	2.01	Acrylonitrile	0.45	90	1000 atm.	192
	0.32	Acrylonitrile	0.9	-60	$NaNH_2$	13
	0.13	Acrylonitrile	0.01	-78	γ-rays	167
	1.30	Acrylonitrile	0.10	-20 to 52 60	γ-rays	167
	56	Allyl chloride	-	60		150
	40.7	Allyl glycidyl ether	0.035	70		165
	0.07 ± 0.02	m-Aminophenyl vinyl ether	0.75 ± 0.05	60		158
	10.0	Bicyclo(2.2.1)hepta-2,5-diene	0	50		191
	3.58	Δ^3-Carene	0.22	h		145
	7.4	4-Cyclopenten-1,3-dione	0.083	65		63
	2.2 ± 0.4	Deuteromethyl acrylate	0.42 ± 0.06	130		155
	1.85 ± 0.05	N,N-Di-n-butyl acrylamide	0.42 ± 0.04	50		24
	2.02 ± 0.05	Diethylphosphonoethyl acrylate	0.15 ± 0.03	65		136
	1.38 ± 0.03	Diethylphosphonomethyl acrylate	0.27 ± 0.01	75		136
	1.43 ± 0.05	Diethylphosphonomethyl methacrylate	0.50 ± 0.03	68		136
	30 ± 10	Diisobutyl vinyl phosphine oxide	0	60		141

COPOLYMERIZATION PARAMETER

M_1	r_1	M_2	r_2	T, °C	Remarks	Ref.
Methyl methacrylate	0.25 ± 0.01	2,5-Dimethoxystyrene	0.72 ± 0.04	70		87
	1.8 ± 0.18	N,N-Dimethylacrylamide	0.45 ± 0.08	50		132
	1.68 ± 0.06	N-(1,1-Dimethyl-3-oxobutyl)-acrylamide	0.57 ± 0.03	60		39
	0.12	1,2-Dimethyl-5-vinylpyridinium methyl sulfate	1.8	50		159
	2.35	Dipentene	0.30	h		145
	0.32 ± 0.02	Diphenyl 4-vinylphenyl-phosphine	0.91 ± 0.12	60		142
	0.29 ± 0.01	Diphenyl 4-vinylphenyl-phosphine sulfide	1.22 ± 0.34	60		142
	5.1 ± 0.2	Diphenyl vinylphosphine	0	60		141
	11 ± 4	Diphenyl vinylphosphine oxide	0	60		141
	13 ± 3	Diphenyl vinylphosphine sulfide	0	60		141
	1.70 ± 0.10	N,N-Ethylene-N'-vinylurea	0.08 ± 0.04	60		79
	0.75	Glycidyl methacrylate	0.94	80		166
	14.4 ± 2.4	Glycidyl vinylsulfonate	0.01 ± 0.13	70		77
	1.70	N-Isopropenylglycidyl-urethane	0.12	60		79
	4.63 ± 1.14	Maleic anhydride	-0.18 ± 0.28	30		131
	2.50	Maleimide	0.17	75		183
	1.65 ± 0.05	Methacrylamide	0.49 ± 0.02	70		122
	0.55 ± 0.02	Methacrylic acid	1.55 ± 0.06	45		148
	0.98 ± 0.04	Methacrylic acid	0.68 ± 0.05	45		148
	2.0 ± 0.5	Methacrylonitrile	0.30 ± 0.05	-78	$PhMgBr/Et_2O$	44
	5.0 ± 0.5	Methacrylonitrile	0.05 ± 0.02	-30	$PhMgBr/Et_2O$	44
	1.91	Methyl acrylate	0.504	130		155
	3.24	N-Methylcitraconimide	0.15	70		110

M_1	r_1	M_2	r_2	T, °C	Remarks	Ref.
Methyl methacrylate	2.03	Methyl ethacrylate	0.1	30,60		19
	1.15	Methyl ethacrylate	0.96	30	Na	19
	1.54 ± 0.05	N-Methylmethacrylamide	0.24 ± 0.02	70		122
	1.66 ± 0.02	N-Methylolmethacrylamide methyl ether	0.27 ± 0.03	70		122
	1.60	2-Nitrobutyl acrylate	0.22	70		175
	3.50 ± 0.06	N-n-Octylacrylamide	0.24 ± 0.06	50		24
	3.6 ± 0.04	N-tert-Octylacrylamide	0.24 ± 0.04	50		24
	3.5	Phenyl vinyl ether	0.01	-		70
	6.60	α-Pinene	0.07	h		145
	0.45 ± 0.016	Styrene	0.43 ± 0.013		$CdEt_2$	58
	0.49	Styrene	0.53	60		185
	0.005	Styrene	20	-78	γ-rays, d	1
	0.45	Styrene	0.52	50	1 atm./C_6H_6	11
	0.48	Styrene	0.58	50	100 atm./C_6H_6	11
	0.58	Styrene	0.72	50	1000 atm./C_6H_6	11
	0.46	Styrene	0.49	50	1 atm./$ClCH_2CH_2Cl$	11
	0.52	Styrene	0.53	50	100 atm./$ClCH_2CH_2Cl$	11
	0.66	Styrene	0.63	50	1000 atm./$ClCH_2CH_2Cl$	11
	0.50	Styrene	0.44	50	1 atm./pyridine	11
	0.57	Styrene	0.49	50	100 atm./pyridine	11
	0.80	Styrene	0.56	50	1000 atm./pyridine	11
	0.47	Styrene	0.45	50	1 atm./EtOH	11
	0.52	Styrene	0.49	50	100 atm./EtOH	11
	0.62	Styrene	0.59	50	1000 atm./EtOH	11
	0.50 ± 0.07	Styrene	0.63 ± 0.09	25	γ-ray	35
	>>1	Styrene	0	-50 to -20	PhMgBr/tol.	44

M_1	r_1	M_2	r_2	T,°C	Remarks	Ref.
Methyl methacrylate	>1	Styrene	0	-78	PhMgBr/tol.	44
	25.0 ± 2	Styrene	0.01 ± 0.01	-30	PhMgBr/tol.	44
	4.5 ± 1	Styrene	0.07 ± 0.02	20	PhMgBr/tol.	44
	20 ± 2	Styrene	0.02 ± 0.01	-78	PhMgBr/Et$_2$O	44
	14.0 ± 2	Styrene	0.05 ± 0.02	-30	PhMgBr/Et$_2$O	44
	2.0 ± 0.3	Styrene	0.30 ± 0.05	20	PhMgBr/Et$_2$O	44
	240 ±20	Tetrachloroethylene	-	60		150
	0.465 ± 0.05	trans-2,3,4,5-tetrachloro-1,3,5-hexatriene	1.82 ± 0.075			8
	0.09 ± 0.105	trans-2,3,4,5-tetrachloro-1,3,5-hexatriene	0.315 ± 0.14	70		106
	28.6	Vinyl acetate	0.035	30		15
	2.75	N-Vinylglycidylurethan	0.10	60		79
	0.34	Vinylhydroquinone dibenzoate	0.41	78		86
	0.20 ± 0.03	2-Vinylpyridine	0.84 ± 0.13	25	γ-rays	35
	2.99	2-Vinylthianthrene	0.07	60		67
N-Methylolacrylamide	0.9 ± 0.2	Acrylamide	2.9 ± 0.4			90
	1.2 ± 0.1	Acrylonitrile	0.7 ± 0.1			89
	0.61 ± 0.17	n-Butyl acrylate	0.87 ± 0.05			88
	1.4 ± 0.2	Ethyl acrylate	1.4 ± 0.2			89
	1.9 ± 0.7	Methyl acrylate	1.3 ± 0.2			88
N-Methylolmethacrylamide methyl ether	0.27 ± 0.03	Methyl methacrylate	1.66 ± 0.02	70		122
4-Methyl-1-pentene	3.67 ± 0.22	Styrene	0.89 ± 0.05	45	e	9
Methyl α-phenylacrylate	0.4 ± 0.2	Styrene	0.03 ± 0.02	65		38
Methyl α-n-propylacrylate	0.22 ± 0.04	Styrene	0.86 ± 0.08	65		38
α-Methylstyrene	0.25 ± 0.06	Acrylonitrile	0.08 ± 0.03		Liq. SO$_2$	115
	0.75 ± 0.07	2-Chloroethyl vinyl ether	2.0 ± 0.2	-30	BF$_3$·2HOAc	33
	0.48 ± 0.04	2-Chloroethyl vinyl ether	3.9 ± 0.15	0	BF$_3$·2HOAc	33

M_1	r_1	M_2	r_2	T, °C	Remarks	Ref.
α-Methylstyrene	0.07 ± 0.01	2-Chloroethyl vinyl ether	4.5 ± 0.5	25	BF$_3$·2HOAc	33
	1.0	p-Dimethylaminostyrene	1.0			193
	0.11	Vinylhydroquinone dibenzoate	0.30	78		86
p-Methylstyrene	5	2-Chloroethyl vinyl ether	45	30	d	91
	6.5	p-Chlorostyrene	0.19	30	d	91
	0.30	p-Methoxystyrene	4.3	30	d	91
	0.13	Styrene	5.3	25	e	154
	4.2	Styrene	0.20	30	d	91
2-Methyl-α,β,β-trifluoro-styrene	0.403	Styrene	1.177	60		52
3-Methyl-α,β,β-trifluoro-styrene	0.50	2,5-Dimethylstyrene	0.20	60		52
	0.73	Styrene	0.40	60		52
4-Methyl-α,β,β-trifluoro-styrene	0.7	2,5-Dimethylstyrene	0.44	60		52
	0.63	Styrene	0.40	60		52
Methyl vinyl ketone	5.05 ± 0.95	α-(2-Cyanoethyl)acrylonitrile	1.24 ± 0.76			176
	4.4	Phenyl vinyl ether	0.01			70
2-Methyl-5-vinylpyridine	0.32 ± 0.065	Triethyleneglycol dimeth-acrylate	0.59 ± 0.06			42
2-Methyl-5-vinyl pyridinium HCl	2.3	Acrylonitrile	0.15			50
2-Nitrobutyl acrylate	1.58	Acrylonitrile	0.90	70		175
	0.22	Methyl methacrylate	1.60	70		175
	0.115	Styrene	0.58	70		175
β-Nitrostyrene	0	Styrene	0.4	80		105
N-n-Octadecylacrylamide	1.44 ± 0.019	Acrylonitrile	1.10 ± 0.035	60		85
	6.11 ± 0.045	Vinyl acetate	0.027 ± 0.009	60		85
	1.37 ± 0.008	Vinylidene chloride	0.438 ± 0.008	60		85

References page II-336

M_1	r_1	M_2	r_2	T, °C	Remarks	Ref.
n-Octadecyl vinyl ether	0.0 ± 0.2	Acrylonitrile	0.85 ± 0.05	50		5
	0 ± 0.35	Vinyl acetate	4.50 ± 0.58	50		4
	-0.1 ± 0.2	Vinyl chloride	2.10 ± 0.20	50		3
1-Octene	-	Ethylene	3.66 ± 0.15	130-220	25,000 psi	23
N-n-Octylacrylamide	0.24 ± 0.06	Methyl methacrylate	3.50 ± 0.06	50		24
	0.20 ± 0.05	Styrene	2.70 ± 0.10	50		24
N-tert-Octylacrylamide	0.24 ± 0.04	Methyl methacrylate	3.6 ± 0.04	50		24
	0.25 ± 0.06	Styrene	2.8 ± 0.10	50		24
n-Octyl vinyl ether	0.0 ± 0.2	Acrylonitrile	0.81 ± 0.05	50		5
	0.0 ± 0.04	Styrene	65 ± 5	70		6
	0 ± 0.31	Vinyl acetate	3.47 ± 0.51	50		4
	0.1 ± 0.1	Vinyl chloride	1.90 ± 0.20	50		3
1,4-Pentadiene	<0.01	Acrylonitrile	1.116	50		18
Phenyl vinyl ether	0.01	Methyl methacrylate	3.5			70
	0.01	Methyl vinyl ketone	4.4			70
	0.01	Styrene	1.7			70
	0.8	Vinyl chloroacetate	1.0	60		157
α-Pinene	0.07	Methyl methacrylate	6.60	h		145
Potassium itaconate	0.10	Acrylonitrile	0.43	50		124
β-Propiolactone	0.05 ± 0.05	3,3-Bis(chloromethyl)oxetane	16 ± 3	-50	BF_3/Et_2O	174
	0.06 ± 0.05	3,3-Bis(chloromethyl)oxetane	38 ± 3	0	BF_3/Et_2O	174
	0.04 ± 0.04	3,3-Bis(chloromethyl)oxetane	30 ±10	-50	$Et_3Al \cdot H_2O$	174
	0.1 ± 0.1	3,3-Bis(chloromethyl)oxetane	30 ±10	0	$Et_3Al \cdot H_2O$	174
	0.05	3,3-Bis(chloromethyl)oxetane	3.5	0	$Et_3Al \cdot H_2O$	174

M_1	r_1	M_2	r_2	T, °C	Remarks	Ref.
β-Propiolactone	18 ± 2	γ-Buryrolactone	0.36 ± 0.10	0	$Et_3Al \cdot H_2O$	172
	0.1 ± 0.1	Tetrahydrofuran	5.5 ± 0.1	h	$Et_3Al \cdot H_2O$	173
	0.4 ± 0.2	Tetrahydrofuran	2.9 ± 0.5	h	BF_3/Et_2O	173
	-0.16	DL-Valine N-carboxyanhydride	11	35	Et_3N	45
Propylene	0.1	Acrylonitrile	0.8		e	93
	4.39	1-Butene	0.227	0-75	e	125
	4.04	1-Butene	0.252	0-75	e	125
	-	Ethylene	3.43 ± 0.15	130-220	25,000 psi	23
	1.9 ± 0.2	Ethylene	0.9 ± 0.1	120	e	36
	0.065	Ethylene	17.95	0-75	e	125
	0.088	Ethylene	7.08	0-75	e	125
	0.145	Ethylene	5.61	0-75	e	125
	0.032	Ethylene	33.36	0-75	e	125
	0.11	Ethylene	15.72	0-75	e	125
	0.11	Ethylene	15.72	0-75	e	125
	7.70	Styrene	0.12	60	e	65
	20.0 ± 3.5	Styrene	0.20 ± 0.13	4C	$i\text{-}Bu_3Al/TiCl_3$	12
	20.5 ± 3.0	Styrene	0.30 ± 0.15	4C	$Et_3Al/TiCl_3$	12
	7.2 ± 0.7	Styrene	0.16 ± 0.08	4C	Et_3Al/VCl_3	12
	0.62	Styrene	0.93	45	$Et_3Al/TiCl_3$	37
	3.7	Styrene	2.0	60	$Et_3Al/TiCl_4$	66
	1.0	Styrene	1.5	60	$Et_3Al/VOCl_3$	66
	2.4	Styrene	1.9	60	Et_3Al/VCl_4	66
	5.4	Styrene	1.0	60	Et_3Al/VCl_3	66
	1.0	Tetrafluoroethylene	0.06	-78	γ-rays	161,162
α-Pyrrolidone	5.0	ε-Caprolactam	0.75	90	Na	97

References page II-336

M_1	r_1	M_2	r_2	T, °C	Remarks	Ref.
Sodium Allylsulfonate	0.18 ± 0.05	Acrylonitrile	0.69 ± 0.05	60		120
	0.07 ± 0.06	Acrylonitrile	4.94 ± 0.06	30	m	120
p-Sodium styrenesulfonate	1.40 ± 0.04	Acrylonitrile	0.05 ± 0.01	45	pH 7	82
Styrene	0.17	Acrylic anhydride	0.1	35		161
	0	Acrylonitrile	0.28	-20	γ-rays	168
	0	Acrylonitrile	0	-78	γ-rays	168
	0.33	Acrylonitrile	0.03	0,15	γ-rays	168
	0.36	Acrylonitrile	0.03	20		36
	0.02 ± 0.01	Acrylonitrile	20.0 ± 2.0	-70 to 0	PhMgBr/tol.	44
	0.05 ± 0.02	Acrylonitrile	15.0 ± 1.0	-45	PhMgBr/tol.	44
	0.005	Acrylonitrile	33.0	-78	e	117
	0.09	Acrylonitrile	0.17	40		152
	0.37	Acrylonitrile	0.07	90	1 atm.	192
	0.43	Acrylonitrile	0.13	90	100 atm.	192
	0.55	Acrylonitrile	0.14	90	1000 atm.	192
	0.005	Acrylonitrile	33	-78	e	2
	30	Allyl chloride	-	60		150
	0.02	Atroponitrile	0.7	80		104
	0.125	Benzylidenemalononitrile	0	80	t	104
	2.2 ± 0.4	Bis(β-chloroethyl)vinyl phosphonate	0.2 ± 0.2			133
	0.15	Bis(triethyleneglycol)-phthalate dimethacrylate	0.75	0	TiCl₄/EtCl	111
	1.13	1,4-Bis(4-vinylphenyl)butane	0.78	61		190
	1.05	1,2-Bis(4-vinylphenyl)ethane	0.87	61		190
	0.94	Bis(4-vinylphenyl)ether	1.06	61		190
	1.01	Bis(4-vinylphenyl)methane	0.93	61		190

M_1	r_1	M_2	r_2	T, °C	Remarks	Ref.
Styrene	1.11	1,3-Bis(4-vinylphenyl)propane	0.89	61		190
	0.60	Bis(4-vinylphenyl)sulfide	1.50	61		190
	0.49	Bornyl methacrylate	0.44	60		74
	0.85 ± 0.01	p-(β-Bromoethyl)styrene	0.79 ± 0.01	50		28
	0.8 ± 0.3	p-Bromostyrene	0.4 ± 0.1	-20 to 10	$BF_3/SO_2/SO_2$	178
	1.8 ± 0.6	p-Bromostyrene	0.3 ± 0.2	-15 to 10	$BF_3/SO_2/CCl_4$	178
	0.06	1,3-Butadiene	3.0	29	e	121
	-0.1	1,3-Butadiene	7.0	30	e	108
	0.1 ± 0.03	α-Chloroacrylonitrile	0.08 ± 0.02	80		29
	16.0 ± 0.04	2-Chloro-1,3-butadiene	0.065 ± 0.01	0	d	135
	6.9 ± 0.5	2-Chloro-1,3-butadiene	0.04 ± 0.01	0	d	135
	12.8 ± 0.3	2-Chloro-1,3-butadiene	0.06 ± 0.01	0	d	135
	33.0 ± 0.5	2-Chloro-1,3-butadiene	0.15 ± 0.05	0	d	135
	2.157	β-Chloro-α,β-difluoro-4-methylstyrene	0.294	60		52
	2.099	β-Chloro-α,β-difluorostyrene	0.402	60		52
	0.06 ± 0.02	2-Chloroethyl vinyl ether	8.0 ± 1.0	-30	Fullers earth	52
	0.04	2-Chloroethyl vinyl ether	16.0 ± 1.5	-30	$BF_3 \cdot Et_2O$	33
	0.12 ± 0.05	2-Chloroethyl vinyl ether	30.5 ± 8.0	-30	$BF_3 \cdot 2HOAc$	33
	0.06 ± 0.02	2-Chloroethyl vinyl ether	12.0 ± 1.0	25	$HgCl_2$	33
	0.11 ± 0.04	2-Chloroethyl vinyl ether	24.0 ± 3.0	25	$BF_3 \cdot Et_2O$	33
	0.08 ± 0.03	2-Chloroethyl vinyl ether	24.0 ± 2.0	25	$BF_3 \cdot 2HOAc$	33
	0 ± 0.01	2-Chloroethyl vinyl ether	51.0 ±15	25	$BF_3 \cdot 2HOAc$	33
	3	2-Chloroethyl vinyl ether	36	30		91
	0.69 ± 0.03	4-(Chloromethyl dimethyl silyl)styrene	0.86 ± 0.03	80	d	60

COPOLYMERIZATION PARAMETER

M_1	r_1	M_2	r_2	T,°C	Remarks	Ref.
Styrene	1.01 ± 0.08	ω-Chloromethyl-ω'-(4-vinyl-phenyl)tetramethyldisiloxane	1.08 ± 0.16	80		60
	1.02 ± 0.04	ω-Chloromethyl-ω'-(4-vinyl-phenyl)hexamethyltrisiloxane	0.97 ± 0.10	80		60
	0.98 ± 0.04	ω-Chloromethyl-ω'-(4-vinyl-phenyl)octamethyltetra-siloxane	1.08 ± 0.08	80		60
	2.5	p-Chlorostyrene	0.45	30	d	91
	1.85 ± 0.03	Cinnamic acid	0	60		17
	2.2	Cinnamonitrile	0	80	t	104
	20.0 ± 0.5	Crotononitrile	0	60	n	84
	0.85 ± 0.06	α-(2-Cyanoethyl)acrylonitrile	0.25 ± 0.15			176
	0.34 ± 0.02	Di-n-amyl itaconate	0.52 ± 0.02	60		26
	1.65 ± 0.03	N,N-Di-n-butylacrylamide	0.32 ± 0.02	50		24
	0.40 ± 0.05	Di-n-Butyl itaconate	0.38 ± 0.02	60		26
	5.4	Di-n-butyl vinyl phosphonate	0.3	60		99
	0.38	2,5-Dichlorostyrene	1.77	70		186
	0.30 ± 0.02	Diethyl itaconate	0.33 ± 0.02	60		26
	32 ± 5	N-Diethyl-O-vinylcarbamate	0.03 ± 0.01	66		143
	4.4 ± 0.6	N-Diethyl-S-vinylmonothiol-carbamate	0.14 ± 0.03	66		143
	8.87 ± 0.14	Diethyl vinyl phosphonate	0.06 ± 0.02			179
	4.1	Diethyl vinyl phosphonate	0	60		99
	0.54	α-Difluoromethylstyrene	1.313	60		52
	0.044	2,5-Difluorostyrene	2.195	60		52
	17.2	Diglycidyl 1,2-dimethyl-3-cyclohexen-1,5-dicarboxylate	0	100		78
	17 ± 5	Diisobutyl vinyl phosphine oxide	0	60		141

M_1	r_1	M_2	r_2	T,°C	Remarks	Ref.
Styrene	4.4	Diisobutyl vinyl phosphonate	0.5	60		99
	2.39	Diisopropyl vinyl phosphonate	0	60		99
	0.77 ± 0.07	2,5-Dimethoxystyrene	1.13	70		87
	1.23 ± 0.43	N,N-Dimethylacrylamide	0.23 ± 0.13	50		132
	0.89	p-Dimethylaminostyrene	0.62			189
	0.32 ± 0.02	Dimethyl itaconate	0.25 ± 0.02	60		26
	1.77 ± 0.08	N-(1,1-Dimethyl-3-oxobutyl)-acrylamide	0.49 ± 0.06	60		39
	4.61	Dimethyl vinyl phosphonate	0.4	60		99
	0.35 ± 0.03	Di-n-octyl itaconate	0.60 ± 0.02	60		26
	0.52 ± 0.05	Diphenyl 4-vinylphenylphosphine	1.43 ± 0.25	60		142
	0.42 ± 0.02	Diphenyl 4-vinylphenyl phosphine oxide	1.40 ± 0.15	60		142
	0.43 ± 0.05	Diphenyl 4-vinylphenyl phosphine sulfide	1.49 ± 0.33	60		142
	7 ± 1	Diphenyl vinylphosphine	0	60		141
	5 ± 1	Diphenyl vinyl phosphine oxide	0	60		141
	2.1 ± 0.3	Diphenyl vinyl phosphine sulfide	0	60		141
	2.03	Diphenyl vinyl phosphonate	0	60		99
	0.25 ± 0.03	Di-n-propyl itaconate	0.41 ± 0.04	60		26
	4.24	Di-n-propyl vinyl phosphonate	0.9	60		99
	0.65	m-Divinylbenzene	0.60	60		190
	0.92	o-Divinylbenzene	1.0	80		188
	0.14	p-Divinylbenzene	0.5	80		188
	56 ± 5	n-Dodecyl vinyl ether	0.0 ± 0.05	70		6
	27 ± 2	n-Dodecyl vinyl ether	0.0 ± 0.05	100		6
	0.46	c-Eleostearic acid	4	h		146
	0.3	Ethyl benzylidenecyanoacetate	0	80	t	104

M_1	r_1	M_2	r_2	T, °C	Remarks	Ref.
Styrene	2.7 ± 0.3	Ethyl cinnamate	0.05	75		144
	0.40	Ethyleneglycol dimeth-acrylate	0.65	61		190
	15.7 ± 0.8	N,N-Ethylene-N'-iso-propenylurea	0.01 ± 0.03	60		79
	14.5 ± 0.9	N,N-Ethylene-N'-vinylurea	0.05 ± 0.04	60		79
	13 ± 3	S-Ethyl-N-methyl-N-vinyl monothiolcarbamate	0.025 ± 0.01	66		143
	0.50 ± 0.15	4-Fluoro-4'-vinylbiphenyl	0.88 ± 0.07	70		22
	0.441 ± 0.007	Glycidyl methacrylate	0.544 ± 0.004	60		164
	0.50	Glycidyl methacrylate	0.60	120		164
	0.45 ± 0.001	Glycidyl methacrylate	0.55 ± 0.002	60		163
	21.0	Glycidyl 1-methyl-3-cyclohexen-1-carboxylate	0	100		78
	0	Glycidyl methyl ether	1.8	50	d	83
	0	Glycidyl n-Propyl ether	4.9	50	d	83
	1.19 ± 0.11	Glycidyl vinylsulfonate	0.03 ± 0.08	70		77
	0.70	Isobornyl methacrylate	0.32	60		74
	1.1	Isobutylene	3.1	-78	d	71
	1.1	Isobutylene	2.2	-78	d	71
	1.0	Isobutylene	1.5	-78	d	71
	0.5	Isobutylene	0.8	-78	d	71
	0.6	Isobutylene	1.9	-78	d	71
	0.6	Isobutylene	3.0	-103	d	196
	0.33	Isobutylene	3.5	-78	d	1
	3.7	Isobutylene	0.5	0	γ-rays	140
	0.2	Isobutylene	3.3	0	γ-rays/ZnO	140
	0.14 ± 0.02	Isoprene	7.0 ± 0.6	30	e	103
	0.50	Isoprene	1.92	100		187

M_1	r_1	M_2	r_2	T, °C	Remarks	Ref.
Styrene	0.54	Isoprene	1.92	80		187
	0.65	Isoprene	1.18	22	γ-rays	187
	0.03	Isoprene	5.89	30	BuLi	187
	0.8	Isoprene	0.1	0 to -30	$SnCl_4/C_2H_5Cl$	195
	2.6	Isopropenyl acetate	0.5	30	d	69
	1.11 ± 0.01	p-Isopropylstyrene	0.54 ± 0.01	50		28
	7.16	Linoleic acid	0.29	150		156
	0.019	Maleic anhydride	0	50		10
	0.040	Maleic anhydride	0.015	50		130
	0.097 ± 0.002	Maleic anhydride	0 ± 0.002	50		68
	0.1	Maleimide	0.1	75		183
	0.2 ± 0.02	Methacrylic acid	0.66 ± 0.08	45		148
	0.53 ± 0.02	Methacrylic acid	0.45 ± 0.06	45	DMF	148
	0.12	Methacrylic anhydride	0.26	36.6		161
	0.05 ± 0.02	Methacrylonitrile	12.0 ± 1.0	-78 to -30	$PhMgBr/Et_2O$	44
	1.05 ± 0.02	Methacrylyl triethyl germanium	0.93 ± 0.08	60		98
	0.11 ± 0.04	o-Methoxystyrene	3.6 ± 0.8	-20	d	72
	0.20 ± 0.02	o-Methoxystyrene	3.9 ± 0.7	30	d	72
	0.5	p-Methoxystyrene	38.0	30	d	72
	0.70 ± 0.10	p-Methoxystyrene	1.5 ± 0.22	25	γ-rays	35
	1.05	p-Methoxystyrene	0.79	-		189
	19	p-Methoxystyrene	0.045	25	e	154
	0.30 to 1.50	Methyl acrylate	0.13	0	BF_3/SO_2	116
	0.75 ± 0.11	Methyl acrylate	0.18 ± 0.03	25	γ-rays	35
	0.59 ± 0.05	Methyl α-benzylacrylate	0.17 ± 0.03	65		38
	0.80 ± 0.05	Methyl α-n-butylacrylate	0.20 ± 0.05	65		38

References page II-336

M_1	r_1	M_2	r_2	T, °C	Remarks	Ref.
Styrene	2.25 ± 0.05	Methyl α-sec-butylacrylate	0	65		38
	0.153	N-Methylcitraconimide	0.24	70		110
	1.65 ± 0.05	Methyl α-cyclohexylacrylate	0	65		38
	0.82 ± 0.08	Methyl ethacrylate	0.21 ± 0.02	65		38
	0.591 ± 0.057	5-Methyl-1-hexene	4.00 ± 0.28	35	e	9
	0.96 ± 0.05	Methyl α-isobutylacrylate	0.20 ± 0.03	65		38
	1.85 ± 0.07	Methyl α-isopropylacrylate	0	65		38
	0.63 ± 0.09	Methyl methacrylate	0.50 ± 0.07	25	γ-rays	35
	20	Methyl methacrylate	0.005	-78	γ-rays, d	1
	0.52	Methyl methacrylate	0.45	50	1 atm./C_6H_6	11
	0.58	Methyl methacrylate	0.48	50	100 atm./C_6H_6	11
	0.72	Methyl methacrylate	0.58	50	1000 atm./C_6H_6	11
	0.49	Methyl methacrylate	0.46	50	1 atm./$ClCH_2CH_2Cl$	11
	0.53	Methyl methacrylate	0.52	50	100 atm./$ClCH_2CH_2Cl$	11
	0.63	Methyl methacrylate	0.66	50	1000 atm./$ClCH_2CH_2Cl$	11
	0.44	Methyl methacrylate	0.50	50	1 atm./pyridine	11
	0.49	Methyl methacrylate	0.57	50	100 atm./pyridine	11
	0.56	Methyl methacrylate	0.80	50	1000 atm./pyridine	11
	0.45	Methyl methacrylate	0.47	50	1 atm./EtOH	11
	0.49	Methyl methacrylate	0.52	50	100 atm./EtOH	11
	0.59	Methyl methacrylate	0.62	50	1000 atm./EtOH	11
	0	Methyl methacrylate	$>>1$	-50 to -20	PhMgBr/tol.	44
	0	Methyl methacrylate	1	-78	PhMgBr/tol.	44
	0.01 ± 0.01	Methyl methacrylate	25 ± 2	-30	PhMgBr/tol.	44
	0.07 ± 0.02	Methyl methacrylate	4.5 ± 1.0	20	PhMgBr/tol.	44
	0.02 ± 0.01	Methyl methacrylate	20.0 ± 2	-78	PhMgBr/Et_2O	44
	0.05 ± 0.02	Methyl methacrylate	14.0 ± 2	-30	PhMgBr/Et_2O	44

M_1	r_1	M_2	r_2	T, °C	Remarks	Ref.
Styrene	0.30 ± 0.05	Methyl methacrylate	2.0 ± 0.3	20	PhMgBr/Et$_2$O	44
	0.43 ± 0.013	Methyl methacrylate	0.45 ± 0.016		CdEt$_2$	58
	0.53	Methyl methacrylate	0.49	60		185
	0.89 ± 0.05	4-Methyl-1-pentene	3.67 ± 0.22	45	e	9
	0.03 ± 0.02	Methyl α-phenylacrylate	0.4 ± 0.2	55		38
	0.86 ± 0.08	Methyl α-n-propylacrylate	0.22 ± 0.04	55		38
	5.3	p-Methylstyrene	0.18	25	e	154
	0.20	p-Methylstyrene	4.2	30	d	91
	1.177	2-Methyl-α,β,β-trifluoro-styrene	0.403	60		52
	0.40	3-Methyl-α,β,β-trifluoro-styrene	0.73	60		52
	0.40	4-Methyl-α,β,β-trifluoro-styrene	0.63	60		52
	0.58	2-Nitrobutyl acrylate	0.115	70		175
	0.4	β-Nitrostyrene	0	80		105
	2.70 ± 0.10	N-n-Octylacrylamide	0.20 ± 0.05	50		24
	2.8 ± 0.10	N-tert-Octylacrylamide	0.25 ± 0.06	50		24
	65 ± 5	n-Octyl vinyl ether	0 ± 0.04	70		6
	1.7	Phenyl vinyl ether	0.01			70
	0.12	Propylene	7.70	60	e	65
	0.93	Propylene	0.62	45	Et$_3$Al/TiCl$_3$	37
	2.0	Propylene	3.7	60	Et$_3$Al/TiCl$_4$	66
	1.5	Propylene	1.0	60	Et$_3$Al/VOCl$_3$	66
	1.9	Propylene	2.4	60	Et$_3$Al/VCl$_4$	66
	1.0	Propylene	5.4	60	Et$_3$Al/VCl$_3$	66
	0.20 ± 0.13	Propylene	20.0 ± 3.5	40	i-Bu$_3$Al/TiCl$_3$	22
	0.30 ± 0.15	Propylene	20.5 ± 3.0	40	Et$_3$Al/TiCl$_3$	12

References page II-336

M_1	r_1	M_2	r_2	T,°C	Remarks	Ref.
Styrene	0.16 ± 0.08	Propylene	7.2 ± 0.7	40	Et_3Al/VCl_3	12
	200 ± 20	Tetrachloroethylene	-	60		150
	0.21	trans-2,3,4,5-tetrachloro-1,3,5-hexatriene	0.84	70		7
	0.501	Tetrahydrofurfuryl acrylate	0.485	70		129
	0.07 ± 0.03	1,1,2-Trichloro-1,3-butadiene	1.18 ± 0.08	60		100
	0.603	3-Trifluoromethylstyrene	0.806	60		52
	0.81	α,β,β-Trifluorostyrene	0.50	60		52
	6.5	Vinyl acetate	0.15	30	$BF_3/PhNO_2$	69
	0.81	1-Vinylanthracene	0.57	65		92
	2.12	9-Vinylanthracene	0.25	100		92
	30	endo-Vinyl bicyclo(2.2.1)-heptane-2-carboxylate	0.01	60		73
	30	exo-Vinyl bicyclo(2.2.1)-heptane-2-carboxylate	0.01	60		73
	0.98 ± 0.04	4-Vinylbiphenyl	0.92 ± 0.08	70		22
	1.0	Vinyl chloroacetate	0.05	60		157
	1.25	Vinyl cinnamate	0.25 ± 0.1	70		144
	10.4 ± 0.02	N-Vinylglycidylurethan	0.02 ± 0.02	60		79
	0.22	Vinylhydroquinone dibenzoate	0.43	78		86
	1.80 ± 0.27	Vinylidene chloride	0.15 ± 0.02	25	γ-rays	35
	3.4	Vinylidene chloride	0.015	26	e	102
	1060.	Vinylmesitylene	0.004	25	e	154
	0.58	9-Vinylphenanthrene	2.36	60		92
	0.46 ± 0.03	4-Vinylphenyl diphenyl arsine	1.18 ± 0.04	65		27
	0.63 ± 0.05	4-Vinylphenyl diphenyl bismuthine	1.35 ± 0.10	65		27
	0.46 ± 0.07	4-Vinylphenyl diphenyl phosphine	1.11 ± 0.12	65		27

M_1	r_1	M_2	r_2	T, °C	Remarks	Ref.
Styrene	0.6	4-Vinylphenyl diphenyl stibine	1.3	65		27
	0.90 ± 0.03	4-Vinylphenyl heptamethyl-trisiloxane	1.2 ± 0.2	80		59
	1.15 ± 0.05	4-Vinylphenyl nonamethyl-tetrasiloxane	1.1 ± 0.5	80		59
	1.04 ± 0.06	4-Vinylphenyl pentamethyl-disiloxane	1.2 ± 0.4	80		59
	1.11 ± 0.01	4-Vinylphenyl undecamethyl-pentasiloxane	1.2 ± 0.1	80		59
	8.3 ± 0.3	N-Vinylphthalimide	0.075 ± 0.03	85		126
	0.50 ± 0.07	2-Vinylpyridine	1.27 ± 0.19	25	γ-rays	35
	0.57 ± 0.03	2-Vinylpyridine	1.33 ± 0.04	50		149
	0.16 ± 0.02	2-Vinylpyridinium acetate	0.36 ± 0.04	22		149
	0.477	2-Vinylthianthrene	0.133	60		67
p-Styrenesulfonic acid	1.20 ± 0.10	Acrylonitrile	0.10 ± 0.02	45	pH 3.0	82
Tetrachloroethylene	–	Methyl methacrylate	240 ±20	60		150
	–	Styrene	200 ±20	60		150
trans-2,3,4,5-tetrachloro-1,3,5-hexatriene	4.05	Acrylonitrile	0.20	70		7
	0.2 ± 0.07	2-Chloro-1,3-butadiene	3.6 ± 0.17	70		106
	1.58 ± 0.1	Isoprene	0.58 ± 0.02	70		106
	3.17 ± 0.27	Methyl acrylate	0.27 ± 0.04			8
	1.82 ± 0.075	Methyl methacrylate	0.465 ± 0.05			8
	0.315 ± 0.14	Methyl methacrylate	0.09 ± 0.105	70		106
	0.84	Styrene	0.21	70		7
	32	Vinyl acetate	0.013	70		7
Tetrafluoroethylene	0	Isobutylene	0	-78	γ-rays	169
	0.06	Propylene	1.0	-78	γ-rays	170,171

References page II-336

M_1	r_1	M_2	r_2	T, °C	Remarks	Ref.
Tetrahydrofuran	1.00 ± 0.05	3,3-Bis(chloromethyl)oxetane	0.82 ± 0.05	0	d	151
	3.9	Epichlorohydrin	0.06	0	d	81
	2.2	Ethylene oxide	0.08	0	d	81
	2.2	Ethylene oxide	0.08	0	d	123
	2.5	Glycidyl acetate	0.25	0	d	134
	2.5	Glycidyl methacrylate	0.25	0	d	134
	5.5 ± 0.1	β-Propiolactone	0.1 ± 0.1	h	Et_3Al/H_2O	173
	2.9 ± 0.5	β-Propiolactone	0.4 ± 0.2	h	BF_3/Et_2O	173
Tetrahydrofurfuryl acrylate	0.665	Acrylonitrile	0.689	70		129
	0.485	Styrene	0.501	70		129
Tetrahydrofuryl acrylate	0.91	Acrylonitrile	1.577	25	γ-rays	16
Tetrahydrofuryl methacrylate	1.01	Acrylonitrile	0.477	25	γ-rays	16
Tetravinyl silane	0.133 ± 0.006	Methyl acrylate	8.87 ± 0.07	h		160
1,1,2-Trichloro-1,3-butadiene	1.18 ± 0.08	Styrene	0.07 ± 0.03	60		100
Triethyleneglycol dimethacrylate	0.59 ± 0.06	2-Methyl-5-vinylpyridine	0.32 ± 0.065			42
3-Trifluoromethylstyrene	0.806	Styrene	0.603	60		52
α,β,β-Trifluorostyrene	0.50	Styrene	0.81	60		52
DL-Valine-N-carboxy-anhydride	11	β-Propiolactone	-0.16	35	Et_3N	45
Vinyl acetate	0.1 ± 0.05	Acrolein	3.3 ± 0.1	50	Heterogeneous	153
	0.05	Acrylonitrile	4.2	50		46,47
	1.30	Allyl chloride	-	60		150
	0.740 ± 0.087	N-Allylstearamide	0.532 ± 0.012	70		85
	0.82	Bicyclo(2.2.1)hepta-2,5-diene	1.28	60		139
	0.71 ± 0.1	n-Butyl vinyl ether	0.2 ± 0.05			95
	0.24 ± 0.05	Carbon monoxide	0.33 ± 0.05	60		119

M_1	r_1	M_2	r_2	T, °C	Remarks	Ref.
Vinyl acetate	0.0	1,3-Dichloro-2-butene	4.8 ± 0.9	50		49
	1.8 ± 0.4	N-Diethyl-O-vinyl carbamate	0.25 ± 0.08	66		143
	0.16 ± 0.08	N-Diethyl-S-vinyl monothiol-carbamate	1.5 ± 0.3	66		143
	1.005 ± 0.08	Divinyl acetal	0.99 ± 0.08	60		114
	1.005 ± 0.015	Divinyl n-butyral	1.06 ± 0.01	60		114
	1.012 ± 0.107	Divinyl formal	1.005 ± 0.105	60		114
	1.04 ± 0.08	Divinyl isoamylal	0.987 ± 0.057	60		114
	1.002 ± 0.047	Divinyl isobutyral	0.985 ± 0.05	60		114
	3.67 ± 0.45	n-Dodecyl vinyl ether	0 ± 0.23	50		4
	1.08 ± 0.19	Ethylene	1.07 ± 0.06	90	1000 atm.	34,192
	0.6 ± 0.1	S-Ethyl-N-methyl-N-vinyl mono-thiol carbamate	1.3 ± 0.2	66		143
	0.035	Methyl methacrylate	28.6	30		15
	0.027 ± 0.009	N-n-Octadecylacrylamide	6.11 ± 0.045	60		85
	4.50 ± 0.58	n-Octadecyl vinyl ether	0 ± 0.35	50		4
	3.47 ± 0.51	n-Octyl vinyl ether	0 ± 0.31	50		4
	0.15	Styrene	6.5	30	$BF_3/PhNO_2$	69
	0.013	trans-2,3,4,5-tetrachloro-1,3,5-hexatriene	32	70		7
	0.04	Vinyl cinnamate	1.20 ± 0.13	70		144
	1.04 ± 0.2	Vinyl 4-ketostearate	1.18 ± 0.22	60		113
	1.03 ± 0.05	Vinyl 9(10)-ketostearate	1.49 ± 0.25	60		113
	1.07 ± 0.02	Vinyl 12-ketostearate	1.26 ± 0.08	60		113
	0.07	N-Vinylphthalimide	2.4	60		128
	0.75 ± 0.04	Vinyl pivalate	0.43 ± 0.05	60		76
	0.175	N-Vinylsuccinimide	5.1	65		127
1-Vinylanthracene	0.57	Styrene	0.81	65		92

M_1	r_1	M_2	r_2	T, °C	Remarks	Ref.
9-Vinylanthracene	0.25	Styrene	2.12	100		92
endo-Vinyl bicyclo(2.2.1)-heptane-2-carboxylate	0.01	Styrene	30	60		73
exo-Vinyl bicyclo(2.2.1)-heptane-2-carboxylate	0.01	Styrene	30	60		73
4-Vinylbiphenyl	0.92 ± 0.08	Styrene	0.98 ± 0.04	70		22
Vinyl bromide	70 ±16	Acrylamide	0 ± 0.1	50	Heterogeneous	181
	90 ±15	Methacrylic acid	0 ± 0.1	50		181
N-Vinylcarbazole	4.77	Vinyl chloride	0.17			75
Vinyl chloride	0.001	Acenaphthylene	64			75
	0.74	Bicyclo(2.2.1)hepta-2,5-diene	0.35	50		191
	0.06	Bornyl methacrylate	12.5	60		74
	1.93 ± 0.15	n-Dodecyl vinyl ether	0.15 ± 0.2	50		3
	3.60 ± 0.30	Ethylene	0.24 ± 0.07	90	1000 atm.	34,192
	1.85 ± 0.2	Ethylene	0.20 ± 0.02	70	300 atm.	54
	0.04	Glycidyl methacrylate	8.84			75
	0.12	Isobornyl methacrylate	10.0	60		74
	2.10 ± 0.20	n-Octadecyl vinyl ether	-0.1 ± 0.2	50		3
	1.90 ± 0.20	n-Octyl vinyl ether	0.1 ± 0.1	50		3
	0.17	N-Vinylcarbazole	4.77			75
	0.5	Vinylidene chloride	0.001	25	e	102
	0.874 ± 0.044	Vinyl 4-ketostearate	0.320 ± 0.076	60		113
	0.963 ± 0.01	Vinyl 12-ketostearate	0.248 ± 0.01	60		113
Vinyl chloroacetate	1.0 ± 0.02	n-Butyl vinyl ether	0.5 ± 0.02			95
	1.01	n-Butyl vinyl ether	0.46	60		157
	0.98	Ethyl vinyl ether	0.26	60		157
	1.0	Phenyl vinyl ether	0.8	60		157
	0.05	Styrene	1.0	60		157

M₁	r₁	M₂	r₂	T, °C	Remarks	Ref.
Vinyl cinnamate	0.15 ± 0.06	Methacrylonitrile	4.6 ± 0.4	70		144
	0.25 ± 0.1	Styrene	1.25 ± 0.1	70		144
	1.20 ± 0.10	Vinyl acetate	0.04	70		144
	1.20	N-Vinylpyrrolidone	0.01	70		144
Vinyl N,N-diethylcarbamate	0.09	Acrylic acid	5.55	80		62
	0.035	Maleic anhydride	0	80		62
	0.01	Methyl acrylate	4.45	80		62
Vinyl fluoride	0.16 ± 0.05	Ethylene	4.39 ± 0.77	160	1000 atm.	34
N-Vinylglycidylurethan	1.5 ± 0.5	Acrylonitrile	0.066 ± 0.004	60		79
	0.10	Methyl methacrylate	2.75	60		79
	0.02 ± 0.02	Styrene	10.4 ± 0.02	60		79
	3.2 ± 0.3	Vinyl acetate	0.26 ± 0.04	50		79
Vinylhydroquinone dibenzoate	0.75	Methyl acrylate	0.46	78		86
	0.41	Methyl methacrylate	0.34	78		86
	0.30	α-Methylstyrene	0.11	78		86
	0.43	Styrene	0.22	78		86
	0.40	4-Vinylpyridine	0.48	78		86
	0.26	N-Vinylpyrrolidone	0.98	60		182
Vinylidene chloride	0.49	Acrylonitrile	1.20	45		137
	0.390	Acrylonitrile	0.585	32.8		112
	5.23 ± 0.067	N-Allylstearamide	0 ± 0.136	80		85
	1.41	Bicyclo(2.2.1)hepta-2,5-diene	0.08	50		191
	0.71	Maleimide	0.48	75		183
	0.005	Methyl acrylate	38	50	e	102
	0.438 ± 0.008	N-n-Octadecylacrylamide	1.37 ± 0.008	60		85
	0.15 ± 0.02	Styrene	1.80 ± 0.27	25	γ-rays	35
	0.015	Styrene	3.4	26	e	102

References page II-336

M_1	r_1	M_2	r_2	T, °C	Remarks	Ref.
Vinylidene chloride	0.001	Vinyl chloride	0.5	25	e	102
	3.8 ± 0.6	Vinyl 4-ketostearate	0 ± 0.17	60		113
	3.7 ± 0.3	Vinyl 9(10)-ketostearate	0.01 ± 0.09	60		113
	4.0 ± 0.5	Vinyl 12-ketostearate	0 ± 0.16	60		113
Vinyl 4-ketostearate	1.18 ± 0.22	Vinyl acetate	1.04 ± 0.2	60		113
	0.320 ± 0.076	Vinyl chloride	0.874 ± 0.044	60		113
	0 ± 0.17	Vinylidene chloride	3.8 ± 0.6	60		113
Vinyl 9(10)-ketostearate	0 ± 0.091	Acrylonitrile	2.96 ± 0.12	60		113
	1.49 ± 0.25	Vinyl acetate	1.03 ± 0.05	60		113
	0.01 ± 0.09	Vinylidene chloride	3.7 ± 0.3	60		113
Vinyl 12-ketostearate	0 ± 0.02	Acrylonitrile	3.11 ± 0.05	60		113
	1.26 ± 0.08	Vinyl acetate	1.07 ± 0.02	60		113
	0.248 ± 0.01	Vinyl chloride	0.963 ± 0.01	60		113
	0 ± 0.16	Vinylidene chloride	4.0 ± 0.5	60		113
Vinylmesitylene	0.004	Styrene	1060.	25	e	154
2-Vinylnaphthalene	0.187	N-Methylcitraconimide	0.256	70		110
β-Vinyloxyethyl methacrylate	0.004	n-Butyl vinyl ether	0.82	26	$Al_2(SO_4)_3/H_2SO_4$	109
9-Vinylphenanthrene	2.36	Styrene	0.58	60		92
4-Vinylphenyl diphenyl arsine	1.18 ± 0.04	Styrene	0.46 ± 0.03	65		27
4-Vinylphenyl diphenyl bismuthine	1.35 ± 0.10	Styrene	0.63 ± 0.05	65		27
4-Vinylphenyl diphenyl phosphine	1.11 ± 0.12	Styrene	0.46 ± 0.07	65		27
4-Vinylphenyl diphenyl stibine	1.3	Styrene	0.6	65		27
4-Vinylphenyl heptamethyl trisiloxane	1.2 ± 0.2	Styrene	0.90 ± 0.03	80		59
4-Vinylphenyl nonamethyl tetrasiloxane	1.1 ± 0.3	Styrene	1.15 ± 0.05	80		59

M_1	r_1	M_2	r_2	T, °C	Remarks	Ref.
4-Vinylphenyl pentamethyl disiloxane	1.2 ± 0.4	Styrene	1.04 ± 0.06	80		59
4-Vinylphenyl undecamethyl pentasiloxane	1.2 ± 0.1	Styrene	1.11 ± 0.01	80		59
N-Vinylphthalimide	0.075 ± 0.03	Styrene	8.3 ± 0.3	85		126
	2.4	Vinyl acetate	0.07			128
Vinyl pivalate	0.43 ± 0.05	Vinyl acetate	0.75 ± 0.04	60		76
2-Vinylpyridine	0	Acrolein	4.0	50	Homogeneous	153
	1.38 ± 0.04	Methacrylic acid	0.44 ± 0.02	h		147
	0.84 ± 0.13	Methyl methacrylate	0.20 ± 0.03	25	γ-rays	35
	1.27 ± 0.19	Styrene	0.50 ± 0.07	25	γ-rays	35
	1.33 ± 0.04	Styrene	0.57 ± 0.03	50		149
4-Vinylpyridine	0.48	Vinylhydroquinone dibenzoate	0.40	78		86
2-Vinylpyridinium acetate	0.36 ± 0.04	Styrene	0.16 ± 0.02	22		149
N-Vinylpyrrolidone	0.01	Vinyl cinnamate	1.20	70		144
	0.98	Vinylhydroquinone dibenzoate	0.26	60		182
N-Vinylsuccinimide	5.1	Vinyl acetate	0.175	65		127
Vinylsulfonic acid	0.15	Acrylonitrile	1.5			107
2-Vinylthianthrene	0.314	Ethyl acrylate	0.07	60		67
	0.07	Methyl methacrylate	2.99	60		67
	0.133	Styrene	0.477	60		67

1. A. D. Abkin, A. P. Sheinker, and L. P. Mezhirova, Zh. Fiz. Khim. $\underline{33}$, 2636 (1959);
    through J. Polymer Sci. $\underline{53}$, 39 (1961).
2. A. D. Abkin, A. P. Sheinker, M. K. Yakovleva, and L. P. Mezhirova, J. Polymer
    Sci. $\underline{53}$, 39 (1961).
3. G. Akazome, S. Sakai, Y. Choshi, and K. Murai, Kobunshi Kagaku $\underline{17}$, 478 (1960);
    through Chem. Zentr. $\underline{135}$(9), 119 (1964).
4. G. Akazome, S. Sakai, and K. Murai, Kobunshi Kagaku $\underline{17}$, 449 (1960); through
    Chem. Zentr. $\underline{135}$(9), 119 (1964).
5. G. Akazome, S. Sakai, and K. Murai, Kobunshi Kagaku $\underline{17}$, 452 (1960); through
    Chem. Zentr. $\underline{135}$(9), 119 (1964).
6. G. Akazome, S. Sakai, and K. Murai, Kobunshi Kagaku $\underline{17}$, 482 (1960); through
    Chem. Zentr. $\underline{135}$(9), 119 (1964).
7. A. N. Akopyan and G. Ye. Krbekyan, Vysokomolekul.Soedin. $\underline{5}$, 201 (1963); Polymer
    Sci. U.S.S.R. $\underline{4}$, 595 (1963).
8. A. N. Akopyan, G. E. Krbekyan, and E. G. Sinanyan, Vysokomolekul.Soedin. $\underline{5}$, 681
    (1963); Polymer Sci. U.S.S.R. $\underline{4}$, 1383 (1963).
9. I. H. Anderson, G. M. Burnett, and P. J. T. Tait, J. Polymer Sci. $\underline{56}$, 391 (1962).
10. T. L. Ang and H. J. Harwood, ACS Polymer Preprints $\underline{5}$(1), 306 (1964).
11. H. Asai and T. Imoto, J. Polymer Sci. $\underline{B2}$, 553 (1964).
12. N. Ashikari, T. Kanemitsu, K. Yanagisawa, K. Nakagawa, H. Okamoto, S. Kobayashi,
    and A. Nishioka, J. Polymer Sci. $\underline{A2}$, 3009 (1964).
13. M. A. Askarov and S. N. Trubitsyna, Vysokomolekul.Soedin. $\underline{5}$, 1235 (1963); Polymer
    Sci. U.S.S.R. $\underline{5}$, 306 (1964).
14. C. Aso and K. Sadakata, Kogyo Kagaku Zasshi $\underline{62}$, 1610 (1959); through Chem. Abstr.
    $\underline{57}$, 16836e (1962).
15. J. N. Atherton and A. M. North, Trans. Faraday Soc. $\underline{58}$, 2049 (1962).
16. A. S. Bank, S. D. Savranskaya, and M. A. Askarov, Khim. i Fiz.-Khim. Prirodn.
    i Sintetich. Polimerov, Akad. Nauk Uz. S.S.R., Inst. Khim. Polimerov No. $\underline{2}$, 110
    (1964); through Chem. Abstr. $\underline{61}$, 13425h (1964).
17. C. A. Barson, J. Polymer Sci. $\underline{62}$, S-128 (1962).
18. J. M. Barton, G. B. Butler, and E. C. Chapin, ACS Polymer Preprints $\underline{5}$(1), 216
    (1964).
19. J. C. Bevington and B. W. Malpass, Trans. Faraday Soc. $\underline{60}$, 1268 (1964).
20. K. I. Beynon, J. Polymer Sci. $\underline{A1}$, 3343 (1963).
21. K. I. Beynon, J. Polymer Sci. $\underline{A1}$, 3357 (1963).
22. V. D. Bezuglyi, T. A. Alekseeva, L. I. Dmitrievskaya, A. V. Chernobai, and
    L. P. Kruglyak, Vysokomolekul Soedin. $\underline{6}$, 125 (1964); through Chem. Abstr. $\underline{60}$,
    10789d (1964).
23. L. Bogetich, G. A. Mortimer, and G. W. Daues, J. Polymer Sci. $\underline{61}$, 3 (1962).
24. J. F. Bork, D. P. Wyman, and L. E. Coleman, J. Appl. Polymer Sci. $\underline{7}$, 451 (1963).
25. E. E. Brando and A. I. Dintses, Neftekhimiya $\underline{4}$, 68 (1964); through Chem. Abstr.
    $\underline{61}$, 728d (1964).
26. D. Braun and T.-O. Ahn, Kolloid Z. $\underline{188}$, 1 (1963).
27. D. Braun, H. Daimon, and G. Becker, Makromol. Chem. $\underline{62}$, 183 (1963).
28. D. Braun and H.-G. Keppler, Makromol. Chem. $\underline{78}$, 100 (1964).
29. S. Bresadola and P. Canal, J. Polymer Sci. $\underline{B1}$, 523 (1963).
30. L. S. Bresler, B. A. Dolgoplosk, M. F. Kolechkova, and E. N. Kropacheva, Dokl.
    Akad. Nauk S.S.S.R. $\underline{144}$, 347 (1962); through Chem. Abstr. $\underline{57}$, 8716h (1962).
31. L. S. Bresler, B. A. Dolgoplosk, M. F. Kolechkova, and E. N. Kropacheva,
    Vysokomolekul Soedin. $\underline{5}$, 357 (1963); through Chem. Abstr. $\underline{59}$, 1819h (1963).
32. L. S. Bresler, B. A. Dolgoplosk, and E. N. Kropacheva, Dokl. Akad. Nauk S.S.S.R.
    $\underline{149}$, 595 (1963); through Chem. Abstr. $\underline{59}$, 4044h (1963).
33. G. R. Brown and D. C. Pepper, J. Chem. Soc. $\underline{1963}$, 5930.
34. R. D. Burkhart and N. L. Zutty, J. Polymer Sci. $\underline{A1}$, 1137 (1963).
35. W. J. Burlant and D. H. Green, J. Polymer Sci. $\underline{31}$, 227 (1958).
36. A. Chapiro and A.-M. Jendrychowska-Bonamour, J. Polymer Sci. $\underline{C1}$, 1211 (1963).
37. R. P. Chernovskaya, V. P. Lebedev, K. S. Minsker, and G. A. Razuvaev,
    Vysokomolekul Soedin. $\underline{6}$, 1313 (1964); through Chem. Abstr. $\underline{61}$, 12095c (1964).
38. K. Chikanishi and T. Tsuruta, Makromol. Chem. $\underline{73}$, 231 (1964).
39. L. E. Coleman, J. F. Bork, and D. P. Wyman, ACS Polymer Preprints $\underline{5}$(1), 250 (1964).
40. P. Colombo, M. Steinberg, and J. Fontana, J. Polymer Sci. $\underline{B1}$, 447 (1963).
41. F. S. Dainton and W. D. Sisley, Trans. Faraday Soc. $\underline{59}$, 1385 (1963).
42. A. B. Davankov, L. B. Zubakova, and A. A. Gurov, Vysokomolekul.Soedin. $\underline{6}$, 237 (1964);
    through Chem. Abstr. $\underline{60}$, 14680b (1964).
43. F. Dawans, J. Polymer Sci. $\underline{A2}$, 3297 (1964).
44. F. Dawans and G. Smets, Makromol. Chem. $\underline{59}$, 163 (1963).
45. O. C. Dermer and W. A. Ames, J. Polymer Sci. $\underline{A2}$, 4151 (1964).
46. I. S. Dorokhina, A. D. Abkin, and V. S. Klimenkov, Khim. Volokna, $\underline{1962}$(1), 49;
    through Chem. Abstr. $\underline{59}$, 2956h (1963).
47. I. S. Dorokhina, A. D. Abkin, and V. S. Klimenkov, Vysokomolekul.Soedin. $\underline{5}$, 385
    (1963); Polymer Sci. U.S.S.R. $\underline{4}$, 1044 (1964).

48. A. A. Durgaryan and R. M. Beginyan, Vysokomolekul. Soedin. 5, 28 (1963); through Chem. Abstr. 59, 2957d (1963).
49. A. A. Durgaryan, A. S. Grigoryan, and O. A. Chaltykyan, Izvest. Akad. Nauk Arm. S. S. R., Khim. Nauki 15, 455 (1962); through Chem. Abstr. 58, 14104g (1963).
50. V. S. Dyurnbaum and V. S. Klimenkov, Khim. Volokna 1963(4), 8; through Chem. Abstr. 59, 11711b (1963).
51. F. H. C. Edgecombe, Nature 198, 1085 (1963).
52. E. I. Egorova and A. F. Dokukina, Vysokomolekul. Soedin., Karbotsepnye Vysokomolekul. Soedin., Sb. Statei 1963, 40; through Chem. Abstr. 61, 4493h (1964).
53. D. D. Eley and J. Saunders, J. Chem. Soc. 1954, 1677.
54. B. Erussalimsky, F. Duntoff, and N. Tumarkin, Makromol. Chem. 66, 205 (1963).
55. E. S. Ferdinandi, W. P. Garby, and D. G. L. James, Can. J. Chem. 42, 2568 (1964).
56. K. Fukui, T. Shimidzu, T. Yagi, S. Fukumoto, T. Kagiya, and S. Yuasa, J. Polymer Sci. 55, 321 (1961).
57. J. Furukawa, T. Saegusa, T. Narvyama, and S. Kurahashi, Kogyo Kagaku Zasshi 65, 2082 (1962); through Chem. Abstr. 58, 14263b (1963).
58. J. Furukawa, T. Tsuruta, T. Fueno, V. Sakata, and K. Ito, Makromol. Chem. 30, 109 (1959).
59. G. Greber and E. Reese, Makromol. Chem. 55, 96 (1962).
60. G. Greber and J. Tölle, Makromol. Chem. 67, 98 (1963).
61. V. F. Gromov, P. M. Khomikovskii, and A. D. Abkin, Vysokomolekul. Soedin. 3, 1015 (1961); through J. Polymer Sci. 59, S-53 (1962).
62. G. Hügele, H. Fröhlich, D. Bischoff, and K. Hamann, Makromol. Chem. 75, 98 (1964).
63. F. L. Hamb and A. Winston, J. Polymer Sci. A2, 4475 (1964).
64. H. Hayashi, I. Ito, T. Saegusa, and J. Furukawa, Kogyo Kagaku Zasshi 65, 1634 (1962); through Chem. Abstr. 58, 9237f (1963).
65. I. Hayashi, Kogyo Kagaku Zasshi 66, 1350 (1963); through Chem. Abstr. 60, 13324a (1964).
66. I. Hayashi, Kogyo Kagaku Zasshi 67, 258 (1964); through Chem. Abstr. 61, 1947e (1964).
67. H. Hopff and H. Gutenberg, Makromol. Chem. 60, 129 (1963).
68. M. B. Huglin, Polymer 3, 335 (1962).
69. M. Ibonai, T. Kato, and Y. Yamashita, Kogyo Kagaku Zasshi 67, 1068 (1964); through Chem. Abstr. 61, 12095d (1964).
70. F. Ida, K. Uemura, and S. Abe, Kagaku to Kogyo (Osaka) 38, 215 (1964); through Chem. Abstr. 61, 7105d (1964).
71. M. Iino and N. Tokura, Bull. Chem. Soc. Japan 37, 23 (1964).
72. Y. Imanishi, A. Mizote, T. Higashimura, and S. Okamura, Kobunshi Kagaku 20, 58 (1963); through Makromol. Chem. 70, 77 (1964).
73. M. Imoto, T. Otsu, and W. Fukuda, J. Polymer Sci. B1, 225 (1963).
74. M. Imoto, T. Otsu, K. Tsuda, and T. Ito, J. Polymer Sci. A2, 1407 (1964).
75. M. Imoto and S. Shimizu, Kobunshi Kagaku 18, 747 (1961); through Makromol. Chem. 53, 228 (1962).
76. S. Imoto, J. Ukida, and T. Kominami, Kobunshi Kagaku 14, 101 (1957); through Chem. Abstr. 52, 1669h (1958).
77. Y. Iwakura and N. Nakabayashi, Makromol. Chem. 66, 142 (1963).
78. Y. Iwakura, N. Nakabayashi, and M. H. Lee, Makromol. Chem. 78, 157 (1964).
79. Y. Iwakura, N. Nakabayashi, and H. Suzuki, Makromol. Chem. 78, 168 (1964).
80. T. Iwata, G. Wasai, T. Saegusa, and J. Furukawa, Makromol. Chem. 77, 229 (1964).
81. S. Iwatsuki, N. Takigawa, M. Okada, Y. Yamashita, and Y. Ishii, J. Polymer Sci. B2, 549 (1964).
82. Z. Izumi, H. Kiuchi, and M. Watanabe, J. Polymer Sci. A1, 705 (1963).
83. H. Jahn and J. Neels, Z. Chem. 2(12), 370 (1962); through Chem. Abstr. 59, 4044d (1963).
84. D. G. L. James and T. Ogawa, J. Polymer Sci. B2, 991 (1964).
85. E. F. Jordan, Jr., and A. N. Wrigley, J. Appl. Polymer Sci. 8, 527 (1964).
86. H. Kamogawa and H. G. Cassidy, J. Polymer Sci. A1, 1971 (1963).
87. H. Kamogawa and H. G. Cassidy, J. Polymer Sci. A2, 2409 (1964).
88. H. Kamogawa, R. Murase, and T. Sekiya, Kogyo Kagaku Zasshi 62, 1749 (1959); through Chem. Abstr. 58, 3511e (1963).
89. H. Kamogawa and T. Sekiya, Kogyo Kagaku Zasshi 62, 1117 (1959); through Chem. Abstr. 58, 3511c (1963).
90. H. Kamogawa and T. Sekiya, Kogyo Kagaku Zasshi 63, 1631 (1960); through Chem. Abstr. 56, 13084h (1962).
91. N. Kanoh, A. Gotoh, T. Higashimura, and S. Okamura, Makromol. Chem. 63, 106 (1963).
92. D. Katz, J. Polymer Sci. A1, 1635 (1963).
93. W. Kawai, Kogyo Kagaku Zasshi 66, 249 (1963); through Chem. Abstr. 59, 10243b (1963).

94. A. D. Ketley, J. Polymer Sci. B1, 121 (1963).
95. A. M. Khomutov, Vysokomolekul. Soedin. 5, 1121 (1963); through Chem. Abstr. 59, 11670g (1963).
96. S. Kimura and M. Imoto, Makromol. Chem. 50, 155 (1961).
97. F. Kobayashi and K. Matsuya, J. Polymer Sci. A1, 111 (1963).
98. G. S. Kolesnikov, S. L. Davydova, and N. V. Klimentova, Vysokomolekul.Soedin. 4, 1098 (1962); through Chem. Abstr. 59, 761a (1963).
99. G. S. Kolesnikov, E. F. Rodionova, and I. G. Safaralieva, Izvest. Akad. Nauk S.S.S.R., Ser. Khim. 1963, 2028; through Chem. Abstr. 60, 6933f (1964).
100. H. S. Kolesnikov, A. P. Suprun, T. A. Soboleva, V. A. Ershova, and V. B. Bondareva, Vysokomolekul. Soedin. 4, 743 (1962); Polymer Sci. U.S.S.R. 3, 977 (1962).
101. A. R. Kol'k, A. A. Konkin, and Z. A. Rogovin, Khim. Volokna 1963(4), 12; through Chem. Abstr. 59, 11670d (1963).
102. A. Konishi, Bull. Chem. Soc. Japan 35, 395 (1962).
103. A. A. Korotkov, and G. V. Rakova, Vysokomole ul Soedin. 3, 1482 (1961); through Chem. Abstr. 56, 11777g (1962).
104. M. Kreisel, U. Garbatski, and D. H. Kohn, J. Polymer Sci. A2, 105 (1964).
105. M. Kreisel, U. Garbatski, and D. H. Kohn, J. Polymer Sci. B2, 81 (1964).
106. G. E. Krybekyan, E. G. Sinanyan, and A. N. Akopyan, Izvest. Akad. Nauk Arm. S.S.R., Khim. Nauki 15, 527 (1962); through Chem. Abstr. 59, 1762h (1963).
107. S. Kunichika and T. Katagiri, Kogyo Kagaku Zasshi 64, 929 (1961); through Chem. Abstr. 57, 7480c (1962).
108. I. Kuntz, J. Polymer Sci. 54, 569 (1961).
109. J. Lal and J. E. McGrath, J. Polymer Sci. A2, 3369 (1964).
110. G. N. Larina, Z. V. Borisova, and T. V. Sheremeteva, Vysokomolekul. Soedin. 3, 1664 (1961); through Chem. Abstr. 56, 10386i (1962).
111. T. E. Lipatova and V. M. Siderko, Vysokomolekul. Soedin. 6, 910 (1964); through Chem. Abstr. 61, 5771a (1964).
112. L. Marker, O. J. Sweeting, and J. G. Wepsic, J. Polymer Sci. 57, 855 (1962).
113. C. S. Marvel, T. K. Dykstra, and F. C. Magne, J. Polymer Sci. 62, 369 (1962).
114. S. G. Matsoyan, M. G. Voskanyan, and A. A. Cholakyan, Vysokomolekul. Soedin. 5, 1035 (1963); through Chem. Abstr. 59, 11668d (1963).
115. M. Matsuda, M. Iino, and N. Tokura, Makromol. Chem. 65, 232 (1963).
116. M. Matsuda, K. Ohshima, and N. Tokura, J. Polymer Sci. A2, 4271 (1964).
117. L. P. Mezhirova, A. P. Sheinker, and A. D. Abkin, Polymer Sci. U.S.S.R. 3, 22 (1962).
118. L. P. Mezhirova, Z. Smigasevich, A. P. Sheinker, and A. D. Abkin, Vysokomolekul. Soedin. 5, 473 (1963); through Chem. Abstr. 59, 767e (1963).
119. A. Mitsutani, and M. Yano, Kogyo Kagaku Zasshi 67, 935 (1964); through Chem. Abstr. 61, 10794e (1964).
120. K. Miyamichi, A. Suzuki, S. Harada, and M. Katayama, Kobunshi Kagaku 21, 79 (1964); through Chem. Abstr. 61, 7111c (1964).
121. M. Morton and F. R. Ells, J. Polymer Sci. 61, 25 (1962).
122. E. Müller, K. Dinges, and W. Graulich, Makromol. Chem. 57, 27 (1962).
123. W. J. Murbach and A. Adicoff, Ind. Eng. Chem. 52, 772 (1960).
124. S. Nagai, Bull. Chem. Soc. Japan 36, 1459 (1963).
125. G. Natta, G. Mazzanti, A. Valvassori, G. Sartori, and A. Barbagalio, J. Polymer Sci. 51, 429 (1961).
126. A. F. Nikolaev and M. N. Tereshchenko, Vysokomolekul.Soedin. 6, 379 (1964); through Chem. Abstr. 61, 5771c (1964).
127. A. F. Nikolaev, S. N. Ushakov, and L. S. Mishkileeva, Vysokomole ul Soedin. 6, 287 (1964); through Chem. Abstr. 61, 729b (1964).
128. A. F. Nikolaev, S. N. Ushakov, L. P. Vishnevetskaya, N. A. Voronova, and E. I. Rodina, Vysokomolekul.Soedin. 4, 1053 (1962); through Chem. Abstr. 59, 10243f (1963).
129. K. Noma and M. Niwa, Kobunshi Kagaku 21, 17 (1964); through Chem. Abstr. 61, 7109a (1964).
130. K. Noma, M. Niwa, and K. Iwasaki, Kobunshi Kagaku 20, 646 (1963); through Makromol. Chem. 73, 250 (1964).
131. A. M. North and D. Postlethwaite, Polymer 5, 237 (1964).
132. A. M. North and A. M. Scallan, Polymer 5, 447 (1964).
133. V. A. Orlov and O. G. Tarakanov, Plasticheskie Massy 1964, 6; through Chem. Abstr. 61, 8412h (1964).
134. T. Otsu, K. Goto, S. Aoki, and M. Imoto, Makromol. Chem. 71, 150 (1964).
135. C. G. Overberger and V. G. Kamath, J. Am. Chem. Soc. 85, 446 (1963).
136. C. G. Overberger and E. Sarlo, J. Polymer Sci. A2, 1017 (1964).
137. R. B. Parker, Jr. and B. V. Mokler, J. Polymer Sci. B2, 19 (1964).
138. T. R. Paxton, J. Polymer Sci. B1, 73 (1963).
139. J. Pellon, R. L. Kugel, R. Marcus, and R. Rabinowitz, J. Polymer Sci. A2, 4105 (1964).

140. A. I. Popova, A. P. Sheinker, and A. D. Abkin, Dokl. Akad. Nauk S.S.S.R. 157, 1192 (1964); through Chem. Abstr. 61, 13423h (1964).
141. R. Rabinowitz, R. Marcus, and J. Pellon, J. Polymer Sci. A2, 1233 (1964).
142. R. Rabinowitz, R. Marcus, and J. Pellon, J. Polymer Sci. A2, 1241 (1964).
143. H. Ringsdorf, N. Weinshenker, and C. G. Overberger, Makromol. Chem. 64, 126 (1963).
144. J. Roovers and G. Smets, Makromol. Chem. 60, 89 (1963).
145. A. M. Rozhkov, Izvest. Sibirsk. Otd., Akad. Nauk S.S.S.R., Ser. Khim. Nauk 1963, 103; through Chem. Abstr. 60, 15989c (1964).
146. N. N. Rozovskaya and A. D. Abkin, Lakokrasochnye Materiali i ikh Primenenie 1961, 9; through Chem. Abstr. 55, 20500c (1961).
147. A. V. Ryabov, Yu. D. Semchikov, and N. N. Slavnitskaya, Tr. po Khim. i Khim. Tekhnol. 1963, 334; through Chem. Abstr. 61, 5771e (1964).
148. A. V. Ryabov, Yu. D. Semchikov, and N. N. Slavnitskaya, Dokl. Akad. Nauk S.S.S.R. 145, 822 (1962); through Chem. Abstr. 57, 15344a (1962).
149. A. V. Ryabov, Yu. D. Semchikov, and V. N. Vakhrusheva, Tr. po Khim. i Khim. Tekhnol. 1963, 188; through Chem. Abstr. 60, 9448h (1964).
150. M. K. Saha, P. Ghosh, and S. R. Palit, J. Polymer Sci. A2, 1365 (1964).
151. T. Saegusa, H. Imai, and J. Furukawa, Makromol. Chem. 56, 55 (1962).
152. I. Sakurada, T. Okada, S. Hatakeyama, and F. Kimura, J. Polymer Sci. C1, 1233 (1963).
153. R. C. Schulz, E. Kaiser, and W. Kern, Makromol. Chem. 58, 160 (1962).
154. M. Shima, D. N. Bhattacharyya, J. Smid, and M. Szwarc, J. Am. Chem. Soc. 85, 1306 (1963).
155. M. Shima and A. Kotera, J. Polymer Sci. A1, 1115 (1963).
156. V. V. Shneiderova, Lakokrasochnye Materiali i ikh Primenenie 1962(4), 33; through Chem. Abstr. 58, 579d (1963).
157. M. F. Shostakovskii, A. M. Khomutov, and A. P. Alimov, Izvest. Akad. Nauk S.S.S.R., Ser. Khim. 1963, 1839; through Chem. Abstr. 60, 4259g (1964).
158. M. F. Shostakovskii, G. G. Skvortsova, and M. Ya. Samoilova, Vysokomolekul. Soedin. 5, 966 (1963); through Chem. Abstr. 59, 7656e (1963).
159. W. P. Shyluk, J. Polymer Sci. A2, 2191 (1964).
160. I. Simek and L. Komora, Chem. Zvesti 17, 757 (1963); through Chem. Abstr. 60, 9362g (1964).
161. G. Smets, N. Deval and P. Hous, J. Polymer Sci. A2, 4835 (1964).
162. G. Smets and W. Van Humbeeck, J. Polymer Sci. A1, 1227 (1963).
163. M. F. Sorokin and I. M. Kochnov, Plasticheskie Massy 1963(1), 7; through Chem. Abstr. 58, 12680d (1963).
164. M. F. Sorokin and I. M. Kochnov, Vysokomolekul. Soedin. 6, 798 (1964); through Chem. Abstr. 61, 5770f (1964).
165. M. F. Sorokin, V. K. Latov, Zh. T. Korkishko, and Z. A. Kochnova, Plasticheskie Massy 1963(5), 11.
166. M. F. Sorokin, K. A. Lyalyushko, R. A. Dudakova, V. S. Vasil'ev, and A. N. Shuvalova, Plasticheskie Massy 1963(3), 3; through Chem. Abstr. 59, 4044e (1963).
167. Y. Tabata, Y. Hashizume, and H. Sobue, J. Polymer Sci. A2, 2647 (1964).
168. Y. Tabata, Y. Hashizume, and H. Sobue, J. Polymer Sci. A2, 3649 (1964).
169. Y. Tabata, K. Ishigure, K. Oshima, and H. Sobue, J. Polymer Sci. A2, 2445 (1964).
170. Y. Tabata, K. Ishigure, and H. Sobue, Kogyo Kagaku Zasshi 65, 1626 (1962); through Chem. Abstr. 58, 6931f (1963).
171. Y. Tabata, K. Ishigure, and H. Sobue, J. Polymer Sci. A2, 2235 (1964).
172. K. Tada, Y. Numato, T. Saegusa, and J. Furukawa, Makromol. Chem. 77, 220 (1964).
173. K. Tada, T. Saegusa, and J. Furukawa, Kogyo Kagaku Zasshi 66, 1501 (1963); through Chem. Abstr. 61, 727f (1964).
174. K. Tada, T. Saegusa, and J. Furukawa, Makromol. Chem. 71, 71 (1964).
175. A. Tanaka, K. Sasaki, Y. Hozumi, and O. Hashimoto, J. Appl. Polymer Sci. 8, 1787 (1964).
176. M. Tanaka, S. Asai, and S. Takeya, Kogyo Kagaku Zasshi 62, 1786 (1959); through Chem. Abstr. 57, 13972i (1962).
177. H. Tatemichi and S. Suzuki, Kogyo Kagaku Zasshi 63, 1843 (1960); through Chem. Abstr. 56, 13084d (1962).
178. N. Tokura, M. Matsuda, and M. Iino, Bull. Chem. Soc. Japan 36, 278 (1963).
179. T. Tsuda and Y. Yamashita, Kogyo Kagaku Zasshi 65, 811 (1962); through Chem. Abstr. 57, 15344g (1962).
180. Y. Tsuda, Kogyo Kagaku Zasshi 62, 1112 (1959); through Chem. Abstr. 57, 13972e (1962).
181. A. Ulinska and Z. Mankowski, Studia Soc. Sci. Torun., Sect. B 2(2), 16 (1960); through Chem. Abstr. 59, 5270d (1963).

182. S. N. Ushakov, O. M. Klimova, O. S. Karchmarchik, and E. M. Smul'skaya, Dokl. Akad. Nauk S.S.S.R. 143, 231 (1962); through Chem. Abstr. 57, 3620i (1962).
183. G. Van Paesschen and D. Timmerman, Makromol. Chem. 78, 112 (1964).
184. G. S. Wich and N. Brodoway, J. Polymer Sci. A1, 2163 (1963).
185. R. H. Wiley and B. Davis, J. Polymer Sci. 62, S-132 (1962).
186. R. H. Wiley and B. Davis, J. Polymer Sci. 62, S-140 (1962).
187. R. H. Wiley and B. Davis, J. Polymer Sci. A1, 2819 (1963).
188. R. H. Wiley and B. Davis, J. Polymer Sci. B1, 463 (1963).
189. R. H. Wiley, L. K. Heidemann, and B. Davis, J. Polymer Sci. B1, 521 (1963).
190. R. H. Wiley and G. L. Mayberry, J. Polymer Sci. A1, 217 (1963).
191. N. L. Zutty, J. Polymer Sci. A1, 2231 (1963).
192. N. L. Zutty and R. D. Burkhart, Advances in Chem. Series #34, "Polymerization and Condensation Processes," ACS, Washington, D. C., 1962, pp. 52-9.
193. G. E. Ham, J. Polymer Sci. 14, 484 (1954).
194. P. M. Kamath and H. C. Haas, J. Polymer Sci. 24, 143 (1957).
195. T. E. Lipatova, A. R Gantmakher, and S. S. Medvedev, Zh. Phys. Chem. 30, 1752 (1956).
196. B. R. Tegge, U. S. 2,643,993 (to Standard Oil Development Co.), 1953.

TABULATION OF Q-e VALUES

Lewis J. Young

The Dow Chemical Company
Plastics Department Research Laboratory
Midland, Michigan

These Q-e values are average values calculated by the use of the following two equations:

$$e_2 = e_1 \pm (-\ln r_1 r_2)^{\frac{1}{2}}$$

and

$$Q_2 = Q_1/r_1 \exp[-e_1(e_1 - e_2)]$$

The validity of the experimental r data was not normally a factor considered during the averaging process. Hence the values presented here may not agree with other sources.

The author wishes also to caution the reader to become familiar with the possible problems involved when the monomer is either a 1,2- or 1,1-disubstituted ethylene. (See G. E. Ham, "Copolymerization", Interscience Publisher, New York, 1964, Chapter II, Section III.) For systems which involve these hindered ethylenes, the Q-e values should be used only when no r data are available and then only with a forewarning of the possibility that the results may be widely at variance with the true experimental results.

For convenience, the data have been presented in two tables. Table I lists the monomers in order of increasing e-value, while Table II lists the monomers alphabetically.

TABLE I

Monomer	e	Q	Notes
N,N-Ethylene-N'-isopropenylurea	-2.16	0.19	b
1,1-Bis(p-anisyl)ethylene	-1.96	1.46	a
2,3-Dimethyl-1,3-butadiene	-1.81	5.86	
Isobutyl vinyl ether	-1.77	0.023	
m-Divinylbenzene	-1.77	3.35	b
1-Vinylanthracene	-1.68	2.50	b
2-Vinylthianthrene	-1.68	4.30	
2-Hydroxyethyl vinyl sulfide	-1.65	0.33	d
Vinylcyclohexene	-1.64	0.060	a,b
N-Vinylurethan	-1.62	0.12	
9-Vinylanthracene	-1.60	0.90	b
tert-Butyl vinyl ether	-1.58	0.15	b
N,N-Divinylaniline	-1.54	0.19	
N-Ethyl-N'-vinylurea	-1.53	0.13	
4-Isopropylstyrene	-1.52	1.60	b
N-Vinylphthalimide	-1.52	0.36	
N,N-Diethyl-S-vinyl monothiolcarbamate	-1.46	0.30	

Table I (Cont'd.) Monomer	e	Q	Notes
Vinyl thiolacetate	-1.46	0.31	b
Methyl vinyl sulfide	-1.45	0.32	
4-(β-Bromoethyl)styrene	-1.43	0.71	b
Phenyl vinyl sulfide	-1.40	0.34	
9-Vinylcarbazole	-1.40	0.41	
Diethyleneglycol monovinyl ether	-1.39	0.046	b
p-Dimethylaminostyrene	-1.37	1.51	
1,1-Diphenylethylene	-1.35	1.50	c
1-Chloro-1-propene	-1.34	0.049	b
trans-1,2-Bis(2-pyridyl)ethylene	-1.34	0.66	
Methylallyl acetate	-1.33	0.037	a
2-Butenyl triethoxysilane	-1.32	0.040	a
Isopropyl vinyl ether	-1.31	45.40	b
S-Ethyl-N-methyl-N-vinyl monothiolcarbamate	-1.29	0.11	
Divinyl ether	-1.28	0.037	
Methoxymethyl vinyl sulfide	-1.27	0.28	d
α-Methylstyrene	-1.27	0.98	
Dimethyl-phenyl-4-vinylphenyl-silane	-1.27	1.63	
Diphenylacetylene	-1.23	0.0025	a
Isoprene	-1.22	3.33	
Phenyl vinyl ether	-1.21	0.082	
n-Butyl vinyl ether	-1.20	0.087	c
N,N-Ethylene-N'-vinylurea	-1.19	0.18	
Bis(β-chloroethyl) vinyl phosphonate	-1.19	0.76	
N-(p-Anisyl)methacrylamide	-1.19	2.80	b
Sodium methacrylate	-1.18	1.36	
Ethyl vinyl ether	-1.17	0.032	c
1,4-Bis(4-vinylphenyl)butane	-1.17	1.20	b
N-Vinyl glycidylurethan	-1.15	0.18	
N-Vinylpyrrolidone	-1.14	0.14	
Allyl acetate	-1.13	0.028	c
2-Chloroallyl acetate	-1.12	0.53	a
4-Vinylbiphenyl	-1.12	1.32	b
1-Vinylnaphthalene	-1.12	1.94	b
Divinyl sulfide	-1.11	0.58	
Bis(4-vinylphenyl)methane	-1.11	1.28	b
p-Methoxystyrene	-1.11	1.36	
N-Methyl-N-vinyl-p-toluenesulfonamide	-1.10	0.082	a
Vinylmesitylene	-1.10	0.22	
1,3-Cyclohexadiene	-1.09	1.48	b
Bis(4-vinylphenyl)sulfide	-1.09	2.07	b
Propenyltriethoxysilane	-1.08	0.0034	a
1,2-Bis(4-vinylphenyl)ethane	-1.08	1.18	b
Bis(4-vinylphenyl)ether	-1.07	1.36	b
N,N-Diethyl-O-vinyl carbamate	-1.06	0.028	

Table I (Cont'd.) Monomer	e	Q	Notes
Bicyclo-[2.2.1]hepta-2,5-diene	-1.06	0.09	
1,3-Butadiene	-1.05	2.39	
β-Isopropenylnaphthalene	-1.04	0.92	c
2,5-Dimethoxystyrene	-1.04	1.75	
Indene	-1.03	0.36	c
Isopropenyl isocyanate	-1.02	0.23	
Dimethyl-vinyl-4-vinylphenyl-silane	-1.01	1.20	
Triallyl cyanurate	-1.00	0.020	c
N-(p-Chlorophenyl)methacrylamide	-0.98	0.70	b
p-Methylstyrene	-0.98	1.27	
p-Acetylaminostyrene	-0.98	1.43	b
Isobutylene	-0.96	0.033	c
2,5-Dimethylstyrene	-0.96	0.97	
Diallyl melamine	-0.95	0.017	c
Allyltriethoxysilane	-0.94	0.024	a
1-Chloro-1-propene	-0.94	0.031	b
2-Vinyl mercaptobenzothiazole	-0.92	1.68	b
Methallyl chloride	-0.91	0.12	a
1,3-Bis(4-vinylphenyl)propane	-0.91	0.98	b
N-Ethylmethacrylamide	-0.88	0.70	b
p-Trimethoxysilylstyrene	-0.88	1.50	b
Diethoxymethylvinylsilane	-0.86	0.020	a
N-Isopropenyl glycidylurethan	-0.86	0.26	b
1,1-Bis(p-chlorophenyl)ethylene	-0.84	2.16	a
Vinyl formate	-0.82	0.17	
2-Vinylquinoline	-0.82	3.79	
Trimethylsiloxylvinyldimethylsilane	-0.81	0.034	
4-Hydroabietyl alcohol	-0.80	0.056	a,b
N-Vinyl-2-oxazolidinone	-0.80	0.057	
Acenaphthylene	-0.80	0.26	b
p-Trimethylsilylstyrene	-0.80	1.00	b
Styrene	(-0.80)	(1.00)	Assumed
m-Vinylphenol	-0.80	1.10	b
9-Vinylphenanthrene	-0.80	1.73	b
3-Vinylphenanthrene	-0.80	2.26	b
2-Vinylthiophene	-0.80	2.86	b
n-Octyl vinyl ether	-0.79	0.061	c
Propylene	-0.78	0.002	
Bis(trimethylsiloxyl)vinylmethylsilane	-0.78	0.036	
N-Phenyl methacrylamide	-0.78	0.85	b
o-Methylstyrene	-0.78	0.90	b
N-(p-Tolyl)methacrylamide	-0.76	1.20	b
n-Dodecyl vinyl ether	-0.74	0.033	c
Vinyl isocaproate	-0.74	0.043	b
5-Ethyl-2-vinylpyridine	-0.74	1.37	

Table I (Cont'd) Monomer	e	Q	Notes
m-Styrenesulfonyl fluoride	-0.73	1.33	
m-Methylstyrene	-0.72	0.91	
2-Chloro-1-propene	-0.71	0.035	c
1-Hexyne	-0.70	0.014	a
Vinyl isocyanate	-0.70	0.16	
Tris(trimethylsiloxyl)vinylsilane	-0.69	0.030	
Vinyl pelargonate	-0.68	0.030	
Vinyl dichloroacetate	-0.68	0.17	
2-Vinylphenanthrene	-0.67	1.96	
Phenylacetylene	-0.66	0.35	
Vinylene carbonate	-0.65	0.0073	
Vinyl chloroacetate	-0.65	0.074	c
α-Acetoxystyrene	-0.65	0.82	b
Vinyl undecylenate	-0.64	0.035	c
Methacrylyl triethyl germanium	-0.64	0.84	b
tert-Butylethylene	-0.63	0.007	a,b
n-Octadecyl vinyl ether	-0.63	0.069	c
1-Pentene	-0.63	0.074	a,b
4-Methacryloxybenzylidine-4'-chloroaniline	-0.63	4.83	b
Triallyl isocyanurate	-0.60	0.011	c
N-Methyl methacrylamide	-0.60	0.32	b
Sodium p-styrenesulfonate	-0.59	2.49	
Potassium itaconate	-0.58	0.16	b
Pentachlorophenyl vinyl sulfide	-0.58	0.22	
2-Methyl-5-vinylpyridine	-0.58	0.99	
N-Allylstearamide	-0.57	0.040	c
Vinyl benzoate	-0.55	0.061	
Vinyl levulinate	-0.53	0.027	b
Vinyl stearate	-0.52	0.034	
Vinyl 12-ketostearate	-0.50	0.032	c
Isopropenyl acetate	-0.50	0.045	
Δ^3-Cyclohexenyltriethoxysilane	-0.50	0.050	a
N,N-Dimethylacrylamide	-0.50	1.08	b
2-Vinylpyridine	-0.50	1.30	
Vinyl 4-ketostearate	-0.48	0.037	c
Vinyl caproate	-0.47	0.025	
Allyl chloroacetate	-0.43	0.011	a,b
2-Fluoro-1,3-butadiene	-0.43	2.08	
Triethoxyvinylsilane	-0.42	0.028	a
n-Propyl methacrylate	-0.41	1.47	
Vinylacetylene	-0.40	0.69	b
Diphenyl p-vinylphenyl bismuthine	-0.40	1.15	b
p-Iodostyrene	-0.40	1.17	
Di-n-nonyl maleate	-0.39	0.22	b
β-Chloro-α,β-difluorostyrene	-0.39	0.34	b

Table I (Cont'd.) Monomer	e	Q	Notes
Di-n-nonyl fumarate	-0.39	0.60	b
Trimethoxyvinylsilane	-0.38	0.031	a
Diethoxyphenylvinylsilane	-0.38	0.034	a
2-Vinylnaphthalene	-0.38	1.25	
Diphenyl 4-vinylphenyl phosphine sulfide	-0.38	1.53	
β-Bromovinyl ethyl ether	-0.37	0.012	c
Triisopropoxyvinylsilane	-0.36	0.031	a
m-Chlorostyrene	-0.36	1.03	
o-Chlorostyrene	-0.36	1.28	
Diethoxyethylvinylsilane	-0.35	0.011	a,b
Vinyl pinonate	-0.35	0.034	
6-Triethoxysilyl bicyclo-[2,2,1]-2-heptene	-0.35	0.072	a
Diphenyl-vinylphosphine	-0.35	0.10	a
tert-Butyl methacrylate	-0.35	1.18	b
N-Vinylsuccinimide	-0.34	0.13	
p-Chlorostyrene	-0.33	1.03	
n-Amyl methacrylate	-0.32	0.82	b
p-Bromostyrene	-0.32	1.04	
Diphenyl-4-vinylphenylphosphine	-0.32	1.29	
Vinyl caprylate	-0.31	0.021	
2,4-Difluorostyrene	-0.31	0.65	b
4-Chloro-1-vinylnaphthalene	-0.31	0.74	
n-Octyl methacrylate	-0.31	0.78	
Diphenyl p-vinylphenyl stibine	-0.30	1.12	b
Potassium p-styrenesulfonate	-0.30	1.41	
Vinyl 9(10)-ketostearate	-0.29	0.039	c
2-Ethyl-1-vinylacetylene	-0.29	0.60	
3-Trifluoromethylstyrene	-0.29	0.92	
1-Hexene	-0.28	0.019	a
Vinyl butyrate	-0.26	0.042	
Ethyl vinyl oxalate	-0.26	0.092	
p-Styrenesulfonic acid	-0.26	1.04	b
Vinyl bromide	-0.25	0.047	
Sodium allylsulfonate	-0.24	0.15	b
n-Butyl methacrylate	-0.23	0.72	
Vinyl acetate	-0.22	0.026	
Divinyl acetal	-0.22	0.026	b
Divinyl butyral	-0.22	0.026	b
Divinyl formal	-0.22	0.026	b
Divinyl isoamylal	-0.22	0.026	b
Divinyl isobutyral	-0.22	0.026	b
Diphenyl 4-vinylphenyl phosphine oxide	-0.22	1.38	
m-Bromostyrene	-0.21	1.07	
α-Difluoromethylstyrene	-0.21	1.16	b
p-Cyanostyrene	-0.21	1.86	

Table I (Cont'd.) Monomer	e	Q	Notes
Ethylene	-0.20	0.015	
4-Vinylpyridine	-0.20	0.82	
Isopropenylacetylene	-0.18	0.54	
Ethyl ethacrylate	-0.18	0.61	b
2,4-Dimethoxy-6-(β-itaconylhydrazino)-s-triazine	-0.17	0.52	b
Allyl-dimethyl-4-vinylphenylsilane	-0.16	0.87	b
1,2-Dimethyl-5-vinylpyridinium methyl sulfate	-0.16	2.49	
Dimethallyl oxalate	-0.15	0.038	b
Isopropyl methacrylate	-0.15	1.20	b
β-Chloro-α,β-difluoro-4-methylstyrene	-0.13	0.27	b
6-Chloro-2-vinylnaphthalene	-0.13	1.35	
Ethyl vinyl sulfide	-0.12	0.37	
n-Hexyl methacrylate	-0.12	0.70	b
Sodium acrylate	-0.12	0.71	
p-Fluorostyrene	-0.12	0.83	
N-(1,1-Dimethyl-3-oxobutyl)acrylamide	-0.11	0.42	
Vinyl caprate	-0.10	0.020	
N-tert-Octylacrylamide	-0.10	0.20	
5-Ethyl-2-vinylpyridine-N-oxide	-0.10	4.52	
4-Methacryloxybenzylideneaniline	-0.09	2.24	b
Vinyl 2-ethylhexanoate	-0.08	0.024	
trans-Stilbene	-0.08	0.030	
Diethyl allyl phosphonate	-0.07	0.019	b
Diallyl phenyl phosphonate	-0.07	0.051	b
Vinyl propionate	-0.07	0.052	
Diallyl n-butyl phosphonate	-0.07	0.053	b
Lauryl methacrylate	-0.07	0.99	d
N,N-Di-n-butylacrylamide	-0.05	0.32	
2,5-Bis(trifluoromethyl)styrene	-0.05	1.11	
Isobutyl methacrylate	-0.04	0.77	b
Dimethyl-4-vinylphenylsilane	-0.04	0.97	b
cis-Stilbene	-0.03	0.017	b
Vinyl palmitate	-0.02	0.026	
Vinylsulfonic acid	-0.02	0.093	c
N-n-Octylacrylamide	-0.02	0.19	
Diphenyl p-vinylphenyl arsine	-0.02	1.16	b
2-Chloro-1,3-butadiene	-0.02	7.26	
Vinyl laurate	-0.01	0.018	
Methacrolein	-0.01	1.75	
2-Vinylpyridine-N-oxide	-0.01	3.77	
Diphenyl p-vinylphenyl phosphine	0.02	1.13	b
Trimethylvinylsilane	0.04	0.029	c
2-(N,N-Dimethylamino)-4-vinylpyrimidine	0.04	1.45	b
2-Methyl-α,β,β-trifluorostyrene	0.06	0.43	b
2,5-Dichlorostyrene	0.09	1.60	

Table I (Cont'd.) Monomer	e	Q	Notes
Glycidyl methacrylate	0.10	0.85	
Allyl chloride	0.11	0.056	c
n-Nonyl methacrylate	0.14	0.91	b
Ethyl methacrylate	0.17	0.56	
tert-Butylaminoethyl methacrylate	0.17	0.98	d
2-Methyl-5-vinylpyridinium hydrochloride	0.17	1.16	b
Ethyl β-ethoxyacrylate	0.18	0.015	c
α-Chlorovinyltriethoxysilane	0.18	0.23	a
Methacryloxymethylpentamethyldisiloxane	0.19	0.74	
Vinyl chloride	0.20	0.044	
2 Hydroxypropyl methacrylate	0.20	0.79	d
2-Hydroxyethyl methacrylate	0.20	0.80	b,d
p-Styrenesulfonyl fluoride	0.20	1.64	
Ethyl acrylate	0.22	0.52	
α,β,β-Trifluorostyrene	0.22	0.75	
Vinyl trans-cinnamate	0.24	0.24	
sec-Butyl methacrylate	0.24	0.72	d
4-Methyl-α,β,β-trifluorostyrene	0.24	0.88	
Ethyleneglycol dimethacrylate	0.24	0.88	
Diethyl vinyl phosphonate	0.25	0.09	c
Vinyl isothiocyanate	0.25	0.54	
Methyl bicyclo-[2.2.1]-2-heptene-5 carboxylate	0.26	0.059	
5-Cyanobicyclo-[2.2.1]-hept-2-ene	0.28	0.07	d
1-Cyano-1,3-butadiene	0.28	5.98	a,b
Vinyl endo-bicyclo-[2.2.1]-heptane-2-carboxylate	0.30	0.014	b
Vinyl exo-bicyclo-[2.2.1]-heptane-2-carboxylate	0.30	0.014	b
Isobornyl methacrylate	0.31	0.91	
Glycidyl 1-methyl-3-cyclohexen-1-carboxylate	0.32	0.014	c
sec-Butyl acrylate	0.34	0.41	d
Diisobutyl vinyl phosphine oxide	0.35	0.024	a
Tetrahydrofuryl methacrylate	0.35	0.45	b
n-Butyl crotonate	0.36	0.007	a,b
n-Propyl crotonate	0.36	0.011	a,b
Crotonaldehyde	0.36	0.013	a,b
Diallyl phthalate	0.36	0.044	b
Allyl alcohol	0.36	0.048	
Vinylidene chloride	0.36	0.22	
N-Methylolacrylamide	0.36	0.31	
Tetrahydrofurfuryl acrylate	0.36	0.54	
Benzyl methacrylate	0.36	3.60	b
p-Sulfonamidostyrene	0.37	1.62	b
2-Ethylhexyl acrylate	0.39	0.41	d
p-Nitrostyrene	0.39	1.63	
Methyl methacrylate	0.40	0.74	
Sodium vinylsulfonate	0.41	0.064	a

Table I (Cont'd.) Monomer	e	Q	Notes
Diethylaminoethyl methacrylate	0.42	2.08	
2-Chloroallyl chloride	0.44	0.27	c
Ethyl α-acetoxyacrylate	0.44	0.44	
3-Methyl-α,β,β-trifluorostyrene	0.44	1.07	
Crotonic acid	0.45	0.013	c
4-Vinylpyrimidine	0.45	2.18	b
Dimethylaminoethyl methacrylate	0.47	0.68	
Hexafluoro-1,3-butadiene	0.47	0.93	
Methyl α-isobutylacrylate	0.48	0.37	b
2-(Diethylphosphato)ethyl methacrylate	0.48	0.97	d
n-Decyl methacrylate	0.48	1.37	b
2,3-Dichloro-1,3-butadiene	0.48	12.86	c
Methyl cinnamate	0.49	0.12	a
Methyl α-n-propylacrylate	0.49	0.41	b
Diphenyl vinyl phosphine oxide	0.50	0.07	a
Ethyl 2-ethyl-2-methyl-1-butenoate	0.50	0.14	
Cinnamic acid	0.50	0.19	a,b
Itaconic acid	0.50	0.76	
Acrylic anhydride	0.51	1.27	
1-(Diethylphosphono)ethyl methacrylate	0.51	1.41	d
Pentachlorostyrene	0.52	0.22	
Methyl ethacrylate	0.52	0.42	b
Di-n-amyl itaconate	0.52	1.02	b
Allyl laurate	0.53	0.031	b
Methyl isopropenyl ketone	0.53	1.49	
trans-Crotononitrile	0.54	0.016	b
β-Chloroethyl acrylate	0.54	0.41	c
Ethyl methacrylylaminoacetate	0.54	0.72	b
Isopropyl acrylate	0.55	0.41	d
Methyl α-n-butylacrylate	0.55	0.42	b
2-Chloroallyl alcohol	0.56	0.24	a
α-(2-Cyanoethyl)acrylonitrile	0.56	0.29	
Stearyl methacrylate	0.56	1.07	b
2-Bromoethyl methacrylate	0.57	0.95	d
Vinyl perfluorobutyrate	0.58	0.038	b
2-Methoxyethyl acrylate	0.58	0.46	d
Methyl thiolacrylate	0.58	1.23	b
Bornyl methacrylate	0.59	0.79	
Methyl acrylate	0.60	0.42	
Ethyl cinnamate	0.62	0.12	b
Phenyl methacrylate	0.62	0.46	d
2-Isocyanatoethyl methacrylate	0.62	0.94	d
2-Butoxyethyl acrylate	0.63	0.42	d
3-Pyridalacetophenone	0.64	0.64	a,b
2-Ethylsulfinylethyl methacrylate	0.64	1.94	d

Table I (Cont'd.) Monomer	e	Q	Notes
Methyl 4-chlorocinnamate	0.65	0.15	a,b
Methacrylic acid	0.65	2.34	
N-(m-Fluorosulfonylphenyl)acrylamide	0.66	0.55	
α-Chloro-β-fluorostyrene	0.67	0.15	b
Hydronopyl acrylate	0.67	0.50	
1-Acrylamido-1-deoxy-D-glucitol	0.68	0.15	
Methyl vinyl ketone	0.68	0.69	
β,β-Difluorostyrene	0.70	0.029	a
Di-n-propyl itaconate	0.71	1.19	b
Triethyleneglycol dimethacrylate	0.71	1.46	b
Dimethyl 2-methylene-5-methyladipate	0.72	0.17	d
Methyl α-benzylacrylate	0.72	0.50	b
α,β-Difluorostyrene	0.73	0.12	b
Acrolein	0.73	0.85	
2,5-Difluorostyrene	0.73	6.70	b
Cinnamonitrile	0.75	0.32	b
trans-2,3,4,5-Tetrachlorohexa-1,3,5-triene	0.75	1.85	
n-Butyl cinnamate	0.76	0.33	b
N-(m-Fluorosulfonylphenyl)methacrylamide	0.76	0.69	b
Hexachloro-1,3-butadiene	0.76	1.31	
3,3,5-Trimethylcyclohexyl methacrylate	0.77	0.70	d
Acrylic acid	0.77	1.15	
Methyl α-chloroacrylate	0.77	2.02	
α-Acetoxyacrylonitrile	0.78	2.14	
1,1,2-Trichloro-1,3-butadiene	0.78	4.04	
Di-n-octyl itaconate	0.79	0.96	
3-Cinnamoylpyridine	0.80	0.33	b
Methacrylonitrile	0.81	1.12	
m-Nitrostyrene	0.81	2.47	
Methyl 2-chlorocinnamate	0.85	0.28	a
2-Chloro-1-propene	0.86	0.035	c
Ethyl α-cyanocinnamate	0.87	1.24	a,b
2,4-Dimethyl-6-vinyl-s-triazine	0.87	2.56	
β-Fluorostyrene	0.88	0.044	b
Ethyleneglycol dichloroacrylate	0.88	0.43	b
N-Benzylidene-4-methacryloxyaniline	0.88	1.08	b
Itaconic anhydride	0.88	2.50	
3,3,5-Trimethylcyclohexyl acrylate	0.90	0.65	d
Benzyl acrylate	0.90	0.68	
n-Propyl thiolacrylate	0.92	1.21	d
2-Methyl-5-cinnamoylpyridine	0.96	0.26	b
Glycidyl acrylate	0.96	0.55	
Ethyl acid fumarate	0.96	1.33	b
Methyl vinyl sulfoxide	0.98	0.057	b
Abityl acrylate	0.98	0.40	b

Table I (Cont'd.) Monomer	e	Q	Notes
Diethylphosphonomethyl methacrylate	0.98	0.65	b
Diethyl itaconate	0.98	0.94	
2-Chlorobenzalacetophenone	0.99	0.37	b
N-(1,1-Dihydroperfluorobutyl)-N-ethyl-acrylamide	1.01	1.22	b
Allyl diethylphosphinic acid	1.02	0.031	b
Poly(1,3-butyleneglycol fumarate)	1.02	0.29	c
Acrylyl chloride	1.02	1.78	
Methacrylic anhydride	1.03	1.60	
Vinyl trifluoroacetate	1.06	0.033	b
n-Butyl acrylate	1.06	0.50	
n-Octyl acrylate	1.07	0.35	
Di-2-ethylhexyl maleate	1.08	0.10	a,b
Di-n-butyl itaconate	1.09	1.07	
N,N,N-Triethyl-N-(2-methacryloxyethyl)ammonium iodide	1.10	2.10	b
n-Octadecyl acrylate	1.12	0.42	
N-n-Octadecylacrylamide	1.13	0.66	
trans-Trimethyl aconitate	1.14	0.0054	b
2-Nitrobutyl acrylate	1.15	0.61	
1,1-Dihydroperfluorobutyl acrylate	1.15	0.78	
Vinyl hydroquinone dibenzoate	1.17	1.80	
Phenyl vinyl sulfone	1.18	0.069	
n-Butyl vinylsulfonate	1.19	0.13	
Acrylonitrile	1.20	0.60	
Diisopropyl itaconate	1.21	0.89	b
Tetrafluoroethylene	1.22	0.049	c
Methacrylamide	1.24	1.46	
cis-Dichloroethylene	1.25	0.003	c
Diethyl fumarate	1.25	0.61	c
α-Cyanostyrene	1.26	9.60	b
Dimethyl maleate	1.27	0.09	
trans-Dichloroethylene	1.28	0.010	c
Vinyl fluoride	1.28	0.012	b
Methyl vinyl sulfone	1.29	0.11	c
1-Deoxy-1-methacrylamido-᛫-glucitol	1.30	0.089	
N-Methylolmethacrylamide methyl ether	1.30	0.64	b
Acrylamide	1.30	1.18	
Methyl α-phenylacrylate	1.30	6.20	b
Dibenzyl maleate	1.32	0.34	
Divinyl sulfone	1.33	0.14	
N-Methacryloxy-ε-caprolactam	1.34	0.18	a,b
Dimethyl itaconate	1.34	1.03	
Diphenyl vinyl phosphine sulfide	1.35	0.083	a
Maleimide	1.35	0.44	
3,3,3-Trichloro-1-propene	1.37	0.056	c

Table I (Cont'd.) Monomer	e	Q	Notes
4-Cyclopenten-1,3-dione	1.40	0.22	
α-Chloroacrylonitrile	1.40	1.72	b
Glycidyl vinylsulfonate	1.41	0.14	
Dioctyl fumarate	1.45	0.24	
Chlorotrifluoroethylene	1.48	0.020	
N-Methylcitraconimide	1.48	2.35	
Diethyl maleate	1.49	0.059	c
1-(Diethylphosphono)ethyl acrylate	1.49	0.57	b
Dimethyl fumarate	1.49	0.76	b
Diethylphosphonomethyl acrylate	1.50	0.76	
2-Hydroxyethyl acrylate	1.51	4.08	b
Di-β-chloroethyl itaconate	1.52	0.38	c
Ethyl acid maleate	1.52	1.23	b
Triethyl aconitate	1.54	0.28	c
Di-n-butyl maleate	1.60	0.042	a,b
cis-Trimethyl aconitate	1.62	0.32	c
Dimethyl methacrylyliminodiacetate	1.64	0.073	b
Diethyl chloromaleate	1.65	0.056	a,b
Citraconic anhydride	1.75	0.87	b
N-Butylmaleimide	1.75	3.08	
Crotonamide	1.76	0.0085	b
4,6-Diamino-2-vinyl-s-triazine	1.76	5.52	b
Dimethyl dithiolfumarate	1.78	1.23	
Diisobutyl maleate	1.85	0.094	b
Trichloroethylene	1.86	0.019	c
Poly(ethyleneglycol fumarate)	1.93	0.42	
Fumaronitrile	1.96	0.80	c
Tetrachloroethylene	2.03	0.0028	a
Diisopropyl maleate	2.06	0.084	c
N-Methylolcrotonamide	2.10	0.035	b
1,1-Dichloro-2,2-difluoroethylene	2.10	0.041	a
Methyl α-cyanoacrylate	2.10	high	d
N-Vinylpyridinium fluoroborate	2.12	1.12	
Methyl acid maleate	2.19	0.10	c
Maleic anhydride	2.25	0.23	c
Maleonitrile	2.32	0.42	a,b
Vinylidene cyanide	2.58	20.13	c

a r_2 assumed zero.

b   1 set of data only.

c   Some r_2 assumed zero.

d   Rohm and Haas values (no $r_1 r_2$).

COPOLYMERIZATION PARAMETER

TABLE II

Monomer	e	Q	Notes
Abityl acrylate	0.98	0.40	b
Acenaphthylene	-0.80	0.26	b
α-Acetoxyacrylonitrile	0.78	2.14	
α-Acetoxystyrene	-0.65	0.82	b
p-Acetylaminostyrene	-0.98	1.43	b
Acrolein	0.73	0.85	
Acrylamide	1.30	1.18	
1-Acrylamido-1-deoxy-ᴅ-glucitol	0.68	0.15	
Acrylic acid	0.77	1.15	
Acrylic anhydride	0.51	1.27	
Acrylonitrile	1.20	0.60	
Acrylyl chloride	1.02	1.78	
Allyl acetate	-1.13	0.028	c
Allyl alcohol	0.36	0.048	
Allyl chloride	0.11	0.056	c
Allyl chloroacetate	-0.43	0.011	a,b
Allyl diethylphosphinic acid	1.02	0.031	b
Allyl-dimethyl-4-vinylphenylsilane	-0.16	0.87	b
Allyl laurate	0.53	0.031	b
N-Allylstearamide	-0.57	0.040	c
Allyl triethoxysilane	-0.94	0.024	a
n-Amyl methacrylate	-0.32	0.82	b
N-(p-Anisyl)methacrylamide	-1.19	2.80	b
Benzyl acrylate	0.90	0.68	
N-Benzylidene-4-methacryloxyaniline	0.88	1.08	b
Benzyl methacrylate	0.36	3.60	b
Bicyclo-[2.2.1]-hepta-2,5-diene	-1.06	0.09	
1,1-Bis(p-anisyl)ethylene	-1.96	1.46	a
Bis(β-chloroethyl)vinyl phosphonate	-1.19	0.76	
1,1-Bis(p-chlorophenyl)ethylene	-0.84	2.16	a
trans-1,2-Bis(2-pyridyl)ethylene	-1.34	0.66	
2,5-Bis(trifluoromethyl)styrene	-0.05	1.11	
Bis(trimethylsiloxyl)vinylmethylsilane	-0.78	0.036	
1,4-Bis(4-vinylphenyl)butane	-1.17	1.20	b
1,2-Bis(4-vinylphenyl)ethane	-1.08	1.18	b
Bis(4-vinylphenyl)ether	-1.07	1.36	b
Bis(4-vinylphenyl)methane	-1.11	1.28	b
1,3-Bis(4-vinylphenyl)propane	-0.91	0.98	b
Bis(4-vinylphenyl)sulfide	-1.09	2.07	b
Bornyl methacrylate	0.59	0.79	
2-Bromoethyl methacrylate	0.57	0.95	d
4-(β-Bromoethyl)styrene	-1.43	0.71	b
m-Bromostyrene	-0.21	1.07	

Table II (Cont'd.) Monomer	e	Q	Notes
p-Bromostyrene	-0.32	1.04	
β-Bromovinyl ethyl ether	-0.37	0.012	c
1,3-Butadiene	-1.05	2.39	
2-Butenyltriethoxysilane	-1.32	0.040	a
2-Butoxyethyl acrylate	0.63	0.42	d
n-Butyl acrylate	1.06	0.50	
sec-Butyl acrylate	0.34	0.41	d
tert-Butylaminoethyl methacrylate	0.17	0.98	d
n-Butyl cinnamate	0.76	0.33	b
n-Butyl crotonate	0.36	0.007	a,b
tert-Butylethylene	-0.63	0.007	a,b
N-Butylmaleimide	1.75	3.08	
n-Butyl methacrylate	-0.23	0.72	
sec-Butyl methacrylate	0.24	0.72	d
tert-Butyl methacrylate	-0.35	1.18	b
n-Butyl vinyl ether	-1.20	0.087	c
tert-Butyl vinyl ether	-1.58	0.15	b
n-Butyl vinylsulfonate	1.19	0.13	
α-Chloroacrylonitrile	1.40	1.72	b
2-Chloroallyl acetate	-1.12	0.53	a
2-Chloroallyl alcohol	0.56	0.24	a
2-Chloroallyl chloride	0.44	0.27	c
2-Chlorobenzalacetophenone	0.99	0.37	b
2-Chloro-1,3-butadiene	-0.02	7.26	
β-Chloro-α,β-difluoro-4-methylstyrene	-0.13	0.27	b
β-Chloro-α,β-difluorostyrene	-0.39	0.34	b
β-Chloroethyl acrylate	0.54	0.41	c
α-Chloro-β-fluorostyrene	0.67	0.15	b
N-(p-Chlorophenyl)methacrylamide	-0.98	0.70	b
1-Chloro-1-propene	-0.94	0.031	b
2-Chloro-1-propene	-0.71	0.035	c
m-Chlorostyrene	-0.36	1.03	
o-Chlorostyrene	-0.36	1.28	
p-Chlorostyrene	-0.33	1.03	
Chlorotrifluoroethylene	1.48	0.020	
4-Chloro-1-vinylnaphthalene	-0.31	0.74	
6-Chloro-2-vinylnaphthalene	-0.13	1.35	
α-Chlorovinyl triethoxysilane	0.18	0.23	a
Cinnamic acid	0.50	0.19	a,b
Cinnamonitrile	0.75	0.32	b
3-Cinnamoylpyridine	0.80	0.33	b
Citraconic anhydride	1.75	0.87	b
Crotonaldehyde	0.36	0.013	a,b
Crotonamide	1.76	0.0085	b
Crotonic acid	0.45	0.013	c

Table II (Cont'd.)　　Monomer	e	Q	Notes
trans-Crotononitrile	0.54	0.016	b
5-Cyanobicyclo-[2.2.1]-2-heptene	0.28	0.07	d
1-Cyano-1,3-butadiene	0.28	5.98	a,b
α-(2-Cyanoethyl)acrylonitrile	0.56	0.29	
α-Cyanostyrene	1.26	9.60	b
p-Cyanostyrene	-0.21	1.86	
1,3-Cyclohexadiene	-1.09	1.48	b
Δ^3-Cyclohexenyltriethoxysilane	-0.50	0.050	a
4-Cyclopenten-1,3-dione	1.40	0.22	
n-Decyl methacrylate	0.48	1.37	b
1-Deoxy-1-methacrylamido-ᴅ-glucitol	1.30	0.089	
Diallyl n-butyl phosphonate	-0.07	0.053	b
Diallyl melamine	-0.95	0.017	c
Diallyl phenyl phosphonate	-0.07	0.051	b
Diallyl phthalate	0.36	0.044	b
4,6-Diamino-2-vinyl-s-triazine	1.76	5.52	b
Di-n-amyl itaconate	0.52	1.02	b
Dibenzyl maleate	1.32	0.34	b
N,N-Di-n-butylacrylamide	-0.05	0.32	
Di-n-butyl itaconate	1.09	1.07	
Di-n-butyl maleate	1.60	0.042	a,b
2,3-Dichloro-1,3-butadiene	0.48	12.86	c
1,1-Dichloro-2,2-difluoroethylene	2.10	0.041	a
cis-Dichloroethylene	1.25	0.003	c
trans-Dichloroethylene	1.28	0.010	c
Di-β-chloroethyl itaconate	1.52	0.38	c
2,5-Dichlorostyrene	0.09	1.60	
Diethoxyethylvinylsilane	-0.35	0.011	a,b
Diethoxymethylvinylsilane	-0.86	0.020	a
Diethoxyphenylvinylsilane	-0.38	0.034	a
Diethyl allyl phosphonate	-0.07	0.019	b
Diethylaminoethyl methacrylate	0.42	2.08	
Diethyl chloromaleate	1.65	0.056	a,b
Diethyleneglycol monovinyl ether	-1.39	0.046	c
Diethyl fumarate	1.25	0.61	c
Di-2-ethylhexyl maleate	1.08	0.10	a,b
Diethyl itaconate	0.98	0.94	
Diethyl maleate	1.49	0.059	c
2-(Diethylphosphato)ethyl methacrylate	0.48	0.97	d
1-(Diethylphosphono)ethyl acrylate	1.49	0.57	b
1-(Diethylphosphono)ethyl methacrylate	0.51	1.41	d
Diethylphosphonomethyl acrylate	1.50	0.76	
Diethylphosphonomethyl methacrylate	0.98	0.65	b
N,N-Diethyl-o-vinyl carbamate	-1.06	0.028	
N,N-Diethyl-S-vinyl monothiolcarbamate	-1.46	0.30	

Table II (Cont'd.) Monomer	e	Q	Notes
Diethyl vinylphosphonate	0.25	0.09	c
α-Difluoromethylstyrene	-0.21	1.16	b
α,β-Difluorostyrene	0.73	0.12	b
β,β-Difluorostyrene	0.70	0.029	a
2,4-Difluorostyrene	-0.31	0.65	b
2,5-Difluorostyrene	0.73	6.70	b
1,1-Dihydroperfluorobutyl acrylate	1.15	0.78	
N-(1,1-Dihydroperfluorobutyl)-N-ethyl-acrylamide	1.01	1.22	b
Diisobutyl maleate	1.85	0.094	b
Diisobutyl vinyl phosphine oxide	0.35	0.024	a
Diisopropyl itaconate	1.21	0.89	b
Diisopropyl maleate	2.06	0.084	c
Dimethallyl oxalate	-0.15	0.038	b
2,4-Dimethoxy-6-(β-itaconylhydrazino)s-triazine	-0.17	0.52	b
2,5-Dimethoxystyrene	-1.04	1.75	
N,N-Dimethylacrylamide	-0.50	1.08	b
Dimethylaminoethyl methacrylate	0.47	0.68	
p-Dimethylaminostyrene	-1.37	1.51	
2-(N,N-Dimethylamino)-4-vinylpyrimidine	0.04	1.45	b
2,3-Dimethyl-1,3-butadiene	-1.81	5.86	
Dimethyl dithiolfumarate	1.78	1.23	
Dimethyl fumarate	1.49	0.76	b
Dimethyl itaconate	1.34	1.03	
Dimethyl maleate	1.27	0.09	
Dimethyl methacrylyliminodiacetate	1.64	0.073	b
Dimethyl 2-methylene-5-methyladipate	0.72	0.17	d
N-(1,1-Dimethyl-3-oxobutyl)acrylamide	-0.11	0.42	
Dimethyl-phenyl-4-vinylphenylsilane	-1.27	1.63	
2,5-Dimethylstyrene	0.96	0.97	
Dimethyl-4-vinylphenylsilane	-0.04	0.97	b
1,2-Dimethyl-5-vinylpyridinium methyl sulfate	-0.16	2.49	
2,4-Dimethyl-6-vinyl-s-triazine	0.87	2.56	
Dimethyl-vinyl-4-vinylphenylsilane	-1.01	1.20	
Di-n-nonyl fumarate	-0.39	0.60	b
Di-n-nonyl maleate	-0.39	0.22	b
Dioctyl fumarate	1.45	0.24	
Di-n-octyl itaconate	0.79	0.96	
Diphenylacetylene	-1.23	0.0025	a
1,1-Diphenylethylene	-1.35	1.50	c
Diphenyl 4-vinylphenyl arsine	-0.02	1.16	b
Diphenyl 4-vinylphenyl bismuthine	-0.40	1.15	b
Diphenyl 4-vinylphenyl phosphine	-0.32	1.29	
Diphenyl 4-vinylphenyl phosphine oxide	-0.22	1.38	
Diphenyl 4-vinylphenyl phosphine sulfide	-0.38	1.53	
Diphenyl 4-vinylphenyl stibine	-0.30	1.12	b

Table II (Cont'd.) Monomer	e	Q	Notes
Diphenyl vinyl phosphine	-0.35	0.10	a
Diphenyl vinyl phosphine oxide	0.50	0.07	a
Diphenyl vinyl phosphine sulfide	1.35	0.083	a
Di-n-propyl itaconate	0.71	1.19	b
Divinyl acetal	-0.22	0.026	b
N,N-Divinylaniline	-1.54	0.19	
m-Divinylbenzene	-1.77	3.35	b
Divinyl butyral	-0.22	0.026	b
Divinyl ether	-1.28	0.037	
Divinyl formal	-0.22	0.026	b
Divinyl isoamylal	-0.22	0.026	b
Divinyl isobutyral	-0.22	0.026	b
Divinyl sulfide	-1.11	0.58	
Divinyl sulfone	1.33	0.14	
n-Dodecyl vinyl ether	-0.74	0.033	c
Ethyl α-acetoxyacrylate	0.44	0.44	
Ethyl acid fumarate	0.96	1.33	b
Ethyl acid maleate	1.52	1.23	b
Ethyl acrylate	0.22	0.52	
Ethyl cinnamate	0.62	0.12	b
Ethyl α-cyanocinnamate	0.87	1.24	a,b
Ethylene	-0.20	0.015	
Ethyleneglycol dichloroacrylate	0.88	0.43	b
Ethyleneglycol dimethacrylate	0.24	0.88	
N,N-Ethylene-N'-isopropenylurea	-2.16	0.19	b
N,N-Ethylene-N'-vinylurea	-1.19	0.18	
Ethyl ethacrylate	-0.18	0.61	b
Ethyl β-ethoxyacrylate	0.18	0.015	c
Ethyl 2-ethyl-2-methyl-1-butenoate	0.50	0.14	
2-Ethylhexyl acrylate	0.39	0.41	d
N-Ethylmethacrylamide	-0.88	0.70	b
Ethyl methacrylate	0.17	0.56	
Ethyl methacrylylaminoacetate	0.54	0.72	b
S-Ethyl-N-methyl-N-vinyl monothiolcarbamate	-1.29	0.11	
2-Ethylsulfinylethyl methacrylate	0.64	1.94	d
2-Ethyl-1-vinylacetylene	-0.29	0.60	
Ethyl vinyl ether	-1.17	0.032	a
Ethyl vinyl oxalate	-0.26	0.092	
5-Ethyl-2-vinylpyridine	-0.74	1.37	
5-Ethyl-2-vinylpyridine-N-oxide	-0.10	4.52	
Ethyl vinyl sulfide	-0.12	0.37	
N-Ethyl-N'-vinylurea	-1.53	0.13	
2-Fluoro-1,3-butadiene	-0.43	2.08	
β-Fluorostyrene	0.88	0.044	b
p-Fluorostyrene	-0.12	0.83	

Table II (Cont'd.) Monomer	e	Q	Notes
N-(m-Fluorosulfonylphenyl)acrylamide	0.66	0.55	
N-(m-Fluorosulfonylphenyl)methacrylamide	0.76	0.69	b
Fumaronitrile	1.96	0.80	c
Glycidyl acrylate	0.96	0.55	
Glycidyl methacrylate	0.10	0.85	
Glycidyl 1-methyl-3-cyclohexen-1-carboxylate	0.32	0.014	c
Glycidyl vinylsulfonate	1.41	0.14	
Hexachloro 1,3-butadiene	0.76	1.31	
Hexafluoro-1,3-butadiene	0.47	0.93	
1-Hexene	-0.28	0.019	
n Hexyl methacrylate	-0.12	0.70	b
1-Hexyne	-0.70	0.014	a
4-Hydroabietyl alcohol	-0.80	0.056	a,b
Hydronopyl acrylate	0.67	0.50	
2-Hydroxyethyl acrylate	1.51	4.08	b
2-Hydroxyethyl methacrylate	0.20	0.80	b,d
2-Hydroxyethyl vinyl sulfide	-1.65	0.33	d
2-Hydroxypropyl methacrylate	0.20	0.79	d
Indene	-1.03	0.36	c
p-Iodostyrene	-0.40	1.17	
Isobornyl methacrylate	0.31	0.91	
Isobutylene	-0.96	0.033	c
Isobutyl methacrylate	-0.04	0.77	b
Isobutyl vinyl ether	-1.77	0.023	
2-Isocyanatoethyl methacrylate	0.62	0.94	d
Isoprene	-1.22	3.33	
Isopropenyl acetate	-0.50	0.045	
Isopropenylacetylene	-0.18	0.54	
N-Isopropenyl glycidylurethan	-0.86	0.26	b
Isopropenyl isocyanate	-1.02	0.23	
β-Isopropenylnaphthalene	-1.04	0.92	c
Isopropyl acrylate	0.55	0.41	d
Isopropyl methacrylate	-0.15	1.20	b
4-Isopropylstyrene	-1.52	1.60	b
Isopropyl vinyl ether	-1.31	45.40	b
Itaconic acid	0.50	0.76	c
Itaconic anhydride	0.88	2.50	
Lauryl methacrylate	-0.07	0.99	d
Maleic anhydride	2.25	0.23	c
Maleimide	1.35	0.44	
Maleonitrile	2.32	0.42	a,b
Methacrolein	-0.01	1.75	
Methacrylamide	1.24	1.46	
Methacrylic acid	0.65	2.34	
Methacrylic anhydride	1.03	1.60	

Table II (Cont'd.) Monomer	e	Q	Notes
Methacrylonitrile	0.81	1.12	
4-Methacryloxybenzylidene-aniline	-0.09	2.24	b
4-Methacryloxybenzylidene-4'-chloroaniline	-0.63	4.83	b
Methacryloxymethyl pentamethyl disiloxane	0.19	0.74	
N-Methacryloyl-ε-caprolactam	1.34	0.18	a,b
Methacrylyl triethyl germanium	-0.64	0.84	b
Methallyl acetate	-1.33	0.037	a
Methallyl chloride	-0.91	0.12	a
2-Methoxyethyl acrylate	0.58	0.46	d
Methoxymethyl vinyl sulfide	-1.27	0.28	d
p-Methoxystyrene	-1.11	1.36	
Methyl acid maleate	2.19	0.10	c
Methyl acrylate	0.60	0.42	
Methyl α-benzylacrylate	0.72	0.50	b
Methyl bicyclo-[2.2.1]-2-heptene-5-carboxylate	0.26	0.059	
Methyl α-n-butylacrylate	0.55	0.42	b
Methyl α-chloroacrylate	0.77	2.02	
Methyl 2-chlorocinnamate	0.85	0.28	a
Methyl 4-chlorocinnamate	0.65	0.15	a,b
Methyl cinnamate	0.49	0.12	a
2-Methyl-5-cinnamoylpyridine	0.96	0.26	b
N-Methylcitraconimide	1.48	2.35	
Methyl α-cyanoacrylate	2.10	high	d
Methyl ethacrylate	0.52	0.42	b
Methyl α-isobutylacrylate	0.48	0.37	b
Methyl isopropenyl ketone	0.53	1.49	
N-Methylmethacrylamide	-0.60	0.32	b
Methyl methacrylate	0.40	0.74	
N-Methylolacrylamide	0.36	0.31	
N-Methylolcrotonamide	2.10	0.035	b
N-Methylolmethacrylamide methyl ether	1.30	0.64	b
Methyl α-phenylacrylate	1.30	6.20	b
Methyl α-n-propylacrylate	0.49	0.41	b
α-Methylstyrene	-1.27	0.98	
m-Methylstyrene	-0.72	0.91	
o-Methylstyrene	-0.78	0.90	b
p-Methylstyrene	-0.98	1.27	
Methyl thiolacrylate	0.58	1.23	b
2-Methyl-α,β,β-trifluorostyrene	0.06	0.43	b
3-Methyl-α,β,β-trifluorostyrene	0.44	1.07	
4-Methyl-α,β,β-trifluorostyrene	0.24	0.88	
Methyl vinyl ketone	0.68	0.69	
2-Methyl-5-vinylpyridine	-0.58	0.99	
2-Methyl-5-vinylpyridinium hydrochloride	0.17	1.16	b
Methyl vinyl sulfide	-1.45	0.32	

Table II (Cont'd.) Monomer	e	Q	Notes
Methyl vinyl sulfone	1.29	0.11	c
Methyl vinyl sulfoxide	0.98	0.057	b
N-Methyl-N-vinyl-p-toluenesulfonamide	-1.10	0.082	a
2-Nitrobutyl acrylate	1.15	0.61	
m-Nitrostyrene	0.81	2.47	
p-Nitrostyrene	0.39	1.63	
n-Nonyl methacrylate	0.14	0.91	b
N-n-Octadecylacrylamide	1.13	0.66	
n-Octadecyl acrylate	1.12	0.42	
n-Octadecyl vinyl ether	-0.63	0.069	c
N-n-Octylacrylamide	-0.02	0.19	
N-tert-Octylacrylamide	-0.10	0.20	
n-Octyl acrylate	1.07	0.35	
n-Octyl methacrylate	-0.31	0.78	
n-Octyl vinyl ether	-0.79	0.061	c
Pentachlorophenyl vinyl sulfide	-0.58	0.22	
Pentachlorostyrene	0.52	0.22	
1-Pentene	-0.63	0.074	a,b
Phenylacetylene	-0.66	0.35	
N-Phenylmethacrylamide	-0.78	0.85	b
Phenyl methacrylate	0.62	0.46	d
Phenyl vinyl ether	-1.21	0.082	
Phenyl vinyl sulfide	-1.40	0.34	
Phenyl vinyl sulfone	1.18	0.069	
Poly(1,3-butyleneglycol fumarate)	1.02	0.29	c
Poly(ethyleneglycol fumarate)	1.93	0.42	
Potassium itaconate	-0.58	0.16	b
Potassium p-styrenesulfonate	-0.30	1.14	
Propenyltriethoxysilane	-1.08	0.0034	a
n-Propyl crotonate	0.36	0.011	a,b
Propylene	-0.78	0.002	
n-Propyl methacrylate	-0.41	1.47	
n-Propyl thiolacrylate	0.92	1.21	d
3-Pyridalacetophenone	0.64	0.64	a,b
Sodium acrylate	-0.12	0.71	
Sodium allylsulfonate	-0.24	0.15	b
Sodium methacrylate	-1.18	1.36	
Sodium p-styrenesulfonate	-0.59	2.49	
Sodium vinylsulfonate	0.41	0.064	a
Stearyl methacrylate	0.56	1.07	b
trans-Stilbene	-0.08	0.030	
cis-Stilbene	-0.03	0.017	b
Styrene	(-0.80)	(1.00)	Assumed
p-Styrenesulfonic acid	-0.26	1.04	b
m-Styrenesulfonyl fluoride	-0.73	1.33	

Table II (Cont'd.) Monomer	e	Q	Notes
p-Styrenesulfonyl fluoride	0.20	1.64	
p-Sulfonamidostyrene	0.37	1.62	b
Tetrachloroethylene	2.03	0.0028	a
trans-2,3,4,5-Tetrachlorohexa-1,3,5-triene	0.75	1.85	
Tetrafluoroethylene	1.22	0.049	c
Tetrahydrofurfuryl acrylate	0.36	0.54	
Tetrahydrofuryl methacrylate	0.35	0.45	b
N-(p-tolyl)methacrylamide	-0.76	1.20	b
Triallyl cyanurate	-1.00	0.020	c
Triallyl isocyanurate	-0.60	0.011	c
1,1,2-Trichloro-1,3-butadiene	0.78	4.04	
Trichloroethylene	1.86	0.019	c
3,3,3-Trichloro-1-propene	1.37	0.056	c
6-Triethoxysilyl-bicyclo-[2.2.1]-2-heptene	-0.35	0.072	a
Triethoxyvinylsilane	-0.42	0.028	a
Triethyl aconitate	1.54	0.28	c
Triethyleneglycol dimethacrylate	0.71	1.46	b
N,N,N-Triethyl-N-[2-methacryloxyethyl] ammonium iodide	1.10	2.10	b
3-Trifluoromethylstyrene	-0.29	0.92	
α,β,β-Trifluorostyrene	0.22	0.75	
Triisopropoxyvinylsilane	-0.36	0.031	a
p-Trimethoxysilylstyrene	-0.88	1.50	b
Trimethoxyvinylsilane	-0.38	0.031	a
trans-Trimethyl aconitate	1.14	0.0054	b
cis-Trimethyl aconitate	1.62	0.32	c
3,3,5-Trimethylcyclohexyl acrylate	0.90	0.65	d
3,3,5-Trimethylcyclohexyl methacrylate	0.77	0.70	d
Trimethylsiloxylvinyldimethylsilane	-0.81	0.034	
p-Trimethylsilylstyrene	-0.80	1.00	b
Trimethylvinylsilane	0.04	0.029	c
Tris(trimethylsiloxyl)vinylsilane	-0.69	0.030	
Vinyl acetate	-0.22	0.026	
Vinylacetylene	-0.40	0.69	g
1-Vinylanthracene	-1.68	2.50	b
9-Vinylanthracene	-1.60	0.90	b
Vinyl benzoate	-0.55	0.061	
Vinyl endo-bicyclo-[2.2.1]-heptane-2-carboxylate	0.30	0.014	b
Vinyl exo-bicyclo-[2.2.1]-heptane-2-carboxylate	0.30	0.014	b
4-Vinylbiphenyl	-1.12	1.32	b
Vinyl bromide	-0.25	0.047	
Vinyl n-butyrate	-0.26	0.042	
Vinyl caprate	-0.10	0.020	
Vinyl caproate	-0.47	0.025	
Vinyl caprylate	-0.31	0.021	

Table II (Cont'd.) Monomer	e	Q	Notes
9-Vinylcarbazole	-1.40	0.41	
Vinyl chloride	0.20	0.044	
Vinyl chloroacetate	-0.65	0.074	c
Vinyl trans-cinnamate	0.24	0.24	
Vinyl cyclohexene	-1.64	0.060	a,b
Vinyl dichloroacetate	-0.68	0.17	
Vinylene carbonate	-0.65	0.0073	
Vinyl 2-ethylhexanoate	-0.08	0.024	
Vinyl fluoride	1.28	0.012	b
Vinyl formate	-0.82	0.17	
N-Vinyl glycidylurethan	-1.15	0.18	
Vinylhydroquinone dibenzoate	1.17	1.80	
Vinylidene chloride	0.36	0.22	
Vinylidene cyanide	2.58	20.13	c
Vinyl isocaproate	-0.74	0.043	b
Vinyl isocyanate	-0.70	0.16	
Vinyl isothiocyanate	0.25	0.54	
Vinyl 4-ketostearate	-0.48	0.037	c
Vinyl 9(10)-ketostearate	-0.29	0.039	c
Vinyl 12-ketostearate	-0.50	0.032	c
Vinyl laurate	-0.01	0.018	
Vinyl levulinate	-0.53	0.027	b
2-Vinyl mercaptobenzothiazole	-0.92	1.68	b
Vinylmesitylene	-1.10	0.22	
1-Vinylnaphthalene	-1.12	1.94	b
2-Vinylnaphthalene	-0.38	1.25	
N-Vinyl-2-oxazolidinone	-0.80	0.057	
Vinyl palmitate	-0.02	0.026	
Vinyl pelargonate	-0.68	0.030	
Vinyl perfluorobutyrate	0.58	0.038	b
2-Vinylphenanthrene	-0.67	1.96	
3-Vinylphenanthrene	-0.80	2.26	b
9-Vinylphenanthrene	-0.80	1.73	b
m-Vinylphenol	-0.80	1.10	b
N-Vinylphthalimide	-1.52	0.36	
Vinyl pinonate	-0.35	0.034	
Vinyl propionate	-0.07	0.052	
2-Vinylpyridine	-0.50	1.30	
4-Vinylpyridine	-0.20	0.82	
2-Vinylpyridine-N-oxide	-0.01	3.77	
N-Vinylpyridinium fluoroborate	2.12	1.12	
4-Vinylpyrimidine	0.45	2.18	b
N-Vinylpyrrolidone	-1.14	0.14	
2-Vinylquinoline	-0.82	3.79	
Vinyl stearate	-0.52	0.034	

Table II (Cont'd.) Monomer	e	Q	Notes
N-Vinylsuccinimide	-0.34	0.13	
Vinylsulfonic acid	-0.02	0.093	c
2-Vinylthianthrene	-1.68	4.30	
Vinyl thiolacetate	-1.46	0.31	b
2-Vinylthiophene	-0.80	2.86	b
Vinyl trifluoroacetate	1.06	0.033	b
Vinyl undecylenate	-0.64	0.035	c
N-Vinylurethan	-1.62	0.12	

[a] r_2 assumed zero.

[b] 1 set of data only.

[c] Some r_2 assumed zero.

[d] Rohm and Haas values (no r_1r_2).

HEATS AND ENTROPIES OF POLYMERIZATION, CEILING
TEMPERATURES, AND EQUILIBRIUM MONOMER CONCENTRATIONS

K. J. Ivin

Department of Physical Chemistry,
University of Leeds
Leeds, England

Contents

TABLE A - HEATS OF POLYMERIZATION

<u>Symbols</u>: The subscripts xx to ΔH denote the state of the monomer (first letter) and
the state of the polymer (second letter), as follows:

g   gaseous state (hypothetical in case of polymer)
c   condensed amorphous state
c'   crystalline or partially crystalline state
l   liquid state
s   in solution; solvent specified in sixth column (ls denotes polymer dissolved in
      monomer).

For emulsion polymerization the subscript is given as lc and a note added in the
sixth column. In all cases where monomer or polymer is present in solution, the
value of ΔH will depend to some extent on the composition. Where the polymer is
crystalline ΔH will depend on the degree of crystallinity.

ΔH values are in kcal per mole of monomer and are generally the limiting values for
high degree of polymerization n.

<u>Example</u>: $C_2H_4(g) \rightarrow \frac{1}{n} (C_2H_4)_n$ (g), ΔH_{gg} = -22.35 kcal

<u>Precision</u>: generally 0.1 - 1.0 kcal mole^{-1} (for details see ref. 1).

<u>Methods of determination</u>: These are summarized below using the numbering system in
                                 ref. 1.

2   Combustion of monomer or polymer or both.
3b   Non-isothermal (i) integral; (ii) differential; (iii) self-heating.
3c   Isothermal, vaporization, integral.
3d   Isothermal, fusion (i) integral; (ii) differential; (iii) extrapolation to 100%
      reaction.
3e   Isothermal, Tian-Calvet method, integral.
4a   Thermodynamic (Van't Hoff isochore).
4b   Semi-empirical rules applied to evaluate heat of formation of polymer or monomer
      or both.

1 - MONOMERS GIVING SATURATED HYDROCARBON POLYMERS

a. Olefinic Monomers (Listed by increasing carbon number)

Monomer	State of Monomer and Polymer xx	$-\Delta H_{xx}$	T°C	Method	Solvent/Notes	Reference
Ethylene	gg	22.35	25	4b		2
	gc'	25.4	25	2		2
	gc'	25.9	25	2		3
	gc	24.2	25	2	ΔH_{fus} (polymer) taken as 1.2	2,4
Propene	gg	20.7	25	4b		5
	gc'	24.9	25	2		3
	lc	20.1	25	4b		5
	sc	16.5	-78	3c	n-butane	6
1-Butene	gg	20.7	25	4b		5
	lc	20.0	25	4b		5
2-Butene cis	gg	19.1	25	4b		5
	lc	17.9	25	4b		5
trans	gg	18.1	25	4b		5
	lc	17.0	25	4b		5
Isobutene	gc	17.2	25	2		7
	lc	11.5	25	2	low polymer	2,8
	ss	12.8	25	?	solvent? low polymer	8
	ss	12.9	-35	3b(iii)?	CH_2Cl_2, polymer swollen*	9
2-Pentene cis	gg	19.2	25	4b		10
trans	gg	18.1	25	4b		10
1-Hexene	lc	19.8	25	4b		5
1-Heptene	gg	20.6	25	4b		5

* partial allowance for unreacted monomer

References page II-396

HEATS OF POLYMERIZATION

Monomer	State of Monomer and Polymer xx	$-\Delta H_{xx}$	T°C	Method	Solvent/Notes	Reference
	b. Cyclic Monomers	(Listed by increasing ring size)				
Cyclopropane	1c	27.0	25	2		11
-- , methyl-	1c	25.1	25	4b		11
-- , 1,1-dimethyl-	1c	23.3	25	4b		11
Cyclobutane	1c	25.1	25	2		12
-- , methyl-	1c	23.9	25	4b		11
-- , 1,1-dimethyl-	1c	22.3	25	4b		11
Cyclopentane	1c	5.2	25	2		12
-- , methyl-	1c	4.1	25	4b		11
-- , 1,1-dimethyl-	1c	3.2	25	4b		11
Cyclohexane	1c	-0.7	25	2		12
-- , methyl-	1c	-2.2	25	4b		11
-- , 1,1-dimethyl-	1c	-1.8	25	4b		11
Cycloheptane	1c	5.1	25	2		12
Cyclooctane	1c	8.3	25	2		12
Cyclononane	1c	11.2	25	2		13
Cyclodecane	1c	11.5	25	2		13
Cycloundecane	1c	10.8	25	2		13
Cyclododecane	1c	3.4	25	2		13
Cyclotridecane	1c	5.3	25	2		13
Cyclotetradecane	1c	1.7	25	2		13
Cyclopentadecane	1c	2.9	25	2		13
Cyclohexadecane	1c	1.9	25	2		13
Cycloheptadecane	1c	2.0	25	2		13

2 - VINYL MONOMERS (listed alphabetically)

Monomer	State of Monomer and Polymer xx	$-\Delta H_{xx}$	T°C	Method	Solvent/Notes	Reference
Acenaphthylene	ss	23.5	26.9	3d(i)	o-dichlorobenzene	14
	ss	24.0	25.9	3d(i)	"	14
	ss	16	74.5	3c	"	15
	ss	16	74.5	3c	benzene	15
	c'c	19.6	26.9	3d(i)		14
Allyl chloride	ls	18.5	74.5	3c		15
Biphenyl, p-isopropenyl-	ss	8.1	-15	4a	tetrahydrofuran	16
Ethylene, tetrafluoro-	gg	37	25	2		22
	gc'	41	25	2		22,23
	lc'	39±4	25	2		1
Maleic anhydride	ls	14	74.5	3c		15
Maleimide	ss	16.1	74.5	3c	chlorobenzene	24
	ss	21.4	74.5	3c	dioxane	24
	ss	21.2	74.5	3c	acetonitrile	24
	ss	20.9	74.5	3c	dimethylformamide	24
Methyl vinyl ketone	lc	17.7	74.5	3c		17
Naphthalene, 2-isopropenyl-	ss	8.7	-5	4a	tetrahydrofuran	16
Styrene	gg	17.8	25	4b		25
	lc	16.7	25	2		26
	lc	16.1	76.8	3c		27
	lc	16.5	74.5	3c		17
	lc	16.4	26.9	3d(i)		14
	lc	17.4	127	4a		28,29
	ls	17.5	25	2		26
	ls	17.4	26.9	3c(i)		14

Monomer	State of Monomer and Polymer xx	$-\Delta H_{xx}$	T°C	Method	Solvent/Notes	Reference
Styrene (Cont'd.)	1s	17.7	26.9	3d(ii)		14
	ss	15.9	-60	3b(iii)?	methylene chloride	30
-- , o-chloro-	1c	16.4	76.8	3c		27
-- , p-chloro-	1c	16.0	76.8	3c		27
-- , 2,5-dichloro-	1c	16.5	76.8	3c		27
-- , ar-ethyl-	1c	16.3	76.8	3c		27
-- , α-methyl-	1c	8.4	25	2		31
	1c	8.2	-20	4a		32,29
	ss	8.0	-20	4a	tetrahydrofuran	32,29
	ss	7.0	30	4a	"	33
	ss	8.5	-20	4a	"	16
-- , 2,4,6-trimethyl-	1c	16.7	26.9	3d(i)		14
Vinyl acetate	1c	21.3	76.8	3c		21
	1c	21.0	74.5	3c		17,34
	1s	21.4	25	3b(iii)		35
	ss	21.5	74.5	3c	acetone	17
	ss	20.7	74.5	3c	hexane	17
	ss	20.5	74.5	3c	benzene	17
Vinyl benzoate	1c	20.2	74.5	3c		34
N-Vinylcarbazole	sc'	15.2	74.5	3c	hexane	15
Vinyl chloride	gc	31.5	25	2		18,19
	gc	30.7	25	2		18,20
	1c	17	25	4b		10
	1c	26.7	25	2	ΔH_{fus} (monomer) taken as 4.8	18

Monomer	State of Monomer and Polymer xx	$-\Delta H_{xx}$	T°C	Method	Solvent/Notes	Reference
Vinyl 2-ethylhexoate	1c	21.0	74.5	3c		34
Vinylidene chloride	1c'	14.4	76.8	3c		21
	1c'	18.0	25	2		18
	1c'	17.5	74.5	3c		15
Vinyl propionate	1c	20.5	74.5	3c		17,34
2-Vinylpyridine	1c	17.1	74.5	3c		15
	1s	18.0	74.5	3c		15
	sc	17.6	74.5	3c	benzene	15
4-Vinylpyridine	1c	18.7	74.5	3c		17
	ss	18.7	74.5	3c	benzene, hexane	17

Monomer	State of Monomer and Polymer xx	$-\Delta H_{xx}$	T°C	Method	Solvent/Notes	Reference
3 - ACRYLIC MONOMERS (Listed alphabetically)						
Acrolein	lc	19.1	74.5	3c		15
	ss	13.8	74.5	3c	hexane	17
	ss	19.5	74.5	3c	water	17
Acrylamide	ss	19.8	26.9	3d(ii)	water	14
	ss	19.5	74.5	3c	water	17
	ss?	16.9	74.5	3c	acetone	17
	sc	14.4	74.5	3c	benzene	17
	sc	13.8	74.5	3c	hexane	17
Acrylic acid	lc	16.0	74.5	3c		15
	ss	18.5	20	3b(i)	water	36
	ss	18.4	25	3e	water	37
	sc	17.6	74.5	3c	benzene	15
	sc	17.2	74.5	3c	carbon tetrachloride	15
	sc	17.8	74.5	3c	hexane	15
-- , n-butyl ester	lc	19.1	25	3e	emulsion (aq)	37
	lc	18.6	74.5	3c		17
	ss	18.4	74.5	3c	acetone	17
	ss	18.9	74.5	3c	butanone	17
	ss	18.2	74.5	3c	benzene	17
	ss	18.1	74.5	3c	carbon tetrachloride	17
	ss	18.6	74.5	3c	hexane	17
-- , ethyl ester	lc	18.8	25	3e	emulsion (aq)	37
	lc	18.6	74.5	3e		34
-- , methyl ester	lc	18.7	76.8	3c		21
	lc	18.8	74.5	3c		34

Monomer	State of Monomer and Polymer xx	$-\Delta H_{xx}$	T°C	Method	Solvent/Notes	Reference
Acrylic acid						
-- , methyl ester (Cont'd.)	1c	18.6	25	3e	emulsion (aq)	37
	ss	20.2	20	3b(i)	ethyl alcohol	36
	ss	19.4	74.5	3c	hexane	34
Acrylonitrile	1c'	17.3	76.8	3c		21
	1c'	18.3	25	3b(i)	emulsion (aq)	38
	1c'	18.3	74.5	3c		17
	sc'	18.5	74.5	3c	benzene	17
Itaconic acid, dimethyl ester	ss	14.5	26.9	3d(ii)	o-dichlorobenzene	14
Methacrolein	1c	15.6	74.5	3c		15
Methacrylamide	ss	13.4	74.5	3c	water	17
	ss	10.2	74.5	3c	chloroform	17
	ss	9.4	74.5	3c	acetone	17
	ss	8.4	74.5	3c	benzene	17
Methacrylic acid	1c	10.1	74.5	3c		15
	ss	15.8	20	3b(i)	water	36
	ss	13.5	25	3e	water	37
	sc	13.6	74.5	3c	methanol*	15
-- , benzyl ester	1c	13.4	76.8	3c	≠	39
-- , n-butyl ester	1c	13.9	25	3e	emulsion (aq)	37
	1c	13.5	76.8	3c		39
	1c	13.7	74.5	3c		34
-- , tert-butyl ester	1s	14.3	26.9	3d(ii)		14
	1s	13.0	26.9	3d(ii)		14

* Value given is for dilute solution. Values determined for complete range of composition; maximum (14.4) at 50 mole % monomer.
≠ No allowance for unreacted monomer.

References page II-396

Methacrylic acid (Cont'd.)

Monomer	State of Monomer and Polymer xx	$-\Delta H_{xx}$	T°C	Method	Solvent/Notes	Reference
-- , cyclohexyl ester	lc	12.2	76.8	3c		39
	ls	12.7	26.9	3d(ii)		14
-- , 2-ethoxyethyl ester	lc	13.7	74.5	3c		34
	ls	14.8	26.9	3d(ii)		14
-- , ethyl ester	lc	14.4	120	4a		40
	lc	13.8	25	3e	emulsion (aq)	37
	lc	14.2	74.5	3c		34
	ls	13.8	26.9	3d(ii)		14
-- , n-hexyl ester	lc	14.0	25	3e	emulsion (aq)	37
	ls	14.4	26.9	3d(ii)		14
-- , 2-hydroxyethyl ester	lc	11.9	25	3e	emulsion (aq)	37
-- , 2-hydroxypropyl ester	lc	12.1	25	3e	emulsion (aq)	37
-- , isobutyl ester	lc	14.3	74.5	3c		34
-- , isopropyl ester	lc	14.3	74.5	3c		34
-- , methyl ester	lc	13.9	76.8	3c		41
	lc	13.4	130	4a		42,43,29
	lc	12.9	20	3b(i)	emulsion (aq)	36
	lc	13.6	25	3e	emulsion (aq)	37
	lc	13.3	74.5	3c		17,34
	ls	13.8	26.9	3d(ii)		14
	ss	12.9	130	4a	o-dichlorobenzene	42,29
	ss	14.0	74.5	3c	acetonitrile	34
	ss	13.7	74.5	3c	tetrahydrofuran	34
	ss	14.0	74.5	3c	hexane	34

Monomer	State of Monomer and Polymer xx	$-\Delta H_{xx}$	T°C	Method	Solvent/Notes	Reference
Methacrylic acid (Cont'd.)						
-- , phenyl ester	lc	12.3	76.8	3c	≠	39
-- , n-propyl ester	lc	13.7	74.5	3c		34
Methacrylonitrile	lc	13.5	74.5	3c		15
	ss	15.3	130	4a	benzonitrile	44,29
4 - DIENE MONOMERS (Listed alphabetically)						
1,3-Butadiene	gg	17.4	25	4b	1:2 polymerization	10
	gg	18.7	25	4b	1:4 polymerization	10
	lc	17.4	25	2	*	45
Chloroprene	lc	16.2	61.3	3c		41
Isoprene	gg	16.9	25	4b		10
	lc	17.9	25	2		46
	ls	17	74.5	3c		15
	ls?**	15.7	34.6	3c		47

≠ No allowance for unreacted monomer. * Corrected for end-group effects.

** The states of monomer and/or polymer are not explicitly stated in ref. but are likely to be ls.

5 - MONOMERS GIVING POLYOXIDES (Listed by increasing ring size)

Monomer	State of Monomer and Polymer xx	$-\Delta H$ xx	T°C	Method	Solvent/Notes	Reference
Acetaldehyde	lc	0	25	4b	*	48
Acetone	lc	-6	25	4b		48
Chloral	gc'	17±2	50	4a		50
	lc'	9±2	50	4a		50
	sc'	8.0	13	4a	pyridine	50
Formaldehyde	gc'	12.2	25	4a		49
	gc'	13	25	2		see 49
	gc'	13.2	25	2		7
Ethylene oxide	gg	24.9	25	4b		14
	lc'	22.6	25	2		51
Propylene oxide	gg	18.0	25	4b		14,52
Styrene oxide	lc	24.3	26.9	3d(iii)		14
-- , 3-nitro-	lc	24.1	26.9	3d(iii)		14
Oxetane $OCH_2CH_2CH_2$	ss	19.3	-9	3c	methyl + ethyl chloride	53
-- , 3,3-di(chloromethyl)-	lc	20.2	26.9	3d(iii)		14
-- , 3,3-dimethyl-	ss	16.1	-9	3c	methyl + ethyl chloride	53
-- , 3,3-di(phenoxymethyl)-	ss	19.8	26.9	3d(iii)		14
Dioxolane $OCH_2OCH_2CH_2$	gg	6.2	20	4b	o-dichlorobenzene	54,129
Tetrahydrofuran	gg	5.0	20	4b		55
	gg	2.9	25	4b		56
	lc'	9.1	25	2		56,57
	ls	4.3	40	4a		57
	ls	5.3	40	4a		58
	ls	4.0	25	?		58

* Zero heat not necessarily in conflict with observed polymerizability below -40°C. Additional loss of free energy may be provided by the crystallization of the polymer.

Monomer	State of Monomer and Polymer xx	$-\Delta H_{xx}$	T °C	Method	Solvent/Notes	Reference
Tetrahydropyran	gg	0.4	20	4b		55,56,59
m-Dioxane	gg	0.0	20	4b		54,59,60
1,3-Dioxepane $\overline{OCH_2O(CH_2)_3CH_2}$	gg	4.7	20	4b		54
	ss?	3.5	120	4a	benzene	87
1-Oxa-4,5-dithiepane $\overline{OCH_2CH_2SSCH_2CH_2}$	lc	1.8	26.9	3d(iii)		61
	ss	2.1	26.9	3d(iii)	dioxane	61
	ss	1.9	26.9	3d(iii)	benzene	61
1,3-Dioxocane $\overline{OCH_2O(CH_2)_4CH_2}$	gg	12.8	20	4b		54

6 - MONOMERS GIVING POLYAMIDES   (Listed by ring size)

Monomer	State of Monomer and Polymer xx	$-\Delta H_{xx}$	T °C	Method	Solvent/Notes	Reference
2-Pyrrolidinone	lc	1.1	75	4b		62
	lc	1.3	25	4b		63
-- , 1-methyl-	lc	0.8	25	4b		64
2-Piperidone	lc	2.2	75	4b		62
	lc	1.1	25	4b		63
-- , 1-methyl-	lc	-0.5	25	4b		64
ε-Caprolactam	lc	3.8	75	4b		62
	lc	3.3	220	3b(i)		65
	lc	3.0	25	4b		63
	ls	3.6	250	4a		66
	ls	4.5	240	4a		67
	ls	4.0	250	4a		68

References page II-396

Monomer	State of Monomer and Polymer xx	$-\Delta H_{xx}$	T°C	Method	Solvent/Notes	Reference
ε-Caprolactam						
-- , 1-methyl-	lc	2.3	25	4b		64
-- , 5-methyl-	lc	3.8	75	4b		62
-- , 7-methyl-	lc	3.8	75	4b		62
ζ-Enantholactam	lc	5.3	75	4b		62
-- , 1-methyl-	lc	5.7	25	4b		63
	lc	3.9	25	4b		64

7 - MONOMERS GIVING POLYSULFIDES (Listed by increasing ring size)
(Polysulfones listed under Copolymers)

Monomer	State of Monomer and Polymer xx	$-\Delta H_{xx}$	T°C	Method	Solvent/Notes	Reference
Thiacyclopropane	gg	19.4	25	4b	*	69,70, 71
-- , 2,2-dimethyl-	gg	16.9	25	4b	*	69,70, 71
-- , cis-2,3-dimethyl-	gg	15.1	25	4b	*	69,70, 71
-- , trans-2,3-dimethyl-	gg	13.3	25	4b	*	69,70, 71
-- , 2-methyl-	gg	17.0	25	4b	*	69,70, 71
Thiacyclobutane	gg	19.1	25	4b	*	69,70, 71

* Value calculated by the compiler of this table from data in reference cited.

Monomer	State of Monomer and Polymer xx	$-\Delta H_{xx}$	T°C	Method	Solvent/Notes	Reference
1,2-Dithiolane $\overline{SS\ CH_2CH_2CH_2}$	ss	6.3	30	4a	ethyl alcohol	72
Thiacyclopentane	gg	1.8	25	4b	*	69,70, 71
o-Dithiane $\overline{SS(CH_2)_3}CH_2$	lc	0.5	26.9	3d(iii)		14
Thiacyclohexane	gg	-0.6	25	4b	*	69,70, 71
1,2-Dithiepane $\overline{SS(CH_2)_4}CH_2$	lc	2.5	26.9	3d(iii)		14
	sc	2.7	26.9	3d(iii)		14
1-Oxa-4,5-dithiepane $\overline{OCH_2CH_2SS\ CH_2CH_2}$	lc	1.8	26.9	3d(iii)	dioxane	61
	ss	2.1	26.9	3d(iii)	dioxane	61
	ss	1.9	26.9	3d(iii)	benzene	61
Thiacycloheptane	gg	3.5	25	4b	*	69,70, 71
1,2-Dithiocane $\overline{SS(CH_2)_5}CH_2$	lc	3.8	26.9	3d(iii)		14
Sulfur S_8	ls	-3.2	200	4a		73,74

* Value calculated by the compiler of this table from data in references cited.

8 - INORGANIC AND SEMI-INORGANIC MONOMERS

Monomer	State of Monomer and Polymer xx	$-\Delta H_{xx}$	T°C	Method	Solvent/Notes	Reference
Cyclotrisiloxane, hexamethyl-	lc	3.5	25	3		84
Phosphonitrile chloride,						
-- , cyclic trimer	gc	14.6	230	*		125
-- , cyclic trimer	lc	1.4	230	*		125
-- , cyclic tetramer	gc	16.2	230	*		125
-- , cyclic tetramer	lc	0.9	230	*		125
-- , cyclic pentamer	gc	19.0	230	*		125
-- , cyclic pentamer	lc	0.8	230	*		125
-- , cyclic hexamer	gc	21.0	230	*		125
-- , cyclic hexamer	lc	0.3	230	*		125
-- , cyclic heptamer	gc	23.1	230	*		125
-- , cyclic heptamer	lc	0	230	*		125
Selenium Se$_8$	ls	-2.3	400	4a		85
Sulfur S$_8$	ls	-3.2	200	4a		73,74
Sulfur trioxide	gc'	13.4	13	4a		86
Sulfur trioxide	lc'	3.0	25	4a		86

* Differential thermal analysis.

9 - COPOLYMERS* (Listed alphabetically under Monomer A)

Monomer A	Monomer B	State of Monomer and polymer xx	$-\Delta H_{xx}$	T°C	Method	Solvent/Notes	Reference
Acrylonitrile	Methacrylic acid,	sc		25	3b(I)	emulsion (aq)	38
	methyl ester	ss		30.5	3b(iii)		76
	Styrene	ss		20	3b(iii)		76
	Vinyl acetate	ss		20	3b(iii)		76
	Vinylidene chloride	sc		25	3b(i)?**	emulsion (aq)	75
Allyl chloride	Maleic anhydride	ss	17.7	74.5	3c		34
1,3-Butadiene	Styrene	lc		25	2		45
1-Butene	Sulfur dioxide	ss	10.6	26.9	3d(ii)	excess B	5
		ss	10.4	55	4a	excess B	77
2-Butene, cis	Sulfur dioxide	ss	10.1	26.9	3d(ii)	excess B	5
		ss	10.4	25	4a	excess B	5
-- , trans	Sulfur dioxide	ss	9.4	26.9	3d(ii)	excess B	5
		ss	9.7	25	4a	excess B	5
Cyclohexene	Sulfur dioxide	ss	9	25	4a	excess B	78
Cyclopentene	Sulfur dioxide	ss	10.8	26.9	3d(i)	excess B	5
Fumaric acid, diethyl ester	Vinyl acetate	ss?**	18.6	76.8	3c	excess B	79
Fumaroyl chloride	Styrene	ss	19.1	74.5	3c	hexane	34

* Numerical values for heats of copolymerization are listed only for those systems yielding 1:1 copolymers. The values refer to the copolymerization of 0.5 mole of each monomer. In all other cases listed the copolymers have a range of composition; details of the corresponding heats of copolymerization are given in the references cited.

Where no solvent is specified in the seventh column, the symbol ΔH_{ss} denotes that the measured heat is for a liquid mixture of monomers going to a solution of copolymer. ΔH_{lc} denotes the heat change for pure liquid monomers going to condensed amorphous polymer. (This symbolism differs from that in ref. 1).

**The states of monomer and/or polymer are not explicitly stated in ref. but are likely to be the ones given.

Monomer A	Monomer B	State of Monomer and Polymer xx	$-\Delta H_{xx}$	T°C	Method	Solvent/Notes	Reference
Fumaroyl chloride	Styrene, α-methyl	ss	17.1	74.5	3c	excess B	34
Isobutene	Sulfur dioxide	1c	7.4	25	2		82
	Sulfur dioxide	1c	9.4	0	4a	*	83
1-Hexadecene	Sulfur dioxide	ss	10.0	26.9	3d(ii)	chloroform	5
	Sulfur dioxide	ss	9.6	30	4a	chloroform	80
1-Hexene	Sulfur dioxide	ss	10.4	26.9	3d(ii)	excess B	5
Isopropenyl acetate	Maleic anhydride	sc	17.8	76.8	3c	excess B	79
Maleic acid, diethyl ester	Vinyl acetate	ss?**	20.0	76.8	3c	excess B	79
Maleic anhydride	Allyl chloride	ss	17.7	74.5	3c		34
	Isopropenyl acetate	sc	17.8	76.8	3c		79
	Styrene	ss	19.3	74.5	3c	benzene	34
	Styrene	ss	19.7	74.5	3c	acetonitrile	34
	Styrene, α-methyl-	ss	17.3	74.5	3c	excess B	34
	Vinyl acetate	sc	20.2	76.8	3c	excess B	79
	Vinyl n-butyl ether	ss	21.5	74.5	3c	benzene	34
Maleimide	Styrene	ss	20.9	74.5	3c	acetonitrile	34
	Styrene, α-methyl-	ss	17.2	74.5	3c	acetonitrile	34
Methacrylic acid, methyl ester	Acrylonitrile	sc		25	3b(i)	emulsion (aq)	38
	Styrene	ss		30.5	3b(iii)		76
	Styrene	ss		24	3b(iii)		81
	Vinyl acetate	ss		24	3b(iii)		81
Propene	Sulfur dioxide	sc	10.1	26.9	3d(i)	excess B	5
Styrene	Acrylonitrile	ss		20	3b(iii)		76
	1,3-Butadiene	1c		25	2		45

* Value calculated from measurements on mixtures containing excess B.
** The states of monomer and/or polymer are not explicitly stated in ref. but are likely to be the ones given.

Monomer A	Monomer B	State of Monomer and Polymer xx	$-\Delta H_{xx}$	T°C	Method	Solvent/Notes	Reference
Styrene	Fumaroyl chloride	ss	19.1	74.5	3c	hexane	34
	Maleic anhydride	ss	19.3	74.5	3c	benzene	34
		ss	19.7	74.5	3c	acetonitrile	34
	Maleimide	ss	20.9	74.5	3c	acetonitrile	34
	Methacrylic acid, methyl ester	ss		24	3b(iii)	acetonitrile	81
	Vinyl acetate	ss		35	3b(iii)		81
Styrene, α-methyl-	Fumaroyl chloride	ss	17.1	74.5	3v	excess A	34
	Maleic anhydride	ss	17.3	74.5	3c	excess A	34
	Maleimide	ss	17.2	74.5	3c	acetonitrile	34
Sulfur dioxide	1-Butene	ss	10.6	26.9	3d(ii)	excess A	5
		ss	10.4	55	4a	excess A	77
	2-Butene, cis	ss	10.1	26.9	3d(ii)	excess A	5
		ss	10.4	25	4a	excess A	5
	--, trans	ss	9.4	26.9	3d(ii)	excess A	5
		ss	9.7	25	4a	excess A	5
	Cyclohexane	ss	9	25	4a	excess A	78
	Cyclopentene	ss	10.8	26.9	3d(i)	excess A	5
	1-Hexadecene	ss	10.0	26.9	3d(ii)	chloroform	5
		ss	9.6	30	4a	chloroform	80
	1-Hexene	ss	10.4	26.9	3d(ii)	excess A	5
	Isobutene	lc	7.4	25	2		82
		lc	9.4	0	4a	*	83
Vinyl acetate	Propene	sc	10.1	26.9	3d(i)	excess A	5
	Acrylonitrile	ss	18.6	20	3b(iii)	excess A	76
	Fumaric acid, diethyl ester	ss?**		76.8	3c	excess A	79

* Value calculated from measurements on mixtures containing excess A.
** The states of monomer and/or polymer are not explicitly stated in ref. but are likely to be the ones given.

Monomer A	Monomer B	State of Monomer and Polymer xx	$-\Delta H_{xx}$	T°C	Method	Solvent/Notes	Reference
Vinyl acetate	Maleic acid, diethyl ester	ss?**	20.0	76.8	3c	excess A	79
	Maleic anhydride	sc	20.2	76.8	3c	excess A	79
	Methacrylic acid, methyl ester	ss		24	3b(iii)		81
	Styrene	ss	21.5	35	3b(iii)		81
Vinyl n-butyl ether	Maleic anhydride	ss		74.5	3c	benzene	34
Vinylidene chloride	Acrylonitrile	sc		25	3b(i)?**	emulsion (aq)	75

** The states of monomer and/or polymer are not explicitly stated in ref. but are likely to be the ones given.

TABLE B - ENTROPIES OF POLYMERIZATION

Symbols: The subscripts to $\Delta S°$ denote the state of the monomer (first letter) and the state of the polymer (second letter) as in Table A. The standard state of the monomer is 1 atm for the gaseous state and 1 mole litre-1 in solution, unless otherwise stated. In all cases where monomer or polymer is present in solution, the value of $\Delta S°$ will depend to some extent on the composition. Where the polymer is crystalline $\Delta S°$ will depend on the degree of crystallinity. ΔS values are in cal deg-1 per mole of monomer and are generally the limiting values for high degree of polymerization.

Precision: generally 0.1 - 2.0 cal deg-1 mole-1.

Methods of determination: (numbering conforms with that in Table A)

1. Third law or statistical
4a. Thermodynamic (Van't Hoff isochore)
4b. Semi-empirical rules applied to evaluate entropy of monomer or polymer or both.

Monomer	State of Monomer and Polymer xx	$-\Delta S°_{xx}$	T°C	Method	Solvent/Notes	Reference
					1 - MONOMERS GIVING SATURATED HYDROCARBON POLYMERS	
					a. Olefinic Monomers (Listed by increasing carbon number)	
Ethylene	gg	34.0	25	4b		2,87
	gc	37.0	25	4b		11
	gc	37.7	25	1		88-91
	gc'	41.1	25	4b		11
	gc'	41.5	25	1	10% cryst. polymer	88-91
Propene	gg	39.9	25	4b		5
	lc	27.0	25	4b		5
	lc	27.8	25	1	isotactic polymer	88
	lc	27.6	25	1	atactic polymer	88,92
	lc'	32.4	25	1	100% cryst. isotactic	88,92

Monomer		State of Monomer and Polymer xx	$-\Delta S°_{xx}$	T°C	Method	Solvent/Notes	Reference
1-Butene		gg	39.8	25	4b		5
		gc	45.4	25	1	isotactic polymer	88
		gc'	52.3	25	1	100% cryst. isotactic	88
		lc	26.9	25	4b		5
		lc	26.8	25	1	isotactic polymer	88
		lc'	33.7	25	1	100% cryst. isotactic	88
2-Butene,	cis	gg	39.1	25	4b		5
		lc	24.9	25	4b		5
-- ,	trans	gg	38.0	25	4b		5
		lc	24.0	25	4b		5
Isobutene		gg	41.0	25	4b		5
		lc	26.7	25	4b		5
		lc	28.8	25	1		11,93
1-Hexene		lc	26.9	25	4b		5
1-Heptene		gg	40.1	25	4b		5

b. Cyclic Monomers (Listed by increasing ring size)

Monomer	State of Monomer and Polymer xx	$-\Delta S°$ xx	T°C	Method	Solvent/Notes	Reference
Cyclopropane	1c	16.5	25	4b		11
-- , methyl-	1c	20.2	25	4b		87
-- , 1,1-dimethyl-	1c	22.3	25	4b		87
Cyclobutane	1c	13.2	25	4b		11
-- , methyl-	1c	17.2	25	4b		87
-- , 1,1-dimethyl-	1c	18.0	25	4b		87
Cyclopentane	1c	10.2	25	4b		11
-- , methyl-	1c	15.3	25	4b		87
-- , 1,1-dimethyl-	1c	15.7	25	4b		87
Cyclohexane	1c	2.5	25	4b		11,87
-- , methyl-	1c	7.6	25	4b		87
-- , 1,1-dimethyl-	1c	8.5	25	4b		87
Cycloheptane	1c	3.8	25	4b	*	11,94
Cyclooctane	1c	0.8	25	4b	*	11,94

* Value in ref. 11 corrected using entropy of monomer in ref. 94.

References page II-396

2,3,4 - VINYL MONOMERS, INCLUDING DIENES AND ALL SUBSTITUTED ETHYLENES

(Listed alphabetically)

Monomer	State of Monomer and Polymer xx	$-\Delta S°$ xx	T°C	Method	Solvent/Notes	Reference
Biphenyl, p-isopropenyl-	ss	28.3	-20	4a	tetrahydrofuran	16
1,3-Butadiene	1c	21.2	25	1		95,96
	1c	20.1	25	1	cis-1,4-polymer	97
Ethylene, tetrafluoro-	gc'	47.1	-75.7	1		98,99
	1c'	26.8	-75.7	1		98,99
Isoprene	1c	24.2	25	1		100,101
Methacrylic acid, ethyl ester	1c	30	120	4a		40
-- , methyl ester	1c	28	127	4a		42,43, 102
	c'c	9.6	-63	1		102,103
	ss	31	127	4a	o-dichlorobenzene	42,29
Methacrylonitrile	ss	36	127	4a	benzonitrile	44,29
Naphthalene, 2-isopropenyl-	ss	29.1	-5	4a	tetrahydrofuran	16
Styrene	gg	35.5	25	4b		25
	1c	21.6	-23	1		104
	1c	24.9	25	1		104
	1c	27.7	127	1		104
	1c	24.8	127	4a	*	28
	1c	25.2	25	1	isotactic polymer	88
	1c	26.7	25	1		105
	1c'	26.5	25	1	100% cryst. isotactic	88
-- , α-methyl-	1c	26.3	-20	4a	tetrahydrofuran	32
	ss	31	-20	4a	tetrahydrofuran	32,29, 16

* From measurements in both benzene and cyclohexane.

Monomer	State of Monomer and Polymer xx	$-\Delta S^\circ$ xx	T°C	Method	Solvent/Notes	Reference
5 - MONOMERS GIVING POLYOXIDES (Listed by increasing ring size)						
Chloral	gc'	46±7	50	4a		50
	lc'	23±7	50	4a		50
	sc'	28.0	13	4a	pyridine *	50
Formaldehyde	gc'	41.7	25	1		106
Oxetane, 3,3-di(chloromethyl)-	lc	19.9	25	1		107
Tetrahydrofuran	ls	~16	40	4a		57,58
6 - MONOMERS GIVING POLYAMIDES (Listed by increasing ring size)						
2-Pyrrolidinone	c'c'	7.3	25	1/4b		63
2-Piperidone	c'c'	6.0	25	1/4b		63
(ε-Caprolactam)	c'c'	1.1	25	1		63
(ζ-Enantholactam)	ls	6.9	250	4a		68
	c'c	4.0	25	1		63
8 - INORGANIC MONOMERS						
Selenium Se$_8$	ls	-6.4	200	4a	from estimated T_c	85,111
Sulfur S$_8$	ls	-7.4	159	4a		73,74, 111
Sulfur trioxide	gc'	42.6	41	4a		86

* Standard state: mole fraction of monomer = 0.1

References page II-396

9 - COPOLYMERS* (Listed alphabetically under Monomer A)

Monomer A	Monomer B	State of Monomer and Polymer xx	$-\Delta S°$ xx	T°C	Method	Solvent/Notes	Reference
1,3-Butadiene	Styrene	lc	27.6	30	1		108
1-Butene	Sulfur dioxide	lc	34.8	25	1		109
		ss	34.9	64	4a	excess B	110
2-Butene, cis	"	ss	33.4	25	4a	excess B	5
-- , trans	"	ss	32.1	25	4a	excess B	5
Cyclopentene	"	ss	33.2	102	4a	excess B	110
1-Hexadecene	"	lc	27.8	30	4a	chloroform	110
1-Hexene	"	ss	34.6	25	1		109
Isobutene	"	lc	32.1	60	4a	excess B	110
Propene	"	lc	27.9	0	4a	**	83
		sc	31.1	25	1		109
				90	4a	excess B	110

* Numerical values for entropies of polymerization listed only for systems yielding 1:1 copolymers. The values refer to the copolymerization of 0.5 mole of each monomer. The symbolism and standard states are the same as used for the heats of copolymerization (Table A9).

** Value calculated from measurements on mixtures containing excess B.

TABLE C - CEILING TEMPERATURES AND EQUILIBRIUM MONOMER CONCENTRATIONS

Most addition polymerization reactions are exothermic and exentropic. The free energy of polymerization per monomer unit therefore becomes less negative as the temperature is raised. At the ceiling temperature T_c the free energy of polymerization under the prevailing conditions is zero and above this temperature polymerization to long-chain polymer is impossible (just as in physical aggregation a liquid cannot form a solid when the temperature is above the melting point). The reverse phenomenon of a floor temperature is also known, e.g. for sulfur.

In general a pure liquid monomer which gives an insoluble polymer will have a single well-defined ceiling temperature, given by $T_c = \Delta H_{1c}/\Delta S_{1c}$. A pure liquid monomer which gives a soluble polymer will have a series of ceiling temperatures corresponding to different percentage conversions of monomer to polymer. The condition for equilibrium is then

$$-\Delta \overline{G}_1 + \Delta G_{1c} + \Delta \overline{G}_2 = 0$$

The partial molar free energy per mole of monomer, $\Delta \overline{G}_1$ and per base-mole of polymer, $\Delta \overline{G}_2$, are then functions of composition and may be evaluated from an appropriate equation for mixing of monomer and polymer, e.g. the Flory-Huggins equation. For a monomer dissolved in a solvent the situation is more complex and the ceiling temperature at a given monomer concentration (or the equilibrium concentration of monomer at a given temperature) is dependent on the nature of the solvent and the composition of the medium (refs. 28, 29, 112, 113, 114). For the case where both monomer and polymer are in solution the variation of T_c with concentration is given to a first approximation by

$$T_c = \Delta H^\circ_{ss}/(\Delta S^\circ_{ss} + R \ln[M])$$

where [M] is the concentration of monomer and ΔH°_{ss} and ΔS°_{ss} refer to the heat and entropy changes in an appropriate standard state. A more general expression may be derived from the free energy condition by insertion of suitable expressions for $\Delta \overline{G}_1$ and $\Delta \overline{G}_2$. These will contain the various interaction parameters appropriate to the polymer-monomer-solvent system.

The values of T_c quoted in the Table are mostly obtained from experimental values by interpolation or short extrapolation. Some unpolymerizable monomers are included where these are structurally closely related to monomers which do polymerize and where the cause of non-polymerization appears to be thermodynamic.

Table C is divided into three sections:

1 - Equilibria involving pure liquid monomers (lc, lc', ls)
2 - Equilibria involving gaseous monomers (gc, gc')
3 - Equilibria involving monomers in solution (sc, sc', ss)

For meaning of symbols see Table A.

References page II-396

1 - EQUILIBRIA INVOLVING PURE LIQUID MONOMERS (Listed alphabetically)

(Mole fractions based on total monomer units)

Monomer	State of Monomer and Polymer	T_c °C	Mole Fraction Monomer at Equilibrium	Notes	Reference
Acetaldehyde	ls	-31	1	atactic polymer	115
	ls	-39	1	isotactic polymer	115
ε-Caprolactam	ls	220	0.055	trace of water	68
	ls	254	0.079	present	68
m-Dioxane	l*	<100	1		116
1,3-Dioxepane $\overline{CH_2O(CH_2)_3}CH_2$	ls?**	100	0.10		116
		140	0.16		
-- , 2-phenyl-	ls?**	20	0.36		116
Dioxolane $\overline{CH_2O}\,CH_2\,CH_2$	ls?**	100	0.30		116
2-Piperidone	ls	60	0.5		118
Propionaldehyde	ls	-31	1	atactic polymer	115
	ls	-39	1	isotactic polymer	115
Selenium	ls	83	1	x	85
Styrene, α-methyl-	ls	61	1	1 atm	119
	ls	170	1	6480 atm	119
Sulfur	ls	159	1	≠	73,111
Sulfur trioxide	lc'	30.4	1		86
Tetrahydrofuran	ls	70±5	1		58
-- , 2-methyl-	l*	<20	1		117
-- , 2,5-dimethyl-	l*	<20	1		117
31 Lactams				discussion of polymerizability	128

x Floor temperature (hypothetical for supercooled liquid). ≠ Floor temperature

* No polymer is formed, therefore not known if soluble in the monomer.

** The states of monomer and/or polymer are not explicitly stated in ref. but are likely to be the ones given.

2 - EQUILIBRIA INVOLVING GASEOUS MONOMERS

Monomer	State of Monomer and Polymer	T_c °C	Equilibrium pressure (mm Hg) (Listed alphabetically)	Notes	Reference
Chloral	gc'	96	760		50
Ethylene, tetrafluoro-	gc	560	96	≠	120,23
Formaldehyde	gc'	126	760	*	49
Methacrylic acid,					
-- , ethyl ester	gs	173	760	⌁	40
-- , methyl ester	gs	164	760	⌁	43
Sulfur trioxide	gc'	27.0	279		86
		0.0	30.6		86

≠   Calculated value. Not measurable experimentally because of side reactions.

*   Composition of vapour in some doubt, see refs. 106, 114.

⌁   Small amount of vapour dissolved in the polymer; approximately gc.

3 - EQUILIBRIA INVOLVING MONOMERS IN SOLUTION

[M] = concentration in mole litre^{-1}, except where otherwise stated.

a. Homopolymerization (Listed alphabetically)

Monomer	State of Monomer and Polymer	T_c °C	[M]	Solvent/Notes	Reference
Biphenyl,					
-- , p-isopropenyl-	ss	0	0.515	tetrahydrofuran	16
-- , p-isopropenyl-	ss	-30	0.079	"	16
2-tert-Butylacrylic acid, methyl ester	sc'	<-80		ammonia	126
Chloral	ss**	12.5#	0.100x	pyridine	50
1,3-Dioxepane $\overline{OCH_2O(CH_2)_3CH_2}$	sc	100	~1.7	benzene	116
1,2-Dithiolane	s*	<20	0.05	95% ethanol	121
Ethylene, 1,1-diphenyl-		<-80		tetrahydrofuran	16
Formaldehyde	sc'	30	0.06	methylene chloride	122
n-Hexyl isocyanate (giving n-hexyl-1-nylon)	sc	-22	~2	dimethylformamide	127
Methacrylic acid, methyl ester	ss	110.7	0.139	o-dichlorobenzene	42
Methacrylic acid, methyl ester	ss	155.5	0.821	"	42
Methacrylonitrile	ss	145	0.27	benzonitrile	44
Naphthalene,					
-- , 1-isopropenyl-	s*	<-80	0.284	tetrahydrofuran	16
-- , 2-isopropenyl-	ss	0		tetrahydrofuran	16
-- , 2-isopropenyl-		-20	0.081	"	16
Styrene	ss	110	1.2×10^{-4}	benzene	28
Styrene	ss	150	9.1×10^{-4}	"	28

*,** See footnotes * and ** page II-390

d T_c/dP = 19 deg kbar^{-1}.

x Mole fraction of monomer.

Monomer	State of Monomer and Polymer	T_c °C	[M]	Solvent/Notes	Reference
a. Homopolymerization (Cont'd.)					
Styrene (Cont'd.)					
ss	110	0.78×10^{-4}	cyclohexane	28
ss	150	6.5×10^{-4}	"	28
-- , α-methyl-	ss	-40	0.060	tetrahydrofuran	32
ss	0	0.76	"	16,32, 123
ss	0	0.4	x "	112
-- , -- , 2,4-dimethyl-	s*	<-80		tetrahydrofuran	16

x Solution containing 2.8 mole liter^{-1} polymer
* See footnote page II-390

b. Copolymerization (1:1 copolymers)

(Listed alphabetically under Monomer A)

Monomer A	Monomer B	State of Monomer and Polymer	T_c °C	$[A][B]$ mole^2 litre^{-2}	Solvent/Notes	Reference
Allyl acetate	Sulfur dioxide	ss	45	27	excess B	110
Allyl alcohol	"	sc	76	27	"	110
Allyl ethyl ether	"	ss	68	27	"	110
Allyl formate	"	sc	45	27	"	110
1-Butene	"	ss	64	27	"	110
-- , 2-ethyl-	"		<-80		all compositions	110
-- , 3-methyl-	"	sc	36	27	excess B	110
2-Butene, cis	"	ss	46*	27	"	110
-- , trans	"	ss	38*	27	"	110
2-Butene (50% cis)	"	ss	34.6‡	27	"	110
-- , 2-methyl-	"		<-80		all compositions	110
Cycloheptene	"	ss	11	27	excess B	124
Cyclohexene	"	ss	24	27	"	110
Cyclopentene	"	ss	103	27	excess B	110
Ethylene	"	sc'	>135	27	"	110
2-Heptene (88% cis)	"	ss	-38‡	33	"	110
1-Hexadecene	"	sc	69	27	"	110
		ss	30	1.15	chloroform	80
1-Hexene	"	ss	60	27	excess B	110
-- , 2-ethyl-	"		<-80		all compositions	110
1-Pentene	"	ss	63	27	excess B	110

* Corrected for isomerization effect.

‡ Uncorrected for isomerization effect.

b. Copolymerization (1:1 copolymers) (Cont'd.)

Monomer A	Monomer B	State of Monomer and Polymer	T_c °C	$[A][B]$ $mole^2$ $litre^{-2}$	Solvent/Notes	Reference
1-Pentene, 2-methyl-	Sulfur dioxide	ss	-34	27	excess B	110
-- , 4,4-dimethyl-	"	sc	14	27	"	110
-- , 2,4,4-trimethyl-	"		<-80		all compositions	110
2-Pentene (50% cis)	"	ss	8.5#	32		110
2-Pentene, 4-methyl-	"		<-80		all compositions	110
4-Pentenoic acid	"	sc	66	27	excess B	110
Propene	"	sc	90	27	"	110
Isobutene	"	sc	5	27	"	110

Uncorrected for isomerization effect.

References page II-396

1. F. S. Dainton and K. J. Ivin, in H. A. Skinner, Ed., "Experimental Thermochemistry," Vol. II, Interscience, New York-London, 1962, p. 251.
2. R. S. Jessup, J. Chem. Phys., 16, 661 (1948).
3. J. W. Richardson and G. S. Parks, J. Am. Chem. Soc., 61, 3545 (1939).
4. F. A. Quinn and L. Mandelkern, J. Am. Chem. Soc., 80, 3178 (1958).
5. F. S. Dainton, J. Diaper, K. J. Ivin and D. R. Sheard, Trans. Faraday Soc., 53, 1269 (1957).
6. C. M. Fontana and G. A. Kidder, J. Am. Chem. Soc., 70, 3745 (1948).
7. G. S. Parks and H. P. Mosher, J. Polymer Sci., A1, 1979 (1963).
8. A. G. Evans and M. Polanyi, Nature, 152, 738 (1943).
9. R. H. Biddulph, P. H. Plesch and P. P. Rutherford, Polymer, 1, 521 (1960).
10. D. E. Roberts, J. Res. Natl. Bur. Std., 44, 221 (1950).
11. F. S. Dainton, T. R. E. Devlin and P. A. Small, Trans. Faraday Soc., 51, 1710 (1955).
12. S. Kaarsemaker and J. Coops, Rec. Trav. Chim., 71, 261 (1952).
13. H. van Kamp, J. Coops, W. A. Lambregts, B. J. Visser and H. Dekker, Rec. Trav. Chim., 79, 1226 (1960).
14. F. S. Dainton, K. J. Ivin and D. A. G. Walmsley, Trans. Faraday Soc., 56, 1784 (1960).
15. R. M. Joshi, Makromol. Chem., 55, 35 (1962).
16. H. Hopff and H. Lüssi, Makromol. Chem., 62, 31 (1963).
17. R. M. Joshi, J. Polymer Sci., 56, 313 (1962).
18. G. C. Sinke and D. R. Stull, J. Phys. Chem., 62, 397 (1958).
19. J. R. Lacher, E. E. Merz, E. Bohmfalk and J. D. Park, J. Phys. Chem., 60, 492 (1956).
20. J. R. Lacher, H. B. Gottlieb and J. D. Park, Trans. Faraday Soc., 58, 2348 (1962).
21. L. K. J. Tong and W. O. Kenyon, J. Am. Chem. Soc., 69, 2245 (1947).
22. W. M. D. Bryant, J. Polymer Sci., 56, 277 (1962).
23. C. R. Patrick, Tetrahedron, 4, 26 (1958).
24. R. M. Joshi, Makromol. Chem., 62, 140 (1963).
25. F. S. Dainton and K. J. Ivin, Trans. Faraday Soc., 46, 331 (1950).
26. D. E. Roberts, W. W. Walton and R. S. Jessup, J. Res. Natl. Bur. Std., 38, 627 (1947).
27. L. K. J. Tong and W. O. Kenyon, J. Am. Chem. Soc., 69, 1402 (1947).
28. S. Bywater and D. J. Worsfold, J. Polymer Sci., 58, 571 (1962).
29. S. Bywater, Makromol. Chem., 52, 120 (1962).
30. R. H. Biddulph, W. R. Longworth, J. Penfold, P. H. Plesch and P. P. Rutherford, Polymer, 1, 521 (1960).
31. D. E. Roberts and R. S. Jessup, J. Res. Natl. Bur. Std., 46, 11 (1951).
32. D. J. Worsfold and S. Bywater, J. Polymer Sci., 26, 299 (1957).
33. H. W. McCormick, J. Polymer Sci., 25, 488 (1957).
34. R. M. Joshi, Makromol. Chem., 66, 114 (1963).
35. W. I. Bengough, Trans. Faraday Soc., 54, 1560 (1958).
36. A. G. Evans and E. Tyrrall, J. Polymer Sci., 2, 387 (1947).
37. K. G. McCurdy and K. J. Laidler, Can. J. Chem., 42, 818 (1964).
38. J. H. Baxendale and G. W. Madaras, J. Polymer Sci., 19, 171 (1956).
39. L. K. J. Tong and W. O. Kenyon, J. Am. Chem. Soc., 68, 1355 (1946).
40. R. E. Cook and K. J. Ivin, Trans. Faraday Soc., 53, 1132 (1957).
41. S. Ekegren, S. Öhrn, K. Granath and P. Kinell, Acta Chem. Scand., 4, 126 (1950).
42. S. Bywater, Trans. Faraday Soc., 51, 1267 (1955).
43. K. J. Ivin, Trans. Faraday Soc., 51, 1273 (1955).
44. S. Bywater, Can. J. Chem., 35, 552 (1957).
45. R. A. Nelson, R. S. Jessup and D. E. Roberts, J. Res. Natl. Bur. Std., 48, 275 (1952).
46. R. S. Jessup and A. D. Cummings, J. Res. Natl. Bur. Std., 13, 357 (1934).
47. A. A. Korotkov and E. N. Marandzheva, Russ. J. Phys. Chem. (English Transl.) 37, 135 (1963).
48. V. A. Kargin, V. A. Kabanov, V. P. Zubov and I. M. Papisov, Dokl. Akad. Nauk S.S.S.R., 134, 1098 (1960); Chem. Abst., 55, 8282 (1961).
49. F. S. Dainton, K. J. Ivin and D. A. G. Walmsley, Trans. Faraday Soc., 55, 61 (1959).
50. W. K. Busfield and E. Whalley, Trans. Faraday Soc., 59, 679 (1963).
51. H. C. Raine, R. B. Richards and H. Ryder, Trans. Faraday Soc., 41, 56 (1945).
52. P. Gray and A. Williams, Trans. Faraday Soc., 55, 760 (1959).
53. J. B. Rose, J. Chem. Soc., 1946, 546.
54. S. M. Skuratov, A. A. Strepikheev, S. M. Shtekher and A. V. Volokhina, Dokl. Akad. Nauk S.S.S.R., 117, 263 (1957).
55. S. M. Skuratov, A. A. Strepikheev and M. P. Kozina, Dokl. Akad. Nauk. S.S.S.R., 117, 452 (1957).
56. R. C. Cass, S. E. Fletcher, C. T. Mortimer, H. D. Springall and T. R. White, J. Chem. Soc., 1958, 1406.
57. D. Sims, J. Chem. Soc., 1964, 864

58. C. E. H. Bawn, R. M. Bell and A. Ledwith, Polymer, 6, 95 (1965).
59. A. Snelson and H. A. Skinner, Trans. Faraday Soc., 57, 2125 (1961).
60. S. E. Fletcher, C. T. Mortimer and H. D. Springall, J. Chem. Soc., 580 (1959).
61. F. S. Dainton, J. A. Davies, P. P. Manning and S. A. Zahir, Trans. Faraday Soc., 53, 813 (1957).
62. A. A. Strepikheev, S. M. Skuratov, O. N. Kachinskaya, R. S. Muramova, E. P. Brildina and S. M. Shtekher, Dokl. Akad. Nauk S.S.S.R., 102, 105 (1955).
63. V. P. Kolesov, I. E. Paukov and S. M. Skuratov, Zh. Fiz. Khim., 36, 770 (1962); Russ. J. Phys. Chem., 36, 401 (1962).
64. M. P. Kozina and S. M. Skuratov, Dokl. Akad. Nauk S.S.S.R., 127, 561 (1959).
65. S. M. Skuratov, A. A. Strepikheev and E. N. Kanarskaya, Kolloidn. Zh., 14, 185 (1952).
66. A. B. Meggy, J. Chem. Soc., 1953, 796.
67. P. F. Van Velden, G. M. Van der Want, D. Heikens, C. A. Kruissink, P. H. Hermans and A. J. Staverman, Rec. Trav. Chim., 74, 1376 (1955).
68. A. V. Tobolsky and A. Eisenberg, J. Am. Chem. Soc., 81, 2302 (1959).
69. H. Mackle and P. A. G. O'Hare, Tetrahedron, 19, 961 (1963).
70. S. Sunner, Acta Chem. Scand., 17, 728 (1963).
71. H. Mackle and R. G. Mayrick, Trans. Faraday Soc., 58, 230 (1962).
72. J. A. Barltrop, P. M. Hayes, and M. Calvin, J. Am. Chem. Soc., 76, 4348 (1954).
73. F. Fairbrother, G. Gee and G. T. Merrall, J. Polymer Sci. 16, 459 (1955).
74. A. V. Tobolsky and A. Eisenberg, J. Am. Chem. Soc., 81, 780 (1959).
75. H. Nagao and T. Yamaguchi, J. Chem. Soc., Japan, Ind. Eng. Chem. Sect., 59, 1363 (1956).
76. H. Miyama and S. Fujimoto, J. Polymer Sci., 54, S 32 (1961).
77. F. S. Dainton and K. J. Ivin, Proc. Roy. Soc. (London), A 212, 207 (1952).
78. J. E. Hazell and K. J. Ivin, Trans. Faraday Soc., 58, 342 (1962).
79. L. K. J. Tong and W. O. Kenyon, J. Am. Chem. Soc., 71, 1925 (1949).
80. F. S. Dainton, K. J. Ivin and D. R. Sheard, Trans. Faraday Soc., 52, 414 (1956).
81. M. Suzuki, H. Miyama and S. Fujimoto, J. Polymer Sci., 31, 212 (1958).
82. K. J. Ivin, W. A. Keith and H. Mackle, Trans. Faraday Soc., 55, 262 (1959).
83. R. E. Cook, K. J. Ivin and J. H. O'Donnell, Trans. Faraday Soc., 61, 000 (1965).
84. W. A. Piccoli, G. G. Haberland and R. L. Merker, J. Am. Chem. Soc., 82, 1883 (1960).
85. A. Eisenberg and A. V. Tobolsky, J. Polymer Sci., 46, 19 (1960).
86. D. C. Abercromby, R. A. Hyne and P. F. Tiley, J. Chem. Soc., 5832 (1963).
87. F. S. Dainton and K. J. Ivin, Quart. Rev., 12, 61 (1958).
88. F. S. Dainton, D. M. Evans, F. E. Hoare and T. P. Melia, Polymer, 3, 277, 286 (1962).
89. E. Passaglia and H. K. Kevorkian, J. Appl. Polymer Sci., 7, 119 (1963).
90. R. W. Warfield and M. C. Petree, Makromol. Chem., 51, 113 (1962).
91. B. Wunderlich, J. Chem. Phys., 37, 1203 (1962).
92. E. Passaglia and H. K. Kevorkian, J. Appl. Phys., 34, 90 (1963).
93. G. T. Furukawa and M. L. Reilly, J. Res. Natl. Bur. Std., 56, 285 (1956).
94. H. L. Finke, D. W. Scott, M. E. Gross, J. F. Messerly and G. Waddington, J. Am. Chem. Soc., 78, 5469 (1956).
95. R. B. Scott, C. H. Meyers, R. D. Rands, F. G. Brickwedde and N. Bekkedahl, J. Res. Natl. Bur. Std., 35, 39 (1945).
96. G. T. Furukawa and R. E. McCoskey, J. Res. Natl. Bur. Std., 51, 321 (1953).
97. F. S. Dainton, D. M. Evans, F. E. Hoare and T. P. Melia, Polymer, 3, 297 (1962).
98. G. T. Furukawa, R. E. McCoskey and M. L. Reilly, J. Res. Natl. Bur. Std., 51, 69 (1953).
99. G. T. Furukawa, R. E. McCoskey and G. J. King, J. Res. Natl. Bur. Std., 49, 273 (1952).
100. N. Bekkedahl and L. A. Wood, J. Res. Natl. Bur. Std., 19, 551 (1937).
101. N. Bekkedahl and H. Matheson, J. Res. Natl. Bur. Std., 15, 503 (1935).
102. T. P. Melia, Polymer, 3, 317 (1962).
103. R. W. Warfield and M. C. Petree, J. Polymer Sci., A1, 1701 (1963).
104. R. H. Boundy and R. F. Boyer, "Styrene," Reinhold, New York, 1952, p. 67.
105. R. W. Warfield and M. C. Petree, J. Polymer Sci., 55, 497 (1961).
106. F. S. Dainton, D. M. Evans, F. E. Hoare and T. P. Melia, Polymer, 3, 263 (1962).
107. F. S. Dainton, D. M. Evans, F. E. Hoare and T. P. Melia, Polymer, 3, 271 (1962).
108. R. J. Orr, Polymer, 2, 74 (1961).
109. F. S. Dainton, D. M. Evans, F. E. Hoare and T. P. Melia, Polymer, 3, 310 (1962).
110. R. E. Cook, F. S. Dainton and K. J. Ivin, J. Polymer Sci., 26, 351 (1957).
111. G. Gee, Chemical Society (London) Special Publication 15, 67 (1961).
112. A. Vrancken, J. Smid and M. Szwarc, Trans. Faraday Soc., 58, 2036 (1962).
113. A. V. Tobolsky, A. Rembaum and A. Eisenberg, J. Polymer Sci., 45, 347 (1960).
114. K. J. Ivin, Pure Appl. Chem., 4, 271 (1962).
115. A. M. North and D. Richardson, Polymer, 6, 000 (1965).

116. A. A. Strepikheev and A. V. Volokhina, Dokl. Akad. Nauk S.S.S.R., $\underline{99}$, 407 (1954).
117. C. L. Hamermesh and V. E. Haury, J. Org. Chem., $\underline{26}$, 4748 (1961).
118. N. Yoda and A. Miyake, J. Polymer Sci., $\underline{43}$, 117 (1960).
119. J. G. Kilroe and K. E. Weale, J. Chem. Soc., $\underline{1960}$, 3849.
120. H. H. G. Jellinek and H. Kachi, Makromol. Chem. (in press).
121. R. B. Whitney and M. Calvin, J. Chem. Phys., $\underline{23}$, 1750 (1955).
122. W. Kern and V. Jaacks, J. Polymer Sci., $\underline{48}$, 399 (1960).
123. H. W. McCormick, J. Polymer Sci., $\underline{25}$, 488, (1957).
124. J. E. Hazell and K. J. Ivin, Trans. Faraday Soc., $\underline{58}$, 176 (1962).
125. J. K. Jacques, M. F. Mole and N. L. Paddock, J. Chem. Soc., $\underline{1965}$, 2112.
126. J. W. C. Crawford, J. Chem. Soc., $\underline{1953}$ 2658.
127. V. E. Shashoua, W. Sweeny and R. E. Tierz, J. Am. Chem. Soc., $\underline{82}$, 866 (1960).
128. R. C. P. Cubbon, Makromol. Chem., $\underline{80}$, 44 (1964).
129. P. H. Plesch and P. H. Westermann, Symposium on Macromolecular Chemistry,
      Prague, 1965 (additional data, not shown in the Tables).

CRITICAL MICELLE CONCENTRATION

H. Gerrens

Badische Anilin und Soda Fabrik
Ludwigshafen, Germany

Contents

A. Introduction

In an aqueous solution of a surface active agent (surfactant) the surfactant is molecularly dispersed at low concentrations. At higher concentrations, however, when a
certain critical concentration is reached the molecules form micelles. These micelles
are in equilibrium with the free surfactant molecules. In the case of ionic surfactants the micelles contain about 50-200 molecules. The concentration that must be
reached in order that micelles are formed is called the critical micelle concentration
(CMC). Many physical properties of the surfactant solution when plotted against the
concentration show more or less sudden changes at the CMC. By measuring such properties as electrical conductivity, interfacial tension, surface tension, refractive
index, viscosity and light scattering as a function of the concentration of the surfactant the CMC is determined as the concentration at which the property versus concentration curve shows a change in slope. The hydrophobic part of the surfactant
molecule is situated at the inside of the micelle, the hydrophilic part at the outside. Inside the micelles lipophilic substances may be solubilized. Certain dye-
stuffs show a spectral change when they are solubilized in the micelles. This effect
too, is used for the measurement of the CMC.

In emulsion polymerization the monomer is emulsified in the solution of a surfactant
(emulsifier) in water. Part of the monomer is solubilized in the micelles. As free
radicals enter the micelles the monomer in them is polymerized and polymer particles
(latex particles) are formed. The surfactant molecules are adsorbed at the surface of
the particles and protect them from coagulation. According to the theory of Smith
and Ewart (1), the number N of latex particles formed in emulsion polymerization is
given by

$$N = 0.43 \cdot \left(\frac{\rho}{\mu}\right)^{2/5} \cdot (a_s [S])^{3/5} \qquad (I)$$

N = number of latex particles per cm^3 of emulsion $[cm^{-3}]$

ρ = rate of formation of free radicals $[cm^{-3} sec^{-1}]$

μ = rate of volume increase of a particle $[cm^3 \cdot sec^{-1}]$

a_s = interfacial area occupied by one surfactant molecule in micelles or at the
    surface of latex particles $[cm^2 \cdot molecule^{-1}]$

[S] = concentration of surfactant [molecules $\cdot$ cm^{-3}]

Colloidal and technological properties of a polymer are to a large extent determined by the size and the number of the latex particles. The rate of polymerization R_p in emulsion is also governed by the number N of latex particles and can be expressed as

$$R_p = (1/2 \cdot N_A) N \cdot k_p \cdot [M] \qquad (II)$$

R_p = overall rate of polymerization [mole $\cdot$ cm^{-3} $\cdot$ sec^{-1}]

1/2 = average number of radicals per latex particles

N_A = Avogadro's number

k_p = propagation constant [cm^3 $\cdot$ mole^{-1} $\cdot$ sec^{-1}]

[M] = monomer concentration [mole $\cdot$ cm^{-3}]

In the derivation of equation I the molecularly dissolved portion of the emulsifier is neglected. Technical emulsion polymerizations, however, frequently use very low emulsifier concentrations. Here the simplification is no longer permissible and the factor [S] in equation I must be substituted by ([S] - CMC) (2). Generally, with decreasing CMC the number of latex particles N and the rate of polymerization R_p will increase.

In a homologous series, there is found a linear dependence of the logarithm of the CMC on the number n of carbon atoms in the paraffin chain of the surfactant (3) or on the number m of ethylene oxide units in the polyethylene glycol chain of ethylene oxide adducts,

$$\log \text{CMC} = A - B \cdot n \qquad (III)$$

and

$$\log \text{CMC} = A' - B' \cdot m \qquad (IV)$$

Literature values of the CMC were plotted according to equations III or IV and the best straight line was drawn through the points. The constants A, B, A' and B' of equations III and IV are listed in tables 1 - 3 together with the numerical values of the CMC calculated with the aid of these constants. Comparing the values for ionic surfactants obtained by different authors, it was observed that the deviations from the straight line given by equation III were always greater than the differences caused by different temperatures. Therefore, only the temperature range of the measurements is given in tables 1 and 2. Table 4 shows the temperature dependence of the CMC for some selected examples. For ionic surfactants the CMC increases slightly with increasing temperature, for nonionics it decreases. Table 4 includes values of the conventional heat of micelle formation ΔH_m, which according to Stainsby and Alexander (4), is given by the relation:

$$\Delta H_m = -RT^2 \, (d \ln \text{CMC}/dT) \qquad (V)$$

Addition of salts lowers the CMC of ionic surfactants. Equation III changes to

$$\log \text{CMC} = K_1 - K_2 \, n - K_3 \cdot \log c_G \qquad (IIIa)$$

where c_G is the total concentration of counterions ("gegenionen"), K_1, K_2 and K_3 are constants. K_3 is generally of the order 0.5. For theoretical foundations of equations III, IIIa and IV see ref. (5).

The Krafft point (6) is the triple point where three phases are in equilibrium: the molecular dissolved surfactant, the micellar surfactant and the crystalline or gel-like surfactant. The Krafft point can be determined by measurements of the solubility of the surfactant with increasing temperature. The solubility suddenly increases when the temperature of the Krafft point is reached. This temperature is listed in tables 1 and 2. Most nonionic surfactants exhibit no Krafft points. For emulsion polymerizations the polymerization temperature should be above the Krafft point, or not all of the emulsifier will participate in the reaction. This effect may be desirable in certain special cases, for instance the formation of monodisperse latices (7). Table 5 shows the influence of counterions on the Krafft point (8).

When the aqueous solution of a nonionic surface active agent is heated, it suddenly becomes cloudy within a narrow temperature range. This is called the Cloud Point. Further heating causes separation in two phases (9). No micelles are present above the cloud point. Emulsion polymerization therefore should be carried out at temperatures below the cloud point. Temperatures of cloud points are given in table 3. The cloud point can be influenced by electrolytes and by solubilized organic substances. At low surfactant concentrations its temperature is practically independent of the concentration (10).

The surface area a_s occupied by a surfactant molecule adsorbed on a latex particle is most conveniently determined by soap titration (11-22), but measurements have been published for only a few surfactants. The nature of the polymer that forms the latex particles appears to have little influence on the adsorption area a_s. In tables 1-3 values for a_s determined by soap titration are marked with an asterisk. Another method for the determination of approximate values of a_s is the evaluation of measurements of the interfacial tension γ of a surfactant solution against air or better against an organic solvent immiscible with water (20). In the presence of an excess of salt (constant ionic strength) Gibbs' equation (23,24) for the interfacial concentration Γ of the surfactant is valid

$$\Gamma = -1/RT \ (d\gamma/d \ \ln \ C) \quad [\text{mole cm}^{-2}] \qquad \qquad (VI)$$

$$a_s = 10^{16}/\Gamma \cdot N_A \qquad \qquad [\overset{\circ}{A}{}^2/\text{molecule}] \qquad \qquad (VIa)$$

In the absence of salt the factor 1/2 must be added to the right side of equation VI (25,26).

Table 1 - Critical Micelle Concentration, Krafft Point and Adsorption Area of Anionic Surfactants

Surfactant	Mol. Wt.	Temp. [°C]	C M C [mole/1]	C M C [g/1]	Krafft Point [°C]	Adsorption Area a_s [$\mathring{A}^2$/molecule]	References
Na- and K-Salts of Saturated Fatty Acids $C_n H_{2n-1} OONa(K)$			$\log CMC = 1.96 - 0.296n^x$				
$C_5 H_9 O_2$ Na	124.12	20	3.0	3.7×10^2			27
K	140.22	25		4.2×10^2			28
$C_6 H_{11} O_2$ Na	138.14	20	1.5	2.1×10^2			27
K	154.24	25		2.3×10^2			28,29,30
$C_7 H_{13} O_2$ Na	152.17	20	7.7×10^{-1}	1.2×10^2			27
K	168.27	25		1.3×10^2			29,30
$C_8 H_{15} O_2$ Na	166.19	20	3.9×10^{-1}	6.5×10^1			27,31
K	182.30	25		7.1×10^1			28,29,30
$C_9 H_{17} O_2$ Na	180.22	20	1.95×10^{-1}	3.5×10^1			27,31
K	196.32	25		3.8×10^1			29
$C_{10} H_{19} O_2$ Na	194.25	20	1.0×10^{-1}	1.9×10^1			27,31
K	210.35	25		2.1×10^1			28,29,30,31
$C_{11} H_{21} O_2$ Na	208.28	-		1.0×10^1			-
K	224.38	25	5.0×10^{-2}	1.1×10^1			29
$C_{12} H_{23} O_2$ Na	222.30	20-70	2.5×10^{-2}	5.6	36	41.4*	8,11,16,27,31,32
K	238.40	20-25		6.0	<0		8,11,28,29,31
$C_{13} H_{25} O_2$ Na	236.33	-		3.1			-
K	252.43	25	1.3×10^{-2}	3.3			29

x No significant differences between the CMC of Na- and K-compounds.

* Determined by soap titration, all other values of a_s derived from measurements of surface or interfacial tension.

Table 1 (Cont'd.) - Critical Micelle Concentration, Krafft Point and Adsorption Area of Anionic Surfactants

Surfactant	Mol. Wt.	Temp. [°C]	C M C [mole/l]	C M C [g/l]	Krafft Point [°C]	Adsorption Area a_s [Å²/molecule]	References
$C_{14}H_{27}O_2$ Na	250.35	50-70	6.5×10^{-3}	1.6	53	34.1*	8,11,16,32
$C_{14}H_{27}O_2$ K	266.45	20-25	-	1.7	8		8,11,28,29,31
$C_{15}H_{29}O_2$ Na	264.38	-	3.3×10^{-3}	8.7×10^{-1}			-
$C_{15}H_{29}O_2$ K	280.48	-		9.3×10^{-1}			-
$C_{16}H_{31}O_2$ Na	278.40	50-70	1.7×10^{-3}	4.7×10^{-1}	62	25.1*	8,11,16,31,34
$C_{16}H_{31}O_2$ K	294.50	35		5.0×10^{-1}	30		8,11,28
$C_{17}H_{33}O_2$ Na	292.43	-	8.6×10^{-4}	2.5×10^{-1}			-
$C_{17}H_{33}O_2$ K	308.53	-		2.65×10^{-1}			-
$C_{18}H_{35}O_2$ Na	306.45	50-60	4.4×10^{-4}	1.3×10^{-1}	71	23.4*	8,11,16,31
$C_{18}H_{35}O_2$ K	322.55			1.4×10^{-1}	46		8,11

Sodium n-Alkyl Sulfates $C_nH_{2n-1}OSO_3Na$ log CMC = 1.43 - 0.290n

Surfactant	Mol. Wt.	Temp. [°C]	C M C [mole/l]	C M C [g/l]	Krafft Point [°C]	Adsorption Area a_s [Å²/molecule]	References
$C_6 H_{13}SO_4Na$	204.22	-	4.9×10^{-1}	9.9×10^{-1}		-	-
$C_8 H_{17}SO_4Na$	232.27	25-50	1.3×10^{-1}	3.0×10^{-1}	<0	-	8,25,33,34
$C_{10}H_{21}SO_4Na$	260.33	25-50	3.4×10^{-2}	8.85	8	50;52	8,25,34
$C_{12}H_{25}SO_4Na$	288.38	35-60	9.0×10^{-3}	2.6	20	49;52	3,25,33,34,35
$C_{14}H_{29}SO_4Na$	316.43	40-60	2.4×10^{-3}	7.5×10^{-1}	33	50;51	3,25,33,34,35
$C_{16}H_{33}SO_4Na$	344.48	40-60	6.2×10^{-4}	2.15×10^{-1}	46		3,25,33,34,35
$C_{18}H_{37}SO_4Na$	372.54	40-60	1.65×10^{-4}	6.2×10^{-2}	58		3,25,33,34,35

References page II-418

Table 1 (Cont'd.) - Critical Micelle Concentration, Krafft Point and Adsorption Area of Anionic Surfactants

Surfactant	Mol. Wt.	Temp. [°C]	C M C [mole/1]	C M C [g/1]	Krafft Point [°C]	Adsorption Area a_s [Å²/molecule]	References
Sodium n-Alkyl Sulfonates $C_nH_{2n+1}SO_3Na$ log CMC = 1.53 - 0.290n							
$C_6H_{13}SO_3Na$	188.22	-	6.2×10^{-1}	1.2×10^2	-		
$C_8H_{17}SO_3Na$	216.27	25	1.6×10^{-1}	3.5×10^1	(15)		8,28,36,37
$C_{10}H_{21}SO_3Na$	244.33	25-80	4.3×10^{-2}	1.0×10^1	24;22.5		8,28,36-40
$C_{12}H_{25}SO_3Na$	272.38	35-80	1.1×10^{-2}	2.3	33;31.5		8,28,36-40
$C_{14}H_{29}SO_3Na$	300.43	40-80	2.9×10^{-3}	8.7×10^{-1}	42;39.5	63*	8,17,28,36-40
$C_{16}H_{33}SO_3Na$	328.48	50	7.7×10^{-4}	2.5×10^{-1}	51;47.5		8,28,37,38
$C_{18}H_{37}SO_3Na$	356.53	57	2.0×10^{-4}	7.2×10^{-2}	60;57.0		8,38
Sodium n-Alkylbenzene Sulfonates $C_nH_{2n+1}C_6H_4SO_3Na$ log CMC = 0.084 - 0.253n							
$C_6H_{13}C_6H_4SO_3Na$	264.31	75	3.7×10^{-2}	9.8			41
$C_7H_{15}C_6H_4SO_3Na$	278.34	75	2.1×10^{-2}	5.85			41
$C_8H_{17}C_6H_4SO_3Na$	292.37	20-75	1.15×10^{-2}	3.4			41-45
$C_9H_{19}C_6H_4SO_3Na$	306.39	75	6.5×10^{-3}	2.0			41
$C_{10}H_{21}C_6H_4SO_3Na$	320.42	50-75	3.6×10^{-3}	1.2			41,42,46
$C_{11}H_{23}C_6H_4SO_3Na$	334.44	-	2.0×10^{-3}	6.7×10^{-1}			-
$C_{12}H_{25}C_6H_4SO_3Na$	348.47	50-75	1.15×10^{-3}	4.0×10^{-1}			41,42,44-46
$C_{14}H_{29}C_6H_4SO_3Na$	376.52	70-75	3.45×10^{-4}	1.3×10^{-1}			41,46
$C_{16}H_{33}C_6H_4SO_3Na$	404.57	50-75	1.1×10^{-4}	4.4×10^{-2}			41,45,46

Table 1 (Cont'd.) - Critical Micelle Concentration, Krafft Point and Adsorption Area of Anionic Surfactants

Surfactant	Mol. Wt.	Temp. [°C]	C M C [mole/l]	[g/l]	Krafft Point [°C]	Adsorption Area a_s [Å²/molecule]	References
$C_{18}H_{37}C_6H_4SO_3Na$	432.63	-	3.4×10^{-5}	1.5×10^{-2}			-
Sodium p-1-Methyl Alkylbenzene Sulfonates $\quad C_nH_{2n+1}CH(CH_3)C_6H_4SO_3Na \quad$ log CMC = -0.456 - 0.215n							
$C_{10}H_{21}$-CH-$C_6H_4SO_3Na$ $\vert$ CH_3	348.47	19-40	2.5×10^{-3}	8.7×10^{-1}	19.0		42
$C_{12}H_{25}$-CH-$C_6H_4SO_3Na$ $\vert$ CH_3	376.52	28-40	9.3×10^{-4}	3.5×10^{-1}	27.7		42
$C_{14}H_{29}$-CH-$C_6H_4SO_3Na$ $\vert$ CH_3	404.57	33-40	3.45×10^{-4}	1.4×10^{-1}	32.6		42
$C_{16}H_{33}$-CH-$C_6H_4SO_3Na$ $\vert$ CH_3	432.63	45-50	1.3×10^{-4}	5.6×10^{-2}	45.5		42
Sodium di-n-Alkyl Sulfosuccinates $\quad NaO_3S$-CH COOR $\vert$ CH$_2$COOR $\quad R = C_nH_{2n+1} \quad$ log CMC = 2.08 - 0.681n							
R = C_4 H_9	332.34	50	2.25×10^{-1}	7.5×10^1			45,47
R = C_5 H_{11}	360.40	50	4.7×10^{-2}	1.7×10^1			45,47
R = C_6 H_{13}	388.44	50	9.7×10^{-3}	3.8			45,47
R = C_7 H_{15}	416.50	50	2.0×10^{-3}	8.3×10^{-1}			45
R = C_8 H_{17}	444.55	50	4.3×10^{-4}	1.9×10^{-1}			45,47
R = C_9 H_{19}	472.60	50	9.0×10^{-5}	4.25×10^{-2}			45
R = $C_{10}H_{21}$	500.65	50	1.85×10^{-5}	9.3×10^{-3}			45

Table 1 (Cont'd) - Critical Micelle Concentration, Krafft Point and Adsorption Area of Anionic Surfactants

Surfactant	Mol. Wt.	Temp. [°C]	C M C [mole/l]	C M C [g/l]	Krafft Point [°C]	Adsorption Area a_s [Å²/molecule]	References
R = $C_{11}H_{23}$	528.71	-	3.8×10^{-6}	2.0×10^{-3}			-
R = $C_{12}H_{25}$	556.76	50	8.0×10^{-7}	4.45×10^{-4}			45
Potassium n-Alkyl Malonates $\quad RCH\!<^{COOK}_{COOK}\quad R = C_n H_{2n+1}\quad \log CMC = 1.30 - 0.219n$							
R = $C_8 H_{17}$	292.44	20-25	3.5×10^{-1}	1.0×10^2			48
R = $C_{10}H_{21}$	320.50	25	1.3×10^{-1}	4.2×10^1			48
R = $C_{12}H_{25}$	348.55	20-25	4.7×10^{-2}	1.6×10^1			48
R = $C_{14}H_{29}$	376.60	20-25	1.7×10^{-2}	6.4			48
R = $C_{16}H_{33}$	404.65	20-25	6.2×10^{-3}	2.5			48
R = $C_{18}H_{37}$	432.70	25	2.3×10^{-3}	1.0			48
Potassium Alkyl Tricarboxylates $\quad RCH\!-\!CH\!<^{COOK}_{COOK}$ COOK $\quad R = C_n H_{2n+1}\quad \log CMC = 1.26 - 0.227n$							
R = $C_6 H_{13}$	360.52	25	7.9×10^{-1}	2.8×10^2			49
R = $C_8 H_{17}$	388.57	25	2.8×10^{-1}	1.1×10^2			-
R = $C_{10}H_{21}$	416.62	25	9.7×10^{-2}	4.0×10^1			49
R = $C_{12}H_{25}$	444.67	25	3.4×10^{-2}	1.5×10^1			-
R = $C_{14}H_{29}$	472.73	25	1.2×10^{-2}	5.7			49

Table 1 (Cont'd.) - Critical Micelle Concentration, Krafft Point and Adsorption Area of Anionic Surfactants

Surfactant	Mol. Wt.	Temp. [°C]	C M C [mole/l]	[g/l]	Krafft Point [°C]	Adsorption Area a_s [Å²/molecule]	References
Alkyl Betaines $\quad$ RCHCOO$^{\ominus}$ $\;\mid$ $\oplus$N(CH$_3$)$_3$	$R = C_n H_{2n+1}$	$\log$ CMC $= 2.75 - 0.469n$					
$R = C_6 H_{13}$	201.30	-	8.5×10^{-1}	1.7×10^{2}			-
$R = C_8 H_{17}$	229.35	27-60	9.7×10^{-2}	2.2×10^{1}	a)	60.0	50-53
$R = C_{10} H_{21}$	257.41	27-60	1.15×10^{-2}	3.0	a)	59.5	50-53
$R = C_{12} H_{25}$	285.46	27-60	1.3×10^{-3}	3.7×10^{-1}	a)	53.9	50-53
$R = C_{14} H_{29}$	313.51	-	1.5×10^{-4}	4.7×10^{-2}			-
Ether Alcohol Sulfates $\quad$ R·(OCH$_2$CH$_2$)$_m$·OSO$_3$Na		$\log$ CMC $= - 2.12 - 0.198m$					
$R = C_{12} H_{25}$							
$C_{12}H_{25}$(OCH$_2$CH$_2$)$_0$OSO$_3$Na	288.38	50	7.6×10^{-3}	2.2	12		54
$C_{12}H_{25}$(OCH$_2$CH$_2$)$_1$OSO$_3$Na	332.43	50	4.9×10^{-3}	1.6	<0		54
$C_{12}H_{25}$(OCH$_2$CH$_2$)$_2$OSO$_3$Na	376.48	50	3.05×10^{-3}	1.1	-		54
$C_{12}H_{25}$(OCH$_2$CH$_2$)$_3$OSO$_3$Na	420.53	50	1.95×10^{-2}	8.2×10^{-1}	-		54
$C_{12}H_{25}$(OCH$_2$CH$_2$)$_4$OSO$_3$Na	464.59	50	1.2×10^{-3}	5.6×10^{-1}	-		54
$R = C_{14} H_{29}$		$\log$ CMC $= - 2.61 - 0.200m$					
$C_{14}H_{29}$(OCH$_2$CH$_2$)$_0$OSO$_3$Na	316.43	50	2.45×10^{-3}	7.7×10^{-1}	29		54
$C_{14}H_{29}$(OCH$_2$CH$_2$)$_1$OSO$_3$Na	360.48	50	1.55×10^{-3}	5.6×10^{-1}	14		54

a) Krafft point and Cloud point do not seem to exist between 0 and 100°C

References page II-418

Table 1 (Cont'd.) - Critical Micelle Concentration, Krafft Point and Adsorption Area of Anionic Surfactants

Surfactant	Mol. Wt.	Temp. [°C]	C M C [mole/l]	C M C [g/l]	Krafft Point [°C]	Adsorption Area a_s [Å²/molecule]	References
$C_{14}H_{29}(OCH_2CH_2)_2OSO_3Na$	404.53	50	9.9×10^{-4}	4.0×10^{-1}	~0		54
$C_{14}H_{29}(OCH_2CH_2)_3OSO_3Na$	448.59	50	6.2×10^{-4}	2.8×10^{-1}	-		54
$R = C_{16}H_{33}$ log CMC = -3.42 - 0.219m (25°C) log CMC = -3.21 - 0.188m (50°C)							
$C_{16}H_{33}(OCH_2CH_2)_0OSO_3Na$	344.48	25 / 50	3.8×10^{-4} / 6.2×10^{-4}	1.3×10^{-1} / 2.1×10^{-1}	46		55 / 54
$C_{16}H_{33}(OCH_2CH_2)_1OSO_3Na$	388.53	25 / 50	2.3×10^{-4} / 4.0×10^{-4}	8.9×10^{-2} / 1.55×10^{-1}	31		55 / 54
$C_{16}H_{33}(OCH_2CH_2)_2OSO_3Na$	432.58	25 / 50	1.4×10^{-4} / 2.6×10^{-4}	6.1×10^{-2} / 1.1×10^{-1}	26		55 / 54
$C_{16}H_{33}(OCH_2CH_2)_3OSO_3Na$	476.63	25 / 50	8.5×10^{-5} / 1.7×10^{-4}	4.05×10^{-2} / 8.1×10^{-2}	19.4		55 / 54
$C_{16}H_{33}(OCH_2CH_2)_4OSO_3Na$	520.68	25 / 50	(5.1×10^{-5}) / 1.1×10^{-4}	(2.7×10^{-2}) / 5.7×10^{-2}	16		55 / 54
$R = C_{18}H_{37}$ log CMC = -3.78 - 0.165m (25°C) log CMC = -3.65 - 0.187m (50°C)							
$C_{18}H_{37}(OCH_2CH_2)_0OSO_3Na$	372.53	25 / 50	1.65×10^{-4} / 2.25×10^{-4}	6.15×10^{-2} / 8.4×10^{-2}	56		55 / 54
$C_{18}H_{37}(OCH_2CH_2)_1OSO_3Na$	416.58	25 / 50	1.1×10^{-4} / 1.45×10^{-4}	4.6×10^{-2} / 6.0×10^{-2}	47.5		55 / 54
$C_{18}H_{37}(OCH_2CH_2)_2OSO_3Na$	460.63	25 / 50	7.8×10^{-5} / 9.5×10^{-5}	3.6×10^{-2} / 4.3×10^{-2}	40		55 / 54
$C_{18}H_{37}(OCH_2CH_2)_3OSO_3Na$	504.68	25 / 50	5.3×10^{-5} / 6.1×10^{-5}	2.7×10^{-2} / 3.1×10^{-2}	34		55 / 54

Table 1 (Cont'd.) - Critical Micelle Concentration, Krafft Point and Adsorption Area of Anionic Surfactants

Surfactant	Mol. Wt.	Temp. [°C]	C M C [mole/l]	C M C [g/l]	Krafft Point [°C]	Adsorption Area a_s [$\overset{\circ}{A}^2$/molecule]	References
$C_{18}H_{37}(OCH_2CH_2)_4OSO_3Na$	548.73	25 50	3.6×10^{-5} 4.0×10^{-5}	2.0×10^{-2} 2.2×10^{-2}	30		55 54
$R = C_8H_{17}CH=CHC_8H_{16}$ $\qquad$ log CMC $= -2.45 - 0.173m$							
$R(OCH_2CH_2)_0OSO_3Na$	370.52	50	3.6×10^{-3}	1.3			54
$R(OCH_2CH_2)_1OSO_3Na$	414.57	50	2.4×10^{-3}	9.9×10^{-1}			54
$R(OCH_2CH_2)_2OSO_3Na$	458.62	50	1.6×10^{-3}	7.3×10^{-1}			54
$R(OCH_2CH_2)_3OSO_3Na$	502.67	50	1.1×10^{-3}	5.5×10^{-1}			54

Table 2 - Critical Micelle Concentration, Krafft Point and Adsorption Area of Cationic Surfactants

Surfactant	Mol. Wt.	Temp. [°C]	C M C [mole/l]	C M C [g/l]	Krafft Point [°C]	Adsorption Area a_s [Å²/molecule]	References
n-Alkylamine Hydrochlorides	RNH$_2$.HCl	$R = C_nH_{2n+1}$	$\log CMC = 1.51 - 0.286n$				
$R = C_6 H_{13}$	137.65	-	6.2×10^{-1}	8.5×10^1			-
$R = C_8 H_{17}$	165.71	-	1.65×10^{-1}	2.7×10^1			-
$R = C_{10}H_{21}$	193.76	25	4.4×10^{-2}	8.5			28
$R = C_{12}H_{25}$	221.81	30-50	1.2×10^{-2}	2.7	26		8,15,28,31
$R = C_{14}H_{29}$	249.86	40	3.2×10^{-3}	8.0×10^{-1}			28
$R = C_{16}H_{33}$	277.91	50	8.6×10^{-4}	2.4×10^{-1}			28
$R = C_{18}H_{37}$	305.97	60	2.3×10^{-4}	7.0×10^{-2}	56		8,28
n-Alkyltrimethylammonium Bromides	RN(CH$_3$)$_3$Br	$R = C_nH_{2n+1}$	$\log CMC = 1.98 - 0.311n$				
$R = C_8 H_{17}$	252.24	25	3.1×10^{-1}	7.8×10^1			28
$R = C_{10}H_{21}$	280.29	25;60	7.5×10^{-2}	2.1×10^1			28
$R = C_{12}H_{25}$	308.35	25;60	1.75×10^{-2}	5.4			28
$R = C_{14}H_{29}$	336.40	60	4.2×10^{-3}	1.4			28
$R = C_{16}H_{33}$	364.45	60	1.0×10^{-3}	3.6×10^{-1}			28
$R = C_{18}H_{37}$	392.50	-	2.4×10^{-4}	9.4×10^{-2}			-
di-n-Alkyldimethylammonium Chlorides	R$_2$N(CH$_3$)$_2$Cl	$R = C_nH_{2n+1}$	$\log CMC = 2.77 - 0.548n$				
$R = C_8 H_{17}$	305.97	30	2.7×10^{-2}	8.3			56
$R = C_{10}H_{21}$	362.07	30	2.1×10^{-3}	7.8×10^{-1}			56
$R = C_{12}H_{25}$	418.17	30	1.8×10^{-4}	7.5×10^{-2}			56

Table 3 - Critical Micelle Concentration, Cloud Point and Adsorption Area of Nonionic Surfactants

Surfactant	Mol. Wt.	Temp. [°C]	C M C [mole/l]	[g/l]	Cloud Point [°C]	Adsorption Area a_s [Å²/molecule]	References
Alkyl Glucosides $RC_6H_{11}O_6$ $R = C_nH_{2n+1}$ $\log CMC = 1.64 - 0.531n$							
$R = C_8H_{17}$	292.37	25	2.5×10^{-2}	7.3		41	57
$R = C_{10}H_{21}$	320.42	25	2.2×10^{-3}	7.05×10^{-1}		47	58
$R = C_{12}H_{25}$	348.47	25	1.9×10^{-4}	6.6×10^{-2}		36	58
Saccharose Monoesters of Fatty Acids $ROOC_{12}H_{21}O_{10}$ $R = C_nH_{2n-1}$ $\log CMC = 0.514 - 0.348n$ (25-27.5°C) $\log CMC = -0.668 - 0.350n$ (50°C)							
$R = C_{12}H_{23}$	524.59	20-27.5	2.2×10^{-4}	1.2×10^{-1}			59,60
		50	1.35×10^{-5}	7.1×10^{-3}			
$R = C_{14}H_{27}$	552.64	20	4.5×10^{-5}	2.5×10^{-2}			50
		50	2.7×10^{-6}	1.5×10^{-3}			
$R = C_{16}H_{31}$	530.70	20	9.1×10^{-6}	5.3×10^{-3}			60
		50	5.5×10^{-7}	3.2×10^{-4}			
$R = C_{18}H_{35}$	608.75	20-27.5	1.85×10^{-6}	1.1×10^{-3}			59,60
		50	1.1×10^{-7}	6.7×10^{-5}			
Saccharose Dipalmitate							
$C_{12}H_{20}O_9(C_{16}H_{31}O_2)_2$	819.10	20	1.34×10^{-5}	1.1×10^{-2}			60
Polyoxyethylene Monododecyl Ethers $C_{12}H_{25}(OCH_2CH_2)_mOH$			$\log CMC = -4.51 + 0.056m$ (23°C)	$\log CMC = -4.40 + 0.009m$ (25°C)	$\log CMC = -4.80 + 0.013m$ (55°C)		62 61,65 61,65
$C_{12}H_{25}(OCH_2CH_2)_4OH$	362.54	25	4.3×10^{-5}	1.6×10^{-2}		44	61
		55	1.8×10^{-5}	6.5×10^{-3}		44	61
$C_{12}H_{25}(OCH_2CH_2)_5OH$	406.59	23	5.9×10^{-5}	2.4×10^{-2}	25	54	62,63

References page II-418

Table 3 (Cont'd.) - Critical Micelle Concentration, Cloud Point and Adsorption Area of Nonionic Surfactants

Surfactant	Mol. Wt.	Temp. [°C]	C M C [mole/l]	C M C [g/l]	Cloud Point [°C]	Adsorption Area a_s [Å²/molecule]	References
$C_{12}H_{25}(OCH_2CH_2)_6OH$	450.64	23	7.6×10^{-5}	3.8×10^{-2}	48	59	63,64
$C_{12}H_{25}(OCH_2CH_2)_7OH$	494.69	25	4.6×10^{-5}	2.3×10^{-2}		48	62
		55	1.95×10^{-5}	9.6×10^{-3}		46	65
$C_{12}H_{25}(OCH_2CH_2)_9OH$	582.80	23	9.9×10^{-5}	5.8×10^{-2}		71	62
$C_{12}H_{25}(OCH_2CH_2)_{12}OH$	670.90	23	1.45×10^{-4}	9.7×10^{-2}		77	62
$C_{12}H_{25}(OCH_2CH_2)_{14}OH$	803.06	25	5.35×10^{-5}	4.3×10^{-2}		65	65
		55	2.4×10^{-5}	1.9×10^{-2}		65	65
$C_{12}H_{25}(OCH_2CH_2)_{23}OH$	1199.53	25	6.5×10^{-5}	7.8×10^{-2}		82	65
		55	3.3×10^{-5}	4.0×10^{-2}		80	65
$C_{12}H_{25}(OCH_2CH_2)_{30}OH$	1507.89	25	7.5×10^{-5}	1.1×10^{-1}		107	65
		55	3.9×10^{-5}	5.9×10^{-2}		105	65
Polyoxyethylene Monotridecyl Ethers	$C_{13}H_{27}(OCH_2CH_2)_mOH$		$\log CMC = -4.04 + 0.011m$ (25°C) $\log CMC = -4.23 + 0.008m$ (55°C)				
$C_{13}H_{27}(OCH_2CH_2)_5\,OH$	420.62	25	1.05×10^{-4}	4.4×10^{-2}		60	61
		55	6.6×10^{-5}	2.8×10^{-2}		58	61
$C_{13}H_{27}(OCH_2CH_2)_{9.5}OH$	618.85	25	1.15×10^{-4}	7.1×10^{-2}		74	61
		55	7.2×10^{-5}	4.5×10^{-2}		71	61
$C_{13}H_{27}(OCH_2CH_2)_{14}OH$	817.09	25	1.3×10^{-4}	1.1×10^{-1}			61
		55	7.8×10^{-5}	6.3×10^{-2}			61

Table 3 (Cont'd.) - Critical Micelle Concentration, Cloud Point and Adsorption Area of Nonionic Surfactants

Surfactant	Mol. Wt.	Temp. [°C]	C M C [mole/l]	C M C [g/l]	Cloud Point [°C]	Adsorption Area a_s [$\mathring{A}^2$/molecule]	References
$C_{13}H_{27}(OCH_2CH_2)_{20}OH$	1081.40	25	1.55×10^{-4}	1.7×10^{-1}			61
		55	8.8×10^{-5}	9.5×10^{-2}			61
$C_{13}H_{27}(OCH_2CH_2)_{30}OH$	1521.92	25	2.0×10^{-4}	3.0×10^{-1}		89	61
		55	1.05×10^{-4}	1.6×10^{-1}		87	61
Polyoxyethylene Monohexadecyl Ethers $C_{16}H_{33}(OCH_2CH_2)_mOH$			log CMC =	$-5.95 + 0.028m$			
$C_{16}H_{33}(OCH_2CH_2)_6OH$	506.74	25	1.65×10^{-6}	8.4×10^{-4}	32		63,66
$C_{16}H_{33}(OCH_2CH_2)_7OH$	550.30	25	1.75×10^{-6}	9.6×10^{-4}			66
$C_{16}H_{33}(OCH_2CH_2)_9OH$	638.90	25	2.0×10^{-6}	1.3×10^{-3}			66
$C_{16}H_{33}(OCH_2CH_2)_{12}OH$	771.06	25	2.4×10^{-6}	1.85×10^{-3}			66
$C_{16}H_{33}(OCH_2CH_2)_{15}OH$	903.21	25	2.9×10^{-6}	2.6×10^{-3}			66
$C_{16}H_{33}(OCH_2CH_2)_{21}OH$	1167.52	25	4.3×10^{-6}	5.0×10^{-3}			66
Polyoxyethylene Monooctadecyl Ethers $C_{18}H_{37}(OCH_2OH_2)_mOH$							
$C_{18}H_{37}(OCH_2CH_2)_{14}OH$	887.21	25	6.0×10^{-5}	5.3×10^{-2}		94	61
		55	2.0×10^{-5}	1.8×10^{-2}		92	61
$C_{18}H_{37}(OCH_2CH_2)_{100}OH$	4675.68	25	2.0×10^{-5}	9.35×10^{-2}		150	61
		55				145	61
Methoxy Polyoxyethylene Decanoates $C_9H_{19}CO(OCH_2CH_2)_mOCH_3$			log CMC =	$-3.29 + 0.036m$			
$C_9H_{19}CO(OCH_2CH_2)_5OCH_3$	406.55	27	7.7×10^{-4}	3.1×10^{-1}			-
$C_9H_{19}CO(OCH_2CH_2)_7OCH_3$	494.65	27	9.2×10^{-4}	4.55×10^{-1}	44		67

Table 3 (Cont'd.) - Critical Micelle Concentration, Cloud Point and Adsorption Area of Nonionic Surfactants

Surfactant	Mol. Wt.	Temp. [°C]	C M C [mole/l]	C M C [g/l]	Cloud Point [°C]	Adsorption Area a_s [Å²/molecule]	References
$C_9H_{19}CO(OCH_2CH_2)_{10,3}OCH_3$	640.03	27	1.2×10^{-3}	7.7×10^{-1}	65		67
$C_9H_{19}CO(OCH_2CH_2)_{11,9}OCH_3$	710.51	27	1.38×10^{-3}	9.8×10^{-1}	74		67
$C_9H_{19}CO(OCH_2CH_2)_{16}OCH_3$	891.12	27	1.9×10^{-3}	1.7			67
Methoxy Polyoxyethylene Dodecanoates $C_{11}H_{23}CO(OCH_2CH_2)_mOCH_3$, log CMC = $- 3.97 + 0.038m$							
$C_{11}H_{23}CO(OCH_2CH_2)_6OCH_3$	478.65	27	1.8×10^{-4}	8.7×10^{-2}	31		67
$C_{11}H_{23}CO(OCH_2CH_2)_{8,4}OCH_3$	584.38	27	2.3×10^{-4}	1.3×10^{-1}	53		67
$C_{11}H_{23}CO(OCH_2CH_2)_{11,2}OCH_3$	707.72	27	2.9×10^{-4}	2.05×10^{-1}	74		67
$C_{11}H_{23}CO(OCH_2CH_2)_{12,5}OCH_3$	764.99	27	3.25×10^{-4}	2.5×10^{-1}	79		67
$C_{11}H_{23}CO(OCH_2CH_2)_{15}OCH_3$	875.12	27	4.0×10^{-4}	3.5×10^{-1}			-
Polyoxyethylene Nonyl Phenyl Ethers $C_9H_{19}C_6H_4(OCH_2CH_2)_mOH$, log CMC = $- 4.54 + 0.014m$ (55°C)							
$C_9H_{19}C_6H_4(OCH_2CH_2)_{10}OH$	660.86	25	$7.5-9.0 \times 10^{-5}$	$5.0-6.0 \times 10^{-2}$	60	55-60	65,68,69
		55	4.0×10^{-5}	2.6×10^{-2}			65
$C_9H_{19}C_6H_4(OCH_2CH_2)_{15}OH$	881.12	25	$1.1-1.3 \times 10^{-4}$	$9.7-11 \times 10^{-2}$	95	72	65,68,69
		55	4.7×10^{-5}	4.1×10^{-2}			65
$C_9H_{19}C_6H_4(OCH_2CH_2)_{20}OH$	1101.38	25	$1.3-1.8 \times 10^{-4}$	$1.4-2.0 \times 10^{-1}$		82;89*,78*	21,65,68
		55	5.6×10^{-5}	6.2×10^{-2}			65
$C_9H_{19}C_6H_4(OCH_2CH_2)_{30}OH$	1541.90	25	$1.8-3.0 \times 10^{-4}$	$2.8-4.6 \times 10^{-1}$		101	65,68
		55	7.8×10^{-5}	1.2×10^{-1}			65

Table 3 (Cont'd.) - Critical Micelle Concentration, Cloud Point and Adsorption Area of Nonionic Surfactants

Surfactant	Mol. Wt.	Temp. [°C]	C M C [mole/l]	[g/l]	Cloud Point [°C]	Adsorption Area a_s [$\overset{\circ}{A}^2$/molecule]	References
$C_9H_{19}C_6H_4(OCH_2CH_2)_{32}OH$	1630.00	26	1.5×10^{-4}	2.4×10^{-1}		116*, 103*	21
$C_9H_{19}C_6H_4(OCH_2CH_2)_{50}OH$	2422.94	25	2.8×10^{-4}	6.8×10^{-1}			65
		55	1.5×10^{-4}	3.6×10^{-1}			55
$C_9H_{19}C_6H_4(OCH_2CH_2)_{100}OH$	4625.54	25	1.0×10^{-3}	4.6		173	58

References page II-418

Table 4 - Temperature Dependence of Critical Micelle Concentration

Surfactant	Temp. [°C]	C M C [mole/l]	ΔH_m [kcal/mole]	References
$C_{12}H_{23}OOK$	25	2.55×10^{-2}	-0.5	28
	30	2.60	-1.1	
	35	2.70	-1.8	
	45	3.05	-2.6	
	55	3.50	-3.3	
	65	4.20×10^{-2}	-5.4	
$C_{14}H_{27}OOK$	25	6.6×10^{-3}	-1.0	28
	35	7.0	-1.0	
	45	7.4	-1.3	
	55	7.9	-1.6	
	65	8.6×10^{-3}	-2.2	
$C_{12}H_{25}SO_4Na$	20	6.3×10^{-3}	-0.4	35
	40	6.7	-0.9	
	60	7.9	-2.3	
	75	9.5×10^{-3}	-2.8	
$C_8 H_{17}SO_3Na$	25	1.55×10^{-1}	-0.2	28
	40	1.62	-1.0	
	50	1.77×10^{-1}	-2.1	
$C_{10}H_{21}SO_3Na$	25	4.1×10^{-2}	-0.3	28
	35	4.2	-0.8	
	45	4.5	-1.5	
	55	4.9	-2.1	
	65	5.5×10^{-2}	-3.5	
$C_{12}H_{25}SO_3Na$	35	1.0×10^{-2}	-1.5	28
	45	1.1	-1.9	
	55	1.2	-2.5	
	65	1.4×10^{-2}	-3.9	
$C_8H_{17}-CH-COO^{\ominus}$ $\quad \overset{\oplus}{N}(CH_3)_3$	6	10.4×10^{-2}	0.7	52
	27	9.7	0.7	
	45	9.1	0.7	
	60	8.6×10^{-2}	0.7	
$C_{12}H_{25}-CH-COO^{\ominus}$ $\quad \overset{\oplus}{N}(CH_3)_3$	10	1.39×10^{-3}	0.6	52
	27	1.32	0.6	
	45	1.25	0.6	
	60	1.20×10^{-3}	0.6	
$C_{10}H_{21} N(CH_3)_3Br$	25	6.8×10^{-2}	-0.6	28
	60	7.5×10^{-2}		
$C_{12}H_{25} N(CH_3)_3Br$	10	3.52×10^{-3}	-0.2	70
	20	3.56	-0.4	
	30	3.72	-1.1	
	40	4.02	-1.9	
	50	4.48	-2.7	
	60	5.12	-3.0	
	70	5.97	-3.2	
	80	6.88×10^{-3}	-3.6	
$C_{10}H_{21}(OCH_2CH_2)_4OH$	1	1.45×10^{-3}	7.0	71
	6.8	1.12	6.9	
	10	0.98	6.0	
	15	0.90	4.2	
	20	0.73	3.4	
	25	0.68×10^{-3}	2.3	

References page II-418

Table 4 (Cont'd.)

Surfactant	Temp. [°C]	C M C [mole/l]	ΔH_m [kcal/mole]	References
$C_{10}H_{21}(OCH_2CH_2)_5OH$	0.8	1.75×10^{-3}	8.2	71
	5	1.41	6.9	
	10	1.18	5.5	
	15	0.97	4.2	
	20	0.90	3.3	
	25	0.81	2.7	
	30	0.76	2.2	
	35	0.72	1.9	
	40	0.68×10^{-3}	1.5	
$C_{10}H_{21}(OCH_2CH_2)_8OH$	5	2.1×10^{-3}	7.1	71
	10	1.72	7.1	
	15	1.4	7.1	
	20	1.1	7.1	
	25	0.9	5.1	
	35	0.77×10^{-3}	2.2	
$C_{10}H_{21}(OCH_2CH_2)_{12}OCH_3$	9.7	17×10^{-4}	3.9	72
	29.0	11	3.6	
	50.7	7.8	3.1	
	58.5	7.0	2.7	
	69.7	6.2	2.3	
	73.4	6.0	0.6	
	75.0	6.0×10^{-4}	0.4	
$C_7H_{15}CO(OCH_2CH_2)_{7,6}OCH_3$	11	12.5×10^{-3}	3.4	73
	25	9.8	2.5	
	40	8.2	2.2	
	43	7.8×10^{-3}	2.2	

Table 5 - Krafft Points (°C) for Various Counterions

Counterion	Li^+	Na^+	K^+	Rb^+	Cs^+
$C_{12}H_{23}OO^-$	124	36	<0	-	-
$C_{14}H_{27}OO^-$	134	53	8	-	-
$C_{16}H_{31}OO^-$	140	62	30	-	-
$C_{18}H_{35}OO^-$	(148)	71	46	51	48

Counterion	F^-	Cl^-	Br^-	J^-
$C_{12}H_{25}NH_3^+$	(22)	26	34	39
$C_{18}H_{37}NH_3^+$	(50)	56	(62)	(68)

C. References

1. W. V. Smith and R. H. Ewart,   J. Chem. Phys. 16, 592 (1948).
2. H. Gerrens,   Fortschr. Hochpolymer. Forsch. 1, 234 (1959).
3. J. Stauff,   Z. Physik. Chem. (Leipzig) A183, 55 (1938/39).
4. G. Stainsby and A. E. Alexander,   Trans. Faraday Soc. 46, 587 (1950).
5. K. Shinoda, T. Nakagawa, B. Tamamushi and T. Isemura,   Colloidal Surfactants, Academic Press, New York - London, 1963, p. 25-48.
6. F. Krafft and H. Wiglow, Ber. 28, 2566 (1895), F. Krafft, Ber. 32, 1596 (1899).
7. A. H. Loranger, T. T. Serafini, W. v. Fischer and E. G. Bobalek,   Off. Dig. Federation Paint and Varnish Prod. Clubs 31,482 (1959).
8. D. G. Dervichian,   Proceedings, 3rd International Congress of Surface Activity, Cologne (Köln), 1960, Vol. 1, Sect. A, p. 182.
9. B. Wurzschmitt, Z. Anal. Chem. 130, 105 (1950).
10. W. N. Maclay,   J. Colloid Sci. 11, 272 (1956).
11. S. H. Maron, M. E. Elder and J. N. Ulevitch, J. Colloid Sci. 9, 89 (1954).
12. S. H. Maron, M. E. Elder and C. Moore,   J. Colloid Sci. 9, 104 (1954).
13. S. H. Maron and M. E. Elder,   J. Colloid Sci. 9, 263 (1954).
14. S. H. Maron and M. E. Elder,   J. Colloid Sci. 9, 347 (1954).
15. S. H. Maron and M. E. Elder,   J. Colloid Sci. 9, 353 (1954).
16. S. H. Maron, M. E. Elder and J. N. Ulevitch,   J. Colloid Sci. 9, 382 (1954).
17. B. Jacobi, Angew. Chem. 64, 539 (1952).
18. E. A. Willson, J. R. Miller and E. H. Rowe,   J. Phys. and Colloid Chem. 53, 357 (1949).
19. M. Morton, J. A. Cala and M. W. Altier,   J. Polymer Sci. 19, 547 (1956).
20. J. G. Brodnyan and G. L. Brown, J. Colloid. Sci. 15, 76 (1960).
21. R. J. Orr and L. Breitman,   Can. J. Chem. 38, 668 (1960).
22. R. J. Orr,   Rubber Plastics Age 41, 1027 (1960).
23. J. W. Gibbs,   Trans. Conn. Acad. Arts Sci. 3, 108 and 343 (1874-1878).
24. C. P. Roe and P. D. Brass,   J. Am. Chem. Soc. 76, 4703 (1954).
25. W. Kling and H. Lange, Proceedings, 2nd International Congress of Surface Activity, London 1957, Vol. I, p. 295 and 308.
26. B. A. Pethica, Trans. Faraday Soc. 50, 413 (1954).
27. K. Hess, W. Philippoff and H. Kiessig,   Kolloid-Z. 88, 40 (1939).
28. H. B. Klevens,   J. Phys. and Colloid Chem. 52, 130 (1948).
29. S. H. Herzfeld,   J. Phys. Chem. 56, 953 (1952).
30. K. Shinoda,   J. Phys. Chem. 58, 541 (1954).
31. K. Tyuzyo,   Bull. Chem. Soc. Japan 31, 117 (1958).
32. J. Powney and C. C. Addison,   Trans. Faraday Soc. 34, 372 (1938).
33. H. C. Evans, J. Chem. Soc. 579 (1956).
34. E. K. Götte,   J. Colloid Sci. 4, 459 (1949).
35. J. Powney and C. C. Addison,   Trans. Faraday Soc. 33, 1243 (1937).
36. H. V. Tartar and A. L. M. Lelong,   J. Phys. Chem. 59, 1185 (1955).
37. H. B. Klevens,   J. Phys. and Colloid Chem. 51, 1143 (1947).
38. H. V. Tartar and K. A. Wright,   J. Am. Chem. Soc. 63, 539 (1939).
39. K. A. Wright, A. D. Abbott, V. Sivertz and H. V. Tartar,   J. Am. Chem. Soc. 61, 549 (1939).
40. E. C. Lingafelter, O. L. Wheeler and H. V. Tartar, J. Am. Chem. Soc. 68, 1490 (1946).
41. W. Griess, Fette, Seifen, Anstrichmittel 57, 24 (1955).
42. J. W. Gershman,   J. Phys. Chem. 61. 581 (1957).
43. R. G. Paquette, E. C. Lingafelter and H. V. Tartar,   J. Am. Chem. Soc. 65, 686 (1943).
44. M. S. Schick and F. M. Fowkes,   J. Phys. Chem. 61, 1062 (1957).
45. H. Schuller, private communication.
46. H. Lange, 4th International Congress of Surface Activity, Brussels 1964, Preprints, paper No. B/IV.1.
47. E. F. Williams, N. T. Woodberry and J. K. Dixon,   J. Colloid Sci. 12, 452 (1957).
48. K. Shinoda,   J. Phys. Chem. 59, 432 (1955).
49. K. Shinoda,   J. Phys. Chem. 60, 1439 (1956).
50. K. Tori and T. Nakagawa,   Kolloid-Z. 180, 47 (1962).
51. K. Tori and T. Nakagawa,   Kolloid-Z. 187, 44 (1963).
52. K. Tori and T. Nakagawa,   Kolloid-Z. 189, 50 (1963).
53. K. Tori and T. Nakagawa,   Kolloid-Z. 191 42,48 (1963).
54. E. Götte,   Proceedings, 3rd International Congress of Surface Activity, Cologne (Köln), 1960, Vol. 1, Sect. A, p. 45.
55. J. K. Weil, R. G. Bistline and A. J. Stirton,   J. Phys. Chem. 62, 1083 (1958).
56. A. W. Ralston, D. N. Eggenberger and P. L. Du Brow,   J. Am. Chem. Soc. 70, 977 (1948).

57. K. Shinoda, T. Yamanaka and K. Kinoshita,   J. Phys. Chem. $\underline{63}$, 648 (1959).
58. K. Shinoda, T. Yamaguchi and R. Hori,   Bull. Chem. Soc. Japan $\underline{34}$, 237 (1961).
59. L. Ossipow, F. D. Snell and J. Hickson,   Proceedings, 2nd International Congress
     of Surface Activity, London 1957, Vol. I, p. 50.
60. W. Wachs and J. Hayano,   Kolloid-Z. $\underline{181}$, 139 (1962).
61. M. S. Schick, J. Colloid Sci. $\underline{17}$, 801 (1962).
62. H. Lange, Proceedings, 3rd International Congress of Surface Activity, Cologne
     (Köln) 1960, Vol. I, Sect. A, p. 279.
63. B. A. Mulley, Proceedings, 3rd International Congress of Surface Activity,
     Cologne (Köln) 1960, Vol. I, Sect. A. p. 31.
64. R. R. Balmbra, J. S. Clunie, J. M. Corkill and J. F. Goodman,   Trans.
     Faraday Soc. $\underline{58}$, 1661 (1962).
65. M. S. Schick, S. M. Atlas and F. R. Eirich,   J. Phys. Chem. $\underline{66}$, 1326 (1962).
66. P. H. Elworthy and C. B. Macfarlane,   J. Chem. Soc. $\underline{1963}$, 537.
67. T. Nakagawa, K. Kuriyama and K. Tori, J. Chem. Soc. Japan, Pure Chem. Sect.
     $\underline{78}$, 1573 (1957), through ref. (5).
68. L. Hsiao, H. V. Dunning and P. B. Lorenz,   J. Phys. Chem. $\underline{60}$, 657 (1956).
69. C. F. Jelinek and R. L. Mayhew,   Textile Res. J. $\underline{24}$, 765 (1954).
70. J F. Addison and H. Taylor, 4th International Congress of Surface Activity,
     Brussels, 1964, Preprints, paper No. B/IV. 17.
71. R. A. Hudson and B. A. Pethica,   4th International Congress of Surface
     Activity, Brussels, 1964, Preprints, paper No. B/IV. 21.
72. K. Kuriyama, H. Inoue and T. Nakagawa,   Ann. Rept. Shionogi Res. Lab. $\underline{9}$,
     1061 (1959), through ref. (5).
73. T. Nakagawa, H. Inoue, K. Tori and K. Kuriyama,   J. Chem. Soc. Japan,
     Pure Chem. Sect. $\underline{79}$, 1194 (1958), through ref. (5).

RATE OF POLYMERIZATION, AVERAGE MOLECULAR WEIGHTS, AND
MOLECULAR WEIGHT DISTRIBUTIONS OF POLYMERS

Leighton H. Peebles, Jr.

Chemstrand Research Center
Durham, North Carolina

Contents

A. INTRODUCTION

An attempt is made to present a systematic guide to the literature dealing with rates
of polymerization, average molecular weights, and molecular weight distributions of
polymers for various types of polymerization. This chapter is an abridgement
of a review to be published elsewhere (1) in which all equations are given in
detail: here we present only references to the literature.

The theoretical description of the molecular weight distribution of a polymer and its
rate of polymerization is dependent on the assumed mechanism of polymerization and on
the mathematical simplifications used to obtain analytical expressions. As the number
of distinct reactions is increased, such as the various transfer reactions, the mathematical expressions can become quite complex and unwieldy. In general, the equations
for the rate of polymerization are the most difficult to describe, the distribution
equations are somewhat easier, and the average molecular weights are the simplest.
In condensation polymerization, many of the distribution formulas are derived by considering the probability of a given reaction instead of the kinetics of the reaction.
Therefore, the emphasis is on the distribution functions and their averages, while
the rates of polymerization are given only if they have been derived from the kinetics
of the reaction.

The chapter is divided into several sections and tables, each treating various types
of polymerization. Only the Stockmayer distribution function for condensation polymers
is given in detail here, because of its general applicability and usefulness. For all
the other expressions, the reader must refer to the original literature. Many of the
simpler functions are adequately described in textbooks of polymer chemistry. Flory
(2), Bamford, Barb, Jenkins, Onyon (3), and Küchler (4) give extended descriptions of
many systems.

Section B presents a series of tables describing the main assumptions or conditions
imposed on the theoretical models and references to the articles where the equations
may be found. Tables 1 and 2 present rate equations and the distribution formulas
for addition polymerization by a variety of mechanisms. No distinction is made among
free radical, cationic, anionic, or coordination-type polymerization. Table 1 treats
those cases where the monomer concentration is held constant, whereas Table 2 treats
those cases where the monomer concentration is allowed to vary. The distributions

for addition-type copolymers are omitted. However, see Küchler (4) for an extended discussion of copolymerization distributions. Table 3 contains distribution formulae for linear condensation polymers, in which the polymer is assumed to be perfectly linear and to contain no rings. Table 4 treats equilibrium polymerization and finally Table 5 describes non-linear systems.

Section C lists a number of distribution functions and their properties. Among them is the generalized exponential function which is a good approximation to many real systems.

Section D presents the Stockmayer distribution function for condensation polymerization wherein molecules of various types of kind A react with molecules of various types of kind B.

B.   TABLES OF REFERENCES FOR THE CALCULATION OF RATES OF POLYMERIZATION, AVERAGE MOLECULAR WEIGHTS, AND MOLECULAR WEIGHT DISTRIBUTIONS OF POLYMERS FOR VARIOUS TYPES OF POLYMERIZATION.

R_p is the rate of polymerization

P_r is the molecular weight distribution

k_i is the rate constant for initiation

k_p is the rate constant for propagation

C   Catalyst concentration

M   Monomer concentration

$\overline{M}_n$ and $\overline{M}_w$ are the number average and the weight average molecular weights, respectively.

There is no correspondence between the set numbers in Table 1 and in Table 2.

No distinction is made among free radical, cationic, anionic, or coordination-type polymerizations.

The rate of initiation may be held constant throughout the polymerization, or it may depend on some function of the catalyst and monomer concentrations, or it may be instantaneous (instant.) in which case only the total number of initiating species need be known.

Transfer reactions may occur to monomer, solvent, or to polymer.

Termination of active species may occur by first order deactivation, or by second order combination (comb.) or disproportionation (disprop.) reactions, or not at all ("living polymers").

Confusion exists over the meaning of the transfer-to-catalyst reaction. In free radical systems, it means transfer of the active species to the initiator by a second order mechanism. In ionic polymerization, it means the expulsion of an active fragment from a growing center by a first order mechanism to form polymer and an active initiator fragment. This first order mechanism is called here the "catalyst expulsion reaction" (cat ex).

1 - Addition Polymerization With Constant Monomer Concentration

Set	Initiation	Transfer	Termination	R_p	P_r	$\overline{M}_n$ & $\overline{M}_w$
1	Constant	none	2nd order comb.	2,3,4	2,3,4	2,3,4
2	Constant	none	2nd order disprop.	2,3,4	2,3,4	2,3,4
3	Constant	monomer solvent	2nd order disprop.	2,3,29-31	2,3	2,3
4	Constant	monomer solvent	2nd order disprop. & comb.	3	3	3
5	Constant (two active ends)	none	2nd order disprop.	3	3	3
6	Constant (two active ends)	monomer	2nd order comb.	3	3	3
7	Constant	monomer	1st order	4	4	4
8	Constant	monomer	2nd order with monomer	4	4	4
9	Constant (grafting reaction)	monomer polymer	2nd order disprop.	3,32	3,32	-
10	Constant (long chain branching)	monomer polymer	2nd order disprop.	-	33	33
11	$k_i C$ (active species formed by reaction between catalyst and activator) (derived without steady state assumptions)	none	2nd order disprop.	34,35	-	34,35
12	$k_i C$ (see comment, set 11) (derived without steady state assumptions)	none	2nd order comb.	35	-	35
13	$k_i MC$	none	1st order	4,36	4,36	4,36
14	$k_i MC$	monomer solvent	1st order	4,37	4,37	4,37
15	$k_i MC$	cat ex	none	4,35	4,35	4,35
16	$k_i MC$	monomer solvent	none	1,38	1,38	1,38
17	$k_i M^2$	monomer	1st order	4	4	4
18	Instant.	monomer cat ex	1st order	39,40	39,40	39,40
19	Instant.	cat ex	none	1,41	-	1,41
20	Instant.	none	2nd order disprop. & comb.	39	2,3	2,3
21	Instant. (active species in equilibrium with inactive species)	none	none	42	-	42
22	Instant.	catalyst activator	none	-	-	43
23	Instant.	none	2nd order with impurity in monomer	-	44,45	44,45

2 - Addition Polymerization with Variable Monomer Concentration

Set	Initiation	Transfer	Termination	R_p	P_r	$\bar{M}_n$ & $\bar{M}_w$
1	Constant	solvent	2nd order disprop. & comb.	3	3	3
2	Constant	monomer solvent	2nd order disprop.	3,32	3,32	-
3	Constant	monomer solvent	2nd order comb.	3,32	3,32	-
4	Constant	none	2nd order monomer	4,46	4,46	4,46
5	$k_i MC$ ($k_i = k_p$ "living polymer")	none	none	2,47,48	2,47,48	2,47,48
6	$k_i MC$ ($k_i \neq k_p$ "living polymer")	none	none	47,70	47	47
7	$k_i MC$ (k_p varies with chain length)	none	none			
a.	general case			-	49	-
b.	all propagation constants are different			-	49	-
c.	$k_i:k_1:k_2:k_3:\ldots.k_n = m:(m-1):(m-2):(m-3):\ldots.1$			-	49	-
d.	$k_1 \neq k_2 \ldots \neq k_m = k_{m+1} = \ldots = k_n$			-	49	-
e.	$k_i \neq k_1 \neq k_2 = k_m$			-	49	-
8	$k_i MC$ (two active species in equilibrium)	none	none	50	-	50
9	$k_i MC$	monomer	none	51	51	51
10	$k_i MC$	none	1st order	46	46	46
11	$k_i MC$	solvent	1st order	-	-	52
12	$k_i MC$	monomer solvent	1st order	-	-	52
13	$k_i MC$	solvent	1st order & 2nd order solvent	46	46	46
14	$k_i MC$	monomer	2nd order monomer	46	46	46
15	$k_i M^2$	none	1st order	4,46	4,46	4,46
16	$k_i M^2$	monomer	2nd order disprop. & comb.	3,4	3,4	3,4
17	$k_i M^2$	monomer	2nd order disprop.	-	3	-
18	Instant.	monomer	none	1,41	-	1,41
19	Instant.	none	1st order	1,41	-	1,41
20	Instant.	monomer	1st order	1,41	-	1,41
21	Instant. (active species in equilibrium with inactive species)	none	none	42	-	42
22	$k_i MC_o exp(-k_d t)$ (dead end polymerization)	monomer	2nd order disprop. or comb.	67,39	68	67-69

3 - Linear Condensation Polymerization Without Ring Formation

Set	Conditions	References
1	Bifunctional monomer AA reacting with bifunctional monomer BB. The nylon case of hexamethylene diamine and adipic acid.	22
2	AA reacting with BC. BC is an anhydride. Within a given molecule, B must react before C.	22
3	AA reacting with BC. BC is an unsymmetrical acid or glycol. B reacts only with A at a different rate from that of C reacting with A.	22
4	AB reacting with C and itself. B and C react only with A. C is a terminator or capping material.	22
5	AA reacting with BB and C. The nylon case again with acetic acid as terminator.	22
6	AA reacting with BC. A and B react with C.	22
7	AB reacting with CD. AB and CD are both hydroxy acids or similar materials.	22
8	AA reacting with BB and CC. A reacts with B and C only and vice versa. BB and CC could be adipic and sebacic acids, respectively.	22
9	AA and BB reacting with CC and DD. A and B react only with C and D and vice versa.	22
10	AA reacting with BC and DD. A reacts only with B, C, and D only.	22
11	AA and DD reacting with BC. A and B react only with C and D and vice versa.	22
12	Poisson distribution polymers	Section C
13	AB polymerized to extent of conversion α, then coupled with CC.	24,71
14	AB polymerized to extent of conversion α, then coupled with CD. A and B can react with C or D.	24
15	AA and BB polymerized to extent of conversion α, then coupled with an excess of CC.	24
16	Poisson-distribution polymer of AA coupled with BC.	24
17	Monomer AB polymerized to extent of conversion α, then coupled with excess CC to extent of conversion γ, then recoupled with excess DD.	24
18	Particularly narrow distributions via coupling reactions. I. AA and BB (great excess)→ BBAABB, then remove excess BB. CC and BBAABB (great excess)→ BBAABBCCBBAABB, then remove excess BBAABB, and continue in like manner. II. AA and 2BC → CBAABC CBAABC and 2DE → EDCBAABCDE etc. III. AB and CD → ABCD ABCD and EF → ABCDEF etc.	25
19	AB reacts with CC or CD. Rate of reaction of A dependent upon whether or not B has reacted.	26

Table 3 (Cont'd.)

Set	Conditions	References
20	Blocks of polymers of known distributions are coupled together.	
	I. A series of Poisson-type polymers coupled together	
	II. Poisson-type polymers coupled to "Most Probable"-type polymers	
	III. A series of "Most Probable"-type polymers coupled together	26,71
21	Condensation of molecules of type AB where the <u>initial</u> distribution is a geometric distribution $P_r^o = b\alpha^{r-1}$.	28
22	Condensation of molecules of type AB where the <u>initial</u> distribution is a superposition of two geometric distributions.	28
23	Condensation of molecules of type AA with molecules of type BB where the <u>initial</u> distribution of AA is $P_r^{oa} = a\alpha^{r-1}$ and of BB is $P_r^{ob} = b\beta^{r-1}$, type BB molecules in excess and reaction has gone to completion.	28

4 - Equilibrium Polymerization

Set	Conditions	References
1	The "most probable" distribution of Flory has been derived for condensation polymerization when all reactions are assumed to have the same probability, regardless of chain length, and whether or not exchange reactions occur:	Section C
	$$P_r + P_s \rightleftharpoons P_{r+s-i} + P_i \qquad i < r + s$$	
	Here P_i can be a by-product such as water, or a polymer molecule whose size is smaller than r+s. The same distribution results when random scission occurs to infinitely long chains.	2,53 54
2	The theoretical equilibrium molecular weight distribution for the system $\qquad rM = P_r$	
	depends upon the thermodynamic definition of the final product. If the change in Gibbs free energy of formation and polymerization is a linear function of molecular size r, then two cases can be considered:	
	a. The monomer is polymerized to a pure perfectly ordered state (solid). This gives the "most probable" distribution.	Section C
	b. The monomer is polymerized to a pure randomly ordered state (liquid). A completely different distribution results.	55
3	Initiation, propagation, and termination reactions are all equilibrium reactions. An initiator is required.	56
4	Initiation, propagation, and termination reactions are all equilibrium reactions. The system is self-initiating.	56
5	Equilibrium initiation and equilibrium propagation with a multifunctional initiator.	57

Table 4 (Cont'd.)

Set	Conditions	References
6	The catalyst can form an active species with any polymer molecule, and the total number of <u>moles</u> of the system is kept constant (constant pressure and volume if all polymer molecules are ideal gases).	58
7	Addition polymerization, instantaneous initiation, no transfer, no termination, monomer concentration held constant, active species in equilibrium with inactive species.	42
8	Addition polymerization, rate of initiation equals k_iMC, no transfer, no termination, two active species in equilibrium, monomer concentration varies.	50
9	Addition polymerization, instantaneous initiation, no transfer, no termination, active species in equilibrium with inactive species, monomer concentration varies.	42
10	Polyphosphate equilibria.	59

5 - Non-Linear Polymerization Systems

In this table, systems are treated where branching reactions, ring formation, or gelation may occur. The symbol RA_f means a monomer containing f reactive A units.

Set	Conditions	References
1	The general distribution function for various molecules of type A reacting with various molecules of type B. A can only react with B. All functional groups have equal reactivity, independent of position within the molecule or the size of the molecule. Ring formation is excluded. (However, see set 22)	Section D
2	The grafting reaction. Addition polymerization, constant rate of initiation, monomer concentration held constant, transfer to monomer and polymer, second order termination by disproportionation.	3,32
3	Long chain branching. Addition polymerization, constant rate of initiation, monomer concentration held constant, transfer to monomer and polymer, second order termination by disproportionation.	33
4	Branching density as a function of conversion. Branches formed by polymerization through a vinyl group (diene polymers) or by transfer-to-polymer reaction.	2
5	Copolymer of RA_f and AB, where A can only react with B. In this system, rings cannot form.	2,60
6	Homopolymer of $A-R-B_{f-1}$ where A can only react with B. In this system rings cannot form.	2,61
7	Copolymer of ARB_{f-1} and AB, where A can only react with B. In this system, rings cannot form.	2,61
8	Homopolymer of RA_f where A can react with A. Formation of rings excluded prior to gelation.	2,61-63

Table 5 (Cont'd.)

Set	Conditions	References
9	Copolymer of RA_f and AA, where A can react with A. Formation of rings excluded prior to gelation.	2,62
10	Crosslinking of molecules of constant length r.	2,62,63
11	Crosslinking or coupling of a polymer with a known primary distribution.	Sections B.3. and D.
12	Gelation conditions for AA reacting with $B_f C_g$. A can react with B and C, but with different velocities. B cannot react with C.	64
13	Application of kinetics to set 12.	64
14	Gelation condition for AA and BB and C reacting with D$\top$D and $\underset{E}{}$ FF. A, B, and C individually can react with D, E, and F, but with different velocities.	64
15	Gelation condition for A$\top$A and C$\mid$C and G-G reacting with D-E $\underset{B}{\overset{C}{}}$ $\underset{C}{}$ and F. DE is an anhydride or similar material. Part D must react first and may have a different velocity of reaction from part E. A, B, C, and G may react with different velocities.	64
16	Gelation condition for A-B and C-D reacting with E$\top$E and GG $\underset{F}{}$ where AB and CD are anhydrides or similar materials where A must react before B and C must react before D. A, B, C, and D may react with different velocities.	64
17	Gelation condition for AA and BC reacting with D$\top$D and F-G $\underset{E}{}$ where BC is an anhydride, B reacting first and F-G is like an unsymmetrical glycol. Different species may react with different velocities.	64
18	Ring formation in the system AA.	65
19	Ring formation in the system AB.	2,65
20	Ring formation in the system AA and BB.	2,65
21	Ring formation and gelation in the system RA_f, AA, and BB, where f⩾3, A can only react with B.	66
22	Ring formation and the Stockmayer distribution function.	21
23	Equilibrium polymerization with a multifunctional initiator.	57

C. SOME DISTRIBUTION FUNCTIONS AND THEIR PROPERTIES

The frequency function, $F(r)$, is the fraction of molecules of size r. Furthermore, $F(r)$ is normalized

$$\sum_1^\infty F(r) = \int_0^\infty F(r)\, dr = 1 \tag{C1}$$

the weight fraction of molecules of size r is

$$W(r) = r\,F(r) / \sum_1^\infty r\,F(r)$$

$$= r\,F(r) / \int_0^\infty r\,F(r)\, dr \tag{C2}$$

Averages of any distribution are defined by

$$\overline{r}_i = \sum_1^\infty r^i F(r) / \sum_1^\infty r^{i-1} F(r)$$

$$= \int_0^\infty r^i F(r)\, dr / \int_0^\infty r^{i-1} F(r)\, dr \tag{C3}$$

The number average degree of polymerization is defined by

$$\overline{r}_n = \sum_1^\infty r\,F(r) / \sum_1^\infty F(r)$$

$$= \sum_1^\infty W(r) / \sum_1^\infty W(r)/r \tag{C4}$$

Thus, by the definitions of $F(r)$ and $W(r)$

$$W(r) = r\,F(r) / \overline{r}_n \tag{C5}$$

The weight average degree of polymerization is

$$\overline{r}_w = \sum_1^\infty r^2 F(r) / \sum_1^\infty r\,F(r)$$

$$= \sum_1^\infty r\,W(r) / \sum_1^\infty W(r) \tag{C6}$$

The "z" average and the "z+1" averages are defined by equation (C3) with i set equal to 3 and 4. There is no need to restrict averages of a distribution to positive integers--any useful average can be defined; such as the $(-5/2)$ average. If the intrinsic viscosity of a polymer is related to the degree of polymerization through the equation

$$[\eta] = K\,\overline{r}_v^{\,a} \tag{C7}$$

where $\overline{r}_v$ is the "viscosity average degree of polymerization," then it is related to the frequency function by

$$\overline{r}_v = \left[\sum_1^\infty r^{1+a} F(r) / \sum_1^\infty r\,F(r) \right]^{1/a} \tag{C8}$$

As a approaches unity, $\overline{r}_v$ approaches $\overline{r}_w$. In principle, a distribution function can be determined if sufficient averages of the distribution can be determined. In practice, only the number, weight, and perhaps "z" averages can be found, which are insufficient to define any distribution without making further assumptions.

The degree of polymerization is a useful concept as long as one is describing polymers made with a single monomer or with monomers of equal molecular weight. When considering copolymers, one must work with the actual molecular weight of the reacted unit. This is done in condensation polymerization. The molecular weight distribution of addition copolymers is not included here because of the extreme complexity of these systems.

When performing the summation of a distribution equation to find an average of the distribution, use is frequently made of the following sums.

$$\sum_{x=1}^{\infty} p^{x-1} = 1/(1-p) \qquad p < 1$$

$$\sum_{x=1}^{\infty} xp^{x-1} = 1/(1-p)^2 \qquad p < 1$$

$$\sum_{x=1}^{\infty} x^2 p^{x-1} = (1+p)/(1-p)^3 \qquad p < 1$$

$$\sum_{x=1}^{\infty} x^n p^{x-1} = \frac{d}{dp} [p \sum_{x=1}^{\infty} x^{n-1} p^{x-1}] \quad p < 1$$

$$\sum_{i=0}^{n} a^{n-i} b^i n!/(n-i)! \, i! = (a+b)^n \quad n \text{ is an integer}$$

$$\sum_{i=0}^{n} a^i i n!/(n-i)! i! = na(1+a)^{n-1}$$

$$\sum_{i=0}^{n} a^i i^2 n!/(n-i)! i! = na(1+na)(1+a)^{n-2}$$

$$\sum_{n=1}^{\infty} A^{n-1}/(n-1)! = \exp A$$

$$\sum_{n=1}^{\infty} n A^{n-1}/(n-1)! = (1+A) \exp A$$

$$\sum_{n=1}^{\infty} n^2 A^{n-1}/(n-1)! = (1+3A+A^2) \exp A$$

$$\sum_{n=1}^{\infty} n^p A^{n-1}/(n-1)! = \frac{d}{dA} [A \sum_{n=1}^{\infty} n^{p-1} A^{n-1}/(n-1)!]$$

1. Normal Distribution Function (Gaussian Distribution)

$$F(r) = \frac{\exp \{-(r-\bar{r})^2/2\sigma^2\}}{(2\pi)^{1/2} \sigma}$$

$$W(r) = (r/\bar{r}) F(r)$$

$$\bar{r} = \int_{-\infty}^{+\infty} \frac{r \exp \{-(r-\bar{r})^2/2\sigma^2\}}{(2\pi)^{1/2} \sigma} = \bar{r}_n$$

$$\sigma^2 = \int_{-\infty}^{+\infty} \frac{(r-\bar{r})^2 \exp \{-(r-\bar{r})^2/2\sigma^2\}}{(2\pi)^{1/2} \sigma}$$

$$\bar{r}_w = \frac{\sigma^2}{\bar{r}} + \bar{r}$$

Values of $F(r)$ and $\int_0^t F(r) dr$ are found in many statistical tables (5). ∘

2. Generalized Logarithmic Normal Distribution Function (6,7)

$$F_s(r) = \frac{r^{s-1} \exp\{-(\ln r/\bar{r}_s)^2/2\sigma_s^2\}}{(2\pi)^{1/2} \sigma_s \bar{r}_s^s \exp\{s^2\sigma_s^2/2\}}$$

$$W_s(r) = \frac{r^s \exp\{-(\ln r/\bar{r}_s)^2/2\sigma_s^2\}}{(2\pi)^{1/2} \sigma_s \bar{r}_s^{s+1} \exp\{(s+1)^2\sigma_s^2/2\}}$$

where $\bar{r}_s$ is a constant

$$\bar{r}_n = \bar{r}_s \exp\{(2s+1)\sigma_s^2/2\}$$

$$\bar{r}_w = \bar{r}_s \exp\{(2s+3)\sigma_s^2/2\}$$

$$\bar{r}_z = \bar{r}_s \exp\{(2s+5)\sigma_s^2/2\}$$

$$\bar{r}_i = \bar{r}_s \exp\{[2(s+i)-1]\sigma_s^2/2\}$$

For each value of s, $\bar{r}_s$ will remain invarient as σ_s is varied (6). When
$s = -\frac{1}{2}$, $\bar{r}_{(-\frac{1}{2})} = \bar{r}_n$. Note that $\bar{r}_w/\bar{r}_n = \bar{r}_z/\bar{r}_w = \bar{r}_{z+1}/\bar{r}_z$.

a. The Wesslau distribution (8) also known as the logarithmic normal distribution
is obtained by setting s = -1 here $\bar{r}_{-1}$ is the median value of r (that value of
r where $\frac{1}{2}$ of the molecules have lower values, the other $\frac{1}{2}$ have higher values).
σ_{-1} is the standard deviation of ln r. Let $\bar{r}_0$ be that value of r at the maximum of the distribution.

Then

$$\ln \bar{r}_0 = \ln \bar{r}_{-1} - \sigma_{-1}^2$$

$$\bar{r}_{-1} = [\prod_{i=1}^{i=n} r_i]^{1/n}$$

This distribution is skewed to large values of r, but Kotliar (7 9) shows that
this distribution is not a good representation of a polymer after either low
or high molecular weight material is removed or degradation has occurred.

b. The distribution function of Lansing and Kramer (10) also known as the zeroth-
order logarithmic distribution is obtained by setting s = 0. Here $\bar{r}_0$ is that
value of r at the maximum of the distribution and hence does not shift when σ_0
is varied.

The standard deviation of this distribution is (6)

$$\sigma = \sigma_0 [\exp(4\sigma_0^2) - \exp(3\sigma_0^2)]^{1/2}$$

3. Generalized Exponential Distribution (7) (11)

$$F_{m,a,y}(r) = my^{a/m} r^{a-1} [\exp(-yr^m)]/\Gamma(a/m)$$

$$W_{m,a,y}(r) = my^{(a+1)/m} r^a [\exp(-yr^m)]/\Gamma[(a+1)/m]$$

$$\bar{r}_n = \Gamma[(a+1)/m]/y^{1/m}\Gamma[a/m]$$

$$\bar{r}_w = \Gamma[(a+2)/m]/y^{1/m}\Gamma[(a+1)/m]$$
$$\bar{r}_z = \Gamma[(a+3)/m]/y^{1/m}\Gamma[(a+2)/m]$$
$$\bar{r}_i = \Gamma[(a+i)/m]/y^{1/m}\Gamma[(a+i-1)/m]$$

a. The distribution function of Schulz (12) and Zimm(13) is obtained by setting $m = 1$ and requiring that $a > 0$. This reduces to Flory's "most probable" distribution when $a = 1$. (See also below.)

The cumulative number or weight fraction may be computed (14) from

$$\int_0^r F_{1,a,y}(r) = \frac{ay^a}{\Gamma(1+a)} \sum_{i=0}^{\infty} \frac{(-1)^i y^i r^{a+i}}{i!(a+i)}$$

$$\int_0^r W_{1,a,y}(r) = \frac{y^{a+1}}{\Gamma(1+a)} \sum_{i=0}^{\infty} \frac{(-1)^i y^i r^{a+i+1}}{i!(a+i+1)}$$

b. The Tung distribution (15) is obtained by setting $m = 1+a$ and $a > -1$. This distribution is usually seen in the form

$$\int_0^r W(r)\,dr = 1 - \exp[-yr^{(1+a)}]$$

Kotliar shows that evaluation of $\underline{y}$ and $\underline{a}$ by the Tung method can lead to erroneous values of $\bar{r}_w/\bar{r}_n$ (16).

c. The Flory distribution, as noted above, occurs when $a = m = 1$, provided that $\ln p$ can be replaced by $-(1-p)$, i.e., $p \approx 1$. The Flory distribution is also written

$$F(r) = p^{r-1}(1-p)$$
$$W(r) = rp^{r-1}(1-p)^2$$
$$\bar{r}_n = 1/(1-p)$$
$$\bar{r}_w = (1+p)/(1-p)$$

and with the approximation $\ln p = p - 1$

$$\int_0^r W(r)\,dr \cong (1/p) - [1 + (1-p)r]p^{r-1}$$

4. Korshak Distribution (17)

$$F(r) = \exp[-\bar{r}_n] \cdot (\bar{r}_n)^r/r!$$
$$W(r) = \exp[-\bar{r}_n] \cdot \bar{r}_n^{r-1}/(r-1)!$$

The theoretical validity of these equations is discussed by Howard (18).

5. Poisson Distribution

$$F(r) = \exp(-\nu) \cdot \nu^{r-1}/(r-1)!$$
$$W(r) = [\nu/(\nu+1)]r \exp(-\nu) \cdot \nu^{r-2}/(r-1)!$$
$$\bar{r}_n = 1 + \nu$$
$$\bar{r}_w = 1 + \nu + \nu/(1+\nu)$$

D. MOLECULAR WEIGHT DISTRIBUTION IN CONDENSATION POLYMERS: THE STOCKMAYER DISTRIBUTION FUNCTION

Stockmayer (19) has presented a generalized distribution formula for a variety of monomers containing end groups of type A which can only react with a variety of monomers containing end groups of type B. In the original mixture there are A_1, A_2, A_3, ... A_i, ... moles of reactants bearing respectively f_1, f_2, f_3, ... f_i, ... functional groups of type A each, together with B_1, B_2, ... B_i, ... moles of reactants of functionalities g_1, g_2, ... g_i, ... in groups of type B. All functional groups of a given type are equally reactive and ring formation does not occur appreciably; which obviously is not true near the gel point. The system reacts until a fraction α of the A groups and a fraction β of the B groups have reacted. Further

$$\alpha \, \Sigma_i f_i A_i = \beta \, \Sigma_j g_j B_j$$

Now $N\{m_i, n_j\}$ represents the number of moles of that species which consists of m_1, m_2, ...m_i,.... monomer units of the A type combined with $n_1, n_2, ...n_j....$ units of the B type.

$$N\{m_i,n_j\} = \frac{K(\Sigma_i f_i m_i - \Sigma_i m_i)!\,(\Sigma_j g_j n_j - \Sigma_j n_j)!\,\prod_i (x_i{}^{m_i}/m_i!)\,\prod_j (y_j{}^{n_j}/n_j!)}{(\Sigma_i f_i m_i - \Sigma_i m_i - \Sigma_j n_j + 1)!\,(\Sigma_j g_j n_j - \Sigma_j n_j - \Sigma_i m_i + 1)!} \tag{D1}$$

where

$$x_i = \left[\frac{f_i A_i}{(\Sigma_i f_i A_i)}\right]\left[\frac{\beta (1 - \alpha)^{f_i - 1}}{(1 - \beta)}\right] \qquad y_j = \left[\frac{g_j B_j}{(\Sigma_j g_j B_j)}\right]\left[\frac{\alpha (1 - \beta)^{g_j - 1}}{(1 - \alpha)}\right]$$

$$K = (\Sigma_i f_i A_i)(1 - \alpha)(1 - \beta)/\alpha = (\Sigma_j g_j B_j)(1 - \alpha)(1 - \beta)/\alpha \tag{D2}$$

an example will illustrate the use of Eq. (D1).

Suppose we have the monomers acetic acid (CH_3COOH, A_1, $f_1 = 1$) and adipic acid ($HOOC(CH_2)_4COOH$, A_2, $f_2 = 2$) reacting with ethylene glycol ($HOCH_2CH_2OH$, B_2, $g_2 = 2$) and glycerol ($HOCH_2CHOHCH_2OH$, B_3, $g_3 = 3$) (all hydroxyl groups of the glycerol are considered equally reactive). What is the number of molecules which contain exactly 1 acetic acid unit, 4 adipic acid units, 3 glycol units and 2 glycerol units? It is $N(1,4,3,2)$ and

$$N(1,4,3,2) = \frac{K(1 + 8 - 1 - 4)!\,(6 + 6 - 3 - 2)!}{(1 + 8 - 1 - 4 - 3 - 2 + 1)!\,(6 + 6 - 3 - 2 - 1 - 4 + 1)!} \tag{D3}$$

$$\times \frac{x_1^1}{1!} \times \frac{x_2^4}{4!} \times \frac{y_2^3}{3!} \times \frac{y_3^2}{2!}$$

$$x_1 = \left[\frac{A_1}{A_1 + 2A_2}\right]\left[\frac{\beta}{1 - \beta}\right] \qquad x_2 = \left[\frac{2A_2}{A_1 + 2A_2}\right]\left[\frac{\beta(1 - \alpha)}{(1 - \beta)}\right]$$

$$y_2 = \left[\frac{2B_2}{B_2 + 3B_3}\right]\left[\frac{\alpha(1 - \beta)}{(1 - \alpha)}\right] \qquad y_3 = \left[\frac{3A_3}{2B_2 + 3B_3}\right]\left[\frac{\alpha(1 - \beta)^2}{1 - \alpha}\right]$$

$$K = (A_1 + 2A_2)(1 - \alpha)(1 - \beta)/\beta \tag{D4}$$

If each species i has an effective molecular weight M_i, which is lower than the original molecular weight by the term $W_o f_i / 2$, where W_o is the molecular weight of the by-product, then

$$W = \Sigma_i M_i A_i + \Sigma_j B_j M_j \tag{D5}$$

The number of molecules of the end of the reaction is, neglecting by-product,

$$N = \Sigma_i A_i + \Sigma_j B_j - a \Sigma_i f_i A_i \qquad (D6)$$

The number average molecular weight is

$$\overline{M}_n = W/N \qquad (D7)$$

The weight average molecular weight is

$$\overline{M}_w = \{ \beta \frac{\Sigma_i M_i^2 A_i}{\Sigma_i f_i A_i} + a \frac{\Sigma_j M_j^2 B_i}{\Sigma_j g_j B_j}$$

$$+ \frac{a\beta [a(f_e - 1) M_b^2 + \beta (g_e - 1) M_a^2 + 2M_a M_b]}{1 - a\beta (f_e - 1)(g_e - 1)} \}$$

$$\times \{ \beta \frac{\Sigma_i M_i A_i}{\Sigma_i f_i A_i} + a \frac{\Sigma_j M_j B_j}{\Sigma_j g_j B_j} \}^{-1} \qquad (D8)$$

where

$$f_e = (\Sigma_i f_i^2 A_i)/(\Sigma_i f_i A_i)$$

$$g_e = (\Sigma_j g_j^2 B_j)/(\Sigma_j g_j B_j)$$

$$M_a = (\Sigma_i M_i f_i A_i)/(\Sigma_i f_i A_i)$$

$$M_b = (\Sigma_j M_j g_j B_j)/(\Sigma_j g_j B_j) \qquad (D9)$$

$$(a\beta)_c = 1/(f_e - 1)(g_e - 1) \qquad (D10)$$

The gel point is $(a\beta)_c = 1/(f_e - 1)(g_e - 1)$

Extensive computations of $N\{m_i, n_j\}$ for the case $f_1 = 1$, $f_2 = 2$, $f_4 = 4$ and $g_2 = 2$ have appeared recently (20).

Hoeve has extended the Stockmayer distribution function to include ring formation (21).

E. References

1. L. H. Peebles, Jr. to be published.
2. P. J. Flory, "Principles of Polymer Chemistry," Cornell University Press, Ithaca, N. Y., 1953.
3. C. H. Bamford, W. G. Barb, A. D. Jenkins, and P. F. Onyon, "The Kinetics of Vinyl Polymerization by Radical Mechanisms," Academic Press, New York, 1958.
4. L. Küchler, "Polymerizationskinetik," Springer-Verlag, Berlin, 1951.
5. "Handbook of Chemistry and Physics," Volume 34 et seq. Chemical Rubber Publishing Co., Cleveland.
6. W. F. Espenscheid, M. Kerker, and E. Matijevic, J. Phys. Chem., $\underline{68}$, 3093 (1964).
7. A. M. Kotliar, J. Polymer Sci., $\underline{A2}$, 4303 (1964).
8. H. Wesslau, Makromol. Chem., $\underline{20}$, 111 (1956).
9. A. M. Kotliar, J. Polymer Sci., $\underline{A2}$, 4327 (1964).
10. W. D. Lansing and E. O. Kramer, J. Am. Chem. Soc., $\underline{57}$, 1369 (1935).
11. L. T. Muus and W. H. Stockmayer, quoted by F. W. Billmeyer, Jr., in "Textbook of Polymer Science," Interscience, New York-London, 1962.
12. G. V. Schulz, Z. Physik. Chem., $\underline{B43}$, 25 (1939).
13. B. H. Zimm, J. Chem. Phys., $\underline{16}$, 1099 (1948).
14. L. H. Peebles, Jr., Unpublished results.
15. L. H. Tung, J. Polymer Sci., $\underline{20}$, 495 (1956).
16. A. M. Kotliar, J. Polymer Sci., $\underline{A2}$, 1373 (1964).
17. S. E. Bresler, V. V. Korshak, S. A. Pavlova, P. A. Finogenov, C. R. Acad. Sci. USSR $\underline{87}$, 961 (1952); S. E. Bresler, V. V. Korshak, S. A. Pavlova, and P. A. Finogenov, Bull. Acad. Sci. USSR (Otdel. Khim. Nauk.) pp. 344,354 (1954).
18. G. J. Howard in "Progress in High Polymers", Vol. 1, edited by J. C. Robb and F. W. Peaker, Academic Press Inc., New York, 1961.
19. W. H. Stockmayer, J. Polymer Sci., $\underline{9}$, 69 (1952); $\underline{11}$, 424 (1953).
20. I. Nakamura, R. Yokouchi, T. Ito, D. Miura, and K. Fujii, Kobunshi Kagaku $\underline{21}$, 553 (1964).
21. C. A. J. Hoeve, J. Polymer Sci., $\underline{21}$, 11 (1956).
22. L. C. Case, J. Polymer Sci., $\underline{29}$, 455 (1958).
23. J. J. Hermans, unpublished results, available from author on request.
24. L. C. Case, J. Polymer Sci., $\underline{37}$, 147 (1959).
25. L. C. Case, J. Polymer Sci., $\underline{39}$, 175 (1959).
26. L. C. Case, J. Polymer Sci., $\underline{48}$, 27 (1960).
27. L. C. Case, J. Polymer Sci., $\underline{39}$, 183 (1959).
28. J. J. Hermans, Makromol. Chem. in press,
29. G. M. Burnett and L. D. Loan, Trans. Faraday Soc., $\underline{51}$, 214 (1955).
30. L. H. Peebles, Jr., J. T. Clarke, and W. H. Stockmayer, J. Am. Chem. Soc., $\underline{82}$, 4780 (1960).
31. J. L. Kice, J. Am. Chem. Soc. $\underline{76}$, 6274 (1954).
32. C. H. Bamford and H. Tompa, Trans. Faraday Soc., $\underline{50}$, 1097 (1954).
33. J. K. Beasley, J. Am. Chem. Soc., $\underline{75}$, 6123 (1953).
34. J. C. W. Chien, J. Polymer Sci., $\underline{A1}$, 1839 (1963).
35. J. C. W. Chien, J. Am. Chem. Soc., $\underline{81}$, 86 (1959).
36. P. H. Plesch, Ed., "The Chemistry of Cationic Polymerization," MacMillan Co., New York, 1963.
37. A. A. Korotkov, S. P. Mitsengendler, and V. N. Krasulina, J. Polymer Sci., $\underline{53}$, 217 (1961).
38. H. J. L. Schuurmans, private communication,
39. H. N. Friedlander, J. Polymer Sci. $\underline{A2}$, 3885 (1964).
40. R. E. Burton and D. C. Pepper, Proc. Roy. Soc., $\underline{A263}$, 58 (1961).
41. R. Chiang and J. J. Hermans, unpublished results, available from authors on request.
42. M. Szwarc and J. J. Hermans, Polymer Letters, $\underline{B2}$, 815 (1964).
43. J. C. W. Chien, J. Polymer Sci., $\underline{A1}$, 425 (1963).
44. T. A. Orofino and F. Wenger, J. Chem. Phys. $\underline{35}$, 532 (1961).
45. B. D. Coleman, F. Gornick and G. Weiss, J. Chem. Phys. $\underline{39}$, 3233 (1963).
46. D. O. Jordan and A. R. Mathieson, J. Chem. Soc., $\underline{1952}$, 2358.

Note: Eqns. 13-17 and 23-29 are incorrect. The correct equations are quoted in Ref. 1.

47. L. Gold, J. Chem. Phys., $\underline{28}$, 91 (1958).
48. P. J. Flory, J. Am. Chem. Soc., $\underline{62}$, 1561 (1940).
49. H. J. R. Maget, J. Polymer Sci., $\underline{A2}$, 1281 (1964).
50. R. V. Figini, Makromol. Chem. $\underline{71}$, 193 (1964).
51. W. T. Kyner, J. R. M. Radok, and M. Wales, J. Chem. Phys., $\underline{30}$, 363 (1959).
52. M. Litt, J. Polymer Sci., $\underline{43}$, 567 (1960).
53. P. J. Flory, Chem. Revs., $\underline{39}$, 137 (1946).

54. W. Kuhn, Chem. Ber., 63, 1503 (1930).
55. J. L. Lundberg, J. Polymer Sci., A2, 1121 (1964).
56. A. V. Tobolsky, J. Polymer Sci., 25, 220 (1957); J. Polymer Sci., 31, 126 (1958). A. V. Tobolsky and A. Eisenberg, J. Am. Chem. Soc., 81, 2302 (1959); J. Am. Chem. Soc., 82, 289 (1960).
57. M. E. Baur and A. Eisenberg, J. Chem. Phys., 42, 85 (1965).
58. C. M. Fontana in P. H. Plesch, "The Chemistry of Cationic Polymerization, MacMillan Co., New York, 1963.
59. J. R. Van Wazer, "Phosphorus and Its Compounds," Vol. 1, Interscience Publishers, Inc., New York, 1958.
60. J. R. Schaefgen and P. J. Flory, J. Am. Chem. Soc., 70, 2709 (1948).
61. P. J. Flory, J. Am. Chem. Soc., 74, 2718 (1952).
62. W. H. Stockmayer, J. Chem. Phys., 11, 45 (1943).
63. P. J. Flory, J. Am. Chem. Soc., 63, 3091 (1941).
64. L. C. Case, J. Polymer Sci., 26, 333 (1957)
65. H. Jacobson and W. H. Stockmayer, J. Chem. Phys., 18, 1600 (1950).
66. R. W. Kilb, J. Phys. Chem., 62, 969 (1958).
67. A. V. Tobolsky, J. Am. Chem. Soc., 80, 5927 (1958). A. V. Tobolsky, L. E. Rogers, and R. D. Brinkman, ibid., 82, 1277 (1960).
68. C. H. Bamford, Polymer, 6, 63 (1965).
69. A. V. Tobolsky, R. H. Gobran, R. Böhme, and R. Schaffhauser, J. Phys. Chem., 67, 2336 (1963).
70. L. F. Beste and H. K. Hall, Jr., J. Phys. Chem., 68, 269 (1964).
71. C. H. Bamford and A. D. Jenkins, Trans. Faraday Soc., 56, 907 (1960).

III.
SOLID STATE PROPERTIES

CRYSTALLOGRAPHIC DATA FOR VARIOUS POLYMERS

Robert L. Miller

Chemstrand Research Center
Durham, North Carolina

Contents

A. INTRODUCTION

The following table presents crystallographic data for about 225 polymers. They have
been grouped, according to the generic structure of the chain repeat unit, into:
poly-olefins, poly-vinyls and poly-vinylidens, poly-aromatics, poly-dienes, poly-amides,
poly-esters, poly-ethers, poly-oxides, poly-sulfides and polysulfones, poly-urethans
and poly-ureas, cellulosics, and others. Where a polymer might be included in more
than one group, the following group definitions were used:

1. Poly-olefins: Those α-olefin polymers not containing aromatic rings; all sub-
    stituted derivatives of these, excluding the vinyl and vinylidene polymers. For
    example, polyethylene, poly(tetrafluoroethylene), and polycyclopentene, but not
    polystyrene, or poly(vinyl chloride).

2. Poly-vinyls and Poly-vinylidenes: Those vinyl and vinylidene polymers containing
    atoms other than carbon and hydrogen, excepting the poly-ethers. Thus, poly(vinyl
    chloride), but not poly(methyl vinyl ether).

3. Poly-aromatics: Those hydrocarbon polymers containing aromatic rings. Thus, poly-
    styrene and poly(p-xylylene).

4. The remaining specific categories contain polymers according to functional groups,
    as, for example, the poly-amides and the poly-esters. Poly-ethers and poly-oxides
    are differentiated according to whether the ether linkage is in the side-group or
    in the backbone, respectively. For example, poly(1-butoxy-2-chloroethylene) is a
    poly-ether and polyformaldehyde is a poly-oxide.

5. Those polymers not otherwise categorized, such as poly(phosphonitrile chloride),
    are listed in the "other" category.

Within each category, polymers are listed alphabetically according to the basic
structure ignoring substituents. Substituted polymers are listed alphabetically
according to the substituent under the entry for the unsubstituted polymer. Thus,
poly(tetrafluoroethylene) and poly(4-methyl-1-pentene) appear, respectively, under
polyethylene and poly(1-pentene).

Included as part of the polymer name is the molecular weight of the chemical repeat
unit in the chain. This appears below the name and is bracketed by asterisks, *.
Unless otherwise indicated, the reference cited in the second column applies to the
entire line of the table. Where an entry has been taken from a source other than that
listed in column 2, a slash (/) separates the value of the entry from the reference.
For example, one value of the heat of fusion of polyethylene is listed as 1.88/85
which is to be read as 1.88 kcal./mole according to reference 85. The crystal system,
where known, is given according to the abbreviations given below. Following this is
the space group symbol (the Schoenflies notation is used because of the limitations
of electronic data processing symbolisms). In the space group indication, the subscript appears before the superscript. Thus, according to reference 14, the polyethylene crystal is orthorhombic (ORTHO) with space group D_{2h}^{16} (D2H-16). For a fuller
discussion of space group symbols, see "International Tables for X-ray Crystallography,"
Vol. I, Kynoch Press, Birmingham, England, 1952.

The dimensions of the unit cell (a, b, and c) are given in Angstroms. Unless otherwise
indicated (by an *) c is the fiber axis. Where required, unit cell angles are given
in the order: α, β, and γ. Where only one angle is needed it is identified according
to the abbreviations given below. The next entry is the number of chemical repeat
units ("monomers") in the unit cell of dimensions listed. The densities of the crystal
and of the completely amorphous polymer are those appropriate (normally) for room
temperature. The melting point is in °C and the heat of fusion, in kcal/mole, corresponds to the unit of molecular weight listed under the polymer name.

The last column of the table indicates the conformation of the polymer chain in the
crystal. The notation, n*p-q, specifies the number (n) of skeletal atoms in the
asymmetric unit of the chain and the number of such units (p) per q turns of the helix
in the crystallographic repeat. Thus, polyethylene has two carbon atoms in the backbone with one such unit per turn in the repeat (2*1-1). Note that polyethylene considered to be polymethylene would be designated 1*2-1, an entirely equivalent description of the conformation. Isotactic polypropene, then, has two atoms in the backbone
unit and three units per turn (2*3-1). On the other hand, syndiotactic polypropene
has four atoms in the backbone unit (two chemical monomers) and two such units per
turn (4*2-1). A fuller discussion of this notation is given in Hughes and Lauer,
J. Chem. Phys. 30, 1165 (1959) and Nagai and Kobayashi, J. Chem. Phys. 36, 1268 (1961).

This list of polymers is not considered to be exhaustive. The compiler expands it as
rapidly as new information is unearthed. All of the data in this table cannot be
considered to have the same validity - the number of polymers for which detailed
crystal structure analyses have been conducted is quite limited.

Abbreviations used in this table: TRI - triclinic, MONO - monoclinic, ORTHO - orthorhombic, TET - tetragonal, RHO - rhombohedral, HEX - hexagonal, P - pseudo, A - α,
B - β, and G - γ. The symbol, #, means "equals." @ means "prime;" % means "left
parenthesis;" and + means "right parenthesis."

References page III-51

POLY-OLEFINS

POLYMER	REF	CRYST SYST.	SPACE GROUP	UNIT CELL PARAMETERS				MON UNIT CELL	DENSITY G./CC.		MELT POINT	HEAT OF FUSION KCAL/MON	CHAIN CONF.
				A	B	C	ANGLES		CRYSTAL	AMORPH.			
POLY-OLEFINS													
POLY-ACETYLENE *26.04*	69 76	PHEX		4.2 4.22	4.2	2.43			1.15				2*1-1
POLY-ALLENE													
---, TETRAFLUORO- *112.03*	38	TET	C4-2 - D4-5	6.88	6.88	15.4		8	2.02		126		2*4-1
POLY-1-BUTENE I. *56.10*	35 126 252 391	RHO RHO	D3D-6 D3D-6	17.7 17.7	17.7 17.7	6.50 6.50		18	0.95/12 0.950	0.8/45 0.868 .860	126/12 132/250 136/277 135/345 142/313 155/320 138/380	3.35/82 1.45/277 1.7/345 1.6E/320	2*3-1 2*3-1
II.	9 207 350	TET TET TET	S4-1	7.49 14.89 14.85	7.49 14.89 14.85	6.85 20.87 20.6		44 44	0.90 0.886 0.90		124/277 122/345 126/313 130/380	1.50/277 0.97/320	2*4-1 2*11-3 2*11-3
III.	207	ORTHO		12.49	8.96						106/277	1.55/277	
---, 3-METHYL- *70.13*	9 152 355	MONO PORT		9.55 19.25	8.54 17.20	6.84 6.84 6.85	G#116.5 G#116.5	4 16	0.93 0.92		30/148 310/90 300/282	4.13/82	2*4-1 2*4-1 2*4-1
---, 3-METHYL- ±VIA HYDRIDE SHIFT+ *70.13*	332			5.4		7.8					55 66/319		
---, 4-PHENYL- *132.20*	61					6.55					160/90 168/187 159/282		2*3-1

POLYMER	REF	CRYST. SYST.	SPACE GROUP	A	B	C	ANGLES	MON UNIT CELL	DENSITY CRYSTAL	DENSITY AMORPH	MELT POINT	HEAT OF FUSION KCAL/MON	CHAIN CONF.
POLY-CYCLOPENTENE TRANS- *68.11*	147	ORTHO	C2V-9 OR D2H-16	7.28	4.97	11.9		4	1.05		23		5*2-1
POLY-1-DECENE I. *140.26*	150					13.2					34/250		
POLY-1-DODECENE I. *168.31*	150					13.2					45/48 49/250		
POLY-ETHYLENE *28.05*	14 15 363 138 406	ORTHO	D2H-16	7.40 7.36	4.93 4.92	2.534 2.534		2	1.00 1.014 0.9988 0.991	0.852/57 0.8866 0.855 0.811	110/46 137/85 141/206 141/286 142/315	1.88/65 1.84/86 2.00/260 1.86/156	2*1-1
%SINGLE CRYSTAL+	72	TRI		7.84	5.56	120	65,71,82	48	1.013				
%SECOND FORM+	58 233 254	PMONO MONO TRI	C2H-5	4.05 8.09 4.285	4.85 2.53* 4.820	2.54 4.79 2.54	G#105 B#107.9 90113108	1 2	0.965 0.997 1.00				2*1-1
---, CHLOROTRIFLUORO *116.48*	208 21 116 139 205 296	HEX HEX HEX		6.34 6.5 6.385	6.34 6.5 6.385	35 35 43 42		14 16	2.19/49 2.10 2.192 2.20	2.08/49 2.032 1.925	220/49 210/46 215 222/341	1.20/88	2*14-1 2*16-1 2*17-
---, TETRAFLUORO- *100.02*	11 154 209 266	PHEX TRI TRI		5.54 5.59 4.882	5.54 5.59 4.875	16.8 16.88 5.105	G#119.5 G#119.3 90,87,81	13	2.40 2.346		327/46		2*13-1 2*13-1 1*13-6
ABOVE 20C	11 209	HEX HEX		5.61 5.66	5.61 5.66	16.8 19.50			2.36 2.302 2.304/66		330 330/101	1.37/91	2*13-1 1*15-7
---, TRIFLUORO- *82.05*	389	HEX		5.59	5.59	2.50			2.01				

References page III-51

POLYMER	REF	CRYST SYST.	SPACE GROUP	UNIT CELL PARAMETERS				MON UNIT CELL	DENSITY CRYSTAL	G./CC. AMORPH.	MELT POINT	HEAT OF FUSION KCAL/MON	CHAIN CONF.
				A	B	C	ANGLES						
POLY-ETHYLENE-CO-2-BUTENE *84.16*	191 247 324	MONO MONO	C2H-5 C2H-5	10.92 10.92	5.94 7.73	9.15 9.15 9.10	A # 130	4	0.95	0.87	135		4*2-1
POLY-ETHYLENE-CO-CYCLOHEPTENE *124.22*	259					9.0					74		
POLY-ETHYLENE-CO-CYCLOPENTENE *96.18*	228 247 412	ORTHO ORTHO OR	D2H-17 D2H-14	8.76 8.76	7.83 8.05	9.00 9.02 9.00		4	1.03 1.054 1.00		185		4*2-1
POLY-ETHYLIDENE *28.05*	178			12.38	6.28	2.5			0.958				
POLY-1-HEPTENE I. *98.18*	359 150					6.45					-40/48 117/250		2*3-1 2*3-1
---, 5-METHYL- *112.21*	67					5.40					52/129		2*3-1
POLY-1-HEXADECENE II. *224.42*	150	ORTHO		7.5	63.2	5.6		8	0.95		68/250		2*4-1
POLY-1-HEXENE *84.16* OR	150 150	MONO ORTHO		22.2 11.7	8.89 26.9	13.7 13.7	G#94.5	14 28	0.73 0.91		-55/48		2*7-2 2*7-2
---, 4-METHYL- *98.18*	9 67	TET		19.64 19.64	19.64 19.64	14.00 14.00		28	0.845		200		2*7-2
---, 5-METHYL- *98.18*	9 67	HEX		10.2 10.2	10.2 10.2	6.50 6.50			0.84		130 110/282		2*3-1 2*3-1
POLY-ISOBUTENE *56.10*	34 115 139	ORTHO ORTHO	D2-4	6.94 6.94	11.96 11.96	18.63 18.63		16 16	0.937	0.915 0.912/53 0.842	44/46	2.87/82	2*8-5

POLYMER	REF	CRYST SYST.	SPACE GROUP	UNIT CELL PARAMETERS				MON UNIT CELL	DENSITY G./CC.		MELT POINT	HEAT OF FUSION KCAL/MON	CHAIN CONF.
				A	B	C	ANGLES		CRYSTAL	AMORPH.			
POLY-1-OCTADECENE II *252.47*	150	ORTHO		7.5	70.4	6.6		8	0.95		80/6 100/90		2*4-1
POLY-1-PENTENE IA. *70.13*	355	MONO	OR	11.35 21.15	20.85 11.20	6.49	B#99.6	12	0.92 0.96/408	0.85/408	130/276 130/380		2*3-1
IB.	355					6.5							2*3-1
IIA.	152 355	PORT		19.30	16.90	6.60 7.08	G#116	16	0.90		75/48 80/9 78/282		2*4-1
IIB.	355	PORT		19.60	15.75	7.08	G#115.3	16	0.885				2*4-1
---, 4-METHYL- *84.16*	55 67 94 333	TET TET	S4-1	18.66 18.60 18.50	18.66 18.63 18.50	13.80 13.84 13.76		28	0.813 0.816 0.828 0.832	0.838	235/48 228/282 250	4.71/82 2.85/370	2*7-2 IRREG.
---, 5-TRIMETHYL-SILYL- *122.28*	70					6.55					153/71		2*3-1
POLY-PROPENE ISOTACTIC I. *42.08*	19 127 6 131 136 170 308 330	MONO MONO MONO MONO TRI MONO MONO	C2H-6 C2H-6 C2H-5 CI-1 C2H-3	6.65 6.65 6.666 6.64 6.69 13.36 6.66	20.96 20.96 20.87 20.88 20.98 6.50* 20.78	6.50 6.50 6.488 6.51 6.504 10.99 6.495	B#99.3 B#99.3 B#98.2 B#98.7 B#99.5 87,10899 B#99.62	12 12 12 12	0.936 0.937 0.940 0.9323 0.934 0.943	0.85/45 0.8535	176/10 180/250 165/282 178/349 183/380 186/394 189/392	2.37/82 1.89/251 2.60/83 2.40/358 1.47/182 2.1/394	2*3-1
II.	166 196	HEX RHO	D3-4 OR -6	12.74 6.38	12.74 6.38	6.35 6.33		3	0.939 0.939	.907/112			2*3-1
	308 308	ORTHO HEX	OR	19.08 22.03	11.01 22.03	6.490 6.490		18 18	0.88/167 0.920 0.920				2*3-1 2*3-1
III.	308	TRI		6.47	10.71		G#99.07						2*3-1

References page III-51

POLYMER	REF	CRYST SYST.	SPACE GROUP	UNIT CELL PARAMETERS A	B	C	ANGLES	MON UNIT CELL	DENSITY G./CC. CRYSTAL	AMORPH.	MELT POINT	HEAT OF FUSION KCAL/MON	CHAIN CONF.
SYNDIOTACTIC I.	67 169 409	ORTHO ORTHO	D2-5	14.50 14.5	5.81 5.8	7.3 7.4		8 8	0.91 0.90 0.898	.858/395			4*2-1
II.	306	PHEX				5.05				0.858	160		4*1-1
---, HEXAFLUORO- *150.03*	268												2*4-1
---, 3-PHENYL- %ALLYLBENZENE+ *118.17*	67					6.40					230/90 208/187 185/282		2*3-1
---, 3-SILYL- *72.15*	70 67					6.45 6.45					128/71		2*3-1 2*3-1
---, TRIMETHYLSILYL- *114.23*	70 67					6.50 6.50					360/71		2*3-1 2*3-1
POLY-1-TETRADECENE II. *196.35*	150	ORTHO		7.5	56.0	6.6		8	0.95		57//250		2*4-1
POLY-VINYLCYCLO- HEXANE *110.19*	60 67 95	TET TRI	C4H-6	21.9 21.76 11.6	21.9 21.76 7.8	6.5 6.50 6.6	92,10898	16 16 3	0.95 0.951 0.982		305/90 300/282 383/328		2*4-1
POLY-VINYLCYCLO- PENTANE *96.18*	95	TRI		10.5	7.4	6.6	92,10899	3	0.986		292/328		
POLY-VINYLCYCLO- PROPANE I. *68.11*	175 95	TRI				6.5					230		

POLYMER	REF	CRYST SYST.	SPACE GROUP	UNIT CELL PARAMETERS A	B	C	ANGLES	MON UNIT CELL	DENSITY G./CC. CRYSTAL	AMORPH.	MELT POINT	HEAT OF FUSION KCAL/MON	CHAIN CONF.
POLY-VINYLS AND POLY-VINYLIDENES													
POLY-ACRYLAMIDE													
---, N,N-DIBUTYL- *183.29*	95	HEX		26.3	26.3	6.3		12	1.06				2*3-1
---, N-ISOPROPYL- *113.16*	102								1.118	1.070	200		
POLY-ACRYLATES													
---, ALLYL- *112.12*	278					6.5					90		2*3-1
---, SEC-BUTYL- *128.17*	192 202 401	MONO	CS-2	17.92	10.34	6.49 6.49 6.5			1.06		130		2*3-1
---, TERT-BUTYL- *128.17*	67 192 202 401	RHO	C3-2	17.92	10.50	6.45 6.48 6.48 6.5			1.04		193/16 200		2*3-1 2*3-1 2*3-1
---, ISOBUTYL- *128.17*	192 202 401	ORTHO		17.92	17.92	6.42 6.42 6.5			1.24		81		2*3-1 2*3-1
---, ISOPROPYL- *114.14* ISOTACTIC	67 149					6.5 6.32			1.08		162/120 162		2*3-1
SYNDIOTACTIC	113					5.18	G#120		1.18		115		
POLY-ACRYLONITRILE SYNDIOTACTIC *53.06*	76 133 162 210 322	HEX ORTHO ORTHO ORTHO PHEX	C2V-16	5.99 10.20 18.1 10.55 6.1	5.99 6.10 6.12 5.80 6.11	5.10 5.00		4 8 4	1.11 1.27 1.14		317/77	1.16/77	4*1-1

References page III-51

POLYMER	REF	CRYST SYST.	SPACE GROUP	UNIT CELL PARAMETERS A	B	C	ANGLES	MON UNIT CELL	DENSITY G./CC. CRYSTAL	AMORPH.	MELT POINT	HEAT OF FUSION KCAL/MON	CHAIN CONF.
ISOTACTIC	133	TET		4.74	4.74	2.55			1.54				
POLY-ISOPROPENYL-METHYL KETONE *84.11*	347	TET		15.08	15.08	6.54		16	1.15		240		2*4-1
	198	TET		15.0	15.0	6.5		16	1.166		240		2*4-1
											200/379		
											240/255		
POLY-METHACRYLATES ---, METHYL- *100.11* ISOTACTIC	30	PORT		21.08	12.17	10.55		20	1.23	1.22/31	160/31		2*5-2
SYNDIOTACTIC	30									1.19/31	200/31		4*5-2
POLY-THIOLACRYLATES ---, SEC-BUTYL- *144.23*	201	RHO	C3-2			5.35							2*3-1
	401					6.5							
---, ISOBUTYL- *144.23*	201	MONO	C5-2			6.42							
	401												
---, ISOPROPYL- *130.20*	200	RHO	C3-2			6.42							
	401												
---, PROPYL- *130.20*	200	MONO	C5-2			6.4							2*3-1
	401					6.5							
POLY-VINYL ALCOHOL *44.05*	29	MONO	C2H-2	7.81	2.52*	5.51	B#91.7	2	1.35	1.29/71	232/310		
	132			7.805	2.533	5.485	B#92.2	2	1.35	.26/53	265/323		
	184	MONO	C2H-2	7.81	2.52	5.50	B#92	2	1.345	.269			
	261			7.81		5.43	B#91.5		1.35				
	316								1.34/410	1.27/410			
QUENCHED	261	ORTHO	C2V-20	7.42	2.52	5.25		2	1.49				2*1-1
SINGLE CRYSTAL	151	HEX		5.45	5.45	2.51		1	1.15				4*1-1
POLY-VINYL CHLORIDE *62.50*	7	ORTHO	D2H-11	10.6	5.4	5.1		4	1.44	1.41/415	273/372	2.7/372	4*1-1
	64	ORTHO		10.11	5.27	5.12			1.522		212/143	0.65/145	
	140	MONO		10.65	5.15*	5.20	B#90	4	1.455				
	235	ORTHO	D2H-11	10.40	5.30	5.10		4	1.48				

POLYMER	REF	CRYST SYST.	SPACE GROUP	UNIT CELL PARAMETERS				MON UNIT CELL	DENSITY G./CC.		MELT POINT	HEAT OF FUSION KCAL/MON	CHAIN CONF.
				A	B	C	ANGLES		CRYSTAL	AMORPH.			
POLY-VINYL FLUORIDE *46.04*	62	HEX		4.93	4.93	2.53		1	1.44		200/79	1.80/79	2*7-2
	236	ORTHO	C2V-14	8.57	4.95	2.52		2	1.430				2*7-2
POLY-VINYL FORMATE *72.02*													
ISOTACTIC	232	RHO	C3V-6- D3D-6	15.9	15.9	6.55		18	1.49				
SYNDIOTACTIC	232					5.0							
POLY-VINYL METHYL KETONE *70.09*	164	TET	S4-1	14.52	14.52	14.40		28	1.216				
	379	TET		14.56	14.56	14.10		29	1.216		170		
POLY-VINYLIDENE BROMIDE *185.87*	33	MONO		25.88	4.77*	13.87	B#70.2	16	3.065				
POLY-VINYLIDENE CHLORIDE *96.95*	32	MONO		13.69	4.67*	6.296	B#55.2	4	1.949	1.66/43	190/46		4*1-1
	33	MONO	C2-2	22.54	4.68*	12.53	B#84.2	16	1.959				
	245	MONO		6.73	4.68*	12.54	B#123.6	4	1.96				
	231												
POLY-VINYLIDENE FLUORIDE *64.02*	171	MONO		5.02	25.4*	4.62	B#107				171/373		2*2-1
POLY-AROMATICS													
POLY-STYRENE *104.14*	67	RHO	C3V-6-	21.90	21.90	6.63		18	1.12	1.04 TO	240/10	2.15/89	2*3-1
	128	RHO	D3D-6	21.9	21.9	6.65		18	1.126	1.065/17	250/90	2.00/174	
	6	RHO		22.08	22.08	6.626			1.111	1.024	235/282		
	139								1.12/45	1.052			
	411								1.114				
---, O-FLUORO- *122.14*	70	RHO	C3V-6	22.1	22.1	6.63		18	1.296		270/75		2*3-1
	73	RHO		22.15	22.15	6.65		18	1.29				2*3-1
	123					6.63							
	168												

References page III-51

POLYMER	REF	CRYST SYST.	SPACE GROUP	UNIT CELL PARAMETERS				MON UNIT CELL	DENSITY G./CC.		MELT POINT	HEAT OF FUSION KCAL/MON	CHAIN CONF.
				A	B	C	ANGLES		CRYSTAL	AMORPH.			
---, P-FLUORO- *122.14*	70					8.30					265/75		2*4-1
	168												
---, A-METHYL- *130.18*	357	RHO				6.6							
---, O-METHYL- *130.18*	67	TET	C4V-12	19.01	19.01	8.10		16	1.071		360/74		2*4-1
	125	TET	C4V-12	19.01	19.01	8.10		16	1.07				2*4-1
---, P-FLUORO- *136.16*	70					8.05					360/75		2*4-1
	67					8.05							
---, M-METHYL- *130.18*	67	TET	S4-1	19.81	19.81	21.74		44	1.010		215/74		2*11-3
	80	TET		19.81	19.81	21.74		44	1.02		215		2*11-3
	163					57.1							2*29-8
	103					57.0							
---, P-METHYL- *130.18*	103					12.9				1.04/67			
---, TRIMETHYLSILYL- *176.30*	103					60.4					284		
POLY-2-VINYLPYRIDINE *105.13*	185					6.7					212		
POLY-P-XYLYLENE ALPHA *82.14*	223	MONO		11.68	6.10	9.16	B#102.5				375/142	7.20/82	
											420/219		
											375/82		
											435/323		
											400/395		
BETA	223	MONO		8.10	5.25	6.53	B#95	2	0.986		412		
	224					6.55							
POLY-1-VINYL NAPHTHALENE *154.20*	67	TET	C4V-12	21.20	21.20	8.10		16	1.124		360/75		2*4-1
	122	TET	C4V-12	21.20	21.20	8.10		16	1.12				2*4-1
	70					8.20							

| POLYMER | REF | CRYST SYST. | SPACE GROUP | UNIT CELL PARAMETERS | | | | MON UNIT CELL | DENSITY G./CC. | | MELT POINT | HEAT OF FUSION KCAL/MON | CHAIN CONF. |
				A	B	C	ANGLES		CRYSTAL	AMORPH.			
POLY-DIENES													
1,2-POLY-1,3-BUTADIENE *54.09*													
SYNDIOTACTIC	7	ORTHO	D2H-11	10.98	6.60	5.14		4	0.963		154		4*1-1
ISOTACTIC	12 152	RHO	D3D-6	17.3	17.3	6.5 6.5		18	0.96 0.96		120 125/44		2*3-1
1,4-POLY-1,3-BUTADIENE *54.09*													
TRANS- I.	31	PHEX		4.54	4.54	4.9		1	1.02		100/352	2.4/552	
II.	154	PHEX		4.88	4.88	4.68		1	0.930		141/352 148/44	1.10/352 1.43/342	
%ABOVE 65+													
CIS-	36 124	MONO MONO	C2H-6 CS-4- C2H-6	4.60 4.60	9.50 9.50	8.60 8.60	B#109 B#109	4 4	1.01 1.01		1/287 1 6.3/335	2.2/553	8*1-1
---, 2-TERT-BUTYL-CIS- *110.19*	367	TRI		13.95	20.78	15.3		22	0.906		106/299		4*11-3
---, 2-CHLORO-TRANS- %CHLOROPRENE+ *88.54*	229 109 40	PORTH ORTHO ORTHO	C2H-5	5.83 9.0 8.84	10.38 8.23 10.24	8.95 4.79 4.29	B#90	4 4 4	1.086 1.657 1.51		115 80/81	2.00/81	
---, 1-CYANO-TRANS- *79.1C*	275					4.8							
---, 2,3-DICHLORO-TRANS- *122.99*	221					4.86							

References page III-51

POLYMER	REF	CRYST SYST.	SPACE GROUP	UNIT CELL PARAMETERS				MON UNIT CELL	DENSITY G./CC.		MELT POINT	HEAT OF FUSION KCAL/MON	CHAIN CONF.
				A	B	C	ANGLES		CRYSTAL	AMORPH.			
---, 2,3-DIMETHYL- *82.14* TRANS-	104					4.55					260 212/221		
CIS-	225					7.0					192		
---, 2-METHYL- %ISOPRENE+ *68.11* TRANS-, BETA	23 283	ORTHO ORTHO	D2-4	7.78 11.9	11.78 4.8*	4.72 7.85		4 4	1.11 1.01		65/46 74/81 68/287	3.04/81	4*1-1
CIS- *68.11*	40 283	MONO ORTHO	C2H-5	12.46 8.97	8.89 8.20	8.10 25.12	B#92	8 16	1.00 0.97	0.906/53 0.910/47	28/81 14/287 36/50	1.05/81	8*1-1
---, 3-CHLORO- TRANS- *102.56*	165					4.9							
---, 2-METHYLACETOXY TRANS- *140.18*	165	ORTHO		16.2	9.3	4.75		4	1.30		155		
---, 2-PROPYL- TRANS- *96.17*	368 165			10.95	6.65	9.2 9.2		4	0.95		42 42		d*1-1
1,4-POLY-1,3- HEPTADIENE *96.17* TRANS- ISOTACTIC	371 375	MONO	C2-2	8.62	7.95	4.85 4.85	B#99	2	0.97		85		4*1-1
---, 6-METHYL- *110.19* TRANS- ISOTACTIC	371					4.85					119		

POLYMER	REF	CRYST SYST.	SPACE GROUP	UNIT CELL PARAMETERS A	B	C	ANGLES	MON UNIT CELL	DENSITY G./CC. CRYSTAL	AMORPH.	MELT POINT	HEAT OF FUSION KCAL/MON	CHAIN CONF.
1,2-POLY-1,5- HEXADIENE *82.14*	267	ORTHO		7.69	6.21	4.80		2	1.188		146		
	340	ORTHO		13.30	15.52	4.80		8	1.10		128		
1,4-POLY-1,3- HEXADIENE *82.14* TRANS- ISOTACTIC	371	ORTHO	D2-4	14.02	8.02	4.85		4	1.00		82		4*1-1
	274					4.85							
--, 5-METHYL- *96.17* TRANS- ISOTACTIC	371					4.85					88		
2,5-POLY-2,4- HEXADIENE --, 2,5-DIMETHYL- *110.19* TRANS-	183					4.8					265 265/376		
2,5-POLY-2,4- HEXADIENOATES TRANS-ERYTHRO- ISOTACTIC --, BUTYL- *168.23*	384			11.36	9.70	4.80							
--, ETHYL- *140.18*	384					4.80							
--, ISOAMYL- *182.25*	384					4.80							
--, ISOBUTYL- *168.23*	384					4.80							
--, ISOPROPYL- *154.20*	384					4.80							

References page III-51

POLYMER	REF	CRYST SYST.	SPACE GROUP	UNIT CELL PARAMETERS				MON UNIT CELL	DENSITY G./CC.		MELT POINT	HEAT OF FUSION KCAL/MON	CHAIN CONF.
				A	B	C	ANGLES		CRYSTAL	AMORPH.			
---, METHYL- *126.15*	384					4.80							
1,4-POLY-1,3- OCTADIENE *110.19* TRANS- ISOTACTIC	371					4.85					87		
POLY-ISOPRENE SEE POLY-BUTADIENE, ---, 2 METHYL-													
1,4-POLY-1,3- PENTADIENE *68.11* TRANS- ISOTACTIC	37 189	P HEX ORTHO		5.25 19.73	5.25 4.85	7.82 7.8		1 4	0.98 0.985		95		
CIS- SYNDIOTACTIC	234					8.50					53		8*1-1
ISOTACTIC	263					8.15					44		4*2-1
2,5-POLY-5-PHENYL- 2,4-PENTADIENOATES TRANS-ERYTHRO- ISOTACTIC ---, BUTYL- *230.29*	384					4.80							
---, METHYL- *188.22*	384					4.80							

POLYMER	REF	CRYST SYST.	SPACE GROUP	UNIT CELL PARAMETERS				MON UNIT CELL	DENSITY G./CC.		MELT POINT	HEAT OF FUSION KCAL/MON	CHAIN CONF.
				A	B	C	ANGLES		CRYSTAL	AMORPH.			
POLY-AMIDES													
POLY-2-AMINOACETIC ACID. 2 *57.05* %GLYCINE+	275	HEX	C3-2	4.8	4.8	9.3		1	1.54				3*3-1
POLY-4-AMINOBUTYRIC ACID 4 *85.10*	272	MONO		9.44	12.1*	8.22	B#64	8	1.34		260/337		
POLY-10-AMINOCAPRIC ACID 10 *169.26*	61	HEX		4.9	4.9	26.5		2	1.019		177/146		
	65	PHEX	C2-2					2			192/177		
POLY-6-AMINOCAPROIC ACID ALPHA %CAPROLACTAM+ 6 *113.16*	3	MONO	C2-2	9.56	17.2*	8.01	H # 67.5	8	1.23		215	4.96/155	
	65			4.81	17.10	7.61	B # 79.5	2	1.21		214/304	5.15/343	
	26	MONO	C2-2	9.65	17.2	8.11	H # 66.3	4	1.208		223/153	4.32/216	
	135	MONO	C2-2	9.45	8.02	17.08	G # 68	8	1.241		233/244	5.5/405	
	212	MONO	C2-2						1.23		226/293		
	213												
	334	MONO						8	1.21		228/346	4.26/346	
BETA	222	HEX		4.8	4.8	8.6	G #65	1	1.10	1.10			
GAMMA	262	MONO	C2H-5	9.35	16.6*	4.91	R#120	4	1.14				
	272	HEX		4.79	4.79	16.7		2	1.13				
	279	ORTHO		4.82	7.82	16.70		4	1.19				
	336	MONO	C2H-5	9.35	16.6*	4.81	B#120	4	1.16				
	246	MONO	C2H-5	9.33	16.9*	4.78	B#121	4	1.16				
ABOVE 150	26	RHO		4.9	16.28	8.22		4	1.32				
POLY-8-AMINOCAPRYLIC ACID ALPHA 8 *141.21*	272	MONO	C2-2	9.8	22.4*	8.3	H#65	8	1.15		185/146		
	65	PHEX							1.18/153		202/153		
											207/244		
BETA	121	MONO											

POLYMER	REF	CRYST SYST.	SPACE GROUP	UNIT CELL PARAMETERS A	B	C	ANGLES	MON UNIT CELL	DENSITY CRYSTAL	G./CC. AMORPH.	MELT POINT	HEAT OF FUSION KCAL/MON	CHAIN CONF.
GAMMA	272	HEX		4.79	4.79	21.7		2	1.09				
	61	HEX		4.9	4.9	21.7		2	1.058				
POLY-7-AMINOENANTHIC ACID 7 *127.13*	61	TRI	CI-1 -	4.9	5.4	9.85	49,77.63	1	1.211		225/146		
	65		CI-1					1	1.20/153		217/153 235/215 223/291		
POLY-9-AMINO-PELARGONIC ACID 9 *155.24*	65							1			194/146 209/177		
POLY-11-AMINO-UNDECANOIC ACID 11 *183.29*	59	TRI	CI-1 -	9.6	4.2	15.0	72,90,64	2	1.192		194/101	9.9/343	
	61	TRI	CI-1	4.9	5.4	14.9	49,77,63	1	1.228		182/146		
	65					18.9	82,75,66	1	1.168		185/292		
	243			4.78	4.13	13.1	86,75,66	1	1.12		186		
	365			4.78	4.13						220		
POLY-DECAMETHYLENE ADIPAMIDE 10.6 *282.42*	110					22.0					230 236/244		
POLY-DECAMETHYLENE AZELAAMIDE 10.9 *324.49*	65	P-HEX						2			214/137	8.76/159 16.3/405	
GAMMA													
POLY-DECAMETHYLENE SEBACAMIDE 10.10 *338.52*	110	TRI			25.6			1			196 203/244 216/137	8.29/159 12.2/118 7.82/160 17.24/05	
	65												
POLY-HEPTAMETHYLENE PIMELAMIDE 7.7 *254.36*	63	PHEX	CS-1	4.82	19.0*	4.82	B # 60	1	1.108		214/244 196/359 205/2		
CAMMA	65	PHEX		18.95									
POLY-HEXAMETHYLENE ADIPAMIDE ALPHA 6.6 *226.31*	25	TRI	CI-1	4.9	5.4	17.2	48,77,65	1	1.24	1.09/52	265/2	11.10/82	
	402	TRI		15.7	10.5	17.3	6 # 73		1.22/54	1.069/54	270/289	9.7/55 8.79/216 11.24/05	
	407			5.00	4.17	17.3	81,76,65						

POLYMER	REF	CRYST SYST.	SPACE GROUP	A	B	C	ANGLES	MON UNIT CELL	DENSITY G./CC. CRYSTAL	AMORPH.	MELT POINT	HEAT OF FUSION KCAL/MON	CHAIN CONF.
BETA	25	TRI	CI-1	4.9	8.0	17.2	90,77,67	2	1.248				
POLY-HEXAMETHYLENE AZELAAMIDE *268.39*	402			7.8	*0.15	5.3	B # 87				226/244 185/339		
POLY-HEXAMETHYLENE SEBACAMIDE ALPHA 6.10 *282.42*	25 153 54	TRI	CI-1	4.95	5.4	22.4	49,76,63	1	1.16 1.17 1.152 1.189/52	1.041	228/51 216 233/244 215/291	7.32/160 13.5/137 14.0/405	
BETA	25	TRI	CI-1	4.9	8.0	22.4	90,77,67	2	1.196				
POLY-NONAMETHYLENE AZELAAMIDE 9.9 *310.47*	110					24.0					177 165/339 189/2		
GAMMA	65	PHEX						1					
POLY-PENTAMETHYLENE AZELAAMIDE 5.9 *254.36*	2					19.5					178/339 179/291		
POLY-P-PHENYLENE PHTHALAMIDE *238.24*	396	ORTHO	D2H-14	22.8	5.5	8.1							
POLY-PIPERAZINE ADIPAMIDE *196.24*	386					9.2					355		
POLY-PIPERAZINE SEBACAMIDE *201.95*											180/81	6.20/81	
POLY-M-XYLYLENE ADIPAMIDE *226.30*	84			5.10	4.70	15.2	G#69.6	1	1.20		246/326		
POLY-P-XYLYLENE SEBACAMIDE *282.40*	204	TRI		5.74	4.87	20.6	76,55,65	1	1.169		300/290 268/291 281/385		

References page III-51

POLYMER	REF	CRYST SYST.	SPACE GROUP	UNIT CELL PARAMETERS				MON UNIT CELL	DENSITY G./CC.		MELT POINT	HEAT OF FUSION KCAL/MON	CHAIN CONF.
				A	B	C	ANGLES		CRYSTAL	AMORPH.			
POLY-ESTERS													
POLY-1,3-CYCLO-BUTYLENE CARBONATE ---, 2,2,4,4-TETRAMETHYL- *170.20*													
TRANS-	364	TRI		9.25	8.28		G#96.5		1.08		360		
CIS-	364	ORTHO		9.16	8.22	12.9		4	1.10		253		
POLY-1,4-CYCLO-HEXYLENEDIMETHYLENE TEREPHTHALATE *274.30*													
TRANS-	199	TRI		6.37	6.63	14.2	89.47111	1	1.265				
CIS-	199	TRI		6.02	6.01	13.7	89.53112	1					
POLY-DECAMETHYLENE ADIPATE 10.6 *284.38*	106	MONO		5.0	7.4	22.1					80/81 77/300	10.2/31 10.9/405	Z
POLY-DECAMETHYLENE AZELAATE 10.9 *326.46*	106	MONO		5.0	7.4	51.7					69/137	10.0/31 12.1/405	Z
POLY-DECAMETHYLENE GLUTARATE 10.5 *270.36*	106	MONO		5.0	7.4	41.6							Z
POLY-DECAMETHYLENE OXALATE 10.2 *228.38*	106	MONO		5.28	7.00	17.0					79/305		Z
POLY-DECAMETHYLENE SEBACATE 10.10 *340.49*	106	MONO		5.0	7.4	27.1					80/137 75/291	12.0/81 12.3/160 7.2/31 15.5/405	Z

POLYMER	REF	CRYST SYST.	SPACE GROUP	A	B	C	ANGLES	MON UNIT CELL	CRYSTAL	AMORPH.	MELT POINT	HEAT OF FUSION KCAL/MON	CHAIN CONF.
POLY-DECAMETHYLENE SUBERATE 10.8 *312.44*	106	MONO		5.0	7.4	24.6							Z
POLY-DECAMETHYLENE SUCCINATE 10.4 *256.33*	106	MONO		5.0	7.4	19.6					68/290		Z
POLY-DECAMETHYLENE TEREPHTHALATE 10.T *304.37*	68	TRI		4.62	6.30	20.10	107 96 113	1	1.012		138/81 129/99	11.00/81 13.54/405	
POLY-DIKETENE *84.07*	217	MONO		5.50	7.78	9.06	B#92	4	1.438		115/190 115		Z
POLY-ETHYLENE ADIPATE 2.6 *172.18*	105 108 203 211	MONO MONO	C2H-5	25.7 5.0 5.47 7.26	30.7 7.4 7.23 5.40	11.71 11.71 11.72 10.85	B#103.8 D#113.5 A#67.7	40 2 2	1.250 1.34 1.453		52/27 47/265 54/291 50/46	3.80/265	
POLY-ETHYLENE AZELAATE 2.9 *214.25*	105 108 107	ORTHO ORTHO		25.7 7.45 5.0	30.7 4.97 7.4	31.2 31.5 31.2	H#103.8	80 4	1.172 1.220				Z
POLY-ETHYLENE ISOPHTHALATE I. II. 2.1 *192.16*	111 398 398					14.8 21.0			1.358	1.346	240 143		
POLY-ETHYLENE-P-OXYBENZOATE *164.15*	556					15.7					2.3/327 220/354		
POLY-ETHYLENE 1,4-PIPERAZINE DICARBOXYLATE *200.19*	386					10.4					245		
POLY-ETHYLENE SEBACATE 2.10 *228.28*	105 100 108	MONO MONO		25.7 5.5 5.0	30.7 15 7.4	16.67 16.9 16.83	H#103.8 B#65	40 4	1.148 1.120		78/302 72/265 76/137 79/46	6.11/158 3.50/265 6.95/137 8.3/405	Z Z

POLYMER	REF	CRYST SYST.	SPACE GROUP	UNIT CELL PARAMETERS				MON UNIT CELL	DENSITY G./CC.		MELT POINT	HEAT OF FUSION KCAL/MON	CHAIN CONF.
				A	B	C	ANGLES		CRYSTAL	AMORPH.			
POLY-ETHYLENE SUBERATE 2.8 *200.23*	108 203	MONO MONO	C2H-5	5.0 5.51	7.4 7.25	14.1 14.28	B#114.5	2	1.281		55/27		
POLY-ETHYLENE SUCCINATE 2.4 *144.12*	105 108	MONO		9.05 5.0	11.09 7.4	8.32 8.32	B#102.8	4	1.358		103/302 108/290		
POLY-ETHYLENE TEREPHTHALATE 2.T *192.16*	27 430 195	TRI TRI	CI-1	4.56 4.52 5.54	5.94 5.98 4.14	10.75 10.77 10.86	98118112 101,1811 10711292	1	1.455 1.498	1.335 1.337	265 265/290 284/264 267/265 270/374	5.76/87 3.98/155 5.40/157 2.2/265 5.9/405	
POLY-GLYCOLIDE 2 *116.07*	312	ORTHO D2-4		6.36	5.13	7.04		4	1.700		223/305		
POLY-HEXAMETHYLENE SEBACATE 6.10 *284.38*											67/290	5.2/301	
POLY-HEXAMETHYLENE TEREPHTHALATE 6.T *248.27*	68	TRI		4.57	6.10	15.40	10598114	1	1.131		160/81 154/99 161/405	8.3/81 8.44/152 8.0/405	
POLY-10-HYDROXY-DECANOIC ACID 10 *170.24*	108	ORTHO		7.45	4.96	27.1		4	1.127		80/309		
POLY-4,4@-ISOPROPYL-IDENEDIPHENYLENE CARBONATE *254.27*	5 283	ORTHO D2-2- D2-3		11.9	10.1	21.5		8	1.30 1.30	1.20	267/57 263/310		6*2-1
POLY-NONAMETHYLENE AZELAATE 9.9 *312.44*											65/405	10.3/159 11.7/405	
POLY-OXYDIETHYLENE SEBACATE *272.33*	105	TET		17.6	17.6	38.0			1.128		44/325		

POLYMER	REF	CRYST SYST.	SPACE GROUP	UNIT CELL PARAMETERS				MON UNIT CELL	DENSITY G./CC.		MELT POINT	HEAT OF FUSION KCAL/MON	CHAIN CONF.
				A	B	C	ANGLES		CRYSTAL	AMORPH.			
POLY-PIVALOLACTONE *100.11*	321	MONO	C2H-5	9.02	11.64	6.02	B#121.5	4	1.23				4*2-1
POLY-B-PROPIOLACTONE ALPHA 3 *72.06*	314					7.02					122/317		4*2-1
BETA	314					4.82							4*1-1
POLY-TETRAMETHYLENE ISOPHTHALATE 4.1 *220.21*	111								1.309	1.268	152.5	10.1	
POLY-TETRAMETHYLENE SEBACATE 4.10 *256.33*											60/325	4.0/301	
POLY-TETRAMETHYLENE TEREPHTHALATE 4.T *220.21*									1.08/111		232/99	7.6/111 7.5/405	
POLY-TRIMETHYLENE ADIPATE 3.6 *186.20*	107	MONO		5.0	7.4	21.5					38 45/300		/
POLY-TRIMETHYLENE AZELAATE 3.9 *228.28*	107	MONO		5.0	7.4	27.7					5.		/
POLY-TRIMETHYLENE DODECANEDIOATE 3.12 *270.36*	107	MONO		5.0	7.4	35.8					61		/
POLY-TRIMETHYLENE GLUTARATE 3.5 *172.18*	107	MONO		5.0	7.4	15.4					59		/
POLY-TRIMETHYLENE OCTADECANEDIOATE 3.18 *354.51*	107	MONO		5.0	7.4	51.6					76 76/301		/

References page III-51

| POLYMER | REF | CRYST SYST. | SPACE GROUP | UNIT CELL PARAMETERS | | | | MON UNIT CELL | DENSITY G./CC. CRYSTAL | AMORPH. | MELT POINT | HEAT OF FUSION KCAL/MON | CHAIN CONF. |
				A	B	C	ANGLES						
POLY-TRIMETHYLENE PIMELATE 3.7 *200.23*	107	MONO		5.0	7.4	25.5					37		Z
POLY-TRIMETHYLENE SEBACATE 3.10 *242.31*	105 107	PTET MONO		31.2 5.0	31.2 7.4	33.5 31.3	G # 90		1.090		56/305 55		Z
POLY-TRIMETHYLENE SUBERATE 3.8 *214.25*	107	MONO		5.0	7.4	26.1					41		Z
POLY-TRIMETHYLENE SUCCINATE 3.4 *153.15*	107	MONO		5.0	7.4	15.2					47 52/300		Z
POLY-TRIMETHYLENE UNDECANEDIOATE 3.11 *256.33*	107	ORTHO		5.0	7.4	32.4					59		Z
POLY-URETHANS AND POLY-UREAS													
POLY-HEPTAMETHYLENE-UREA *154.21*												2.54/404	
POLY-HEXAMETHYLENE-UREA *140.18*												3.31/404	
POLY-TETRAMETHYLENE HEXAMETHYLENE-DIURETHAN *258.31*	402 334			4.95 9.05	8.69 19.1	19.17 8.38	90 10 460 90,63,65		1.24		160/291 173/101		

POLYMER	REF	CRYST SYST.	SPACE GROUP	A	B	C	ANGLES	MON UNIT CELL	DENSITY CRYSTAL	DENSITY AMORPH.	MELT POINT	HEAT OF FUSION KCAL/MON	CHAIN CONF.
POLY-ETHERS													

POLY-ETHYLENE													
---, 1-BUTOXY-2-CHLORO-													
134.60													
TRANS-	242					6.5							2*3-1
CIS-	242					8.6							2*4-1
---, 1-CHLORO-2-ISOBUTOXY-													
134.60													
TRANS-	242					20.8							2*10-3
---, 1-ISOBUTOXY-2-METHYL-													
114.18													
TRANS-	67				13.77	13.8					226		2*7-2
	141					.							
POLY-A-METHYLVINYL METHYL ETHER SYNDIOTACTIC *72.10*	383	TET		15.2	15.2	16.4		32	1.011				2*8-3
POLY-VINYL ETHERS													
---, BENZYL- *134.17*	253					6.30					162/114		2*3-1
---, BUTYL- *100.14*	360	RHO	C31-2	23.7	23.7	6.50		18	0.945	0.92	64/114		2*3-1
---, SEC-BUTYL- *100.14*	382					35.5					1/0		2*17-5
---, TERT-BUTYL- *100.14*	269	TET	C4H-6	18.84	18.84	7.65		16	0.978		160 260/114 238/281		2*4-1

POLYMER	REF	CRYST SYST.	SPACE GROUP	UNIT CELL PARAMETERS				MON UNIT CELL	DENSITY G./CC.		MELT POINT	HEAT OF FUSION KCAL/MON	CHAIN CONF.
				A	B	C	ANGLES		CRYSTAL	AMORPH.			
---, ISOBUTYL- *100.14*	8 269 152	ORTHO		16.8	9.70	6.50		6	0.940 0.94		115/46 117 165/114 170/281		 2*3-1
---, ISOPROPYL- *86.13*	161 269	TET		17.2	17.2	35.5		68	0.926 0.93		191/281 98 190/114		2*17-5
---, METHYL- *58.07*	176 67	RHO	D3D-6	16.20	16.20	6.50 6.30		18	1.175		144/114		2*3-1 2*3-1
---, 2-METHYLBUTYL- *114.17*	382					6.50					140		2*3-1
---, NEOPENTYL- *114.17*	161 269	ORTHO		18.2	10.5	6.50		6	0.916 0.91		216/281 155 216/114		2*3-1

POLYMER	REF	CRYST SYST.	SPACE GROUP	UNIT CELL PARAMETERS				MON UNIT CELL	DENSITY G./CC.		MELT POINT	HEAT OF FUSION KCAL/MON	CHAIN CONF.
				A	B	C	ANGLES		CRYSTAL	AMORPH.			
POLY-OXIDES													
POLY-ACETALDEHYDE *44.05*	92	TET	C4H-6	14.60	14.60	4.79		16	1.14		165/329		2*4-1
	97	TET		14.63	14.63	4.79		16	1.14				2*4-1
---, 2-CHLORO- *78.50*	387	TET	C4H-6			4.80							2*4-1
---, 2,2-DICHLORO- *112.95*	387	TET	C4H-6			5.22							2*4-1
---, 2,2,2-TRICHLORO *147.40*	387	TET	C4H-6			6.45					220/388		2*4-1
POLY-ACETONE *58.07*	214	TET	S4-1	14.65	14.65	10.22		28	1.231		60		2*7-2
POLY-2-BUTENE OXIDE *72.10*													
TRANS-	397	ORTHO	D2-4	13.72	4.50	6.90		4	1.099		114/399		3*2-1
CIS-	397	ORTHO		11.20	10.44	7.01		8	1.168		162/399		3*2-1
POLY-BUTYRALDEHYDE *72.10*	92	TET	C4H-6	20.01	20.01	4.78		16	1.00		225/529		2*4-1
	96								0.997				
	240	TET	C4H-6	20.00	20.00	4.80		16	0.998				
POLY-1,3-CYCLO-BUTYLENE FORMAL ---, 2,2,4,4-TETRA-METHYL- *156.21*													
TRANS- ALPHA	361					11.5					260 260/369		
BETA	361					5.75							
CIS- ALPHA	361					11.5					285 285/369		

POLYMER	REF	CRYST SYST.	SPACE GROUP	UNIT CELL PARAMETERS				MCN UNIT CELL	DENSITY G./CC.		MELT POINT	HEAT OF FUSION KCAL/MON	CHAIN CONF.
				A	B	C	ANGLES		CRYSTAL	AMORPH.			
BETA	361					5.75							
POLY-2,6-DIMETHYL-1,4-PHENYLENE OXIDE *120.14*	226			8.45	6.02		B#91				261		
POLY-EPICHLORODHYDRIN *92.53*	119	ORTHO	D2-40R	12.14	4.90	7.05		4	1.461		117		
	194		C2V-9			7.07					121 135/318		
POLY-ETHYLENE OXIDE *44.04*	109	MONO		9.5	19.5	12.0	B#101	36	1.205	1.15/366	66/81	1.28/61	3*7-2
	194	MONC	CS-2	8.03	13.09	19.52	B#125.1	28	1.220		62/180	2.36/543	3*7-2
	185	MONC		7.95	13.11	19.39	B#124.6	28	1.23		72/218		
	227	MONC		8.02	13.4	19.25	B#126.9	30	1.333				
	348	ORTHO		12.83	12.83	19.3		56	1.29		66		
	303					19.3		4	1.234	1.123			3*7-2
	190								1.222	1.124		1.75	3*7-2
	390								1.235				
POLY-FORMALDEHYDE %OXYMETHYLENE+ *30.02*	42	HEX	C3-2 -	4.46	4.46	17.30		9	1.506	1.25	181	0.090/91	2*9-5
	134		C3-3								198/217	1.52/186	2*2-1
	231										178/529	1.76/343	2*2?-
	270	HEX		4.470	4.470	56.00							16
	258	HEX		4.43	4.43	17.25			1.530				2*9-5
	362	HEX		4.47	4.47	56.00		27	1.492				2*2?-
	284	HEX		7.74	7.74	56.0		81	1.492				16
	280												
II-	270	ORTHO	D2-4	4.767	7.600	3.563		4	1.54				2*2-1
	271	ORTHO	D2-4	4.77	7.65	3.56		4	1.533				2*2-1
	351	ORTHC	D2-4	4.767	7.660	3.563		18	1.50				2*2-1
	249	ORTHO		7.75	4.46	17.30							
POLY- ISOBUTYRALDEHYDE *72.10*	96	TET				5.2					260/329		
POLY- ISOVALERALDEHYDE *86.13*	96	TET		20.6	20.6	5.2		16	1.037				2*4-1

POLYMER	REF	CRYST SYST.	SPACE GROUP	UNIT CELL PARAMETERS A	B	C	ANGLES	MON UNIT CELL	DENSITY G./CC. CRYSTAL	AMORPH.	MELT POINT	HEAT OF FUSION KCAL/MON	CHAIN CONF.
POLY-OXACYCLOBUTANE ---, 3,3-BISCHLORO-METHYL- ALPHA *155.03*	344 148 378	ORTHO ORTHO	D2H-2	17.85 8.16	8.16 17.85	4.8 4.8 4.82		4 4	1.47 1.47/343 1.469	1.39/343	190/173 180	5.49/343	3*1-1
BETA	172 378	MONO MONO	CS-1 - CS-2 CS-3	6.85 11.42	11.42 7.06	4.75 4.82	B#109.8 G#114.5	2 2	1.47 1.455				3*1-1 3*1-1
POLY-PROPIONALDEHYDE *58.08*	92 246	TET TET	C4H-6 C4H-6	17.52 17.50	17.52 17.50	4.78 4.80		16 16	1.05 1.050		185/329		2*4-1
POLY-PROPYLENE OXIDE *58.07*	13	ORTHO	C2V-9- D2-4	10.52	4.67	7.16		4	1.096	.998/139	75/18 75/377 73/285	1.03/18 2.0/377	3*2-1
	41 78	ORTHO ORTHO	D2-4 D2-4	10.52 10.40	4.68 4.64	7.10 6.92			1.102 1.154				
---, 3-PHENOXY- *150.17*	258	ORTHC		17.0	8.2	5.48		4	0.7860	0.7660	215 210/297 208/318		
POLY-TETRAHYDROFURAN *72.10* %TETRAMETHYLENE OXIDE+	348 403	MONO MONO	C2H-6 C2H-6	5.48 5.61	8.73 8.92	12.10 12.25	B#134.2 B#134.5	4 4	1.18 1.09		35 60/366 37/180		5*2-1 5*2-1
POLY-SULFIDES AND POLY-SULFONES													
POLYMER OF SULFUR *32.06*	288	MONO	C2H-2	26.4	9.26*	12.32	B#79.25		2.34				
POLY-DIMETHYLENE SULFIDE *60.11*	181 241	HEX		4.92	4.92	6.74		2	1.413		190 210		3*2-1

POLYMER	REF	CRYST SYST.	SPACE GROUP	UNIT CELL PARAMETERS				MON UNIT CELL	DENSITY G./CC.		MELT POINT	HEAT OF FUSION KCAL/MON	CHAIN CONF.
				A	B	C	ANGLES		CRYSTAL	AMORPH.			
POLY-ETHYLENE DISULFIDE *92.17*	134					8.8					130/294 113/295		4*1-1
POLY-ETHYLENE TETRASULFIDE *156.29*	134 256 257	ORTHO MONO		8.57 8.68	5.0 5.03	4.32 4.27 4.32	G # 87	1	1.418 1.378				
POLY-HEXAMETHYLENE PENTAMETHYLENE SULFONE *282.41*	39	MONO		9.88	9.26	34.00	B#121.7	8	1.42				
POLY-HEXAMETHYLENE SULFONE *119.36*	39	MONO		9.38	9.26	18.24	B#121.7	8	1.39				
POLY-HEXAMETHYLENE TETRAMETHYLENE SULFONE *268.38*	39	MONO		9.38	9.26	15.68	B#121.7	4	1.46				
POLY-METHYLENE SULFIDE *46.09*	331 237 311	HEX ORTHO ORTHO		5.07 12.7 12.0	5.07 12.0 12.7	36.52 5.10 5.10		17 16	1.60 1.55		245/181 260/298 260		2*17-9
POLY-PENTAMETHYLENE SULFONE *105.34*	39	MONO		9.88	9.26	7.76	B#121.7	4	1.48				
POLY-PENTAMETHYLENE TETRAMETHYLENE SULFONE *254.35*	39	MONO		9.88	9.26	28.33	B#121.7	8	1.53				

POLYMER	REF	CRYST. SYST.	SPACE GROUP	UNIT CELL PARAMETERS				MON UNIT CELL	DENSITY G./CC.		MELT POINT	HEAT OF FUSION KCAL/MON	CHAIN CONF.
				A	B	C	ANGLES		CRYSTAL	AMORPH.			
CELLULOSICS**													
** CF. TABLE OF PROPERTIES OF CELLULOSE													
CELLULOSE I *162.14*	22 28*	MONO		8.35	10.3 10.34	7.9	B#84	2	1.592				Z
	20 98	MONO	C2-2	8.20	10.3*	7.90	B#83.3		1.625				
CELLULOSE II *162.14*	22 28*	MONO		8.14	10.3 10.34	9.14	B#62	2	1.583				Z
	98	MONO		8.02	10.3*	9.03	B#62.8		1.62				
CELLULOSE III *162.14*	28								1.62				
CELLULOSE IV *162.14*	98 234	MONO		8.12 7.9	10.3 10.3*	7.99	B#90		1.61				
CELLULOSE X *162.14*	98 218	MONO		8.10 8.12	10.3* 10.3*	8.16 7.99	B#78.3 B#90.0		1.615 1.61				
CELLULOSE TRIACETATE *288.25*	4	PORT	C2-2	24.5	11.6*	10.43		4	1.30		306/144		Z
CELLULOSE TRIBUTYRATE *372.40*											207/118 206/46	3.0/118	
CELLULOSE TRICAPRYLATE *540.72*											116/117	3.1/117	
CELLULOSE TRINITRATE *297.14*	24	ORTHO		12.25	25.4*	9.3		4	1.41		697/77 700/81	0.9 – 1.5/77	Z
CELLULOSE-2.44-NITRATE											617/81	1.35/81	

POLYMER	REF	CRYST SYST.	SPACE GROUP	UNIT CELL PARAMETERS				MON UNIT CELL	DENSITY G./CC.		MELT POINT	HEAT OF FUSION KCAL/MON	CHAIN CONF.
				A	B	C	ANGLES		CRYSTAL	AMORPH.			
OTHER POLYMERS													
POLY-DIMETHYL KETENE *70.09* I	179					8.8		4			250 255/130		
140.18 II											170/179 180/248		
POLY-HYDROXY- METHYLENE *30.03*	338					2.5							
POLY-KETONE %ETHYLENE-CO- CARBON MONOXIDE+ *56.06*	193	ORTHO	D2H-16	7.97	4.76	7.57		4	1.296				3*2-1
POLY-PHOSPHONITRILE CHLORIDE *115.90*	230 56	ORTHO	C2V-9	11.07 11.07	4.92* 4.92*	12.72 12.72		8 8	2.222 2.21	1.91			2*2-1
POLY-SILOXANE ---, DIMETHYL- *74.13*	197	MONO		13.0	8.3*	7.75	B#60	8	1.07	0.98			
POLY-TETRAMETHYL-P- SILPHENYLENE SILOXANE *208.35*											148/225	4.55/225	

C.   MELTING POINTS OF VARIOUS POLYMERS

The following table presents melting points for about 850 polymers. Entries are
alphabetical according to the basic structure of the polymer ignoring substituents.
Substituted polymers are listed alphabetically (according to the substituent) under
the entry for the unsubstituted polymer. The molecular weight is that of the chemical repeat in the polymer. Melting points in °C are taken from the reference cited.

    %   MEANS LEFT PARENTHESIS
    +   MEANS RIGHT PARENTHESIS
    ā   MEANS PRIME

POLYMER	MOLECULAR WEIGHT	MELTING POINT	REF.
CELLULOSE TRIACETATE	288.25	306	144
CELLULOSE TRIBUTYRATE	372.40	207	118
		206	46
CELLULOSE TRICAPRATE	624.93	88	144
CELLULOSE TRICAPROATE	456.56	94	144
CELLULOSE TRICAPRYLATE	540.72	116	117
CELLULOSE TRIHEPTYLATE	498.64	88	144
CELLULOSE TRILAURATE	709.03	91	144
CELLULOSE TRIMYRISTATE	751.11	106	144
CELLULOSE TRINITRATE	297.14	697	77
		700	81
CELLULOSE 2.44-NITRATE		617	81
CELLULOSE TRIPALMITATE	793.18	105	144
CELLULOSE TRIPROPIONATE	330.33	234	144
CELLULOSE TRIVALERATE	414.48	122	144
POLY-ACETALDEHYDE	44.05	165	329
---, 2,2,2-TRICHLORO-	147.40	220	388
POLY-ACETONE	58.07	60	214
POLY-ACRYLAMIDE, N-ISOPROPYL-	113.16	200	102
POLY-ACRYLATES			
---, ALLYL-	112.12	90	278
---, BUTYL-	128.17	47	202
---, SEC-BUTYL-	128.17	130	202
---, TERT-BUTYL-	128.17	193	16
		200	202
---, ISOBUTYL-	128.17	81	202
---, ISOPROPYL-	114.14		
ISOTACTIC		162	120
		162	149
SYNDIOTACTIC		115	113
POLY-ACRYLONITRILE	53.06		
SYNDIOTACTIC		317	77
POLY-ADIPIC ANHYDRIDE	128.12	85	840
		98	841
		77	826
POLY-ALLENE	40.06	122	818
---, TETRAFLUORO-	112.03	126	38
POLY-4-AMINOBUTYRIC ACID	85.10	260	337

POLYMER	MOLECULAR WEIGHT	MELTING POINT	REF.
POLY-10-AMINOCAPRIC ACID	169.26	177	146
		188	337
		192	177
POLY-6-AMINOCAPROIC ACID	113.16	215	3
		214	304
		223	153
		233	244
		226	293
		228	346
---, 6-METHYL-	127.18	185	402
POLY-8-AMINOCAPRYLIC ACID	141.21	185	146
		202	153
		209	244
POLY-22-AMINODOCOSANOIC ACID	337.57	145	177
POLY-7-AMINOENANTHIC ACID	127.18	225	146
		211	153
		233	215
		233	291
---, N-METHYL-	141.21	65	828
POLY-17-AMINOHEPTADECANOIC ACID	267.44	150	292
POLY-P-AMINOHYDROCINNAMIC ACID	147.17	310	402
POLY-12-AMINOLAURIC ACID	197.31	179	177
POLY-9-AMINOPELARGONIC ACID	155.24	194	146
		198	292
		209	177
POLY-3-AMINOPROPIONIC ACID	71.08	260	244
		330	337
---, 2,2-DIMETHYL-	99.13	270	402
---, N-ISOPROPYL-	113.16	130	869
---, N-METHYL-	85.10	225	863
		202	869
---, N-PHENYL-	147.17	205	869
POLY-6-AMINOTHIOCAPROIC ACID	129.22	120	402
POLY-7-AMINOTHIOENANTHIC ACID	143.24	235	402
POLY-A-AMINOTOLUIC ACID	133.14	300	836
POLY-13-AMINOTRIDECANOIC ACID	211.34	183	177
POLY-11-AMINOUNDECANOIC ACID	182.29	194	101
		182	146
		183	292
		186	243
		188	836
		220	365
---, N-ALLYL-	223.35	350	402
---, N-ETHYL-	209.32	-30	402
---, 2-METHYL-	197.31	130	402
---, N-METHYL-	198.32	80	402
---, N-PHENYL-	259.38	-30	402
---, N-PIPERAZINE-	239.39	142	402
POLY-5-AMINOVALERIC ACID	99.13	223	244
		258	402
POLY-ARABONOLACTONE, 2,3,4-TRIMETHYL-	170.19	138	305
POLY-AZELAIC ANHYDRIDE	170.20	54	823
POLY-BENZALDEHYDE-CO-DIMETHYLKETENE	176.21	290	817
POLY-4,4a-BIPHENYLDICARBOXALDEHYDE	210.22	250	801
POLY-4,4a-BIPHENYLENE ADIPAMIDE	294.34	400	402
POLY-4,4a-%2,2a-2,2a-BIPHENYLENEDITHIAZOLE+-OXY-P-DIPHENYLENE	486.58	240	810
POLY-4,4a-%2,2a-2,2a-BIPHENYLENEDITHIAZOLE+-P-PHENYLENE	394.49	250	810
POLY-4,4a-BIPHENYLENE SEBACAMIDE	350.44	435	402
POLY-4,4a-BIPHENYLENE TEREPHTHALAMIDE	314.33	500	402
---, 3,3a-DIMETHYL-	342.38	440	402
---, ---, N,Na-DIETHYL-	398.48	254	870
---, N,Na-DIETHYL-	370.43	316	870
POLY-%3-BROMO-4-CARBOXYPHENOXY+-ACETIC ANHYDRIDE	257.05	179	827
1,2-POLY-1,3-BUTADIENE	54.09		
SYNDICTACTIC		154	7
ISOTACTIC		120	12
		125	44

POLYMER		MOLECULAR WEIGHT	MELTING POINT	REF.
1,4-POLY-1,3-BUTADIENE		54.09		
TRANS-	I.		100	352
	II.		141	352
			148	44
CIS-			1	287
			1	124
			6	335
---, 2-TERT-BUTYL-		110.19		
CIS-			106	299
---, 2-CHLORO- %CHLOROPRENE+		88.54		
TRANS-			115	229
			80	81
---, 2,3-DIMETHYL-		82.14		
TRANS-			260	104
			272	221
CIS-			192	220
---, 1-METHOXY-		84.11		
TRANS-			118	329
---, 2-METHYL- %ISOPRENE+		68.11		
TRANS-			65	46
			74	81
			68	287
CIS-			28	81
			14	287
			36	50
---, 2-METHYLACETOXY-		140.18		
TRANS-			135	165
---, 2-PROPYL-		96.17		
TRANS-			42	165
POLY-BUTADIENE OXIDE		70.09	74	809
POLY-1-BUTENE	I.	56.10	126	12
			132	250
			136	277
			135	345
			142	313
			135	320
	II.		124	277
			122	345
			126	313
			122	320
	III.		106	277
---, 4-CYCLOHEXYL-		138.24	170	282
			138	328
---, 3,3-DIMETHYL-		84.16	260	282
---, 3-METHYL-		70.13	300	48
			310	90
			300	282
---, 3-METHYL- %VIA HYDRIDE SHIFT+		70.13	55	332
			66	319
---, 3-PHENYL-		132.20	360	90
---, 4-PHENYL-		132.20	160	90
			168	187
			159	282
---, 4-O-TOLYL-		146.22	235	187
---, 4-P-TOLYL-		146.22	196	187
---, 4,4,4-TRIFLUORO-		110.08	263	813
---, ---, 3-METHYL-		124.11	300	813
---, 5,5,5-TRIFLUORO-4-METHYL-		124.11	225	813
POLY-2-BUTENE OXIDE		72.10		
TRANS-			114	399
CIS-			162	399
POLY-4,4a-BUTYLIDENEDIPHENYLENE CARBONATE		268.30	170	858
POLY-4,4a-%2,2-BUTYLIDENE+-DIPHENYLENE CARBONATE		268.30	222	858
POLY-BUTYLISOCYANATE		99.13	175	814
POLY-BUTYRALDEHYDE		72.10	225	329
POLY-E-CAPROLACTONE		114.14	55	824
POLY-CAPRYLALDEHYDE		128.21	35	329
POLY-M-%CARBOXYPHENOXY+-ACETIC ANHYDRIDE		178.14	134	827
POLY-P-CHLOROBENZALDEHYDE-CO-DIMETHYLKETENE		210.66	260	817
POLY-CYCLOBUTENE		54.09		
	I.		210	864
	II.		150	864

POLYMER	MOLECULAR WEIGHT	MELTING POINT	REF.
POLY-1,3-CYCLOBUTYLENE CARBONATE,			
2,2,4,4-TETRAMETHYL-	170.20		
TRANS-		360	364
CIS-		253	364
POLY-1,3-CYCLOBUTYLENE FORMAL,			
---, 2,2,4,4-TETRAMETHYL-	156.21		
TRANS-		260	361
		260	369
CIS-		285	361
		285	369
1,4-POLY-1,3-CYCLOHEXADIENE	80.12		
TRANS-		380	221
POLY-1,3-CYCLOHEXYLENE ADIPAMIDE	224.30		
TRANS-		300	402
CIS-		170	402
POLY-1,4-CYCLOHEXYLENE ADIPAMIDE	224.30	400	402
POLY-1,3-CYCLOHEXYLENE AZELAAMIDE	266.37		
TRANS-		300	402
CIS-		125	402
POLY-1,4-CYCLOHEXYLENE 3,3ω-DIBENZOAMIDE	320.38	390	402
POLY-1,4-CYCLOHEXYLENEDIMETHYLENE ADIPAMIDE	252.35		
TRANS-		345	385
POLY-1,4-CYCLOHEXYLENEDIMETHYLENE AZELAAMIDE	294.43		
TRANS-		275	385
POLY-1,4-CYCLOHEXYLENEDIMETHYLENE DODECANEDIAMIDE	336.50		
TRANS-		278	385
POLY-1,4-CYCLOHEXYLENEDIMETHYLENE FORMAL	156.22		
TRANS-		78	369
POLY-1,4-CYCLOHEXYLENEDIMETHYLENE GLUTARAMIDE	238.32		
TRANS-		290	385
POLY-1,4-CYCLOHEXYLENEDIMETHYLENE ISOPHTHALAMIDE	272.34		
TRANS-		310	385
POLY-1,4-CYCLOHEXYLENEDIMETHYLENE			
OCTAMETHYLENEDIURETHAN	340.45		
TRANS-		160	402
		160	291
POLY-1,4-CYCLOHEXYLENEDIMETHYLENE PIMELAMIDE	266.37		
TRANS-		293	385
POLY-1,4-CYCLOHEXYLENEDIMETHYLENE SEBACAMIDE	308.45		
TRANS-		300	385
POLY-1,4-CYCLOHEXYLENEDIMETHYLENE SUBERAMIDE	280.40		
TRANS-		311	385
POLY-%1,4-CYCLOHEXYLENEDIOXY+-DITRIMETHYLENE			
ADIPAMIDE	340.45	196	402
POLY-%1,4-CYCLOHEXYLENEDIOXY+-DITRIMETHYLENE			
4,4@-%ETHYLENEDIOXY+-DIBENZOAMIDE	496.58	250	402
POLY-%1,4-CYCLOHEXYLENEDIOXY+-DITRIMETHYLENE			
4,4@-%HEXAMETHYLENEDIOXY+-DIBENZOAMIDE	552.69	215	402
POLY-%1,4-CYCLOHEXYLENEDIOXY+-DITRIMETHYLENE			
CXAMIDE	284.35	246	402
POLY-%1,4-CYCLOHEXYLENEDIOXY+-DITRIMETHYLENE			
4,4@-%OXYDIETHYLENEDIOXY+-DIBENZOAMIDE	540.64	125	402
POLY-%1,4-CYCLOHEXYLENEDIOXY+-DITRIMETHYLENE			
%P-PHENYLENEDIOXY+-DIACETAMIDE	420.49	160	402
POLY-%1,4-CYCLOHEXYLENEDIOXY+-DITRIMETHYLENE			
TEREPHTHALAMIDE	360.44	384	402
POLY-%1,4-CYCLOHEXYLENEDIOXY+-DITRIMETHYLENE			
4,4@-%TETRAMETHYLENEDIOXY+-DIBENZOAMIDE	524.64	224	402
POLY-1,4-CYCLOHEXYLENE FORMAL	128.17		
TRANS-		209	369
POLY-1,4-CYCLOHEXYLENE 3,3ω-METHYLENEDIBENZOAMIDE	334.40	174	402
POLY-1,4-CYCLOHEXYLENE OCTAMETHYLENEDIURETHAN	312.40		
TRANS-		255	866
		255	402
		221	291
POLY-1,3-CYCLOHEXYLENE SEBACAMIDE	280.40		
TRANS-		290	402
CIS-		120	402
POLY-1,4-CYCLOHEXYLENEURETHAN	141.17	355	836
POLY-4,4@-CYCLOHEXYLIDENEDIPHENYLENE CARBONATE	294.33	260	858
POLY-CYCLOPENTENE	68.11		
TRANS-		23	147
POLY-4,4@-CYCLOPENTYLIDENEDIPHENYLENE CARBONATE	280.31	250	858

POLYMER	MOLECULAR WEIGHT	MELTING POINT	REF.
POLY-CYCLOPROPANE CYCLOPROPANEDICARBOXAMIDE	166.18	285	865
POLY-1,2-CYCLOPROPANEDIMETHYLENE CYCLOPROPANEDICARBOXAMIDE	194.23	220	865
POLY-1,2-CYCLOPROPANEDIMETHYLENE CYCLOPROPANE-DIURETHAN	226.23		
TRANS-		210	865
CIS-		175	865
POLY-1,2-CYCLOPROPANEDIMETHYLENE ISOPHTHALAMIDE	230.26	220	865
POLY-1,2-CYCLOPROPANEDIMETHYLENE ISOPHTHALATE	232.22	100	860
POLY-1,2-CYCLOPROPANEDIMETHYLENE SEBACAMIDE	266.37	223	865
POLY-1,2-CYCLOPROPANEDIMETHYLENE TEREPHTHALATE	232.22	130	860
POLY-CYCLOPROPANE ISOPHTHALAMIDE	202.21	250	865
POLY-CYCLOPROPANE SEBACAMIDE	238.32	220	865
POLY-DECAMETHYLENE ADIPAMIDE	282.42	230	110
		236	244
POLY-DECAMETHYLENE ADIPATE	284.38	80	81
		77	300
POLY-DECAMETHYLENE ADIPYLDIURETHAN	370.44	164	402
POLY-DECAMETHYLENE AZELAAMIDE	324.49	214	137
POLY-DECAMETHYLENE AZELAATE	326.46	69	137
POLY-DECAMETHYLENE CARBONAMIDE	198.30	200	402
POLY-DECAMETHYLENE CARBONATE	200.27	55	820
POLY-DECAMETHYLENE %DECAMETHYLENEDISULFONYL+-DICAPROAMIDE	634.95	207	402
POLY-DECAMETHYLENE DECAMETHYLENEDIUREA	396.60	210	291
POLY-DECAMETHYLENE DECAMETHYLENEDIURETHAN	398.57	145	291
POLY-DECAMETHYLENE 4,4a-%3,3a-DIMETHYL+-DIPHENYLENEDIURETHAN	438.55	219	866
POLY-DECAMETHYLENE DISULFIDE	204.38	45	868
POLY-DECAMETHYLENE DODECANEDIAMIDE	366.57	191	244
POLY-DECAMETHYLENE EICOSANEDIAMIDE	478.78	171	244
POLY-DECAMETHYLENE 4,4a-%ETHYLENEDIOXY+-DIBENZOATE	440.52	135	290
POLY-DECAMETHYLENE 4,4a-%ETHYLENEDIPHENYLENE+-DIOXYDIACETAMIDE	466.60	220	402
POLY-DECAMETHYLENE 4,4a-ETHYLIDENEDIBENZOAMIDE	406.55	150	402
POLY-DECAMETHYLENE FORMAL	186.29	57	825
POLY-DECAMETHYLENE FUMARAMIDE	252.35	50	402
POLY-DECAMETHYLENE 2,5-FURANDIPROPIONAMIDE	348.47	140	402
POLY-DECAMETHYLENE HEXAMETHYLENE AMINE	254.45	102	829
POLY-DECAMETHYLENE %HEXAMETHYLENEDISULFONYL+-DICAPROAMIDE	578.85	218	402
POLY-DECAMETHYLENE HEXAMETHYLENEDIUREA	340.50	210	402
POLY-DECAMETHYLENE HEXAMETHYLENE SULFIDE	288.54	78	819
POLY-DECAMETHYLENE ISOPHTHALAMIDE	302.40	186	868
POLY-DECAMETHYLENE 4,4a-%ISOPROPYLIDENEDI-PHENYLENE+-DIOXYDIACETAMIDE	480.63	105	402
POLY-DECAMETHYLENE 3,3a-METHYLENEDIBENZOAMIDE	392.52	65	402
POLY-DECAMETHYLENE 4,4a-METHYLENEDIBENZOAMIDE	392.52	100	402
POLY-DECAMETHYLENE OCTAMETHYLENEDIURETHAN	370.52	146	402
POLY-DECAMETHYLENE OXALATE	228.38	79	305
POLY-DECAMETHYLENE OXAMIDE	226.31	229	291
		290	402
POLY-DECAMETHYLENE OXIDE	156.26	79	181
		72	180
		60	291
POLY-DECAMETHYLENE %PENTAMETHYLENEDISULFONYL+-DICAPROAMIDE	564.82	223	402
POLY-DECAMETHYLENE P-PHENYLENEDIACETAMIDE	330.46	242	291
POLY-DECAMETHYLENE %P-PHENYLENEDIOXY+-DIACETAMIDE	362.46	188	402
POLY-DECAMETHYLENE P-PHENYLENEDIPROPIONAMIDE	358.51	265	402
POLY-DECAMETHYLENE PHTHALAMIDE	302.40	115	868
POLY-DECAMETHYLENE SEBACAMIDE	338.52	196	110
		203	244
		216	137
POLY-DECAMETHYLENE SEBACATE	340.49	80	137
		73	291
POLY-DECAMETHYLENE SEBACYLDIURETHAN	426.54	153	402
POLY-DECAMETHYLENE SUBERAMIDE	310.47	217	244
		208	291
POLY-DECAMETHYLENE SUCCINATE	256.33	68	290
POLY-DECAMETHYLENE SULFIDE	172.32	78	819
		91	181
POLY-DECAMETHYLENE TEREPHTHALAMIDE	302.40	276	868

References page III-51

POLYMER	MOLECULAR WEIGHT	MELTING POINT	REF.
POLY-DECAMETHYLENE TEREPHTHALATE	304.37	138	81
		129	99
POLY-DECAMETHYLENE TETRADECANEDIAMIDE	394.62	189	2
POLY-DECAMETHYLENE 2,5-TETRAHYDROFURAN-			
DIPROPIONAMIDE	352.50	178	402
POLY-DECAMETHYLENE %TETRAMETHYLENEDISULFONYL+-			
DICAPROAMIDE	550.80	236	402
POLY-DECAMETHYLENE TETRAMETHYLENEDIURETHAN	314.42	171	866
POLY-DECAMETHYLENE TRIDECANEDIAMIDE	380.60	175	339
POLY-1-DECENE	140.26	34	250
POLY-2,2-DIETHYLTRIMETHYLENE			
4,4a-METHYLENEDIPHENYLENEDIURETHAN	382.44	150	402
POLY-DIKETENE	84.07	115	190
		115	217
POLY-4,4a-DIMETHYLBIPHENYL	180.24	550	832
POLY-DIMETHYLENE SULFIDE	60.11	190	181
		210	241
POLY-4,4-DIMETHYLHEPTAMETHYLENE			
4,4a-SULFONYLDIBENZAMIDE	428.53	268	835
POLY-DIMETHYL KETENE I.	70.09	250	179
		255	130
II.	140.18	170	179
		180	248
POLY-2,6-DIMETHYL-1,4-PHENYLENE OXIDE	120.14	261	226
POLY-2,5-DIMETHYLPIPERAZINE ISOPHTHALAMIDE	242.27	315	833
POLY-2,5-DIMETHYLPIPERAZINE PHTHALAMIDE	242.27	350	833
POLY-2,5-DIMETHYLPIPERAZINE TEREPHTHALAMIDE	242.27	350	833
POLY-2,2-DIMETHYLTRIMETHYLENE			
4,4a-SULFONYLDIBENZAMIDE	372.43	284	835
POLY-1,3-DIOXOLANE	74.08	55	852
POLY-DIPHENYLMETHANE %DIPHENYLMETHYLENE+	166.21	220	831
---, 4,4a-DIMETHYL-	194.26	255	832
POLY-DITOLYLMETHANE	194.26	180	831
POLY-DIVINYLBENZAL	176.21	100	830
---, 2-METHYL-	190.23	95	830
---, 4-METHYL-	190.23	115	830
POLY-DIVINYLFURFURAL	166.17	145	830
POLY-DODECAMETHYLENE ADIPAMIDE	310.47	210	339
POLY-DODECAMETHYLENE DODECAMETHYLENEDIURETHAN	454.68	128	866
POLY-DODECAMETHYLENE SEBACAMIDE	366.57	173	339
POLY-DODECANEDIOIC ANHYDRIDE	212.28	87	823
POLY-1-DODECENE	168.31	45	48
		49	250
POLY-EICOSAMETHYLENE MALONATE	382.57	69	868
POLY-ENANTHALDEHYDE	114.18	150	329
POLY-EPIBROMOHYDRIN	136.99	112	809
POLY-EPICHLOROHYDRIN	92.53	117	119
		121	194
		135	318
POLY-EPIFLUOROHYDRIN	76.07	68	119
POLY-A-ETHYLACRYLONITRILE	81.11	200	853
POLY-ETHYLENE	28.05	110	46
		137	85
		141	206
		141	286
		142	315
---, CHLOROTRIFLUORO-	116.48	210	46
		220	49
		215	116
		222	341
---, 1-ETHOXY-2-METHOXY-	102.13		
TRANS-		217	141
---, 1-ETHOXY-2-METHYL-	86.13		
TRANS-		243	141
---, 1-ISOBUTOXY-2-METHYL-	114.18		
TRANS-		226	141
---, 1-METHOXY-2-METHYL-	72.10		
TRANS-		210	141
---, TETRAFLUORO-	100.02	327	46
		330	11
		330	101
POLY-ETHYLENE ADIPAMIDE	170.21	310	402

POLYMER	MOLECULAR WEIGHT	MELTING POINT	REF.
POLY-ETHYLENE ADIPATE	172.18	52	27
		47	265
		54	291
		50	46
POLY-ETHYLENE ADIPYLDIUREA	356.26	241	402
POLY-ETHYLENE ADIPYLDIURETHAN	258.23	210	402
POLY-ETHYLENE-CO-2-BUTENE	84.16	135	191
POLY-ETHYLENE CARBONAMIDE	86.09	400	402
POLY-ETHYLENE P-%CARBOXYPHENOXY+-ACETATE	222.19	140	290
POLY-ETHYLENE P-%CARBOXYPHENOXY+-BUTYRATE	250.24	85	290
POLY-ETHYLENE P-%CARBOXYPHENOXY+-CAPROATE	278.29	45	290
POLY-ETHYLENE P-%CARBOXYPHENOXY+-HEPTANOATE	292.32	55	290
POLY-ETHYLENE P-%CARBOXYPHENOXY+-UNDECANOATE	348.42	65	290
POLY-ETHYLENE P-%CARBOXYPHENOXY+-VALERATE	264.27	55	290
POLY-ETHYLENE-CO-CYCLOHEPTENE	124.22	74	259
POLY-ETHYLENE-CO-CYCLOPENTENE	96.18	185	228
POLY-ETHYLENE CYCLOPROPANEDICARBOXAMIDE TRANS-	154.17		
		350	860
POLY-4,4a-ETHYLENEDIBENZOIC ANHYDRIDE	252.26	340	854
POLY-4,4a-%ETHYLENEDIOXY+-3,3a-BISMETHOXY-DIBENZOIC ANHYDRIDE	344.31	220	855
POLY-3,3a-%ETHYLENEDIOXY+-DIBENZOIC ANHYDRIDE	284.26	237	854
POLY-4,4a-%ETHYLENEDIOXY+-DIBENZOIC ANHYDRIDE	284.26	208	854
		215	827
POLY-%ETHYLENEDIOXY+-DIETHYLENE ADIPAMIDE	258.31	160	291
		190	402
POLY-%ETHYLENEDIOXY+-DIETHYLENE 1,4-PIPERAZINE-DIACETAMIDE	314.38	115	291
POLY-4,4a-ETHYLENEDIPHENYLENE ADIPAMIDE	322.39	400	402
POLY-4,4a-ETHYLENEDIPHENYLENE CARBONATE	240.25	300	858
POLY-4,4a-ETHYLENEDIPHENYLENE SEBACAMIDE	378.50	360	402
POLY-ETHYLENE DISULFIDE	92.17	130	294
		113	295
POLY-%ETHYLENEDISULFONYL+-DIACETIC ANHYDRIDE	256.24	185	856
POLY-%ETHYLENEDISULFONYL+-DIPROPIONIC ANHYDRIDE	284.30	255	856
POLY-4,4a-%2,2a-ETHYLENEDITHIAZOLE+-P-PHENYLENE	270.36	265	810
POLY-%ETHYLENEDITHIO+-DIACETIC ANHYDRIDE	192.24	83	827
POLY-%ETHYLENEDITHIO+-DIPROPIONIC ANHYDRIDE	220.30	75	827
POLY-ETHYLENE DODECANEDIAMIDE	254.36	261	244
POLY-ETHYLENE 4,4a-%ETHYLENEDIOXY+-DIBENZOATE	328.31	243	290
		240	291
POLY-ETHYLENE 4,4a-%ETHYLENEDITHIO+-DIBENZOATE	328.37	190	291
POLY-ETHYLENE FUMARAMIDE	140.14	50	402
POLY-ETHYLENE HEXAMETHYLENEDIURETHAN	230.26	184	402
POLY-ETHYLENE HEXAMETHYLENE SULFIDE	176.33	86	819
POLY-ETHYLENE ISOPHTHALATE	192.16	240	111
		143	398
POLY-ETHYLENE 4,4a-METHYLENEDIBENZOATE	282.28	220	291
POLY-ETHYLENE MUCONAMIDE	172.22	61	402
POLY-ETHYLENE OXALATE	116.07	172	821
POLY-ETHYLENE OXIDE	44.04	66	81
		62	180
		72	518
		66	348
---, 1,1-BISCHLOROMETHYL-	141.00	180	816
POLY-ETHYLENE-P-OXYBENZOATE	164.15	220	354
		203	327
POLY-ETHYLENE 4,4a-OXYDIBENZOATE	284.26	152	291
POLY-ETHYLENE-P-OXYPHENYLENEACETATE	178.18	172	841
POLY-ETHYLENE P-PHENYLENEDIACETATE	220.22	107	325
		137	341
POLY-ETHYLENE P-PHENYLENE OXIDE	136.14	270	868
POLY-ETHYLENE PHTHALAMIDE	190.20	250	833
POLY-ETHYLENE 1,4-PIPERAZINEDICARBOXYLATE	200.19	245	386
POLY-ETHYLENE SEBACAMIDE	226.31	276	244
		254	291
		280	402
POLY-ETHYLENE SEBACATE	228.28	78	302
		72	265
		76	137
		79	46
POLY-ETHYLENE SEBACYLDIUREA	312.36	228	402
POLY-ETHYLENE SEBACYLDIURETHAN	314.33	198	402

References page III-51

POLYMER	MOLECULAR WEIGHT	MELTING POINT	REF.
POLY-ETHYLENE SUBERATE	200.23	55	27
POLY-ETHYLENE SUCCINATE	144.12	103	302
		108	290
POLY-ETHYLENE 4,4a-SULFONYLDIBENZAMIDE	330.35	380	835
POLY-ETHYLENE TEREPHTHALAMIDE	190.20	455	834
---, N,Na-DIBUTYL-	302.41	190	834
---, N,Na-DIETHYL-	246.30	230	834
---, N,Na-DIMETHYL-	218.25	379	834
POLY-ETHYLENE TEREPHTHALATE	192.16	265	27
		265	290
		284	264
		267	265
POLY-ETHYLENE 2,5-TETRAHYDROFURANDIPROPIONAMIDE	240.30	218	402
POLY-ETHYLENE 4,4a-TETRAMETHYLENEDIBENZOATE	324.36	173	291
POLY-ETHYLENE 4,4a-%TETRAMETHYLENEDIOXY+-DIBENZOATE	356.36	252	841
POLY-ETHYLENE 4,4a-THIODIBENZOATE	300.32	200	291
POLY-ETHYLENE THIODIENANTHAMIDE	314.48	210	402
POLY-ETHYLENE THIODIVALERAMIDE	258.37	220	402
POLY-4,4a-ETHYLIDENEDIPHENYLENE CARBONATE	240.25	195	858
POLY-FORMALDEHYDE %OXYMETHYLENE+	30.02	181	42
		198	217
		178	329
POLY-2,5-FURANDIPROPIONIC ANHYDRIDE	194.18	67	827
POLY-FURFURAL-CO-DIMETHYLKETENE	166.17	180	817
POLY-GLYCOLIC ACID LACTONE, HYDROXYETHYL-	102.09	89	305
POLY-GLYCOLIDE	116.07	223	305
1,4-POLY-1,3-HEPTADIENE	96.17		
TRANS-			
ISOTACTIC		85	371
---, 6-METHYL-	110.19		
TRANS-			
ISOTACTIC		119	371
POLY-HEPTAMETHYLENE ADIPAMIDE	240.34	250	244
		209	291
		226	339
		245	859
POLY-HEPTAMETHYLENE AZELAAMIDE	282.42	201	244
POLY-HEPTAMETHYLENE DISULFIDE	162.30	130	868
POLY-HEPTAMETHYLENE P-PHENYLENEDIACETAMIDE	288.38	234	402
POLY-HEPTAMETHYLENE PIMELAMIDE	254.36	214	244
		196	339
		205	2
POLY-HEPTAMETHYLENE SEBACAMIDE	296.44	208	244
		187	339
POLY-HEPTAMETHYLENE SUBERAMIDE	268.39	230	244
POLY-HEPTAMETHYLENE 2,5-TETRAHYDROFURAN-DIPROPIONAMIDE	310.42	148	402
POLY-HEPTAMETHYLENE UNDECANEDIAMIDE	310.47	195	2
POLY-1-HEPTENE	98.18	-46	48
		17	250
---, 6,6-DIMETHYL-	126.23	104	282
---, 5-METHYL-	112.21	52	129
POLY-4,4a-%4,4-HEPTYLIDENE+-DIPHENYLENE CARBONATE	310.38	200	858
POLY-1-HEXADECENE	224.42	68	250
1,2-POLY-1,5-HEXADIENE	82.14	146	267
		128	340
1,4-POLY-1,3-HEXADIENE	82.14		
TRANS-			
ISOTACTIC		82	371
---, 5-METHYL-	96.17		
TRANS-			
ISOTACTIC		88	371
2,5-POLY-2,4-HEXADIENE, 2,5-DIMETHYL-	110.19		
TRANS-		265	376
		265	183
POLY-HEXAMETHYLENE ADIPAMIDE	226.31	265	2
		270	289
---, N,Na-DIMETHYL-	254.36	75	402
---, N-METHYL-	240.34	145	291
POLY-HEXAMETHYLENE ADIPATE	228.28	56	290
POLY-HEXAMETHYLENE ADIPYLDIURETHAN	314.33	206	402
POLY-HEXAMETHYLENE AZELAAMIDE	268.39	226	244
		185	339

POLYMER	MOLECULAR WEIGHT	MELTING POINT	REF.
POLY-HEXAMETHYLENE 5-TERT-BUTYLISOPHTHALAMIDE	302.40	210	402
POLY-HEXAMETHYLENE CARBONAMIDE	142.20	300	402
POLY-HEXAMETHYLENE CARBONATE	144.17	60	820
POLY-HEXAMETHYLENE P-%CARBOXYPHENOXY+-ACETATE	278.29	50	290
POLY-HEXAMETHYLENE P-%CARBOXYPHENOXY+-CAPROATE	334.40	60	290
POLY-HEXAMETHYLENE P-%CARBOXYPHENOXY+-UNDECANOATE	404.53	72	290
POLY-HEXAMETHYLENE P-%CARBOXYPHENOXY+-VALERATE	320.37	60	290
POLY-HEXAMETHYLENE 1,2-CYCLOHEXYLENEDIACETAMIDE	280.40	255	402
POLY-HEXAMETHYLENE 1,2-CYCLOHEXYLENEDICARBOXAMIDE TRANS-	252.35	242	402
POLY-HEXAMETHYLENE 1,3-CYCLOHEXYLENEDICARBOXAMIDE TRANS-	252.35	312	402
POLY-HEXAMETHYLENE 1,4-CYCLOHEXYLENEDICARBOXAMIDE TRANS-	252.35	360	402
POLY-HEXAMETHYLENE CYCLOPROPANEDICARBOXAMIDE TRANS-	210.27	300	860
CIS-			860
POLY-HEXAMETHYLENE CYCLOPROPANEDIUREA	240.30	180	865
POLY-HEXAMETHYLENE %DECAMETHYLENEDISULFONYL+-DICAPROAMIDE	578.85	210	402
POLY-HEXAMETHYLENE DECAMETHYLENEDIURETHAN	342.47	154	291
POLY-HEXAMETHYLENE 2,2@-DIBENZOAMIDE	322.39	175	402
POLY-HEXAMETHYLENE 3,3@-DIBENZOAMIDE	322.39	142	402
POLY-HEXAMETHYLENE 4,4@-DIBENZOAMIDE	322.39	360	402
POLY-4,4@-HEXAMETHYLENEDIBENZOIC ANHYDRIDE	308.36	151	854
POLY-HEXAMETHYLENE 2,5-DIHYDROXYTEREPHTHALAMIDE	278.30	334	402
POLY-HEXAMETHYLENE DIMETHYLMALONAMIDE	212.29	117	402
POLY-HEXAMETHYLENE 2,5-DIMETHYLTEREPHTHALAMIDE	274.35	143	402
POLY-3,3@-%HEXAMETHYLENEDIOXY+-DIBENZOIC ANHYDRIDE	340.36	157	854
POLY-4,4@-%HEXAMETHYLENEDIOXY+-DIBENZOIC ANHYDRIDE	340.36	157	854
POLY-HEXAMETHYLENE DISULFIDE	148.28	57	868
POLY-HEXAMETHYLENE DITHIOTEREPHTHALAMIDE	278.42	190	402
POLY-HEXAMETHYLENE DODECANEDIAMIDE	310.47	217	244
POLY-HEXAMETHYLENE EICOSANEDIAMIDE	422.68	189	244
POLY-HEXAMETHYLENE 4,4@-%ETHYLENEDIOXY+-DIBENZOATE	384.41	175	290
POLY-HEXAMETHYLENE 4,4@-ETHYLIDENEDIBENZOAMIDE	350.44	175	402
POLY-HEXAMETHYLENE FORMAL	130.18	38	825
POLY-HEXAMETHYLENE 2,5-FURANDIPROPIONAMIDE	292.37	190	402
POLY-HEXAMETHYLENE GLUTARAMIDE	212.29	241	402
POLY-HEXAMETHYLENE %HEXAMETHYLENEDIOXY+-DIPROPIONAMIDE	342.47	105	402
POLY-HEXAMETHYLENE %HEXAMETHYLENEDISULFONYL+-DICAPROAMIDE	522.74	222	402
POLY-HEXAMETHYLENE HEXAMETHYLENEDITHIOUREA	288.50	160	402
POLY-HEXAMETHYLENE HEXAMETHYLENEDIUREA	284.40	300	291
		270	802
POLY-HEXAMETHYLENE HEXAMETHYLENEDIURETHAN	286.36	150	291
		290	402
POLY-HEXAMETHYLENE ISOPHTHALAMIDE	246.30	220	402
		198	868
POLY-HEXAMETHYLENE ISOPHTHLATE	248.27	140	111
POLY-HEXAMETHYLENE 4,4@-ISOPROPYLIDENEDIBENZOAMIDE	364.45	180	402
POLY-HEXAMETHYLENE 3-METHYLADIPAMIDE	240.34	216	291
		230	859
POLY-HEXAMETHYLENE 1-METHYLCYCLOPROPANE-DICARBOXAMIDE TRANS-	224.30	115	860
POLY-HEXAMETHYLENE 3-METHYLCYCLOPROPANE-DICARBOXAMIDE TRANS-	224.30	270	860
POLY-HEXAMETHYLENE 3,3@-METHYLENEDIBENZOAMIDE	336.42	113	402
POLY-HEXAMETHYLENE 4,4@-METHYLENEDIBENZOAMIDE	336.42	132	402
POLY-HEXAMETHYLENE 4,4@-%METHYLENEDIPHENYLENE+-DIOXYDIACETAMIDE	396.47	174	402
POLY-HEXAMETHYLENE %1-METHYL-2,5-PYRROLE+-DIPROPIONAMIDE	305.41	180	402
POLY-HEXAMETHYLENE %1-METHYL-2,5-PYRROLIDINE+-DIPROPIONAMIDE	309.44	200	402
POLY-HEXAMETHYLENE METHYLTEREPHTHALAMIDE	260.33	248	402
POLY-HEXAMETHYLENE OCTAMETHYLENEDITHIOUREA	344.57	160	402
POLY-HEXAMETHYLENE OCTAMETHYLENEDIURETHAN	342.47	153	866
POLY-HEXAMETHYLENE OXALATE	172.16	66	305
POLY-HEXAMETHYLENE OXAMIDE	170.21	320	402

References page III-51

POLYMER	MOLECULAR WEIGHT	MELTING POINT	REF.
POLY-HEXAMETHYLENE OXIDE	100.16	58	181
POLY-HEXAMETHYLENE OXYDIACETAMIDE	214.26	143	402
POLY-HEXAMETHYLENE 4,4ə-%OXYDIPHENYLENE+-DIOXY-			
DIACETAMIDE	398.44	220	402
POLY-HEXAMETHYLENE %PENTAMETHYLENEDISULFONYL+-			
DICAPROAMIDE	508.72	226	402
POLY-HEXAMETHYLENE PENTAMETHYLENE SULFIDE	190.35	65	819
POLY-HEXAMETHYLENE %P-PHENOXY+-DIACETAMIDE	290.35	86	402
POLY-HEXAMETHYLENE M-PHENYLENEDIACETAMIDE	274.35	182	402
POLY-HEXAMETHYLENE %P-PHENYLENEDIOXY+-DIACETAMIDE	306.35	237	402
POLY-HEXAMETHYLENE P-PHENYLENEDIPROPIONAMIDE	302.40	290	291
		295	402
POLY-HEXAMETHYLENE P-PHENYLENE OXIDE	192.25	170	868
POLY-HEXAMETHYLENE PHTHALAMIDE	246.30	150	833
POLY-HEXAMETHYLENE PIMELAMIDE	240.34	228	244
		202	339
POLY-HEXAMETHYLENE 1,4-PIPERAZINEDIACETAMIDE	282.38	168	291
POLY-HEXAMETHYLENE SEBACAMIDE	282.42	228	51
		216	153
		233	244
		215	291
POLY-HEXAMETHYLENE SEBACATE	284.38	67	290
POLY-HEXAMETHYLENE SEBACYLDIURETHAN	370.44	158	402
POLY-HEXAMETHYLENE SUBERAMIDE	254.36	232	244
		235	291
POLY-HEXAMETHYLENE SUBERATE	256.33	58	291
POLY-HEXAMETHYLENE SUCCINAMIDE	198.26	212	402
POLY-HEXAMETHYLENE SUCCINATE	200.23	57	305
POLY-HEXAMETHYLENE SULFIDE	116.22	79	181
		68	295
		76	819
POLY-HEXAMETHYLENE 4,4ə-SULFONYLDIBENZAMIDE	368.45	310	835
POLY-HEXAMETHYLENE SULFONYLDIVALERAMIDE	346.48	215	402
POLY-HEXAMETHYLENE TEREPHTHALAMIDE	246.30	371	834
		350	291
---, N,Nə-DIETHYL-	302.40	182	834
---, N,Nə-DIMETHYL-	274.35	260	834
POLY-HEXAMETHYLENE TEREPHTHALATE	248.27	160	81
		154	99
		161	405
POLY-HEXAMETHYLENE TETRADECANEDIAMIDE	338.52	209	2
POLY-HEXAMETHYLENE 2,5-TETRAHYDROFURAN-			
DIPROPIONAMIDE	296.40	182	402
POLY-HEXAMETHYLENE %TETRAMETHYLENEDIOXY+-			
DIPROPIONAMIDE	314.42	110	402
POLY-HEXAMETHYLENE %TETRAMETHYLENEDISULFONYL+-			
DICAPROAMIDE	494.69	241	402
POLY-HEXAMETHYLENE TETRAMETHYLENE SULFIDE	204.38	67	819
POLY-HEXAMETHYLENE TETRAMETHYLENEDIURETHAN	258.31	180	866
POLY-HEXAMETHYLENE THIODIBUTYRAMIDE	286.42	200	291
POLY-HEXAMETHYLENE THIODIENANTHAMIDE	370.58	170	402
POLY-HEXAMETHYLENE THIODIPROPIONAMIDE	258.37	216	859
		219	402
POLY-HEXAMETHYLENE THIODIVALERAMIDE	314.48	180	402
POLY-HEXAMETHYLENE 2,5-THIOPHENEDIPROPIONAMIDE	308.43	232	402
POLY-HEXAMETHYLENE 4,4ə-%TRIMETHYLENEDIPHENYLENE+-			
DIOXYDIACETAMIDE	424.52	80	402
1,6-POLY-1,3,5-HEXATRIENE	80.12	250	848
POLY-1-HEXENE	84.16	-55	48
---, 4,4-DIMETHYL-	112.21	350	90
---, 3-METHYL-	98.18	285	861
---, 4-METHYL	98.18	200	9
---, 5-METHYL-	98.18	130	9
		110	282
POLY-4,4ə-%2,2-HEXYLIDENE+-DIPHENYLENE CARBONATE	296.35	200	858
POLY-P-HYDROXYBENZOIC ACID	120.10	320	839
POLY-3-HYDROXYBUTYRIC ACID	86.09	176	842
POLY-10-HYDROXYDECANOIC ACID	170.24	80	509
POLY-ISOBUTENE	56.10	44	46
POLY-ISOBUTYLENE OXIDE	72.10	158	816
		155	318
POLY-ISOBUTYRALDEHYDE	72.10	260	329
POLY-ISOPHTHALALDEHYDE	134.13	80	801

POLYMER	MOLECULAR WEIGHT	MELTING POINT	REF.
POLY-ISOPHTHALIC ANHYDRIDE	148.11	259	827
POLY-ISOPRENE, SEE POLY-BUTADIENE, --- 2-METHYL-			
POLY-ISOPROPENYLMETHYL KETONE	84.11	240	347
		240	255
		240	198
		200	379
POLY-A-ISOPROPYLACRYLONITRILE	95.14	310	853
POLY-4,4ā-ISOPROPYLIDENEDIBENZOIC ANHYDRIDE	266.28	235	854
		240	855
POLY-ISOPROPYLIDENEDIMETHYLENE			
4,4ā-METHYLENEDIPHENYLENEDIURETHAN	354.39	190	402
POLY-4,4ā-ISOPROPYLIDENEDIPHENYLENE ADIPATE	338.38	80	837
POLY-4,4ā-ISOPROPYLIDENEDIPHENYLENE CARBONATE	254.27	267	57
		230	858
		265	370
POLY-4,4ā-ISOPROPYLIDENEDIPHENYLENE			
CYCLOPROPANEDICARBOXYLATE	322.34		
TRANS-		180	860
CIS-		130	860
POLY-%4,4ā-ISOPROPYLIDENEDIPHENYLENEDIOXY+-			
DIACETIC ANHYDRIDE	326.33	202	855
POLY-4,4ā-ISOPROPYLIDENEDIPHENYLENE FUMARATE	308.32	240	837
POLY-4,4ā-ISOPROPYLIDENEDIPHENYLENE HEXAMETHYLENE-			
DIURETHAN	396.47	130	402
POLY-4,4ā-ISOPROPYLIDENEDIPHENYLENE ISOPHTHALATE	358.37	280	837
POLY-4,4ā-ISOPROPYLIDENEDIPHENYLENE MALONATE	296.31	96	868
POLY-4,4ā-ISOPROPYLIDENEDIPHENYLENE			
1-METHYLCYCLOPROPANEDICARBOXYLATE	336.37		
TRANS-		90	860
POLY-4,4ā-ISOPROPYLIDENEDIPHENYLENE			
3-METHYLCYCLOPROPANEDICARBOXYLATE	336.37		
TRANS-		130	860
POLY-4,4ā-ISOPROPYLIDENEDIPHENYLENE			
4,4ā-METHYLENEDIPHENYLENEDIURETHAN	478.52	193	402
POLY-4,4ā-ISOPROPYLIDENEDIPHENYLENE OXALATE	282.28	155	837
POLY-4,4ā-ISOPROPYLIDENEDIPHENYLENE			
%P-PHENYLENEDIOXY+-DIACETATE	418.43	165	837
POLY-4,4ā-ISOPROPYLIDENEDIPHENYLENE			
4,4ā-SULFONYLDIBENZOATE	498.53	230	837
POLY-4,4ā-ISOPROPYLIDENEDIPHENYLENE TEREPHTHALATE	358.37	350	837
POLY-METHACRYLATES			
---, TERT-BUTYL-	142.20		
ISOTACTIC		104	851
SYNDIOTACTIC		165	851
---, METHYL-	100.11		
ISOTACTIC		160	31
SYNDIOTACTIC		200	31
POLY-METHACRYLONITRILE	67.09	250	853
POLY-P-METHOXYBENZALDEHYDE-CO-DIMETHYLKETENE	206.23	240	817
POLY-4,4ā-METHYLENEDIBENZOIC ANHYDRIDE	238.23	322	854
POLY-4,4ā-%METHYLENEDIOXY+-DIBENZOIC ANHYDRIDE	270.23	220	854
POLY-4,4ā-METHYLENEDIPHENYLENE ADIPAMIDE	308.37	356	402
---, 3,3ā-DIMETHYL-	336.42	326	402
---, N,Nā-DIETHYL-	364.47	62	402
---, N,Nā-DIMETHYL-	336.42	120	402
POLY-4,4ā-METHYLENEDIPHENYLENE AZELAAMIDE	350.44	275	402
---, N,Nā-DIETHYL-	406.55	41	402
---, N,Nā-DIMETHYL-	378.50	58	402
POLY-4,4ā-METHYLENEDIPHENYLENE CARBONATE	226.20	300	858
POLY-4,4ā-METHYLENEDIPHENYLENE HEXAMETHYLENEDIUREA	352.42	250	402
POLY-4,4ā-METHYLENEDIPHENYLENE SEBACAMIDE	364.47	280	402
---, N,Nā-DIETHYL-	420.57	32	402
---, 3,3ā-DIMETHYL-	392.52	227	402
---, N,Nā-DIMETHYL-	392.52	55	402
POLY-4,4ā-METHYLENEDIPHENYLENE TEREPHTHALAMIDE	328.35	420	402
---, N,Nā-DIBUTYL-	440.56	195	870
---, N,Nā-DIETHYL-	384.46	182	870
---, 3,3ā-DIMETHYL-	356.41	380	402
---, ---, N,Nā-DIBUTYL-	468.61	159	870
---, ---, N,Nā-DIETHYL-	412.51	178	870
---, ---, N,Nā-DIMETHYL-	384.46	229	870
---, ---, N,Nā-DIPROPYL-	440.56	190	870
---, N,Nā-DIMETHYL-	356.41	264	870
---, N,Nā-DIPROPYL-	412.51	156	870

References page III-51

POLYMER	MOLECULAR WEIGHT	MELTING POINT	REF.
POLY-METHYLENE SULFIDE	46.09	245	181
		260	298
		260	311
POLY-3-METHYLHEXAMETHYLENE ADIPAMIDE	240.34	180	291
POLY-METHYLIMINODITRIMETHYLENE OXAMIDE	199.25	202	291
POLY-4,4a-%2,2-4-METHYLPENTYLIDENE+-DIPHENYLENE CARBONATE	296.35	220	858
POLY-3-METHYL-M-PHENYLENE ADIPAMIDE	232.27	225	402
POLY-3-METHYL-M-PHENYLENE SEBACAMIDE	288.38	200	402
POLY-2-METHYLPIPERAZINE ISOPHTHALAMIDE	228.24	280	833
POLY-2-METHYLPIPERAZINE PHTHALAMIDE	228.24	350	833
POLY-2-METHYLPIPERAZINE TEREPHTHALAMIDE	228.24	350	833
POLY-%N-METHYL-2,5-PYRROLE+-DIPROPIONIC ANHYDRIDE	207.22	188	827
POLY-%N-METHYL-2,5-TETRAHYDROPYRROLE+-DIPROPIONIC ANHYDRIDE	211.25	103	827
POLY-1-METHYLTRIMETHYLENE OCTAMETHYLENEDIURETHAN	286.36	82	866
POLY-1-METHYLTRIMETHYLENE 4,4a-SULFONYLDIBENZAMIDE	358.40	272	835
POLY-M-NITROBENZALDEHYDE-CO-DIMETHYLKETENE	221.21	240	817
POLY-NONAMETHYLENE ADIPAMIDE	268.39	205	339
POLY-NONAMETHYLENE AZELAAMIDE	310.47	177	110
		165	339
		189	2
POLY-NONAMETHYLENE AZELAATE	312.44	65	405
POLY-NONAMETHYLENE DISULFIDE	190.35	55	868
POLY-NONAMETHYLENE FORMAL	172.26	55	825
POLY-NONAMETHYLENE HEXAMETHYLENEDIURETHAN	328.44	147	866
POLY-NONAMETHYLENE PIMELAMIDE	282.42	196	2
POLY-NONAMETHYLENE SEBACAMIDE	324.49	176	339
		202	402
POLY-NONAMETHYLENE TEREPHTHALATE	290.34	85	99
POLY-NONAMETHYLENE 2,5-TETRAHYDROFURAN-DIPROPIONAMIDE	338.48	149	402
POLY-NONAMETHYLENE TRIDECANEDIAMIDE	366.57	183	2
POLY-NONAMETHYLENE UNDECANEDIAMIDE	338.52	196	2
POLY-1-NONENE	126.23	19	250
POLY-4,4a-%2,2-NONYLIDENE+-DIPHENYLENE CARBONATE	338.43	190	858
POLY-OCTADECAMETHYLENE 4,4a-%ETHYLENEDIOXY+-DIBENZOATE	552.72	122	290
POLY-OCTADECAMETHYLENE FORMAL	298.49	72	825
POLY-OCTADECAMETHYLENE TEREPHTHALATE	416.58	116	290
POLY-OCTADECANEDIOIC ANHYDRIDE	296.44	95	823
POLY-1-OCTADECENE	252.47	80	6
		110	90
1,4-POLY-1,3-OCTADIENE	110.19		
TRANS-		87	371
ISOTACTIC			
POLY-OCTAMETHYLENE ADIPAMIDE	254.36	250	244
		235	291
POLY-OCTAMETHYLENE ADIPYLDIUREA	340.42	209	402
POLY-OCTAMETHYLENE AZELAAMIDE	296.44	206	244
POLY-4,4a-%2,2a-OCTAMETHYLENEDITHIAZOLE+-P-PHENYLENE	354.51	164	810
POLY-OCTAMETHYLENE DODECANEDIAMIDE	338.52	202	244
		194	291
POLY-OCTAMETHYLENE DODECANEDIOATE	340.49	73	291
POLY-OCTAMETHYLENE EICOSANEDIAMIDE	450.73	179	244
POLY-OCTAMETHYLENE HEXAMETHYLENEDIUREA	312.45	225	402
POLY-OCTAMETHYLENE ISOPHTHALAMIDE	274.35	186	868
POLY-OCTAMETHYLENE OCTAMETHYLENEDITHIOUREA	372.62	190	402
POLY-OCTAMETHYLENE OCTAMETHYLENEDIUREA	340.50	260	291
POLY-OCTAMETHYLENE OCTAMETHYLENEDIURETHAN	342.47	144	402
POLY-OCTAMETHYLENE 2,5-%1,3,4-OXADIAZOLE+	180.24	100	862
POLY-OCTAMETHYLENE PHTHALAMIDE	274.35	123	868
POLY-OCTAMETHYLENE SEBACAMIDE	310.47	207	153
		210	244
POLY-OCTAMETHYLENE SEBACYLDIUREA	396.52	212	402
POLY-OCTAMETHYLENE SUBERAMIDE	282.42	225	244
		216	291
POLY-OCTAMETHYLENE TEREPHTHALAMIDE	274.35	315	868
POLY-OCTAMETHYLENE TEREPHTHALATE	276.31	132	99
POLY-OCTAMETHYLENE TETRADECANEDIAMIDE	366.57	196	2
POLY-OCTAMETHYLENE 2,5-TETRAHYDROFURAN-DIPROPIONAMIDE	324.45	180	402

POLYMER	MOLECULAR WEIGHT	MELTING POINT	REF.
POLY-OCTAMETHYLENE TETRAMETHYLENEDITHIOUREA	316.52	160	402
POLY-1-OCTENE	112.21	-38	48
POLY-N-OCTYLPHOSPHINIDENEDITRIMETHYLENE ADIPAMIDE	370.51	135	859
POLY-OXACYCLOBUTANE *TRIMETHYLENE OXIDE+	58.07	36	180
		35	806
		34	181
---, 3,3-BISBROMOMETHYL-	243.95	220	807
---, 3,3-BISCHLOROMETHYL-	155.03	190	173
		180	148
---, 3,3-BISETHOXYMETHYL-	174.23	83	808
---, 3,3-BISFLUOROMETHYL-	122.11	135	805
---, 3,3-BISHYDROXYMETHYL-	118.13	280	280
---, 3,3-BISIODOMETHYL-	337.98	290	807
---, 3,3-DIMETHYL-	86.13	47	806
POLY-4,4a-OXYDIBENZOIC ANHYDRIDE	240.20	296	854
POLY-*OXYDIETHYLENE+-DIBENZOIC ANHYDRIDE	328.31	190	854
POLY-OXYDIETHYLENE HEXAMETHYLENEDIURETHAN	274.31	120	866
POLY-OXYDIETHYLENE P-PHENYLENEOXIDE	180.20	136	868
POLY-OXYDIETHYLENE SEBACATE	272.33	44	325
POLY-*OXYDIMETHYLENE+-DIBENZOIC ANHYDRIDE	300.26	192	854
POLY-OXYDITETRAMETHYLENE HEXAMETHYLENEDIURETHAN	330.42	124	866
POLY-OXYDITRIMETHYLENE ADIPAMIDE	242.31	190	291
1,4-POLY-1,3-PENTADIENE	68.11		
TRANS-			
ISOTACTIC		95	189
CIS-			
SYNDIOTACTIC		53	234
ISOTACTIC		44	263
POLY-PENTAMETHYLENE ADIPAMIDE	212.52	223	339
		225	402
POLY-PENTAMETHYLENE ADIPYLDIUREA	298.34	222	402
POLY-PENTAMETHYLENE AZELAAMIDE	254.36	178	339
		179	291
POLY-PENTAMETHYLENE CARBONATE	130.14	46	820
POLY-PENTAMETHYLENE CYCLOPROPANEDIURETHAN	228.24	170	865
POLY-PENTAMETHYLENE *DECAMETHYLENEDISULFONYL+-DICAPROAMIDE	564.82	202	402
POLY-4,4a-PENTAMETHYLENEDIBENZOIC ANHYDRIDE	294.33	118	854
POLY-4,4a-*PENTAMETHYLENEDIOXY+-DIBENZOIC ANHYDRIDE	326.33	188	854
POLY-3,3a-*PENTAMETHYLENEDIOXY+-DIBENZOIC ANHYDRIDE	326.33	176	854
POLY-PENTAMETHYLENE DISULFIDE	134.25	44	295
POLY-PENTAMETHYLENE FORMAL	116.16	39	825
POLY-PENTAMETHYLENE GLUTARAMIDE	198.26	198	291
POLY-PENTAMETHYLENE *HEXAMETHYLENEDISULFONYL+-DICAPROAMIDE	508.72	210	402
POLY-PENTAMETHYLENE HEXAMETHYLENEDIURETHAN	272.34	151	866
		235	402
POLY-PENTAMETHYLENE MALONAMIDE	170.21	191	402
POLY-PENTAMETHYLENE OCTADECANEDIAMIDE	380.60	167	339
POLY-PENTAMETHYLENE OXYDIACETAMIDE	200.23	130	291
POLY-PENTAMETHYLENE *PENTAMETHYLENEDISULFONYL+-DICAPROAMIDE	494.69	212	402
POLY-PENTAMETHYLENE P-PHENYLENE OXIDE	178.22	164	868
POLY-PENTAMETHYLENE PIMELAMIDE	226.31	183	291
POLY-PENTAMETHYLENE SEBACAMIDE	268.39	195	339
POLY-PENTAMETHYLENE SEBACYLDIUREA	354.44	205	402
POLY-PENTAMETHYLENE SUBERAMIDE	240.34	202	339
POLY-PENTAMETHYLENE SULFIDE	102.19	65	295
POLY-PENTAMETHYLENE TEREPHTHALAMIDE	232.28	353	854
POLY-PENTAMETHYLENE TEREPHTHALATE	234.23	134	99
		116	291
POLY-PENTAMETHYLENE TETRADECANEDIAMIDE	324.49	178	339
POLY-PENTAMETHYLENE 2,5-TETRAHYDROFURAN-DIPROPIONAMIDE	280.36	153	402
POLY-PENTAMETHYLENE TRIDECANEDIAMIDE	310.47	176	339
POLY-PENTAMETHYLENE UNDECAMETHYLENEDIURETHAN	342.47	123	866
POLY-PENTAMETHYLENE UNDECANEDIAMIDE	282.42	176	291
POLY-PENTAMETHYLENEURETHAN	129.16	150	291
		155	836

POLYMER		MOLECULAR WEIGHT	MELTING POINT	REF.
POLY-1-PENTENE	IA.	70.13	130	276
	IIA.		75	48
			80	9
			78	282
---, 5-CYCLOHEXYL-		152.27	123	328
---, 4,4-DIMETHYL-		98.18	350	90
			231	282
			380	861
---, 3-METHYL-		84.16	273	129
---, 4-METHYL-		84.16	235	48
			228	282
			250	94
---, 5,5,5-TRIFLUORO-4-METHYL-		138.13	255	813
---, 5-TRIMETHYLSILYL-		122.28	133	71
POLY-4,4a-%2,2-PENTYLIDENE+-DIPHENYLENE CARBONATE		282.32	220	858
POLY-M-PHENYLENE ADIPAMIDE		218.25	296	402
			250	868
POLY-O-PHENYLENE ADIPAMIDE		218.25	179	868
POLY-P-PHENYLENE ADIPAMIDE		218.25	262	402
POLY-P-PHENYLENE ADIPATE		220.22	190	837
POLY-M-PHENYLENE CYCLOPROPANEDICARBOXYLATE		204.16		
TRANS-			105	860
CIS-			65	860
POLY-P-PHENYLENE CYCLOPROPANEDICARBOXYLATE		204.16		
TRANS-			280	860
CIS-			160	860
POLY-P-PHENYLENEDIACETIC ANHYDRIDE		178.16	92	827
			152	855
POLY-P-PHENYLENEDIETHYLENE ADIPAMIDE		274.35	310	402
POLY-P-PHENYLENEDIETHYLENE AZELAAMIDE		316.43	250	402
POLY-P-PHENYLENEDIETHYLENE OCTAMETHYLENEDIURETHAN		362.46	212	402
			212	291
POLY-P-PHENYLENEDIETHYLENE M-PHENYLENEDIACETAMIDE		322.39	222	402
POLY-P-PHENYLENEDIETHYLENE SEBACAMIDE		330.46	285	841
POLY-%M-PHENYLENEDIOXY+-DIACETIC ANHYDRIDE		208.16	130	827
POLY-%P-PHENYLENEDIOXY+-DIACETIC ANHYDRIDE		208.16	158	855
			152	827
POLY-%P-PHENYLENEDIOXY+-DIETHYLENE OCTAMETHYLENE-				
DIURETHAN		394.46	212	866
POLY-P-PHENYLENEDIPROPIONIC ANHYDRIDE		204.22	92	827
POLY-4,4a-%2,2a-M-PHENYLENEDITHIAZOLE+-OXY-				
P-DIPHENYLENE		410.49	340	810
POLY-%P-PHENYLENEDITHIO+-DIPROPIONIC ANHYDRIDE		268.34	55	827
			50	857
POLY-P-PHENYLENEDITRIMETHYLENE HEXAMETHYLENE-				
DIURETHAN		362.46	158	866
			240	291
POLY-M-PHENYLENE HEXAMETHYLENEDIURETHAN		278.30	150	402
POLY-M-PHENYLENE ISOPHTHALATE		240.20	245	837
POLY-P-PHENYLENE MALONATE		178.14	233	868
POLY-M-PHENYLENE SEBACAMIDE		274.35	205	868
			256	402
POLY-O-PHENYLENE SEBACAMIDE		274.35	125	868
POLY-P-PHENYLENE SEBACAMIDE		274.37	145	402
			325	868
POLY-P-PHENYLENE SEBACATE		276.32	150	837
POLY-M-PHENYLENE SUBERAMIDE		246.30	196	868
POLY-O-PHENYLENE SUBERAMIDE		246.30	150	868
POLY-P-PHENYLENE SUCCINATE		192.16	230	837
			300	841
POLY-P-PHENYLENE SULFIDE		108.15	290	849
---, 2-METHYL-		122.18	100	849
POLY-P-PHENYLENE TRIMETHYLENE OXIDE		150.17	166	868
POLY-4,4a-PHENYLETHYLIDENEDIPHENYLENE CARBONATE		316.34	230	858
POLY-PHENYLISOCYANATE		119.12	275	814
POLY-PIMELIC ANHYDRIDE		142.15	55	823
POLY-PIPERAZINE ADIPAMIDE		196.24	355	386
POLY-PIPERAZINE AZELAAMIDE		238.32	148	402
POLY-PIPERAZINE CYCLOPROPANEDICARBOXAMIDE		180.20		
TRANS-			330	860
POLY-PIPERAZINE CYCLOPROPANEDIUREA		210.23	260	865
POLY-1,4-PIPERAZINEDIETHYLENE HEXAMETHYLENE-				
DIURETHAN		342.43	165	291

POLYMER	MOLECULAR WEIGHT	MELTING POINT	REF.
POLY-PIPERAZINE HEXAMETHYLENEDIUREA	254.33	245	402
		265	838
POLY-PIPERAZINE ISOPHTHALAMIDE	216.23	540	833
POLY-PIPERAZINE 1-METHYLCYCLOPROPANEDICARBOXAMIDE TRANS-	194.23	130	860
POLY-PIPERAZINE 3-METHYLCYCLOPROPANEDICARBOXAMIDE TRANS-	194.23	280	860
POLY-PIPERAZINE PHTHALAMIDE	216.23	325	833
POLY-PIPERAZINE SEBACAMIDE	201.95	180	81
POLY-PIPERAZINE SUBERAMIDE	168.19	300	402
POLY-PIPERAZINE TEREPHTHALAMIDE	216.23	350	833
		380	402
POLY-PIPERAZINE %TRIMETHYLENEDITHIO+- DIPROPIONAMIDE	302.44	100	402
POLY-1,4-PIPERIDINEURETHAN	127.14	270	836
POLY-PROPENE	42.08		
ISOTACTIC		176	10
		180	250
		165	282
		178	349
---, 3-CYCLOHEXYL-	124.22	230	90
		215	282
		214	328
---, 3-CYCLOPENTYL-	110.19	225	90
		210	328
---, HEXAFLUORO-	150.03	160	268
---, 3-PHENYL- %ALLYLBENZENE+	118.17	230	90
		208	187
		185	282
---, ---, 2,5-DIMETHYL-	146.22	338	187
---, ---, 3,4-DIMETHYL-	146.22	275	187
---, ---, 3,5-DIMETHYL-	146.22	252	187
---, 3-SILYL-	72.15	128	71
---, 3-M-TOLYL-	132.20	180	187
---, 3-O-TOLYL-	132.20	290	187
---, 3-P-TOLYL-	132.20	240	187
---, 3-TRIMETHYLSILYL-	114.23	360	71
POLY-PROPENYL ETHERS			
---, ETHYL-	86.13	230	804
---, METHYL-	72.10	287	804
---, PROPYL-	100.16	168	804
POLY-B-PROPIOLACTONE	72.06	122	317
POLY-PROPIONALDEHYDE	58.08	185	329
POLY-A-PROPYLACRYLONITRILE	95.14	210	853
POLY-PROPYLENE OXALATE	130.10	180	305
POLY-PROPYLENE OXIDE	58.07	75	18
		75	377
		73	285
---, 2-CHLOROMETHYL-	106.55	126	816
---, 3-PHENOXY-	150.17	215	238
		210	297
		208	318
POLY-PROPYLENE 4,4a-SULFONYLDIBENZAMIDE	344.37	335	855
POLY-SEBACIC ANHYDRIDE	184.13	80	826
		82	822
POLY-STYRENE	104.14	240	10
		250	90
		235	282
---, 2,4-DIMETHYL-	144.21	310	75
		350	74
---, 2,5-DIMETHYL-	144.21	330	75
		340	74
---, 3,4-DIMETHYL-	144.21	240	75
---, 3,5-DIMETHYL-	144.21	270	75
---, O-FLUORO-	122.14	270	75
---, P-FLUORO-	122.14	265	75
---, O-METHYL-	130.18	360	74
---, ---, P-FLUORO-	156.16	360	75
---, M-METHYL-	130.18	215	74
		215	80
---, TRIMETHYLSILYL-	176.30	284	103
POLY-STYRENE OXIDE	120.14	149	809
		140	318

References page III-51

POLYMER	MOLECULAR WEIGHT	MELTING POINT	REF.
POLY-SUBERIC ANHYDRIDE	156.18	66	823
POLY-SULFONYLDIPROPIONIC ANHYDRIDE	192.18	237	856
POLY-SULFUR TRIOXIDE	80.06	32	288
POLY-TEREPHTHALALDEHYDE	134.13	120	801
---, 2,5-DIMETHYL-	162.18	140	801
POLY-TEREPHTHALIC ANHYDRIDE	148.11	410	826
		400	827
POLY-TETRADECAMETHYLENE FORMAL	242.39	69	825
POLY-TETRADECANEDIOIC ANHYDRIDE	240.33	91	823
POLY-1-TETRADECENE	196.36	57	250
POLY-TETRAHYDROFURAN %TETRAMETHYLENE OXIDE+	72.10	57	180
		35	348
		60	366
POLY-2,5-TETRAHYDROFURANDIPROPIONIC ANHYDRIDE	198.21	135	827
POLY-TETRAMETHYLENE ADIPAMIDE	198.26	295	291
		308	51
POLY-TETRAMETHYLENE ADIPATE	200.23	48	325
POLY-TETRAMETHYLENE AZELAAMIDE	240.34	223	339
		253	402
POLY-TETRAMETHYLENE AZELAATE	242.31	37	325
POLY-TETRAMETHYLENE CARBONAMIDE	114.14	400	402
POLY-TETRAMETHYLENE CARBONATE	116.11	59	320
POLY-TETRAMETHYLENE 1,4-CYCLOHEXYLENEDIURETHAN	256.30	260	866
POLY-TETRAMETHYLENE CYCLOPROPANEDIURETHAN	214.22	180	865
POLY-TETRAMETHYLENE %DECAMETHYLENEDISULFONYL+-DICAPROAMIDE	550.80	219	402
POLY-4,4a-TETRAMETHYLENEDIBENZOIC ANHYDRIDE	280.31	263	854
POLY-4,4a-%TETRAMETHYLENEDIOXY+-3,3a-BISMETHOXY-DIBENZOIC ANHYDRIDE	372.36	172	855
POLY-3,3a-%TETRAMETHYLENEDIOXY+-DIBENZOIC ANHYDRIDE	312.31	199	854
POLY-4,4a-%TETRAMETHYLENEDIOXY+-DIBENZOIC ANHYDRIDE	312.31	204	854
POLY-%TETRAMETHYLENEDIOXY+-DITRIMETHYLENE OXAMIDE	258.31	162	291
		167	402
POLY-TETRAMETHYLENE DISULFIDE	120.22	39	295
POLY-4,4a-%2,2a-TETRAMETHYLENEDITHIAZOLE+-P-PHENYLENE	298.41	252	810
POLY-4,4a-%TETRAMETHYLENEDITHIO+-DIBENZOIC ANHYDRIDE	344.43	206	854
POLY-TETRAMETHYLENE DODECANEDIAMIDE	282.42	245	153
POLY-TETRAMETHYLENE 4,4a-%ETHYLENEDIOXY+DIBENZOATE	356.36	180	290
POLY-TETRAMETHYLENE %HEXAMETHYLENEDISULFONYL+-DICAPROAMIDE	494.69	228	402
POLY-TETRAMETHYLENE HEXAMETHYLENEDIURETHAN	258.31	180	291
		173	101
		184	402
---, 1,4-DIMETHYL-	286.36	104	866
POLY-TETRAMETHYLENE ISOPHTHALATE	220.21	152	111
POLY-TETRAMETHYLENE NONAMETHYLENEDIURETHAN	300.39	140	866
POLY-TETRAMETHYLENE OCTAMETHYLENEDIURETHAN	286.36	160	866
POLY-TETRAMETHYLENE %PENTAMETHYLENEDISULFONYL+-DICAPROAMIDE	480.67	232	402
POLY-TETRAMETHYLENE PENTAMETHYLENEDIURETHAN	244.29	159	866
POLY-TETRAMETHYLENE P-PHENYLENEDIACETATE	248.27	63	325
POLY-TETRAMETHYLENE PIMELAMIDE	212.52	235	339
		238	402
POLY-TETRAMETHYLENE SEBACAMIDE	254.36	254	153
		239	291
POLY-TETRAMETHYLENE SEBACATE	256.33	60	325
POLY-TETRAMETHYLENE SUBERAMIDE	226.31	250	291
POLY-TETRAMETHYLENE SUBERATE	228.28	56	291
POLY-TETRAMETHYLENE SUCCINAMIDE	170.21	287	402
---, N,Na-DIMETHYL-	198.26	123	402
POLY-TETRAMETHYLENE SULFIDE	88.16	67	161
POLY-TETRAMETHYLENE SULFONE	101.31	100	845
POLY-TETRAMETHYLENE 4,4a-SULFONYLDIBENZAMIDE	358.40	358	855
POLY-TETRAMETHYLENE TEREPHTHALAMIDE	218.25	436	854
---, N,Na-DIMETHYL-	246.30	272	854
POLY-TETRAMETHYLENE TEREPHTHALATE	220.21	232	99
POLY-TETRAMETHYLENE 2,5-TETRAHYDROFURAN-DIPROPIONAMIDE	268.35	210	402
POLY-TETRAMETHYLENE TETRAMETHYLENEDITHIOUREA	260.41	213	402

POLYMER	MOLECULAR WEIGHT	MELTING POINT	REF.
POLY-TETRAMETHYLENE TETRAMETHYLENEDIURETHAN	230.26	193	291
		193	866
POLY-TETRAMETHYLENE THIODITRIMETHYLENEDIURETHAN	290.37	133	866
POLY-TETRAMETHYLENE UNDECAMETHYLENEDIURETHAN	328.44	146	866
POLY-TETRAMETHYLENE UNDECANEDIAMIDE	268.39	208	339
POLY-TETRAMETHYL-P-SILPHENYLENESILOXANE	208.35	148	225
POLY-THIODIETHYLENE HEXAMETHYLENEDIURETHAN	290.37	134	866
POLY-THIODIPROPIONIC ANHYDRIDE	160.18	55	857
POLY-THIODITETRAMETHYLENE HEXAMETHYLENEDIURETHAN	346.48	125	866
POLY-2,5-THIOPHENEDIPROPIONIC ANHYDRIDE	210.24	78	827
POLY-4,4a-TOLYLIDENEDIPHENYLENE CARBONATE	302.31	215	858
POLY-TRIDECANEDIOIC ANHYDRIDE	226.31	78	823
POLY-TRIMETHYLENE ADIPATE	186.20	45	300
		38	107
POLY-TRIMETHYLENE AZELAATE	228.28	50	107
POLY-TRIMETHYLENE CYCLOPROPANEDICARBOXAMIDE	168.19		
TRANS-		310	860
POLY-TRIMETHYLENE CYCLOPROPANEDIURETHAN	200.19	170	865
POLY-4,4a-TRIMETHYLENEDIBENZOIC ANHYDRIDE	266.28	215	854
POLY-3,3a-%TRIMETHYLENEDIOXY+-DIBENZOIC ANHYDRIDE	298.28	197	854
POLY-4,4a-%TRIMETHYLENEDIOXY+-DIBENZOIC ANHYDRIDE	298.28	267	854
---, 3,3a-BISMETHOXY-	358.33	175	855
POLY-TRIMETHYLENE DISULFIDE	106.20	67	295
POLY-TRIMETHYLENE DODECANEDIOATE	270.36	61	107
POLY-TRIMETHYLENE GLUTARATE	172.18	39	107
POLY-TRIMETHYLENE HEXAMETHYLENEDIURETHAN	244.29	167	866
POLY-TRIMETHYLENE ISOPHTHALATE	206.18	132	111
POLY-TRIMETHYLENE OCTADECANEDIOATE	354.51	76	307
		76	107
POLY-TRIMETHYLENE OXALATE	130.10	86	821
		88	305
POLY-TRIMETHYLENE-P-OXYBENZOATE	178.18	185	841
		211	327
POLY-TRIMETHYLENE PIMELATE	200.23	37	107
POLY-TRIMETHYLENE SEBACATE	242.31	56	305
		53	107
POLY-TRIMETHYLENE SUBERATE	214.25	41	107
POLY-TRIMETHYLENE SUCCINATE	158.15	47	107
		52	300
POLY-TRIMETHYLENE SULFIDE	74.14	100	181
POLY-TRIMETHYLENE 4,4a-SULFONYLDIBENZAMIDE	344.37	298	835
POLY-TRIMETHYLENE TEREPHTHALAMIDE	204.22	399	834
---, N,Na-DIETHYL-	260.33	160	834
---, N,Na-DIMETHYL-	232.28	220	834
POLY-TRIMETHYLENE TEREPHTHALATE	206.18	233	99
		221	291
---, 2,2-DIMETHYL-	234.24	140	291
POLY-TRIMETHYLENE UNDECANEDIOATE	256.33	59	107
POLY-UNDECAMETHYLENE SEBACAMIDE	352.55	169	339
POLY-UNDECANEDIOIC ANHYDRIDE	198.25	70	823
POLY-VALERALDEHYDE	86.13	155	329
POLY-D-VALEROLACTONE	100.11	55	844
		53	305
POLY-VINYL ALCOHOL	44.05	232	310
		265	323
POLY-VINYL-TERT-BUTYL KETONE	112.17	150	812
		240	843
POLY-VINYL CHLORIDE	62.50	212	143
		273	372
POLY-VINYLCYCLOBUTANE	82.13	228	847
POLY-VINYLCYCLOHEPTANE	124.21	300	847
POLY-VINYLCYCLOHEXANE	110.19	305	90
		300	282
		383	328
---, O-METHOXY-	140.22	195	815
---, 3-METHYL-	124.22	355	867
---, 4-METHYL-	124.22	250	867
POLY-VINYLCYCLOHEXENE	108.18	418	850
POLY-VINYLCYCLOHEXYL KETONE	138.20	240	843
POLY-VINYLCYCLOPENTANE	96.18	292	28
POLY-VINYLCYCLOPROPANE	68.11	230	175
POLY-N-VINYLDIPHENYLAMINE	195.25	320	811

References page III-51

POLYMER	MOLECULAR WEIGHT	MELTING POINT	REF.
POLY-VINYL ETHERS			
---, BENZYL-	134.17	162	114
---, BUTYL-	100.14	64	114
---, SEC-BUTYL-	100.16	170	382
---, TERT-BUTYL-	100.41	160	269
		260	114
		238	281
---, 2-CHLOROETHYL-	106.55	150	114
---, ETHYL-	72.10	86	114
---, ISOBUTYL-	110.14	115	46
		117	269
		165	114
		170	281
---, ISOPROPYL	86.13	191	281
		98	269
		190	114
---, 2-METHOXYETHYL-	86.13	73	114
---, METHYL-	58.07	144	114
---, 2-METHYLBUTYL-	114.19	140	382
---, NEOPENTYL-	114.17	216	281
		155	269
		216	114
---, PROPYL-	86.13	76	114
---, 2,2,2-TRIFLUOROETHYL-	126.08	128	114
POLY-VINYL FLUORIDE	46.04	200	79
POLY-VINYLISOPROPYL KETONE	98.14	220	843
POLY-VINYLMETHYL KETONE	70.09	170	379
POLY-1-VINYLNAPHTHALENE	154.20	360	75
POLY-2-VINYLPYRIDINE	105.13	212	185
POLY-VINYL STEARATE	310.50	54	846
POLY-VINYLIDENE CHLORIDE	96.95	190	46
POLY-VINYLIDENE FLUORIDE	64.02	171	373
POLY-M-XYLYLENE, 4,6-DIMETHYL-	132.20	135	832
POLY-P-XYLYLENE	82.14	375	142
		420	219
		375	82
		435	323
		412	224
		400	395
---, BROMO-	183.05	270	395
---, CHLORO-	138.59	290	395
---, CYANO-	129.15	270	395
---, 2,5-DICHLORO-	173.04	183	831
		300	395
---, 2,5-DIMETHYL-	132.20	350	832
---, ETHYL-	132.20	170	395
---, METHYL-	118.17	210	395
		230	142
POLY-M-XYLYLENE ADIPAMIDE	226.30	246	326
POLY-P-XYLYLENE ADIPAMIDE	246.30	333	385
		340	402
POLY-P-XYLYLENE ADIPATE	248.27	70	325
POLY-M-XYLYLENE AZELAAMIDE	288.38	172	402
POLY-P-XYLYLENE AZELAAMIDE	288.38	263	385
POLY-P-XYLYLENE AZELAATE	290.35	59	325
POLY-P-XYLYLENE CARBONATE	164.15	185	820
POLY-%P-XYLYLENEDISULFONYL+-DIACETIC ANHYDRIDE	316.34	170	856
POLY-%P-XYLYLENEDISULFONYL+-DIPROPIONIC ANHYDRIDE	344.39	260	856
POLY-%P-XYLYLENEDITHIO+-DIACETIC ANHYDRIDE	268.34	88	827
			857
POLY-%P-XYLYLENEDITHIO+-DIPROPIONIC ANHYDRIDE	296.39	91	827
		55	857
POLY-P-XYLYLENE DOCOSANEDIAMIDE	470.72	240	402
POLY-P-XYLYLENE DODECANEDIAMIDE	330.46	272	385
POLY-P-XYLYLENE GLUTARAMIDE	232.27	280	402
POLY-M-XYLYLENE ISOPHTHALAMIDE	266.29	225	402
POLY-P-XYLYLENE ISOPHTHALAMIDE	266.29	279	385
POLY-P-XYLYLENE MALONAMIDE	204.22	110	402
POLY-P-XYLYLENE OCTADECANEDIAMIDE	414.61	235	402
POLY-P-XYLYLENE OCTAMETHYLENEDIURETHAN	334.40	168	402
POLY-P-XYLYLENE P-PHENYLENEDIACETATE	296.31	146	291
POLY-P-XYLYLENE PHTHALAMIDE	266.29	230	402
POLY-M-XYLYLENE PIMELAMIDE	260.33	192	402

POLYMER	MOLECULAR WEIGHT	MELTING POINT	REF.
POLY-P-XYLYLENE PIMELAMIDE	260.33	284	385
POLY-M-XYLYLENE SEBACAMIDE	302.40	193	402
POLY-P-XYLYLENE SEBACAMIDE	282.40	300	290
		281	385
		268	291
POLY-P-XYLYLENE SEBACATE	304.37	84	325
POLY-M-XYLYLENE SUBERAMIDE	274.35	213	402
POLY-P-XYLYLENE SUBERAMIDE	274.35	305	385
POLY-P-XYLYLENE SUCCINAMIDE	218.25	360	402
POLY-M-XYLYLENE TEREPHTHALAMIDE	266.29	300	402
POLY-P-XYLYLENE TEREPHTHALAMIDE	266.29	350	402
POLY-M-XYLYLENE TETRADECANEDIAMIDE	358.51	192	402

References page III-51

1. H. Tadokoro, K. Kozai, S. Seki, and I. Nitta, J. Polymer Sci. 26, 379 (1957).
2. W. P. Slichter, J. Polymer Sci. 35, 77 (1959).
3. D. R. Holmes, C. W. Bunn, and D. J. Smith, J. Polymer Sci. 17, 159 (1955).
4. W. J. Dulmage, J. Polymer Sci. 26, 277 (1957).
5. A. Prietzschk, Kolloid-Z. 156, 8 (1958).
6. R. L. Miller, unpublished results.
7. G. Natta and P. Corradini, J. Polymer Sci. 20, 251 (1956); Atti Accad. Nazl. Lincei, Rend., Classe Sci. Fis., Mat. Nat. 19, 229 (1955).
8. G. Natta, I. W. Bassi, and P. Corradini, Makromol. Chem. 18/19, 455 (1956).
9. G. Natta, P. Corradini, and I. W. Bassi, Atti Accad. Nazl. Lincei, Rend., Classe Sci. Fis., Mat. Nat. 19, 404 (1955).
10. G. Natta, SPE Journal 15, 373 (1959).
11. C. W. Bunn and E. R. Howells, Nature 174, 549 (1954).
12. G. Natta, L. Porri, P. Corradini, and D. Morero, Atti Accad. Nazl. Lincei, Rend. Classe Sci. Fis., Mat. Nat. 20, 560 (1956).
13. G. Natta, P. Corradini, and G. Dall'Asta, Atti Accad. Nazl. Lincei, Rend., Classe Sci. Fis., Mat. Nat. 20, 408 (1956).
14. C. W. Bunn, Trans. Faraday Soc. 35, 482 (1939).
15. E. R. Walter and F. P. Reding, J. Polymer Sci. 21, 561 (1956).
16. M. L. Miller and C. E. Rauhut, J. Polymer Sci. 38, 63 (1959).
17. G. Natta, J. Polymer Sci. 16, 143 (1955).
18. C. C. Price, M. Osgan, R. E. Hughes, and J. Shambelan, J. Am. Chem. Soc. 78, 690 (1956).
19. G. Natta, P. Corradini, and M. Cesari, Atti Accad. Nazl. Lincei, Rend., Classe Sci. Fis., Mat. Nat. 21, 365 (1956).
20. C. Legrand, Acta Cryst. 5, 800 (1952).
21. H. S. Kaufman, J. Am. Chem. Soc. 75, 1477 (1953).
22. P. H. Hermans, "Physics and Chemistry of Cellulose Fibers," Elsevier Publishing Co., Inc., New York, 1949.
23. C. W. Bunn, "Chemical Crystallography," Clarendon Press, Oxford, 1946.
24. H. S. Peiser, H. P. Rooksby, and A. J. C. Wilson, "X-ray Diffraction by Polycrystalline Materials," Chapman and Hall Ltd., London, 1955.
25. C. W. Bunn and E. V. Garner, Proc. Roy. Soc. (London) A189, 39 (1947).
26. A. Okada, Chem. High Polymers (Tokyo) 7, 122 (1950).
27. R. de P. Daubeny, C. W. Bunn, and C. J. Brown, Proc. Roy. Soc. (London) A226, 531 (1954).
28. H. J. Wellard, J. Polymer Sci. 13, 471 (1954).
29. C. W. Bunn, Nature 161, 929 (1948).
30. J. D. Stroupe and R. E. Hughes, J. Am. Chem. Soc. 80, 1768 (1958).
31. T. G. Fox, B. S. Garrett, W. E. Goode, S. Gratch, J. F. Kincaid, A. Spell, and J. D. Stroupe, J. Am. Chem. Soc. 80, 1768 (1958).
32. R. C. Reinhardt, Ind. Eng. Chem. 35, 422 (1943).
33. S. Narita and K. Okuda, J. Polymer Sci. 38, 270 (1959).
34. C. S. Fuller, S. J. Frosch, and N. R. Pape, J. Am. Chem. Soc. 62, 1905 (1940).
35. G. Natta, P. Corradini, and I. W. Bassi, Makromol. Chem. 21, 240 (1956).
36. G. Natta and P. Corradini, Angew. Chem. 68, 615 (1956).
37. G. Natta, P. Corradini, and L. Porri, Atti Accad. Nazl. Lincei, Rend., Classe Sci. Fis., Mat. Nat. 20, 728 (1956).
38. J. D. McCullough, R. S. Bauer, and T. L. Jacobs, Chem. Ind. (London) 1957, 706.
39. H. D. Noether, J. Polymer Sci. 25, 217 (1957).
40. C. W. Bunn, Proc. Roy. Soc. (London) A180, 40 (1942).
41. C. Shambelan, Ph.D. Thesis, Univ. of Penna., 1959; Dissertation Abstracts 20, 120 (1959).
42. C. F. Hammer, T. A. Koch, and J. F. Whitney, J. Appl. Polymer Sci. 1, 169 (1959).
43. W. Goggin and R. Lowry, Ind. Eng. Chem. 34, 327 (1942).
44. G. Natta, Chem. Ind. (London) 1957, 1520.
45. G. Natta, P. Pino, P. Corradini, F. Danusso, E. Mantica, G. Mazzanti, and G. Moraglio, J. Am. Chem. Soc. 77, 1708 (1955).
46. R. Boyer, Compt. Rend. de la 2e Reunion de Chimie Physique (2 - 7 June 1952, Paris) p. 383.
47. D. E. Roberts and L. Mandelkern, J. Am. Chem. Soc. 80, 1289 (1958).
48. F. P. Reding, J. Polymer Sci. 21, 547 (1956).
49. J. D. Hoffman and J. J. Weeks, J. Res. Natl. Bur. Std. 60, 465 (1958).
50. L. Wood, N. Bekkedahl, and R. E. Gibson, J. Chem. Phys. 13, 475 (1945).
51. R. Beaman and F. Cramer, J. Polymer Sci. 21, 223 (1956).
52. H. Starkweather, Jr., G. Moore, J. Hansen, T. Roder, and R. Brooks, J. Polymer Sci. 21, 189 (1956).
53. R. Wiley, Ind. Eng. Chem. 38, 959 (1946).
54. H. W. Starkweather, Jr. and R. E. Moynihan, J. Polymer Sci. 22, 363 (1956).
55. F. C. Frank, A. Keller, and A. O'Connor, Phil. Mag. 4, 200 (1959).

56. K. H. Meyer, W. Lotmar, and G. W. Pankow, Helv. Chim. Acta 19, 930 (1936).
57. L. E. Nielsen, unpublished results.
58. P. W. Teare and D. R. Holmes, J. Polymer Sci. 24, 496 (1957).
59. K. Little, Brit. J. Appl. Phys. 10, 225 (1959).
60. G. Natta, P. Corradini, and I. W. Bassi, Makromol. Chem. 33, 247 (1959).
61. W. P. Slichter, J. Polymer Sci. 36, 259 (1959).
62. R. C. Golike, J. Polymer Sci. 42, 583 (1960).
63. Y. Kinoshita, Makromol. Chem. 33, 21 (1959).
64. P. H. Burleigh, J. Am. Chem. Soc. 82, 749 (1960).
65. Y. Kinoshita, Makromol. Chem. 33, 1 (1959).
66. R. E. Moynihan, J. Am. Chem. Soc. 81, 1045 (1959).
67. G. Natta, Makromol. Chem. 35, 93 (1960).
68. J. Bateman, R. E. Richards, G. Farrow, and I. M. Ward, Polymer 1, 63 (1960).
69. P. Corradini, Atti Accad. Nazl. Lincei, Rend., Classe Sci. Fis., Mat. Nat. 25, 517 (1958).
70. G. Natta, P. Corradini, and I. W. Bassi, Gazz. Chim. Ital. 89, 784 (1959).
71. G. Natta, G. Mazzanti, P. Longi, and F. Bernardini, Chim. Ind. (Milan) 40, 813 (1958).
72. W. D. Niegisch and P. R. Swan, J. Appl. Phys. 31, 1906 (1960).
73. P. Corradini, G. Natta, and I. W. Bassi, Angew. Chem. 70, 598 (1958).
74. D. Sianesi, G. Natta, and P. Corradini, Gazz. Chim. Ital. 89, 775 (1959).
75. G. Natta, F. Danusso, and D. Sianesi, Makromol. Chem. 28, 253 (1958): D. Sianesi, M. Rampichini, and F. Danusso, Chim. Ind. (Milan) 41, 287 (1959).
76. G. Natta, G. Mazzanti, and P. Corradini, Atti Accad. Nazl. Lincei, Rend., Classe Sci. Fis., Mat. Nat. 25, 3 (1958).
77. W. R. Krigbaum and N. Tokita, J. Polymer Sci. 43, 467 (1960).
78. E. Stanley and M. Litt, J. Polymer Sci. 43, 453 (1960).
79. D. I. Sapper, J. Polymer Sci. 43, 383 (1960).
80. P. Corradini and P. Ganis, J. Polymer Sci. 43, 311 (1960).
81. L. Mandelkern, Chem. Revs. 56, 903 (1956).
82. J. R. Schaefgen, J. Polymer Sci. 38, 549 (1959).
83. F. Danusso, G. Moraglio, and E. Flores, Atti Accad. Nazl. Lincei, Rend., Classe Sci. Fis., Mat. Nat. 25, 520 (1958).
84. N. Yoda and I. Matsubara, J. Polymer Sci. A2, 253 (1964).
85. F. A. Quinn, Jr. and L. Mandelkern, J. Am. Chem. Soc. 80, 3178 (1958).
86. F. W. Billmeyer, Jr., J. Appl. Phys. 28, 1114 (1957).
87. M. Dole, J. Polymer Sci. 19, 347 (1956).
88. A. M. Bueche, J. Am. Chem. Soc. 74, 65 (1952).
89. F. Danusso and G. Moraglio, Atti Accad. Nazl. Lincei, Rend., Classe Sci. Fis., Mat. Nat. 27, 381 (1959).
90. T. W. Campbell and A. C. Haven, Jr., J. Appl. Polymer Sci. 1, 73 (1959).
91. H. W. Starkweather, Jr. and R. H. Boyd, J. Phys. Chem. 64, 410 (1960).
92. G. Natta, G. Mazzanti, P. Corradini, and I. W. Bassi, Makromol. Chem. 37, 156 (1960).
93. D. V. Badami, Polymer 1, 273 (1960).
94. J. H. Griffith and B. G. Ranby, J. Polymer Sci. 44, 369 (1960).
95. C. G. Overberger, A. E. Borchert, and A. Katchman, J. Polymer Sci. 44, 491 (1960).
96. G. Natta, G. Mazzanti, P. Corradini, A. Valvassori, and I. W. Bassi, Atti Accad. Nazl. Lincei, Rend., Classe Sci. Fis., Mat. Nat. 28, 18 (1960).
97. G. Natta, G. Mazzanti, P. Corradini, P. Chini, and I. W. Bassi, Atti Accad. Nazl. Lincei, Rend., Classe Sci. Fis., Mat. Nat. 28, 8 (1960).
98. O. Ellefsen, Norelco Reporter 7, 104 (1960).
99. G. Farrow, J. McIntosh, and I. M. Ward, Makromol. Chem. 38, 147 (1960).
100. N. G. Esipova, L. Pan-Tun, N. S. Andreeva, and P. V. Kozlov, Vysokomolekul. Soedin. 2, 1109 (1960).
101. A. G. M. Last, J. Polymer Sci. 39, 543 (1959).
102. D. J. Shields and H. W. Coover, Jr., J. Polymer Sci. 39, 532 (1959).
103. S. Murahashi, S. Nozakura, and H. Tadokoro, Bull. Chem. Soc. Japan 32, 534 (1959).
104. T. F. Yen, J. Polymer Sci. 38, 272 (1959).
105. C. S. Fuller and C. L. Erickson, J. Am. Chem. Soc. 59, 344 (1937).
106. C. S. Fuller and C. J. Frosch, J. Am. Chem. Soc. 61, 2575 (1939).
107. C. S. Fuller, C. J. Frosch, and N. R. Pape, J. Am. Chem. Soc. 64, 154 (1942).
108. C. S. Fuller and C. S. Frosch, J. Phys. Chem. 43, 323 (1939).
109. C. S. Fuller, Chem. Revs. 26, 143 (1940).
110. W. O. Baker and C. S. Fuller, J. Am. Chem. Soc. 64, 2399 (1942).
111. A. Conix and R. van Kerpel, J. Polymer Sci. 40, 521 (1959).
112. J. A. Gailey and R. H. Ralston, SPE Trans. 4, 29 (1964).
113. H. S. Yanai, Quoted in C. F. Ryan and J. J. Gormley, Macromol. Synth. 1, 30 (1963).
114. E. J. Vandenberg, R. F. Heck, and D. S. Breslow, J. Polymer Sci. 41, 519 (1960).
115. A. M. Liquori, Acta Cryst. 8, 345 (1955).

116. S. Furuya and M. Honda, J. Polymer Sci. $\underline{28}$, 232 (1958).
117. P. Goodman, J. Polymer Sci. $\underline{24}$, 307 (1960).
118. L. Mandelkern and P. J. Flory, J. Am. Chem. Soc. $\underline{73}$, 3206 (1951).
119. S. Ishida and S. Murahashi, J. Polymer Sci. $\underline{40}$, 571 (1959).
120. B. S. Garrett, W. E. Goode, S. Gratch, J. F. Kincaid, C. L. Levesque, A. Spell, J. D. Stroupe and W. H. Watanabe, J. Am. Chem. Soc. $\underline{81}$, 1007 (1959).
121. D. C. Vogelsong and E. M. Pearce, J. Polymer Sci. $\underline{45}$, 546 (1960).
122. P. Corradini and P. Ganis, Nuovo Cimento, Suppl. $\underline{15}$, 104 (1960).
123. G. Natta, P. Corradini, I. W. Bassi, Nuovo Cimento, Suppl. $\underline{15}$, 83 (1960).
124. G. Natta and P. Corradini, Nuovo Cimento, Suppl. $\underline{15}$, 111 (1960).
125. P. Corradini and P. Ganis, Nuovo Cimento. Suppl. $\underline{15}$, 96 (1960).
126. G. Natta, P. Corradini, and I. W. Bassi, Nuovo Cimento, Suppl. $\underline{15}$, 52 (1960).
127. G. Natta and P. Corradini, Nuovo Cimento, Suppl. $\underline{15}$, 40 (1960).
128. G. Natta, P. Corradini, and I. W. Bassi, Nuovo Cimento, Suppl. $\underline{15}$, 68 (1960).
129. P. Pino and G. P. Lorenzi, J. Am. Chem. Soc. $\underline{82}$, 4745 (1960).
130. G. Natta, G. Mazzanti, G. Pregaglia, M. Binaghi, and M. Peraldo, J. Am. Chem. Soc. $\underline{82}$, 4742 (1960).
131. Z. W. Wilchinsky, J. Appl. Phys. $\underline{31}$, 1969 (1960).
132. T. Mochizuki, J. Chem. Soc. Japan, Pure Chem. Sect. $\underline{81}$, 15 (1960).
133. R. Stefani, M. Chevreton, M. Garnier, and C. Eyraud, Compt. Rend. $\underline{251}$, 2174 (1960).
134. M. L. Huggins, J. Chem. Phys. $\underline{13}$, 37 (1945).
135. C. Ruscher and H. J. Schroder, Faserforsch. Textiltech. $\underline{11}$, 165 (1960).
136. Z. Mencik, Chem. Prumysl $\underline{10}$, 377 (1960).
137. M. Dole and B. Wunderlich, Makromol. Chem. $\underline{34}$, 29 (1959).
138. G. Allen, G. Gee, and G. J. Wilson, Polymer $\underline{1}$, 456 (1960).
139. G. Allen, G. Gee, D. Mangaraj, D. Sims, and G. J. Wilson, Polymer $\underline{1}$, 466 (1960).
140. M. Asahina and K. Okuda, Chem. High Polymers (Tokyo) $\underline{17}$, 607 (1960).
141. G. Natta, M. Farino, M. Peraldo, P. Corradini, G. Bressan, and P. Ganis, Atti Accad. Nazl. Lincei, Rend., Classe Sci. Fis., Mat. Nat. $\underline{28}$, 442 (1960).
142. L. A. Auspos, C. W. Burnam, L. Hall, J. K. Hubbard, W. Kirk, J. R. Schaefgen, and S. B. Speck, J. Polymer Sci. $\underline{15}$, 19 (1955).
143. A. T. Walter, J. Polymer Sci. $\underline{13}$, 207 (1954).
144. C. J. Malm, J. W. Mench, D. L. Kendall, and G. D. Hiatt, Ind. Eng. Chem. $\underline{43}$, 688 (1951).
145. C. E. Anagnostopoulos, A. Y. Coran, and H. R. Gamrath, J. Appl. Polymer Sci. $\underline{4}$, 181 (1960).
146. C. F. Horn, B. T. Freure, H. Vineyard, and H. J. Decker, Angew. Chem. $\underline{74}$, 531 (1962).
147. G. Natta, G. Dall'Asta, and G. Mazzanti, Angew. Chem. $\underline{76}$, 765 (1964).
148. A. C. Farthing and W. J. Reynolds, J. Polymer Sci. $\underline{12}$, 503 (1954).
149. H. S. Yanai, quoted in W. E. Goode, R. P. Fellman, and F. H. Owens, Macromol. Synth. $\underline{1}$, 25 (1963).
150. A. Turner-Jones, Makromol. Chem. $\underline{71}$, 1 (1964).
151. M. Niinomi, T. Fukuda, and M. Takayanagi, J. Polymer Sci. in press.
152. G. Natta, Angew. Chem. $\underline{68}$, 393 (1956).
153. G. F. Schmidt and H. A. Stuart, Z. Naturforschung $\underline{13a}$, 222 (1958).
154. G. Natta and P. Corradini, Nuovo Cimento, Suppl. $\underline{15}$, 9 (1960).
155. F. Rybnikar, Chem. Listy $\underline{52}$, 1042 (1958).
156. B. Wunderlich and M. Dole, J. Polymer Sci. $\underline{24}$, 201 (1957).
157. C. W. Smith and M. Dole, J. Polymer Sci. $\underline{20}$, 37 (1956).
158. B. Wunderlich and M. Dole, J. Polymer Sci. $\underline{32}$, 125 (1958).
159. P. J. Flory, H. D. Bedon, and E. H. Keefer, J. Polymer Sci. $\underline{28}$, 151 (1958).
160. R. D. Evans, M. R. Mighton, and P. J. Flory, J. Am. Chem. Soc. $\underline{72}$, 2018 (1950).
161. G. Dall'Asta and N. Oddo, Chim. Ind. (Milan) $\underline{42}$, 1234 (1960).
162. Z. Mencik, Vysokomolekul. Soedin. $\underline{2}$, 1635 (1960).
163. Y. Chatani, J. Polymer Sci. $\underline{47}$, 491 (1960).
164. G. Wasai, T. Tsuruta, and J. Furukawa, J. Chem. Soc. Japan, Ind. Chem. Sect. $\underline{66}$, 1339 (1963).
165. M. Cesari, private communication.
166. H. D. Keith, F. J. Padden, Jr., N. M. Walter, and H. W. Wyckoff, J. Appl. Phys. $\underline{30}$, 1485 (1959).
167. G. Natta, M. Peraldo, and P. Corradini, Atti Accad. Nazl. Lincei, Rend., Classe Sci. Fis., Mat. Nat. $\underline{26}$, 14 (1959).
168. D. Sianesi, R. Serra, and F. Danusso, Chim. Ind. (Milan) $\underline{41}$, 515 (1959).
169. G. Natta, I. Pasquon, P. Corradini, M. Peraldo, M. Pegoraro, and A. Zambelli, Atti Accad. Nazl. Lincei, Rend., Classe Sci. Fis., Mat. Nat. $\underline{28}$, 539 (1960).
170. N. M. Walter, quoted in C. Y. Liang, and F. G. Pearson, J. Mol. Spectry. $\underline{5}$, 290 (1960).
171. S. S. Leshchenko, V. L. Karpov, and V. A. Kargin, Vysokomolekul. Soedin. $\underline{1}$, 1538 (1959).

172. D. J. H. Sandiford, J. Appl. Chem. $\underline{8}$, 188 (1958).
173. M. Hatano and S. Kambara, Polymer $\underline{2}$, 1 (1961).
174. R. Dedeurwaerder and J. F. M. Oth, Bull. Soc. Chim. Belges $\underline{70}$, 37 (1961).
175. G. Natta, D. Sianesi, D. Morero, I. W. Bassi, and G. Caporiccio, Atti Accad. Nazl. Lincei, Rend., Classe Sci. Fis., Mat. Nat. $\underline{28}$, 551 (1960).
176. I. W. Bassi, Atti Accad. Nazl. Lincei, Rend., Classe Sci. Fis., Mat. Nat. $\underline{29}$, 193 (1960).
177. G. Champetier, M. Laualov, and J. P. Pied, Bull. Soc. Chim. France $\underline{1958}$, 708.
178. A. G. Nasini, L. Trossarelli, and G. Saini, Makromol. Chem. $\underline{44/46}$, $\underline{550}$ (1961).
179. G. Natta, G. Mazzanti, G. F. Pregaglia, and M. Binaghi, Makromol. Chem. $\underline{44/46}$, 537 (1961).
180. J. C. Swallow, Proc. Roy. Soc. (London) $\underline{A238}$, 1 (1956).
181. J. Lal and G. S. Trick, J. Polymer Sci. $\underline{50}$, 13 (1961).
182. R. J. Wilkinson and M. Dole, J. Polymer Sci. $\underline{58}$, 1089 (1962).
183. F. B. Moody, 140th National American Chemical Society Meeting, Chicago, September 1961; ACS Polymer Preprints $\underline{2}$, 285 (1961).
184. I. Sakurada, K. Nukushina, and Y. Sone, Chem. High Polymers (Tokyo) $\underline{12}$, 506, 517 (1955).
185. G. Natta, G. Mazzanti, P. Longi, G. Dall'Asta, and F. Bernardini, J. Polymer Sci. $\underline{51}$, 487 (1961).
186. M. Inoue, J. Polymer Sci. $\underline{51}$, S18 (1961).
187. J. A. Price, M. R. Lytton, and B. G. Ranby, J. Polymer Sci. $\underline{51}$, 541 (1961).
188. F. P. Price and R. W. Kilb, J. Polymer Sci. $\underline{57}$, 395 (1962).
189. G. Natta, L. Porri, P. Corradini, G. Zanini, and F. Ciampelli, J. Polymer Sci. $\underline{51}$, 463 (1961).
190. P. Arlie and A. Skoulious, Compt. Rend. $\underline{258}$, 2570 (1964).
191. G. Natta, G. Dall'Asta, G. Mazzanti, I. Pasquon, A. Valvassori, and A. Zambelli, J. Am. Chem. Soc. $\underline{83}$, 3343 (1961).
192. A. Kawasaki, J. Furukawa, T. Tsuruta, G. Wasai, and T. Makimoto, Makromol. Chem. $\underline{49}$, 76 (1961).
193. Y. Chatani, T. Takizawa, S. Murahashi, Y. Sakata, and Y. Nishimura, Makromol. Chem. $\underline{49}$, 76 (1961).
194. J. R. Richards, Ph.D. Thesis, Univ. of Penna., 1961; Dissertation Abstr. $\underline{22}$, 1029 (1961).
195. H. G. Kilian, H. Haboth, and E. Jenckel, Kolloid-Z. $\underline{172}$, 166 (1960).
196. E. J. Addink and J. Beintema, Polymer $\underline{2}$, 185 (1961).
197. G. Damaschun, Kolloid-Z. $\underline{180}$, 65 (1962).
198. R. Koyama, Bull. Inst. Chem. Res., Kyoto Univ. $\underline{41}$, 207 (1963).
199. C. A. Boye, J. Polymer Sci. $\underline{55}$, 275 (1961).
200. A. Kawasaki, J. Furukawa, T. Tsuruta, Y. Nakayama, and G. Wasai, Makromol. Chem. $\underline{49}$, 112 (1961).
201. A. Kawasaki, J. Furukawa, T. Tsuruta, Y. Nakayama, and G. Wasai, Makromol. Chem. $\underline{49}$, 136 (1961).
202. T. Makimoto, T. Tsuruta, and J. Furukawa, Makromol. Chem. $\underline{50}$, 116 (1961).
203. A. Turner-Jones and C. W. Bunn, Acta Cryst. $\underline{15}$, 105 (1962).
204. D. C. Vogelsong, J. Polymer Sci. $\underline{57}$, 895 (1962).
205. C. Y. Liang and S. Krimm, J. Chem. Phys. $\underline{25}$, 563 (1956).
206. M. G. Broadhurst, J. Res. Natl. Bur. Std. $\underline{66A}$, 241 (1962); J. Chem. Phys. $\underline{36}$, 2578 (1962).
207. R. L. Miller and V. F. Holland, J. Polymer Sci. $\underline{B2}$, 519 (1964).
208. A. V. Ermolina, G. S. Markova, and V. A. Kargin, Kristallografiya $\underline{2}$, 623 (1957).
209. E. S. Clark and L. T. Muus, Z. Krist. $\underline{117}$, 119 (1962).
210. V. F. Holland, S. B. Mitchell, W. L. Hunter, P. H. Lindenmeyer, J. Polymer Sci. $\underline{62}$, 145 (1962).
211. J. J. Point, Bull. Classe Sci. Acad. Roy. Belg. $\underline{30}$, 435 (1953).
212. L. G. Wallner, Monatsh. Chem. $\underline{79}$, 279 (1948).
213. H. Hendus, K. Schmieder, G. Schnell, and K. A. Wolf, Festschrift Carl Wurster der BASF vom 2.12.1960.
214. J. Furukawa, T. Saegusa, T. Tsuruta, S. Ohta, and G. Wasai, Makromol. Chem. $\underline{52}$, 230 (1962).
215. G. Champetier and J. P. Pied, Makromol. Chem. $\underline{44/46}$, 64 (1961).
216. F. Rybnikar, Collection Czech. Chem. Commun. $\underline{24}$, 2861 (1959).
217. S. Okamura, K. Hayashi, and Y. Kitanishi, J. Polymer Sci. $\underline{58}$, 925 (1962).
218. O. Ellefsen and N. Norman, J. Polymer Sci. $\underline{58}$, 769 (1962).
219. L. A. Errede and R. S. Gregorian, J. Polymer Sci. $\underline{60}$, 21 (1962).
220. T. F. Yen, J. Polymer Sci. $\underline{35}$, 533 (1959).
221. J. F. Brown, Jr. and D. M. White, J. Am. Chem. Soc. $\underline{82}$, 5671 (1960).
222. A. Ziabicki, Kolloid-Z. $\underline{167}$, 132 (1959).
223. C. J. Brown and A. C. Farthing, J. Chem. Soc. $\underline{1953}$, 3270.
224. M. H. Kaufman, H. F. Mark. and R. R. Mesrobian, J. Polymer Sci. $\underline{13}$, 3 (1954).
225. R. L. Merker and M. J. Scott, J. Polymer Sci. $\underline{A2}$, 15 (1964).

226. W. A. Butte, C. C. Price, and R. E. Hughes, J. Polymer Sci. 61, S28 (1962).
227. E. R. Walter and F. P. Reding, 133rd National American Chemical Society Meeting, San Francisco, April 1958.
228. G. Natta, G. Dall'Asta, G. Mazzanti, I. Pasquon, A. Valvassori, and A. Zambelli, Makromol. Chem. 54, 95 (1962).
229. C. W. Bunn and E. V. Garner, J. Chem. Soc. 1942, 654.
230. E. Giglio, F. Pompa, and A. Ripamonti, J. Polymer Sci. 59, 293 (1960).
231. P. de Santis, E. Giglio, A. M. Liquori, and A. Ripamonti, J. Polymer Sci. A1, 1383 (1963).
232. K. Fujii, T. Mochizuki, S. Imoto, J. Ukida, and M. Matsumoto, Makromol. Chem. 51, 225 (1962).
233. K. Tanaka, T. Seto, and T. Hara, J. Phys. Soc. Japan 17, 873 (1962).
234. G. Natta, L. Porri, A. Carbonaro, F. Ciambelli, and G. Allegra, Makromol. Chem. 51, 229 (1962).
235. G. Natta, I. W. Bassi, and P. Corradini, Atti Accad. Nazl. Lincei, Rend., Classe Sci. Fis., Mat. Nat. 31, 17 (1961).
236. G. Natta, I. W. Bassi, and G. Allegra, Atti Accad. Nazl. Lincei, Rend., Classe Sci. Fis., Mat. Nat. 31, 350 (1961).
237. J. B. Lando and V. Stannett, J. Polymer Sci. B2, 375 (1964).
238. A. Takahashi and S. Kambara, Makromol. Chem. 72, 92 (1964).
239. T. Petitpas and J. Mering, Compt. Rend. 254, 2611 (1962).
240. I. W. Bassi, Rend. Ist. Lombardo Sci. Lettere A94, 579 (1960).
241. S. Boileau, J. Coste, J.-M. Raynal, and P. Sigwalt, Compt. Rend. 254, 2774 (1962).
242. G. Natta, M. Peraldo, M. Farina, and G. Bressan, Makromol. Chem. 55, 139 (1962).
243. R. Aclion, Ann. Chim. (Paris) 3, 5 (1948).
244. K. Dachs and E. Schwartz, Angew. Chem. 74, 540 (1962).
245. K. Okuda, J. Polymer Sci. A2, 1749 (1964).
246. H. Arimoto, J. Polymer Sci. A2, 2283 (1964).
247. G. Natta, G. Allegra, I. W. Bassi, P. Corradini, and P. Ganis, Makromol. Chem. 58, 242 (1962); G. Natta, P. Corradini, P. Ganis, I. W. Bassi, and G. Allegra, Chim. Ind. (Milan) 44, 532 (1962).
248. Y. Yamashita and S. Nunomoto, Makromol. Chem. 58, 244 (1962).
249. L. Becker, Wiss. Z. Karl-Marx-Univ. Leipzig, Math.-Naturw. Reihe 11, 3 (1962).
250. K. J. Clark, A. Turner-Jones, and D. J. H Sandiford, Chem. Ind. (London) 1962, 2010.
251. E. Passaglia and H. K. Kevorkian, J. Appl. Phys. 34, 90 (1963).
252. A. Nishioka and K. Yanigisawa, Chem. High Polymers (Tokyo) 19, 667 (1962).
253. S. Murahashi, H. Yuki, T. Sano, U. Yonemura, H. Tadokoro, and Y. Chatani, J. Polymer Sci. 62, S77 (1962).
254. A. Turner-Jones, J. Polymer Sci. 62, S53 (1962).
255. H. Watanabe, R. Koyama, H. Nagai, and A. Nishioka, J. Polymer Sci. 62, S74 (1962).
256. J.-J. Trillat and R. Tertian, Compt. Rend. 219, 395 (1944).
257. L. Ulicky, Chem. Zvesti 16, 818 (1962).
258. E. Sauter, Z. Physik. Chem. B18, 417 (1932).
259. G. Natta, G. Dall'Asta, and G. Mazzanti, Chim. Ind. (Milan) 44, 1212 (1962).
260. M. G. Broadhurst, J. Res. Natl. Bur. Std. 67A, 233 (1963).
261. L. Becker, Plaste Kautschuk 8, 557 (1961).
262. M. Ogawa, T. Ota, O. Yoshizaki, and E. Nagai, J. Polymer Sci. B1, 57 (1963).
263. G. Natta, L. Porri, G. Stoppa, G. Allegra, and F. Ciampelli, J. Polymer Sci. B1, 67 (1963).
264. G. W. Taylor, Polymer 3, 543 (1962).
265. O. B. Edgar and E. Ellery, J. Chem. Soc. 1952, 2633.
266. H. G. Kilian, Kolloid-Z. 185, 13 (1962).
267. H. S. Makowski, K. C. Shim, and Z. W. Wilchinsky, J. Polymer Sci. A2, 1549 (1964); ACS Polymer Preprints 4, 43 (1963).
268. D. Sianesi and G. Caporiccio, Makromol. Chem. 60, 213 (1963).
269. I. W. Bassi, G. Dall'Asta, U. Campigli, and E. Strepparola, Makromol. Chem. 60, 202 (1963).
270. G. Carazzolo, S. Leghissa, and M. Mammi, Makromol. Chem. 60, 171 (1963).
271. G. Carazzolo and M. Mammi, J. Polymer Sci. A1, 965 (1963).
272. D. C. Vogelsong, J. Polymer Sci. A1, 1055 (1963).
273. F. H. C. Crick and A. Rich, Nature 176, 780 (1955).
274. G. Perego and I. W. Bassi, Makromol. Chem. 61, 198 (1963).
275. U. Giannini, M. Cambini, and A. Cassata, Makromol. Chem. 61, 246 (1963).
276. F. Danusso and G. Gianotti, Makromol. Chem. 61, 164 (1963).
277. F. Danusso and G. Gianotti, Makromol. Chem. 61, 139 (1963).
278. M. Donati and M. Farina, Makromol. Chem. 60, 233 (1963).
279. E. M. Bradbury and A. Elliott, Polymer 4, 47 (1963).
280. G. Carazzolo, Gazz. Chim. Ital. 92, 1345 (1962).
281. E. J. Vandenberg, J. Polymer Sci. C, No. 1, 207 (1963).

282. K. R. Dunham, J. Vandenberghe, J. W. H. Faber and L. E. Contois, J. Polymer Sci. A1, 751 (1963).
283. M. Tomika, Chem. High Polymers (Tokyo) 20, 145 (1963).
284. G. A. Carazzolo, J. Polymer Sci. A1, 1573 (1963).
285. N. S. Chu and C. C. Price, J. Polymer Sci. A1, 1105 (1963).
286. K. H. Meyer and A. van der Wyk, Helv. Chim. Acta 20, 1313 (1937).
287. W. Cooper and R. K. Smith, J. Polymer Sci. A1, 159 (1963).
288. K. H. Meyer, "Natural and Synthetic High Polymers," Interscience, New York, 1950.
289. J. R. Whinfield, Nature 158, 930 (1946).
290. E. F. Izard, J. Polymer Sci. 8, 503 (1952).
291. R. Hill and E. E. Walker, J. Polymer Sci. 3, 609 (1948).
292. D. D. Coffman, M. L. Cox, E. L. Martin, W. E. Mochel, and F. J. van Natta, J. Polymer Sci. 3, 85 (1948).
293. J. R. Schaefgen and P. J. Flory, J. Am. Chem. Soc. 70, 2709 (1948).
294. J. C. Patrick, Trans. Faraday Soc. 32, 347 (1936).
295. C. W. Bunn, J. Polymer Sci. 16, 323 (1955).
296. E. L. Gal'perin, S. S. Dubov, E. V. Volkova, and M. P. Mlenik, Kristallografiya 9, 102 (1964); Soviet Phys. - Cryst. 9, 81 (1964).
297. A. Noshay and C. C. Price, J. Polymer Sci. 34, 165 (1959).
298. E. Gipstein, E. Wellisch, and O. J. Sweeting, J. Polymer Sci. B1, 237 (1963).
299. W. Marconi, A. Mazzei, S. Cucinella, and M. Cesari, J. Polymer Sci. A2, 4261 (1964).
300. W. H. Carothers and J. A. Arvin, J. Am. Chem. Soc. 51, 2560 (1929).
301. K. Ueberreiter and N. Steiner, Makromol. Chem. 74, 158 (1964).
302. W. H. Carothers and G. L. Dorough, J. Am. Chem. Soc. 52, 711 (1930).
303. H. Tadokoro, Y. Chatani, T. Yoshihara, S. Tahara, and S. Murahashi, Makromol. Chem. 73, 109 (1964).
304. W. H. Carothers and G. J. Berchet, J. Am. Chem. Soc. 52, 5289 (1930).
305. W. H. Carothers, Chem. Revs. 8, 353 (1931).
306. G. Natta, M. Peraldo, and G. Allegra, Makromol. Chem. 75, 215 (1964).
307. W. H. Carothers and J. W. Hill, J. Am. Chem. Soc. 54, 1559 (1932).
308. A. Turner-Jones, J. M. Aizlewood, and D. R. Beckett, Makromol. Chem. 75, 134 (1964).
309. W. H. Carothers, J. Am. Chem. Soc. 55, 4714 (1933).
310. M. I. Bessonov and A. P. Rudakov, Fiz. Tverd. Tela 6, 1333 (1964).
311. J. B. Lando and V. Stannett, 148th National American Chemical Society Meeting, Chicago, September 1964 - ACS Polymer Preprints 5, 969 (1964).
312. K. Hirono, G. Wasai, T. Sacgusa, and J. Furukawa, J. Chem. Soc. Japan, Ind. Chem. Sect. 67, 604 (1964).
313. J. Boor, Jr. and J. C. Mitchell, J. Polymer Sci. A1, 59 (1963).
314. G. Wasai, T. Saegusa, and J. Furukawa, J. Chem. Soc. Japan, Ind. Chem. Sect. 67, 601 (1964).
315. B. Wunderlich and T. Arakawa, J. Polymer Sci. A2, 3697 (1964).
316. K. Tsuboi and T. Mochizuki, J. Polymer Sci. B1, 531 (1963).
317. K. Hayashi, Y. Kitanishi, M. Nishii, and S. Okamura, Makromol. Chem. 47, 237 (1961).
318. S. Kambara and A. Takahashi, Makromol. Chem. 63, 89 (1963).
319. J. P. Kennedy, J. J. Elliott, and B. Groten, Makromol. Chem. 77, 26 (1964).
320. H. Wilski and T. Grewer, J. Polymer Sci. C, No. 6, 33 (1964).
321. G. Carazzolo, Chim. Ind. (Milan) 46, 525 (1964).
322. G. W. Urbanczyk, Zeszyty Nauk. Politech. Lodz, Wlokiennictwo 9, 79 (1962); Through Chem. Abstr. 61, 5836b (1964).
323. K. Fujii, T. Mochizuki, S. Imoto, J. Ukida, and M. Matsumoto, J. Polymer Sci. A2, 2327 (1964).
324. P. Corradini and P. Ganis, Makromol. Chem. 62, 97 (1963).
325. E. N. Zilberman, A. E. Kulikova, and N. M. Teplyakov, J. Polymer Sci. 56, 417 (1962).
326. G. Allegra, A. Ponoglio, and I. Pasquon, Rend. Ist. Lombardo Sci. Lettere A95, 335 (1961).
327. M. Ishibashi, J. Polymer Sci. A2, 4361 (1964).
328. A. D. Ketley and R. J. Ehrig, J. Polymer Sci. A2, 4461 (1964).
329. O. Vogl, J. Polymer Sci. A2, 4621 (1964).
330. A. Chiba, H. Futama, and J. Furuichi, Reports on Progress in Polymer Physics in Japan 7, 51 (1964).
331. G. Carazzolo and M. Mammi, J. Polymer Sci. B2, 1057 (1964).
332. J. P. Kennedy and R. M. Thomas, Makromol. Chem. 64, 1 (1963).
333. M. Litt, J. Polymer Sci. A1, 2219 (1964).
334. R. Brill, Z. Physik. Chem. B53, 61 (1943).
335. J. C. Mitchell, J. Polymer Sci. B1, 285 (1963).
336. T. Ota, O. Yoshizaki, and E. Nagai, Chem. High Polymers (Tokyo) 20, 225 (1963).

337. E. Mueller, Melliand Textilber. 44, 484 (1963).
338. J. R. Schaefgen and R. Zbinden, J. Polymer Sci. A2, 4865 (1964).
339. D. D. Coffman, G. J. Berchet, U. R. Peterson, and E. W. Spanagel, J. Polymer Sci. 2, 306 (1947).
340. H. S. Makowsky, B. K. C. Shim, and Z. W. Wilchinsky, J. Polymer Sci. A2, 4973 (1964).
341. F. Rybnikar, Collection Czech. Chem. Commun. 27, 2864 (1962).
342. L. Mandelkern, M. Tryon, and F. A. Quinn, Jr., J. Polymer Sci. 19, 77 (1956).
343. M. Inoue, J. Polymer Sci. A1, 2697 (1963).
344. I. Heber, Kolloid-Z. 189, 110 (1963).
345. H. Wilski and T. Grewer, 145th National American Chemical Society Meeting, New York, September 1963 - ACS Polymer Preprints 4, 464 (1963).
346. G. B. Gechele and L. Crescentini, J. Appl. Polymer Sci. 7, 1349 (1963).
347. A. Nishioka, H. Watanabe, R. Koyama, and H. Nagai, Reports on Progress in Polymer Physics in Japan 6, 311 (1963).
348. H. Tadokoro, Y. Chatani, M. Kobayashi, T. Yoshihara, and S. Murahashi, Reports on Progress in Polymer Physics in Japan 6, 303 (1963).
349. H. W. Wyckoff, J. Polymer Sci. 62 83 (1962).
350. A. Turner-Jones, J. Polymer Sci. B1, 455 (1963).
351. G. Carazzolo and G. Putti, Chim. Ind. (Milan) 45, 771 (1963).
352. G. Natta and G. Moraglio, Rubber Plastics Age 44, 42 (1963).
353. G. Natta and G. Moraglio, Makromol. Chem. 66, 218 (1963).
354. M. Ishibashi, Polymer 5, 305 (1964).
355. A. Turner-Jones and J. M. Aizlewood, J. Polymer Sci. B1, 471 (1963).
356. M. Ishibashi, J. Polymer Sci. B1, 629 (1963).
357. Y. Sakurada, M. Matsumoto, K. Imai, A. Nishioka, and Y. Kato, J. Polymer Sci. B1, 633 (1963).
358. I. Kirshenbaum, Z. W. Wilchinsky, and B. Groten, J. Appl. Polymer Sci. 8, 2723 (1964).
359. N. P. Borisova and T. M. Birshtein, Vysokomolekul. Soedin. 5, 279 (1963).
360. G. Dall'Asta and I. W. Bassi, Chim. Ind. (Milan) 43, 999 (1961).
361. C. A. Boye, Bull. Am. Phys. Soc. 8, 266 (1963).
362. H. Tadokoro, T. Yasumoto, S. Murahashi, and I. Nitta, J. Polymer Sci. 44, 266 (1960).
363. P. R. Swan, J. Polymer Sci. 42, 525 (1960).
364. A. Turner-Jones and R. P. Palmer, Polymer 4, 525 (1963).
365. M. Genas, Angew. Chem. 74, 535 (1962).
366. N. C. Gaylord, Editor, "Polyethers." Vol. I, Interscience, New York, 1963.
367. M. Cesari, J. Polymer Sci. B2, 453 (1964).
368. W. Marconi, A. Mazzei, S. Cucinella, M. Cesari, and E. Pauluzzi, J. Polymer Sci. A3, 123 (1965).
369. W. J. Jackson, Jr. and J. R. Caldwell, J. Appl. Polymer Sci. 7, 1975 (1963).
370. R. B. Isaacson, I. Kirshenbaum and W. C. Feist, J. Appl. Polymer Sci. 8, 2789 (1964).
371. C. Natta, L. Porri, and M. C. Gallazzi, Chim. Ind. (Milan) 46, 1158 (1964).
372. D. C. Kockott, Kolloid-Z. 198, 17 (1964).
373. F. S. Ingraham and D. F. Wooley, Jr., Ind. Eng. Chem. 56, No. 9, 53 (1964).
374. R. Janssen, H. Ruysschaert, and R. Vroom, Makromol. Chem. 77, 153 (1964).
375. G. Natta, I. W. Bassi, and G. Perego, Atti Accad. Nazl. Lincei, Rend., Classe Sci. Fis., Mat. Nat. 36, 291 (1964).
376. F. B. Moody, Makromol. Synth. 1, 67 (1963).
377. G. Allen, C. Booth, M. N. Jones, D. J. Marks, and W. D. Taylor, Polymer 5, 547 (1964).
378. G. Wasai, T. Saegusa, and J. Furukawa, J. Chem. Soc. Japan, Ind. Chem. Sect. 67, 1428 (1964).
379. T. Tsuruta, R. Fujio, and J. Furukawa, Makromol. Chem. 80, 172 (1964).
380. F. Danusso and G. Gianotti, Makromol. Chem. 80, 1 (1964).
381. F. Danusso, G. Gianotti, and G. Polizzotti, Makromol. Chem. 80, 13 (1964).
382. G. P. Lorenzi, E. Benedetti, and E. Chiellini, Chim. Ind. (Milan) 46, 1474 (1964).
383. M. Goodman and Y.-L. Fan, J. Am. Chem. Soc. 86, 4922 (1964).
384. G. Natta, P. Corradini, and P. Ganis, J. Polymer Sci. A3, 11 (1965).
385. A. Bell, J. G. Smith, and C. J. Kibler, J. Polymer Sci. A3, 19 (1965).
386. E. L. Wittbecker, W. S. Spliethoff, and G. R. Stine, J. Appl. Polymer Sci. 9, 213 (1965).
387. G. Wasai, T. Iwata, K. Hirono, M. Kuragano, T. Saegusa, and J. Furukawa, J. Chem. Soc. Japan, Ind. Chem. Sect. 67, 1920 (1964).
388. D. E. Ilyina, B. A. Krentzel, and G. E. Semenido, J. Polymer Sci. C, No. 4, 999 (1964).
389. E. L. Gal'perin and Yu. V. Strogalin, Vysokomolekul. Soedin. 7, 16 (1965).
390. F. T. Simon and J. M. Rutherford, Jr., J. Appl. Phys. 35, 82 (1964).
391. J. Powers, J. D. Hoffman, J. J. Weeks, and F. A. Quinn, Jr., In press.
392. G. Farrow, Polymer 4, 191 (1963).

393. F. Danusso, G. Moraglio, W. Chiglia, L. Motto, and G. Talamini, Chim. Ind. (Milan) 41, 748 (1959).
394. W. R. Krigbaum and I. Uematsu, J. Polymer Sci. A3, 767 (1965).
395. W. F. Gorham, ACS Polymer Preprints 6, 73 (1965).
396. H. Morawetz, S. Z. Zakabhazy, J. B. Lando, and B. Post, Proc. Natl. Acad. Sci. US 49, 789 (1963).
397. M. Barlow, J. Polymer Sci., in press.
398. R. Yamadera and C. Sonoda, J. Polymer Sci. B3, 411 (1965).
399. E. J. Vandenberg, J. Polymer Sci. 47, 489 (1965).
400. Yu. Ya. Tomashpolskii and G. S. Markova, Vysokomolekul. Soedin. 6, 274 (1964); Polymer Sci. (USSR) (English Transl.) 6, 316 (1964).
401. G. Wasai, J. Furukawa, and A. Kawasaki, J. Chem. Soc. Japan, Ind. Chem. Sect. 68, 210 (1965).
402. V. V. Korshak and T. M. Frunze, "Synthetic Hetero-chain Polyamides," Daniel Davey and Co., New York, 1964 (translated by N. Kaner).
403. M. Cesari, G. Perego, and A. Mazzei, Makromol. Chem. 83, 196 (1965).
404. H. Iiyama, M. Asakura, and K. Kimoto, J. Chem. Soc. Japan, Ind. Chem. Sect. 68, 243 (1965).
405. I. Kirshenbaum, J. Polymer Sci. A3, 1869 (1965).
406. H. Kojima and K. Yamaguchi, Chem. High Polymers (Tokyo) 19, 715 (1962).
407. F. Echochard, J. Chim. Phys. 43, 113 (1946).
408. F. A. Quinn, Jr. and J. Powers, J. Polymer Sci. B1, 341 (1963).
409. G. Natta and M. Pegoraro, Atti Accad.Nazl. Lincei, Rend. Classe Sci. Fis., Mat. Nat. 34, 110 (1963).
410. H. Tadokoro, S. Seki, and I. Nitta, Bull. Chem. Soc. Japan 28, 559 (1958).
411. G. Natta, F. Danusso, and G. Moraglio, Makromol. Chem. 28, 166 (1958).
412. G. Natta, G. Allegra, I. W. Bassi, P. Corradini, and P. Ganis, Atti Accad. Nazl. Lincei, Rend., Classe Sci. Fis., Mat. Nat. 36, 433 (1964).
413. V. P. Lebedev, N. A. Okladnov, K. S. Minsker, and B. P. Shtarkman, Vysokomolekul. Soedin. 7, 655 (1965).

801. Yu. V. Mitin, Yu. N. Sazanov, G. P. Vlasov, and M. M. Koton, Vysokomolekul. Soedin. 2, 716 (1960); Polymer Sci. (USSR) (English Transl.) 2, 423 (1961).
802. P. J. Flory, "Principles of Polymer Chemistry," Cornell University Press, Ithaca, New York, 1953.
803. R. F. Heck and D. S. Breslow, J. Polymer Sci. 41, 521 (1960).
804. R. F. Heck and D. S. Breslow, J. Polymer Sci. 41, 520 (1960).
805. Y. Etienne, Ind. Plastiques Mod. (Paris) 9, 37 (1957).
806. J. B. Rose, J. Chem. Soc. 1956, 542, 546.
807. T. W. Campbell, J. Org. Chem. 22, 1029 (1957).
808. A. C. Farthing, J. Chem. Soc. 1955, 3648.
809. E. J. Vandenberg, J. Polymer Sci. 47, 486 (1960).
810. W. C. Sheehan, T. B. Cole, and L. G. Picklesimer, J. Polymer Sci. A3, 1443 (1965).
811. P. Longi, Atti Accad. Nazl. Lincei, Rend., Classe Sci. Fis., Mat. Nat. 31, 273 (1961).
812. C. G. Overberger and A. M. Schiller, J. Polymer Sci. 54, S30 (1961).
813. C. G. Overberger and E. B. Davidson, J. Polymer Sci. 62, 23 (1962).
814. G. Natta, J. Di Pietro, and M. Cambini, Makromol. Chem. 56, 200 (1962).
815. G. Natta, G. Dall'Asta, G. Mazzanti, and A. Casale, Makromol. Chem. 58, 217 (1962).
816. S. Kambara, and A. Takahashi, Makromol. Chem. 58, 226 (1962).
817. G. Natta, G. Mazzanti, G. F. Pregaglia, and G. Pozzi, J. Polymer Sci. 58, 1201 (1962).
818. W. P. Baker, Jr., J. Polymer Sci. A1, 655 (1963).
819. C. S. Marvel and R. R. Chambers, J. Am. Chem. Soc. 70, 993 (1948).
820. W. H. Carothers and F. J. van Natta, J. Am. Chem. Soc. 52, 314 (1930).
821. W. H. Carothers, J. A. Arvin, and G. L. Dorough, J. Am. Chem. Soc. 52, 3292 (1930).
822. J. W. Hill and W. H. Carothers, J. Am. Chem. Soc. 54, 1569 (1932).
823. J. W. Hill and W. H. Carothers, J. Am. Chem. Soc. 55, 5023 (1933).
824. F. J. van Natta, J. W. Hill and W. H. Carothers, J. Am. Chem. Soc. 56, 455 (1934).
825. J. W. Hill and W. H. Carothers, J. Am. Chem. Soc. 57, 925 (1935).
826. N. Yoda and A. Miyake, Bull. Chem. Soc. Japan 32, 1120 (1959).
827. N. Yoda, J. Polymer Sci. A1, 1323 (1963).
828. R. S. Muromova, A. A. Strepikheyev, and Z. A. Rogovin, Vysokomolekul. Soedin. 5, 1096 (1963); Polymer Sci. (USSR) (English Transl.) 5, 157 (1964).
829. H. Zahn and G. B. Gleitsmann, Makromol. Chem. 63, 129 (1963).
830. S. G. Matsoyan and L. M. Akopyan, Vysokomolekul. Soedin. 3, 1311 (1961); Polymer Sci. (USSR) (English Transl. 3, 915 (1962).

831. V. V. Korshak, S. L. Sosin, and V. P. Alekseyeva, Vysokomolekul. Soedin. 3, 1332 (1961); Polymer Sci. (USSR) (English Transl.) 3, 925 (1962).
832. E. P. Melnikova, A. A. Vansheidt, M. G. Krakovyak, and L. V. Kukharcva, Vysokomolekul. Soedin. 2, 1817 (1960); Polymer Sci. (USSR) (English Transl.) 3, 494 (1962).
833. M. Katz, J. Polymer Sci. 40, 337 (1959).
834. V. E. Shashova and W. M. Eareckson, III, J. Polymer Sci. 40, 343 (1959).
835. C. W. Stephens, J. Polymer Sci. 40, 359 (1959).
836. J. R. Schaefgen, F. H. Koontz, and R. F. Tietz, J. Polymer Sci. 40, 377 (1959).
837. W. M. Eareckson, III, J. Polymer Sci. 40, 399 (1959).
838. D. J. Lyman and S. L. Jung, J. Polymer Sci. 40, 407 (1959).
839. J. R. Caldwell and R. Gilkey, 134th National American Chemical Society Meeting, Chicago, September, 1958.
840. J. W. Hill, J. Am. Chem. Soc. 52, 4110 (1930).
841. O. B. Edgar and R. Hill, J. Polymer Sci. 8, 1 (1952).
842. W. G. C. Forsyth, A. C. Hayward, and J. B. Roberts, Nature 182, 800 (1958).
843. P. R. Thomas, G. J. Tyler, T. E. Edwards, A. T. Radcliffe, and R. C. P. Cubbon, Polymer 5, 525 (1964).
844. W. H. Carothers, G. L. Dorough, and F. J. van Natta, J. Am. Chem. Soc. 54, 761 (1932).
845. E. Wellisch, E. Gipstein, and O. J. Sweeting, J. Polymer Sci. B2, 35 (1964).
846. D. A. Lutz and L. P. Witnauer, J. Polymer Sci. B2, 31 (1964).
847. C. G. Overberger, H. Kaye, and G. Walsh, J. Polymer Sci. A2, 755 (1964).
848. V. L. Bell, J. Polymer Sci. A2, 5291 (1964).
849. S. Tsunawaki and C. C. Price, J. Polymer Sci. A2, 1511 (1964).
850. W. Marconi, S. Cesca, and G. D. Fortuna, J. Polymer Sci. B2, 301 (1964).
851. K. Matsuzaki, T. Okamoto, A. Ishida, and H. Sobue, J. Polymer Sci. A2, 1105 (1964).
852. M. Okada, Y. Yamashita, and Y. Ishii, Makromol. Chem. 80, 196 (1964).
853. G. Natta and G. Dall'Asta, Chim. Ind. (Milan) 46, 1429 (1964).
854. A. Conix, J. Polymer Sci. 29, 343 (1958).
855. N. Yoda, Makromol. Chem. 32, 1 (1959).
856. N. Yoda, Chem. High Polymers (Tokyo) 19, 495 (1959).
857. N. Yoda, Chem. High Polymers (Tokyo) 19, 553 (1959).
858. H. Schnell, Angew. Chem. 68, 633 (1956).
859. J. Pellon, J. Polymer Sci. A1, 3561 (1963).
860. R. Oda, T. Shono, A. Oku, and H. Takao, Makromol. Chem. 67, 124 (1963).
861. J. A. Faucher and F. P. Reding, "Crystalline Olefin Polymers," Part I, p. 677, R. A. V. Raff and K. W. Doak, Editors, Interscience, New York, 1965.
862. M. Hasegawa and T. Unishi, J. Polymer Sci. B2, 237 (1964).
863. T. Kagiya, H. Kishimoto, S. Narisawa and K. Fukui, J. Polymer Sci. A3, 145 (1965).
864. G. Natta, G. Dall'Asta, G. Mazzanti, and G. Motroni, Makromol. Chem. 69, 163 (1963).
865. T. Shono, T. Morikawa, R.-I. Okayama, and R. Oda, Makromol. Chem. 81, 142 (1965).
866. O. Bayer, Angew. Chem. A59, 257 (1957).
867. C. G. Overberger and J. E. Mulvaney, J. Am. Chem. Soc. 81, 4697 (1959).
868. P. W. Morgan, "Condensation Polymers: By Interfacial and Solution Methods" (Polymer Reviews, Vol. 10), Interscience, New York, 1965.
869. A. Leoni, M. Guaita, and G. Saini, Chim. Ind. (Milan) 47, 373 (1965).
870. O. Ya. Fedotova, M. L. Kerber, and I. P. Losev. Vysokomolekul. Soedin. 6, 452 (1964); Polymer Sci. (USSR) (English Transl.) 6, 502 (1964).

THE GLASS TRANSITION TEMPERATURES OF POLYMERS

W. A. Lee and G. J. Knight

Royal Aircraft Establishment
Farnborough, Hants, England

Contents

A. DEFINITION OF THE GLASS TRANSITION TEMPERATURE

The glass transition temperature (T_g) of a polymer is a characteristic of the amorphous phase. At this temperature a transition occurs in the temperature (and pressure) derivatives of the energy, heat content, entropy, and volume, but these quantities are themselves continuous functions of temperature (1). Thus, on heating through the glass transition region there is an abrupt increase in the coefficient of expansion, compressibility and specific heat, but no significant absorption of latent heat. The transition is not sharp and is taken as the mid-point of the temperature interval over which the discontinuity takes place.

All physical properties of amorphous polymers which are dependent on the segmental relaxation rate (e.g. viscous flow, mechanical and dielectric relaxation, creep, crystallization, diffusion and chemical reactivity) show a major change on heating through the glass transition region. The magnitude of the property change observed is variable and depends on several factors, in particular the degree of crystallinity of the sample being studied. A polymer sample which is largely amorphous will show, in general, a large drop in Young's modulus (perhaps 3 orders of magnitude) (2) and at the same time a discontinuity in the temperature dependence, or a marked change, in such properties as diffusion coefficient (3-8) and solubility (of gases) (8), glazing (9, 10), creep properties (3, 11, 12), refractive index (13-17), and chemical reactivity (8). The rate of crystallization is extremely slow near the transition interval (8).

On a molecular scale, the glass temperature is the temperature above which the polymer has acquired sufficient thermal energy for rotational motion, or considerable torsional oscillation, to occur about the majority of bonds in the main chain. Below the glass temperature this form of motion takes place very infrequently and the majority of in-chain groups have fixed conformations. In most polymers the glass temperature is unambiguous because considerable cooperation between neighbouring segments is required for rotation about most in-chain bonds, in a manner analogous to the interaction of a set of engaging cog wheels. Transitions also occur at temperatures below T_g where some of the bonds become free to rotate and there is always the possibility of further transitions of this type taking place above T_g. Boyer (8) has classified the various transitions and proposed that $T<T_g$ transition and $T>T_g$ transitions be called $T_{g.g}$ and $T_{\ell\ell}$ transitions respectively.

B. ASSESSMENT OF PUBLISHED DATA

Published values for the glass temperatures of individual polymers sometimes differ greatly. Such discrepancies arise mainly from the use of different rates and methods of measurement, different purities of samples, from the use of polymer samples which are not in corresponding states, and from different interpretations of experimental data.

1. Rate Effects and Dynamic Methods of Measurement

Two kinds of inconsistency derive from rate effects. The first of these is caused by lack of near-equilibrium conditions during measurements and the second by the use of high frequency methods. Fast heating, or cooling rates obviously do not permit the complete polymer sample to attain the temperature recorded in an experiment.   The best criterion for heating rate is that halving or doubling it has no significant effect on the results. Most reproducible results are obtained using a rising temperature scale (18) of approximately 1 °C per hour. True equilibrium conditions are very difficult to attain near the transition region and very slow drifts with time in such quantities as volume, heat content, etc., commonly occur. Such rate effects have been extensively studied (8, 19-28).

Rate dependent methods, for example, torsion pendulum (29-39), creep and stress relation (40-42), resilience (43-46), dynamic mechanical loss (47-52), power factor (53, 54), NMR (21, 55-60) have been widely used and discussed (8, 61, 62). The use of these methods leads to high glass temperatures which should be corrected to zero rates, or frequencies of the order of 10^{-4} cycles/sec. for comparison with glass temperatures obtained by relatively static methods e.g. dilatometry. Though of rare occurrence, it is worth remembering that relaxation processes with different activation energies can be unresolved at particular frequencies (8). This situation is countered by the use of several frequencies and temperatures. In the table which follows glass temperatures determined by rate dependent methods are prefixed "less than" (<) temperatures and are not corrected to one frequency. A correction (45) for frequency may be applied by the use of the WLF relationship (63), by the use of the Lewis equations (61), or by suitable extrapolation to very low frequencies e.g. 10^{-4} cycles/sec. of the data quoted in the references given against the T_g's. Glass temperatures determined by rate dependent methods are usually 20° to 40°C above those determined dilatometrically.

2. Static Methods of Measurement

At least twenty relatively static methods have been employed in the determination of glass temperatures, but many of these are variants of the same principle. For example, the β-ray transition method (64, 65) is based on the change in dimensions of the sample on heating rather than on a change in β-ray transmission characteristics. Other techniques include dilatometry (22, 25, 26, 31, 66-80), dilatometry by differential pressure measurements (81), bouyancy (82-84), coefficient of linear expansion (76), X-ray diffraction (85), refractometry (14, 15, 17, 86-91), calorimetry (24, 92-102), differential thermal analysis (24, 97, 103-109), resistivity (110), penetrometer (111-113), brittle point (13, 21, 74, 114, 115), softening point (43, 116-118), velocity of sound (said to be frequency independent) (119), and infrared spectra measurements (120). Volume/temperature measurements on a rising temperature scale, using the aforementioned heating rate, give the most reliable results (121). Length/temperature methods are not so reproducible as volume methods especially when internal stresses are present. T_g's from refractive index and dilatometric measurements agree well and spurious data arising from glass/polymer interactions of the type observed by Landel (122) and Bills (123) have not been reported. Mechanical techniques, such as penetrometer measurements, brittle points, and softening point in which the sample is under load can give high and low results, but correlations with glass temperatures determined dilatometrically can be established (111, 117). For this reason, these data have been included in the table to provide an approximate value for T_g, but the use of such methods is noted. In many cases a correction to the observed value has been applied.

This correction has been estimated by comparison of the data with that obtained by more reliable methods and is not necessarily the same for ostensibly similar softening point determinations, presumably because of slight differences in the techniques employed by different workers.

3. Purity of Sample

Much of the divergence of published data of glass temperatures is caused by the use of impure samples, especially those containing such impurities as unpolymerized monomer and water. Great care should be taken to remove such diluents because the glass temperatures can be shifted as much as 40°C by small concentrations of impurities (17, 21, 124-126). A full description of the precautions taken to exclude diluents in the preparation of samples is necessary if the validity of published results is to be properly assessed.

4. State of Sample

For the determination and comparison of transition temperatures, polymers must be in corresponding states. This is particularly so with respect to molecular weights, structure, degrees of crystallinity and orientation, and internal stress. Thus the T_g should be determined using a polymer with molecular weight in the high molecular weight range where T_g is independent of molecular weight; this should either be proved, or the T_g should be associated with a particular molecular weight. If the polymer possesses an asymmetric in-chain tetravalent atom, or a double bond, then the sample may be predominantly stereoregular, or in a cis, or trans, configuration. As the glass temperature of some polymers is greatly affected by structural variations of these kinds, the mode of preparation of the polymer sample must be carefully described, or the structure determined, for the results to be of most value. [See data for poly(methyl methacrylate) and poly(1,3-butadiene).] Ideally, samples should be free from internal stress, unorientated and amorphous. Wherever possible, the degree of crystallinity and its effect on the glass temperature (if any) should be quoted.

5. Interpretation of Data

The glass temperature is not always unambiguously determined in some polymers, e.g. polyethylene, polytetrafluoroethylene, Nylon 66, and cellulose triacetate; different authors are wont to call the same transitions by different names (8). Until there is some method of distinguishing between the $T_{g,g}$, T_g, and $T_{\ell,\ell}$ transitions it is necessary to note all the observed transitions which might be called the glass temperature. For this reason, more than one value has been reported for some polymers in the accompanying table. Boyer (8) has suggested a formidable list of criteria for T_g requiring extensive experimentation on each polymer but, unfortunately, very few polymers have been investigated to this extent.

The foregoing remarks emphasize the need for considerable caution in the determination of T_g and show why many literature values should be regarded as probable rather than fully authenticated. Tabulated T_g values have been selected by consideration of the data in the publications referenced. It should be noted that these are often not all in accord and that the temperature selected for the glass temperature is not necessarily quoted in any of the publications referenced. It may be an average of several fairly close values or an estimate from Vicat softening point data. As new data become available a reassessment of all published results based on the accepted criterion for selecting T_g should be made.

C. TABULATED ARRANGEMENT OF POLYMERS

Polymers are subdivided into 16 groups according to structure and are arranged alphabetically within these groups. Polymers having very complex names are not named, but arranged by chemical formulae in order of increasing complexity, placing linear aliphatic polymers first, then alicyclic, aromatic, and lastly polymers containing atoms uncommon to the majority of polymers in their class.

K- 273 = °C

Polymer	$T_g(°K)$	Remarks	References
		1 - POLYOLEFINS AND POLYHALO-OLEFINS	
Polyacenaphthylene	487 <537	Conflicting data	9,117,195,196
Poly(allyl derivatives) See Poly(propene derivatives)			
Poly(1-butene)	249	Wide spread in published data	3,51,64,65,76, 119,176,205-208
Poly(chlorotrifluoroethylene)	318		3,8,20,21,43,53, 56,145,151, 209-218
Poly(cyclohexylethylene) [Poly(vinylcyclohexane)]	<363		48
Poly(4-cyclohexyl-1-butene)	<313		48
Poly(5-cyclohexyl-1-pentene)	~248	Softening point	219
Poly(3-cyclohexyl-1-propene)	<348		48
Poly(cyclopentylethylene) [Poly(vinylcyclopentane)]	<348		48
Poly(3-cyclopentyl-1-propene)	<333		48
Poly(1-decene)	232		51,220
Poly(1,1-dichloroethylene)	254		3,8,21,72,81, 145,221,222
Poly(1,1-dichloro-2-fluoroethylene)	~320	Mechanical method	223
Poly(1,1-difluoroethylene)	228		3,209
Poly(1,2-difluoroethylene)	323		224
Poly(1,1-dimethylbutane)	253	Frequency 1 cycle/sec.	225
Poly(3,3-dimethyl-1-butene)	<337	Softening point; highly crystalline sample; stereoregular	219
Poly(6,6-dimethyl-1-heptene)	<313	Softening point; crystalline sample; stereoregular	219
Poly(5,5-dimethyl-1-hexene)	<326	Softening point; amorphous sample; stereoregular	219
Poly(4,4-dimethyl-1-pentene)	<332	Softening point; crystalline sample, stereoregular	219
Poly(1,1-dimethylpropane)	263	Frequency 1 cycle/sec.	225
Poly(1-dodecene)	<267		51
Polyethylene	148	Conflicting interpretations. Homopolymer always highly crystalline. Branch-point transition at 252°K.	3,8,21,43,48,51, 52,65,70,76,84, 91,101,119,145, 176,189,190,207, 222,227-247
Poly(1-heptene)	<242	Frequency 180 cycles/sec.	51
Poly(1-hexadecene)	<313	Frequency 30 cycles/sec.	51
Poly(hexafluoropropylene)	438	High pressure synthesis	249
Poly(1-hexene)	223		3,51,52,76,185, 219,220,250
Polyindene	358		251
Polyisobutene See Poly(2-methylpropene)			
Poly(3-methyl-1-butene)	<323		48,253

Polymer	$T_g(°K)$	Remarks	References
Polymethylene	155		76
Poly(6-methyl-1-heptene)	<239	Softening point, stereo-regular, amorphous	219
Poly(5-methyl-1-hexene)	<259	Softening point, stereo-regular, amorphous	219
Poly(4-methyl-1-pentene)	302		3,55,188,253-256
Poly(3-o-methylphenylpropene)	353	Crystalline sample	257
Poly(3-m-methylphenylpropene)	313	Crystalline sample	257
Poly(3-p-methylphenylpropene)	338	Less crystalline than o and m isomers	257
Poly(2-methylpropene)	200		3,27,50,63,65, 86,87,94,149, 191,221,243,258-260
Poly(1-nonene)	<226	Frequency method	51
Poly(1-octadecene)	<328	Frequency 25 cycles/sec.	51
Poly(1-octene)	208 to 228		3,51,76,220
Poly(1-pentene)	~233	Conflicting data. T_g lies between 220 and 248°K	3,51,52,76,119, 185,220,253
Poly(4-phenyl-1-butene)	283	Crystalline sample	48,219,257
Poly(5-phenyl-1-pentene)	<245	Softening point	219
Poly(3-phenyl-1-propene)	333		43,219,257
Polypropylene atactic	253	Transition at 298°K has been called T_g^2 (22)	3,8,21,22,51,52, 55,64,65,76,106, 176,205-208,237, 243,246,261-269
isotactic	263	Transition at 298°K has been called T_g^2 (22)	22,43,55,119, 176,264,266
Poly(1-tetradecene)	<283		51
Polytetrafluoroethylene	160, 400	Conflicting data, two major amorphous transitions observed	3,8,36,43,119, 190,229,237,244, 270-277

Polymer	$T_g(°K)$	Remarks	References
2 - POLYACRYLATES			
Poly(butyl acrylate)	218		3,48,86,127, 128
Poly(sec-butyl acrylate)	253		129,130
Poly(tert-butyl acrylate)	251		130
Poly[2-(2-cyanoethylthio)ethyl acrylate]	223		131
Poly[3-(2-cyanoethylthio)propyl acrylate]	215		131
Poly[2-(cyanomethylthio)ethyl acrylate]	249		131
Poly[6-(cyanomethylthio)hexyl acrylate]	214		131
Poly[2-(3-cyanopropylthio)ethyl acrylate]	215		131
Poly(cyclohexyl acrylate)	289		130
Poly[2-(1',1'-dihydroperfluorobutoxy)ethyl acrylate]	228		132
Poly(1,1-dihydroperfluorobutyl acrylate)	243		133
Poly(1,1-dihydroperfluoroethyl acrylate)	263		133
Poly(1,1-dihydroperfluorohexyl acrylate)	234		133
Poly(1,1-dihydroperfluorooctyl acrylate)	256		133
Poly(1,1-dihydroperfluoropentyl acrylate)	236		133
Poly(1,1-dihydroperfluoropropyl acrylate)	247		133
Poly(dodecyl acrylate)	270	Brittle point	128
Poly(2-ethoxyethyl acrylate)	223		132
Poly(3-ethoxypropyl acrylate)	205 218	Conflicting data	132,134
Poly(ethyl acrylate)	249		48,86,127,128, 130
Poly(2-ethylbutyl acrylate)	223	Brittle point	129
Poly(2-ethylhexyl acrylate)	223	Brittle point	128
Poly(5-ethyl-2-nonyl acrylate)	233	Brittle point	129
Poly(2-ethylthioethyl acrylate)	202		134
Poly(3-ethylthiopropyl acrylate)	197		134
Poly(fluoromethyl acrylate)	288	Estimated from homologous series	135
Poly(heptyl acrylate)	213	Brittle point	128
Poly(2-heptyl acrylate)	235	Brittle point	129

References page III-85

Polymer	$T_g(°K)$	Remarks	References
Poly(hexadecyl acrylate)	308		86,128,136
Poly(hexyl acrylate)	216	Brittle point	128
Poly[2-(2'-hydroperfluoroethoxy)ethyl acrylate]			
	251		132
Poly(isobornyl acrylate)	367		130
Poly(isobutyl acrylate)	249	Brittle point	129
Poly(isopropyl acrylate)	270		129,130
Poly(2-methoxyethyl acrylate)	223		132
Poly(3-methoxypropyl acrylate)	198	Conflicting data	132,134
	215		
Poly(methyl acrylate)	279		13,17,86,114, 127,128,130, 134, 137-140
Poly(2-methylbutyl acrylate)	241	Brittle point	129
Poly(3-methylbutyl acrylate)	228	Brittle point	129
Poly(2-methyl-7-ethyl-4-undecyl acrylate)			
	253	Brittle point	129
Poly(2-methylpentyl acrylate)	235		129
Poly(4-methyl-2-pentyl acrylate)	258		129
Poly(4-methylthiobutyl acrylate)	203		134
Poly(2-methylthioethyl acrylate)	213		134
Poly(3-methylthiopropyl acrylate)	208		134
Poly(nonyl acrylate)	215	Brittle point	128
Poly(octyl acrylate)	208	Brittle point	128
Poly(2-octyl acrylate)	228	Brittle point	129
Poly(3-pentyl acrylate)	257	Brittle point	129
Poly(3-perfluorobutoxy-1,1-dihydroperfluoropropyl acrylate)			
	205		132
Poly(3-perfluoroethoxy-1,1-dihydroperfluoropropyl acrylate)			
	224		132
Poly(3-perfluoromethoxy-1,1-dihydroperfluoropropyl acrylate)			
	218		132
Poly(3-perfluoropropoxy-1,1-dihydroperfluoropropyl acrylate)			
	205		132
Poly(propyl acrylate)	~225		86
Poly(tetradecyl acrylate)	293		86,128,136
Poly[2-(3',3',4',4'-tetrafluorobutoxy)ethyl acrylate]			
	233		132
Poly[2-(2',2',2'-trifluoroethoxy)ethyl acrylate]			
	235		132
Poly(1,1,3-trihydroperfluorobutyl acrylate)			
	251		133
Poly(1,1,5-trihydroperfluoropentyl acrylate)			
	238		133

Polymers	$T_g(°K)$	Remarks	References

3 - POLYMETHACRYLATES

Poly(2-N-tert-butylaminoethyl methacrylate)

	304 to 312		141
Poly(butyl methacrylate)			
atactic	293		17,27,52,127, 128,130,142
isotactic	249		130
Poly(2-butyl methacrylate)	∿318	Vicat softening point 333°K	116
Poly(2-chloroethyl methacrylate)	∿376	Vicat softening point 391°K	116
Poly(cyclohexyl methacrylate)			
random	339		130
isotactic	324		130
Poly(decyl methacrylate)	203		86,128,136
Poly(N,N-diethylaminoethyl methacrylate)			
	∿289 to 297		141
Poly(3,3-dimethylbutyl methacrylate)	∿318	Vicat softening point 332°K	116
Poly(3,3-dimethyl-2-butyl methacrylate)			
	∿381	Vicat softening point 396°K	116
Poly(dodecyl methacrylate)	208		3,128,142
Poly(2-ethylhexyl methacrylate)	263	Brittle point	128
Poly(ethyl methacrylate)			
random	338		17,27,38,128, 130,141-147
isotactic	285		130
Poly(glycidyl methacrylate)	319		148
Poly(hexadecyl methacrylate)	288	Brittle point	128
Poly(hexyl methacrylate)	268		27,142
Poly(isobornyl methacrylate)	383		130
Poly(isobutyl methacrylate)			
random	326		128,130
isotactic	281		130
Poly(isopropyl methacrylate)			
random	354		130
isotactic	300		130
syndiotactic	358		130
Poly(2-methoxyethyl methacrylate)	∿286 to 292		141
Poly(methyl methacrylate)			
random	378		3,17,55,88-90, 100,114,118,127, 128,130,140,142, 149-158
isotactic	318 328		8,130,152,155, 159
syndiotactic	388		130,159

Polymers	T_g (°K)	Remarks	References
Poly(octadecyl methacrylate)	173		3
Poly(octyl methacrylate)	253 203	Conflicting data	27,86,128,136, 142
Poly(pentyl methacrylate)	268	Brittle point	128
Poly(phenyl methacrylate)	∼378	Vicat softening point 393°K	116
Poly(propyl methacrylate)	308		17,52,128,141, 142
Poly(tetradecyl methacrylate)	264		86,128,136
Poly(1,1,1-trifluoroisopropyl methacrylate)			
	∼339	Vicat softening point 354°K	116

4 - POLYCHLOROACRYLATES

Poly(butyl chloroacrylate)	∼315	Vicat softening point 330°K	116
Poly(2-butyl chloroacrylate)	∼332	Vicat softening point 347°K	116
Poly(cyclohexyl chloroacrylate)	∼372	Vicat softening point 387°K	116
Poly(ethyl chloroacrylate)	∼351	Vicat softening point 366°K	116
Poly(isobutyl chloroacrylate)	363		161
Poly(isopropyl chloroacrylate)	∼348	Vicat softening point 363°K	116
Poly(methyl chloroacrylate)	∼398	Vicat softening point 413°K	116
Poly(propyl chloroacrylate)	∼329	Vicat softening point 344°K	116

Polymer	$T_g(°K)$	Remarks	References

5 - POLYSTYRENES

Polymer	$T_g(°K)$	Remarks	References
Poly(4-bromostyrene)	∿410	Conflicting data	163-165
Poly(4-[(2-butoxyethoxy)methyl]styrene)			
[Poly(4-(2,5-dioxanonyl)styrene)]	<235		162
Poly[4-(butoxymethyl)styrene]	<283		162
Poly(4-butoxystyrene)	∿320	Mechanical methods	162,166
Poly(5-tert-butyl-2-methylstyrene)	360		163
Poly(4-butylstyrene)	279 <321	Conflicting data	162,167
Poly(4-tert-butylstyrene)	403		117,168,169
Poly(4-chloro-3-fluorostyrene)	395		163
Poly(4-chloro-2-methylstyrene)	418		163
Poly(4-chloro-3-methylstyrene)	387		163
Poly(2-chlorostyrene)	392		163
Poly(3-chlorostyrene)	363		163
Poly(4-chlorostyrene)	399 383	Conflicting data	117,163-165
Poly(4-decylstyrene)	208		167
Poly(2,4-dichlorostyrene)	406		163,170
Poly(2,5-dichlorostyrene)	379		163,171
Poly(2,6-dichlorostyrene)	∿440	Estimated from softening point data	117,172
Poly(3,4-dichlorostyrene)	401		163,171
Poly(2,5-difluorostyrene)	∿374	Softening point	117
Poly(2,4-diisopropylstyrene)	∿435	Softening point	117
Poly(2,5-diisopropylstyrene)	∿441	Softening point	117
Poly(2,4-dimethylstyrene)	385		163
Poly(2,5-dimethylstyrene)	416		163
Poly(3,4-dimethylstyrene)	382		163
Poly(4-dodecylstyrene)	221		167
Poly[4-(2-ethoxyethoxymethyl)styrene]			
	<273		162
Poly(4-ethoxystyrene)	∿359	Mechanical method	166
Poly[4-(1-ethylhexoxymethyl)styrene]			
[Poly(4-(2-oxa-3-ethyloctyl)styrene)]	250		162
Poly(4-ethylstyrene)	300 <351	Conflicting data	162,167
Poly(4-fluorostyrene)	356 368 379 383	Conflicting data	163-165
Poly(4-hexadecylstyrene)	278		167
Poly[4-(hexoxymethyl)styrene]	<253		162
Poly(4-hexylstyrene)	246		167
Poly[4-(4-hydroxybutoxymethyl)styrene]			
	<293		162

References page III-85

Polymer	$T_g(°K)$	Remarks	References
Poly[4-(2-hydroxyethoxymethyl)styrene]			
	<319		162
Poly(2-hydroxymethylstyrene)	433		3
Poly(3-hydroxymethylstyrene)	<398		3
Poly(4-hydroxymethylstyrene	413		3
Poly(4-iodostyrene)	429		164
Poly(4-isopentoxystyrene)	~330	Mechanical method	166
Poly[4-(methoxymethyl)styrene]	<350		162
Poly(4-methoxystyrene)	~362	Mechanical method	166
Poly(4-methylstyrene)	366		173
Poly(α-methylstyrene)	443 465	Conflicting data	8,117
Poly(2-methylstyrene)	409		163
Poly(3-methylstyrene)	370		163,173
Poly(4-nonadecylstyrene)	305		3
Poly(4-nonylstyrene)	220		167
Poly(4-octadecylstyrene)	305		167
Poly[4-(octoxymethyl)styrene]	<231		162
Poly(2-octoxystyrene)	286		174
Poly(4-octylstyrene)	228		167
Poly[4-(2-oxa-3-methylpentyl)styrene]	<313		162
Poly(4-phenoxystyrene)	~373	Softening point	117
Poly[4-(propoxymethyl)styrene]	<295		162
Poly(4-propoxystyrene)	343	Mechanical method	166
Polystyrene			
isotactic, atactic	373		16,17,24,26, 43, 55,64,68,72,88, 127,137,138,140, 150,153,158,163, 173,175,176-192
Poly(4-tetradecylstyrene)	237		167
Poly(α,β,β-trifluorostyrene)	513	Softening point	117,193,194
Poly(2,4,5-trimethylstyrene)	~409	Softening point	117
Poly(2,4,6-trimethylstyrene)	~435	Softening point	117

Polymer	$T_g\,(°K)$	Remarks	References
6 - MISCELLANEOUS VINYL AND VINYLIDENE POLYMERS			
Poly(acrylic acid)	∿360		197,198
Polyacrylonitrile	∿378	Conflicting data. Two transitions present.	3,21,24,82,89, 137,145,151,153, 187,193,199-204
Poly(4-carbutoxyphenylmethacrylamide)			
	401		160
Poly(4-carbethoxyphenylmethacrylamide)			
	441		160
Poly(4-carbmethoxyphenylmethacrylamide)			
	453		160
Poly(4-carboxyphenylmethacrylamide)	473		160
Poly(diphenylvinylphosphine oxide)	453		226
Poly(ethyl-vinylphosphonic-dimethylamide)			
$[CH_2=CHP(O)(OEt)NMe_2]$	305		248
Poly(methacrylic anhydride)	∿417	Estimated from Vicat softening point (10 mms) 432°K	252
Poly(methacrylonitrile)	393		3
Poly(phenyl vinylphosphonic dimethylamide)			
$[CH_2=CHP(O)(OPh)NMe_2]$	300		248
Poly(vinyl acetal)	355		3
Poly(vinyl acetate)	301		3,14,17,27,54, 81,97,127,136, 139,140,151,157, 199,203,221,243, 251,278,279
Poly(vinyl alcohol)	358		3,43,221,251
Poly(vinyl butyl ether)	221		3
Poly(vinyl tert-butyl ether)	361		3
Poly(vinyl butyral)	322		3,175
Poly(vinylcarbazole)	357, 423, 481	Conflicting values reported	3,52,139,251
Poly(vinyl chloride)	354	Temperature of polymerization important in determining T_g	2,3,16,21,24, 50,140,175,187, 273,281
Poly(vinylene fluoride) See Poly(1,2-difluoroethylene)			
Poly(vinyl ethyl ether)	254		3,145,243,251, 282,283
Poly(vinyl fluoride)	253 or <313	Conflicting interpretations	3,8,145
Poly(vinyl formal)	378		3
Poly(vinyl formate)	304	Temperature of polymerization affects T_g	284
Poly(vinylidene chloride) See Poly(1,1-dichloroethylene)			
Poly(vinylidene fluoride) See Poly(1,1-difluoroethylene)			

References page III-85

Polymer	$T_g(°K)$	Remarks	References
Poly(vinyl isobutyl ether)	246		3,243,251,283, 285
Poly(vinyl isobutyral)	329		3
Poly(vinyl methyl ether)	260		3,243,283
Poly(1-vinylnaphthalene)	∿435	B.S.1493 softening point	117
Poly(vinyl propional)	345		3
Poly(2-vinylpyridine)	377		286
Poly(vinylpyrrolidine)	327		251
Poly(vinylpyrrolidone)	359		3,6

7 - POLYDIENES

Polymer	$T_g(°K)$	Remarks	References
Poly(1,2-butadiene)	269	polymer 1,2-	287
Poly(1,3-butadiene)			
cis	165	polymer 1,4-	65,76,87,104, 137,288-291
trans	255	polymer 1,4-	291,292
Poly(2-tert-butyl-1,3-butadiene)	293		21,115
Poly(2-chloro-1,3-butadiene)			
cis	253		3,87,293-297
trans	225		294
Poly(2-decyl-1,3-butadiene)	220		3
Poly(2,3-dimethyl-1,3-butadiene)	262		137
Poly(2-ethyl-1,3-butadiene)	197		298
Poly(2-heptyl-1,3-butadiene)	190		21,115
Poly(2-isopropyl-1,3-butadiene)	223		115,298
Poly(2-methyl-1,3-butadiene)			
cis	200		76,299
trans	213, 220		76,300

Polymer	$T_g(°K)$	Remarks	References

8 - POLYAMIDES

Polymer	$T_g(°K)$	Remarks	References
Poly(10-aminocapric acid) (Nylon 10)	315		309
Poly(6-aminocaproic acid) [poly(ε-caprolactam)] (Nylon 6)			
	323 to 348	T_g observed highest when sample dry	3,43
Poly(8-aminocaprylic acid) (Nylon 8)	323		309
Poly(7-aminoenanthic acid) (Nylon 7)	335		309
Poly(12-aminolauric acid) (Nylon 12)	310		309
Poly(9-aminopelargonic acid) (Nylon 9)	323		309
Poly(13-aminotridecanoic acid) (Nylon 13)			
	314		309
Poly(11-aminoundecanoic acid) (Nylon 11)			
	319		309
Poly(γ-benzyl L-glutamate)	∿288	Frequency 0.18 cycles/sec.	208
Poly(heptamethylene adipamide) (Nylon 7.6)			
	318		267,308
Poly(hexamethylene adipamide) (Nylon 6.6)			
	∿330	Conflicting data and interpretation. Samples must be dry	8,43,52,145, 189,204,212,244, 299,301-307
Poly(hexamethylene azelaamide) (Nylon 6.9)			
	331		145
Poly[hexamethylene 4,4'-(2,2-butylidene)dibenzamide]			
	427 to 437		310

Poly(hexamethylene [bisdimethylene(phenyl)phosphine oxide]dicarboxamide)

$$-NH-(CH_2)_6-NH-OC-(CH_2)_2-\overset{\overset{O}{\|}}{\underset{|}{P}}-(CH_2)_2-CO-$$

302   308

Poly(hexamethylene[bisdimethylene(phenyl)phosphine sulfide]dicarboxamide)

316   308

$$-NH-(CH_2)_6-NH-OC-(CH_2)_2-\overset{\overset{S}{\|}}{\underset{|}{P}}-(CH_2)_2-CO-$$

Polymer	$T_g(°K)$	Remarks	References
Poly(hexamethylene isocinchomeronamide)			
	322		304
Poly(hexamethylene 3-methyladipamide)			
	290		308
Poly(hexamethylene 4-methylpimelamide)			
	323		145
Poly(hexamethylene pimelamide) (Nylon 6.7)			
	331		308

References page III-85

Polymer	T_g (°K)	Remarks	References
Poly(hexamethylene sebacamide)(Nylon 6.10)			
	323		303
Poly(hexamethylene 4-thiapimelamide)			
	287 to 300		308
Poly[isobutyl(bistrimethylene)phosphine adipamide]			
	344		308

$$-NH-(CH_2)_3-\underset{|}{P}-(CH_2)_3-NH-OC-(CH_2)_4-CO-$$
$$CH_2-CH(CH_3)-CH_3$$

Polymer	T_g (°K)	Remarks	References
Poly[methylimino-bistrimethylene adipamide]			
	278		308
Poly[methyl(bistrimethylene)phosphine oxide adipamide]			
	332		308
Poly[methyl(tetramethylene)(trimethylene)phosphine oxide adipamide]			
	332		308
Poly[octyl(bistrimethylene)phosphine oxide adipamide]			
	285		308
Poly(4-oxaheptamethylene adipamide)	307		267
Poly[phenyl(bistrimethylene)phosphine adipamide]			
	322		308
Poly[phenyl(bistrimethylene)phosphine oxide adipamide]			
	328		308
Poly[piperazine 4,4'-(2,2-butylidene)dibenzamide]			
	492 to 505		310
Poly(piperazine sebacamide)	355		67
Poly[tetramethylene 4,4'-(2,2-butylidene)dibenzamide]			
	446 to 455		310

Polymer	$T_g (°K)$	Remarks	References

9 - POLYANHYDRIDES

Polymer	$T_g (°K)$	Remarks	References
Poly[4,4'-(ethylenedioxy)benzoic anhydride]			
	318		312
Poly[4,4'-hexamethylenebenzoic anhydride]			
	<293		312
Poly(isophthalic anhydride)	413		311
Poly[4,4'-isopropylidenebenzoic anhydride]			
	333		312
Poly[4,4'-methylenebenzoic anhydride]	395		312
Poly[4,4'-(methylenedioxy)benzoic anhydride]			
	357		312
Poly[4,4'-(oxydiethylenedioxy)benzoic anhydride]			
	314		312
Poly[4,4'-(oxydimethylenedioxy)benzoic anhydride]			
amorphous	325		312
crystalline	335		
Poly[4,4'-pentamethylenebenzoic anhydride]			
	312		312
Poly[3,3'-(pentamethylenedioxy)benzoic anhydride]			
	334		312
Poly[4,4'-(pentamethylenedioxy)benzoic anhydride]			
	326		312
Poly[4,4'-tetramethylenebenzoic anhydride]			
	319		312
Poly[3,3'-(tetramethylenedioxy)benzoic anhydride]			
	<295		312
Poly[4,4'-(tetramethylenedioxy)benzoic anhydride]			
	348		312
Poly[4,4'-(tetramethylenedithio)benzoic anhydride]			
	335		312
Poly[3,3'-trimethylenebenzoic anhydride]			
	325		312
Poly[4,4'-(trimethylenedioxy)benzoic anhydride]			
	368		312

10 - POLYCARBONATES

Polymer	$T_g (°K)$	Remarks	References
Poly(4,4'-butylidenediphenylene carbonate)			
	396		189
Poly[4,4'-(2,2-butylidene)diphenylene carbonate]			
	407		189
Poly(4,4'-cyclohexylidenediphenylene carbonate)			
	444		189,314

Polymer	$T_g(°K)$	Remarks	References
Poly(4,4'-ethylidenediphenylene carbonate)			
	403		189
Poly(4,4'-isobutylidenediphenylene carbonate)			
	422		189
Poly[4,4'-isopropylidene-bis(3,5-dichlorophenylene) carbonate]			
	493	Frequency 0.5 cycles/sec.	39
Poly[4,4'-isopropylidene-bis(3-methylphenylene) carbonate]			
	418	Frequency 0.5 cycles/sec.	39
Poly(4,4'-isopropylidenediphenylene carbonate)			
	422		39,189,313,315
Poly(phenolphthalein carbonate)	513		313
Poly(4,4'-phenylethylidenediphenylene carbonate)			
	463	Frequency 0.5 cycles/sec.	39
Poly(4,4'-phenylmethylenediphenylene carbonate)			
	394		189,314
Poly[1,3-(2,2,4,4-tetramethylcyclobutylene)carbonate]			
	<433		316

11 - POLYESTERS

Polymer	$T_g(°K)$	Remarks	References
Poly[1,4-(2-butene) sebacate]			
cis	232		317
trans	233		317
Poly[1,4-(2-butyne) sebacate]	246		317,318
Poly(4,4'-cyclohexylidenediphenylene isophthalate)			
	400		313
Poly(decamethylene adipate)	217		111
Poly(decamethylene terephthalate)	<298	Frequency 102 cycles/sec.	8,320
Poly(3,3'-dimethylphenolphthalein isophthalate)			
	546?	Shows exotherm at this temperature by D.T.A. method	322
Poly(ethylene adipate)	223		3,111,112,299,
	203		319
Poly[ethylene 4,4'-(2,2-butylidene)dibenzoate]			
	378 to 382		310
Poly(ethylene isophthalate)	324		82
Poly(ethylene 1,4-naphthalate)	337		82

Polymer	T_g (°K)	Remarks	References
Poly(ethylene 1,5-naphthalate)			
amorphous	344		82
crystalline	351		
Poly(ethylene 2,6-naphthalate)	386		82
Poly(ethylene 2,7-naphthalate)	392		82
Poly(ethylene terephthalate)	342		3,41,43,52,64, 65,82,112,151, 189,207,209, 299,320-323
Poly(fluoroescein isophthalate)	549		322
Poly(2,2,3,3,4,4-hexafluoropentamethylene adipate)			
	216		75
Poly(hexamethylene terephthalate)	<318	Frequency 160 cycles/sec.	8,320
Poly(4,4'-isopropylidenediphenylene 4,4'-(2,2-butylidene)dibenzoate)			
	477 to 483		310
Poly(4,4'-isopropylidenediphenylene isophthalate)			
	453		313
Poly(N-methylphenolphthalimidine isophthalate) (Poly[N-methyl-3,3-bis(4-phenyl)isooxindole isophthalate])			
	558	Transition indistinct by D.T.A. method	313
Poly(N-methylphenolphthalimidine terephthalate) (Poly[N-methyl-3,3-bis(4-phenyl)isooxindole terephthalate])			
	555	Transition indistinct by D.T.A. method	313
Poly(nonamethylene terephthalate)	<308	Frequency 366 cycles/sec.	8,320
Poly(octamethylene terephthalate)	<318	Frequency 352 cycles/sec.	320
Poly(oxydiethylene adipate)	226		111
Poly(oxydiethylene azelaate)	205		111
Poly(oxydiethylene dodecanedioate)	202		111
Poly(oxydiethylene glutarate)	226		111
Poly(oxydiethylene heptylmalonate)	215		111
Poly(oxydiethylene malonate)	244		111
Poly(oxydiethylene methylmalonate)	244		111
Poly(oxydiethylene nonylmalonate)	214		111
Poly(oxydiethylene octadecanedioate)	205		111
Poly(oxydiethylene oxalate)	265		111
Poly(oxydiethylene pentylmalonate)	226		111
Poly(oxydiethylene pimelate)	213		111
Poly(oxydiethylene propylmalonate)	235		111
Poly(oxydiethylene sebacate)	199		111
Poly(oxydiethylene suberate)	212		111
Poly(oxydiethylene succinate)	244		111

References page III-85

Polymer	T_g (°K)	Remarks	References
Poly(pentamethylene adipate)	204		111
Poly(pentamethylene terephthalate)	<318	Frequency 215 cycles/sec.	8,320
Poly(phenolisatin isophthalate) (Poly[3,3-bis(4-phenyl)oxindole isophthalate])	529		313
Poly(phenol-5,7-dichloroisatin isophthalate) [Poly(5,7-dichloro-3,3-bis(4-phenyl)oxindole isophthalate)]	543		313
Poly(phenolphthalein 5-tert-butylisophthalate)	552		313
Poly(phenolphthalein 5-chloroisophthalate)	586		313
Poly(phenolphthalein isophthalate)	591		313
Poly(phenolphthalimidine isophthalate) (Poly[3,3-bis(4-phenyl)isooxindole isophthalate])	598		313
Poly(phenolphthalimidine terephthalate) (Poly[3,3-bis(4-phenyl)isooxindole terephthalate])	600		313
Poly[4,4'-phenylmethylenediphenylene isophthalate]	433		324
Poly[4,4'-phenylmethylenediphenylene terephthalate]	473		324
Poly(propylene terephthalate)	341		112
Poly(tetramethylene adipate)	205		21,111
Poly(tetramethylene sebacate)	216	T_g decreased as intrinsic viscosity increased	3,317,318
Poly(trimethylene adipate)	214		111
Poly(tetramethylene terephthalate)	<353	Frequency 215 cycles/sec.	8,320
Poly(trimethylene terephthalate)	<368	Frequency 275 cycles/sec.	320,322

Polymer	T_g (°K)	Remarks	Reference
	12 - POLYOXIDES		
Polyacetaldehyde	243		325
Poly[3,3-bis(chloromethyl)oxacyclobutane)]	283		3,327,328
Poly(butadiene oxide)	198		243,326
Poly(2-butene oxide) [trans]	277		243
Poly(1-butene oxide)	190		243
Poly(tert-butylethylene oxide)	308		326
Poly(dodecene oxide)	232		243
Poly(ethylene oxide)	206		243,329
Poly(isobutene oxide)	264		243
Polyformaldehyde	188		3,8,43,329-334
Poly(propylene oxide)	198		57,208,243,335
Poly(styrene oxide)	310		243,326,336
Poly(tetramethylene oxide)	194		52,208,337
Poly(trimethylene oxide)	<228	Frequency 40-600 cycles/sec.	52,208

Polyhydroxyoxides

(1) $-\langle\bigcirc\rangle-O-CH_2-CH(OH)-CH_2-O-$ 333   338

(2) $-\langle\bigcirc\rangle-CH_2-\langle\bigcirc\rangle-O-CH_2-CH(OH)-CH_2-O-$ 353   338

(3) $-\langle\bigcirc\rangle-CH(CH(CH_3)CH_3)-\langle\bigcirc\rangle-O-CH_2-CH(OH)-CH_2-O-$ 368   338

(4) $-\langle\bigcirc\rangle-C(CH_3)_2-\langle\bigcirc\rangle-O-CH_2-CH(OH)-CH_2-O-$ 373   338

(5) $-\langle\bigcirc(Cl)\rangle-C(CH_3)_2-\langle\bigcirc(Cl)\rangle-O-CH_2-CH(OH)-CH_2-O-$ 358   338

(6) $-\langle\bigcirc(Cl)(Cl)\rangle-C(CH_3)(Cl)-\langle\bigcirc(Cl)\rangle-O-CH_2-CH(OH)-CH_2-O-$ 388   338

(7) $-\langle\bigcirc\rangle-C(CH_3)_2-CH_2-CH(CH_3)-\langle\bigcirc\rangle-O-CH_2-CH(OH)-CH_2-O-$ 348   338

Polymer	T_g (°K)	Remarks	References

Polyhydroxyoxides (Cont'd.)

(8)

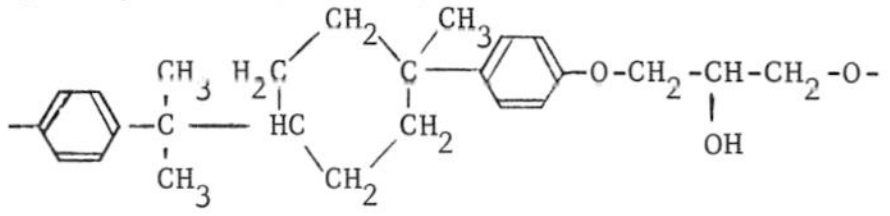

408   338

(9)

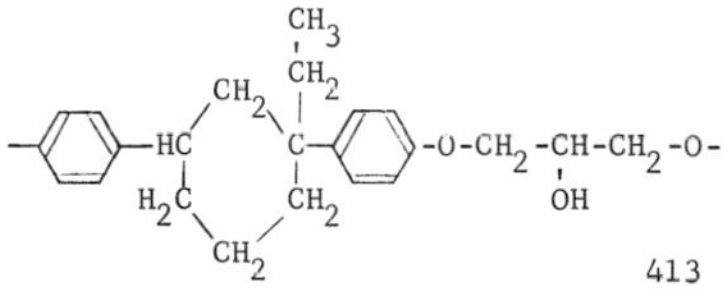

413   338

(10)

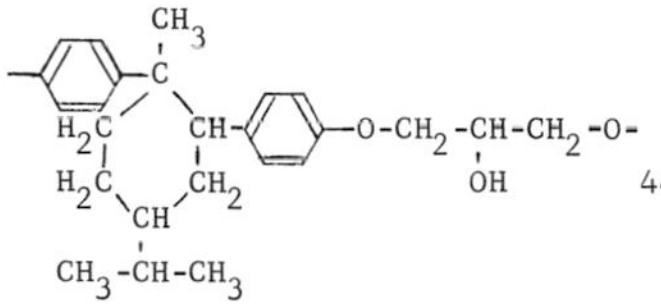

448   338

(11)

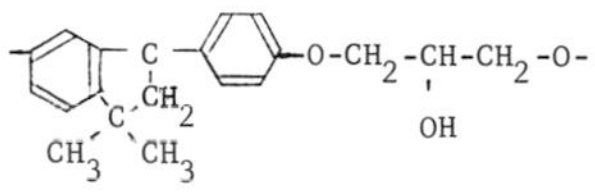

393   338

(12)

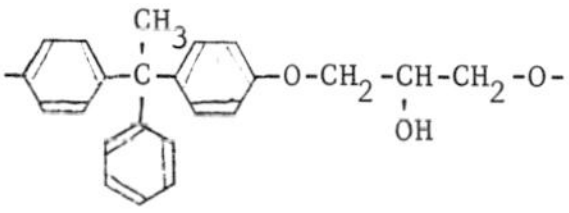

388   339

(13)

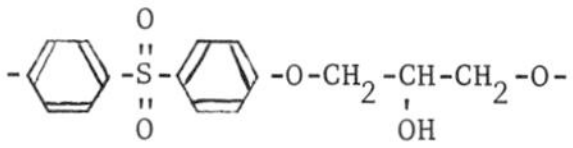

428   339

Polymer	T_g (°K)	Remarks	References

Polyhydroxyoxide derivatives

(1)   -〈◯〉-O-CH$_2$-CH-CH$_2$-O-   322   339
                  O-CO-CH$_3$

(2)   -〈◯〉-C(CH$_3$)$_2$-〈◯〉-O-CH$_2$-CH-CH$_2$-O-   333   339
                              O-CO-CH$_3$

(3)   -〈◯〉-C(CH$_3$)$_2$-〈◯〉-O-CH$_2$-CH-CH$_2$-O-   333   339
                              O-CO-CH$_2$-CH$_3$

(4)   -〈◯〉-C(CH$_3$)$_2$-〈◯〉-O-CH$_2$-CH-CH$_2$-O-   338   339
                              O-CO-CH$_2$Cl

(5)   -〈◯(Cl)(Cl)〉-C(CH$_3$)$_2$-〈◯(Cl)(Cl)〉-O-CH$_2$-CH-CH$_2$-O-   373   339
                              O-CO-CH$_3$

(6)   -〈◯〉-C(CH$_3$)$_2$-〈◯〉-O-CH$_2$-CH-CH$_2$-O-   338   339
                              O-CO-〈◯〉

(7)   -〈◯〉-C(CH$_3$)$_2$-〈◯〉-O-CH$_2$-CH-CH$_2$-O-   339   339
                              O-CO-〈◯〉Cl

(8)   -〈◯〉-HC〈 ... C(CH$_2$-CH$_2$-CH$_3$) ... 〉-〈◯〉-O-CH$_2$-CH-CH$_2$-O-   380   339
                              O-CO-CH$_3$

References page III-85

Polymer	T_g (°K)	Remarks	References

Polyhydroxyoxide derivatives (Cont'd.)

(9)

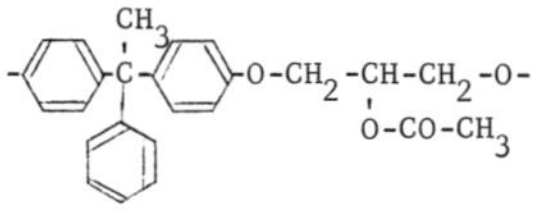

$-O-CH_2-CH-CH_2-O-$
$O-CO-CH_3$ 383   339

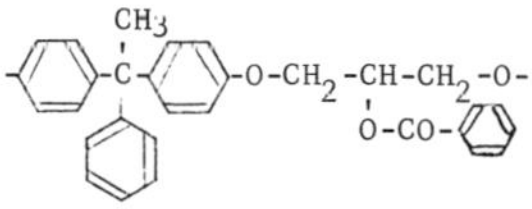

(10)

$-O-CH_2-CH-CH_2-O-$
$O-CO-$ 399   339

(11)

$-O-CH_2-CH-CH_2-O-$
$O-CO-CH_3$ 403   339

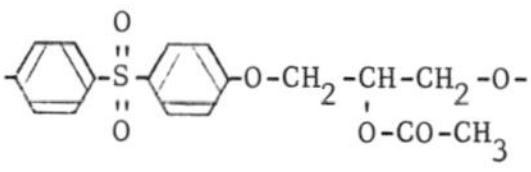

13 - POLYSILOXANES

Polymer	T_g (°K)	Remarks	References
Poly(dimethylsiloxane)	150		3,8,243,340-342
Poly[(heptamethyl)(2-phenylethyl)tetrasiloxane]	171		344
Poly[(heptamethyl)(phenyl)tetrasiloxane]	201		344
Poly[(heptamethyl)(trimethylsiloxy)tetrasiloxane]	148		344
Poly[(methyl)(3,3,3-trifluoropropyl)siloxane]	205	Brittle point	74
Poly(octamethyltetrasiloxane)	221		344
Poly[(phenyl)(methyl)siloxane]	187		340
Poly[tetramethyl(1,4-phenylene)disiloxanylene]	250		343

Polymer	$T_g(°K)$	Remarks	References
14 - CELLULOSE DERIVATIVES			
Cellulose acetate butyrate	323	Same reference gave tri-acetate T_G at 342°K	175
Cellulose acetate propionate	312		175
Cellulose triacetate	430, 378	Conflicting data. 4 transitions observed	3,16,66,69,118, 175,345-348
Cellulose tributyrate	313, 393	Conflicting interpretation of data	3,8,66
Cellulose trinitrate	326, 339		16,118,175,221
Ethyl cellulose	316		3,118

15 - MISCELLANEOUS POLYMERS

Polymer	$T_g(°K)$	Remarks	References
Poly[2,2'-(2,2'-diphenylene)-5,5'-dibenzimidazole]			
	663		32
Poly(ethylene piperazine-1,4-dicarboxylate)			
	333		349
Polymer from perfluorobutyronitrile and perfluoroglutaronitrile			
$\overline{N=C-N=C-N=C}-(CF_2)_2-CF_3$	283 to 291		350
Poly(thiocarbonyl fluoride)	155		351
Poly(tetrafluoroethylene/nitrosotrifluoromethane)			
	222		352,353
Poly(tetramethylene hexamethylene-urethan)			
	215 253 303	Conflicting data and interpretation. $T_{g.g}$ and T_g transitions probably present.	43,189,318
Poly(1,4-(2-butene) hexamethylene-urethan)			
cis	234		317
trans	229		
Poly(1,4-(2-butyne) hexamethylene-urethan)			
	228		318

1. J. H. Gibbs, in J. D. Mackenzie, Ed., "Modern Aspects of the Vitreous State", Butterworths, 1960, p. 152.
2. F. P. Reding, E. R. Walter, and F. J. Welch, J. Polymer Sci., 56, 225 (1962).
3. L. E. Nielsen, "Mechanical Properties of Polymers", Reinhold, 1962.
4. C. A. Kumins and J. Roteman, J. Polymer Sci., A1, 527 (1963).
5. K. Kanamaru and M. Sugiura, Kolloid-Z., 194, 110 (1964).
6. M. Sugiura and E. Fujii, Tokyo Kogyo Shikcnoho Hokoku, 58, 534 (1963)
7. K. Kanamaru and M. Sugiura, J. Chem. Soc. (Japan), 65, 1434 (1962).
8. R. F. Boyer, Rubber Chem. Technol., 36, 1303 (1963).
9. K. R. Dunham, J. Vandenberge, J. W. H. Faber, and W. F. Fowler, Jr., J. Appl. Polymer Sci., 7, 143 (1963).
10. B. Maxwell and L. F. Rohm, Soc. Plastics Engrs. J., 6, 7 (1950).
11. L. E. Nielsen, R. Buchdahl, and R. Levreault, J. Appl. Phys., 21, 607 (1950).
12. F. S. Conant and J. W. Liska, J. Appl. Phys., 15, 767 (1944).
13. R. F. Boyer and R. S. Spencer, "Advances in Colloid Science", Interscience N.Y., 1946, Vol. II.
14. R. H. Wiley, J. Polymer Sci., 2, 10 (1947).
15. L. Turunen, Kunststoffe-Plastics, 52, 672 (1962).
16. B. D. Sully, in "The Science of Surface Coatings", Ernest Benn, 1962, p. 281.
17. R. H. Wiley and G. M. Brauer, J. Polymer Sci., 3, 455 (1948).
18. G. Allen, private communication.
19. A. J. Kovacs, Doctoral Thesis, University of Paris, No. 3566 (1955).
20. R. F. Boyer, J. Appl. Phys., 25, 825 (1954).
21. R. F. Boyer, "Changements des Phases", Soc. de Chim. Phys., Paris, 1952.
22. D. L. Beck, A. A. Hiltz, and J. R. Knox, Soc. Plastics Engrs. Trans., 3, 279 (1963).
23. G. M. Bartenev and Yu. A. Gorbatkina, Rubber Chem. Technol., 34, 1193 (1961).
24. J. J. Keavney and E. C. Eberlin, J. Appl. Polymer Sci., 3, 47 (1960).
25. G. M. Martin and L. Mandelkern, J. Res. Natl. Bur. Std., 62, 141 (1959).
26. R. S. Spencer, J. Colloid Sci., 4, 229 (1949).
27. J. D. Ferry, "Viscoelastic Properties of Polymers", Wiley, New York, 1961.
28. N. I. Shishkin and M. P. Vershinina, Soviet Physics - Solid State (English Transl.), 1, 724 (1958).
29. L. E. Nielsen, Am. Soc. Testing Mater. Bull., No. 165,48 (1950).
30. J. Kumanotani, L. W. Chen, and T. Kuwata, Bull. Chem. Soc. Japan, 35, 1341 (1962).
31. S. D. Gehman, D. E. Woodford, and C. S. Wilkinson, Jr., Ind. Eng. Chem., 39, 1108 (1947).
32. J. K. Gillham, Science, 139, 494 (1963).
33. A. F. Lewis and J. K. Gillham, J. Appl. Polymer Sci., 7, 685 (1963).
34. R. J. Ward and E. G. Bobalek, Ind. Eng. Chem. Prod. Res. Develop., 2, 85 (1963).
35. M. Baer, J. Polymer Sci., A2, 417 (1964).
36. N. G. McCrum, J. Polymer Sci., 34, 355 (1959).
37. K. Schmieder and K. Wolf, Kolloid-Z., 127, 65 (1952).
38. K. M. Sinnott, Soc. Plastics Engrs. Trans., 2, 65 (1962).
39. F. P. Reding, J. A. Faucher, and R. D. Whitman, J. Polymer Sci., 54, S56 (1961).
40. F. S. C. Chang, J. Polymer Sci., 57, 949 (1962).
41. I. M. Ward, Polymer, 5, 59 (1964).
42. A. V. Tobolsky, D. Katz, and M. Takahashi, J. Polymer Sci., A1, 483 (1963).
43. K. Fujimoto, Chem. High Polymer (Japan), 18, 415 (1961).
44. M. Gordon and B. M. Grieveson, J. Polymer Sci., 29, 9 (1958).
45. M. Gordon, "High Polymers - Structure and Physical Properties", Iliffe Books Ltd., London, 1963.
46. L. Bridge, and W. Simpson, Soc. Chem. Ind. Monograph, No. 13, 453 (1961).
47. A. Brown, Textile Res. J., 25, 891 (1955).
48. F. P. Reding, J. A. Faucher, and R. D. Whitman, J. Polymer Sci., 55, 483 (1962).
49. D. W. Robinson, J. Sci. Instr., 32, 2 (1955).
50. H. Eyring and N. Hirai, J. Polymer Sci., 37, 51 (1959).
51. K. J. Clark, A. T. Jones, and D. H. Sandiford, Chem. Ind. (London), 1962, 2010.
52. A. H. Willbourn, Trans. Faraday Soc., 54, 717 (1958).
53. A. H. Scott, D. J. Scheiber, A. J. Curtis, J. I. Lauritzen, Jr., and J. D. Hoffman, J. Res. Natl. Bur. Std., 66A, 269 (1962).
54. J. M. O'Reilly, J. Polymer Sci., 57, 429 (1962).
55. A. E. Woodward, Trans. N. Y. Acad. Sci., 24, 250 (1962).
56. A. Odajima, J. A. Sauer, and A. E. Woodward, J. Polymer Sci., 57, 107 (1962).
57. W. P. Slichter, Makromol. Chem., 34, 67 (1959).
58. W. P. Slichter and D. D. Davis, Rubber Chem. Technol., 36, 318 (1963).
59. J. G. Powles, Polymer, 1, 219 (1960).
60. W. P. Slichter, Am. Soc. Testing Mater. Spec. Tech. Publ., No. 247, 257 (1958).
61. A. F. Lewis, J. Polymer Sci., B1, 649 (1963).

62. R. K. Eby and K. M. Sinnott, J. Appl. Physics, 32, 1765 (1961).
63. M. L. Williams, R. F. Landel, and J. D. Ferry, J. Am. Chem. Soc., 77, 3701 (1955).
64. R. Zannetti, P. Manaresi, and L. Baldi, Chim. Ind. (Milan), 43, 1310 (1961).
65. R. Zannetti, P. Manaresi, and L. Baldi, J. Polymer Sci., 62, S33 (1962).
66. L. Mandelkern and P. J. Flory, J. Am. Chem. Soc., 73, 3206 (1951).
67. P. J. Flory, L. Mandelkern, and H. K. Hall, J. Am. Chem. Soc., 73, 2532 (1951).
68. P. J. Flory and T. G. Fox, J. Appl. Phys., 21, 587 (1950).
69. A. Sharples and F. L. Swinton, J. Polymer Sci., 50, 53 (1961).
70. P. R. Swan, J. Polymer Sci., 42, 525 (1960).
71. N. J. Bekkedahl, J. Res. Natl. Bur. Std., 42, 145 (1949).
72. R. F. Boyer and R. S. Spencer, J. Appl. Phys., 15, 398 (1944).
73. C. J. Bell, J. Sci. Instr., 38, 27 (1961).
74. W. R. Grifftin, Rubber World, 136, 687 (1957).
75. E. V. Gouinlock, Jr., C. J. Verbanic, and G. C. Schweiker, J. Appl. Polymer Sci., 1, 361 (1959).
76. M. L. Dannis, J. Appl. Polymer Sci., 1, 121 (1959).
77. M. L. Dannis, J. Appl. Polymer Sci., 4, 249 (1960).
78. C. A. Kumins and J. Roteman, J. Polymer Sci., 55, 683 (1961).
79. N. Colebourne, E. Collinson, D. J. Currie, and F. S. Dainton, Trans. Faraday Soc., 59, 1357 (1963).
80. I. M. Otchenashenko, V. M. Neimark, N. K. Ermilov, and B. D. Egorov, Ind. Lab. (USSR), 29, 1387 (1964).
81. J. Heller and D. J. Lyman, J. Polymer Sci. B1, 317 (1963).
82. H. J. Kolb and E. F. Izard, J. Appl. Phys., 20, 564 (1949).
83. A. Eisenberg, J. Polymer Sci., B1, 177 (1963).
84. T. Shibukawa, V. D. Gupta, R. Turner, J. H. Dillon, and A. V. Tobolsky, Textile Res. J., 32, 810 (1962).
85. K. H. Illers and E. Jenckel, in K. A. Wolf, Ed., "Kunststoffe", Vol. 1, Springer-Verlag, Berlin, 1962.
86. R. H. Wiley, J. Polymer Sci., 3, 647 (1948).
87. R. H. Wiley, G. M. Brauer, and A. R. Bennett, J. Polymer Sci., 5, 609 (1950).
88. R. B. Beevers, Trans. Faraday Soc., 58, 1465 (1962).
89. R. B. Beevers and E. F. T. White, Trans. Faraday Soc., 56, 1529 (1960).
90. R. B. Beevers and E. F. T. White, Trans. Faraday Soc., 56, 744 (1960).
91. K. H. Illers, Kolloid-Z., 190, 16 (1963).
92. N. Bekkedahl and H. Matheson, J. Res. Natl. Bur. Std., 15, 503 (1935).
93. N. Bekkedahl and R. B. Scott, J. Res. Natl. Bur. Std., 29, 87 (1942).
94. J. D. Ferry and G. S. Parks, J. Chem. Phys., 4, 70 (1936).
95. R. D. Rands, W. J. Ferguson, and J. L. Prather, J. Res. Natl. Bur. Std., 33, 63 (1944).
96. J. Coste, Ind. Plastiques Mod. (Paris), 9, 37 (1957).
97. D. M. Chackraburtty, J. Chem. Phys., 26, 427 (1957).
98. N. D. Scott, Polymer, 1, 114 (1960).
99. B. Wunderlich, J. Phys. Chem., 64, 1052 (1960).
100. R. W. Warfield, M. C. Petree, and P. Donovan, Soc. Plastics Engrs. J., 15, 1055 (1959).
101. F. S. Dainton, D. M. Evans, F. E. Hoare, and T. P. Melia, Polymer, 3, 277 (1962).
102. N. E. Schmidt, Zh. Fiz. Khim, 35, 2814 (1961).
103. S. Strella, J. Appl. Polymer Sci., 7, 569 (1963).
104. M. L. Dannis, J. Appl. Polymer Sci., 7, 231 (1963).
105. L. J. Garfield and S. E. Petrie, J. Phys. Chem., 68, 1750 (1964).
106. B. Ke, J. Polymer Sci., B1, 167 (1963).
107. B. Ke, J. Polymer Sci., A1, 1453 (1963).
108. A. R. Haly and M. Dole, J. Polymer Sci., B2, 285 (1964).
109. S. Strella, J. Polymer Sci. B2, 625 (1964).
110. R. W. Warfield, Soc. Plastics Engrs., J. 15, 1 (1959).
111. B. M. Grieveson, Polymer, 1, 499 (1960).
112. O. B. Edgar, J. Chem. Soc., 1952, 2638.
113. O. B. Edgar and E. J. Ellery, J. Chem. Soc., 1952, 2633.
114. E. H. Riddle, "Monomeric Acrylic Esters," Reinhold, N. Y., 1954, p. 59.
115. C. G. Overberger, L. H. Arond, R. H. Wiley, and R. R. Garrett, J. Polymer Sci., 7, 431 (1951).
116. E. A. W. Hoff, D. W. Robinson, and A. H. Willbourn, J. Polymer Sci., 18, 161 (1955).
117. W. G. Barb, J. Polymer Sci., 37, 515 (1959).
118. F. E. Wiley, Ind. Eng. Chem., 34, 1052 (1942).
119. M. Baccaredda and E. Butta, Chim. Ind. (Milan), 44, 1228 (1962).
120. K. Fukawa, J. Chem. Soc. Japan (Kogyo Kagaku Zasshi) Ind. Chem. Sec., 66, 1605 (1963).

121. G. Allen, J. Appl. Chem. (London), 14, 1 (1964).
122. R. F. Landel, Trans. Soc. Rheol., 2, 53 (1958).
123. K. W. Bills, K. H. Sweeny, and F. S. Salcedo, J. Appl. Polymer Sci., 4, 259 (1960).
124. E. Jenckel and R. Heusch, Kolloid-Z., 130, 89 (1953).
125. H. Jacobs and E. Jenckel, Makromol. Chem., 47, 72 (1961).
126. E. A. Dimarzio and J. H. Gibbs, J. Polymer Sci., A1, 1417 (1963).
127. L. J. Hughes and G. L. Brown, J. Appl. Polymer Sci., 5, 580 (1961).
128. C. E. Rehberg and C. H. Fisher, Ind. Eng. Chem., 40, 1429 (1948).
129. C. E. Rehberg, W. A. Faucette, and C. H. Fischer, J. Am. Chem. Soc., 66, 1723 (1944).
130. J. A. Shetter, J. Polymer Sci., B1, 209 (1963).
131. J. H. Prager, R. M. McCurdy, and G. B. Rathmann, J. Polymer Sci., A2, 1941 (1964).
132. F. A. Bovey and J. F. Abere, J. Polymer Sci., 15, 537 (1955).
133. F. A. Bovey, J. F. Abere, G. B. Rathmann, and C. L. Sandberg, J. Polymer Sci., 15, 520 (1955).
134. R. M. McCurdy and J. H. Prager, J. Polymer Sci., A2, 1185 (1964).
135. G. K. Dyvik, Polymer, 2, 449 (1961).
136. R. H. Wiley and G. M. Brauer, J. Polymer Sci., 4, 351 (1949).
137. R. H. Gerke, J. Polymer Sci., 13, 295 (1954).
138. E. Jenckel and K. Überreiter, Z. Physik. Chem. (Leipzig), A182, 361 (1938).
139. F. Würstlin, in H. A. Stuart, Ed., "Die Physik der Hochpolymeren", Springer-Verlag, Berlin, 1955, Chap. 11.
140. F. Würstlin and H. Thurn, in H. A. Stuart, Ed., "Die Physik der Hochpolymeren", Springer-Verlag, Berlin, 1956.
141. A. V. Tobolsky and M. C. Shen, J. Phys. Chem., 67, 1886 (1963).
142. S. S. Rogers and L. Mandelkern, J. Phys. Chem., 61, 985 (1957).
143. M. O. Samsoen, Ann. Phys., 9, 35 (1928).
144. E. Baer, Offic. Dig. J. Paint Technol. Eng., 36, (472), 464 (1964).
145. K. Schmieder and K. Wolf, Kolloid-Z., 134, 149 (1953).
146. L. de Brouckère and G. Offergeld, Bull. Soc. Chim. Belges, 67, 96 (1958).
147. J. D. Ferry, W. C. Child, R. Zard, D. M. Stern, M. L. Williams, and R. F. Landel, J. Colloid Sci., 12, 53 (1957).
148. I. A. Arbuzova and V. N. Efremova, Vysokomolekul. Soedin., 1, 455 (1959); through Chem. Abstr., 54, 5151h (1960).
149. T. G. Fox and S. Loshaek, J. Polymer Sci., 15, 371 (1955).
150. H. A. Stuart, Ed., "Die Physik der Hochpolymeren", Vol. III, Springer-Verlag, Berlin, 1955.
151. S. Saito and T. Nakajima, J. Appl. Polymer Sci., 2, 93 (1959).
152. T. G. Fox, B. S. Garrett, W. E. Goode, S. Gratch, J. F. Kincaid, A. Spell, and J. D. Stroupe, J. Am. Chem. Soc., 80, 1768 (1958).
153. R. B. Beevers and E. F. T. White, J. Polymer Sci., B1, 171 (1963).
154. S. Loshaek, J. Polymer Sci., 15, 391 (1955).
155. A. Odajima, A. E. Woodward, and J. A. Sauer, J. Polymer Sci., 55, 181 (1961).
156. W. G. Gall and N. G. McCrum, J. Polymer Sci., 50, 489 (1961).
157. G. Allen, D. Sims, and G. J. Wilson, Polymer, 2, 375 (1961).
158. G. M. Martin, S. S. Rogers, and L. Mandelkern, J. Polymer Sci., 20, 579 (1956).
159. G. V. Schulz, W. Wunderlich, and R. Kirste, Makromol. Chem., 75, 23 (1964).
160. G. M. Chetyrkina, T. A. Sokolova, and M. M. Koton, Vysokomolekul. Soedin, Vsesoyuz. Khim. Obshchestvo im. D. I. Mendeleeva, 1, No. 2, 248 (1959); through Chem. Abstr., 53, 230591 (1959).
161. V. A. Kargin and T. I. Sogolova, Zh. Fiz. Khim., 23, 540 (1949).
162. E. C. Chapin, J. G. Abrams, and V. L. Lyons, J. Org. Chem., 27, 2595 (1962).
163. K. R. Dunham, J. W. H. Faber, J. Vandenberghe, and W. F. Fowler, J. Appl. Polymer Sci., 7, 897 (1963).
164. R. Kosfield, Kolloid-Z., 172, 183 (1960).
165. K. H. Illers, Z. Elektrochem., 65, 679 (1961); through Chem. Abstr., 56, 4932h (1962).
166. G. S. Kolesnikov and G. M. Pogosyan, Izv. Akad. Nauk. S.S.S.R. Otd. Khim. Nauk., 1958 (2), 227.
167. C. G. Overberger, C. Frazier, J. Mandelman, and H. F. Smith, J. Am. Chem. Soc., 75, 3326 (1953).
168. U. S. 2,723,261, Nov. 8, 1955.
169. L. L. Ferstandig, J. C. Butler, and A. E. Straus, J. Am. Chem. Soc., 76, 5779 (1954).
170. G. S. Kolesnikov. Izv. Akad. Nauk. S.S.S.R. Otd. Khim. Nauk., 1959, 1333.
171. K. R. Dunham, J. Vandenberghe, J. W. H. Faber, and W. F. Fowler, J. Appl. Polymer Sci., 7, 1531 (1963).
172. Brit. 609,482, Oct. 1, 1948.
173. G. T. Kennedy and F. Morton, J. Chem. Soc., 1949, 2383.

174. G. S. Kolesnikov and G. M. Pogosyan, Izv. Akad. Nauk. S.S.S.R. Otd. Khim. Nauk., 1962, 2098; through Chem. Abstr., 58, 8047a (1963).
175. R. F. Clash and L. M. Runkiewiez, Ind. Eng. Chem., 36, 279 (1944).
176. F. S. Dainton, D. M. Evans, F. E. Hoare, and T. P. Melia, Polymer, 3, 286 (1962).
177. S. Newman and W. P. Cox, J. Polymer Sci., 46, 29 (1960).
178. R. S. Spencer and R. F. Boyer, J. Appl. Phys., 17, 398 (1946).
179. T. G. Fox and P. J. Flory, J. Polymer Sci., 14, 315 (1954).
180. T. G. Fox and P. J. Flory, J. Am. Chem. Soc., 70, 2384 (1948).
181. T. G. Fox and P. J. Flory, J. Phys. and Colloid Chem., 55, 221 (1951).
182. R. H. Boundy and R. F. Boyer, "Styrene", Reinhold, New York, 1952.
183. S. Krimm and A. V. Tobolsky, J. Polymer Sci., 6, 667 (1951).
184. E. Jenckel and K. Überreiter, Z. Physik. Chem. (Leipzig), A182, 361 (1938).
185. G. Natta, F. Danusso, and G. Moraglio, J. Polymer Sci., 25, 119 (1957).
186. W. Patnode and W. J. Scheiber, J. Am. Chem. Soc., 61, 3449 (1939).
187. W. J. Roff, "Fibres, Plastics and Rubbers", Academic Press, New York, 1956.
188. B. G. Ranby, K. S. Chan, and H. Brumberger, J. Polymer Sci., 58, 545 (1962).
189. H. Schnell, Angew. Chem., 68, 633 (1956).
190. A. V. Tobolsky, "Properties and Structures of Polymers", Wiley, New York, 1960.
191. L. A. Wood, in G. S. Wiley, Ed., "Synthetic Rubber", Wiley, New York, 1954, Chap. 10.
192. U. V. Zelenev, Vysokomolekul. Soedin., 4, 1486 (1962).
193. U. S. 2,651,627, Sept. 8, 1953.
194. D. L. Livingston, P. M. Kamath, and R. S. Corley, J. Polymer Sci., 20, 485 (1956).
195. R. J. Schaffhauser, M. C. Shen, and A. V. Tobolsky, J. Appl. Polymer Sci., 8, 2825 (1964).
196. M. Kaufman and A. F. Williams, J. Appl. Chem. (London), 1, 489 (1951).
197. E. Jenckel and E. Braucker, Z. Physik. Chem. (Leipzig), A185, 465 (1940).
198. L. J. T. Hughes and D. B. Fordyce, J. Polymer Sci., 22, 509 (1956).
199. W. H. Howard, J. Appl. Polymer Sci., 5, 303 (1961).
200. L. V. Holroyd, R. S. Codrington, B. A. Mrowca, and E. Guth, Rubber Chem. Technol., 25, 767 (1952).
201. W. R. Krigbaum and N. Tokita, J. Polymer Sci., 43, 467 (1960).
202. T. G. Fox, Bull. Am. Phys. Soc., 1, 123 (1956).
203. R. J. Kokes, F. A. Long, and J. L. Hoard, J. Chem. Phys., 20, 1711 (1952).
204. R. Meredith and B. Hsu, J. Polymer Sci., 61, 271 (1962).
205. G. Natta, Angew. Chem., 68, 393 (1956).
206. F. P. Reding, J. Polymer Sci., 21, 547 (1956).
207. N. G. Gaylord and H. F. Mark, "Linear and Stereoregular Addition Polymers", Interscience, New York, 1959.
208. R. G. Saba, J. A. Sauer, and A. E. Woodward, J. Polymer Sci., Part A1, 1483 (1963).
209. L. Mandelkern, G. M. Martin, and F. A. Quinn, Jr., J. Res. Natl. Bur. Std., 58, 137 (1957).
210. T. Nakajima and S. Saito, J. Polymer Sci., 31, 423 (1958).
211. A. Nishioka, J. Polymer Sci., 37, 163 (1959).
212. R. F. Boyer and R. S. Spencer, J. Appl. Phys., 15, 398 (1944).
213. M. Baccaredda and E. Butta, J. Polymer Sci., 44, 421 (1960).
214. J. D. Hoffman, J. Am. Chem. Soc., 74, 1696 (1952).
215. K. H. Illers and E. Jenckel, Kolloid-Z., 165, 84 (1959).
216. K. H. Illers and E. Jenckel, in K. A. Wolf, Ed., "Kunststoffe", Vol. I, Springer-Verlag, Berlin, 1962.
217. N. G. McCrum, J. Polymer Sci., 60, S3 (1962).
218. F. P. Price, J. Am. Chem. Soc., 74, 311 (1952).
219. K. R. Dunham, J. Vandenberghe, J. W. H. Faber, and L. E. Contois, J. Polymer Sci., A1, 751 (1963).
220. G. Natta, Rend. Accad. Nazl. Lincei, Ser. 8, 24, (1958); through reference 243.
221. R. Houwink, "Fundamentals of Synthetic Polymer Technology", Elsevier, New York, p. 34.
222. N. L. Zutty and C. J. Whitworth, J. Polymer Sci., B2, 709 (1964).
223. G. S. Kolesnikov and M. G. Avetyan, Izv. Akad. Nauk. S.S.S.R. Otd. Khim. Nauk., 1962, 331.
224. W. S. Durrell, 148th Meeting ACS, Division of Fluorine Chemistry, Chicago, Illinois, Sept. 3, 1964 (Discussion).
225. A. Turner and F. E. Bailey, J. Polymer Sci., B1, 601 (1963).
226. B. L. Tsetlin, T. Ya. Medved, Yu. G. Chikishev, Yu. M. Polikarpov, S. R. Rafikov, and M. I. Kabuchnik, Vysokomolekul. Soedin., 3, 1117 (1961); through Chem. Abstr., 56, 2568h (1962).
227. F. Danusso, G. Moraglio, and G. Talamini, J. Polymer Sci., 21, 139 (1956).
228. H. Thurn, Kolloid-Z., 173, 72 (1960).
229. R. Simha and R. F. Boyer, J. Chem. Phys., 37, 1003 (1962).
230. A. Odajima, J. A. Sauer, and A. E. Woodward, J. Phys. Chem., 66, 718 (1962).

231. W. G. Oakes and D. W. Robinson, J. Polymer Sci., 14, 505 (1954).
232. O. D. Frampton and J. F. Nobis, Ind. Eng. Chem., 45, 404 (1953).
233. K. Wolf,and K. Schmieder, Internat. Symposium Macromol. Chem., Ric. Sci., 25, 732 (1955).
234. F. Wurstlin, Kunststoffe-Plastics, 40, 158 (1950).
235. A. E. Woodward and J. A. Sauer, Fortschr. Hochpolymer. Forsch., 1, 114 (1958).
236. B. Wunderlich, J. Polymer Sci., C1, 41 (1963).
237. N. G. McCrum, Makromol. Chem., 34, 50 (1959).
238. P. Manaresi and V. Giannela, J. Appl. Polymer Sci., 4, 251 (1960).
239. R. Nakane, J. Appl. Polymer Sci., 3, 124 (1960).
240. E. Hunter and E. W. Oakes, Trans. Faraday Soc., 41, 49 (1945).
241. F. A. Quinn and L. Mandelkern, J. Am. Chem. Soc., 80, 3178 (1958).
242. D. E. Kline, J. A. Sauer, and A. E. Woodward, J. Polymer Sci., 22, 455 (1956).
243. D. J. Marks, Ph.D. Thesis, Manchester Univ. (1961).
244. K. H. Illers, H. G. Kilian and R. Kosfield, Ann. Rev. Phys. Chem., 12, 49 (1961).
245. E. G. Kontos and W. P. Slichter, J. Polymer Sci., 61, 61 (1962).
246. H. A. Flücke, Kolloid-Z., 180, 118 (1962).
247. W. Pechhold, S. Blasenbrey and S. Woerner, Kolloid-Z., 189, 14 (1963).
248. G. S. Kolesnikov, E. F. Rodionova, L. S. Fedorova, T. Ya. Medved, and
      M. I. Kabacknik, Vysokomolekul.Soedin., 4, 1385 (1962); through Chem. Abstr., 58, 14108e (1963).
249. H. S. Eleuterio and E. P. Morre, 2nd International Symposium on Fluorine Chemistry, Estes Park Colo., U.S.A., 17-20th July, 1962.
250. S. F. Kurath, E. Passaglia, and R. Pariser, J. Appl. Phys., 28, 499 (1957).
251. E. Jenckel, Kolloid-Z., 100, 163 (1942).
252. J. C. H. Hwa, W. A. Fleming, and L. Miller, J. Polymer Sci., A2, 2385 (1964).
253. A. E. Woodward, J. A. Sauer, and R. A. Wall, J. Polymer Sci., 50, 117 (1961).
254. J. H. Griffith and B. G. Ranby, J. Polymer Sci., 44, 369 (1960).
255. R. W. Penn, Trans. Soc. Rheol., 3, 416 (1963).
256. W. A. Hewett and F. E. Weir, J. Polymer Sci., A1, 1239 (1963).
257. J. A. Price, M. R. Lytton, and B. G. Ranby, J. Polymer Sci., 51, 541 (1961).
258. G. T. Furukawa, R. E. McCoskey, and M. L. Reilly, J. Res. Natl. Bur. Std., 55, 127 (1955).
259. G. M. Zhidomirov, U. D. Tsvetkov, and Y. S. Lebedev, Zh. Strukt. Khim., 2, 696 (1961).
260. E. Butta and P. Giusti, Ric. Sci. Rend. Sec.A., 2, 362 (1962).
261. J. J. Maurer and H. C. Tsien, J. Appl. Polymer Sci., 8, 1719 (1964).
262. L. T. Muus, N. G. McCrum, and F. C. McGrew, Soc. Plastics Engrs. J., 15, 368 (1959).
263. N. G. McCrum, J. Polymer Sci., B2, 495 (1964).
264. R. W. Wilkinson and M. Dole, J. Polymer Sci., 58, 1089 (1962).
265. H. Wilski,Kunststoffe-Plastics, 54, 90 (1964).
266. J. A. Sauer, R. A. Wall, N. Fuschills, and A. E. Woodward, J. Appl. Phys., 29, 1385 (1958).
267. F. B. Cramer and R. G. Beaman, J. Polymer Sci., 21, 237 (1956).
268. V. A. Kargin and I. Yu. Marchenko, Polymer Sci. U.S.S.R., 2, 370 (1961).
269. E. Passaglia and G. M. Martin, J. Res. Natl. Bur. Std., 68, 273 (1964).
270. J. A. Sauer and A. E. Woodward, Rev. Mod. Phys., 32, 88 (1960).
271. W. Sorenson and T. W. Campbell, "Preparative Methods of Polymer Chemistry", Interscience, New York, 1961, p. 48.
272. T. Satokawa and S. Koizumi, Kogyo Kagaku Zasshi, 65, 1211 (1962).
273. G. T. Furukawa, R. E. McCoskey, and G. J. King, J. Res. Natl. Bur. Std., 49, 273 (1952).
274. K. H. Illers and E. Jenckel, Kolloid-Z., 160, 97 (1958).
275. M. Baccaredda and E. Butta, J. Polymer Sci., 31, 189 (1958).
276. K. Ohzawa and C. Wasa, "Reports on Progress in Polymer Physics in Japan", p. 147, Kobayasi Institute of Physical Research, Kokubunji, Tokyo, Japan, 1963.
277. C. W. F. T. Pistorius, Polymer, 5, 315 (1964).
278. E. W. Merrill and D. A. Gibbs, Chem. Eng. News, 41 (38), 41 (1963).
279. P. Meares, Trans. Faraday Soc., 53, 31 (1957).
280. L. Bohn, Kunststoffe-Plastics, 53, 93 (1963).
281. F. E. Bailey, J. P. Henry, R. D. Lundberg, and J. M. Whelan, J. Polymer Sci., 2, 447 (1964).
282. H. Thurn and K. Wolf, Kolloid-Z., 148, 16 (1956).
283. E. J. Vandenburg, R. F. Heck, and D. S. Breslow, J. Polymer Sci., 41, 519 (1960).
284. K. Fuju, S. Imoto, T. Mochizuki, J. Ukida, and M. Matsumoto, Chem. High Polymers (Japan), 19, 587 (1962).
285. C. E. Schildknecht, S. T. Gross, H. R. Davidson, J. M. Lambert, and A. O. Zoss, Ind. Eng. Chem., 40, 2104 (1948).
286. C. Noel, Compt. Rend., 258, 3702 (1964).

287. J. N. Short, G. Kraus, R. P. Zelinski, and F. E. Naylor, Rubber Chem. Technol., 32, 614 (1959).
288. M. Baccaredda and E. Butta, Chim. Ind. (Milan), 42, 978 (1960).
289. E. Pedemonte and U. Bianchi, J. Polymer Sci., B2, 1025 (1964).
290. A. W. Meyer, R. R. Hampton, and J. A. Davison, J. Am. Chem. Soc., 74, 2294 (1952).
291. F. S. Dainton, D. M. Evans, F. E. Hoare, and T. P. Melia, Polymer, 3, 297 (1962).
292. M. Baccaredda and E. Butta, J. Polymer Sci., 51, S39 (1961).
293. R. M. Kell, B. Bennett, and P. B. Stickney, J. Appl. Polymer Sci., 2, 8 (1959).
294. J. B. Campbell, Science, 141, 329 (1963).
295. B. L. Dolgoplosk, A. P. Erusalimskii, and A. V. Merkur'eva, Vysokomolekul. Soedin., 4, 1333 (1962); through Chem. Abstr., 59, 4045d (1963).
296. R. R. Garett, Unpublished results quoted by Aufdermarsh and Pariser, J. Polymer Sci., A2, 4727 (1964).
297. C. A. Aufdermarsh and R. Pariser, J. Polymer Sci., A2, 4727 (1964).
298. I. A. Livshits and L. M. Korobova, Dokl. Akad. Nauk. S.S.S.R., 121, 474 (1958).
299. R. G. Beaman, J. Polymer Sci., 9, 470 (1952).
300. K. Überreiter, Z. Physik. Chem., B45, 361 (1940).
301. G. F. D'Alelio, "Fundamental Principles of Polymerization," Wiley, New York, 1952, p. 124.
302. D. W. McCall and E. W. Anderson, J. Chem. Phys., 32, 237 (1960).
303. A. E. Woodward, J. M. Crissman, and J. A. Sauer, J. Polymer Sci., 44, 23 (1960).
304. O. Ishizuka, A. Okada, S. Ueda, T. Muroi, and I. Ikoma, Chem. High Polymer, (Japan), 17, 143 (1960); through Chem. Abstr., 55, 15997c (1961).
305. F. D. Hartley, F. W. Lord, and L. B. Morgan, Internat. Symposium Macromol. Chem., Ric. Sci., 25, 577 (1955).
306. A. M. Thomas, Nature, 179, 862 (1957).
307. F. P. Chappel, M. F. Culpin, R. G. Gosden, and T. C. Tranter, Conference on "Advances in Polymer Science and Technology", 1-3rd May, 1963, London.
308. J. Pellon, J. Polymer Sci., A1, 3561 (1963).
309. G. Champetier and J. P. Pied, Makromol. Chem., 44-6, 64 (1961); through Chem. Abstr. 56, 1584c (1962).
310. A. Schiller, J. C. Petropoulos, and C. S. H. Chen, J. Appl. Polymer Sci., 8, 1699 (1964).
311. J. E. McIntyre and E. C. Pugh, Brit. 838,986, (1960).
312. A. Conix, J. Polymer Sci., 29, 343 (1958).
313. P. W. Morgan, J. Polymer Sci., A2, 437 (1964).
314. H. Schnell, Ind. Eng. Chem., 51, 157 (1959).
315. J. P. Mercier, J. J. Aklonis, and A. V. Tobolsky, "The Viscoelastic Behaviour of Polycarbonates of Bisphenol A", ONR. Tech. Report RLT-60.
316. M. Gawlak, R. P. Palmer, J. B. Rose, D. J. H. Sandiford, and A. Turner-Jones, Chem. Ind. (London), 1962, 1148.
317. C. S. Marvel and C. H. Young, J. Am. Chem. Soc., 73, 1066 (1951).
318. C. S. Marvel and J. H. Johnson, J. Am. Chem. Soc., 72, 1674 (1950).
319. O. B. Edgar and R. Hill, J. Polymer Sci., 8, 1 (1952).
320. G. Farrow, J. McIntosh and J. M. Ward, Makromol. Chem., 38, 147 (1960).
321. J. Bateman, R. E. Richards, G. Farrow, and I. M. Ward, Polymer, 1, 63 (1960).
322. A. B. Thompson and D. W. Woods, Trans. Faraday Soc., 52, 1383 (1956).
323. B. Ke, J. Appl. Polymer Sci., 6, 624 (1962).
324. A. Conix, Ind. Eng. Chem., 51, 147 (1959).
325. G. Williams, Trans. Faraday Soc., 59, 1397 (1963).
326. G. Allen and J. Hurst, Unpublished Work.
327. F. S. Dainton, D. M. Evans, F. E. Hoare, and T. P. Melia, Polymer, 3, 271 (1962).
328. D. J. H. Sandiford, J. Appl. Chem., 8, 188 (1958).
329. J. C. Swallow, Proc. Roy. Soc., London, A238, 1 (1957).
330. B. E. Read and G. Williams, Polymer, 2, 239 (1961).
331. W. H. Linton and H. H. Goodman, J. Appl. Polymer Sci., 1, 179 (1959).
332. N. G. McCrum, J. Polymer Sci., 54, 561 (1961).
333. F. S. Dainton, D. M. Evans, F. E. Hoare, and T. P. Melia, Polymer, 3, 263 (1962).
334. G. Williams, Polymer, 4, 27 (1963).
335. L. E. St. Pierre and C. C. Price, J. Am. Chem. Soc., 78, 3432 (1956).
336. E. J. Vandenberg, J. Polymer Sci., 47, 486 and 489a (1960).
337. D. Sims, private communication: Ministry of Aviation, E.R.D.E., Waltham Abbey, Essex, U.K.
338. N. H. Reinking, A. E. Barnabeo, and W. F. Hale, J. Appl. Polymer Sci., 7, 2135 (1963).
339. N. H. Reinking, A. E. Barnabeo, and W. F. Hale, J. Appl. Polymer Sci., 7, 2153 (1963).
340. K. E. Polmanteer and M. J. Hunter, J. Appl. Polymer Sci., 1, 3, (1959).

341. C. E. Weir, W. H. Leser, and L. A. Wood, J. Res. Natl. Bur. Std., _44_, 367
      (1950).
342. L. A. Wood, J. Polymer Sci., _28_, 319 (1958).
343. S. B. Dolgoplosk, A. L. Klebanskii, L. P. Fomina, V. S. Fekhlengol'ts, and
      E. Yu. Shvarts, Dokl. Akad. Nauk. S.S.S.R., _150_, 813 (1963); through Chem.
      Abstr., _59_, 7664a (1963).
344. K. A. Andrianov and S. E. Yakushkina, Vysokomolekul. Soedin., _4_, 1193 (1962).
345. J. H. Daane and R. E. Barker, J. Polymer Sci., _B2_, 343 (1964).
346. K. Nakamura, Chem. High Polymers (Japan), _13_, 47 (1956).
347. J. Russell and R. G. Van Kerpel, J. Polymer Sci., _25_, 77 (1957).
348. K. Ueberreiter, Z. Physik. Chem., _B48_, 197 (1941).
349. E. L. Wittbecker, Chem. Eng. News, _41_, No. 46, 41 (1963).
350. S. N. Borisov, Kauchuk i Rezina, _20_, 16 (1961).
351. Chem. Eng. News., _41_, No. 38, 46 (1963).
352. D. A. Barr, R. N. Hazeldine, and C. J. Willis, J. Chem. Soc., 1351 (1961).
353. G. H. Crawford and D. E. Rice, Chem. Eng. News, _38_, No. 16, 107 (1960).

RATE OF CRYSTALLIZATION OF POLYMERS

J. Powers*
Washington, D. C.

and

R. L. Miller
Chemstrand Research Center
Durham, North Carolina

Contents

A. INTRODUCTION

In common with other substances, polymers crystallize from their liquids at rates governed by two fundamentally distinct processes: (a) primary crystal nucleation (i.e. formation of microscopic, but viable, crystal nuclei in the liquid phase) and (b) subsequent growth of these nuclei to form structures some of whose dimensions may be macroscopic in extent.

It is apparent that both processes contribute to the over-all transformation rate and that one cannot, from measurement of such over-all rates alone, disentangle the individual contribution of each process. It is possible, nevertheless, in certain limiting cases, to analyze over-all rate data in terms of combined rate constants governing nucleation and growth.

The simplest and best known expression for the time dependence of degree of crystallinity during crystallization at constant temperature is the Avrami equation (1); frequently written as

$$\theta = \exp \left[- Kt^n \right]$$

where θ is the fraction of untransformed phase, t the time, n an integer, and K a constant dependent upon nucleation and growth rates which, in the present case, are presumed to be constant throughout the course of the phase transformation. The value of n is related to the type of nucleation and the growth geometry. Thus, for n = 4, nucleation is homogeneous and growth three dimensional. For n = 3, either nucleation is homogeneous and growth two dimensional or nucleation is heterogeneous (non-sporadic in time) and growth is three dimensional.

If the value of t is known at some given fraction (say 1/2) of the phase transformation and if the value of n is known or assumed, then K may be calculated from

$$K = \frac{\ln 2}{(t_{1/2})^n}$$

* Present address: American Cyanamid Co., Stamford, Connecticut.

where the numerical value of K depends on the unit of time. Thus n and either $t_{1/2}$ or K may be used to characterize overall polymer crystallization rate under isothermal conditions.

Nucleation and growth processes in polymers usually result in the formation of morphological entities termed spherulites (spherical polycrystalline aggregates). Optical microscopy is presumed to measure the growth rate of individual polymeric crystals. Direct measurements of sporadic nucleation rates are more difficult, but several have been reported (2-4). The value of K obtained by kinetic measurements may be compared to that obtained from microscopy. In accord with the above assumptions (based on volume fraction and linear growth rates):

$$K = \frac{\pi}{3} NG^3 \qquad (n = 4)$$

and

$$K = \frac{4\pi}{3} IG^3 \qquad (n = 3) \text{ (heterogeneous nucleation)}$$

or

$$K = \frac{\pi}{3} N\ell_c G^2 \qquad (n = 3)$$

where N is the spherulitic nucleation rate (nuclei/cc/min), G the spherulitic radial growth rate (μ/min) and I the nuclei density (nuclei/cc). ℓ_c represents a constant dimension for the growth process assuming homogeneous nucleation (1,3).

Several papers deal with cases in which the assumptions of the above theory are relaxed. Thus, Avrami (5) treats the case in which nuclei are formed both by homogeneous and by heterogeneous (but sporadic) nucleation. Banks, Sharples, and Hay (6) discuss the case in which nuclei are formed by both homogeneous and non-sporadic processes. Gornick and Mandelkern (7) examine the case of nucleation and growth rates that vary with amount of material transformed. Neither the Avrami theory nor any of the above papers treat the phenomenon of secondary crystallization (8, 8a) (i.e., the small but continuous increase of degree of crystallinity observed at high degrees of crystallinity).

Many isothermal rate data in the literature have been reported in terms of K and n, treated essentially as parameters in purely phenomenological equations. For reasons cited above, molecular interpretation of these parameters (in particular, conclusions drawn from non-integral values of n) should be made with caution. These parameters are nevertheless useful for comparing isothermal rate data of different polymers.

The parameter θ is usually calculated either from specific volume data (as a mass fraction):

$$\theta_m = \frac{V_f - V_t}{V_f - V_o}$$

where V_f represents the final specific volume (cc/g), V_o the initial, and V_t the specific volume of polymer at time t; or from density balance measurements (as a volume fraction):

$$\theta_v = \frac{\rho_f - \rho_t}{\rho_f - \rho_o}$$

where ρ is the polymer density (g/cc) and the subscripts are defined above.

These expressions for measuring crystallinity have been discussed and applied to polymers in many publications [for example, specific volume (1,9), density balance (8), and light transmission (10)]. Typical over-all rate data for selected polymers

are presented in Table B. Literature references to more data are added in parenthesis.
Data for other polymers can be found in the references cited. Variation in the number
of heterogenities from sample to sample can shift the absolute rates by orders of
magnitude. The main value of these over-all rate data lies in their temperature dependence (8). M_v represents a viscosity average molecular weight.

Typical spherulitic growth rates (and when available, nucleation rates) are given in
Table C. These growth data are not influenced by the presence of heterogenities and
hence analysis of rates based on the data in Table C are more reliable than analysis
based on the data in Table B. Several authors using different polymers (for example,
poly-(decamethylene sebacate) (2), poly(ethylene oxide) (3), and polypropylene (11))
have compared values of K obtained by the two techniques.

To obtain these rate data, the sample is first heated in an auxiliary bath at some
arbitrary temperature [T(1)] above the polymer melting point, then transferred rapidly
to a hot stage or liquid bath preset at the desired crystallization temperature
[T(2)]. For microscopy, photographs are then taken of the hot stage field at various
times (t). For kinetic studies the mercury level in a dilatometer is observed or the
weight of the sample is measured at various times (t).

B. OVERALL RATE OF ISOTHERMAL CRYSTALLIZATION

Polymer	T°C	$t_{1/2}$[min]	K[min^{-n}]	n	Remarks	Reference
Polyolefins, Vinyl Polymers:						
Polyethylene						
(Marlex 50)	122	8.8				12
	123	12.5				(13,14)
	124	18.0				
	125	26.0				
	126	57.0				
	127	190.				
	128	580.				
	129	3300.				
	130	19000.				
Polypropylene						
M_v = 50,500	135.	7.9				16
	140.	25.4				(11,15,17,
	145.	114.5				61,63)
	150.	440.				
	155	1950.				
M_v = 96,800	133.	10.6				
	134.	14.9				
	135.	22.6				
	136.	35.4				
	137.	59.4				
	138	87.6				
	139.	134.9				
	140.	185.9				
	141.	272.				
M_v = 307,000	135.	10.7				
	140.	38.				
	145.	190.				
	150.	540.				
	155.	2540.				
Poly(1-butene)						18,19
Polyisobutene						20
Poly(1-pentene)						21
Poly(4-methyl-1-pentene)						60
cis-Polyisoprene						
(Natural Rubber)	-5	920.				23 (24,65,
	-11	330.				66,67,68,
	-16	200.				71)
	-17	170.				
	-22	150.				
	-27	150.				
	-33	240.				
	-38	390.				

Polymer	T°C	$t_{\frac{1}{2}}$[min]	K[min^{-n}]	n	Remarks	Reference
trans-Polyisoprene						
(Gutta Percha)	35	12.8				25 (26)
	40	21.				
	45	113.				
	47	195.				
	49	330.				
	51	530.				
	53	1075.				
	55	2150.				
	57	4850.				
	59	12,000.				
Polystyrene						77
Polyoxides:						
Polyformaldehyde						27
Poly(ethylene oxide)						3,28,70
Poly(3,3-bis(chloromethyl)oxacyclobutane)						29,30
Polyester:						
Poly(decamethylene adipate)						28,70
Poly(decamethylene sebacate)						2,31
Poly(decamethylene terephthalate)						35
Poly(ethylene adipate)						32
Poly(ethylene succinate)						33,34
Poly(ethylene terephthalate)						36 (37,72,
M_n = 16,800	106		1.51×10^{-5}		T(1) 268°C	74)
	108		5.11×10^{-5}			
	110		1.24×10^{-4}			
	120		7.54×10^{-3}			
	130		2.23×10^{-1}			
	247		2.08×10^{-6}			
	249		4.52×10^{-7}			
	250		1.59×10^{-10}			
Polyamides:						
Poly(6-aminocaproic acid)						38 (39,75,
M_n = 14,600	205.0	18.				76)
	207.0	34.				
	208.5	60.				
	209.7	83.				
	212.0	100.				
	215.0	210.				
Poly(hexamethylene adipamide)						40 (69,73)
M_n = 11,600	241		3.22×10^{-4}	3		
	247		3.72×10^{-5}	3		
	250		2.99×10^{-6}	3		
	252		8.67×10^{-9}	4		
	243		6.62×10^{-4}	3		
	247		1.57×10^{-4}	3		

Polymer	T°C	$t\frac{1}{2}$[min]	K[min^{-n}]	n	Remarks	Reference
Poly(hexamethylene adipamide) (Cont'd.)						
M_n = 11,600	250		1.61×10^{-5}	3		40
	252		7.62×10^{-6}	3		
	253		7.39×10^{-9}	4		
	247		3.33×10^{-4}	3		
	250		1.35×10^{-4}	3		
	252		1.34×10^{-5}	3		
	253			3-4		
	254		7.10×10^{-9}	4		
	247		4.06×10^{-4}	3		
	250		1.10×10^{-4}	3		
	252		8.09×10^{-5}	3		
	255			3-4		
	257		3.46×10^{-7}	4		
Poly(m-xylylene adipamide)						64
Poly(chlorotrifluoroethylene)						42 (8)
	180	3		–		
	186	8		3		
	191	25		3		
	193.5	47		3		
	195	70		3		
	196	87		3		
	196.5	143		3		
	197	186		3		

References page III-110

C. RATE OF RADIAL SPHERULITIC GROWTH

Polymer	T(1)[°C]	T(2)[°C]	G[μ/min]	Remarks	Ref.
1 - POLYOLEFINS AND VINYL POLYMERS					
Polyethylene					43
D* = 0	292	120.7	6.7		
	192	122.9	6.2		
	193	125.1	1.09		
	196	127.0	0.065		
	168	122.4	5.3		
	153	122.5	6.0		
D = 20 MR	195	114.0	6.0		
	195	116.4	12.9		
	195	118.9	2.5		
D = 40 MR	195	113.1	17.5		
	195	113.8	13.5		
	195	114.6	13.0		
	195	115.8	3.9		
	195	117.0	2.7		
	195	117.8	0.14		
D = 100 MR	195	100.0	4.3		
	195	100.0	3.7		
	195	101.8	1.9		
	195	104.0	0.47		
M_v = 19,000	200 (20 min)	125.0	7.6		44
		126.0	2.2		
		127.0	1.0		
		128.0	0.2		
Polyethylene (Low Density)					45
M_n = 4000		81.0	30.6	$CH_3/100CH_2$=7.15	
		82.0	20.5		
		83.0	15.4		
		83.9	11.7		
		85.0	8.6		
		86.0	6.2		
		87.1	4.8		
		88.0	3.8		
M_n = 7000		91.0	12.9	$CH_3/100CH_2$=5.32	
		92.1	7.7		
		93.0	5.2		
		94.2	3.6		
		95.2	2.1		
		96.0	1.5		
		97.0	0.84		
		98.0	0.47		

* D = Radiation dose   MR = Megarad

Polymer	T(1)[°C]	T(2)[°C]	G[μ/min]	Remarks	Ref.
Polyethylene (Low Density) Cont'd.)					
M_n = 10,000		92.0	10.5	$CH_3/100CH_2$=4.70	45
		93.0	6.1		
		94.1	4.0		
		95.0	2.4		
		95.9	1.8		
		97.0	1.2		
		98.0	0.69		
M_n = 12,000		90.3	19.0	$CH_3/100CH_2$=4.51	
		92.0	11.1		
		94.2	5.3		
		96.0	2.6		
		98.0	0.73		
		100.3	0.20		
Polypropylene	190-195	125	5.25		46
		130	3.69		
		134	1.72		
		138	0.52		
		140	0.27		
	180 (15 min)	122.0	18.		11
		125.0	12.		
		127.5	7.0		
		130.0	4.3		
		132.5	2.6		
		135.0	1.6		
		138.0	0.86		
		140.0	0.59		
		145.0	0.27		
M_v = 178,000		120	29.4		47
		125	13.0		
		131	3.88		
		135	1.63		
Polypropylene (Pro-fax 6513 E)	220	120.5	28.80		15
		123.5	23.4		
		129.	7.20		
		131.	4.6		
		145.	0.21		
Polypropylene (Pro-fax 6501)		121.	24.5		15
		126	20.4		
		132	2.8		
		140	0.47		
		145	0.14		
Poly(1-butene) M_v = 400,000	160 (10 min)	90	8.8		19
		95	4.4		
		100	1.0		
		105	0.25		

References page III-110

Polymer	T(1)[°C]	T(2)[°C]	G[μ/min]	Remarks	Ref.
Polystyrene (isotactic)					47
M_v = 60,000		140	0.02		
		155	0.09		
		168	0.20		
		177	0.26		
		184	0.25		
		190	0.22		
		200	0.10		
		210	0.03		
M_v = 1,250,000		140	0.05		47
		155	0.13		
		170	0.29		
		177	0.30		
		184	0.27		
		200	0.13		
		210	0.04		
M_v = 190,000	270	150	0.02		48
		170	0.08		
		180	0.08		
		185	0.07		
		190	0.03		
M_v = 1,380,000		130	0.02		48
		150	0.11		
		170	0.27		
		180	0.45		
		185	0.22		
		190	0.19		

2 - POLYOXIDES

Polymer	T(1)[°C]	T(2)[°C]	G[μ/min]	Remarks	Ref.
Polyformaldehyde					49
M_n = 45,000		156.0	20.8		
		157.0	13.8		
		158.0	5.95		
		159.8	4.62		
		160.8	3.39		
		163.0	1.25		
		163.9	0.855		
		164.5	0.288		
		166.1	0.177		
		169.1	0.0285		
Poly(ethylene oxide)					3
M_v = 5,470		42.0	826.		
		44.2	284.		

Polymer	T(1)[°C]	T(2)[°C]	G[μ/min]	Remarks	Ref.
Poly(ethylene oxide) (Cont'd.)					
M_v = 5,470		45.2	133.		3
		47.2	23.7		
M_v = 12,400		47.2	705.		
		48.8	362.		
		51.2	90.8		
		55.2	3.33		
M_v = 33,100		47.6	107.		
		48.2	91.0		
		50.5	21.2		
		51.0	24.6		
		51.0	26.6		
		51.0	25.3		
		53.8	5.65		
		56.4	0.096		
Poly(propylene oxide)					
M_n = 10,300		0	30		62
		4	44.5		
		5	44.8		
		10	43.4		
		15	50.3		
		25	28.6		
		30	24.2		
		35	14.4		
		40	8.74		
		45	3.4		
		40	8.74		
		50	1.41		
		60	0.123		
Poly(3,3-bis(chloromethyl)- oxacyclobutane)		75	12.5		30
		80	11.		
		85	10.		
		90	9.		
		100	7.5		
		105	7.		
		110	6.		
		115	5.		
		120	4.		
		125	3.5		
		130	2.		
		135	1.75		
		140	1.5		

References page III-110

Polymer	T(1)[°C]	T(2)[°C]	G[μ/min]	Remarks	Ref.

3 - POLYESTERS

Polymer	T(1)[°C]	T(2)[°C]	G[μ/min]	Remarks	Ref.
Poly(decamethylene sebacate)				N(nuclei/cc /min)	2
M_v – 10,300	100	67.1	5.24	1.50×10^5	
	(24 hrs)	68.1	1.30	3.72×10^4	
		69.1	0.387	8.95×10^3	
		70.1	0.113	1.12×10^3	
		71.1	0.0350	1.65×10^2	
		72.0	0.00498	1.65×10^1	
Poly(decamethylene terephthalate)				N(nuclei/cc /min)	35
$M_n = 10^4$	160	120.0	0.332	54.6	
	(5 min)	121.0	0.207	22.6	
		121.9	0.154	11.0	
		123.0	0.09550	3.33	
		123.7	0.0660	1.86	
		123.9	0.0655	1.90	
		125.0	0.0373	0.800	
		126.0	0.0153	0.246	
Poly(ethylene adipate)					32
$M_v = 9900$		20	3.98		
		40	1.08		
		44	0.79		
		47	0.54		
Poly(ethylene succinate)					34
$M_w = 5980$		16.4	0.72		
		23.0	1.87		
		24.1	1.44		
		26.3	3.74		
		27.2	2.54		
		28.5	2.65		
		35.6	5.48		
		36.1	6.92		
		36.3	5.51		
		39.6	8.82		
		39.8	7.73		
		40.9	8.40		
		41.8	9.26		
		42.3	9.51		
		49.8	9.73		
		50.3	9.96		
		51.2	9.60		
		53.4	9.01		
		57.0	9.20		
		57.6	7.20		
		58.7	6.96		
		59.8	7.56		
		61.4	4.61		

Polymer	T(1)[°C]	T(2)[°C]	G[μ/min]	Remarks	Ref.
Poly(ethylene succinate) (Cont'd.)					
M_w = 5980		67.6	4.45		34
		72.0	3.08		
		75.2	1.57		
		81.8	0.348		
		85.0	0.180		
Poly(ethylene terephthalate)				N(nuclei/cc /min)	
M_n = 16,800	294	220	2.5	3.2×10^8	36
		240	0.186	4.93×10^6	
		185	7.0		52
		220	1.6		
Poly(4,4'-isopropylidenediphenylene carbonate)					51
(Polycarbonate-A)		190	0.005		
		195	0.0025		
Poly(4,4'-methylenediphenylene carbonate)					51
(Polycarbonate-F)		175	1.0		
		180	0.6		
		185	0.3		
		190	0.2		
Poly(4,4'-thiodiphenylene carbonate)					51
(Polycarbonate-S)		145	1.2		
		150	0.9		
		160	0.5		
		170	0.35		
		180	0.25		

4 - POLYAMIDES

Polymer	T(1)[°C]	T(2)[°C]	G[μ/min]	Remarks	Ref.
Poly(6-aminocaproic acid)					53
M_n = 27,400	300 (30 sec)	102.3	54.0		
		103.5	66.0		
		112.5	88.7		
		113.0	96.9		
		122.0	122		
		130.0	166		
		131.0	180		
		132.0	194		
		139.0	176		
		140.5	188		
		150.5	179		
		151.0	165		
		151.5	169		
		159.0	147		
		159.5	144		

References page III-110

Polymer	T(1)[°C]	T(2)[°C]	G[μ/min]	Remarks	Ref.
Poly(6-aminocaproic acid) (Cont'd.)					
M_n = 27,400		170.0	85.9		53
		171.5	79.5		
		172.0	80.0		
		180.0	42.6		
		180.5	41.8		
		181.5	38.1		
		182.0	36.6		
M_n = 24,700		90	22.5		54
		95	36.6		
		101	38.4		
		107	66.5		
		117	94.3		
		124.5	116.0		
		135	146.3		
		141	146.3		
		148	126.3		
		157	107.4		
		172	59.0		
		184	18.3		
		184.5	14.4		
Poly(hexamethylene adipamide) (Nylon 66)				I (nuclei/cc)	40
M_n = 11,600	295	241	10.	1.06×10^6	
	295	247	3.5	7.60×10^5	
	295	250	0.83	6.08×10^5	
	295	252	0.63	*	
	285	247	4.0	9.13×10^5	
negative spherulites		251	0.86		56
		256	0.50		
		257±1	0.80		55
		259±1	0.55		
		261±1	0.40		
		263±1	0.25		
		265±0.5	0.15		
				N(nuclei/cc /min)	
M_n = 12,900	300	246.0	6.40	1.16×10^6	57
	(30 min)	248.0	3.38	0.88×10^6	
		253.0	0.65	0.12×10^6	
M_n = 13,700	300	141.0	810		53
	(30 sec)	160.0	820		
		180.0	727		
		199.0	534		
		214.0	328		
		215.0	310		

* $N = 6.99 \times 10^3$

Polymer	T(1)[°C]	T(2)[°C]	G[μ/min]	Remarks	Ref.
Poly(hexamethylene adipamide) (Nylon 66) (Cont'd.)					
M_n = 13,700	300	215.0	310		53
	(30 sec)	216.5	282		
		230.0	127		
		234.0	91.8		
		237.0	55.2		
		238.0	53.0		
		239.5	45.9		
		241.0	28.3		
		244.0	22.1		
				N(nuclei/cc /min)	
M_n = 14,600	280	241.5	17.0	48.5×10^6	57
		242.	15.75	39.2×10^6	
		243.	13.8	22.5×10^6	
		245.	10.85	5.73×10^6	
		247.5	6.3	2.85×10^6	
		248.	5.74	2.26×10^6	
		252.	0.88	0.33×10^6	
	300	241.5	12.26	14.4×10^6	57
		242.	11.5	13.0×10^6	
		243.	10.5	10.5×10^6	
		245.	7.7	6.2×10^6	
		247.5	4.1	3.15×10^6	
		248.	3.5	2.80×10^6	
		251.	0.46	0.18×10^6	
		252	0.33		
	315	241.5	16.8	45.0×10^6	57
		242.	14.5	31.7×10^6	
		243.	10.1	10.5×10^6	
		245.	6.8	6.7×10^6	
		247.5	3.95	3.25×10^6	
		248.	3.4	2.89×10^6	
		252.	0.38	0.09×10^6	
positive spherulites					
M_n = 17,200		50	219.		58
		100	286		
		142	405.		
		160	366		
		178	312.		
		198	222.		
		200	174.		
		228	28.		
positive spherulites					
M_n = 25,500	300	180.0	686		53
	(30 sec)	200.0	477		
		202.0	471		

References page III-110

Polymer	T(1)[°C]	T(2)[°C]	G[μ/min]	Remarks	Ref.
Poly(hexamethylene adipamide) (Nylon 66) (Cont'd)					
positive spherulites					
M_n = 25,500	300	211.0	317		53
	(30 sec)	222.0	164		
		229.5	105		
		230.0	96.9		
		233.5	70.0		
		234.5	65.2		
		235.5	40.8		
		240.0	29.0		
Poly(hexamethylene sebacamide) (Nylon 610)					
positive spherulites		200	15.2		58
		205	7.2		
		212	2.2		
		217	0.8		
negative spherulites		205	11.2		58
		212	7.8		
		217	4.4		

5 - MISCELLANEOUS ORGANIC POLYMERS

Polymer	T(1)[°C]	T(2)[°C]	G[μ/min]	Remarks	Ref.
Poly(chlorotrifluoroethylene)					
	305	166.3	27.0		8
	277	169.0	26.4		
	305	169.1	25.8		
	277	171.7	21.6		
	277	174.4	19.2		
	277	177.2	15.9		
	277	180.1	11.7		
	277	180.2	12.6		
	277	183.0	8.3		
	267	185.5	6.6		
	267	185.6	1.05		
	267	188.2	3.9		
	267	188.3	4.2		
	267	191.0	2.4		
	267	193.7	1.2		
		195	0.435		42
		195.3	0.333		
		195.8	0.218		
		196.6	0.173		
		197	0.150		

Polymer	T(1)[°C]	T(2)[°C]	G[μ/min]	Remarks	Ref.
Poly(chlorotrifluoroethylene) (Cont'd.)					
		197.4	0.133		42
		198.4	0.0983		
		199.1	0.0730		
		200	0.0605		
		200.8	0.0428		
		201.5	0.0208		
		202	0.0192		
(Kel-F NST 300)	270 (10 min)	170	24.4		59
		175	18.6		
		180	13.0		
		185	7.45		
		190	2.18		

6 - INORGANIC POLYMERS

Poly(tetramethyl-p-silphenylene siloxane)					78
M_v = 10,100		23	13.1		
		24	14.6		
		25.5	17.6		
		45	55.3		
		60	82.5		
		70	84.5		
		75	72.8		
		85	57.5		
		90	48.2		
		100	21.4		
		110	5.4		
		120	0.98		
		125	0.3		
		130	0.02		
M_v = 25,000		23	8.43		
		30	15.4		
		40	29.2		
		45	34.9		
		60	52.8		
		70	51.8		
		80	44.0		
		90	28.75		
		100	14.4		

References page III-110

Polymer	T(1)[°C]	T(2)[°C]	G[μ/min]	Remarks	Ref.
Poly(tetramethyl-p-silphenylene siloxane) (Cont'd.)					
M_v = 25,000		110	4.77		78
		115	2.83		
		120	1.3		
		125	0.243		
M_v = 56,000		23	4.7		
		26	5.8		
		30	8.35		
		40	17.0		
		45	20.3		
		50	27.5		
		60	30.7		
		70	31.2		
		75	32.5		
		80	27.5		
		90	16.6		
		100	8.6		
		110	3.4		
M_v = 1.09 x 10^5		21.5	3.15		
		22.5	3.55		
		23	4.72		
		24	4.58		
		40	14.85		
		60	24.6		
		70	24.0		
		79	18.17		
		82	18.2		
		90.2	12.92		
		105	3.62		
		110	1.90		
		116	0.85		
		119.8	0.346		
		120	0.317		
		121.3	0.258		
		125	0.124		
		130	0.0265		

D. REFERENCES

1. L. Mandelkern, Chem. Rev. 56, 903 (1956).
2. P. J. Flory and A. D. McIntyre, J. Polymer Sci. 18, 592 (1955).
3. W. J. Barnes, W. G. Luetzel, and F. P. Price, J. Phys. Chem. 65, 80 (1961).
4. R. L. Cormia, F. P. Price, and D. Turnbull, J. Chem. Phys. 37, 1333 (1962).
5. M. Avrami, J. Chem. Phys. 8, 212 (1940).
6. W. Banks, A. Sharples, and J. N. Hay, J. Polymer Sci. A2, 4059 (1964).
7. F. Gornick and L. Mandelkern, J. Appl. Phys. 33, 907 (1962).
8. J. D. Hoffman and J. J. Weeks, J. Chem. Phys. 37, 1723 (1962).
8a. F. Rynikar, J. Polymer Sci. A1, 2031 (1963).
9. N. Bekkedahl, J. Res. Natl. Bur. Std. 13, 411 (1934).
10. J. H. Magill, Polymer 3, 35 (1962).
11. B. von Falkai, and H. A. Stuart, Kolloid-Z 162, 138 (1959).
12. L. Mandelkern, "Growth and Perfection of Crystals," R. H. Doremus, B. W. Roberts
    and D. Turnbull (Editors), John Wiley, New York, 467-497 (1958).
13. J. J. Weeks, J. Res. Natl. Bur. Std. 67A, 44 (1963).
14. W. Banks, M. Gordon, R.-J. Roe, and A. Sharples, Polymer 4, 61 (1963).
15. L. Marker, P. M. Hays, G. P. Tilley, R. M. Early, and O. J. Sweeting, J. Polymer
    Sci. 38, 33 (1959).
16. J. H. Griffith and B. G. Ranby, J. Polymer Sci. 38, 107 (1959).
17. P. Parrini and G. Corrieri, Makromol. Chem. 62 83 (1963).
18. J. Boor, Jr. and J. C. Mitchell, J. Polymer Sci. A1, 59 (1963).
19. J. Powers, J. D. Hoffman, and F. A. Quinn, Jr., J. Res. Natl. Bur. Std. in press.
20. R. M. Kell, B. Bennett, and P. B. Stickney, Rubber Chem. and Technol. 31, 499
    (1958).
21. F. A. Quinn, Jr. and J. Powers, J. Polymer Sci. C1, 341 (1963).
23. L. A. Wood, and N. Bekkedahl, J. Res. Natl. Bur. Std. 36, 489, (1946).
24. E. W. Russell, Trans. Faraday Soc. 47, 539 (1951).
25. L. Mandelkern, F. A. Quinn, Jr. and D. E. Roberts, J. Am. Chem. Soc. 78, 926
    (1956).
26. W. Cooper and G. Vaughan, Polymer 4, 329 (1963).
27. M. Inque and T. Takayanaki, J. Polymer Sci. 47, 498 (1960).
28. L. Mandelkern, F. A. Quinn, Jr. and P. J. Flory, J. Appl. Phys. 25, 830 (1954).
29. M. Hatano and S. Kambara, Polymer 2, 1 (1961).
30. M. Inoue, J. Polymer Sci. 61, 343 (1962).
31. A. D. McIntyre, Thesis, Cornell Univ., 1956, Univ. Microfilm 16,256.
32. M. Takayanagi, Mem. Fac. Eng. Kyushu. Univ. 16(3), 111, (1957).
33. K. Uberreiter, G. Kanig, and A. S. Brenner, J. Polymer Sci. 16, 53 (1955).
34. M. Takayanagi and N. Kusumoto, J. Chem. Soc. Japan (Ind Sect) 62, 587 (1959).
35. A. Sharples and F. L. Swinton, Polymer 4, 119 (1963).
36. F. D. Hartley, F. W. Lord, and L. B. Morgan, Proc. Roy. Soc. (London) A247, 23
    (1954).
37. W. H. Cobbs, Jr. and R. L. Burton, J. Polymer Sci. 10, 257 (1953).
38. M. Inoue, J. Polymer Sci. 55, 753 (1961).
39. P. Cefelin, M. Chmelir, and O. Wichterle, Collection Czech. Chem. Commun. 25,
    1267 (1960).
40. F. D. Hartley, F. W. Lord, and L. B. Morgan, Ric. Sci. Suppl. A25, 577 (1955).
42. F. Rybnikar, Collection Czech. Chem. Commun. 27, 2307 (1962).
43. F. P. Price, J. Phys. Chem. 64, 169 (1960).
44. W. Banks, J. N. Hay, A. Sharples, and G. Thompson, Polymer 5, 163 (1964).
45. T. Naono, J. Sci. Hiroshima Univ. A24, 653 (1960).
46. S. Hoshino, B. Meinecke, J. Powers, S. Newman, and R. S. Stein, unpublished
    results.
47. H. D. Keith and F. J. Padden, Jr., J. Appl. Phys. 35, 1286 (1964).
48. A. S. Kenyon, R. C. Gross, and A. L. Wurstner, J. Polymer Sci. 40, 159 (1959).
49. F. J. Limbert,and E. Baer, J. Polymer Sci. A1, 3317 (1963).
51. B. von Falkai and W. Rellensmann, Makromol. Chem. 75, 112 (1964).
52. A. Keller, G. R. Lester, and L. B. Morgan, Phil. Trans. Roy. Soc. London A247,
    1 (1954).
53. B. B. Burnett and W. F. McDevit, J. Appl. Phys. 28, 1101 (1957).
54. J. H. Magill, Polymer 3, 655 (1962).
55. F. Khoury, J. Polymer Sci. 38, 389 (1958).
56. E. H. Boasson and J. M. Woestenenk, J. Polymer Sci. 24, 57 (1957).
57. J. V. McLaren, Polymer 4, 175 (1963).
58. C. R. Lindegren, J. Polymer Sci. 50, 181 (1961).
59. F. P. Price, J. Am. Chem. Soc. 74, 311 (1952).
60. J. H. Griffith and B. G. Ranby, J. Polymer Sci. 44, 369 (1960).
61. J. H. Magill, Nature 191, 1092 (1961).

62. J. H. Magill, Private communication.
63. J. H. Magill, Polymer 3, 35 (1962).
64. G. Allegra, A. Pontoglio, and I. Pasquon, Rend. Ist. Lombardo Sci. Lettere A95, 335 (1961).
65. A. N. Gent, Trans. Faraday Soc. 50, 521 (1954).
66. A. N. Gent, I. R. I. Trans. 30, 139 (1954).
67. A. N. Gent, I. R. I. Trans. 30, 144 (1954).
68. A. N. Gent, J. Polymer Sci. 18, 321 (1955).
69. P. W. Allen, Trans. Faraday Soc. 48, 1178 (1952).
70. L. Mandelkern, J. Appl. Phys. 26, 443 (1955).
71. A. N. Gent, J. Polymer Sci. 28, 257 (1955).
72. H. G. Zachman and H. A. Stuart, Makromol. Chem. 41, 131 (1960).
73. J. H. Magill, Polymer 2, 221 (1961).
74. R. P. Sheldon, Polymer 3, 27 (1962).
75. F. Rybnikar, Collection Czech. Chem. Commun. 27, 106 (1962).
76. M. Inoue, J. Polymer Sci. A1, 2013 (1963).
77. J. N. Hay, J. Polymer Sci. A3, 433 (1965).
78. J. H. Magill, J. Appl. Phys., 35, 3249 (1964).

CRITICAL SURFACE TENSION OF POLYMERS

E. G. Shafrin

U. S. Naval Research Laboratory
Washington, D. C.

The critical surface tension for spreading (γ_C) defines the wettability of a solid surface by noting the lowest surface tension (γ_L) a liquid can have and still exhibit a contact angle (θ) greater than zero degrees on that solid. The constant is expressed in units of dynes per centimeter and the temperature is specified; the following values are based on measurements made at 20-25°C.

The value of γ_C for a given solid is determined by observing the spreading behavior and the angle θ of a series of liquids of decreasing γ_L. A rectilinear relation exists between cosine θ and γ_L; the intercept of this line with the cos θ = 1 (i.e., θ = zero) line gives a value of γ_C which is independent of the nature of the test liquid and is a parameter characteristic of the solid surface only.

Polymer	Critical Surface Tension (γ_C) [dynes cm.$^{-1}$]	Ref.
Polyolefins and Vinyl Polymers		
Poly(chlorotrifluoroethylene)	31	1
Polyethylene	31	2
	31.5	3
Poly(hexafluoropropylene)	16.2 - 17.1	4
Polystyrene	33 - 35	5
	30 - 35	6
Poly(tetrafluoroethylene)	18.5	7
Poly(trifluoroethylene)	22	8
Poly(vinyl alcohol)	37	9
Poly(vinyl chloride)	39	8
Poly(vinyl fluoride)	28	8
Poly(vinylidene chloride)	40	8
Poly(vinylidene fluoride)	25	8
Acrylic Polymers		
Polyacrylamide	35 - 40	6
Polyacrylate	35	10
Poly(1,1-dihydro-perfluorooctyl methacrylate)	10.6	11
Poly(methyl methacrylate)	33 - 44	12
	39	6
Poly[2-(N-propylperflurooctanesulfonamido)ethyl acrylate]	11.1	11
Polyesters		
Poly(ethylene terephthalate)	43	5
	42.5	3
Polyamides		
Poly(6-aminocaproic acid)	42	13
Poly(11-aminoundecanoic acid)	33	13

Polymer	Critical Surface Tension (γ_C) [dynes cm.$^{-1}$]	Ref.
Polyamides (Cont'd.)		
Poly(decamethylene sebacamide)	32	13
Poly(heptamethylene pimelamide)	43	13
Poly(hexamethylene adipamide)	46	5
Poly(octamethylene suberamide)	34	13
Poly(nonamethylene azelaamide)	36	13
Other Organic Polymers, Copolymers, and Resins		
Polyamide-epichlorohydrin resin	52	10
Poly(tetrafluoro ethylene-co-chlorotrifluoroethylene)		
80:20	20	1
60:40	24	1
Poly(tetrafluoroethylene-co-ethylene)		
50:50	26 - 27	1
Poly(tetrafluoroethylene-co-hexafluoropropylene)		
94:6	19.0	14
92:8	18.3	14
86:14	18.2	14
84:16	18	14
77:23	17.8	14
Poly(vinylidene chloride-co-acrylonitrile)		
80:20	38 - 44	6
91:9	38	3
Urea-formaldehyde resin	61	10
Natural Polymers		
Amylopectin	35	9
Amylose	37	9
Casein	43	10
Cellulose (regenerated)	44	9
Starch	39	9
Wool	45	10
Semiorganic Polymers		
Poly(dimethyl siloxane)	24	15

REFERENCES

1. H. W. Fox and W. A. Zisman, J. Colloid Sci. 7, 109 (1952).
2. H. W. Fox and W. A. Zisman, J. Colloid Sci. 7, 428 (1952).
3. D. K. Owens, J. Appl. Polymer Sci. 8, 1465 (1964).
4. M. K. Bernett and W. A. Zisman, J. Phys. Chem. 65, 2266 (1961).
5. A. H. Ellison and W. A. Zisman, J. Phys. Chem. 58, 503 (1954).
6. N. L. Jarvis, R. B. Fox and W. A. Zisman, in "Advances in Chemistry," Number 43, American Chemical Society, Washington, D. C., 1964, p. 317.
7. H. W. Fox and W. A. Zisman, J. Colloid Sci. 5, 514 (1950).
8. A. H. Ellison and W. A. Zisman, J. Phys. Chem. 58, 260 (1954).
9. B. R. Ray, J. R. Anderson and J. J. Scholz, J. Phys. Chem. 62, 1220 (1958).
10. H. D. Feltman and J. R. McPhee, Textile Research J., 34, 634 (1964).
11. M. K. Bernett and W. A. Zisman, J. Phys. Chem. 66, 1207 (1962).
12. E. Wolfram, Kolloid Z. 182, 75 (1962).
13. T. Fort, Jr., in "Advances in Chemistry," Number 43, American Chemical Society, Washington, D. C., 1964, p. 302.
14. M. K. Bernett and W. A. Zisman, J. Phys. Chem. 64, 1292 (1960).
15. E. G. Shafrin and W. A. Zisman, in "Advances in Chemistry," Number 43, American Chemical Society, Washington, D. C., 1964, p. 145.

IV.
SOLUTION PROPERTIES

VISCOSITY-MOLECULAR WEIGHT RELATIONSHIPS

and

UNPERTURBED DIMENSIONS OF LINEAR CHAIN MOLECULES

Michio Kurata, Masamichi Iwama, and Kensuke Kamada

Institute for Chemical Research, Kyoto University
Kyoto, Japan

Contents

A. INTRODUCTION

1. The Viscosity-Molecular Weight Relationship

The ratio of the viscosity η of a solution to the viscosity η_o of the pure solvent is called the viscosity ratio or the relative viscosity, and is denoted by η_r,

$$\eta_r = \eta/\eta_o .\qquad(1)$$

The relative increase of the viscosity is called the specific viscosity and is denoted by η_{sp},

$$\eta_{sp} = (\eta - \eta_o)/\eta_o = \eta_r - 1 .\qquad(2)$$

This quantity is divided by the concentration c to obtain the viscosity number η_{sp}/c which expresses the average contribution of the solute molecules at concentration c to the viscosity. The limiting viscosity number or the Staudinger index $[\eta]$ which has long been called the intrinsic viscosity is the value of the viscosity number at infinite dilution; i.e.

$$[\eta] = \lim_{c \to 0} \frac{\eta_{sp}}{c} = \lim_{c \to 0} \frac{\eta - \eta_o}{\eta_o c} \tag{3}$$

The limiting viscosity number may also be defined as

$$[\eta] = \lim_{c \to 0} \frac{\ln \eta_r}{c} \tag{4}$$

The concentration c is expressed in grams of solute per milliliter of solution or, more frequently, in grams of solute per 100 milliliters of solution, the limiting viscosity number being given in the reciprocals of these units, i.e. in milliliters per gram or in deciliters per gram. The viscosity of polymer solutions, especially with high molecular weight polymers, is often appreciably dependent on the rate of shear in the range of measurement. The limiting viscosity number should, therefore, be given as the limiting value of η_{sp}/c not only at infinite dilution but also at a shear rate of zero, or the value of the rate of shear should be specified.

The limiting viscosity number of a polymer solution is a measure of the capacity of a polymer molecule to enhance the viscosity, which depends on the size and the shape of the polymer molecule. Within a given series of polymer homologs, the limiting viscosity number increases with the molecular weight M; hence it is a measure of M.

The following Tables B1-B12 give the limiting viscosity number-molecular weight relationships for polymers in various solvents and at various temperatures. The tables contain the constants of the equation

$$[\eta] = KM^a , \tag{5}$$

which is known as the Mark-Houwink-Sakurada equation.

It is now well established that for linear, flexible polymers, under special condition of temperature or solvent, which is usually known as the Flory "theta" temperature or solvent (1) the above equation becomes

$$[\eta]_\theta = K_\theta M^{0.50} \tag{6}$$

The sign θ in front of the data in the tables indicates that these constants were obtained under θ condition. Since Eq. (6) is approximately valid over the whole molecular weight range, K_θ and a = 0.50 may be used, without modification outside of the molecular weight range in which they were determined. However, the constants K and a determined in ordinary solvents are valid only within a rather limited range of M (2,3). It is, therefore, quite probable that the relationships tabulated are in error outside the indicated range of M (see eighth column in the tables). As for the effect of temperature, both K and a mostly become insensitive to the temperature when a exceeds about 0.70, and they may be used in a ten-degree range on either side of the temperature at which the constants were determined.

The method of determination of the molecular weight and the number of fractions (Fr.) or whole polymers (W.P.) used to determine the $[\eta]$-M relationship are also given in the ninth and the sixth or seventh columns, respectively. The abbreviations used are as follows.

(A) Methods yielding the number-average molecular weight, M_n.

CR, cryoscopy.

EB, ebullioscopy.

EG, end-group titration.

OS, osmotic pressure.

VOS, vapor pressure osmometry.

(B) Methods yielding the weight-average molecular weight, M_w.

LS, light scattering.

SA, approach to the sedimentation equilibrium (Archibald's method).

SD, sedimentation and diffusion.

SE, sedimentation equilibrium.

(C) Empirical or semi-empirical methods.

DV, diffusion and viscosity (yielding M_w).

IV, viscosity-molecular weight relationship in other solvents (purely empirical).

MV, melt viscosity-molecular weight relationship (purely empirical).

PR, analysis of polymerization rate (yielding M_n).

SV, sedimentation and viscosity (yielding M_w).

Thus, for example, the constants tabulated are for the $[\eta]$-M relationships expressed in terms of M_n if the method is specified as OS. When well fractionated polymers or whole polymers with a sharp distribution of molecular weight such as anionic polymers were used to determine the constants, the difference between M_n and M_w may be neglected. The so-called "viscosity-average molecular weight" M_v of a heterogeneous polymer can be estimated from $[\eta]$ by the use of the $[\eta]$-M relationship:

$$M_v = (\Sigma_i w_i M_i^a)^{1/a} \tag{7}$$

where M_i and w_i represent the molecular weight and the weight fraction of component i of the heterogenous polymer. As a is generally between 0.5 and 1.0, M_v gives an intermediate between M_n and M_w. Eq. (7) is based on the additivity of $[\eta]$

$$[\eta] = \Sigma_i w_i [\eta]_i \quad , \tag{8}$$

and on the assumption that the same constants K and a are applicable to all components of the whole polymers. This assumption, however, can not be valid in ordinary solvents over a very wide range of molecular weight, but is valid in theta solvents. As a result, the rigorous meaning of the viscosity average becomes more or less obscure in ordinary solvents.

Chain configurations such as branching, tacticity or the sequence length of a component in copolymers often greatly influence the $[\eta]$-M relationships. Detailed information on these factors cannot be given in the tables, and it is desirable that readers refer to the original paper before they use the tabulated constants.

In the tables the polymers are arranged according to their type in subgroups. Within each subgroup, the polymers are, in principle, given in alphabetical order. The suffixes like alpha (α), ortho (o), meta (m), and normal (n) are neglected, but the suffixes di-, tri-, and iso- are used for alphabetical arrangement. Substituted homologs or closely related polymers are listed under the basic underlying structure in order to keep similar polymers together. For instance: polystyrene, poly(p-bromostyrene), poly(p-chlorostyrene), poly(2,5-dichlorostyrene),...; Within each polymer, the solvents are also arranged in alphabetical order, followed by the mixed solvents.

2. Unperturbed Dimensions of Linear Chain Molecules

The dimension of a linear chain molecule is usually expressed in terms of the end-to-end distance r. For a given structure of the basic chain, the mean square value of r is determined by the nature of the hindrance to internal rotation around single bonds and by van der Waals or other type of interactions between non-bonded groups which are separated in the basic chain structure by many valence bonds. This latter interaction is called the long-range interaction, while the hindrance to internal rotation is called the short-range interaction.

In the absence of both types of interaction, the so-called "freely-rotating chain" is obtained, its dimension being easily computed from the given data of bond lengths and bond angles. For instance, the freely-rotating dimension of a chain consisting of only one kind of bond is given as

$$\langle r^2 \rangle_{of} = n\ell^2 [(1 + \cos \theta)/(1 - \cos \theta)] , \tag{9}$$

where n is the number of bonds, ℓ is the bond length, θ is the supplement of the valence bond angle, and the subscript zero denotes the lack of long-range interaction and f denotes the freely-rotating state. For polymethylene chains, $\ell = 1.54$ [Å], $\cos \theta = 1/3$, and $n = M/m = 2M/M_u$; and hence,

$$(\langle r^2 \rangle_{of}/M)^{\frac{1}{2}} = 3.08/M_u^{\frac{1}{2}} = 2.18/m^{\frac{1}{2}} \text{ [Å]} \tag{10}$$

where M is the molecular weight, M_u is the molar weight of the repeating unit of vinyl polymers and m is the average weight per skeletal link. Similar expressions for $r_{of}(=\langle r^2 \rangle_{of}^{\frac{1}{2}})$ can be obtained also for more complicated chains. The results are summarized in Table C.

The hindrance to internal rotations introduces appreciable changes in the average chain dimensions, but it does not alter the proportionality between the mean square end-to-end distance and n. Therefore a chain without long-range interactions is called an unperturbed chain, and its dimension is called the unperturbed dimension. The ratio of the unperturbed dimension r_o to r_{of}, then, represents the effect of steric hindrance:

$$\sigma = r_o/r_{of} = (\langle r^2 \rangle_o/\langle r^2 \rangle_{of})^{\frac{1}{2}} \tag{11}$$

The quantity σ is independent of n.

The long-range interactions, on the contrary, give rise to the so-called "excluded volume effect" which can be described as an osmotic swelling of the randomly coiled chain by the solvent-polymer interactions. As a result of the superposition of short- and long-range interactions, the average end-to-end distance of a real linear macromolecule in dilute solution is generally written as

$$r \equiv \langle r^2 \rangle^{\frac{1}{2}} = \alpha r_o = (\alpha \sigma) r_{of} , \tag{12}$$

in which the linear expansion factor α depends on the number of bonds n. The present theories of the excluded volume effect (2,3,7a) indicate that α^3 (instead of α^5 in the Flory theory (1)) becomes asymptotically proportional to $n^{\frac{1}{2}}$ as the solvent power is increased.

Another measure of the short-range interactions in polymer chains is the persistence length a_p which is defined as the average projection of an infinitely long chain along the direction of its first link. For an unperturbed chain consisting of one kind of bond, a_p can be written as

$$a_p = \ell [(r_o^2/2n\ell^2) + \frac{1}{2}] \tag{13}$$

Similar relations between a_p and r_o are also obtainable for more complicated chains, though not reproduced here. (7b,7c)

Table D gives a list of the unperturbed dimensions of linear chain polymers which are obtained under various conditions of solvent and temperature. The values of

References page IV-64

$r_o/M^{\frac{1}{2}}$, $r_{of}/M^{\frac{1}{2}}$ and σ are given, together with the experimental values of S_{oz}/M_w, a_p
or K_o from which the unperturbed end-to-end distances r_o were computed. S_{oz} which
is the abbreviation of $\langle S^2 \rangle_{oz}^{\frac{1}{2}}$ is the so-called z-average value of the unperturbed
radius of gyration, a_p is the persistence length and K_o is a viscosity constant
identical to K_θ given in Eq. (6). The methods used to determine these quantities are
also indicated in the ninth column of the table by using the following abbreviations.

(A) Light scattering.

   LS(t): Zimm plot in a theta solvent yielding $S_{oz}/M_w^{\frac{1}{2}}$. $r_{oz} = 6^{\frac{1}{2}}S_{oz}$. After a
           heterogeneity correction is made, $r_{ow}/M_w^{\frac{1}{2}}$ is obtained. (See R. Chiang,
           "Dissymmetries and Particle Scattering Factors" in this Handbook.) This
           value is tabulated as $r_o/M^{\frac{1}{2}}$.

   LSd(t): dissymmetry method in a theta solvent. $r_o/M^{\frac{1}{2}}$ can be directly obtained
           by the use of theoretical relations between the dissymmetry coefficient
           and r_o. Less reliable for heterogeneous polymers than the former method.

   LS(g): Zimm plot in good solvents yielding $S_z/M_w^{\frac{1}{2}}$. If this value is determined
           with sufficient accuracy over a wide range of molecular weight, $S_{oz}/M_w^{\frac{1}{2}}$
           can be estimated with the help of the excluded volume theory (2).

(B) X-ray small angle scattering.

   XS(t) and XS(g): X-ray scattering in theta and in good solvents. a_p is obtained
                     irrespective of the solvent nature (7b,7c).

(C) Limiting viscosity number.

   VM(t): viscosity-molecular weight relationship in a theta solvent. K_o is ob-
           tained as $[\eta]_\theta/M^{\frac{1}{2}}$. The Flory-Fox relation, $K_o = \Phi_o(r_o/M^{\frac{1}{2}})^3$, then yields
           r_o. In this table, the following values of Φ_o were used:

           2.87×10^{21} for homogeneous polymers,

           2.7×10^{21} for well-fractionated polymers,

           2.5×10^{21} for poorly-fractionated or whole polymers.

           1.39×10^{21} for the values put in parenthesis for poly(vinylsulfonic
           acid).

   V(t):   essentially the same as above. But K_o was obtained with only one fraction.

   VM(g): viscosity-molecular weight relationship in good solvent. K_o was estimated
           from the $[\eta]$-M relationship by the use of the Kurata-Stockmayer-Fixman
           plot (2,3).

(D) Second virial coefficient.

   A_2(∿t): temperature and molecular weight dependence of A_2 in the vicinity of the
            theta temperature. $r_o/M^{\frac{1}{2}}$ was estimated by the use of the perturbation
            theory of A_2.

The polymers are arranged in Table D in the same order as in Table B. For each polymer,
smoothed values of $r_o/M^{\frac{1}{2}}$ and σ, which were mostly obtained by VM(t,g), are given in
the first line, followed by some typical values obtained by the more direct methods such
as LS(t) or XS(t). Consistency or scattering of these values would help to give a rough
idea of the reliability of the present knowledge of the unperturbed dimensions. In
recent papers, emphasis has often been put on the effect of temperature or solvent

on the unperturbed dimensions. These data are put together at the end of the tabulation for each polymer.

These tables are essentially based on the tables published by W. H. Stockmayer and M. Kurata (2). Data were also taken from the tables published by A. Peterlin (4), G. Meyerhoff (5), H. G. Elias (6), and S. Krause (7), the last one including a number of unpublished data on viscosity-molecular weight relationships of acrylic and methacrylic polymers. We are grateful to these authors. Thanks are tendered also to J. Brandrup and K. Kamide for their help with this compilation.

B. TABLES OF VISCOSITY-MOLECULAR WEIGHT RELATIONSHIPS, $[\eta] = KM^a$

Polymer	Solvent	Temp. [°C]	K × 10^5 [dl/g]	a	No. of Samples Fr. W.P.		Mol. Wt. Range M × 10^-4	Method	Ref.
1 - POLYOLEFINS									
Poly(1-butene)									
atactic	anisole	⊖ 86.2	123	0.50	3	--	10-130	LS	8
	benzene	30	22.4	0.72	11	--	0.03-0.5	EG	9
	ethylcyclohexane	70	7.34	0.80	5	--	4-130	LS	8
isotactic	ethylcyclohexane	70	7.34	0.80	4	--	8-94	LS	8
	decalin	115	9.49	0.73	6	--	4.5-90	LS	49
	heptane	35	4.73	0.80	6	--	4.5-90	LS	49
		60	15.0	0.69	6	--	4.5-90	LS	49
	n-nonane	80	5.85	0.80	4	--	11-94	LS	8
Poly(diphenylmethylene)	benzene	-	218	0.328	?	--	1-90	?	48
Polyethylene low pressure	1-chloronaphthalene	125	138	0.58	?	?	?	LS	10
		125	18.4	0.78	10	--	5-100	LS	11
		125	43	0.67	10	--	5-100	LS	12
		129	27.1	0.71	26	--	5-100	LS	13
	decalin	135	67.7	0.67	--	>10	3-100	LS	14
		135	46	0.73	23	--	3-64	LS	15
		135	62	0.70	3	--	6-34	LS	16
	tetralin	105	16.2	0.83	4	--	13-57	LS	17
		120	23.5	0.78	36	--	5-100	LS	11
		120	32.6	0.77	20	--	0.3-50	LS	18
		130	43.5	0.76	6	--	2-30	OS	19
		130	51	0.725	9	--	0.4-10	OS	20
		130	37.8	0.72	--	10	8-17	LS	21

Polymer	Solvent	Temp. [°C]	$K \times 10^5$ [dl/g]	a	No. of Samples Fr. W.P.	Mol. Wt. Range $M \times 10^{-4}$	Method	Ref.
Polyethylene (Cont'd.) low pressure	p-xylene	105	16.5	0.83	4	--	13-50	LS	17
		105	17.6	0.83	8	--	1-18	OS	22
	paraffin wax (M_n = 390±10)	150	(42)	(0.65)	9	--	0.04-11	LS	23
high pressure	decalin	70	38.73	0.738	8	--	0.2 -3.5	OS	24
	p-xylene	75	135	0.63	--	22	0.2 -7.6	OS	25
		81	105	0.63	7	--	1-10	OS	26
Polyethylene (normal paraffin)	carbon tetrachloride	20	$(-0.0114+104 \times 10^{-5} M)$		--	7	0.024-0.048	CR	27
Poly(chlorotrifluoroethylene)	2,5-dichlorobenzotrifluoride	130	6.15	0.74	7	--	7-51	OS	28
Polyisobutene	anisole	⊖ 105	91	0.50	--	--	--	IV	42
	benzene	⊖ 24	107	0.50	15	--	18-188	IV	42
		25	83	0.53	9	--	0.05-126	OS,CR	43
		30	61	0.56	9	--	0.05-126	OS,CR	43
		40	43	0.60	9	--	0.05-126	OS,CR	43
		60	26	0.66	9	--	0.05-126	OS,CR	43
	carbon tetrachloride	30	29	0.68	12	--	0.05-126	OS,CR	43
	cyclohexane	25	40	0.72	6	--	14-34	OS	44
		30	27.6	0.69	7	--	4-71	OS	45
		30	26.5	0.69	12	--	0.05-126	OS,CR	43, 46
	diisobutylene	20	36	0.64	23	--	1-130	OS	47
	phenetole	⊖ 86	91	0.50	4	--	5-188	IV	42
	toluene	0	40	0.60	8	--	1-146	OS	43
		15	24	0.65	6	--	1-146	OS	43
		25	87	0.56	6	--	14-34	OS	44
		30	20	0.67	5	--	5-146	OS	43
		50	20	0.68	6	--	1-146	OS	43

Polymer	Solvent	Temp. [°C]	K × 10^5 [dl/g]	a	No. of Samples Fr. W.P.	Mol. Wt. Range M × 10^-4	Method	Ref.
Polyisobutene (Cont'd.)	toluene	60	13.5	0.71	4 --	11-146	OS	43
	toluene	90	12.6	0.72	3 --	46-146	OS	43
Polypropylene atactic	benzene	25	27.0	0.71	6 --	6-31	OS	29
	benzene	30	33.8	0.67	6 --	2-34	OS	30
	1-chloronaphthalene	⊖ 74	182	0.50	3 --	4-33	OS	31
	cyclohexane	25	16.0	0.80	6 --	6-31	OS	29
	cyclohexane	30	20.9	0.76	6 --	2-34	OS	30
	cyclohexanone	⊖ 92	172	0.50	4 --	1.5-33	OS	31
	decalin	135	15.8	0.77	6 --	2-39	OS	32
	decalin	135	11.0	0.80	6 --	2-62	LS	29
	decalin	135	54.3	0.55	-- 1C	2-72	LS	33
	isoamyl acetate	⊖ 34	168.5	0.30	6 --	2-34	OS	30
	phenyl ether	145	192	0.47	3 --	3.7-21	OS	31
	phenyl ether	⊖ 153	120	0.50	3 --	3.7-21	OS	31
	tetralin	130	1.24	0.96	-- --	?	?	34
	toluene	30	21.8	0.725	7 --	2-34	OS	30
isotactic	1-chloronaphthalene	139	21.5	0.67	11 --	10-170	LS	35
		145	4.9	0.80	9 --	5-63	LS	36
	decalin	135	11.0	0.80	6 --	2-62	LS	29
	decalin	135	10.0	0.80	4 --	10-100	LS	37
	phenyl ether	⊖ 145	132	0.50	4 --	3.5-48	OS	31
	phenyl ether	153	112	0.54	4 --	3.5-48	OS	31
	tetralin	135	2.5	1.0	5 --	2-11	OS	38
	tetralin	135	9.17	0.80	9 --	4-54	OS	36
Poly(C10-C18 α-olefin)	p-xylene	85	96	0.63	12 --	?	OS	39
	toluene	25	12.7	1.04	12 --	2-18	LS	40
Poly(C12-C18 α-olefin)	cetane	38	21	0.61	10 --	4-700	LS	41

References page IV-64

2 - VINYL AND ALLYL POLYMERS

Polymer	Solvent	Temp. [°C]	K x 10^5 [dl/g]	a	No. of Samples Fr. W.P.	Mol. Wt. Range M x 10^-4	Method	Ref.
Poly(allyl acetate)	benzene	27	66	0.53	8	--	0.14-0.25	CR	165b
Polystyrene atactic	benzene	20	6.3	0.78	18	--	1-300	SD	50
		20	12.3	0.72	7	--	0.6-520	SD	51
		25	22.7	0.72	--	7	0.2-0.8	CR	52
		25	41.7	0.60	9	--	0.1-1	CR	52
		25	34.0	0.65	11	--	0.4-0.8	EG	53
		25	9.52	0.744	6	--	3-61	OS	54
		25	9.18	0.743	6	--	3-70	LS	55
		25	11.3	0.73	10	--	7-180	OS	56
		34	9.8	0.737	10	--	8-80	DV	57
	butanone	25	39	0.58	16	--	1-180	LS	58
		25	30.5	0.60	5	--	7-150	OS	56
		25	19.5	0.635	7	--	12-280	LS	59
		30	23	0.62	7	--	40-370	LS	60
		34	28.9	0.60	10	--	8-80	DV	61, 62
	n-butyl chloride	40.8	15.1	0.659	5	--	29-106	LS	63
	chlorobenzene	25.7	7.4	0.749	4	--	62-424	LS	63
	chloroform	25	7.16	0.76	8	--	12-280	LS	59
		25	11.2	0.73	5	--	7-150	OS	56
		30	4.9	0.794	4	--	19-373	OS	64
	cyclohexane	28	108.0	0.479	7	--	0.6-69	OS	65
		Θ 34	82	0.50	15	--	1-70	IV	54
		Θ 34	90.2	0.503	9	--	0.6-69	OS	65

Polymer	Solvent		Temp. [°C]	K x 10^5 [dℓ/g]	a	No. of Samples Fr. W.P.	Mol. Wt. Range M x 10^{-4}	Method	Ref.
Polystyrene (Cont'd.) atactic									
	cyclohexane	θ	35	80	0.50	3 --	8-42	LS	66
		θ	35	70	0.50	8 --	3-200	SD	67
		θ	35	76	0.50	10 --	4-137	LS	63
			40	41.6	0.554	10 --	4-137	LS	63
			45	34.7	0.575	10 --	4-137	LS	63
			50	26.9	0.599	10 --	4-137	LS	63
	decalin (100%-trans)	θ	20	149	0.44	7 --	14-200	LS	58
		θ	23	98	0.48	7 --	14-200	LS	58
			25	67	0.52	7 --	14-200	LS	68
			30	61	0.53	6 --	14-200	LS	68
			60	22	0.63	4 --	14-200	LS	68
	decalin (73%-trans)	θ	18	77	0.50	4 --	14-140	LS	68
			30	36	0.58	4 --	14-140	LS	68
			40	37	0.58	4 --	14-140	LS	68
			60	22	0.64	4 --	14-140	LS	68
			100	15.7	0.67	6 --	14-200	LS	68
	dichloroethane		25	21.0	0.66	7 --	1-180	LS	58
	dioxane		34	15.0	0.694	10 --	8-80	DV	62
	ethylbenzene		25	17.5	0.68	5 --	7-150	OS	56
	ethylcyclohexane	θ	70	75	C.50	2 --	36-127	IV	69
	methylcyclohexane	θ	70	76	0.50	? ?	?	?	70
	toluene		20	4.16	0.788	10 --	4-137	LS	63
			25	17	0.69	9 --	1-160	LS	58
			25	7.5	0.75	8 --	12-280	LS	59
			25	13.4	0.71	5 --	7-150	OS	56
			25	7.54	0.783	? ?	5-80	OS	71

References page IV-64

Polymer	Solvent	Temp. [C]	$K \times 10^5$ [dℓ/g]	a	No. of Samples Fr.	W.P.	Mol. Wt. Range $M \times 10^{-4}$	Method	Ref.
Polystyrene (Cont'd.) atactic	toluene	25	44	0.65	--	9	0.5-4.5	OS	72
		25	(a increases with M)		10	--	0.08-3.7	CR	73
		25	11.8	0.72	11	--	10-53	IV	426
		30	9.2	0.72	9	--	4-146	LS	74
		30	12.0	0.71	8	--	40-370	LS	60
		30	11.0	0.725	7	--	8-85	OS	75
		34	9.7	0.733	10	--	8-80	DV	62
		34	11.5	0.72	11	--	10-53	IV	426
		45	11.4	0.72	11	--	10-53	IV	426
	benzene/methanol (74/26 vol) ⊖	34	89	0.50	10	--	8-80	DV	57
	butanone/isopropanol (6/1 vol) ⊖	23	73	0.50	9	--	4-146	LS	74
	(82.6/17.4 vol) ⊖	34	71.8	0.50	10	--	8-80	DV	62
	butanone/methanol (97.5/2.5 vol)	25	22.4	0.62	8	--	12-280	LS	59
	(95.0/5.0 vol)	25	26.3	0.60	8	--	12-280	LS	59
	(92.5/7.5 vol)	25	35.7	0.57	8	--	12-280	LS	59
	(89/11 vol) ⊖	25	73	0.50	8	--	12-280	LS	59
	chloroform/methanol (90/10 vol)	25	7.7	0.75	8	--	12-280	LS	59
	(80/20 vol)	25	12	0.68	8	--	12-280	LS	59
	(75/25 vol)	25	46	0.54	8	--	12-280	LS	59
	(74.7/24.3 vol) ⊖	25	73	0.50	8	--	12-280	LS	59
	dioxane/methanol (65.1/34.9 vol) ⊖	34	72.6	0.50	10	--	8-80	DV	62
	toluene/methanol (90/10 vol)	25	10.4	0.715	8	--	12-280	LS	59

Polymer	Solvent	Temp. [°C]	$\bar{X} \times 10^5$ [dℓ/g]	a	No. of Samples Fr. W.P.	Mol. Wt. Range M x 10^-4	Method	Ref.
Polystyrene (Cont'd.) atactic	toluene/methanol (80/20 vol)	25	26	0.612	8	--	12-280	LS	59
	(76.9/23.1 vol)	⊕ 25	92	0.50	12	--	0.07-3.5	DV	76
	(75.2/24.8 vol)	⊕ 34	88	0.50	10	--	8-80	DV	62
		⊕ 34	89.3	0.50	11	--	10-53	IV	426
	(72.8/27.2 vol)	⊕ 45	88.1	0.50	11	--	10-53	IV	426
atactic, anionic	benzene	25	100	0.50	--	8	0.05-1	VOS	77
	cyclohexane	⊕ 34	74.5	0.50	--	?	?	LS	78
		⊕ 34.5	35	0.50	--	4	0.05-150	VOS,IV	77
	toluene	20	11.2	0.72	--	6	3-24	SD	79
		25	9.77	0.73	--	12	1-104	SD	80
		25	14.6	0.69	--	?	?	LS	76
		25	34.5	0.62	--	25	0.4-230	SD	81
		30.3	10.4	0.73	--	15	2.6-50	OS,LS	82
isotactic	benzene	30	9.5	0.77	6	--	4-75	OS	83
		30	10.6	0.735	7	--	4-37	OS	84
	chloroform	30	(25.9)	(0.734)	3	--	9-32	OS	64
	toluene	30	11.0	0.725	7	--	3-37	OS	84
		30	9.3	0.72	5	--	15-71	LS	85
	butanone	25	17	0.69	6	--	0.3-165	LS	58
branched, random type	butanone	25	(a decreases with M)		5	--	30-200	LS	86
	butanone/propanol (83.5/16.5 wt)	⊕ 25	(a decreases with M)		5	--	30-200	LS	86
star type, anionic	cyclohexane	⊕ 34	g' = 0.82(4 branches)* g' = 0.94(3 branches)*					LS	78

* g' = [η] of branched molec./[η] of linear molec. with same mol. wt.

References page IV-64

VISCOSITY–MOLECULAR WEIGHT RELATIONSHIPS

Polymer	Solvent	Temp. [°C]	$K \times 10^5$ [dl/g]	a	No. of Samples Fr.	W.P.	Mol. Wt. Range $M \times 10^{-4}$	Method	Ref.
Polystyrene (Cont'd.) star type, anionic		25	g' = 0.84(4 branches)* / g' = 0.90(3 branches)*					LS	78
Poly(p-bromostyrene)	benzene	⊕ 20	95.5	0.53	10	--	3-30	OS	87
Poly(p-chlorostyrene)	butanone	25	29	0.59	7	--	3-140	LS	88
	toluene	20	24.1	0.605	--	7	2-40	LS	89
		25	13.2	0.645	--	7	1-244	LS	90
		30	13.0	0.64	6	--	3-140	LS	88
Poly(2,5-dichlorostyrene)	toluene	21	12.6	0.69	9	--	7-66	LS	91
	ethyl acetate/ethanol (15/1 wt)	⊕ 30.5	35.5	0.50	8	--	50-130	LS	92
Poly(3,4-dichlorostyrene)	butyl acetate/butanol (13/1 wt)	⊕ 32.9		0.50	8	--	40-540	LS	93
Poly(2,4-dimethylstyrene)	toluene	30	9.52	9.70	--	9	5-120	LS	94
	dioxane	20	33	0.51	10	6	10-118	IV	95
Poly(p-iodostyrene)	butanone	35	8.6	0.68	6	--	1-100	LS	88
Poly(p-methoxystyrene)	toluene	30	18.0	0.62	6	--	1-100	LS	88
Poly(α-methylstyrene)	benzene	30	24.9	0.647	4	--	14-91	OS	96
		30	1.7	0.87	?	--	?	LS	97
	toluene	25	7.81	0.73	--	6	3-60	SD	98
		30	2.2	0.80	6	--	1-100	LS	88
		30	10.8	0.71	--	13	3-66	LS	99
Poly(styrenesulfonic acid)	benzene/methanol (79.4/20.6 mol)	⊕ 30	76.8	0.50	4	--	14-91	OS	96
	aqueous HCl (0.52M)	25	63.5	1.0	3	--	18-46	IV	100
	aqueous NaCl (0.52M)	25	57.5	1.0	3	--	18-46	IV	100

* g' = [η] of branched molec./[η] of linear molec. with same mol. wt.

Polymer	Solvent	Temp. [°C]	$K \times 10^5$ [dℓ/g]	a	No. of Samples / Fr. W.P.	Mol. Wt. Range $M \times 10^{-4}$	Method	Ref.
Poly(vinyl alcohol)	water	25	20	0.75	6 / --	0.6-2.1	OS	101
		25	(300)	(0.50)	4 / --	0.9-17	SD	102
		25	(140)	(0.60)	3 / --	1-7	SD	103
		25	67	0.55	8 / --	2-20	LS	104
		30	66.6	0.64	8 / --	0.6-16	OS	105
		80	94	0.56	-- / 5	10-46	LS	106
	water/phenol (15/85 vol)	30	24.6	0.80	-- / 21	3-12	OS	107
Poly(vinyl bromide)	cyclohexanone	25	32.8	0.55	7 / --	2-10	LS	135
	tetrahydrofuran	25	15.9	0.64	7 / --	2-10	LS	135
	tetrahydrofuran/methanol (83/17 vol)	20	38.8	0.50	7 / --	2-10	LS	165a
Poly(vinyl chloride)	benzyl alcohol	155.4 Θ	156	0.50	9 / --	4-35	LS	163
	chlorobenzene	30	71.2	0.59	7 / --	3-19	SA	152
	cyclohexanone	20	11.6	0.85	6 / --	2.5-9.7	OS	136
		20	13.7	1	7 / 5	7-13	OS	137
		20	112.5	0.53	5 / 3	9-15	OS	137
		25	24	0.77	13 / --	3-14	OS	138
		25	12.3	0.83	11 / --	2-14	OS	139
		25	204	0.56	? / ?	2-15	OS	140
		25	208	0.56	6 / --	6-22	OS	161
		25	174	0.55	6 / --	15-52	LS	161
		30	16.3	0.77	6 / --	3-19	SA	162
	tetrahydrofuran	20	1.63	0.92	-- / 20	2-17	OS	141
		25	49.8	0.69	5 / --	4-40	LS(OS)	142
		25	16.2	0.766	-- / --	2-17	LS	143
		30	219	0.54	16 / --	5-30	LS	144
		30	83.3	0.83	7 / --	3-19	SA	162

References page Iv-64

Poly(vinyl ester)

Polymer	Solvent	Temp. [°C]	$K \times 10^5$ [dl/g]	a	No. of Samples Fr.	W.P.	Mol. Wt. Range $M \times 10^{-4}$	Method	Ref.
Poly(vinyl acetate)	acetone	18	24.5	0.67	6	--	4-34	OS	108
		20	15.8	0.69	6	--	19-72	LS	109
		25	21.4	0.68	6	--	4-34	OS	108
		25	18.8	0.69	?	?	?	LS	110
		25	14.6	0.72	--	6	0.7-1.3	EG	111
		25	10.8	0.72	10	--	0.9-2.5	EG	111
		30	17.6	0.68	--	32	2-163	OS	112
		30	8.6	0.74	8	--	8-66	LS	113
		30	17.4	0.70	?	--	7-68	OS	114
		30	10.2	0.72	--	8	3-126	LS	115
		30	10.1	0.73	11	--	6-150	LS,OS	116
		39	14.8	0.71	6	--	4-34	OS	108
		46	13.8	0.71	6	--	4-34	OS	108
	acetonitrile	25	16.2	0.71	?	--	24-215	LS	117
		30	41.5	0.62	4	--	97-153	LS	118
	benzene	30	22	0.65	5	--	34-102	LS	119
		30	56.3	0.62	24	--	3-86	OS	120
		30	56.3	0.62	12	--	7-54	LS	121, 122
	butanone	35	21.6	0.675	14	--	5-40	LS	123
		25	13.4	0.71	6	--	25-346	LS	124, 125
	chlorobenzene	25	42	0.62	15	--	2-120	SD,LS	126
		30	10.7	0.71	--	13	3-120	LS	115
		25	94.4	0.56	6	--	4-34	OS	108
		39	80.4	0.57	6	--	4-34	OS	108

Polymer	Solvent	Temp. [°C]	$K \times 10^5$ [dℓ/g]	a	No. of Samples Fr. W.P.	Mol. Wt. Range $M \times 10^{-4}$	Method	Ref.
Poly(vinyl acetate) (Cont'd.)								
	chlorobenzene	53	53.7	0.60	6 --	4-34	OS	108
		67	28.9	0.65	6 --	4-34	OS	108
	chloroform	20	15.8	0.74	? ?	7-68	OS	114
		25	20.3	0.72	5 --	4-34	OS	108
		39	16.2	0.74	5 --	4-34	OS	108
		53	14.7	0.74	5 --	4-34	OS	108
	dioxane	25	11.4	0.74	5 --	4-34	OS	108
		53,60	10.2	0.75	5 --	4-34	OS	108
	ethanol	Θ 56.9	90	0.50	5 --	4-150	OS,LS	116
		30	32	0.65	4 --	16-154	LS	118
	ethyl formate	Θ 66	82.0	0.50	-- 9	14-83	LS	127
	ethyl isoamyl ketone	Θ 66	78.0	0.50	3 --	9-150	OS,LS	116
	3-heptanone	Θ 26.8	82.0	0.30	5 --	4-150	OS,LS	116
		Θ 29	92.9	0.50	-- 6	5-83	LS	127
	methanol	Θ 6	101	0.50	9 --	0.3-150	OS,LS,VOS	116
		25	38.0	0.59	5 --	4-22	CS	108
		30	31.4	0.60	-- 13	3-120	LS	115
		39	36.5	0.60	5 --	4-22	OS	108
		53	36.6	0.59	5 --	4-22	OS	108
	methyl isobutyl ketone	30	44.9	0.60	5 --	12-69	LS	118
	toluene	25	108	0.53	4 --	4-15	OS	108
		39	121	0.51	4 --	4-15	OS	108
		53	139	0.50	4 --	4-15	OS	108
		67	156	0.49	4 --	4-15	OS	108

References page IV-64

Polymer	Solvent	Temp. [°C]	$K \times 10^5$ [dℓ/g]	a	No. of Samples Fr.	No. of Samples W.P.	Mol. Wt. Range $M \times 10^{-4}$	Method	Ref.
Poly(vinyl acetate) (Cont'd.)									
	1,2,4-trichlorobenzene	35	33.0	0.623	?	--	5-40	LS	123
	methyl isopropyl ketone/n-heptane (73.2/26.8 vol) ⊕	25	93	0.50	6	--	25-287	LS	127
Poly(vinyl benzoate)	xylene ⊖	32.5	62.0	0.50	5	--	10-24	OS	128
Poly(vinyl p-chlorobenzoate)	water	30	64.0	0.64	7	--	6-35	IV	160
	butanone/n-butanol (53/47 vol) ⊖	60	73	0.50	7	--	6-35	IV	160
Poly(vinyl n-butyrate)	benzene	30	(11.15)	(0.735)	--	4	3-15	OS	129
Poly(vinyl n-caproate)	benzene	30	(15.47)	(0.689)	--	4	3-126	OS	129
Poly(vinyl formate)	acetone	30	29.3	0.63	9	--	3-41	IV	130
	acetonitrile	30	14.1	0.717	9	--	3-41	IV	130
	dioxane	30	20.7	0.68	8	--	3-41	IV	130
	methyl acetate	30	37.6	0.61	7	--	3-24	IV	130
	methyl formate	30	14.1	0.722	7	--	3-24	IV	130
Poly(vinyl isobutyrate)	benzene	30	(11.05)	(0.711)	--	4	5-20	OS	129
Poly(vinyl isocaproate)	benzene	30	(51.0)	(0.575)	--	4	3-17	OS	129
Poly(vinyl pivalate)	acetone	25	2.88	0.77	4	--	40-217	LS	131
	butanone/methanol (0.897 g/ml) ⊖	20	53	0.50	2	--	222-344	LS	131
Poly(vinyl sulfate)	aqueous NaCl(0.5M)	20	0.55	1.06	6	--	1-6	IV	132
Poly(vinyl ether)									
Poly(vinyl methyl ether)	benzene	30	76	0.60	13	--	1-45	LS	133
	butanone	30	92	0.58	13	--	1-45	LS	133
Poly(vinyl octadecyl ether)	benzene	25	170	0.47	--	7	0.1-1.5	LS	134
	tetrahydrofuran	30	224	0.35	--	7	9.4-11	LS	134

Polymer	Solvent	Temp. [°C]	$K \times 10^5$ [dl/g]	a	No. of Samples Fr.	W.P.	Mol. Wt. Range $M \times 10^{-4}$	Method	Ref.
Poly(2-vinylnaphthalene)	benzene	17	1.7	0.80	11	--	10-100	LS	145
	decalin/toluene (1.3/1 wt)	30.2 θ		0.50	8	--	10-100	LS	146
Poly(2-vinylpyridine)	benzene	25	17.0	0.64	14	--	3-93	LS	147
	dimethylformamide	25	14.7	0.67	14	--	3-93	LS	147
	dioxane	25	30.9	0.58	14	--	3-93	LS	147
	ethanol/water (92/8 wt)	25	12.2	0.73	14	--	3-93	LS	147
	methanol	25	11.3	0.73	14	--	3-93	LS	147
Poly(4-vinylpyridine)	ethanol	25	(1.51)	(0.52)	--	3	1-4	SD	148
	ethanol	25	25.0	0.68	8	--	10-185	LS	149
	water	25	22.0	0.687	8	--	10-185	LS	149
	butanone/isopropanol (86/14 wt)	25	38.0	0.57	7	--	7-224	LS	150
	ethanol/water (92/8 wt)	25	12.0	0.73	7	--	7-224	LS	150
Poly(2-methyl-5-vinyl-pyridine)	butanone	25	13.9	0.65	5	--	13-88	LS	152
Poly(vinylpyrrolidone)	dimethylformamide	25	13.0	0.76	6	--	4-40	OS	151
	methanol	25	18.0	0.83	8	--	4-40	OS	151
		25	8.0	0.76	9	--	13-88	LS	152
	chloroform	25	19.4	0.64	4	2	2-23	LS	153
	methanol	30	23	0.65	--	6	2-23	LS	153
	water	20	64	0.58				SD	154
		25	67.6	0.55	12	--	0.7-10	LS	155
		25	4.1	0.85	--	5	1-4	SD	156
		30	14	0.70	9	--	1-340	SD	157
		30	39.3	0.59	6	--	8-110	OS	158
	water/acetone (33.2/66.8 vol)	25 θ	74.0	0.50	--	3	1.2-108	LS	164

References page IV-64

Polymer	Solvent	Temp. [°C]	$K \times 10^5$ [dl/g]	a	No. of Samples Fr. W.P.	Mol. Wt. Range $M \times 10^{-4}$	Method	Ref.
Poly(vinylsulfonic acid) [Poly(ethylenesulfonic acid)]	aqueous KBr (0.347M)	θ 5.7	68.8	0.50	5	--	4-39	LS	165
		15	30.8	0.61	5	--	8-39	LS	165
		30	24.5	0.75	5	--	8-39	LS	165
		40	25.1	0.76	5	--	8-39	LS	165
		50	26.6	0.76	5	--	8-39	LS	165
	aqueous KCl (0.349M)	θ 5.5	68.2	0.50	5	--	4-39	LS	165
		25	16.7	0.79	5	--	4-39	LS	165
	(0.650M)	θ 26.0	79.5	0.50	5	--	4-39	LS	165
	(1.001M)	θ 44.5	80.3	0.50	5	--	4-39	LS	165
	aqueous NaBr (0.346M)	θ -0.6	95.5	0.50	5	--	4-39	LS	165
		10	26.8	0.73	5	--	8-39	LS	165
		20	25.1	0.76	5	--	8-39	LS	165
		30	22.0	0.79	5	--	8-39	LS	165
	(1.008M)	θ 40.1	94.5	0.50	5	--	4-39	LS	165
	aqueous NaCl (1.003M)	θ 32.4	96.1	0.50	5	--	4-39	LS	165
	(0.5M)	20	21.5	0.65	--	6	0.3-3	SD	159

3 - ACRYLIC AND METHACRYLIC POLYMERS

Polymer	Solvent	Temp. [°C]	K x 10^5 [dl/g]	a	No. of Samples	Fr. M.W.P.	Mol. Wt. Range M x 10^{-4}	Method	Ref.
Poly(acrylic acid)	1,4-dioxane	Θ 30	76	0.50	--	4	13-82	OS	156
Poly(acrylic acid), sodium-salt	aqueous NaOH(2M)	25	42.2	0.54	12	--	4-50	OS,IV	157
	aqueous NaCl(1M)	25	15.47	0.30	12	--	4-50	OS,IV	167
	aqueous NaBr (1.5M)	Θ 15	165	0.30	5	--	6-64	IV(OS)	168
		Θ 15	124	0.50	4	--	12-83	LS	169
	(0.502M)	15	52.7	0.628	7	--	1.5-50	IV(LS)	170
	(0.100M)	15	25.4	0.755	7	--	1.5-50	IV(LS)	170
	(0.0502M)	15	28.1	0.77	7	--	1.5-50	IV(LS)	170
	(0.0251M)	15	16.3	0.84	7	--	1.5-50	IV(LS)	170
	(0.0100M)	15	(13.6)	0.89	7	--	1.5-50	IV(LS)	170
	(0.00502M)	15	(44.2)	0.83	7	--	1.5-50	IV(LS)	170
	(0.00251M)	15	(24.9)	0.89	7	--	1.5-50	IV(LS)	170
	aqueous NaSCN (1.25M)	Θ 30	154	0.50	5	--	6-64	IV(OS)	168
Poly(acrylamide)		Θ 30	121	0.50	4	--	12-83	LS	171
	water	30	6.31	0.80	7	--	2-50	SD	238
	methanol	30	68	0.66	--	21	1-20	PR	239
Poly(N,N'-dimethyl-acrylamide)	methanol	25	17.5	0.68	--	3	5-122	LS	240
	water	25	23.2	0.81	--	6	5-122	LS	240
Poly(acrylic acid ester)									
Poly(n-butyl acrylate)	acetone	25	6.85	0.75	--	6	5-27	LS	173
Poly(1,1-dihydroperfluoro-butyl acrylate)	fluorobenzene	26.6	13	0.56	7	3	20-200	LS	186
	methyl perfluorobutytate	26.6	12	0.60	7	3	20-200	LS	186

References page IV-64

Polymer	Solvent	Temp. [°C]	$K \times 10^5$ [dℓ/g]	a	No. of Samples Fr.	No. of Samples W.P.	Mol. Wt. Range $M \times 10^{-4}$	Method	Ref.
Poly(ethyl acrylate)	acetone	30	20.0	0.66	5	--	16-50	OS	174
	acetone	30	25.4	0.66	--	7	14-70	OS	174
	benzene	30	27.7	0.67	--	7	5-67	OS	175
	chloroform	30	31.4	0.68	--	5	9-54	OS	175
	ethyl acetate	30	26.0	0.66	--	5	9-54	OS	175
	methanol	30	48.8	0.55	--	6	6-81	OS	175
Poly(n-hexadecyl acrylate)	n-heptane	20	1.74	0.82	6	--	1-10	LS	176
Poly(isopropyl acrylate)	acetone	30	13.0	0.69	6	--	6-30	LS	177
	benzene	30	11.8	0.71	4	--	7-20	LS	177
	chloroform	30	14.1	0.72	5	--	7-30	LS	178
Poly(methyl acrylate)	acetone	20	(7.40)	(0.76)	--	4	7-32	OS	179
		25	5.5	0.77	8	--	28-160	LS	180
		25	19.8	0.66	9	--	30-250	LS	181
		30	28.2	0.52	7	--	4-45	OS	172
	benzene	25	2.58	0.85	4	--	20-130	OS	182
		30	4.5	0.78	7	7	7-160	LS	183
		35	12.8	0.71	--	5	5-30	OS	184
	butanone	20	3.5	0.81	13	--	6-240	LS	183
		35	(34)	(0.61)	--	3	5-47	IV	185
	chloroform	35	(36)	(0.67)	--	3	5-47	IV	185
	ethyl acetate	35	(48)	(0.60)	--	3	5-47	IV	185
	toluene	35	(45)	(0.56)	--	3	5-47	IV	185
	butanone/isopropanol (42/58 vol)	20	81	0.50	5	--	29-140	LS	180
		20	290	0.40	6	--	37-250	LS	181
	(1/1 vol) θ	27.5	54.4	0.50	4	--	14-83	LS	169
Poly(acrylomorpholide)	dimethylformamide	25	18	0.65	?	?	?	LS	256
	aqueous NaCl (0.1M)	20	64	0.68	?	?	?	LS	256

Polymer	Solvent	Temp. [°C]	$K \times 10^5$ [dl/g]	a	No. of Samples Fr. W.P.	Mol. Wt. Range $M \times 10^{-4}$	Method	Ref.
Polyacrylonitrile	γ-butyrolactone	20	34.4	0.730	5 --	4-40	IV(LS)	243
		30	57.2	0.67	6 --	4-30	SA	244
		30	34.2	0.70	5 --	6-30	SA	244
		50	28.7	0.740	5 --	4-40	LS	243
	dimethylformamide	20	17.7	0.78	5 --	7-30	LS	245
		25	16.6	0.81	5 --	5-27	SE	246
		25	24.3	0.75	-- 4	3-25	LS	247
		25	39.2	0.75	-- 16	3-100	OS	248
		25	15.5	0.80	3 5	3-10	OS,LS,SD	249
		25	57.4	0.73	-- 8	0.3-1.5	EG	250
		25	39.6	0.75	-- 7	4-30	OS	251
		25	44.3	0.70	-- 7	2-20	LS	251
		30	29.6	0.74	7 --	4-30	SA	244
		30	20.9	0.75	7 --	6-30	SA	244
		35	27.8	0.76	9 --	3-58	DV	252
		35	31.7	0.746	12 --	9-76	LS	243
		50	30.0	0.752	22 --	4-102	IV(LS)	243
	dimethylacetamide	20	30.7	0.761	6 --	2-40	IV(LS)	243
		35	27.5	0.767	6 --	2-40	IV(LS)	243
		50	27.4	0.764	6 --	2-40	IV(LS)	243
	dimethyl sulfoxide	20	32.1	0.750	9 --	9-40	IV(LS)	243
		50	28.3	0.758	9 --	9-40	IV(LS)	243
	ethylene carbonate	50	29.5	0.718	13 --	7-40	IV(LS)	243
	hydroxyacetonitrile	20	40.9	0.697	8 --	4-34	IV(LS)	243
		50	35.4	0.707	8 --	4-34	IV(LS)	243

Polymer	Solvent	Temp. [°C]	$K \times 10^5$ [dl/g]	a	No. of Samples Fr. W.P.	Mol. Wt. Range $M \times 10^{-4}$	Method	Ref.
Polyacrylonitrile (Cont'd.)	aqueous HNO_3 (60%)	0	33.9	0.740	6 --	2-40	IV(LS)	243
		20	30.7	0.747	5 --	4-40	IV(LS)	243
Poly(acrylopiperidide)	dimethylformamide	25	32	0.56	? ?	?	LS	256
Poly(ethacrylic acid ester)								
Poly(methyl ethacrylate)	butanone	30	4.27	0.76	12 --	3.8-171	LS	237
Poly(methacrolein)	dimethylformamide	(20)	2.8	0.97	-- ?	0.5-2.1	OS,CR	255
Poly(methacrylic acid)	methanol	26	242	0.51	6 --	4-20	OS,IV	187
	aqueous HCl (0.002M)	30 ⊖	66	0.50	7 --	10-90	IV	188
	aqueous $NaNO_3$ (2M)	25	44.9	0.65	6 --	8-70	OS(LS)	189
Poly(N-phenyl methacrylamide)	acetone	20	28.2	0.75	8 --	10-320	LS	241
Poly(N-p-carbethoxyphenyl-methacrylamide)	acetone	unc.	0.00115	1.35	4 --	26-74	LS	242
	dimethylformamide	unc.	This relation not followed		5 --	48-140	LS	242
	ethyl acetate	unc	0.00446	1.25	5 --	26-11	LS	242
Poly(methacrylic acid ester)								
Poly(benzyl methacrylate)	benzene	30	1.03	0.82	-- 9	17-120	LS	190
Poly(n-butyl methacrylate)	acetone	25	18.4	0.62	5 --	100-600	LS,OS	191
	benzene	30	(4.0)	(0.77)	-- 3	8-300	LS	192
	butanone	23	1.56	0.81	10 --	25-260	LS	193
		25	9.7	0.68	5 --	11-670	LS,OS	191
		30	(1.15)	(0.89)	3 --	67-132	OS	194
	chloroform	20	2.9	0.78	8 --	4-800	LS	195
		25	4.37	0.80	6 --	8-80	OS	196
	isopropanol	21.5 ⊖	29.5	0.50	8 --	30-260	LS	193
		21.5 ⊖	38	0.50	9 --	4-800	LS	195
		23.7 ⊖	36.6	0.50	5 --	40-170	LS	197

Polymer	Solvent	Temp. [°C]	$K \times 10^5$ [dℓ/g]	a	No. of Samples Fr. W.P.	Mol. Wt. Range $M \times 10^{-4}$	Method	Ref.
Poly(p-tert-butylphenyl methacrylate)	acetone	20	5.75	0.68	15 --	6-350	LS	198
	bromobenzene	20	4.1	0.71	7 --	15-2500	LS	199
	carbon tetrachloride	20	4.1	0.71	7 --	20-2500	LS	199
	chloroform	20	2.4	0.78	15 --	6-300	LS	200
Poly(cetyl methacrylate)	n-heptane	25	35.1	0.56	9 --	20-110	LS	201
Poly(cyclohexyl methacrylate)	benzene	30	8.4	0.59	5 --	80-200	LS	202
	n-butanol	23	33.7	0.30	5 --	57-445	LS	258
	butanone	25	5.79	0.58	6 --	57-560	LS	258
	butanone	30	7.0	0.66	5 --	80-200	LS	202
Poly(n-dodecyl methacrylate)	pentanol	29.5 ⊖	34.8	0.50	7 --	27-240	LS	206
	n-butyl acetate	23	8.64	0.64	8 --	26-360	LS	207
	isopropyl acetate	13 ⊖	32.2	0.50	7 --	26-360	LS	207
Poly(ethyl methacrylate)	butanone	23	2.83	0.79	10 --	20-263	LS	203
	isopropanol	36.9 ⊖	47.5	0.50	4 --	22-130	LS	197
	butanone/isopropanol (1/7 vol)	23 ⊖	47.3	0.50	10 --	20-263	LS	203
Poly(2-ethylbutyl methacrylate)	butanone	25	2.21	0.77	8 --	48-332	LS	203
	isopropanol	27.4	33.7	0.50	8 --	48-332	LS	204
Poly(n-hexyl methacrylate)	butanone	23	2.22	0.78	8 --	6-41	LS	205
	isopropanol	32.6 ⊖	43.0	0.50	8 --	6-41	LS	205
Poly(methyl methacrylate) atactic	acetone	20	3.90	0.76	7 --	7-700	SD	208
		25	7.5	0.70	9 --	8-137	LS	209
		25	6.76	0.71	10 --	3-700	SD	210
		25	7.5	0.70	14 --	2-740	LS,SD	211
		25	5.3	0.73	7 --	2-780	LS	212

References page IV-64

Polymer	Solvent	Temp. [°C]	$K \times 10^5$ [dl/g]	a	No of Samples	Fr. W.P.	Mol. Wt. Range $M \times 10^{-4}$	Method	Ref.
Poly(methyl methacrylate) (Cont'd.)									
atactic	acetone	25	9.6	0.69	4	--	180-350	LS	213
		25	7.5	0.70	4	6	3-98	LS	214
		25	2.45	0.80	9	--	6-210	OS	215
		25	6.59	0.71	6	--	5-41	OS	216
		30	7.7	0.70	--	6	6-263	LS	217
		39	6.40	0.72	6	--	5-41	OS	216
		46	6.18	0.72	6	--	5-41	OS	216
	acetonitrile	30	39.3	0.50	6	--	10-86	IV	218
		45	15.3	0.59	6	--	10-260	IV	219
		50	29	0.54	6	--	10-260	IV	219
		65	9.8	0.64	5	--	10-260	IV	219
	benzene	20	8.35	0.73	7	--	7-700	SD	208
		20	15.1	0.70	7	--	8-90	SD	220
		25	7.24	0.76	10	--	6-100	OS	221
		25	5.5	0.76	11	--	2-740	LS	212
		25	3.80	0.79	5	--	24-450	LS	222
		25	83	0.52	7	--	0.03-1	EB	223
		30	5.2	0.76	9	--	6-250	LS	218
		30	6.27	0.76	5	--	4-73	OS	224
		30	104	0.50	9	--	0.02-2	OS	224
		30	195	0.41	5	--	0.3-2	LS	218
		39	6.74	0.75	6	--	5-41	OS	216
		53	6.52	0.76	6	--	5-41	OS	216
	butanone	25	6.8	0.72	9	--	8-137	LS	209
		25	7.1	0.72	7	--	41-330	LS	213

Polymer	Solvent	Temp. [°C]	$K \times 10^5$ [dl/g]	a	No. of Samples Fr. W.P.		Mol. Wt. Range $M \times 10^{-4}$	Method	Ref.
Poly(methyl methacrylate) (Cont'd)									
atactic	butanone	25	6.8	0.72	4	6	3-98	LS	214
	butanone	25	9.39	0.58	15	--	16-910	LS	259
	n-butyl chloride	⊖ 35.4	50.5	0.50	4	--	13-68	SA	225
	chloroform	20	9.6	0.78	18	--	1.4-60	OS	226
		20	4.88	0.82	8	--	6-100	OS	221
		20	4.85	0.80	9	--	8-200	SD	208
		20	6.0	0.79	12	--	3-780	LS	212, 227
		25	4.8	0.80	9	--	8-137	LS	209
		25	3.4	0.83	6	--	40-330	LS	213
		25	5.81	0.79	6	--	5-41	OS	216
		30	4.3	0.80	--	8	13-263	LS	217
		39	5.02	0.80	6	--	5-41	OS	216
		53	3.90	0.79	6	--	5-41	OS	216
		unc.	5.1	0.79	13	--	7-400	LS	228
	p-xymene	⊖ 159.7	57.5	0.50	4	--	6.6-171	IV	260
	1,2-dichloroethane	25	17.0	0.68	4	6	3-98	LS	214
		30	5.3	0.77	--	7	6-263	LS	217
	ethyl acetate	20	21.1	0.64	8	34	6-110	SD	229
	3-heptanone	⊖ 33.7	63.1	0.50	4	--	6.6-171	IV	260
	4-heptanone	⊖ 33.8	59	0.48	5	--	1-170	LS	219
	methyl isobutyrate	30	9.9	0.67	6	--	19-260	IV	218
	methyl methacrylate	30	6.75	0.72	3	--	13-170	IV	218
	nitroethane	25	5.70	0.74	2	6	10-200	LS	230
	3-octanone	⊖ 71	58	0.49	3	--	13-170	IV	219
	n-propanol	⊖ 84.4	67.9	0.50	4	-	6.6-171	IV	260

References page IV-64

Polymer	Solvent	Temp. [°C]	$K \times 10^5$ [dℓ/g]	a	No. of Samples Fr. W.P.	Mol. Wt. Range $M \times 10^{-4}$	Method	Ref.
Poly(methyl methacrylate) (Cont'd.)								
atactic	tetrachloroethane	25	12.8	0.73	6 --	5-41	OS	216
		53	12.2	0.73	6 --	5-41	OS	216
	toluene	25	7.1	0.73	7 --	4-330	LS	213
		25	8.12	0.71	6 --	5-41	OS	216
		30	7.0	0.71	6 --	19-263	IV	218
		39	7.24	0.72	6 --	5-41	OS	216
		53	6.63	0.73	6 --	5-41	OS	216
	butanone/isopropanol (55/45 vol)	23	47.0	0.55	6 --	40-300	LS	213
	(50/50 vol)	θ 25	59.2	0.50	7 --	30-280	LS	231
		θ 25	42.8	0.50	5 --	77-490	LS	259
	toluene/methanol (5/9 vol)	θ 26.2	55.9	0.50	3 --	60-300	LS	197
	acetone	30	23.0	0.63	-- 7	5-128	?	232
	acetonitrile	20	130	0.448	5 --	3-19	IV	233
		θ 27.6	75.5	0.500	5 --	3-19	IV	233
		35	46	0.546	5 --	3-19	IV	233
		50	26.2	0.602	5 --	3-19	IV	233
	benzene	30	5.2	0.76	-- 5	5-128	LS	234
	p-cymene	θ 152.1	56.6	0.50	4 --	7.9-131	IV	260
	3-heptanone	θ 40.0	87.0	0.50	4 --	7.9-131	IV	260
	propanol	75.9	76.1	0.50	4 --	7.9-131	IV	260
	butanone/isopropanol (50/50 vol)	θ 30.3	90.0	0.50	4 --	7.9-131	IV	260
Poly(n-octadecyl methacrylate)	tetrahydrofuran	30	2.5	0.75	-- 4	20-170	LS	236
Poly(n-octyl methacrylate)	n-butanone	θ 16.8	26.8	0.50	10 --	33-1250	LS	235
	butanone	23	4.47	0.69	10 --	33-1250	LS	235

Polymer	Solvent	Temp. [°C]	$K \times 10^5$ [dℓ/g]	a	No. of Samples Fr. M.P.	Mol. Wt. Range -4 $M \times 10$	Method	Ref.
Poly(phenyl methacrylate)	butyl acetate	25	14.7	0.63	8 / --	2-110	SD	257
Poly(methacrylonitrile)	acetone	20	95.5	0.56	-- / 4	35-100	OS	253
	dimethylformamide	29.2	306	0.503	-- / 15	0.6-8	IV	254

4 - POLYDIENES, INCLUDING DIENE COPOLYMERS

Polymer	Solvent	Temp. [°C]	$K \times 10^5$ [dℓ/g]	a	No. of Samples Fr. M.P.	Mol. Wt. Range -4 $M \times 10$	Method	Ref.
Polybutadiene								
98%-cis	benzene	30	33.7	0.715	9 / --	5-50	OS	261
	isobutyl acetate	20.5 Θ	185	0.50	6 / --	5-50	OS	261
	toluene	30	30.5	0.725	9 / --	5-50	OS	261
95%-cis, 1%-trans, 4%-1,2	benzene	30	8.5	0.78	4 / --	15-50	LS	262
	cyclohexane	30	11.2	0.75	4 / --	15-50	LS	262
	diethyl ketone	10.3 Θ	160	0.50	4 / --	10-25	LS,OS	323
	methyl isoamyl ketone	12.6 Θ	130	0.50	4 / --	15-35	LS	262
92%-cis, 3%-trans, 5%-1,2	toluene	30	33.9	0.688	8 / --	10-65	OS	263
84%-cis, 14%-trans, 2%-1,2	benzene	32	10	0.77	13 / --	10-160	LS	264
	benzene	-	13.3	0.78	20 / --	2-80	OS	265
	benzene	-	11.2	0.78	25 / --	2-60	OS	265
	dioxane	34 Θ	145	0.50	30 / --	2-50	OS	265
65%-1,2, 25%-trans, 10%-cis	toluene	25	110	0.62	8 / --	7-70	OS	266
71%-trans, 4%-cis, 25%-1,2	cyclohexane	25	12	0.77	8 / --	230-880	LS	267
79%-trans, 21%-cis	cyclohexane	20	36	0.70	12 / --	23-130	LS	268

References page IV-64

Polymer	Solvent	Temp. [°C]	$K \times 10^5$ [dℓ/g]	a	No. of Samples Fr.	W.P.	Mol. Wt. Range $M \times 10^{-4}$	Method	Ref.
Polybutadiene (Cont'd.) 97%-trans, 3%-cis	cyclohexane	40	28.2	0.70	7	--	4-17	LS	269
	toluene	30	29.4	0.753	6	--	5-16	OS	263
ca. 100%-cis	benzene	32	14.5	0.76	8	--	18-50	LS	270
	hexane(1)/heptane(1)	20	138	0.53	5	--	?	SD	320
5°C-emulsion, randomly branched	diethyl ketone	24	$M^{2/3}/[\eta]^{4/3} = 3320+1610M$		10	--	10-100	OS	271
50°C-emulsion, randomly branched	diethyl ketone	5	$M^{2/3}/[\eta]^{4/3} = 2140+152M$		16	--	5-124	OS	271
Poly(trichlorobutadiene)	benzene	25	31.6	0.66	11	--	29-129	LS	321
Polychloroprene neoprene CG	benzene	25	2.02	0.89	10	--	6-150	OS	272
neoprene GN	benzene	25	14.6	0.73	16	--	2-96	OS	273
neoprene W	benzene	25	15.5	0.71	8	--	5-100	OS	274
type, unspecified	toluene	25	50	0.615	13	--	4-120	OS	266
Polyisoprene natural rubber	benzene	30	18.5	0.74	--	4	8-28	OS	275
	cyclohexane	27	30	0.70	--	?	?	LS,SD	276
	n-propyl ketone Θ	14.5	119	0.50	--	4	8-28	OS	275
	toluene	25	50.2	0.667	20	--	7-100	OS	277
synthetic cis	hexane	20	68.4	0.58	5	--	5-80	SD	322
85-91%-cis	isooctane	30	22.2	0.683	--	8	23-580	LS	278
	toluene	30	20.0	0.728	--	12	14-580	LS	278
	n-heptane/propanol (78/22 vol)	30	37	0.63	--	6	43-580	LS	278
gutta percha	n-propyl acetate Θ	60	232	0.50	--	3	10-20	OS	275
synthetic trans, gutta percha, balata	benzene	32	43.7	0.65	24	--	8-140	LS	279

Polymer	Solvent	Temp. [°C]	$K \times 10^5$ [dl/g]	a	No. of Samples Fr. W.P.	Mol. Wt. Range $M \times 10^{-4}$	Method	Ref.
Poly(butadiene-co-acrylonitrile), Buna-N rubber	acetone	25	50	0.64	5 --	2.5-100	OS	266
	benzene	25	13	0.55	5 --	2.5-100	OS	265
	chloroform	25	54	0.63	5 --	2.5-100	OS	266
	toluene	25	49	0.64	7 --	2.5-100	OS	266
Poly(butadiene-co-styrene), Buna-S, GR-S, or SBR rubber	benzene	25	52.5	0.66	24 --	1-160	OS	280
	benzene	25	54	0.66	-- 8	1-165	OS	281
	cyclohexane	30	31.6	0.70	6 --	5-25	OS	324
	methyl n-propyl ketone	21 Θ	185	0.50	6 --	5-25	OS	324
	toluene	25	52.5	0.66	25 --	2.5-50	OS	277
	toluene	30	16.5	0.78	-- 9	3-25	OS	282
	toluene	30	37.9	0.71	6 --	5-25	OS	324

References page IV-64

5 - COPOLYMERS, EXCLUDING DIENE COPOLYMERS

Polymer	Solvent	Temp. [°C]	$K \times 10^5$ [dℓ/g]	a	No. of Samples Fr. W.P.	Mol. Wt. Range $M \times 10^{-4}$	Method	Ref.
Poly(acrylonitrile-co-glycidyl methacrylate)	dimethylformamide	30	175	0.65	? ?	?	?	403
Poly(acrylonitrile-co-methyl acrylate)	dimethylformamide	20	17.9	0.79	6 --	2-21	LS	404
Poly(acrylonitrile-co-styrene) (38.3/61.7 mole)	butanone	30	36	0.62	14 --	15-120	LS	405
Poly(diethyl fumarate-co-isobutene) (1/1 mole)	benzene/petroleum ether	20	340	0.44	4 --	1.5-14	SD	406
Poly(divinyl styrene-co-styrene)	benzene	25	37.2	0.70	5 --	5-80	SD	407
	n-octane	21	162	0.50	6 --	5-80	SD	407
Poly(methacrylic acid-co-methyl methacrylate) (7.4/92.6)	acetone	20	3.4	0.74	9 --	26-105	LS	408
Poly(methyl methacrylate co-p-isopropylstyrene) (~ 2/3 random)	butanone	25	0.021	1.11	-- 6	31-65	LS	409
Poly(methyl methacrylate-co-styrene) (1/1 random)	butanone	25	15.4	0.675	11 --	5-227	LS	410
(94/6 mole, random)	n-butyl chloride	40.8	27.6	0.617	5 --	20-100	LS	411
(52/48 mole, random)	n-butyl chloride	40.8	49	0.575	5 --	18-115	LS	411
(10/90 mole, random)	n-butyl chloride	40.8	16.6	0.609	5 --	20-82	LS	411
(block)	butanone	30	No simple relation		16 --	28-820	LS	412
Poly(1-hexene-sulfone)	acetone (or chloroform)	20	5.9	0.74	7 --	5-60	LS,SD	318
	n-hexylchloride	⊖ 13	33	0.55	5 --	10-60	LS,SD	318
	butanone/isopropanol (37/63 vol)	⊖ 27	48	0.50	3 --	10-60	LS,SD	318
Poly(styrene-sulfone)	tetrahydrofuran	30	3.89	0.78	4 --	15-40	OS	319

6 - POLYOXIDES AND POLYIMINES

Polymer	Solvent	Temp. [°C]	$K \times 10^5$ [dℓ/g]	a	No. of Samples Fr. W.P.	Mol. Wt. Range $M \times 10^{-4}$	Method	Ref.
Polyacetaldehyde	butanone	25	(1.68)	(0.65)	1 5	9-20	OS	283
Poly(ethylene imine)	water	25	$2.14 \times 10^{-2} N^{0.35}$		4 --	N=4-13*	CR	393
Poly(ethylene oxide)	acetone	25	156	0.50	7 --	0.02-0.3	EG	284
	benzene	20	48	0.68	12 --	0.01-1.9	EG	285
		25	129	0.50	12 --	0.02-0.8	EG	284
	carbon tetrachloride	20	69	0.61	9 --	0.02-1.1	EG	285
	chloroform	25	206	0.50	6 --	0.02-0.15	EG	284
	cyclohexane	20	$(0.005 + 35 \times 10^{-5} M^{0.69})$		11 --	0.006-1.1	EG	285
	dimethylformamide	25	$(0.02 + 24 \times 10^{-5} M^{0.73})$		10 --	0.1-3	LS,SD,SA	286
	dioxane	20	$(0.0075 + 35 \times 10^{-5} M^{0.71})$		13 --	0.006-1.9	EG	285
		25	138	0.50	7 --	0.02-0.15	EG	285
	methanol	20	$(0.02 + 33 \times 10^{-5} M^{0.72})$		12 --	0.006-1.9	EG	285
		25	85.2	0.57	? --	?	LS,SD,SA	287
	toluene	35	14.5	0.70	4 --	0.04-0.4	EG	288
	water	20	$(0.02 + 16 \times 10^{-5} M^{0.76})$		11 --	0.006-1.1	EG	287
		25	156	0.50	5 --	0.019-0.1	EG	289
		30	12.5	0.78	6 --	2-500	LS	290
		35	6.4	0.82	5 --	3-700	IV(LS)	291
		35	16.6	0.32	4 --	0.04-0.4	EG	288
		45	6.9	0.81	5 --	3-700	IV(LS)	291
	aqueous K_2SO_4(0.45M)	Θ 35	130	0.50	5 --	3-700	IV(LS)	291
	aqueous $MgSO_4$(0.39M)	Θ 45	100	0.50	6 --	3-700	IV(LS)	291

* N = number of skeletal atoms

References page IV-64

Polymer	Solvent	Temp. [°C]	$K \times 10^5$ [dl/g]	a	No. of Samples Fr.	No. of Samples W.P.	Mol. Wt. Range $M \times 10^{-4}$	Method	Ref.
Polyformaldehyde	dimethylformamide	150	44	0.66	--	4	8.9-28.5	LS	457
	hexafluoroacetone hydrate	25	87	0.69	--	5	2-19	LS	256
Poly(propylene oxide)	benzene	25	14	0.8	?	--	?	?	292
	benzene	25	11.2	0.77	3	--	3-70	IV(LS)	293
	hexane	46	19.7	0.67	6	10	3.4-367	LS	293
	toluene	25	12.9	0.75	3	--	3-70	IV(LS)	293
Polyurethan (essentially poly(propylene oxide))	benzene	25	41.3	0.64	11	--	1-8	LS	294
	methanol	25	76.9	0.55	10	1	1-7	LS	294
	toluene/isooctane (5/7 vol)	θ 39.5	107.5	0.50	7	--	1-7	LS	294
Poly(tetrahydrofuran)	benzene	30	131	0.60	--	12	2.6-113	LS	295
	cyclohexane	30	176	0.54	--	12	2.6-113	LS	295
	ethyl acetate	30	42.2	0.65	--	12	2.6-113	LS	295
	ethyl acetate/n-hexane (22.7/77.3 wt)	θ 31.8	206	0.49	--	11	2.6-113	LS	295

7 - POLYESTERS

Polymer	Solvent	Temp. [°C]	$K \times 10^5$ [dℓ/g]	a	No. of Samples Fr.	W.P.	Mol. Wt. Range $M \times 10^{-4}$	Method	Ref.
Poly(1,4-cyclohexylene sebacate), cis	chloroform	20	27.8	0.78	--	5	2.1-4.6	OS	298
trans	chloroform	20	18.3	0.86	--	9	1.1-3.7	OS	298
Poly(decamethylene adipate)	chlorobenzene	25	11.7	0.84	--	7	0.3-3	MV	299
	diethyl succinate	79	5.8	0.86	--	12	1-3	MV	299
Poly(ethylene terephthalate)	o-chlorophenol	25	6560	0.72	--	5	1.2-2.5	CS	414
	o-chlorophenol	25	30	0.77	--	34	1.1-2.9	EG	416
		25	17	0.83	--	7	0.8-2.0	EG	417
	m-cresol	25	0.77	0.95	5	--	0.04-1.2	EG	300
	tetrachloroethane	50	13.8	0.87	6	--	0.04-0.1	EG	301
	phenol/tetrachloroethane (60/40)	30	210	0.53	--	5		EG	419
	(50/50)	20	75.5	0.635	--	38		EG	422
		25	21	0.82	--	9	0.5-3	EG	302
			12.7	0.86					418
	phenol/dichloroethane (4/6)		9.2	0.8				EG	423
	phenol/tetrachlorophenol	25	46.8	0.68				LS	415
	phenol/trichlorophenol (10/7)	29.8	28.0	0.775	--	4	0.1-0.4	EG	420
		30	(630)	(0.47)	--	8	1.1-4	OS	303
Poly(hexadecamethylene sebacate)	chloroform	20	74.7	0.70	4	--	2-10	OS	304
Poly(hexamethylene acetylene- dicarboxylate)	benzene	20	151	0.55	?	--	0.1-0.5	OS	305
	chloroform	20	91	0.61	?	--	0.1-0.5	OS	305
Poly(hexamethylene bicyclo-2,2,2-octandione dicarbonate)	chloroform	20	--	--	--	4	1.4-3.9	OS	306

Polymer	Solvent	Temp. [°C]	$K \times 10^5$ [dℓ/g]	a	No. of Samples	Fr. W.P.	Mol. Wt. Range $M \times 10^{-4}$	Method	Ref.
Poly(hexamethylene α,α'-dibutylisebacate)	benzene	20	37.4	0.74	?	--	0.9-2.4	OS	307
Poly(hexamethylene fumarate)	chloroform	20	27.1	0.80	5	--	2-4.3	OS	308
Poly(hexamethylene cis-hexahydro-3,6-endo-methylenephthalate)	benzene	20	4.64	0.86	13	--	2.3-7.5	OS	325
	chloroform	20	9.33	0.83	13	--	2.3-7.5	OS	325
Poly(hexamethylene trans-hexahydro-3,6-endo-methylenephthalate)	benzene	20	17.4	0.75	10	--	3.3-11	OS	325
	chloroform	20	17.9	0.77	11	--	3.3-15	OS	325
Poly(hexamethylene maleate)	benzene	20	76.3	0.60	7	--	1.3-6.6	OS	308
	chloroform	20	36.2	0.73	7	--	1.3-6.6	OS	308
	tetrahydrofuran	20	43.7	0.66	7	--	1.3-6.6	OS	308
Poly(hexamethylene sebacate)	benzene	20	62.7	0.69	9	--	0.6-1.8	OS	307
	chloroform	20	72.5	0.70	9	--	2-10	OS	304
Poly(hexamethylene succinate)	benzene	20	43.3	0.70	22	--	1.5-5	OS	308
	chloroform	20	24.4	0.79	18	--	1.5-5	OS	308
	tetrahydrofuran	20	44.3	0.69	13	--	1.5-5	OS	308
Poly(4,4'-isopropylidene-diphenylene carbonate)	chloroform	20	277	0.50	--	--	1.5-6	LS	296
Poly(octamethylene cis-hexahydroterephthalate)	methylene chloride	25	11.1	0.82	--	6	1-27	SD	297
	tetrahydrofuran	25	39.9	0.70	--	6	1-27	SD	297
	chloroform	20	22.9	0.79	6	--	3.3-5.5	OS	298
Poly(octamethylene trans-hexahydroterephthalate)	chloroform	20	18.9	0.84	6	--	2.4-4.4	OS	298
Poly(ω-oxyundecanoate)	chloroform	20	21.4	0.60	7	--	3-49	OS	304
	chloroform	25	36.3	0.82	--	6	0.5-1.3	EG	309

ε - POLYAMIDES AND POLYURETHANS

Polymer	Solvent	Temp. [°C]	K x 10^5 [dℓ/g]	a	No. of Samples Fr. W. P.	Mol. Wt. Range M x 10^-4	Method	Ref.
Poly(ε-caprolactam) (Nylon 6)	m-cresol	25	320	0.62	6 / --	0.05-0.5	EG	310
	aqueous HCOOH(85%)	20	75	0.70		0.45-1.6	EG	311
	aqueous H₂SO₄(40%)	25	59.2	0.69		0.3-1.3	EG	312
(Monochain, polymerized with stearic acid)	conc. H₂SO₄	25	63	0.75	-- / 7	0.2-1.4	EG	313
(Dichain, polymerized with sebacic acid)	conc. H₂SO₄	25	42	0.79	-- / 14	0.2-2.3	EG	313
(Tetrachain, polymerized with tetrabasic acid)	conc. H₂SO₄	25	55	0.74	-- / 11	0.2-1.9	EG	313
(Octachain, polymerized with octabasic acid)	conc. H₂SO₄	25	13.5	0.86	-- / 5	0.4-2.6	EG	313
Poly(hexamethylene adipamide) (Nylon 66)	m-cresol	25	$0.015 + 35.3 \times 10^{-5} M^{0.792}$		13 / --	0.015-5	LS,EG	326
	dichloroacetic acid	25	$0.005 + 352 \times 10^{-5} M^{0.551}$		13 / --	0.015-5	LS,EG	326
	aqueous HCOOH (90% vol)	25	110	0.72	19 / 2	0.5-2.5	EG	314
		25	32.8	0.74	-- / 19	1-5	EG	315
	aqueous HCOOH (90% vol), ECOONa(0.1M)	25	$0.025 + 13.2 \times 10^{-5} M^{0.875}$		13 / --	0.015-5	LS,EG	326
	aqueous HCOOH (90% vol), KCl(2M)	25	$0.010 + 51.6 \times 10^{-5} M^{0.687}$		6 / --	0.015-5	LS,EG	326
		25	142	0.559	9 / --	0.015-5	LS,EG	326
	aqueous HCOOH (90% vol), KCl(2.3M)	⊖ 25	253	0.500	7 / --	0.015-5	LS,EG	326
	aqueous H₂SO₄ (95% vol)	25	$0.025 + 24.9 \times 10^{-5} M^{0.832}$		12 / --	0.015-5	LS,EG	326
Poly(hexamethylene sebacamide) (Nylon 610)	m-cresol	25	13.5	0.96	-- / 5	0.8-2.4	SD	316
Poly(butyl isocyanate)	benzene	20	1.10	1.11	-- / 7	1.8-21	SD	317
	tetrahydrofuran	20	0.457	1.18	-- / 7	1.8-21	SD	317

References page IV-64

Polymer	Solvent	Temp. [°C]	$K \times 10^5$ [dℓ/g]	a	No. of Samples Fr.	W.P.	Mol. Wt. Range $M \times 10^{-4}$	Method	Ref.
Polyurethan (essentially poly(propylene oxide))	benzene	25	41.3	0.64	11	--	1-8	LS	294
	methanol	25	76.9	0.55	10	1	1-7	LS	294
	toluene/isooctane (5/7 vol)	Θ 39.5	107.5	0.50	7	--	1-7	LS	294
9 - POLYSACCHARIDES									
Amylose	dimethyl sulfoxide	20	3.97	0.82	--	14	2-217	LS	329
		25	1.25	0.87	9	--	22-310	LS	327
		25	30.6	0.64	6	--	27-220	LS	328
	ethylenediamine	25	15.5	0.70	6	--	31-310	LS	327
	formamide	20	22.6	0.67	--	12	2-157	LS	329
	water	20	13.2	0.68	--	12	36-217	LS	329
	dimethyl sulfoxide/acetone (56.5/43.5 vol)	Θ 20	83.1	0.51	--	10	2-157	LS	329
	aqueous KCl (0.33M)	22.5	33.9	0.59	5	--	16-229	LS	330
	(0.50M)	Θ 25	115	0.50	6	--	27-220	LS	328
	(0.50M)	Θ (25)	(61.1)	(0.50)					334
	aqueous KOH (0.5 M)	25	8.50	0.76	6	--	27-220	LS	328
	(1 M)	25	1.18	0.89	5	--	31-310	LS	327
	aqueous NaOH (0.5M)	20	3.65	0.85	--	16	2-217	LS	329

Polymer	Solvent	Temp. [°C]	$K \times 10^5$ [dℓ/g]	a	No. of Samples Fr.	W.P.	Mol. Wt. Range $M \times 10^{-4}$	Method	Ref.
Amylose triacetate	chloroform	30	1.06	0.92	12	--	12-480	LS	332
	methyl acetate	25	(5.60)	(0.80)	--	3	7-19	SD	333
	nitromethane	30	1.10	0.87	14	--	12-480	LS	332
	tetrachloroethane	25			--	3	7-19	SD	333
Amylose tricarbanilate	acetone	20	0.814	0.90	--	26	4-490	LS	334
	dioxane	20	0.906	0.92	--	25	4-360	LS	334
	pyridine	20	0.589	0.92	--	20	4-360	LS	334
Amylose tricarbethoxy-methylcarbamate	acetone	20	27.6	0.63	13	--	9-380	IV	335
Arginic acid (Na salt)	aqueous NaCl (0.2M)	25	7.97	1.0	--	7	5-19	OS	336
Cellulose*	cadoxene	25	34	0.77				SD	392
	cuprammonium	20	105	0.66	9	--	2-25	OS	337
		25	8.5	0.81	--	5	8-96	OS	338
	cupriethylene diamine	25	13.3	0.505	32	--	1-54	OS	339
Cellulose acetatebutyrate	acetic acid	25	14.6	0.83	--	5	1-21	OS	340
	acetone	25	13.7	0.85	--	11	1-21	OS	340
Cellulose triacetate	acetone	20	2.38	1.0	5	--	2-14	SD	341
		25	14.9	0.82	8	--	2-39	OS	342
		25	8.97	0.90	14	--	1-18	OS	343
		25	33.0	0.760	9	--	2-30	OS	337
	chloroform	30	4.5	0.3	5	--	3-18	IV	343, 344
	o-cresol	30	6.15	0.9	5	--	3-18	IV	344
	acetone/water (80/20 vol)	20	2.65	1.0	9	--	2-11	SD	341
		25	21.0	0.803	--	--	2-30	OS	337
	methylene chloride/ethanol (80/20 vol)	25	13.9	0.834	--	--	2-30	OS	337

* See also table on "Properties of Cellulose Materials."

Polymer	Solvent	Temp. [°C]	$K \times 10^5$ [dl/g]	a	No. of Samples Fr.	W.P.	Mol. Wt. Range $M \times 10^{-4}$	Method	Ref.
Cellulose tributyrate	butanone	30	18.2	0.80	7	--	8-22	OS	345
	dodecane/tetralin (75/22 vol) Θ	130	82	0.50	3	--	11-21	OS	345
Cellulose tricaproate	dimethylformamide Θ	41	245	0.50	7	--	6-130	LS	346
	dioxane	35	125	0.57	7	--	4-130	LS	346
Cellulose tricaprylate	dimethylformamide Θ	140	113	0.50	3	--	10-32	OS	345
	γ-phenylpropanol Θ	48	129	0.50	3	--	8-32	OS	345
	toluene	30	17.3	0.70	6	--	8-35	OS	345
Cellulose tricarbanilate	acetone	20	4.66	0.84	--	16	7-270	LS	334
	dioxane	20	4.20	0.88	--	15	7-270	LS	334
	pyridine	20	3.46	0.86	--	12	7-270	LS	334
Cellulose trinitrate*	acetone	20	2.80	1.00	13	--	1-250	SD	347
		25	7.00	0.933	9	--	5-50	OS	337
		25	1.69	1.00	11	--	8-265	LS	348
		25	11.0	0.91	33	--	3-100	OS	339
		25	23.5	0.78	6	--	7-26	OS	349
		25	10.8	0.89	4	--	4-32	LS	350
		25	1.66	0.86	6	--	68-250	LS	351
	amyl acetate	25	1.1	1.04	6	--	7-26	OS	349
	amyl methyl ketone	25	5.0	0.93	6	--	7-26	OS	349
	n-butyl acetate	25	5.68	0.969	9	--	5-50	OS	337
	butyl formate	25	23	0.81	6	--	7-26	OS	349
	cyclohexanone	25	2.24	0.810	6	--	7-22	OS	352
	ethyl acetate	25	3.8	1.03	33	--	3-100	OS	339
		25	8.3	0.90	6	--	7-26	OS	349
		25	1.66	0.86	7	--	68-250	LS	351
		30	2.50	1.01	6	--	4-57	LS	353

* See also table on "Properties of Cellulose Materials."

Polymer	Solvent	Temp. [°C]	$K \times 10^5$ [dl/g]	a	No. of Samples Fr. W.P.	Mol. Wt. Range $M \times 10^{-4}$	Method	Ref.
Cellulose trinitrate* (Cont'd.)								
	ethyl butyrate	25	3.64	1.0	?	5-50	OS	354
	ethyl formate	25	30	0.79	6	7-26	OS	349
	ethyl lactate	25	12.2	0.92	19	3-65	OS	339
	methyl acetate	25	18.3	0.835	6	7-22	OS	352
	nitrobenzene	25	6.1	0.945	6	7-22	OS	352
Ethyl cellulose	benzene	25	29.2	0.81	6	4-14	OS	355
		39	28.0	0.81	6	4-14	OS	355
		60	35.8	0.73	6	4-14	OS	355
	butanone	25	18.2	0.84	6	4-14	OS	355
		39	21.2	0.82	6	4-14	OS	355
		60	26.7	0.79	6	4-14	OS	355
	butyl acetate	25	14.0	0.87	6	4-14	OS	355
		39	14.6	0.86	6	4-14	OS	355
		60	18.1	0.83	6	4-14	OS	355
	chloroform	25	11.8	0.89	6	4-14	OS	355
		46	9.3	0.90	6	4-14	OS	355
	ethyl acetate	25	10.7	0.89	6	4-14	OS	355
		39	14.0	0.86	6	4-14	OS	355
		60	14.0	0.85	6	4-14	OS	355
	methanol	25	52.3	0.65	6	10-41	LS	356
	nitroethane	25	4.2	0.96	6	4-14	OS	355
		39	7.5	0.90	6	4-14	OS	355
		60	22.6	0.79	6	4-14	OS	355
Ethyl hydroxyethyl cellulose	water	25	47.0	0.80	4	5-18	OS(LS, SD)	357
		40	43.7	0.78	4	5-18	OS(LS, SD)	357

References page IV-64

Polymer	Solvent	Temp. [°C]	$K \times 10^5$ [dl/g]	a	No. of Samples Fr. W.P.	Mol. Wt. Range $M \times 10^{-4}$	Method	Ref.
Hydroxyethyl cellulose	cadoxene	25	13	0.79	4 --	8-61	LS	358
	water	25	11	0.87	5 --	8-63	LS	358
Methyl cellulose	water	25	316	0.55	-- 5	12-57	LS	359
Carboxymethyl cellulose (Na salt)	cadoxene	25	33.4	0.73	-- 5	5-106	LS	360
	aqueous NaCl (0.1M)	25	12.3	0.91	8 --	4.5-35	SD	361
	(0.01M)	25	0.646	1.20	3 --	4.5-35	SD	361
	(0.001M)	25	0.100	1.40	8 --	4.5-35	SD	361
Dextran (acid-hydrolyzed)	water	25	97.8	0.50	10 --	2-10	LS	362
Guaran triacetate	water	25	2.62	0.87	4 --	7-85	LS	363
	acetonitrile	25	311	0.52	5 --	206-534	LS	363

10 - POLYPEPTIDES

Polymer	Solvent	Temp. [°C]	$K \times 10^5$ [dℓ/g]	a	No. of Samples Fr.	W.P.	Mol. Wt. Range $M \times 10^{-4}$	Method	Ref.
Collagen (calf-skin, sonically degraded)	citrate buffer (0.15M; pH 3.7)	24.8	0.000123	1.80	--	9	14-37	SV	364
Gelatin	acetate buffer (0.17M; pH 4.75)	35	1.66	0.885	13	--	5-21	OS	365
	aqueous KCNS (2M)	25	29	0.62	--	8	2-10	SE	366
	aqueous NaCl (1M)	40	2.69	0.88	8	--	7-14	OS	389
Poly(n-benzyl-β-alanine)	dichloroacetic acid	25	120	0.525	--	6	0.15-1.8	EG	367
Poly(γ-benzyl-ι-glutamate)	dichloroacetic acid	25	2.78	0.87	--	6	2-34	LS	368
	dimethylformamide	25	0.00029	1.70	--	5	7-34	LS	368
Poly(γ-benzyl-D,ι-glutamate)	dichloroacetic acid	25	2.85	0.85	--	6	1.5-10	LS	369
	dimethylformamide	25	37.7	0.55	--	6	1.5-10	LS	369
Poly(D,ι-phenyl alanine)	chloroform	25	0.00346	1.48	--	11	2.2-14	LS	390
Poly(ι-proline)	water, acetic acid	25	no simple relation		--	5	1-5	OS	391
Poly(sarcosine)	water	20	56	0.88	--	5	0.7-1.6	EG	370

11 - POLYNUCLEOTIDES

Polymer	Solvent	Temp. [°C]	$K \times 10^5$ [dl/g]	a	No. of Samples Fr.	W.P.	Mol. Wt. Range $M \times 10^{-4}$	Method	Ref.
Deoxyribonucleic acid (calf-thymus; native and sonically degraded)	aqueous NaCl(0.2M)	25	14.5	1.12	--	5	30-740	LS	372
(fish sperm; native)	citrate buffer (Na$^+$, 0.2M; pH 7)	?	11	1.0	--	19	400-1300	LS	373
(degraded by acid)	aqueous NaCl(0.2M), HCOOH (0.035M); pH 2.6	25	(60)	(0.50)	--	?	?	LS	378
(degraded by enzyme)	aqueous NaCl(0.2M)	25	(70)	(1.0)	--	?	?	LS	379
(D. pneumoniae; denatured by heat)	phosphate buffer (Na$^+$, 0.012M; pH 6.8)	20	3.46	0.933	--	13	25-330	SV	380
(E. coli; denatured by heat)	citrate buffer (Na$^+$, 0.195M; pH 7.2)	20	73	0.53	--	9	13-480	SV	381
(P. aeruginosa; denatured by heat)	phosphate buffer (Na$^+$, 0.012M; pH 6.8)	20	3.11	0.912	--	9	8-460	SV	380
	citrate buffer (Na$^+$, 0.012M; pH 6.8)	20	6.4	0.81	--	4	305-693	SV	381
Poly(riboadenylic acid)	citrate buffer (Na$^+$, 0.195M; pH 7.1)	25	38	0.65	--	6	1-13	SV	382
Poly(riboinosinic acid)	aqueous NaCl (0.1M)	25	14.8	0.90	--	?	30-100	SV	383
Poly(ribouridylic acid)	citrate buffer (Na$^+$, 0.195M; pH 6.0)	25	8.98	0.75	--	9	2-20	SV	384
Ribonucleic acid (calf liver, native)	phosphate buffer (PO$_4$, 0.01M; pH 7)	20	62	0.53	--	?	2-12	SV	385
	(Na$^+$, 0.2M; pH 7.7)	25	(71)	(0.50)	--	8	1.4-36	SD	386
(TMV virus, native)	phosphate buffer	25		(0.50)				SV	387

12 - SEMIORGANIC AND INORGANIC POLYMERS

Polymer	Solvent	Temp. [°C]	$K \times 10^5$ [dℓ/g]	a	No. of Samples Fr. / W.P.	Mol. Wt. Range $M \times 10^{-4}$	Method	Ref.
Poly(dimethyl siloxane)	benzene	20	12	0.63	4 / --	5.5-12	IV	394
	bromobenzene	Θ 78.7	76	0.53	3 / --	8-106	LS	413
	bromocyclohexane	Θ 28	78	0.50	5 / --	10-92	SD	395
		Θ 29.0	74	0.50	5 / --	3.3-106	LS	413
	butanone	Θ 20	81	0.50	5 / --	5-66	OS	396
		30	48	0.55	8 / --	5-66	OS	396
	ethyl iodide	Θ 2.1	70	0.50	2 / --	34-106	LS	413
	phenetole	Θ 83	79	0.50	-- / 2	5-66	OS	396
		Θ 89.5	73	0.50	4 / --	4.5-106	LS	413
	toluene	25	8.28	0.72	5 / --	10-92	OS	395
		25	21.5	0.65	-- / ?	2-130	OS	397
		25	20.0	0.66	13 / --	0.3-20	OS	424
	bromocyclohexane/phenetole (6/7 vol)	Θ 36.3	75.5	0.50	4 / --	4.5-106	LS	413
	chlorobenzene/dimethyl phthalate (45/6 vol)	Θ 57.5	76	0.50	3 / --	8-106	LS	413
	$C_8H_{18}/C_2Cl_4F_2$ (33.17/66.83 wt) (low cohesive energy density mixture)	Θ 22.5	106	0.50	4 / --	55-120	LS	425
Poly(methyl siloxane) (Me/Si = 1.5)	chlorobenzene	Θ 20	326	0.21	12 / --	0.1-500	LS	398
(Me/Si = 1.8)	chlorobenzene/dimethyl phthalate (90.7/9.3 wt)	Θ 20	240	0.28	3 / --	5-100	LS	398
Poly(tetramethyl-sil-phenylene siloxane)	toluene	25	11.2	0.75	6 / --	7-38	LS	399
Poly(phenylsilsesqui-oxane) (double chain)	benzene	-	?	0.92	? / --	?	LS	400
Poly(phosphoric acid), Na-salt	aqueous NaBr (0.035M)	25.5	69	0.61	-- / 5	0.09-1	EG	401
	(0.35M)	25	6.5	0.69	-- / 6	1-125	LS	402
	(0.415M)	Θ 25	49.4	0.50	-- / 9	1-125	LS	402

References page IV-64

C. CALCULATED UNPERTURBED DIMENSION OF FREELY-ROTATING CHAINS

Chain Type	$r_{of}/M^{\frac{1}{2}} \times 10^8$ [cm. $mole^{\frac{1}{2}}$ $gram^{-\frac{1}{2}}$]		Reference
Polymethylene chain	$3.08/M_u^{\frac{1}{2}}$	$2.18/m^{\frac{1}{2}}$	1
Amylosic chain	$4.26/M_u^{\frac{1}{2}}$	$1.91/m^{\frac{1}{2}}$	427
Cellulosic chain	$7.90/M_u^{\frac{1}{2}}$	$3.53/m^{\frac{1}{2}}$	428
Gutta-percha (trans polydiene)	$5.80/M_u^{\frac{1}{2}}$	$2.90/_m^{\frac{1}{2}}$	428,429
Natural rubber (cis polydiene)	$4.02/M_u^{\frac{1}{2}}$	$2.01/m^{\frac{1}{2}}$	428,429
Polypeptide	$3.83/M_u^{\frac{1}{2}}$	$2.21/m^{\frac{1}{2}}$	428

D. UNPERTURBED DIMENSIONS OF LINEAR POLYMER MOLECULES

Polymer	Solvent	Temp. [°C]	$S_{oz}/M_w^{\frac{1}{2}} \times 10^3$ or a_P [A]	$K_o \times 10^5$ [dl/g]	$r_o/M^{\frac{1}{2}} \times 10^3$ [A]	$r_{of}/M^{\frac{1}{2}} \times 10^3$ [A]	r_o/r_{of}	Method	Ref.*
1 - POLYOLEFINS									
Poly(1-butene)									
atactic	anisole; ethylcyclohexane	~70	--	123±10	775±25	427	1.82±0.05	VM(t,g)	2(8)
	n-nonane	35	590±50	--	1180±70	427	2.76±0.20	LS(t)	8
isotactic	n-nonane	80	510±50	--	1290±90	427	3.00±0.25	LS(=)	8
Polyethylene	1-chloronaphthalene; tetralin; p-xylene	~100	--	230±30	950±40	582	1.63±0.08	VM(g)	2(12, 20,22)
	bis-2-ethylhexyl adipate	145	--	225±10	940±40	582	1.61±0.08	VM(t)	430
		145	690±100	--	1320±150	582	2.27±0.26	LS(t)	430
		140	--	--	1070	582	1.84	V(g)A$_2$	454
Poly(chlorotrifluoro ethylene)(KEL-F)	2,5-dichlorobenzotrifluoride	130	--	52±3	580±15	286	2.03±0.07	VM(g)	2(28)
Polyisobutene	benzene	24	--	107±5	740±20	412	1.80±0.05	VM(t)	42
	phenetole	86	--	91±5	700±20	412	1.70±0.05	VM(t)	42
	anisole	105	--	91±5	700±20	412	1.70±0.05	VM(t)	42
	n-heptane/propanol (80/20 vol)	25	390	166	780	412	1.9	LS(-t)	431
Poly(1-pentene)									
isotactic	isoamyl acetate	31~32	--	~140	801	368	2.2	V(t)	453
	2-pentanol	62.4	--	121	784	368	2.13	VM(t)	455
Polypropylene									
atactic	isoamyl acetate; benzene; cyclohexane; toluene	~30	--	156±15	835±25	475	1.76±0.05	VM(t,g)	2(29, 30)
	decalin	135	--	125±20	775±25	475	1.63±0.08	VM(g)	2(29,32)
	1-chloronaphthalene	74	--	182	880	475	1.85	VM(g)	31
	cyclohexanone	92	--	172	870	475	1.83	VM(t)	31
	phenyl ether	153	--	120	765	475	1.61	VM(t)	31

* References in parenthesis give data which were used for calculation of end-to-end distance in ref. 2.

References page IV-64

Polymer	Solvent	Temp. [°C]	$S_{oz}/M_w^{\frac{1}{2}}$ x 10^3 or a^P [A]	K_o x 10^5 [dl/g]	$r_o/M^{\frac{1}{2}}$ x 10^3 [A]	$r_{of}/M^{\frac{1}{2}}$ x 10^3 [A]	r_o/r_{of}	Method	Ref*
Polypropylene (Cont'd.)									
isotactic	1-chloronaphthalene; decalin; tetralin	~140	--	120±20	765±40	475	1.61±0.08	VM(g)	2(29, 36)
	phenyl ether	145	--	132	790	475	1.66	VM(t)	31
		145	--	94	710	475	1.49	VM(t)	430
		145	370±30	--	685±30	475	1.44±0.07	LS(t)	430
2 - VINYL POLYMERS									
Polystyrene									
atactic	various solvents	~30	--	82±5	670±15	302	2.22±0.05	VM(t,g)	2(54, 57, 59, 62, 68, 74, 77, 78)
	ethyl(or methyl) cyclohexane	~70	--	75±5	650±15	302	2.15±0.05	VM(t)	2(69, 70)
	cyclohexane	34	282±5	--	690±10	302	2.28±0.04	LS(t)	432
		35	306	--	730	302	2.42	LS(t)	58
		35	300	--	670	302	2.22	LS(t)	433
		35	9.2±0.3	--	705±15	302	2.33±0.05	XS(t)	434
	benzene; toluene	25	9.1±0.2	--	700±15	302	2.32±0.04	XS(g)	434
	benzene/ethanol (71.5/28.5 vol)	25	296	--	645	302	2.14	LS(~t)	431
	butanone/isopropanol (87/13 vol)	67	317	--	757	302	2.50	LS(t)	58

Polymer	Solvent	Temp. [°C]	$S_{oz}/M_w^{1/2}$ x 10^3 or a_p [A]	K_o x 10^5 [dl/g]	$r_o/M^{1/2}$ x 10^3 [A]	$r_{of}/M^{1/2}$ x 10^3 [A]	r_o/r_{of}	Method	Ref.*
Polystyrene (Cont'd.) atactic	1-chloro-n-undecane	32.8	--	(78.6)	775	302	2.56	$A_2(\sim t)$	435
	cyclohexane	34.8	--	(86.6)	768	302	2.54	$A_2(\sim t)$	435
	diethyl malonate	35.9	--	(76.9)	762	302	2.52	$A_2(\sim t)$	435
	73%-trans-decalin	18	--	77	655	302	2.17	VM(~)	68
	100%-trans-decalin	24	--	82	670	302	2.22	VM(~)	68
	n-butyl formate	-9	--	77.4	655	302	2.17	V(t)	436
	hexyl-m-xylol	12.5	--	77.0	655	302	2.17	V(t)	436
	decalin	29.5	--	77.9	655	302	2.17	V(t)	436
	diethyl malonate	31	--	70.5	635	302	2.10	V(t)	436
	cyclohexane	34	--	79.5	660	302	2.18	V(t)	436
	diethyl oxalate	51.5	--	72.2	640	302	2.12	V(t)	436
	methylcyclohexane	68	--	78.0	655	302	2.17	V(t)	436
	cyclohexanol	83.5	--	50.8	575	302	1.90	V(t)	436
	1-chloro-n-decane	6.6	--	78.0	655	302	2.17	V(t)	437
	1-chloro-n-undecane	32.8	--	78.7	660	302	2.18	V(t)	437
	1-chloro-n-dodecane	58.6	--	80.7	665	302	2.20	V(t)	437
	cyclohexane/methylcyclohexane (1/0)	34.5	--	77.9	655	302	2.17	V(t)	438
	(2/1 vol)	43.0	--	77.6	655	302	2.17	V(t)	438
	(1/1 vol)	48.0	--	74.8	650	302	2.15	V(t)	438
	(1/2 vol)	54.0	--	73.0	645	302	2.14	V(t)	438
	(0/1)	70.5	--	69.6	635	302	2.10	V(=)	438

References page IV-64

Polymer	Solvent	Temp. [°C]	$S_{oz}/M_w^{1/2} \times 10^3$ or a_p [A]	$K_o \times 10^5$ [dl/g]	$r_o/M^{1/2} \times 10^3$ [A]	$r_{of}/M^{1/2} \times 10^3$ [A]	r_o/r_{of}	Method	Ref*
Polystyrene (Cont'd.) atactic	diethyl malonate/diethyl oxalate	34.2 ~55.8	--	71.8 ~73.0	640~645	302	2.12~2.14	V(t)	438
isotactic	benzene; toluene	30	--	90±10	695±25	302	2.30±0.08	VM(g)	2(83, 84,85)
Poly(p-chlorostyrene)	toluene	25,30	--	50±3	570±15	261	2.18±0.07	VM(g)	2,(88, 90)
Poly(2,5-dichloro-styrene)	ethyl acetate/ethanol (15/1 wt)	30.5	--	35.5	510	234	2.18	VM(t)	2(92)
Poly(3,4-dichloro-styrene)	butyl acetate/butanol (13/1 wt)	32.9	--	71	640	234	2 7	VM(t)	93
Poly(2,4-dimethyl-styrene)	toluene	30	--	60±5	630±15	268	2.35±0.07	VM(g)	94
Poly(α-methylstyrene)	toluene; benzene/methanol (79.4/20.6 vol)	30	--	74±10	655±25	284	2.30±0.10	VM(g,t)	2(96, 99)
Poly(vinyl alcohol)	water	30	--	222±25	950±40	464	2.04±0.10	VM(g)	2(101, 103, 105)
Poly(vinyl bromide)	cyclohexanone; tetrahydrofuran; THF/methanol (83/17 vol)	20	--	40±5	540±20	298	1.82±0.07	VM(t,g)	2(135, 165a)
	1-methylnaphthalene	? 20	(10.9)	--	(763)	298	(2.56)	XS(g)	440
Poly(vinyl chloride)	cyclohexanone; tetrahydrofuran	? 25	--	100±30	720±30	393	1.83±0.15	VM(g)	2(136, 138, 139, 141)
Poly(vinyl ester) benzyl alcohol	benzyl alcohol	155.4	--	156	820	393	2.08	VM(t)	163
Poly(vinyl acetate)	various solvents	? 25	--	93±10	705±30	332	2.12±0.09	VM(t,g)	2(113, 115, 125, 127)

Polymer	Solvent	Temp. [°C]	$S_{oz}/M_w^{1/2} \times 10^3$ or a [A]^p	$K_o \times 10^5$ [dl/g]	$r_o/M^{1/2} \times 10^3$ [A]	$r_{of}/M^{1/2} \times 10^3$ [A]	r_o/r_{of}	Method	Ref.*
Poly(vinyl acetate) (Cont'd.)									
	3-heptanone	29	9.5±0.5	--	790±20	332	2.38±0.07	XS(t)	439
	methyl isopropyl ketone/ n-heptane (73.2/26.8 vol)	25	318±10	--	745±20	332	2.24±0.07	LS(t)	124
	methanol	6	--	101	720	332	2.17	VM(t)	116
	3-heptanone	26.8	--	82.0	670	332	2.02	VM(t)	116
	ethanol	56.9	--	90	690	332	2.08	VM(t)	116
	ethyl isoamyl ketone	66	--	78	660	332	1.99	VM(t)	115
Poly(vinyl benzoate)	xylene	32.5	--	62±8	620±25	252	2.46±0.10	VM(t)	128
Poly(vinyl p-chloro-benzoate)	butanone/n-butanol (53/47 vol)	60	--	73	665	228	2.92	VM(t)	160
Poly(vinyl n-butyrate)	benzene	30	--	80±10	670±35	288	2.32±0.12	VM(g)	2(129)
Poly(vinyl n-caproate)	benzene	30	--	91±10	700±30	258	2.71±0.12	VM(g)	2(129)
Poly(vinyl isobutyrate)	benzene	30	--	80±10	670±35	288	2.32±0.12	VM(g)	2(129)
Poly(vinyl pivalate)	acetone; butanone/methanol (0.897 g/ml)	20	--	53±5	580±20	253	2.29±0.08	VM(t,g)	131
Poly(vinyl sulfate)	aqueous NaCl (0.5M)	20	--	25±15	460±80	278	1.65±0.30	VM(g)	2(132)
Poly(vinyl methyl ether)	benzene; butanone	30	--	195±30	900±50	404	2.23±0.13	VM(g)	2(133)
Poly(2-vinyl-naphthalene)	decalin/toluene (1.3/1 vol)	30.2	--			248	ca. 3.1	VM(t)	146

References page IV-64

Polymer	Solvent	Temp. [°C]	$s_{oz}/M_w^{1/2} \times 10^3$ or a_p [A]	$K_o \times 10^5$ [dl/g]	$r_o/M^{1/2} \times 10^3$ [A]	$r_{of}/M^{1/2} \times 10^3$ [A]	r_o/r_{of}	Method	Ref.*
Poly(2-vinyl-pyridine)	various solvents	25	--	82±10	660±30	300	2.20±0.10	VM(g)	147
Poly(4-vinyl-pyridine)	ethanol; water	25	--	94±10	710±30	300	2.37±0.10	VM(g)	2(149, 150)
Poly(2-methyl-5-vinylpyridine)	butanone; methanol	25	--	69±5	652±15	282	2.31±0.05	VM(g)	152
Poly(vinyl-pyrrolidone)	water	~25	--	100±15	720±40	292	2.48±0.12	VM(g)	2(155, 157)
	water/acetone (33.2/66.8 vol)	25	--	75	650	292	2.22	VM(t)	164
Poly(vinylsulfonic acid)	aqueous NaBr (0.346M)	-0.6	--	95.5	730(882)	296	2.46(2.98)	VM(t)	165, 441
	aqueous KBr (0.347M)	5.7	--	68.8	650(788)	296	2.19(2.66)	VM(t)	165, 441
	aqueous KCl (0.349M)	5.5	--	68.2	650(786)	296	2.19(2.66)	VM(t)	165, 441
	(0.650M)	26.0	--	79.5	685(830)	296	2.31(2.80)	VM(t)	165, 441
	(1.001M)	44.5	--	80.3	690(832)	296	2.33(2.81)	VM(t)	165, 441
	aqueous NaCl (1.003M)	32.4	--	96.1	730(880)	296	2.46(2.97)	VM(t)	165, 441
	aqueous NaBr (1.008M)	40.1	--	94.5	725(875)	296	2.45(2.96)	VM(t)	165, 441

3 - ACRYLIC AND METHACRYLIC POLYMERS

Polymer	Solvent	$S_{oz}/M_W^{1/2} \times 10^3$ or a [A]^p	Temp. [°C]	$K_O \times 10^5$ [dl/g]	$r_O/M^{1/2} \times 10^3$ [A]	$r_{of}/M^{1/2} \times 10^3$ [A]	r_o/r_{of}	Method	Ref*
Poly(acrylic acid)	1,4-dioxane	--	30	76	665	363	1.83	VM(t)	166
Poly(acrylic acid) sodium salt	aqueous NaBr (1.5M)	--	15	124	756	318	2.38	VM(t)	169, 170
		--	15	--	1030	318	3.24	LSd(t)	169
	aqueous NaSCN	--	30	121	752	318	2.36	VM(t)	168
Polyacrylamide	water	--	30	260±40	1000±50	367	2.72±0.10	VM(g)	2(239)
Poly(N,N'-dimethyl-acrylamide)	methanol; water	--	25	78±15	670±40	309	2.17±0.14	VM(g)	2(240)
Poly(acrylic acid ester)									
Poly(ethyl acrylate)	acetone; methanol	--	30	90±10	720±30	308	2.34±0.10	VM(g)	174, 175
Poly(methyl acrylate) various solvents		--	~30	81±10	680±30	332	2.05±0.10	VM(g)	2(179, 185)
	butanone/isopropanol (42/58 vol)	--	20	81	680	332	2.05	VM(t)	180
	(1/1 vol)	--	27.5	54.4	590	332	1.78	VM(t)	169
		--	27.5	--	720	332	2.17	LSd(t)	169
		--	25	70±10	630±40	260	2.42±0.	VM(g)	2(256)
Poly(acrylo-morpholide)	dimethylformamide	--	25	210±15	930±20	422	2.20±0.05	VM(g)	2(246, 247)
Polyacrylonitrile	dimethylformamide								
(polymd. at -30°C)	DMF; γ-butyrolactone	--	30	250	970	422	2.30	VM(g)	244
(polymd. at 60°C)	" "	--	30	200	900	422	2.13	VM(g)	244
Poly(acrylo-piperidide)	dimethylformamide	--	25	58±10	600±40	261	2.30±0.15	VM(g)	2(255)
Poly(ethacrylic acid ester)									
Poly(methyl ethacrylate)	butanone	--	30	65±3	620±5	288	2.15±0.02	VM(g)	237

Polymer	Solvent	Temp. [°C]	$S_{oz}/M_w^{1/2} \times 10^3$ or a_p [A]	$K_o \times 10^5$ [dl/g]	$r_o/M^{1/2} \times 10^3$ [A]	$r_{of}/M^{1/2} \times 10^3$ [A]	r_o/r_{of}	Method	Ref.[*]
Poly(N-phenyl-methacrylamide)	acetone	20	--	38±9	520±40	242	2.15±0.16	VM(g)	2(241)
Poly(methacrylic acid ester)									
Poly(n-butyl methacrylate)	butanone; isopropanol	23	--	34±5	510±20	258	1.98±0.10	VM(t,g)	2(193, 195, 197)
	isopropanol	23	--	--	530	258	2.06	LSd(t)	193
Poly(p-tert-butyl-phenyl methacrylate)	acetone	20	--	35±5	515±20	208	2.48±0.10	VM(g)	2(198)
Poly(cyclohexyl methacrylate)	butanol	23	--	34	510	237	2.15	VM(t)	258
Poly(ethyl methacrylate)	butanone	23	--	49±3	565±15	288	1.96±0.05	VM(g)	2(203)
	butanone/isopropanol (1/7 vol)	23	--	47.3	560	288	1.94	VM(t)	203
		23	--	--	560	288	1.94	LSd(t)	203
Poly(2-ethylbutyl methacrylate)	butanone; isopropanol	~25	--	36±5	510±30	236	2.16±0.13	VM(t,g)	2(204)
	isopropanol	27.4	--	--	500	236	2.12	LSd(t)	204
Poly(n-hexyl methacrylate)	butanone; isopropanol	~30	--	41±4	530±20	236	2.25±0.08	VM(t,g)	2(205)
	isopropanol	32.6	--	--	580	236	2.46	LSd(t)	205
Poly(n-lauryl methacrylate)	n-amyl alcohol; butyl (or iso-propyl) acetate	~25	--	33±5	500±20	193	2.59±0.10	VM(t,g)	2(206, 207)
	n-amyl alcohol	29.5	222±10	--	500±20	193	2.59±0.10	LS(t)	206
Poly(methyl methacrylate)	various solvents	25	--	70±20	640±60	308	2.08±0.20	VM(t,g)	2(209, 211, 212, 213, 220, 230, 231)

Polymer	Solvent	Temp. [°C]	$S_{oz}/M_w^{1/2} \times 10^3$ or a_p [A]	$K_o \times 10^5$ [dℓ/g]	$r_o/M^{1/2} \times 10^3$ [A]	$r_{of}/M^{1/2} \times 10^3$ [A]	r_o/r_{of}	Method	Ref.*
Poly(methyl methacrylate) (Cont'd.)									
	butyl chloride	35.4	219	--	537	308	1.74	LS(t)	442
		40.8	292±6	--	620±15	308	2.01±0.05	LS(t)	63
	benzene; toluene; butanone/ isopropanol	21	7.2±0.5	--	653±25	308	2.12±0.08	XS(t,g)	443
	2-methyl-4-pentanone	-42	--	36.0	500	308	1.62	V(t)	442
	methyl isovalerate	-37	--	41.5	525	308	1.70	V(t)	442
	butyl acetate	-20	--	40.6	520	308	1.69	V(t)	442
	butanone/isopropanol (58.2/41.8 vol)	4.0	--	47.2	550	308	1.78	V(t)	442
	(55/45 vol)	12.8	--	49.3	560	308	1.82	V(t)	442
	(50/50 vol)	22.8	--	50.4	610	308	1.98	V(t)	442
	(46.8/53.2 vol)	28.5	--	50.8	610	308	1.99	V(t)	442
	butyl chloride	35.4	--	52.6	620	308	2.00	V(t)	442
	4-heptanone	40.4	--	53.2	620	308	2.01	V(t)	442
	isoamyl acetate	57.5	--	53.5	620	308	2.01	V(=)	442
	4-heptanone	~33	--	47±4	550±15	308	1.78±0.05	VM(t)	444
	acetonitrile	45	--	49±5	555±15	308	1.80±0.05	VM(t)	444
	3-octanone	72	--	50±3	560±10	308	1.82±0.03	VM(t)	444
isotactic	acetonitrile	27.6	--	75.5	670	308	2.17	VM(t)	233
Poly(n-octyl methacrylate)	n-butanol; butanone	~20	--	30±5	480±20	219	2.19±0.09	VM(t,g)	2(235)
	n-butanol	16.8	--	--	500	219	2.28	LSd(t)	235

References page IV-64

4 - POLYDIENES

Polymer	Solvent	Temp. [°C]	$S_{oz}/M_w^{1/2}$ x 10^3 or a_p [A]	K_o x 10^5 [dl/g]	$r_o/M^{1/2}$ x 10^3 [A]	$r_{of}/M^{1/2}$ x 10^3 [A]	r_o/r_{of}	Method	Ref.*
Polybutadiene 98%-cis,2%-1,2	isobutyl acetate	20.5	--	185	880	547	1.61	VM(t)	261
95%-cis,4%-1,2	diethyl ketone (DEK)	10.3	--	181	875	546	1.57	VM(t)	438
	methyl n-propyl ketone (MNPK)	59.7	--	157	835	546	1.50	VM(t)	438
	DEK/MNPK (3/2 vol)	30.0	--	174	860	546	1.55	V(t)	438
92%-cis,5%-1,2	benzene	32	--	150±20	820±40	545	1.50±0.08	VM(g)	2(264)
84%-cis,14%-trans	dioxane	34	--	145	810	585	1.38	VM(t)	265
71%-trans, 25%-1,2	cyclohexane	25	--	300±40	1030±50	702	1.45±0.08	VM(g)	2(267)
79%-trans, 21%-1,2	cyclohexane	20	--	280±25	1010±30	742	1.36±0.05	VM(g)	2(268)
97%-trans,3%-1,2	cyclohexane	40	--	150±25	820±40	768	1.07±0.05	VM(g)	269
Polychloroprene 85%-trans	benzene	25	--	115±20	750±80	535	1.40±0.15	VM(g)	2(273, 274)
Polyisoprene 100%-cis	benzene; propyl ketone	≈20	--	130±20	810±45	485	1.67±0.09	VM(t,g)	2(275)
	diisopropyl ether	22	7.6	--	847	485	1.74	XS(g)	445
100%-trans	n-propyl acetate	60	--	232	970	703	1.38	VM(t)	275

Polymer	Solvent	Temp. [°C]	$S_{oz}/M_w^{1/2}$ x 10^3 or a_P [A]	K_o x 10^5 [dℓ/g]	$r_o/M^{1/2}$ x 10^3 [A]	$r_{of}/M^{1/2}$ x 10^3 [A]	r_o/r_{of}	Method	Ref.*
5 - COPOLYMERS									
Poly(acrylonitrile-co-styrene) 38.3/61.7 mole	butanone	30	--	124	770	353	2.18±0.05	VM(g)	405
Poly(1-hexene-sulfone)	n-hexyl chloride	13	--	67±2	625±10	350	1.79±0.02	V(t)	447
		13	296±9	--	725±22	350	2.07±0.07	LS(t)	447
	butanone/isopropanol (41.5/58.5 vol.)	4	230±11	--	563±28	350	1.61±0.08	LS(t)	447
	(37/63 vol)	23.5	228±23	--	559±55	350	1.60±0.15	LS(t)	447
		27	--	48±2	560±10	350	1.60±0.03	VM(t)	447
Poly(styrene-sulfone)	tetrahydrofuran	30	--	57.4	649	425	1.53	VM(g)	319
Poly(styrene-co-methyl methacrylate) 0/1	n-butyl chloride	40.8	--	50	583	308	1.89	VM(t)	410
6/94 mole		40.8	--	59	616	308	2.00	VM(g)	410
48/52 mole		40.8	--	95	728	305	2.39	VM(g)	410
90/10 mole		40.8	--	89	707	302	2.34	VM(g)	410
1/0		40.8	--	80	685	302	2.27	VM(g)	410
Poly(trifluoro-nitrosomethane-co-tetrafluoro-ethylene)		35	--	38	510±25	304	1.68±0.08	VM(t)	2(452)

References page IV-64

Polymer	Solvent	Temp. [°C]	$S_{oz}/M_w^{1/2} \times 10^3$ or a_p [Å]	$K_o \times 10^5$ [dℓ/g]	$r_o/M^{1/2} \times 10^3$ [Å]	$r_{of}/M^{1/2} \times 10^3$ [Å]	r_o/r_{of}	Method	Ref.*
6 – POLYOXIDES									
Poly(ethylene oxide)	various solvents	~20	--	110±10	750±30	541	1.38±0.06	VM(g)	2(285, 286)
	aqueous K_2SO_4 (0.45M)	35	--	130	790	541	1.46	VM(t)	291
	aqueous $MgSO_4$ (0.39M)	45	--	100	720	541	1.33	VM(t)	291
Polyformaldehyde	phenol	90	--	280	1000	522	1.9±0.1	VM(g)	421
	hexafluoroacetone hydrate	25	--	380	1100	522	2.1±0.2	VM(g)	456
Poly(propylene oxide)	benzene; methanol	25	--	115±10	750±25	472	1.59±0.05	VM(g)	2(294)
	toluene/isooctane (5/7 vol)	39.5	--	107.5	735	472	1.56	VM(t)	294
Poly(tetra-hydrofuran)	benzene	30	--	330±20	1050±30	556	1.89±0.05	VM(g)	295
	ethyl acetate (EA)	33	--	180±20	860±30	556	1.55±0.05	VM(g)	295
	EA/hexane (227/77.3 wt)	31.8	--	210±10	900±20	556	1.62±0.03	VM(t)	295
7 – POLYESTERS									
Poly(cis-1,4-cyclohexylene sebacate)	chloroform	20	--	140±20	800±30	495	1.62±0.05	VM(g)	2(298)
Poly(trans-1,4-cyclohexylene sebacate)	chloroform	20	--	160±20	840±30	633	1.33±0.05	VM(g)	2(298)
Poly(decamethylene adipate)	chlorobenzene	25	--	100±10	720±25	540	1.33±0.05	VM(g)	2(299)

Polymer	Solvent	Temp. [°C]	$S_{oz} M_w^{1/2} \times 10^3$ or $[A]_a^p$ / $K_o \times 10^5$ [dl/g]	$r_o/M^{1/2} \times 10^3$ [A]	$r_{of}/M^{1/2} \times 10^3$ [A]	r_o/r_{of}	Method	Ref.*
Poly(decamethylene sebacate)		25	-- / 220±30	900±50	549	1.65±0.10	VM(g)	446
Poly(ethylene terephthalate)	phenol/tetrachloroethane (1/1 vol)	25	-- / 160±15	840±25	687	1.22±0.03	VM(g)	2(302)
Poly(hexadeca-methylene sebacate)	chloroform	20	-- / 270±40	1000±50	555	1.80±0.10	VM(g)	2(304)
Poly(hexamethylene acetylene-di-carboxylate)	benzene; chloroform	20	-- / 180±20	870±30	627	1.39±0.05	VM(g)	2(305)
Poly(hexamethylene α,α'-dibutyl-sebacate)	benzene	20	-- / 155±25	835±70	457	1.82±0.15	VM(g)	2(307)
Poly(hexamethylene fumarate)	chloroform	20-50	-- / 180±20	870±30	592	1.47±0.05	VM(g)	2(308)
Poly(hexamethylene maleate)	benzene; tetrahydrofuran; chloroform	20-50	-- / 135±15	790±30	510	1.55±0.05	VM(g)	2(308)
Poly(hexamethylene sebacate)	benzene; chloroform	20	-- / 215±60	910±100	540	1.70±0.17	VM(g)	2(304, 307)
Poly(hexamethylene succinate)	benzene; chloroform; tetrahydrofuran	20-60	-- / 165±30	850±60	522	1.62±0.14	VM(g)	2(308)
Poly(4,4'-iso-propylidene-diphenylene carbonate)	methylene chloride; tetrahydrofuran	25	-- / 180±20	880±40	796	1.10±0.05	VM(g)	2(297)
Poly(octamethylene cis-hexahydro-terephthalate)	chloroform	20	-- / 140±20	800±30	495	1.62±0.05	VM(g)	2(298)

References page IV-64

Polymer	Solvent	Temp. [°C]	$\dfrac{S_{oz}/M_w^{\frac{1}{2}}}{\text{x }10^3}$ or a_p [A]	$K_o \times 10^5$ [dl/g]	$r_o/M^{\frac{1}{2}} \times 10^3$ [A]	$r_{of}/M^{\frac{1}{2}} \times 10^3$	r_o/r_{of}	Method	Ref.*
Poly(octamethylene trans-hexahydro-terephthalate)	chloroform	20	--	160±20	840±30	633	1.33±0.05	VM(g)	2(298)
Poly(ω-oxy-undecanoate)	chloroform	20	--	185±60	880±100	550	1.60±0.16	VM(g)	2(304, 309)
8 - POLYAMIDES									
Poly(ε-caprolactam)	conc. H_2SO_4	25	--	190±10	890±20	545	1.63±0.04	VM(g)	2(313)
Poly(hexamethylene adipamide)	aqueous HCOOH (90% vol)	25	--	190±20	890±40	545	1.63±0.08	VM(g)	2(314, 315)
	aqueous HCOOH (90% vol) KCl (2.3M)	25	--	253	1010	545	1.85	VM(t)	326
	aqueous HCOOH (90% vol) KCl (2.3M)	25	--	192	900	545	1.65	VM(t)	326a

9 - POLYSACCHARIDES

Polymer	Solvent	Temp. [°C]	$S_{oz}/M^{1/2} \times 10^3$ or a_p [A]	$K_o \times 10^5$ [dℓ/g]	$r_o/M^{1/2} \times 10^3$ [A]	$r_{of}/M^{1/2} \times 10^3$ [A]	r_o/r_{of}	Method	Ref.*
Amylose	dimethyl sulfoxide; ethylene-diamine	25	--	56±12	600±50	335	1.79±0.15	VM(g)	2(327)
	aqueous KCl (0.33M); DMS	25	--	110±5	750±25	335	2.24±0.08	VM(t=g)	2(328)
	aqueous KCl (0.5M)	25	--	61	625	335	1.87	VM(t)	331
Amylose triacetate	chloroform; nitromethane	30	--	47±10	580±60	250	2.32±0.24	VM(g)	2(332)
		30	--	48	580	250	2.32	VM(g)	448
		30	--		800±15	250	3.2±0.06	VM(g)	449
Amylose tri-carbanilate	acetone; dioxane; pyridine	20	--	27±5	470±30	187	2.51±0.16	VM(g)	2(334)
Cellulose	cupriethylenediamine	25	--	180±80	900±150	620	1.45±0.25	VM(g)	2(339)
Cellulose triacetate	acetone; chloroform; o-cresol	25-30	--	108±10	750±30	465	1.61±0.07	VM(g)	2(343,344)
Cellulose tributyrate	butanone	30	--	97±15	730±40	408	1.79±0.10	VM(g)	2(345)
	dodecane/tetralin (75/25 vol)	130	--	82	690	408	1.69	VM(t)	345
Cellulose tricaproate	dimethylformamide	~40	--	240	980	370	2.65	VM(t)	346
Cellulose tricaprylate	toluene	30	--	127±15	800±40	340	2.35±0.12	VM(g)	2(345)
	dimethylformamide	140	--	113	770	340	2.27	VM(t)	345
Cellulose carbanilate	acetone; dioxane; pyridine	20	--	130±30	810±70	345	2.34±0.20	VM(g)	2(334)
Cellulose trinitrate	acetone; ethyl acetate	~25	--	130±30	810±50	453	1.77±0.11	VM(g)	2(337,339,347,348)
	acetone	25	360	--	720	458	1.57	LS(g)	2(348)
		22	26±1	--	930±15	458	2.03±0.03	XS(g)	439

References page IV-64

Polymer	Solvent	Temp. [°C]	$S_{oz}/M_w^{1/2}$ x 10^3 or a_p [A]	K_o x 10^5 [dl/g]	$r_o/M^{1/2}$ x 10^3 [A]	$r_{of}/M^{1/2}$ x 10^3	r_o/r_{of}	Method	Ref.*
Cellulose trinitrate (Cont'd.)									
cotton	acetone	~20	40-70	--	1180-1590	458	2.58-3.46	XS(g)	450
wood pulp	acetone	~20	22-28	--	850-975	458	1.85-2.12	XS(g)	450
Ethyl cellulose	methanol	25	--	232±10	970±20	520	1.87±0.03	VM(g)	2(356)
Ethyl hydroxyethyl cellulose	water	~25	--	550±80	1300±50	545	2.38±0.09	VM(g)	2(357)
Methyl cellulose	water	25	--	920±100	1500±60	581	2.58±0.10	VM(g)	2(359)
10 - POLYPEPTIDES									
Gelatin	acetate buffer;	~35	--	40±10	540±50	404	1.34±0.12	VM(g)	2(365, 366,389)
Poly(γ-benzyl-L-glutamate)	dichloroacetic acid	25	--	58±5	600±20	259	2.32±0.08	VM(g)	2(368)
Poly(γ-benzyl-DL-glutamate)	dichloroacetic acid; dimethyl-formamide	25	--	58±5	600±20	259	2.32±0.08	VM(g)	2(369)
Poly(DL-proline)	water	25	--	~25	~570	390	~1.5	V(~t)	2(391)
Poly(sarcosine)	water	20	--	50±20	570±90	455	1.25±0.20	VN(g)	2(370)

Polymer	Solvent	Temp. [°C]	$\dfrac{S_{oz}}{M_w^{1/2}} \times 10^3$ or a_P [A]	$K_o \times 10^5$ [dl/g]	$r_o/M^{1/2} \times 10^3$ [A]	$r_{of}/M^{1/2} \times 10^3$ [A]	r_o/r_{of}	Method	Ref.*
11 - POLYNUCLEOTIDES									
Deoxyribonucleic acid									
denatured	phosphate buffer	20	--	115±20	760±50	330	2.30±0.15	VM(g)	2(381)
native		25	--	6000	2800	--	--	SM	2
Poly(riboadenylic acid)									
neutral pH	citrate buffer	25	--	115±20	760±50	32C	2.38±0.15	VM(g)	2(382)
low pH	citrate buffer	25	--	23±5	440±50	--	--	VM(g)	2(382)
12 - SEMIORGANIC AND INORGANIC POLYMERS									
Poly(dimethyl siloxane)	butanone; toluene	~25	--	80±5	670±20	482	1.39±0.05	VM(≈,g)	2(396, 424)
	various theta solvents	2-90	266±10	--	612±13	482	1.27±0.03	LS(t)	413
	$C_8F_{18}/C_2Cl_4F_2$ (33/67 wt)	22.5	--	106	740	482	1.54	VM(t)	425
	ethyl iodide	2	--	70	640	482	1.33	VM(t)	413
	bromocyclohexane (BCH)	29	--	74	655	482	1.36	VM(t)	413
	BCH/phenetole (6/7 vol)	36	--	75	660	482	1.37	VM(t)	413
	chlorobenzene/dimethyl phthalate (45/6 vol)	57.5	--	76	660	482	1.37	VM(t)	413
	bromobenzene	78.5	--	76	660	482	1.37	VM(t)	413
	phenetole	89.5	--	73	650	432	1.35	VM(t)	413
Poly(phosphate)	aqueous CsCl (0.96M)	30					3.93	LS(t)	451
	aqueous LiCl (2.9M)	30					2.25	LS(t)	451
	aqueous NaCl (0.52M)	30					2.79	LS(t)	451
Poly(metaphosphate)	aqueous NaBr (0.35-0.415M)	25	--	50±3	560±20	370	1.51±0.04	VM(t,g)	2(402)

References page IV-64

E.   REFERENCES

1. P. J. Flory, "Principles of Polymer Chemistry," Cornell University Press, Ithaca, New York, 1953.
2. M. Kurata and W. H. Stockmayer, Fortschr. Hochpolymer Forsch. $\underline{3}$, 196 (1963).
3. W. H. Stockmayer and M. Fixman, J. Polymer Sci. $\underline{C1}$, 137 (1963).
4. G. Meyerhoff, Fortschr. Hochpolymer, Forsch. $\underline{3}$, 59 (1961).
5. A. Peterlin, Viskosität und Form. In "Die Physik der Hochpolymeren," edited by H. A. Stuart, Vol. II. Springer-Verlag, Berlin, 1953.
6. H.-G. Elias, Kunststoffe-Plastics, 4,1 (1961).
7. S. Krause, "Dilute Solution Properties of Acrylic and Methacrylic Polymers," Part I, Revision 1 Rohm & Haas Co., Philadelphia, Pennsylvania, Feb. 1961.
7a. O. P. Ptitsyn, Vysokomolekul. Soedin. $\underline{3}$, 1673 (1963).
7b. A. Peterlin, J. Polymer Sci. $\underline{47}$, 403 (1960).
7c. S. Heine, O. Kratky, G. Porod, and P. J. Schmitz, Makromol. Chem. $\underline{44\text{-}46}$, 682 (1961); S. Heine, ibid. $\underline{48}$, 205 (1961); S. Heine, O. Kratky and J. Roppert, ibid. $\underline{56}$, 150 (1962).
8. W. R. Krigbaum, J. E. Kurz, and P. Smith, J. Phys. Chem. $\underline{65}$, 1984 (1961).
9. R. Endo, K. Iimura, and M. Takeda, Bull. Chem. Soc. Japan, $\underline{37}$, 950 (1964).
10. R. W. Wheatcraft, cited in H. Wesslau, Makromol. Chem. $\underline{20}$, 111 (1956).
11. E. Duch and L. Küchler, Z. Elektrochem. $\underline{60}$, 218 (1956).
12. J. T. Atkins, L. T. Muus, C. W. Smith, and E. T. Pieski, J. Am. Chem. Soc. $\underline{79}$, 5089 (1957).
13. A. Kotera, T. Saito, K. Takamizawa, and Y. Miyazawa, Rept. Progr. Polymer Phys. Japan, $\underline{3}$, 58 (1960).
14. P. S. Francis, R. Cooke, Jr., and J. H. Elliott, J. Polymer Sci. $\underline{31}$, 453 (1957).
15. P. M. Henry, J. Polymer Sci. $\underline{36}$, 3 (1959).
16. R. Chiang, J. Polymer Sci. $\underline{36}$, 91 (1959); J. Am. Chem. Soc. in press.
17. Q. A. Trementozzi, J. Polymer Sci. $\underline{36}$, 113 (1959).
18. H. Wesslau, Makromol. Chem. $\underline{26}$, 96 (1958).
19. H. S. Kaufmann and E. K. Walsh, J. Polymer Sci. $\underline{26}$, 124 (L) (1957).
20. L. H. Tung, J. Polymer Sci. $\underline{24}$, 333 (1957). See also, L. H. Tung, ibid. $\underline{36}$, 287 (1959).
21. C. J. Stacy and R. L. Arnett, J. Polymer Sci. $\underline{A2}$, 167 (1964).
22. W. R. Krigbaum and Q. A. Trementozzi, J. Polymer Sci. $\underline{28}$, 295 (1958).
23. W. F. Busse and R. Longworth, J. Polymer Sci. $\underline{58}$, 49 (1962).
24. K. Überreiter, H.-J. Orthman, and S. Sorge, Makromol. Chem. $\underline{8}$, 21 (1952).
25. I. Harris, J. Polymer Sci. $\underline{8}$, 353 (1952).
26. Q. A. Trementozzi, J. Polymer Sci. $\underline{23}$, 887 (1957).
27. K. H. Meyer and A. van der Wyk, Helv. Chim. Acta, $\underline{18}$, 1067 (1935).
28. E. K. Walsh, and H. S. Kaufman, J. Polymer Sci. $\underline{26}$, 1 (1957).
29. J. B. Kinsinger and R. E. Hughes, J. Phys. Chem. $\underline{63}$, 2002 (1959).
30. F. Danusso and G. Moraglio, Rend. Accad. Naz. Lincei. $\underline{25}$, 509 (1958).
31. J. B. Kinsinger and R. E. Hughes, J. Phys. Chem. $\underline{67}$, 1922 (1963).
32. F. Danusso and G. Moraglio, Makromol. Chem. $\underline{28}$, 250 (1958).
33. L. Westerman, J. Polymer Sci. $\underline{A1}$, 411 (1963).
34. H. J. L. Schuurmans and R. A. Mendelson, Unpublished work; cited in E. Kohn, H. J. L. Schuurmans, J. V. Cavender, and R. A. Mendelson, J. Polymer Sci. $\underline{58}$, 681 (1962).
35. A. Kotera, K. Takamizawa, T. Kamata, and H. Kawaguchi, Rept. Progr. Polymer Phys. Japan, $\underline{4}$, 131 (1961).
36. P. Parrini, F. Sebastiano, and G. Messina, Makromol. Chem. $\underline{38}$, 27 (1960).
37. R. Chiang, J. Polymer Sci. $\underline{28}$, 235 (L) (1958).
38. G. Ciampa, Chim. Ind. (Milan) $\underline{38}$, 298 (1956).
39. F. Ang and H. Mark, Monatsh. Chem. $\underline{88}$, 427 (1957).
40. J. L. Jungnickel and F. T. Weiss, J. Polymer Sci. $\underline{49}$, 437 (1961).
41. D. L. Flowers, W. A. Hewett, and R. D. Mullineaux, J. Polymer Sci. $\underline{A2}$, 2305 (1964).
42. T. G. Fox and P. J. Flory, J. Am. Chem. Soc. $\underline{73}$, 1909 (1951).
43. T. G. Fox and P. J. Flory, J. Phys. Colloid Chem. $\underline{53}$, 197 (1949).
44. C. E. H. Bawn, E. S. Hill, and M. A. Wajid, Trans. Faraday Soc. $\underline{52}$, 1651 (1956).
45. W. R. Krigbaum and P. J. Flory, J. Am. Chem. Soc. $\underline{75}$, 1775 (1953).
46. W. R. Krigbaum and P. J. Flory, J. Polymer Sci. $\underline{11}$, 37 (1953).
47. P. J. Flory, J. Am. Chem. Soc. $\underline{65}$, 372 (1943).
48. V. V. Korshak, S. L. Sosin, and V. P. Alekseeva, J. Polymer Sci. $\underline{52}$, 213 (1961).
49. S. S. Stivala, R. J. Valles, and D. W. Levi, J. Appl. Polymer Sci. $\underline{7}$, 97 (1963).
50. M. Cantow, G. Meyerhoff, and G. V. Schulz, Makromol. Chem. $\underline{49}$, 1 (1961).
51. G. Meyerhoff, Z. Physik. Chem. N.F. $\underline{4}$, 335 (1955).
52. D. C. Pepper, J. Polymer Sci. $\underline{7}$, 347 (1951). See also D. C. Pepper, Proc. Roy. Dublin Soc. $\underline{25}$, 239 (1951).
53. G. S. Misra, R. C. Rastogi, and V. P. Gupta, Makromol. Chem. $\underline{50}$, 72 (1961).

54. W. R. Krigbaum and P. J. Flory, J. Polymer Sci. 11, 37 (1953).
55. T. A. Orofino and F. Wenger, J. Phys. Chem. 67, 566 (1963).
56. C. E. H. Bawn, R. F. J. Freeman, and A. R. Kamaliddin, Trans. Faraday Soc. 46, 1107 (1950).
57. C. Rossi, Chimica delle Macromolecole (Sept. 1961); Consiglio Nazionalle delle Ricerche, Roma, (1963) p. 153.
58. P. Outer, C. I. Carr, and B. H. Zimm, J. Chem. Phys. 18, 830 (1950).
59. J. Oth and V. Desreux, Bull. Soc. Chim. Belges, 63, 285 (1954).
60. T. Oyama, K. Kawahara, and M. Ueda, Nippon Kagaku Zasshi (J. Chem. Soc. Japan, Pure Chem. Sec.), 79, 727 (1958).
61. U. Bianchi, V. Magnasco, and C. Rossi, Ric. Sci. 58, 1412 (1958).
62. U. Bianchi, V. Magnasco, and C. Rossi, Chim. Ind. (Milan), 40, 263 (1958); see also, Ref. 57.
63. H. Utiyama, Dissertation, Kyoto Univ. Kyoto, Japan, Nov. 1962.
64. R. Endo and M. Takeda, J. Polymer Sci. 56, 28 (1962).
65. L. Utracki and R. Simha, J. Phys. Chem. 67, 1052 (1963).
66. T. Homma, K. Kawahara, H. Jujita, and M. Ueda, Makromol. Chem. 67, 132 (1963).
67. H. J. Cantow, Makromol. Chem. 30, 169 (1959).
68. H. Inagaki, T. Matsuo, M. Fujii, and H. Suzuki, private communication.
69. T. G. Fox and P. J. Flory, J. Am. Chem. Soc. 73, 1915 (1951).
70. E. T. Dimitru and L. H. Cragg, unpublished work; cited in ref. 1, p. 615, Table XXVII.
71. R. H. Ewart, H. C. Tingey, and M. Wales, unpublished work, cited in W. V. Smith, J. Am. Chem. Soc. 68, 2063 (1946).
72. C. H. Bamford and M. J. S. Dewar, Proc. Roy, Soc. London, A192, 329 (1948).
73. H. Marzolph and G. V. Schulz, Makromol. Chem. 13, 120 (1954).
74. S. N. Chinai, P. C. Scherer, C. W. Bondurat, and D. W. Levi, J. Polymer Sci. 22, 527 (1956).
75. F. Danusso and G. Moraglio, J. Polymer Sci. 24, 161 (1957).
76. C. Rossi, U. Bianchi, and E. Bianchi, Makromol. Chem. 41, 31 (1960).
77. T. Altares, D. P. Wyman, and V. R. Allen, J. Polymer Sci. A2, 4533 (1964).
78. M. Morton, T. E. Helminiak, S. D. Gadkary, and F. Bueche, J. Polymer Sci. 57, 471 (1962).
79. G. Meyerhoff, Z. Physik. Chem. 23, 100 (1960).
80. H. W. McCormick, J. Polymer Sci. 36, 341 (1959).
81. R. N. Mukherjea and P. Remmp, J. Chim. Phys. 56, 94 (1959).
82. J. M. G. Cowie, D. J. Worsfold, and S. Bywater, Trans. Faraday Soc. 57, 537 (1961).
83. F. Ang, J. Polymer Sci. 25, 126 (1957).
84. G. Natta, F. Danusso, and G. Moraglio, Makromol. Chem. 20, 37 (1956).
85. L. Trossarelli, E. Campi, and G. Saini, J. Polymer Sci. 35, 205 (1959).
86. C. D. Thurmond and B. H. Zimm, J. Polymer Sci. 8, 477 (1952).
87. W. Kern and D. Brawn, Makromol. Chem. 27, 23 (1958).
88. A. Kotera, T. Saito, H. Matsuda, and R. Kamata, Rept. Progr. Polymer Phys. Japan, 3, 51 (1960).
89. G. Greber, J. Tölle, and W. Burchard, Makromol. Chem. 71, 47 (1964).
90. J. E. Davis, Dissertation, Mass. Inst. Tech. (Cambridge, Mass., U.S.A., May 1960).
91. E. F. Frisman and L. F. Shalaeva, Dokl. Akad. Nauk S.S.S.R. 101, 907 (1955).
92. V. E. Eskin and K. Z. Gumargalieva, Vysokomolekul. Soedin., 2, 265 (1960).
93. V. E. Eskin and L. N. Andreeva, Vysokomolekul. Soedin., 3, 435 (1961).
94. C. S. H. Chen and R. F. Stamm, J. Polymer Sci. 58, 369 (1962).
95. D. Braun, T.-O. Ahn, and W. Kern, Makromol. Chem. 53, 154 (1962).
96. S. Okamura, T. Higashimura and Y. Imanishi, Kobunshi Kagaku (Chem. High Polymers, Tokyo), 16, 244 (1959).
97. L. A. Wall; reported in the paper by A. M. Kotliar, J. Appl. Polymer Sci. 2, 134 (1959).
98. H. W. McCormick, J. Polymer Sci. 41, 327 (1959).
99. A. F. Sirianni, D. J. Worsfold and S. Bywater, Trans. Faraday Soc. 55, 2124 (1959).
100. M. Kato, T. Nakagawa, H. Akamatu, Bull. Chem. Soc., 33, 322 (1960).
101. P. J. Flory and F. Leutner, J. Polymer Sci. 3, 880 (1948).
102. K. Dialer, K. Vogler, and F. Patat, Helv. Chim. Acta, 35 869 (1952).
103. H. A. Dieu, J. Polymer Sci. 12, 417 (1954).
104. G. Levy and H. Frank, J. Polymer Sci. 17, 247 (1955).
105. A. Nakajima and K. Furutate, Kobunshi Kagaku (Chem. High Polymers, Tokyo), 6, 460 (1949).
106. T. Matsuo and H. Inagaki, Makromol. Chem. 55, 151 (1962).
107. M. Matsumoto and K. Imai, J. Polymer Sci. 24, 125 (1957).

108. W. R. Moore and M. Murphy, J. Polymer Sci. 56, 519 (1962).
109. P. C. Scherer, A. Tanenbaum, and D. W. Levi, J. Polymer Sci. 43, 531 (1960).
110. G. Saini, L. Maldifassi, and L. Trossarelli, Ann. Chim. (Rome) 44, 1954; cited in H.-G. Elias, Kunststoffe, 4, 8 (1961).
111. G. S. Misra and V. P. Gupta, Makromol. Chem. 71, 110 (1964).
112. R. H. Wagner, J. Polymer Sci. 2, 21 (1947).
113. S. N. Chinai, P. C. Scherer, and D. W. Levi, J. Polymer Sci. 17, 117 (1955).
114. K. Z. Fattakhov, E. S. Pisarenko, and L. N. Verkotina, Kolloidn. Zh. 18, 101 (1956).
115. M. Matsumoto and Y. Ohyanagi, J. Polymer Sci. 46, 441 (1960).
116. M. Ueda and K. Kajitani, private communication.
117. Bevak, Dissertation, Mass. Inst. Tech., Cambridge, Mass., U.S.A., 1955.
118. V. Kalpagam and R. Rao, J. Polymer Sci. A1, 233 (1963).
119. M. R. Rao, and V. Kalpagam, J. Polymer Sci. 49, 514 (1961).
120. A. Nakajima, Kobunshi Kagaku,(Chem. High Polymers, Tokyo), 11, 142 (1954).
121. V. V. Varadiah, J. Polymer Sci. 19, 477 (1956).
122. V. N. Tsvetkov and S. Ya Kotlyar, J. Phys. Chem. (USSR) 30, 1100 (1956).
123. G. C. Berry, L. M. Hobbs, and V. C. Long, Polymer 5, 31 (1964).
124. A. R. Shultz, J. Am. Chem. Soc. 76, 3423 (1954).
125. R. O. Howard, Dissertation, Mass. Inst. Tech., Cambridge, Mass., U.S.A., Nov. 1952.
126. H.-G. Elias and F. Patat, Makromol. Chem. 25, 13 (1957).
127. M. Matsumoto and Y. Ohyanagi, J. Polymer Sci. 50, S1 (1961). See also Ref. 115.
128. I. Sakurada, Y. Sakaguchi, and S. Kokuryo, Kobunshi Kagaku,(Chem. High Polymers, Tokyo), 17, 227 (1960).
129. C. J. Kurian and M. S. Muthana, Makromol. Chem. 29, 1 (1959).
130. K. Fujii, S. Imoto, J. Ukida, and M. Matsumoto, Kobunshi Kagaku,(Chem. High Polymers, Tokyo), 19, 210, 581 (1962).
131. H. Hopff and J. Dohany, Makromol. Chem. 69, 131 (1963).
132. F. Patat and K. Vogler, Helv. Chim. Acta 35, 128 (1952).
133. J. A. Manson and G. J. Arquette, Makromol. Chem. 37, 187 (1960).
134. J. G. Fee, W. S. Port and L. P. Witnauer, J. Polymer Sci., 33, 95 (1958).
135. A. C. Ciferri, M. Kryszewski, and G. Weil, J. Polymer Sci. 27, 167 (1958).
136. J. W. Breitenbach, E. L. Forster, and A. J. Renner, Kolloid-Z, 127, 1 (1952).
137. C. Bier and H. Krämer, Makromol. Chem. 18-19, 151 (1955).
138. F. Danusso, G. Moraglio, and S. Cazzera, Chim. Ind (Milan) 36, 883 (1954).
139. G. Ciampa and H. Schwindt, Makromol. Chem. 21, 169 (1954).
140. Z. Mencik, Collection. Czech. Chem. Commun. 21, 517 (1956).
141. H. Batzer and A. Nisch, Makromol. Chem. 22, 131 (1957).
142. A. Takahashi, M. Obara, and I. Kagawa, Kogyo Kagaku Zasshi, (J. Chem. Soc. Japan, Ind. Chem. Sec.), 66, 960 (1963).
143. M. Freeman and P. P. Manning, J. Polymer Sci. A2, 2017 (1964).
144. T. Kobayashi, Bull Chem. Soc. Japan, 35, 726 (1962).
145. V. E. Eskin and O. Z. Korotkina, Vysokomolekul. Soedin. 1, 1580 (1959).
146. V. E. Eskin and O. Z. Korotkina, Vysokomolekul. Soedin. 2, 272 (1960).
147. S. Arichi, Bull. Chem. Soc. Japan, in press.
148. D. O. Jordan, A. R. Mathieson, and M. R. Porter, J. Polymer Sci. 21, 473 (1956).
149. J. B. Berkowitz, M. Yamin, and R. M. Fuoss, J. Polymer Sci., 28, 69 (1958).
150. A. G. Boyes and U. P. Strauss, J. Polymer Sci. 22, 463 (1956).
151. H. Sato and T. Yamamoto, Nippon Kagaku Zasshi, (J. Chem. Soc. Japan, Pure Chem. Sec.), 80, 1393 (1959).
152. M. Miura and Y. Kubota, Bull. Chem. Soc. Japan, in press.
153. G. B. Levy and H. P. Frank, J. Polymer Sci. 17, 247 (1955).
154. K. Dialer and K. Vogler, Makromol. Chem. 6, 191 (1951).
155. G. B. Levy and H. P. Frank, J. Polymer Sci. 10, 371 (1953).
156. L. W. Miller and F. A. Hamm, J. Phys. Chem. 57, 110 (1953).
157. W. Scholtan, Makromol. Chem. 7, 209 (1951).
158. L. C. Cerney, T. E. Helminiak, and J. F. Meier, J. Polymer Sci. 44, 539 (1960).
159. K. Dialer and R. Kerber, Makromol. Chem. 17, 56 (1955).
160. Y. Sakaguchi, J. Nishino, and K. Tsugawa, Kobunshi Kagaku,(Chem. High Polymer Tokyo), 20, 661 (1963).
161. W. R. Moore and R. J. Hutchinson, Nature, 200, 1097 (1963).
162. H. Inagaki and J. Nakazawa, private communication.
163. M. Sata, Y. Koshiishi, and M. Asahina, J. Polymer Sci. B1, 233 (1963).
164. H.-G. Elias, Makromol. Chem. 50, 1 (1961).
165. H. Eisenberg and D. Woodside, J. Chem. Phys. 36, 1844 (1962).
165a. A. Ciferri and M. Lauretti, Ann. Chim. (Rome), 48, 198 (1958).
165b. M. Litt and F. R. Eirich, J. Polymer Sci. 45, 379 (1960).
166. S. Newman, W. R. Krigbaum, C. Laugier, and P. J. Flory, J. Polymer Sci. 14, 451 (1954).

167. A. Takahashi, N. Hayashi, and I. Kagawa, Kogyo Kagaku Zasshi, (J. Chem. Soc. Japan, Ind. Chem. Sec.), 60, 1059 (1957). See also Ref. 172
168. A. Takahashi, S. Yamori, and I. Kagawa, Nippon Kagaku Zasshi,(J. Chem. Soc. Japan, Pure Chem. Sec.), 83, 11 (1962).
169. A. Takahashi, T. Kamei, and I. Kagawa, Nippon Kagaku Zasshi, (J. Chem. Soc. Japan, Pure Chem. Sec.), 83, 14 (1962).
170. A. Takahashi and M. Nagasawa, J. Am. Chem. Soc. 86, 543 (1964).
171. A. Soda and I. Kagawa, Nippon Kagaku Zasshi,(J. Chem. Soc. Japan, Pure Chem. Sec.), 83, 412 (1962).
172. H. Ito, S. Shimizu, and S. Suzuki, Kogyo Kagaku Zasshi, (J. Chem. Soc., Japan, Ind. Chem. Sec.), 59, 930 (1956).
173. G. Saini and L. Trossarelli, Atti Accad. Sci. Torino, Classe Sci. Fis., Mat. Nat. 90, 410 (1955-56), cf. Ref. 7.
174. H. Sumitomo and Y. Hachihama, Kobunshi Kagaku, (Chem. High Polymers, Tokyo), 10, 544 (1953). See also, Y. Hachihama and H. Sumitomo, Technol. Rept. Osaka Univ. 3, 385 (1953).
175. H. Sumitomo and Y. Hachihama, Kobunshi Kagaku, (Chem. High Polymers, Tokyo), 12, 479 (1955). See also, Y. Hachihama and H. Sumitomo, Technol. Rept. Osaka Univ. 5, 485 (1956).
176. I. G. Soboleva, N. V. Makletsova, and S. S. Medvedev, Dokl. Akad. Nauk. S. S. S. R. 94, 289 (1954).
177. F. S. Cohn, T. A. Orofino, and I. L. Scogna, unpublished work; cited in Ref. 7.
178. S. Krause, unpublished work; cited in Ref. 7.
179. H. Staudinger and H. Warth, Z. Prakt. Chem. 155, 261 (1940).
180. L. Trossareli and G. Saini, Atti. Accad. Sci. Torino, Classe Sci. Fis., Mat. Nat. 90, 419 (1955-56) cited in Ref. 7.
181. L. Trossareli and G. Saini, Atti. Accad. Sci. Torino, Classe Sci. Fis., Mat. Nat. 90, 431 (1955-56); cited in Ref. 7.
182. G. M. Guzman, Anales Real Soc. Espan. Fis Quim. (Madrid), 52B, 377 (1956); cited in Ref. 7.
183. Rohm and Haas, old data; reported in Ref. 7.
184. J. N. Sen, S. R. Chatterjee, and S. R. Palit, J. Sci. Ind. Res. (India), 11B, 90 (1952); cited in Ref. 7.
185. N. T. Srinivasan and M. Santappa, Makromol Chem. 27, 61 (1958).
186. G. B. Rathmann and F. A. Bovey, J. Polymer Sci. 15, 544 (1955).
187. N. M. Wiederhorn and A. R. Brown, J. Polymer Sci. 8, 651 (1952).
188. A. Katchalsky and H. Eisenberg, J. Polymer Sci. 6, 145 (1951).
189. R. Arnold and S. R. Caplan, Trans. Faraday Soc. 51, 857 (1955).
190. E. S. Cohn, unpublished work; cited in Ref. 7.
191. R. Van Leemput and R. Stein, J. Polymer Sci. A1, 985 (1963). K values are given for monodisperse polymers.
192. Rohm and Haas, old data; reported in Ref. 7.
193. S. N. Chinai and R. A. Guzzi, J. Polymer Sci. 21, 417 (1956).
194. A. S. Nair and M. S. Muthana, Makromol. Chem. 47, 114 (1961).
195. V. N. Tsvetkov and S. I. Klenin, Zh. Tekhn. Fiz. 29, 1393 (1959).
196. Z. Menčik, Chem. Listy, 46, 407 (1952).
197. S. N. Chinai and R. J. Valles, J. Polymer Sci. 39, 363 (1959).
198. V. N. Tsvetkov and O. V. Kalisov, Zh. Fiz. Khim. 33, 710 (1959).
199. O. V. Kalisov and I. N. Shtennikova, Vysokomolekul. Soedin. 1, 842 (1959).
200. V. N. Tsvetkov and S. I. Klenin, J. Polymer Sci. 30, 187 (1958).
201. J.-Y. Chieng and M.-H. Shih, Z. Physik. Chem. 207, 60 (1957).
202. E. S. Cohn, I. L. Scogna, and T. A. Orofino, unpublished work; cited in Ref. 7.
203. S. N. Chinai and R. J. Samuels, J. Polymer Sci. 19, 463 (1956).
204. F. R. Didot, S. N. Chinai, and D. W. Levi, J. Polymer Sci. 43, 557 (1960).
205. S. N. Chinai, J. Polymer Sci. 25, 413 (1957).
206. H. T. Lee and D. W. Levi, J. Polymer Sci. 47, 449 (1960).
207. S. N. Chinai and R. A. Guzzi, J. Polymer Sci. 41, 475 (1959).
208. G. Meyerhoff and G. V. Schulz, Makromol. Chem. 7, 249 (1952).
209. J. Bischoff and V. Desreux, Bull. Soc. Chim. Belges, 61, 10 (1952).
210. G. V. Schulz and G. Meyerhoff, Z. Elektrochem. 56, 904 (1952).
211. G. V. Schulz, H.-J. Cantow, and G. Meyerhoff, J. Polymer Sci. 10, 79 (1953).
212. H.-J. Cantow and G. V. Schulz, Z. Physik. Chem. (N.F.) 2, 117 (1954); see also H.-J. Cantow and G. V. Schulz, ibid. 1, 365 (1954).
213. S. N. Chinai, J. D. Matlack, A. L. Resnick, and R. J. Samuels, J. Polymer Sci. 17, 391 (1955).
214. F. W. Billmeyer, Jr., and C. B. de Than, J. Am. Chem. Soc. 77, 4763 (1955).
215. S. L. Kapur, J. Sci. Ind. Res. (India), 15B, 239 (1956).
216. W. R. Moore and R. J. Fort, J. Polymer Sci. A1, 929 (1963).
217. E. Cohn-Ginsberg, T. G. Fox, and H. F. Mason, Polymer 3, 97 (1962).
218. T. G. Fox, H. F. Mason, and E. S. Cohn, unpublished work; cited in Ref. 7.

219. E. S. Cohn and T. G. Fox, unpublished work; cited in Ref. 7.
220. A. F. V. Eriksson, Acta Chem. Scand. 7, 623 (1953).
221. J. H. Baxendale, S. Bywater, and M. G. Evans, J. Polymer Sci. 1, 237 (1946).
222. J.-Y. Chien, L.-H. Shin, and K.-I. Shin, Acta Chim. Sinica, 23, 215 (1957). cf. Ref. 7.
223. K. G. Schoen and G. V. Schulz, Z. Physik. Chem. (N.F.), 2, 197 (1954).
224. T. G. Fox, J. B. Kinsinger, H. F. Mason, and E. M. Schuele, Polymer 3, 71 (1962).
225. H. Inagaki and S. Kawai, Makromol. Chem. 79, 42 (1964). See also, G. V. Schulz and R. Kirste, Z. Physik. Chem. (N.F.) 30, 171 (1961).
226. G. V. Schulz and A. Dinglinger, Z. Prakt. Chem. 158, 137 (1941).
227. H. J. Cantow, J. Pouget, and C. Wippler, Makromol. Chem. 14, 110 (1954).
228. V. N. Tsvetkov and S. I. Klenin, J. Polymer Sci. 30, 187 (1958).
229. A. F. V. Eriksson, Acta Chem. Scand. 10, 378 (1956).
230. E. F. Casassa and W. H. Stockmayer, Polymer 3, 53 (1962).
231. S. N. Chinai and C. W. Bondurant, J. Polymer Sci. 22, 555 (1956).
232. S. Krause and E. Cohn-Ginsberg, cited in S. Krause and E. Cohn-Ginsberg, J. Phys. Chem. 67, 1479 (1963).
233. S. Krause and E. Cohn-Ginsberg, J. Phys. Chem. 67, 1479 (1963).
234. S. Krause and E. Cohn-Ginsberg, Polymer 3, 565 (1962).
235. S. N. Chinai, A. L. Resnick, and H. T. Lee, J. Polymer Sci. 33, 471 (1958).
236. J. G. Fee, W. S. Port, and L. P. Whitnauer, J. Polymer Sci. 33, 95 (1958).
237. M. Kurata, H. Utiyama and M. Iwama, unpublished work.
238. W. Scholtan, Makromol. Chem. 14, 169 (1954).
239. E. Collinson, F. S. Dainton, and G. S. McNaughton, Trans. Faraday Soc. 53, 489 (1957).
240. L. Trossarelli and M. Meirone, J. Polymer Sci. 57, 445 (1962).
241. V. N. Tsvetkov and V. G Aldoshin, Zh. Fiz. Khim. 33, 2767 (1959).
242. G. M. Chetyrkina, V. G. Aldoshin, and S. Y. Frenkel, Vysokomolekul. Soedin. 1, 1133 (1959).
243. Y. Fujisaki and H. Kobayashi, Kobunshi Kagaku, (Chem. High Polymers, Tokyo), 19, 73, 81 (1962).
244. H. Inagaki, K. Hayashi, and T. Matsuo, Makromol. Chem. 84, 80 (1965).
245. W. Scholtan and H. Marzolph, Makromol. Chem. 57, 52 (1962).
246. J. Bisschops, J. Polymer Sci. 17, 81 (1955).
247. R. L. Cleland and W. H. Stockmayer, J. Polymer Sci. 17, 473 (1955).
248. R. F. Onyon, J. Polymer Sci. 22, 13 (1956).
249. W. R. Krigbaum and A. M. Kotliar, J. Polymer Sci. 32, 323 (1958).
250. C. H. Bamford, A. D. Jenkins, R. Johnston, and E. F. T. White, Trans. Faraday Soc. 55, 168 (1959).
251. P. F. Onyon, J. Polymer Sci. 37, 315 (1959).
252. H. Kobayashi, J. Polymer Sci. 39, 369 (1959).
253. N. Fuhrman and R. B. Mesrobian, J. Am. Chem. Soc. 76, 3281 (1954).
254. C. G. Overberger, E. M. Pearce, and N. Mayes, J. Polymer Sci. 34, 109 (1959).
255. R. C. Schulz, S. Suzuki, H. Cherdron, and W. Kern, Makromol. Chem. 53, 145 (1962).
256. J. Parrod and J. Elles, J. Polymer Sci. 29, 411 (1958).
257. V. N. Tsvetkov, V. S. Skazka, N. A. Nikitin, and I. B. Steparenko, Vysokomolekul. Soedin. 6, 69 (1964).
258. J. Hakozaki, Nippon Kagaku Zasshi, (J. Chem. Soc. Japan, Pure Chem. Sec.), 82, 158 (1961).
259. J. Hakozaki, Nippon Kagaku Zasshi, (J. Chem. Soc. Japan, Pure Chem. Sec.), 82, 155 (1961).
260. I. Sakurada, A. Nakajima, O. Yoshizaki, and K. Nakamae, Kolloid-Z. & Z. Polymere, 186, 41 (1962).
261. F. Danusso, G. Moraglio, and G. Gianott, J. Polymer Sci. 51, 475 (1961).
262. H. Fujita, N. Takeguchi, K. Kawahara, T. Abe, H. Utiyama, and M. Kurata, Paper presented at 12th Polymer Symposium, Nagoya, Japan, 1963.
263. M. Takeda and R. Endo, Rept. Progr. Polymer Phys. Japan, 6, 37 (1963).
264. W. G. Cooper, G. Vaughan, D. E. Eaves, and R. W. Madden, J. Polymer Sci. 50, 159 (1961).
265. I. Ya Poddubnyi and E. G. Ehrenburg, J. Polymer Sci. 57, 545 (1962). K = 13.3 in benzene is for Li-type polymer, and 11.2 for Ziegler-types. No difference is found in dioxane.
266. R. L. Scott, W. C. Carter, and M. Magat, J. Am. Chem. Soc. 71, 220 (1949).
267. R. L. Cleland, J. Polymer Sci. 27, 349 (1958).
268. P. L. Ribeyrolles, A. Guyot, and H. Benoit, J. Chim. Phys. 56, 377 (1959).
269. M. Kurata, H. Utiyama, K. Kajitani, T. Koyama, and H. Fujita, Paper presented at 12th Polymer Symposium, Nagoya, Japan, 1963.
270. W. Cooper, D. E. Eaves, and G. Vaughan, J. Polymer Sci. 59, 241 (1962).
271. D. J. Pollock, L. J. Elyash, and T. W. Dewitt, J. Polymer Sci. 15, 335 (1955).
272. W. E. Mochel and J. B. Nichols, J. Am. Chem. Soc. 71, 3435 (1949).

273. W. E. Mochel, J. B. Nichols, and C. J. Mighton, J. Am. Chem. Soc. 70, 2185 (1948).
274. W. E. Mochel and J. B. Nichols, Ind. Eng. Chem. 43, 154 (1951).
275. H. L. Wagner and P. J. Flory, J. Am. Chem. Soc. 74, 195 (1952).
276. K. Altgelt and G. V. Schulz, Makromol. Chem. 36, 209 (1960).
277. W. C. Carter, R. L. Scott, and M. Magat, J. Am. Chem. Soc. 68, 1480 (1946).
278. W. H. Beattie and C. Booth, J. Appl. Polymer Sci. 7, 507 (1963).
279. W. Cooper, D. E. Eaves, and G. Vaughan, J. Polymer Sci. 59, 241 (1962).
280. H. C. Tingey, R. H. Ewart, and G. E. Hulse, unpublished work; cited in Ref. 266. See also, D. M. French and R. H. Ewart, Anal. Chem. 19, 165 (1947).
281. J. A. Yanko, J. Polymer Sci. 3, 576 (1958).
282. J.-Y. Chien, W. Chin, and Y.-S. Cheng,Kolloidn. Zh. 19, 515 (1957).
283. K. Weissermel and W. Schmieder, Makromol. Chem. 51, 39 (1962).
284. C. Rossi and C. Cuniberti, J. Polymer Sci. in press. Private communication.
285. C. Sadron and P. Rempp, J. Polymer Sci. 29, 127 (1958).
286. T. A. Ritscher and H. G. Elias, Makromol. Chem. 30, 48 (1959).
287. H. G. Elias, Kunststoffe, Plastics 4, 1 (1961).
288. D. K. Thomas and A. Charlesby, J. Polymer Sci. 42, 195 (1960).
289. C. Rossi, E. Bianchi, and G. Conio, Chim. Ind. (Milan), 45, 1498 (1963).
290. F. E. Bailey, Jr., J. L. Kucera, and L. G. Imhof, J. Polymer Sci. 32, 517 (L) (1958).
291. F. E. Bailey, Jr., and R. W. Callard, J. Appl. Polymer Sci. 1, 56 (1959).
292. R. E. Hughes and J. Richards, unpublished work; cited in P. E. Ebert and C. C. Price, J. Polymer Sci. 34, 157 (1959).
293. G. Allen, A. C. Booth, and M. N. Jones, Polymer 5, 195 (1964).
294. J. Moacanin, J. Appl. Polymer Sci. 1, 272 (1959).
295. H. Utiyama, K. Kamada, and M. Kurata, unpublished work.
296. A. D. Chirico, Chim. Ind. (Milan), 42, 248 (1960).
297. G. V. Schulz and A. Horbach, Makromol. Chem. 29, 93 (1959).
298. H. Batzer and G. Fritz, Makromol. Chem. 14, 179 (1955).
299. P. J. Flory and P. B. Stickney, J. Am. Chem. Soc. 62, 3032 (1940).
300. H. Zahn, C. Borstlap, and G. Valk, Makromol. Chem. 64, 18 (1963).
301. B. Seidel, J. Polymer Sci. 55, 411 (1961).
302. A. Conix, Makromol. Chem. 26, 226 (1958).
303. W. A. Lanke, reported in W. R. Krigbaum, J. Polymer Sci. 28, 213 (1958).
304. H. Batzer, Makromol. Chem. 5, 5 (1950).
305. H. Batzer and G. Weisenberger, Makromol. Chem. 11, 83 (1953).
306. H. Batzer and G. Benzing, Makromol. Chem. 62, 66 (1963).
307. H. Batzer, Makromol. Chem. 10, 13 (1953).
308. H. Batzer and B. Mohr, Makromol. Chem. 8, 217 (1952).
309. W. O. Baker, C. S. Fuller, and J. H. Heiss, Jr., J. Am. Chem. Soc. 63, 3316 (1941).
310. K. Hoshino and M. Watanabe, Nippon Kagaku Zasshi (J. Chem. Soc. Japan, Pure Chem. Sec.) 70, 24 (1949).
311. R. Bennewitz, Faserforsch. Textiltech. 5, 155 (1954).
312. J.-J. Chien, L.-H. Shih, and K.-I. Shih, Acta Chem. Sinica, 21, 50 (1955).
313. J. R. Schaefgen and P. J. Flory, J. Am. Chem. Soc. 70, 2709 (1948).
314. G. B. Taylor, J. Am. Chem. Soc. 69, 635 (1947).
315. G. J. Howard, J. Polymer Sci. 37, 310 (L) (1959).
316. P. W. Morgan and S. L. Kwolek, J. Polymer Sci. A1, 1147 (1963).
317. W. Burchard, Makromol. Chem. 67, 182 (1963).
318. K. J. Ivin, H. A. Ende, and G. Meyerhoff, Polymer 3, 129 (1962).
319. R. Endo and M. Takeda, Private communication.
320. I. Ya. Poddubnyi and V. A. Grechanovskii, Vysokomolekul. Soedin. 6, 64 (1964).
321. S. A. Pavlova, T. A. Soboleva, and A. P. Suprun, Vysokomolekul. Soedin. 6, 122 (1964).
322. I. Ya. Poddubnyi, V. A. Grechanovskii, and A. V. Podalinskii, Vysokomolekul. Soedin. 5, 1588 (1964).
323. M. Abe, Y. Murakami, and H. Fujita, J. Polymer Sci. to be published. The constants are derived for hypothetical monodisperse fractions.
324. T. Homma and H. Fujita, J. Appl. Polymer Sci., in press. Bound styrene, 24 wt%.
325. H. Batzer and H. Jürgen, Makromol. Chem. 44-49, 179 (1961).
326. H.-G. Elias and R. Schumacher, Makromol. Chem. 76, 23 (1964).
326a. P. R. Saunders, J. Polymer Sci. A2, 3765 (1964).
327. J. M. G. Cowie, Makromol. Chem. 42, 230 (1961).
328. W. W. Everett and J. F. Foster, J. Am. Chem. Soc. 81, 3464 (1959).
329. W. Burchard, Makromol. Chem. 64, 110 (1963).
330. W. Banks and C. T. Greenwood, Makromol. Chem. 67, 49 (1963).
331. J. M. C. Cowie, Makromol. Chem. 53, 13 (1962).
332. J. M. G. Cowie, J. Polymer Sci. 49, 455 (1961).

333. B. A. Dombrow and C. O. Beckmann, J. Phys. Colloid Chem. 51, 107 (1947).
334. W. Burchard and E. Husemann, Makromol. Chem. 44-46, 358 (1961).
335. E. Husemann, R. Resz and R. Wermer, Makromol. Chem. 47, 48 (1961).
336. F. G. Donnan and R. C. Rose, Can. J. Research, B28, 105 (1950).
337. W. G. Harland, in "Recent Advances in Chemistry of Cellulose and Starch"
     edited by Honeyman, Interscience Pub. Inc., New York, 1959, pp. 265-284.
338. N. Gralen and T. Svedberg, Nature 152, 625 (1943).
339. E. H. Immergut, B. G. Ranby, and H. Mark, Ind. Eng. Chem. 45, 2383 (1953).
340. J. W. Tamblyn, D. R. Morey and R. H. Wagner, Ind. Eng. Chem. 37, 573 (1945).
341. F. H. Holmes and D. J. Smith, Trans. Faraday Soc. 53, 67 (1957).
342. W. J. B. Badgley and H. Mark, J. Phys. Colloid Chem. 51, 58 (1947).
343. H. J. Philipp and C. F. Bjork, J. Polymer Sci. 6, 549 (1951).
344. P. J. Flory, O. K. Spurr, Jr., and D. K. Carpenter, J. Polymer Sci. 27, 231
     (1958).
345. L. Mandelkern and P. J. Flory, J. Am. Chem. Soc. 74, 2517 (1952).
346. W. R. Krigbaum and L. H. Sperling, J. Phys. Chem. 64, 99 (1960).
347. G. Meyerhoff, J. Polymer Sci. 29, 399 (1958).
348. A. M. Holtzer, H. Benoit, and P. Doty, J. Phys. Chem. 58, 624 (1954).
349. W. R. Moore and J. A. Epstein, J. Appl. Chem. (London), 6 168 (1956).
350. R. M. Badger and R. H. Blaker, J. Phys. Colloid Chem. 53, 1056 (1949).
351. M. M. Huque, D. A. I. Goring, and S. G. Mason, Can. J. Chem. 36, 952 (1958).
352. W. R. Moore and G. D. Edge, J. Polymer Sci. 47, 469 (1960).
353. M. L. Hunt, S. Newman, H. A. Scheraga, and P. J. Flory, J. Phys. Chem. 60,
     1278 (1956).
354. W. G. Harland, Nature 170, 667 (1952).
355. W. R. Moore and A. M. Brown, J. Colloid Sci. 14, 1, 343 (1959).
356. V. N. Tsvetkov and S. Ya Kotlyar, Zh. Fiz. Khim. 30, 1100 (1956).
357. R. St. J. Manley, Arkiv Kemi, 9, 519 (1956).
358. W. Brown, D. Henley, and J. Öhman, Makromol. Chem. 64, 49 (1963).
359. W. B. Neely, J. Polymer Sci. A1, 311 (1963).
360. W. Brown, D. Henley, and J. Öhman, Makromol. Chem. 62, 164 (1963).
361. G. Sitaramaiah and D. A. I. Goring, J. Polymer Sci. 58, 1107 (1962).
362. F. R. Senti, N. N. Hellman, N. H. Ludwig, G. E. Babcock, R. Tobin, C. A. Class,
     and B. L. Lamberts, J. Polymer Sci. 17, 527 (1955). See also Ref. 371.
363. J. V. Koleska and S. F. Kurath, J. Polymer Sci. A2, 4123 (1964).
364. T. Nishihara and P. Doty, Proc. Natl. Acad. Sci. U. S. 44, 411 (1958).
365. J. Pouradier and A. M. Venet, J. Chim. Phys. 47, 391 (1950).
366. J. W. Williams, W. M. Saunders, and J. S. Cicirelli, J. Phys. Chem. 58, 774
     (1954).
367. A. Zilkha and Y. Burstein, Biopolymers, 2, 147 (1964).
368. P. Doty, J. H. Bradbury, and A. M. Holtzer, J. Am. Chem. Soc. 78, 947 (1956).
369. G. Spach, Compt. Rend. 249, 543 (1959).
370. J. H. Fessler and A. G. Ogston, Trans. Faraday Soc. 47, 667 (1951).
371. E. Antonini, L. Bellelli, M. L. Bonacci, M. R. Bruzzesi, A. Caputo,
     E. Chiancone, and A. Rossi-Fanelli, Biopolymers, 2, 35 (1964).
372. P. Doty, B. B. McGill, and S. A. Rice, Proc. Natl. Acad. Sci. U. S. 44, 432
     (1958). Cf. Ref. 374-377 and 381.
373. J. T. Lett and K. A. Stacey, Makromol. Chem. 38, 204 (1960).
374. Y. Kawade and I. Watanabe, Biochim. Biophys. Acta, 19, 513 (1956).
375. K. Iso and I. Watanabe, Nippon Kagaku Zasshi, (J. Chem. Soc. Japan, Pure Chem.
     Sec.), 78, 1268 (1957).
376. J. A. V. Butler, D. J. R. Laurence, A. B. Robins, and K. V. Shooter, Proc.
     Roy. Soc. London, A250, 1 (1959).
377. L. F. Cavalieri and B. H. Rosenberg, J. Am. Chem. Soc. 81, 5136 (1959).
378. C. A. Thomas, Jr., and P. Doty, J. Am. Chem. Soc. 78, 1854 (1956).
379. C. A. Thomas, Jr., J. Am. Chem. Soc. 78, 1861 (1956).
380. J. Eigner, unpublished work; cited in P. Doty, J. Marmur, J. Eigner, and
     C. Schildkraut, Proc. Natl. Acad. Sci. U.S. 46, 461 (1960). See also Ref. 381.
381. J. Eigner, Dissertation, Harvard University, Cambridge, Mass., U. S. A. April 1960.
382. J. R. Fresco and P. Doty, J. Am. Chem. Soc. 79, 3928 (1957).
383. R. Haselkorn, unpublished work; cited in Ref. 381.
384. E. G. Richards, C. P. Flessel, and J. R. Fresco, Biopolymers, 1, 431 (1963).
385. B. D. Hall and P. Doty, "Microsomal Particles and Protein Synthesis,"
     Washington Acad. Sci. p. 27 (1958).
386. Y. Kawade, Ann. Report Inst. Virus Research, Kyoto Univ. B2, 219 (1959). See
     also Ref. 388.
387. H. Boedtker, J. Mol. Biol. 2, 171 (1960).
388. C. G. Kurland, J. Mol. Biol. 2, 83 (1960).
389. M. Tamura, H. Odani, S. Imai, and S. Nishida, Private communication.
390. J. Marchal and C. Lapp, J. Chim. Phys. 60, 756 (1963).

391. I. Z. Steinberg, W. F. Harrington, A. Berger, M. Sela, and E. Katchalski, J. Am. Chem. Soc. 82, 5263 (1960).
392. D. Henley, Arkiv Kemi, 18, 327 (1961).
393. G. Thomson, S. A. Rice, and M. Nagasawa, J. Am. Chem. Soc. 85, 2537 (1963).
394. V. Crescenzi and P. J. Flory, J. Am. Chem. Soc. 86, 141 (1964).
395. Von A. Haug and G. Meyerhoff, Makromol. Chem. 53, 91 (1962).
396. P. J. Flory, L. Mandelkern, J. B. Kinsinger, and W. B. Schulz, J. Am. Chem. Soc. 74, 3364 (1952).
397. A. Ya Korolev, K. A. Andrianov, L. S. Utesheva, and T. E. Vredenskaya, Dokl. Acad. Nauk, SSSR, 89, 65 (1953).
398. F. P. Price, S. G. Martin, and J. P. Bianchi, J. Polymer Sci. 22, 41 (1956).
399. R. L. Merker and M. J. Scott, J. Polymer Sci. A2, 15 (1964).
400. J. F. Brown, Jr., L. H. Vogt, Jr., A. Katchman, J. W. Eustance, K. M. Kiser, and K. W. Krantz, J. Am. Chem. Soc. 82, 6194 (1960).
401. M. Nakagaki, S. Ohashi, and F. Minato, Bull. Chem. Soc. Japan, 36, 341 (1963).
402. U. P. Strauss and P. L. Wineman, J. Am. Chem. Soc. 80, 2366 (1958).
403. Houtz, cited in Y. Iwakura, T. Kurosaki, and N. Nakabayashi, Makromol. Chem. 44-46, 570 (1961).
404. W. Scholtan and H. Marzolph, Makromol. Chem. 57, 52 (1962).
405. Y. Shimura, I. Mita, and H. Kambe, J. Polymer Sci. B2, 403 (1964).
406. H. Hopff and D. Starck, Makromol. Chem. 48, 50 (1961).
407. I. Ya. Poddubnyi, V. A. Grechanovskii, and M. I. Mosevitskii, Vysokomolekul. Soedin., 5, 1042 (1964).
408. V. A. Myagchenkov, E. V. Kuznetsov, O. A. Iskhakov, and V. M. Lichkina, Vysokomolekul. Soedin. 5, 724 (1963).
409. J. D. Matlack, S. N. Chinai, R. A. Guzzi, and D. W. Levi, J. Polymer Sci. 49, 533 (1961).
410. W. H. Stockmayer, L. D. Moore, Jr., M. Fixman, and B. N. Epstein, J. Polymer Sci. 16, 517 (1955).
411. H. Utiyama, K. Kajitani, and M. Kurata, unpublished work. Cf. Rept. Progr. Polymer Phys. Japan, 6, 29 (1963).
412. S. Krause, J. Phys. Chem. 68, 1948 (1964).
413. G. V. Schulz and A. Haug, Z. Physik. Chem. (Frankfurt), N. F. 34, 328 (1962).
414. I. Marshall and A. Todd, Trans. Faraday Soc. 49, 67, (1953).
415. L. D. Moore, ACS Meeting, Cleveland, Polymer Preprints, 1, Vol. 234 (1960).
416. I. M. Ward, Nature 180, 141 (1957).
417. D. A. S. Ravens and I. M. Ward, Trans. Faraday. Soc., 57, 150 (1961).
418. W. Griehl and S. Neue, Faserforsch. Textiltech. 5, 423 (1954).
419. C. Y. Cha, J. Polymer Sci. B2, 1069 (1964).
420. N. G. Gaylord and S. Rosenbaum, J. Polymer Sci. 39, 545 (1959).
421. V. Kokle, F. W. Billmeyer, J. Polymer Sci. B3, 47 (1965).
422. H. M. Koepp, H. Werner, Makromol. Chem. 32, 79 (1959).
423. E. V. Kuznetsov, A. O. Wisel, I. M. Shermergorn, C. C. Tjulenjeu, Vysokomolekul. Soedin. 2, 205 (1960).
424. A. J. Barry, J. Appl. Phys. 17, 1020 (1946).
425. V. Crescenzi and P. J. Flory, J. Am. Chem. Soc. 86, 141 (1964).
426. U. Bianchi and V. Magnasco, J. Polymer Sci. 41, 177 (1959).
427. J. M. G. Cowie, Makromol. Chem. 42, 230 (1961).
428. H. Benoit, J. Polymer Sci. 3, 376 (1948).
429. H. Markovitz, J. Chem. Phys. 20, 868 (1952).
430. A. Kotera, H. Matsuda, and A. Wada, paper presented at 13th Polymer Symposium, Japan, Tokyo, Nov. 13, 1964.
431. E. D. Kunst, Rec. Trav. Chim. 69, 125 (1950).
432. N. T. Notley and P. J. W. Debye, J. Polymer Sci. 17, 99 (1955).
433. W. R. Krigbaum and D. K. Carpenter, J. Phys. Chem. 59, 1166 (1955).
434. E. Wada and K. Okano, Rept. Prog. Polymer Phys. Japan, 7, 19 (1964).
435. T. A. Orofino and J. W. Mickey, Jr., J. Chem. Phys. 38, 2513 (1963).
436. G. V. Schulz and H. Baumann, Makromol. Chem. 60, 120 (1963).
437. T. A. Orofino and A. Ciferri, J. Phys. Chem. 68, 3136 (1964).
438. M. Abe and H. Fujita, J. Phys. Chem. in press.
439. E. Wada and K. Okano, Rept. Prog. Polymer Phys. Japan, 6, 1 (1963).
440. O. Kratky and G. Porod, Rec. Trav. Chim. 68, 1106 (1949).
441. E. Eisenberg and E. F. Casassa, J. Polymer Sci. 47, 29 (1960).
442. R. Kirste and G. V. Schulz, Z. Physik. Chem. (N.F.), 30, 171 (1961).
443. R. Kirste and O. Kratky, Z. Physik, Chem. (N.F.) 31, 363 (1962).
444. T. G. Fox, Polymer 3, 111 (1962).
445. O. Kratky and H. Sand, Kolloid-Z. 172, 18 (1960).
446. W. Raich, S. B. Thesis, Mass. Inst. Tech., Cambridge, Mass., U.S.A., 1948.
447. K. J. Ivin and H. A. Ende, J. Polymer Sci. 54, S17 (1961).

448. J. M. G. Cowie and P. M. Toporowski, Polymer $\underline{5}$, 601 (1964).
449. R. D. Patel and R. S. Patel, J. Polymer Sci. to be published.
450. S. Heine, O. Kratky, G. Porod, and P. J. Schmitz, Makromol. Chem. $\underline{44\text{-}46}$, 682 (1961).
451. J. K. Peterson, Dissertation, Ohio State Univ., Ohio, U.S.A., 1961.
452. G. A. Morneau, P. I. Roth, and A. R. Shultz, J. Polymer Sci. $\underline{55}$, 609 (1961).
453. G. Moraglio and J. Brzezinski, J. Polymer Sci. $\underline{B2}$, 1105 (1964).
454. P. J. Flory, A. Ciferri, and R. Chiang, J. Am. Chem. Soc. $\underline{83}$, 1023 (1961).
455. J. E. Mark and P. J. Flory, J. Am. Chem. Soc., 1415, 1423 $\overline{(1965)}$.
456. W. H. Stockmayer and L. L. Chan, ACS-Meeting, Detroit, Polymer Preprint 6(1), 333 (1965).
457. I. M. Belgovskii, N. S. Enikolopyan, and L. S. Sakhonenko, Vysokomolekul. Soedin. $\underline{4}$, 1197 (1962).

SEDIMENTATION CONSTANTS, DIFFUSION CONSTANTS,
PARTIAL SPECIFIC VOLUMES, FRICTIONAL RATIOS

and

SECOND VIRIAL COEFFICIENTS OF POLYMERS IN SOLUTION

H. A. Ende

Chemstrand Research Center*
Durham, North Carolina

Contents

---

* Present Address: Monsanto International, Hydrocarbon and Plastics Division,
St. Louis, Missouri

I. SEDIMENTATION CONSTANTS, DIFFUSION CONSTANTS, PARTIAL SPECIFIC VOLUMES, AND
    FRICTIONAL RATIOS OF POLYMERS IN SOLUTION*

    A. Introduction

        1. Sedimentation Constant

        According to Svedberg (Ref. 2) the sedimentation constant s is defined as the
        sedimentation velocity in a unit field (1 dyn)

        $$s = (dr/dt)(1/\omega^2 r) \tag{1}$$

        For a given molecule in a given solvent the sedimentation constant is dependent
        on temperature, polymer concentration, and pressure.

        a. Temperature Dependence

        The Svedberg equation (Ref. 2) (to be discussed in I.A.3), requires that the
        sedimentation constant s, the diffusion constant D, the partial specific vol-
        ume $\bar{v}_2$, and the density ρ, be given at equal temperatures. The temperature
        most commonly used is 20°C. The sedimentation constant, s_{20}, can either be
        measured at 20°C, or be calculated from s_T by equation (2)

        $$s_{20} = s_T \frac{\eta_T}{\eta_{20}} \frac{1 - (\bar{v}_2)_{20}\rho_{20}}{1 - (\bar{v}_2)_T \rho_T} \tag{2}$$

        where η_T and η_{20} are the viscosities of the solvent at T°C and 20°C, respec-
        tively. Especially with aqueous solvents (buffers, salt solutions) it is
        often desirable to reduce s_{20} to a reference solvent (e.g. water). Equation
        (2) becomes then (Ref. 2)

        $$s_{20}^o = s_T \frac{\eta_T}{\eta_{20}^o} \frac{1 - (\bar{v}_2)_{20} \rho_{20}^o}{1 - (\bar{v}_2)_T \rho_T} \tag{3}$$

        with η_{20}^o = viscosity of the reference solvent at 20°C. Most of the sedimen-
        tation constants, determined in aqueous solutions, listed in Table I.B. are
        those defined by Equation (3).

        b. Concentration Dependence

        For the majority of systems studied by ultracentrifugation it is found that
        1/s or s is a linear function of concentration:

        $$\frac{1}{s} = \frac{1}{s_o} (1 + k_s c) \tag{4a}$$

        and

        $$s = s_o (1 - k_s' c) \tag{4b}$$

        where s_o is the sedimentation constant at c = o.

        Behavior according to Equation (4a) is found more frequently than that accord-
        ing to Equation (4b). The dimensions of k_s and k_s' depend on those of c;
        usually, cc/g or 100 cc/g are used. In Table I.B. a concentration dependence
        according to Equation (4a) is denoted by c.a. and that according to Equation
        (4b) by c.b. In rare cases special extrapolation procedures are used. In
        these cases Table I.B. refers to the appropriate reference. For special treat-
        ments see e.g. Gehatia (Refs. 358,359).

        The sector-shape of the ultracentrifugation cell causes a uniform decrease of
        the concentration during sedimentation (Ref. 360). In many cases this decrease
        in concentration has to be taken into account. At time t

        $$c_t = c_o (r_o/r_t)^2 \tag{5}$$

---

* Detailed Bibliography, references 2, 349-357.

References page IV-150

where r_o and r_t are the distances of the meniscus and the distance of the boundary from the axis of rotation, c_o and c_t the concentrations before centrifugation and at time t, respectively.

c. Pressure Dependence

The high pressures encountered within the cell due to the high centrifugal fields applied in ultracentrifugation change appreciably the viscosity and the density of the solvent; likewise, the partial specific volume is influenced by high pressures. Thus, the sedimentation constant, s_p, measured at a pressure p, differs from the sedimentation constant, s_1, measured at 1 atm. The difference between s_p and s_1 is especially large in organic solvents. Mosimann and Signer (Ref. 361) derived an equation analogous to Equation (3) for calculating s_1 from s_p:

$$s_1 = s_p \frac{\eta_p}{\eta_1} \frac{(1 - (\overline{v}_2)_1 \, \rho_1)}{(1 - (\overline{v}_2)_p \, \rho_p)} \tag{6}$$

The calculation requires knowledge of the viscosity η_p, density of the solvent ρ_p, and partial specific volume $(\overline{v}_2)_p$, each at pressure p. Values for η_p are given by Bridgman (Ref. 362), and may be calculated from the compressibilities found in a number of handbooks. Very recently, values for $(\overline{v}_2)_p$ have become available through the work of Andersson (Ref. 148). More precise equations for the calculation of the pressure influence on the sedimentation constant have been worked out by Oth and Desreux (Ref. 363), Wales (Ref. 364), and Fujita (Ref. 365). An elegant and simple extrapolation procedure, which does not require the knowledge of any of the pressure dependent quantities, was suggested by Elias (Ref. 366).

d. Averages of Sedimentation Constants

Most ultracentrifuges are equipped with schlieren optics which measure the refractive index gradient dn/dr versus r. The increment dn/dr is proportional to the concentration gradient dc/dr. Monodisperse polymers yield a symmetrical curve with a maximum. The gradient curve of a polydisperse polymer is a summation of an infinite number of single curves from the single fractions contained in the polymer. Each of the fractions has its own sedimentation constant so that a distribution of sedimentation constants results. In the majority of cases a continuous curve with one maximum is obtained. It can be shown (Ref. 14) that with certain assumptions the gradient curve represents to a fair approximation the distribution function of s,f(s) = dc/ds. Since

$$\frac{dn}{dr} = const. \frac{dc}{ds} \tag{7}$$

it should in principle be possible to evaluate the various averages of sedimentation constants, e.g. $\langle s \rangle_o = s_n$, $\langle s \rangle_1 = s_w$, and $\langle s \rangle_2 = s_z$, from the distribution of the concentration gradient within the cell. The common practice, however, is to determine simply the migration of the maximum which leads to a sedimentation constant s_t, not readily defined with respect to its average. A less common method of evaluating sedimentation constants is by observing the movement of the median, that is the line dividing the gradient curve in two equal areas, yielding, likewise, a rather undefined average s_m. According to Jullander (Ref. 259) s_t and s_m can be related to s_w by

$$s_w = \frac{3s_m - s_t}{2} \tag{8}$$

provided the skewness of the curve is not very pronounced. In Table I.B., we have occasionally listed instead of s_o, the intrinsic sedimentation constant $[s_o] = s_o \, \eta / (1 - \overline{v}_2 \rho)$.

e. Sedimentation Constant - Molecular Weight Relationship

In analogy with the Mark-Houwink (Refs. 367, 368) equation the dependence of the sedimentation constant on molecular weight can often be expressed as follows:

$$s = k' \cdot M^{a'} \tag{9}$$

where k' and a' are constants for a given polymer homologous series in a given solvent. Whenever quoted in the literature, relation (9) is listed in the table rather than single s-values.

2. Diffusion Constant

The diffusion constant D is defined by Fick's first law which states that in the process of translational diffusion the amount of material (in solution) crossing a plane of unit area per unit time is proportional to the concentration gradient $\partial c/\partial x$ through the diffusion constant D. Thus, the rate of flow F is

$$F = -D(\partial c/\partial x) \tag{10}$$

The minus sign in Equation (10) indicates that diffusion takes place in the direction of decreasing concentration. For practical reasons Fick's second law is preferred

$$\partial c/\partial t = D(\partial^2 c/\partial x^2) \tag{11}$$

which, when solved with consideration of certain boundary conditions, allows the determination of D by measuring dc/dx as a function of the time t and the distance x.

The diffusion constant is dependent on temperature and polymer concentration. Constancy of pressure is generally assumed during measurements.

a. Temperature Dependence

The diffusion constant D_{20} for 20°C can be calculated (Ref. 2) from that measured at T°C from Equation (12)

$$D_{20} = D_T \frac{293}{273 + T} \frac{\eta_T}{\eta_{20}} \tag{12}$$

The diffusion constant D_{20}°, reduced to a reference solvent (usually water), is calculated from

$$D_{20}^\circ = D_T \frac{293}{273 + T} \frac{\eta_T}{\eta_{20}^\circ} \tag{13}$$

b. Concentration Dependence

In general, it is possible to describe the concentration dependence by a linear equation:

$$D = D_o (1 + k_D c) \tag{14}$$

The direct measurement of the concentration dependence according to Equation (14) is the method which is used most frequently today. There are, however, methods which determine D_o and k_D from a measurement at only one concentration. Another method is that of Gralén (Ref. 14), and that of Beckmann and Rosenberg (Ref. 13). Whenever one of the latter two methods was used the remarks "Gralén" or "B. + R." are inserted in Table I.B.

c. Averages of Diffusion Constants

Similar considerations as made under A.1.d. on sedimentation constants hold for diffusion constants also. Moments over the concentration gradient curve obtained by schlieren optics yield certain averages of diffusion constants. The schlieren curve has usually one maximum. The abscissa is conveniently chosen such that the zero point is at the maximum of the concentration gradient $dn/dx \sim dc/dx = g(x)$. The moments over the concentration gradient Λ_s are then defined as

$$\Lambda_s = \int_{-\infty}^{\infty} |x|^s g(x) dx \tag{15}$$

References page IV-150

with s = 0, 1, 2, and 4. The following diffusion constants D can then be obtained:

$$D_{0,h} = \frac{1}{t} \frac{\Lambda_o^2}{4\pi h_{max}^2} = D_A \tag{16}$$

$h_{max} = [g(x)]_{max}$

$$D_{2,0} = \frac{1}{t} \frac{\Lambda_2}{2\Lambda_o} = D_w \tag{17}$$

$$D_{4,2} = \frac{1}{t} \frac{\Lambda_4}{6\Lambda_2} = D_z \tag{18}$$

$$D_\sigma = \frac{\sigma^2}{2t} = \frac{\Lambda_2\Lambda_o - \Lambda_1^2}{2t\Lambda_o^2} \tag{19}$$

A somewhat unusual diffusion constant is that defined by Equation (20)

$$D_h = \frac{x_1^2 - x_2^2}{4t\ln\frac{h_2}{h_1}} = \frac{x_1^2}{4t\ln\frac{h_{max}}{h_1}} \tag{20}$$

determined from two points $h_1 = [g(x)]_1$ and $h_2 = [g(x)]_2$ at x_1 and x_2, h_{max} at the latter value being equal to zero.

The averages of the diffusion constants are defined as follows:

$$\langle D \rangle_a = \frac{\int_o^\infty f(D)D^a \, dD}{\int_o^\infty f(D)D^{a-1} dD} \tag{21}$$

Thus, for a = 0, 1, and 2 one obtains D_n, D_w, and D_z, respectively. The diffusion constant $D_A = D_{0,h}$ is larger than D_n. It is defined by Equation (22):

$$D_A = \left[\frac{\int_o^\infty f(D)dD}{\int_o^\infty f(D)D^{-1/2}dD} \right]^2 \tag{22}$$

The diffusion constants most frequently found in the literature are D_A and D_w.

d. Diffusion Constant - Molecular Weight Relationship

The diffusion constant molecular weight dependence frequently takes the form

$$D = k'' \, M^{-a''} \tag{23}$$

with k'' and a'' being constants for a given polymer homologous series in a given solvent. In Table I.B. relation (23) is listed whenever quoted in the literature, in preference to single D- values.

3. Molecular Weight Averages Determined from Sedimentation- and Diffusion-Constants

For calculation of the molecular weight from sedimentation and diffusion data the Svedberg equation (Ref. 2) is used:

$$M = \frac{RTs}{(1-\bar{v}_2\rho)D} \quad (T = °K) \tag{24}$$

Here s and D are the corrected and standardized constants for zero polymer concentration, $\bar{v}_2$ is the partial specific volume of the polymer, ρ is the density of the solution, R and T are the gas constant and absolute temperature, respectively. For polydisperse polymers the various averages of the sedimentation and diffusion constant $\langle s \rangle = s_i$ and $\langle D \rangle = D_j$ are inserted; certain molecular weight averages $\langle M \rangle = M_{i,j}$ are then obtained. Thus, Equation (24) acquires the more general form:

$$M_{i,j} = \frac{RTs_i}{D_j \, (1 - \bar{v}_2 \rho)} \tag{25}$$

For $i = n, w, z$, and $j = n, w, z$, Equation (25) defines nine different molecular weight averages, e.g. $M_{n,n}$, $M_{w,n}$, $M_{w,w}$, etc. (The averages $M_{n,n}$ and $M_{w,w}$ are different from M_n and M_w, respectively.) As described in the preceding sections, the constants with $i = n$ and z, and $j = n$ and z are determinable either not at all, or only with large error. Instead, the constants with $i = t$ and m, and $j = A, w, \sigma$ (and h) are usually evaluated. Thus, rather peculiar averages, e.g. $M_{t,A}$, $M_{m,\sigma}$, and $M_{w,h}$, result. The more straight forward molecular weight averages, e.g. $M_{n,w}$, $M_{w,w}$, $M_{z,w}$, etc., in relation to the familiar averages $\bar{M}_n$, $\bar{M}_w$, and $\bar{M}_z$, are found elsewhere in the literature (Refs. 369-371).

4. Partial Specific Volumes

The volume, v_{12}^{id}, of an ideal two component system can be expressed in terms of the masses m_1 and m_2, and the specific volumes v_1 and v_2 of the two components by the equation

$$v_{12}^{id} = m_1 v_1 + m_2 v_2 \tag{26}$$

Most components do not behave ideally upon mixing; i.e., they react with each other in a way so that the total volume deviates from V_{12}^{id} owing to concentration effects or to expansion of component 1 and/or 2. The total volume can then be written:

$$V_{12} = m_1 \bar{v}_1 + m_2 \bar{v}_2 \tag{27}$$

where $\bar{v}_1$ and $\bar{v}_2$ are the partial specific volumes of components 1 and 2, respectively. When component 2 is polymer and component 1 solvent, then, for practical reasons, it is convenient to introduce the so-called apparent partial specific volume $\bar{v}_2^*$ which is defined by

$$V_{12} = m_1 \bar{v}_1^o + m_2 \bar{v}_2^* \tag{28}$$

where $v_1^o = v_1$, i.e. the specific volume of the solvent. The quantity $\bar{v}_2^*$ now contains the parameters of non-ideal mixing of both the solvent and the polymer but, in practice, is not much different from $\bar{v}_2$ if the polymer concentration is kept low (up to 1%).

Dividing Equation (28) by the total mass $m_1 + m_2$ Equation (29) is obtained:

$$v_{12} = g_1 v_1^o + g_2 \bar{v}_2^* \tag{29}$$

where v_{12} is the specific volume of the solution and $g_1 = m_1/(m_1 + m_2)$, $g_2 = m_2/(m_1 + m_2)$ are the weight fractions of the solvent and the polymer, respectively. With $v_{12} = 1/\rho_{12}$ and $v_1^o = 1/\rho_1$, ρ_{12} and ρ_1 being the density of the solution and the solvent, respectively, it is readily found that

$$\bar{v}_2^* = \frac{1}{g_2} \left(\frac{\rho_1 - g_1 \rho_{12}}{\rho_{12} \rho_1} \right) \tag{30}$$

Equation (30) shows that $\bar{v}_2^*$ can be determined by measuring ρ_1 and ρ_{12}. Numerous methods for determining densities are described in the literature (Refs. 268, 372-379).

In order to determine the partial specific volume from the apparent specific volume, Equation (29) yields

$$\left(\frac{\partial(m_2\bar{v}_2^*)}{\partial m_2}\right)_{m_1} = m_2 \left(\frac{\partial \bar{v}_2^*}{\partial m_2}\right)_{m_1} + \bar{v}_2^* = \left(\frac{\partial V_{12}}{\partial m_2}\right)_{m_1} \tag{31}$$

where $(\partial V_{12}/\partial m_2)_{m_1}$ is, according to definition, equal to $\bar{v}_2$. In terms of weight fractions, Equation (31) can finally be written

$$\bar{v}_2 = \bar{v}_2^* + g_1 g_2 \frac{\partial \bar{v}_2^*}{\partial g_2} \tag{32}$$

Most values reported in the literature are $\bar{v}_2^*$ - values rather than $\bar{v}_2$ - values, since extrapolation according to Equation (32) is usually omitted. The differences between $\bar{v}_2^*$ and $\bar{v}_2$ are, however, often small.

5. Frictional Ratio

The molar frictional constant f_o of an unsolvated spherical molecule may be computed by the formula based on Stokes law

$$f_o = 6\pi\eta \left(\frac{3N^2 M\bar{v}_2}{4\pi}\right)^{1/3} \tag{33}$$

where η is the viscosity of the solvent and N is the Avogadro number. When the shape of a molecule deviates from that of a sphere, or when it is solvated, then the molar frictional constant f of such a molecule is larger than that of the spherical molecule. The frictional ratio f/f_o thus permits to draw conclusions concerning either solvation or shape of the molecule. It is possible to calculate the dimensions of the non-spherical molecule provided a particular model (ellipsoid, cylinder, etc.) for the molecule is adopted and either the degree of solvation is known or assumed to be negligible. The molar frictional constant f can be determined (Ref. 2) either from sedimentation velocity data, provided the molecular weight is known from independent measurements according to

$$f = \frac{M(1 - \bar{v}_2\rho)}{s} \tag{34}$$

or from diffusion measurements, using the relation

$$f = \frac{RT}{D} \quad (T = {}^\circ K) \tag{35}$$

Combining equations (24), (33), and (35) the following relation is found:

$$f/f_o = \frac{1}{\eta} \left(\frac{R^2 T^2 (1 - \bar{v}_2\rho)}{162 \ \pi^2 \ N^2 \ D^2 \ \bar{v}_2 s}\right)^{1/3} \tag{36}$$

For aqueous solutions, Equation (36) reduces to the approximated relation (valid at 20°C):

$$f/f_o = 10^{-8} \left(\frac{1 - \bar{v}_2\rho}{D^2 s\bar{v}_2}\right)^{1/3} \tag{37}$$

Equations (36) and (37) are most frequently used for calculating the frictional ratio; they are termed as a and b, respectively, in the present table. Other relations for the determination of f/f_o are quoted in the literature (Ref. 2). In these cases special reference to the literature is made in the table.

In a few cases, only the molar frictional coefficient f, rather than f/f_o, was quoted in the literature. These values are inserted in the same column as values for the frictional ratio.

6. Miscellaneous

    1. In Table I.B. all concentrations are given in g/liter.

    2. Molecular weights determined from viscosity data, via a Mark-Houwink relation, are called $\overline{M}_v$.

    3. With certain assumptions it is possible to determine the molecular weight from a combination of the intrinsic viscosity $[\eta]$ and the limiting sedimentation constant s_o. Mandelkern and Flory (Ref. 128) derived an expression

$$M = \left[\frac{s_o[\eta]^{1/3}\,\eta N}{P^{-1}\,\Phi^{-1/3}\,(1 - \overline{v}_2\rho)} \right]^{3/2} \qquad (38)$$

in which the parameter $\Phi^{-1/3}P^{-1}$ is assumed to be a constant, equal approximately 2.5×10^6. An expression similar to that of Equation (38) was derived by combining relationships involving D_o and $[\eta]$ (Ref. 128).

In addition, Wales and Van Holde (Ref. 134) derived the following expression

$$M = 9.5 \times 10^{24}\ (1.66\ [\eta])^{0.5} \left(\frac{s_o\eta}{1 - \overline{v}_2\rho} \right) \qquad (39)$$

Equations (38) and (39) are referred to as F + M and W + H, respectively, in Table I.B.,and the molecular weights determined from either one of these or similar relations is termed $\overline{M}_\eta$.

7. Symbols

c	concentration
c_o	initial polymer concentration
c_t	polymer concentration at time t
D	diffusion constant $[cm^2/sec]$
D_n	number average diffusion constant
$D_{o,h} = D_A$	diffusion constant determined from zeroth moment of concentration gradient curve and its maximum height (so-called "area method").
$D_{2,o} = D_w$	diffusion constant determined from second and zeroth moment of concentration gradient, is equal to the weight average of diffusion constant D_w. This is so-called "moment method" (frequently the symbol D_m is used in literature).
$D_{4,2} = D_z$	diffusion constant determined from fourth and second moment of concentration gradient; it is equal to the "z" - average of diffusion constant D_z.

References page IV-150

D_h diffusion constant determined from two heights, h_1 and h_2 at distances x_1 and x_2 of the concentration gradient curve.

D_σ diffusion constant determined from zeroth, first, and second moment.

D_{20} diffusion constant at 20°C.

D_T diffusion constant at T°C.

D_{20}° diffusion constant at 20°C, corrected for water.

η viscosity of solvent

η_1 viscosity of solvent at 1 atm.

η_p viscosity of solvent at p atm.

η_T viscosity of solvent at T°C.

η_{20} viscosity of solvent at 20°C.

η_{20}° viscosity of reference solvent at 20°C.

f_o molar frictional constant of spherical molecules

f molar frictional constant of any polymer molecule

k_D concentration coefficient defined by Equation (14).

k_s concentration coefficient defined by Equation (4a).

k_s' concentration coefficient defined by Equation (4b).

M molecular weight of polymer.

$\overline{M}_n$ number average molecular weight

M_w weight average molecular weight

$\overline{M}_z$ "z" - average molecular weight

M_v molecular weight determined by Mark-Houwink equation

M_η molecular weight determined from Equations (38) or (39) or from similar relations

$M_{i,j}$ molecular weight average determined by Equation (25) from s_j and D_j

$M_{t,w}$ molecular weight determined from s_t and D_w

$M_{t,A}$ molecular weight determined from s_t and D_A

$M_{t,\sigma}$ molecular weight determined from s_t and D_σ

$M_{s,w}$ molecular weight determined with undefined sedimentation constant and D_w

$M_{s,A}$ molecular weight determined with undefined sedimentation constant and D_A

$M_{s,D}$ molecular weight determined from undefined sedimentation constant and undefined diffusion constant

$M_{w,w}$ molecular weight determined from s_w and D_w

n refractive index of polymer solution

ω angular velocity

r distance from center of rotation

r_o distance of meniscus from center of rotation

r_t distance of boundary (maximum) from center of rotation at time t

ρ density of solution $[g/cm^3]$

ρ_T density of solvent at T°C

ρ_{20}° density of reference solvent at 20°C.

ρ_1 density of solvent at 1 atm.

ρ_p density of solvent at p atm.

R gas constant

s sedimentation constant [sec]

s_o	sedimentation constant at zero polymer concentration
$[s_o]$	intrinsic sedimentation constant, see Section I.A.1.d.
s_{20}	sedimentation constant at 20°C.
s_{20}^o	sedimentation constant at 20°C reduced to reference solvent.
s_1	sedimentation constant at 1 atm. pressure
s_p	sedimentation constant at p atm. pressure
s_t	sedimentation constant determined from migration of the gradient curve maximum
s_T	sedimentation constant at T°C.
$s_n = \langle s \rangle_o$	number average of sedimentation constant
$s_w = \langle s \rangle_1$	weight average of sedimentation constant
$s_z = \langle s \rangle_2$	"z" - average of sedimentation constant
s_m	sedimentation constant determined from migration of gradient curve median
T	temperature in °C, unless specified as °K
t	time
v_2	specific volume of polymer
$\bar{v}_2$	partial specific volume of polymer
$(\bar{v}_2)_{20}$	partial specific volume of polymer at 20°C.
$(\bar{v}_2)_T$	partial specific volume of polymer at T°C.
$\bar{v}_2^*$	apparent partial specific volume of polymer
$(\bar{v}_2)_p$	partial specific volume of polymer at p atm.
$(v_2)_1$	partial specific volume of polymer at 1 atm.
$v_1^o = v_1$	specific volume of solvent.

8. Abbreviations

A	Archibald method
LS	Light scattering method
OS	Osmometry
SE	Sedimentation equilibrium
SV	Sedimentation velocity
c.a.	concentration dependence according to Equation (4a) [100 cc/g]
c.b.	concentration dependence according to Equation (4b) [100 cc/g] or [cc/g]
a	frictional ratio determined through Equation (36)
b	frictional ratio determined through Equation (37)
"Gralén"	concentration dependence of diffusion constant, determined by Gralen method (Ref. 14)
"B.+R."	concentration dependence of diffusion constant, determined by the method of Beckmann and Rosenberg (Ref. 13)
F+M	see Section I.A.6.3
W+H	see Section I.A.6.3

1 - POLYOLEFINS AND POLYDIENES

Polymer	Solvent	T°C	$s_o \times 10^{13}$	k_s	$D_o \times 10^7$	k_D	f/f_o	$\bar{v}_2$	$M \times 10^{-4}$	Remarks	Ref.
Polybutadiene 90% 1,4-cis (Al(isobutyl)$_3$/TiI$_4$)	hexane/heptane (1:1)	20	5.35		8.63				5.5	M$_{s,D}$	323
			8.5		5.30				14.2		
			11.7		4.00				26.2		
			13.7		3.10				39.5		
			20.4		2.35				87.5		
			23.0		1.90				108.0		
			$s_o = 2.80 \times 10^{-15} \times M^{0.48}$								323
90% 1,4-cis (Al(isobutyl)$_3$/CoCl$_2$)	hexane/heptane (1:1)		4.3		10.81				3.47		323
			5.3		8.62				5.42		
			7.0		6.79				9.0		
			10.2		5.01				18.6		
			15.2		3.30				44.5		
			24.0		2.00				104.0		
			$s_o = 2.33 \times 10^{-15} \times M^{0.50}$								323
Poly(butadiene-co-styrene) (21% wt. styrene)	methyl n-propyl ketone	21	$s_o = 0.83 \times 10^{-15} \times M^{0.5}$						4.9 -51.4	M$_n$	344
Polyethylene linear, high density	1-bromonaphthalene	110	$s_o = 7.74 \times 10^{-15} \times M^{0.344}$						0.35-27.4	M$_v$	38
linear	1-chloronaphthalene	120	-1.67							[η]=0.51[100 cc/g]	27
			-2.37							=0.90	
			-3.31							=1.69	
branched (fractions) branches per molec. 1.9			-1.06							[η]=0.18[100 cc/g]	
2.6			-1.91							0.33	
3.0			-2.85							0.56	

Polymer	Solvent	T°C	$s_o \times 10^{13}$	k_s	$D_o \times 10^7$	k_D	f/f_o	$\bar{v}_2$	$M \times 10^{-4}$	Remarks	Ref.
Polyethylene (Cont'd.) branched (fractions) branches per molec.											
2.9	1-chloronaphthalene	120	-2.77							[η]=0.60[100 cc/g]	27
4.6			-3.57							0.66	
5.7			-4.11							0.74	
6.4			-4.52							0.88	
13.7			-7.30							1.18	
16.1			-7.87							1.29	
26.3			-11.37							1.39	
Poly(1-hexene sulfone)	acetone	20	11.5		16.2				4.68	s_t; D_A; c.a.; $M_{t,A}$	53
			21.5		6.4				22.2		
			33.8		3.0				57.1		
		20						0.793			54
Polyisobutene	cyclohexane	20	0.925	0.54					3.09	c.a. [100 cc/g]; M_n	32
			1.49	1.28					8.67		
			1.94	1.91					17.2		
			3.33	5.1					67.2		
			4.45	8.36					142		
	ethyl octanoate	22	1.3	55.5			1.106		75	s_t;[cc/g]	237
	octane	20.9					1.072		5.2	M_v	148
		23.2					1.069		160		
		20.7					1.075		160		
Polyisoprene natural rubber, crepe	chloroform	20	15.5		2.24		3.32		27.0	$M_{s,D}$ Determ.of	337
			15.5		1.26		5.10		48.5	f/f_o see ref.	
			27.5		1.16		5.26		93.0		
								1.088			

Polymer	Solvent	T°C	$s_o \times 10^{13}$	k_s	$D_o \times 10^7$	k_D	f/f_o	$\bar{v}_2$	$M \times 10^{-4}$	Remarks	Ref.
Polyisoprene (Cont'd.)											
natural rubber, crepe	chloroform	20			2.63		3.82		12.5	M_n; OS; Determ. of f/f_o see ref.	337
					1.64		4.71		27.5		
					1.55		4.67		33.0		
					1.41		4.64		45.0		
					1.44		3.82		76.0		
natural rubber	cyclohexane	20	4.6		0.48			1.10	160	s_t; c.a.; $M_{t,A}$	29
	hexane	20	9		3				27	$M_{s,D}$	337
			21		1.01				166		
1,4 cis	hexane	20	$s_o = 5.01 \times 10^{-15}$ $\times M^{0.45}$		$D_o = 3.98 \times 10^{-2}$ $\times M^{-0.55}$			1.054		$M_{s,D}$	324
Polymethylene	1-bromonaphthalene	110	1.42						C.47	M_v	38
			2.03						1.42		
			2.39						2.18		
			3.39						5.50		
Poly(o-methylphenylene)	toluene	20	1.10		18.5		1.68	0.841	0.56	$D_{2,o}$; $M_{t,w}$; $\bar{v}_2$ independ. of M	140
			1.36		12.5		1.94		0.93	$D_{2,o}$	
			1.55		11.1		2.04		-.26	D_A	
			1.73		11.0		2.06		1.58	$D_{2,o}$; $M_{t,A}$	
			2.20		12.1				1.68	$D_{2,o}$	
			2.35		9.41		2.04		2.34	D_A; $M_{t,w}$	
			2.87		8.38		2.25		3.67	$D_{2,o}$	
			4.40		5.34		2.42		7.72	$D_{2,o}$; $M_{t,w}$	
			8.25		3.52		2.97		27.0	$D_{2,o}$	

Polymer	Solvent	T°C	$s_o \times 10^{13}$	k_s	$D_o \times 10^7$	k_D	f/f_o	$\bar{v}_2$	$M \times 10^{-4}$	Remarks	Ref.
2 - VINYL POLYMERS											
Polyacrylonitrile	dimethylformamide	25	1.52		3.6			0.830	4.8	s_t; $D_{2,o}$; $M_{t,w}$;	115
			2.08		2.1				11.3		
			2.36		1.75				15.5		
			2.95		1.25				27.0		
		25	2.04					0.830	10.5	s_t; M_w	74
			2.48						21.0		
					7.14				1.6	$D_{2,o}$; D_n given	206
					5.72				2.8	in ref.	
					5.08				6.3		
					4.03				19.3		
		35			3.91				21.4		201
									2.8-57.5		
Poly(α-methylstyrene)	cyclohexane	35	$s_o=1.72 \times M^{0.49} \times 10^{-15}$		$D_o=2.19 \times 10^{-4} \times M^{-0.58}$				3.7-62.7	M_w; A.; M_n given in ref.; s_m	321
					$k_D=2.31 \times 10^{-9} \times D_o^{-1.29}$						
Polystyrene	acetone	25						0.8990	∞	extrapolated value	268
	benzene				27.9				0.132	M_v	180
					25.0				0.195		
					21.1				0.28		
					17.2				0.39		
		20	11.9		1.18				120	s_t; $D_A=D_{2,o}$; $M_{t,w}$	50
			14.5		1.15				150		
branched		20	11.1		1.36				97	s_t; $D_A=D_{2,o}$; $M_{t,w}$	50
			12.3		0.94				150		
			12.5		0.88				169		
			16.7		0.80				245		

Polymer	Solvent	T°C	$s_0 \times 10^{13}$	k_s	$D_0 \times 10^7$	k_D	f/f_0	$\bar{v}_2$	$M \times 10^{-4}$	Remarks	Ref.
Polystyrene (Cont'd.) linear	benzene	25			11.7				1.06	c.a.; SV; M_w;	150
			2.5		4.1				6.7		
			7.14		1.50				60.6		
		25	$s_0 \sim M^{0.47}$		$D_0 \sim M^{-0.53}$			0.910	∞	extrapolated value	150 268
								0.9175	0.118-52		43
								0.9078	0.23-22.2	$_\eta; \bar{v}_2=[\bar{v}_2]_{M=\infty}$ $+ (-23/M)(B_2O_2)$	268
								-0.9177			
	benzene/methanol 1/3.27 vol.	40	19.68	100.4				0.917	400	M_w; LS; c.a.	172
		25						0.660		c.a.	150
	butyl acetate	25						0.9162	∞	extrapolated value	268
	carbon tetrachloride	27			4.43	-1.31			8.2	$D_{2,0}$; B+R method; M_n	12
					2.27	0			14	Gralén-method given in ref.	12
					1.41	0			48		
					1.04	0.5			110		
		?	180		0.45	450			350	k_s[cc/g];k_D[cc/g];	179
			260		0.33	600			500		
	chlorobenzene	27			$D_{2,0}=k \times M_{t,w}^{-0.59}$			0.9087	∞	extrapolated value	268
											12
	chloroform	25						0.9207	∞	extrapolated value	268
		20	9.2	1.8					25	c.a. [100 cc/g]	125
			13.1	3.2					55		
			15.4	4.0					80		
			17.8	5.0					130		
			-15.1		(1.84)		$[f] = 3.86 \times 10^{-5}$		54	s_t; M_w [f]=kT/D_0 in [cm]	3

References page IV-150

Polymer	Solvent	T°C	$s_o \times 10^{13}$	k_s	$D_o \times 10^7$	k_D	f/f_o	$\bar{v}_2$	$M \times 10^{-4}$	Remarks	Ref.
Polystyrene (Cont'd.)	chloroform	20					0.908				5
	chloroform	25					0.9100		∞	extrapolated value	268
			$\log[s_o]=17.922 + 0.415 \log M_w$						11.5–280	$[s_o]=-1.595$ $\times 10^{-2} s_o$	268
	cyclohexane	25						0.9293	∞	extrapolated value	268
		27						0.928				57
		35					$[f] = 0.77$ $\times 10^{-5}$		3.2	M_w; only $[f]=kT/D_o$ in [cm]	6
							1.28		10		
							1.83		20.4		
							1.97		25.3		
							2.42		36.6		
							3.37		61.6		
							3.50		80.8		
							5.01 $\times 10^{-5}$		164		
			(12.1)		1.92		2.95 $\times 10^{-5}$		54	M_w; only $[f]=kT/D_o$ in [cm]	3
								0.934			5
			$s=1.69 \times 10^{-15} \times M^{0.48}$ $s_o=1.35 \times 10^{-15}$ $\times M_w^{0.51}$		$D_o=1.21 \times 10^{-4}$ $\times M_w^{-0.49}$				1.14–104	M_w; A.	107
											96
		35	28.1	5.06							
		45	29.0	15.7				0.928	400	M_w; LS; c.a.	172
		55	34.0	35.7				0.934			
								0.936			
	decalin	27	2.73	0.73	0.50	-0.15			77	$D_{2,o}$; B+R method;M_n	12
	o-dichlorobenzene	25						0.9289	∞	extrapolated value	268
	diethyl ketone	25						0.9106	∞	" "	268

Polymer	Solvent	T°C	$s_0 \times 10^{13}$	k_s	$D_0 \times 10^7$	k_D	f/f_0	$\bar{v}_2$	$M \times 10^{-4}$	Remarks	Ref.
Polystyrene (Cont'd.)	dioxane	25						0.9270	∞	extrapolated value	268
	ethyl acetate	27	9.5	3.55	2.64	0.12			77	$D_{2,o}$; B+R method;M_n	12
		25						0.9132	∞	extrapolated value	268
	ethylbenzene	27			0.96	1.3			77	$D_{2,o}$; B+R method;M_n	12
	mesitylene	25						0.9260	∞	extrapolated value	268
	methyl ethyl ketone	20	7.13						11.0	LS; M: av. of 6 observers	11
			13.41						33.1	LS; M: av. of 6 observers	
			26.0						98.5	LS; M: av. of 6 observers	
			23.8						72.0	OS; M: av. of 3 observers	
			18.4		3.25				52.8	s; D_A; M_w	3
			12.6	0.73					25	c.a. [100 cc/g]	125
			18.2	1.3					55		
			21.3	1.7					80		
			26.0	2.3					130		
			12		12		1.38		9	s_w; $D_{2,o}$; $M_{w,w}$	126
			21		6.4		2.05		13		
			21		2.6		3.18		75		
			22		2.04		3.75		96		
			31		1.70		3.71		170		
			45		1.48		3.59		280		
			30		0.83		6.05		340		
			45		0.84		5.24		500		
			48		0.81		5.25		550		
			17.9		3.4				45	D_A; av. of 4 observers	4

References page IV-150

Polymer	Solvent	T°C	$s_o \times 10^{13}$	k_s	$D_o \times 10^7$	k_D	f/f_o	$\bar{v}_2$	$M \times 10^{-4}$	Remarks	Ref.
Polystyrene (Cont'd.)	methyl ethyl ketone	20			3.75				52.8	$D_{2,o}$ $[f]=kT/D_o\eta;M_{t,A}$	4
		25				[f] = 3.12 $\times 10^{-5}$	0.9078		∞	extrapolated value 268	3
			log[s_o]=17.845 + 0.455 log M_w						32.5	$[s_o]=1.385\times 10^{-2}$ x s_o	169
									-280		
		27	**9.8**	0.43	9.4	-0.86			8.2	[100 cc/g]; $D_{2,o}$ Gralén method;$2,o$	12
			13.3	0.48	5.14	-0.12			14	M_n	
			20.0	1.11	3.32	0.49			48	$D_{2,o}=kxM_{t,w}^{-0.53}$	
					2.51	0			77		
			25.0	1.75	2.64	0.40			110		
	methyl ethyl ketone/ butyl alcohol, φ = 0.26*	?		400	1.1	160			350	k_s[cc/g];k_D[cc/g]	179
		25	18.05						37.25	M_w; LS	169
			26.6	1.23					83		
			32.0	1.62					106.5		
			47.1	2.72					230		
	methyl isopropyl ketone	20	7.2		6.95				9.4	s; $D_A=D_{2,o}$; $M_{t,w}$	66
			7.4		6.4				10.3		
			9.6		5.35				16.1		
			10.3		4.7				19.6		
			8.4		3.45				21.8		
			14.5		3.5				37.0		
			34.0		2.5				120		
	tetrahydrofuran	25						0.9102	∞	extrapolated value 268	3
	toluene	20	8.75		1.95	[f] = 3.55 $\times 10^{-5}$			53.6	s_t; D_A; M_w; [f]= $kT/D_o\eta$ in [cm]	4
			7.92		2.02			0.910	45.0	av. of 3 observers	5

* φ = volume fraction of butyl alcohol

Polymer	Solvent	T°C	$s_o \times 10^{13}$	k_s	$D_o \times 10^7$	k_D	f/f_o	$\bar{v}_2$	$M \times 10^{-4}$	Remarks	
Polystyrene (Cont'd.)	toluene	20	$s \sim M^{0.47}$		$D \sim M^{-0.53}$				0.12-52		43
			6.25		2.50				30	s_t; D_A; M_w	1
			7.20		2.85				4.5	s_w; D_w; M_n	1
			4.75		4.03				14	s_t; D_A; $M_{t,A}$	16
			9.65		1.17				96		
			18.1		0.74				285		
			5.9	1.5					25	c.a.; k_D	125
			7.6	2.5					55	[100 cc/g]	
			9.3	3.1					80		
			11.2	4.0					130		
Szwarc, ("living polymer")		20	3.7		8.05				5.75	$M_{t,A}$;c = 1.0 g/l	44
			4.09		5.35				10.1		
			5.04		3.61				16.0		
			5.20		3.29				22.6		
free radical, linear	toluene	22.7					0.918		19	M_v	148
		23.5	3.24	36.4						s_t;[cc/g]	237
		25.0					0.9169		∞	extrapolated value	268
		27.0					0.917				57
					1.22	0.96			77	$D_{2,o}$; B+R method (ref. 13); M_n	12
	?				3.6	0.1			24	$D_{2,o}$; k_D[100 cc/g];	13
			0.66						0.12	s_t	17
			0.44						0.2		
								0.917	4		1,237
	toluene/methyl ethyl ketone 3:1	20	9.95		2.11		[f] = 3.65-5 × 10-5		52.8	s_t; D_A; [f]= kT/η_o D in [cm]	3
	1:1		12.9		2.45		3.43-5 × 10-5		55.3		

Polymer	Solvent	T°C	$s_o \times 10^{13}$	k_s	$D_o \times 10^7$	k_D	f/f_o	$\bar{v}_2$	$M \times 10^{-4}$	Remarks	Ref.
Polystyrene (Cont'd.)	toluene/methyl ethyl ketone 1:3		15.6		2.82	$[f] = 3.29 \times 10^{-5}$			54.5		3
	m-xylene							0.9205	∞	extrapolated value	268
Poly(styrene-co-divinylbenzene) (30/70)	n-octane	21	$s_o = 1.59 \times 10^{-15} \times M^{0.50}$		$D_o = 1.49 \times M^{-0.50} \times 10^{-4}$			1.05	6.5-71.0	$M_{s,D}$	322
Poly(styrenesulfonic acid)	0.2 M KCl	20	8.6						67	F+M; see ref. 127, 128	127
			9.0						68		
			9.05						81		
			10.6/1-.5						115		
Poly(vinyl acetal)	toluene	20.9						0.848			148
Poly(vinyl acetate)	cyclohexanone	23.8						0.849	4.8	M_v	148
	diethyl ketone	13						0.821			60
		40						0.833			60
	methyl ethyl ketone	20	$s_o = 9.8 \times 10^{-15} \times M^{0.38}$		$D_o = 7.8 \times M^{-0.63} \times 10^{-4}$				1.7-120	s_t; c.a.; D_A; $M_{t,A}$	110, 112
	1,2,3-trichloropropane	13						0.83			60
		40						0.841			60
Poly(vinyl alcohol)	water	20	0.96		7.46			0.765	2.24		129
									1.3	s_t; c.a. [100 cc/g]; $M_{t,w}$	129
			1.26		3.77				3.4		
			1.96		2.68				7.4		
			1.86		2.16				9		
			$s_o = 4.4 \times 10^{-15} \times M^{0.32}$		$D_o = 5.5 \times 10^{-10} \times M^{-0.68}$			0.765			130
		21.6						0.750	2.1	M_v	148
		25	0.61		6.89	2.28			0.85	s_t; c.a.; D_o; $M_{t,\sigma}$	119
			0.96		3.97	2.82			2.33	D_A given in ref.	

Polymer	Solvent	T°C	$s_o \times 10^{13}$	k_s	$D_o \times 10^7$	k_D	f/f_o	$\bar{v}_2$	$M \times 10^{-4}$	Remarks	Ref.
Poly(vinyl alcohol) {Cont'd.}	water	25	1.54		2.3		3.47		6.47	$f/f_o=1.04\ M^{-0.166}$	119
	water	30	2.52		1.45		4.00		16.7		151
								0.769	0.64	M_v	
								0.756	1.98		
								0.763	5.4		
	0.2 M NaCl	25	2.14					0.79		c.a.	152
	0.2 M NaCl (D_2O)		1.22								
Poly(4-vinyl-N-butyl-pyridinium bromide)	0.2 M NaCl	25	1.10						2.5		131
	0.2 M NaCl	20	3.0		2.8		2.38	0.77	11.5	a; c = 1.0 g/l	135
Poly(vinyl butyral)	amyl alcohol	20						0.883		$[\eta]=122[cc/g]$	148
Poly(vinylcarbazole)	chlorobenzene	23.1						0.793		$[\eta]=122$	148
Poly(vinyl chloride)	cyclohexanone	23.4						0.711	94	M_v	148
	cyclohexanone	25	0.622					0.705	1.9	M_n	75
			1.075						5.3		
			1.18						6.6		
			1.56						12.0		
			1.7						13.8		
	tetrahydrofuran	25						0.7429			181
Poly(vinyl chloride-co-vinyl acetate)	cyclohexanone	23.5						0.723		$[\eta]=77.2[cc/g]$	148
Poly(vinyl chloride-co-vinylidene chloride)	cyclohexanone	23.5						0.703		$[\eta]=77.4[cc/g]$	148
Poly(vinyl methyl ether)	amyl alcohol	23.5						0.983	1.5	M_v	148
Poly(4-vinylpyridine)	ethyl alcohol	25	3.6	1.79				0.682	9.7	c.a.[100 cc/g], W+H; ref. 134	132
			6.45	6.29				0.689	43.0		
Poly(vinylpyrrolidone)	methanol	25	3.41		9.60			0.730	2.3	c.a.; from SV; $M_{t,D}$	150
			20.0		1.20				1.08		

References page IV-150

Polymer	Solvent	T°C	$s_o \times 10^{13}$	k_s	$D_o \times 10^7$	k_D	f/f_o	$\bar{v}_2$	$M \times 10^{-4}$	Remarks	Ref.
Poly(vinylpyrrolidone) (Cont'd.)	water	20						0.776	2.0		144
								0.783	50.0		144, 143
			$s_o=8.81 \times 10^{-16} \times M^{0.50}$		$D_A=1.0 \times 10^{-4} \times M^{-0.50}$		1.70	0.802	1.2-7.4	D_A; $M_{t,A}$	
			0.82		7.55				1.3	s_t; D_σ; $M_{t,\sigma}$;$\bar{v}_2$ at 24.85°	40
			1.10		6.33		1.73		2.1		
			1.03		5.94		1.84		2.1	$D_A=5.97$	
			1.13		5.87		1.80		2.3	$D_A=6.19$	
			1.28		4.81		1.96		3.2		
			1.27		4.27		2.14		3.6	$D_A=3.89$	
			1.42		4.14		2.11		4.15		
			10		1.17				94.5	s_t; D_A; $M_{t,A}$	153
			12.20		0.50				270.0	$M_{t,A}$	
			0.85		8.66		1.66		1.06	c=5%; $M_{s,D}$	178
			1.66		4.31		2.12		4.2		
			1.94		2.44		2.94		8.6		
	unfractionated	23.1						0.775	2.9		178
		25						0.781	2.5	M_v	148
		30						0.820	2.0		150
		30						0.784	5.0		144
	0.2 M NaCl	20	1.0				1.46	0.801	1.2	c.a.[1/g]; $M_{t,A}$	144
			1.43	0.068					2.5	$s_t=8.81 \times 10^{-16} \times M^{0.50}$	
			1.59	0.085			2.09		3.92		
			1.76				2.38		5.56		
			4.77	0.391					31.0		

Polymer	Solvent	T°C	$s_o \times 10^{13}$	k_s	$D_o \times 10^7$	k_D	f/f_o	$\bar{v}_2$	$M \times 10^{-4}$	Remarks	Ref.
Poly(vinylpyrrolidone) (Cont'd.)											
	0.2 M NaCl	20	7.13				2.81		58.4		144
			7.13	0.720			4.36		112.9		
			12.5	1.310					190		
			16.7	1.63					342		
	0.1 M phosphate buffer pH = 7	20	7.15						94.5	s_t; $M_{t,A}$	153
Poly(vinylsulfonic acid) sodium salt	0.5 M NaCl	20	1.57		21.3			0.410	0.3	s_t; D_o; $M_{t,o}$	116
			1.96		15.0			0.428	0.5		
			2.32		11.0			0.433	0.9		
			2.94		9.75			0.424	1.25		
			4.27		5.95			0.4C8	2.95		
			4.46		6.40			0.464	2.95		

3 - ACRYLIC AND METHACRYLIC POLYMERS

Polymer	Solvent	T°C	$s_o \times 10^{13}$	k_s	$D_o \times 10^7$	k_D	f/f_o	$\bar{v}_2$	$M \times 10^{-4}$	Remarks	Ref.
Polyacrylamide	water	20	$s_t = 8.17 \times 10^{-15}$ $\times M^{0.31}$		$D_A = 8.46 \times 10^{-4}$ $\times M^{-0.69}$				1.94-53.4	s_t; c.a.; D_A measured in 0.2 M KCl; $M_{t,A}$	266
								0.769			154
Poly(acrylic acid ester):											
Poly(n-butyl acrylate)	methyl isobutyl ketone	23.3						0.944	4.6	M_v	148
Poly(ethyl acrylate)	methyl isobutyl ketone	24.3						0.951	3.4	M_v	148

Polymer	Solvent	T°C	$s_0 \times 10^{13}$	k_S	$D_0 \times 10^7$	k_D	f/f_0	$\bar{v}_2$	$M \times 10^{-4}$	Remarks	Ref.
Poly(p-carbethoxy-phenyl-methacrylamide)	acetone				7.05				47.9	$D_A; M_w$	267
					7.59				57.5		
					3.90				95.5		
					2.52				106.0		
	dimethylformamide (DMF)				2.18				100	$D_A; M_w$	267
	DMF/10% formamide				1.16				74	$D_A; M_w$	267
					1.11				110		
	ethyl acetate				$D_A = 2.8 \times 10^{-4} \times M_w^{-0.69}$				26-74		267
Poly(methacrylic acid) sodium salt	NaCl/water, Y* = 4	20	2.90		1.150				23.7	s_t; apparent M	124
	" = 5		3.87		1.072				33.9		
	" = 7		4.36		0.923				44.2		
	" = 9		4.73		0.838				53.0		
	" = 14		5.46		0.742				69.0		
	" = 19		5.66		0.692				76.8		
	" = 29		6.04		0.643				88.0		
	" = 39		6.28		0.621				94.3		
	" = 49		6.43		0.611				98.6		
	" = 59		6.50		0.602				101.4		
	" = ∞		7.22			3.45			111.2	M of uncharged polymer; b	
	0.01 M HCl pH 2.0	21.3						0.712	6.2	M_v	148
	0.01 M NaOH pH 12.0	21.4						0.385	7.8	M_v	148
	0.01 M NaOH/1M NaCl pH 12.0	21.8						0.412	7.8	M_v	148
Poly(butyl methacrylate):	methyl isobutyl ketone	21.2						0.922	82	M_v	148
	2-propyl alcohol	21.5			$6.3 \times 10^{-5} \times M^{-0.50}$				4-800	M_v	399

* Y = total molarity of sodium ions divided by grund molarity of poly(methacrylic acid).

Polymer	Solvent	T°C	$s_o \times 10^{13}$	k_s	$D_o \times 10^7$	k_D	f/f_o	$\bar{v}_2$	$M \times 10^{-4}$	Remarks	Ref.
Poly-p-tert-butyl phenyl methacrylate)	chloroform				$D = 6.0 \times 10^{-4} \times M_w^{-0.60}$				6.0-3.65	LS; c=0.2 g/l	179
Poly(ethyl meth-acrylate)	methyl isobutyl ketone	22.9						0.863	41	M_v	148
	acetone	20	$s_o \sim M^{0.43}$		$D_o \sim M^{-0.57}$		$f_o \sim M^{0.57}$	0.798	7.7-744	$M_{t,A}$	59
			8.95		17.4			0.7980	3.41	$M_{t,A} = M_{t,w}$(selected values)	18
			9.3		16.0				3.86	s_t	
			9.65		16.0				4.0		
			19.7		4.65				28.0		
			31.8		4.20				50.0		
			33.5		3.55				62.1		
			101		1.15				580		
			108		1.05				685		
			120		0.85				935		
								0.7942	∞	extrapolated value	268
		20	7.45	0.023	20.0	0			2.46	s_t[1/g]; D_A[1/g]	52
			11.6	0.035	12.05	0			6.35	$M_{t,w}$	
			18.8	0.058	8.3	0			14.8		
			25.2	0.102	5.45	0			30.6		
			36.5	0.153	3.95	0.011			61.1		
			48.5	0.267	2.25	0.034			142.0		
			59.5	0.321	1.35	0.039			202		
			69.0	0.407	1.42	0.066			321		
			82.0	0.420	1.18	0.068			459		
			107.0	0.610	0.95	0.063			744		

Polymer	Solvent	T°C	$s_o \times 10^{13}$	k_s	$D_o \times 10^{7}$	k_D	f/f_o	$\bar{v}_2$	$M \times 10^{-4}$	Remarks	Ref.
Poly(methyl methacrylate) (Cont'd.)											
	acetone	20	20.3	72	6.8	18	$[f]=1.97 \times 10^{-5}$	0.798	20.1	s_t; c.a. [cc/g]; D_A k_D[cc/g]; $M_{t,A}$	15
			46.1	224	2.2		5.35×10^{-5}		138		
			88.5	614	0.92		14.1×10^{-5}		635	only $[f]=kT/D_o\eta$ in [cm]	211
		20	$s_o=1.64 + 0.0441\sqrt{M}$								
	benzene	25						0.8273 −0.8077	0.19–7.7	M_η $\bar{v}_2=[\bar{v}_2]_{M=\infty} + 50/M$ (AIBN)	268
								0.8069	∞	$\bar{v}_2=[\bar{v}_2]_{M=\infty} + 39.4/M$ (B_2O_2)	211
	butyl acetate							0.8080	∞	extrapolated value	268
	butyl chloride	35.6	15.7	22	7.18	−30	$[f]=1.65 \times 10^{-5}$	0.82	20	$[f]=kT/D_o\eta$ in [cm]	6; 15
			39.1	41	2.91	−55	4.09×10^{-5}		130	s_t; c.a. [cc/g]; k_A[cc/g]; $M_{t,A}$	268
			86.0	107	1.15	−35	9.38×10^{-5}		655		
	carbon tetrachloride							0.8038	∞	extrapolated value	268
	chloroform				$D=4.5 \times 10^{-4} \times M^{-0.60}$			0.8118	∞	extrapolated value	268
									7–432	M_w; LS; 0.3 g/l	179
	o-dichlorobenzene							0.7942	∞	extrapolated value	268
	diethyl ketone							0.8187	∞	" " "	268
	dioxane							0.8015	∞	" " "	268
		25	2.11	134			$[f]=2.17 \times 10^{-5}$	0.8181	20	s_t; c.a. [cc/g]; M_w	15
			4.5	412			6.35×10^{-5}		130	only $[f]=kT/D_o\eta$ in [cm]	

Polymer	Solvent	T°C	$s_o \times 10^{13}$	k_s	$D_o \times 10^7$	k_D	f/f_o	$\bar{v}_2$	$M \times 10^{-4}$	Remarks	Ref.
Poly(methyl methacrylate) (Cont'd.)	dioxane	25	8.55	1040			$[f]=17.6 \times 10^{-5}$		655	extrapolated value	15
								0.7963		extrapolated value	268
	ethyl acetate	20	7.6	2.5	7.21	0		0.787	∞	c.a. [cc/g]; $D_{2,o}$; $M_{s,D}$ $s_o = -0.06 + 0.026\sqrt{M}$	211
						0			7.9		
			8.8	0.8	5.66				12.7		
			11.7	1.8	4.36				20.7		
			14.1	1.9	3.75				31.5		
			16.3	2.4	3.79				38.1		
			19.4	5.2	3.38				47.3		
			21.5	5.2	2.54				70.1		
			25.0	6.0	2.34				93.1		
		20	9.86	0.59					18	c.a. [cc/g]; $M_{s,w}$	212
			34.0	3.1					196.5		
			$s = 1.51 \times 10^{15} \times 10^{0.48}$						18-196.5		
	methyl ethyl ketone							0.7993	∞	extrapolated value	268
	methyl isobutyl ketone 21.8							0.816	48	M_v	148
	tetrahydrofuran							0.8085	∞	extrapolated value	268
	toluene							0.807	∞	"	268
								0.8101	∞	"	268
	m-xylene	17						0.8063	19	M_v	148
		22.15						0.8019			
		29.5						0.8190			
		45.0						0.8143			

References page IV-150

Polymer	Solvent	T°C	$s_o \times 10^{13}$	k_s	$D_o \times 10^7$	k_D	f/f_o	∇_2	$M \times 10^{-4}$	Remarks	Ref.
4 - CONDENSATION POLYMERS											
Poly(butyl isocyanate)	tetrahydrofuran	20	$s_o=3.05 \times 10^{-14} \times M^{0.16}$		$D_o=1.69 \times 10^{-4} \times M^{-0.85}$				1.8-21.1	$M_{s,D}$	325
Poly(dimethyl siloxane)	bromocyclohexane	28	-2.40		1.66				10.1	$M_{s,D}$	326
			-2.70		1.15				16.5	$M_{s,D}$	
			-4.60		0.59				55.0		
	methyl ethyl ketone	10						1.025			326
		20						1.018	1.6	M_v	148
		35						1.0282			
								1.0468			
	toluene	20	4.09		3.00				30.1	$M_{s,D}$	326
			6.07		1.60				92.0		
		22.4						1.024	0.94	M_v	148
Poly(ethylene oxide)	acetone	25			37.8				0.43	M_w; LS	184
	formamide	25			5.76				0.43	M_w; LS	184
	methanol	25			23.5				0.43	M_w; LS	184
					10.7				2.38		
	water	20	3.18		10.7			0.785	1.92	s_t; $M_{t,D}$	150
					37.0				0.029	$D_{2,o}$	177
					29.2				0.0625		
					24.0				0.125		
					13.3				0.33		
					11.6				0.58		
					10.3				0.88		
					7.2				1.06		
					23.6				0.1426		180
					22.6				0.1470		

Polymer	Solvent	T°C	$s_0 \times 10^{13}$	k_s	$D_0 \times 10^7$	k_D	f/f_0	$\bar{v}_2$	$M \times 10^{-4}$	Remarks	Ref.
Poly(ethylene oxide) (Cont'd.)											
	water	20			19.7				0.1778		180
					20.1				0.1822		148
		22.8						0.834	47	M_v	
		23.0						0.846	0.024		184
		25.0			11.5				0.43		184
			0.59		4.85				23.8		
			0.93		7.35				1.2		
			1.09		4.85				2.38		
					3.95				3.73	M_w, LS	150
Poly(heptamethylene urea)	dimethylformamide	55						0.955		M_w, LS	183
		90						0.949			
	formic acid (97%)	25						0.915			183
	96% sulfuric acid	25						0.574	2.35	M_w, LS	183
		60						0.565			
Poly(hexamethylene adipamide)	98–100% formic acid	22.4						0.890	1.6	M_v	148
Poly(4,4'-isopropyli- denediphenylene car- bonate)	methylene chloride	20	$s_0 = 1.33 \times 10^{-14}$ $\times M_{s,D}^{0.362}$		$1/D_0 = 1.569 \times 10^{-3}$ $\times M_{s,D}^{0.638}$			0.8099			45
	tetrahydrofuran	20						0.7738	0.85–26.6	s_t; c.a. [cc/g]; $M_{t,w}$	45
Poly(metaphosphoric acid)											
magnesium complex	0.4 M NaCl (water)	38				1.39	2.8	0.370	100		139
potassium salt	0.1 M NaCl (water)	14				1.05	5.2	0.311	48	s_t; $D_{2,0}$; a; $M_{t,w}$	139
	0.4 M NaCl (water)	32				1.08	3.8	0.316	110		
	0.1 M NaCl (5% ethanol)	20				1.25	4.1	0.315	57		
	0.1 M NaCl (8% ethanol)	25				1.36	3.6	0.318	65		
Poly(methylphenyl siloxane)	toluene	22						0.996		$[\eta]=132$ [cc/g]	148

Polymer	Solvent	T°C	$s_o \times 10^{13}$	k_s	$D_o \times 10^7$	k_D	f/f_o	$\bar{v}_2$	$M \times 10^{-4}$	Remarks	Ref.
Poly(trimethylhexamethylene urea)	dimethylformamide	55						0.955			183
		90						0.949			
	97% formic acid	25						0.915			

5 - CELLULOSE AND CELLULOSE DERIVATIVES

Polymer	Solvent	T°C	$s_o \times 10^{13}$	k_s	$D_o \times 10^7$	k_D	f/f_o	$\bar{v}_2$	$M \times 10^{-4}$	Remarks	Ref.
Cellulose absorbent cotton	cuam*	20	4.28		2.64				15	s_t; c=1.0 g/l	63
aged, alkali cell.			3.8	1.1	0.84	0.3	5.3	0.508	15	s_t; c.a. [100 cc/g] $D_{2,o}$; a; $M_{t,w}$	14
overaged			1.9	0.2	1.54	0.45	4.6	0.508	4.4		14
cotton (Georgia)			10.4	9.0	0.2	3.5	9.8	0.508	175		14
holo cellulose (spruce)			7.2	3.9	0.72	1.45	4.7	0.508	34		14
linters, unbleached			10.3	6.0	0.23	3.2	9.0	0.508	150		14
bleached			7.2	5.2	0.43	1.3	6.1	0.508	49		14
			9.2	6.9	0.26	2.5	8.6	0.508	120		14
linters, cotton filter paper			3.94		2.83					s_t, c=1.0 g/l	63
flax fiber			17.5	17.0	0.1	12.0	13.1	0.508	590	s_t; c.a.[100 cc/g]; $D_{2,o}$; a; $M_{t,w}$	14
nettle fiber			14.0	10.0	0.25	3.2	7.7	0.508	190		14

* cuam = cuprammonium hydroxide

Polymer	Solvent	T°C	$s_o \times 10^{13}$	k_s	$D_o \times 10^7$	k_D	f/f_o	$\bar{v}_2$	$M \times 10^{-4}$	Remarks	Ref.
Cellulose (Cont'd.)											
ramie fiber	cuam	20	10.8	8.6	0.18	2.5	10.4	0.508	200		14
sulfate cell.			6.5	3.9	0.54	1.05	5.9	0.508	40	s_t; c.a.[100 cc/g] $D_{2,o}$; a; $M_{t,w}$	14
-- , acetylated			6.3		0.37	1.9	7.7	0.508	57		14
-- , precipet.			6.3		0.66	1.65	5.2	0.508	32		14
sulfite cell.			6.3	3.8	0.45	1.15			50		14
-- , bleached			4.28		2.72					s_t; constituent A	63
			2.73		3.67					" B	63
viscose staple fiber (sulfate cellulose) (spruce)			2.6	0.5	1.04	0	4.8	0.508	7.5	s_t; c.a.; $D_{2,o}$; a; $M_{t,w}$	14
(pine)			4.1	1.7	0.54	0.75	6.4	0.508	23	s_t; constituent A	63
wood cellulose (cross and Bevan aspen)			4.28		2.70					" B	63
			2.73		3.53						63
α-Cellulose cotton linters			4.6		5.4			0.642	5.3	s_t	62
holo cellulose			6.5	3.2	0.32	2.95	8.4	0.508	68	s_t; c.a. [100 cc/g] $D_{2,o}$; a; $M_{t,w}$	14
β-Cellulose			1.6	0.5	1.97	0.5	4.0	0.508	2.7		14
Cellulose	cuene*	25	5.5		1.2				17.5	c.a.; $D_{2,o}$; $M_{s,w}$	234
			8.3		0.95				0.95		
								0.65			97
linters hydrol.	cadoxene**	25	1.80	1.53	1.77			0.59	4.3	s_t[100 cc/g]; $D_{2,o}$; $M_{t,w}$	97

* Cuene = cupriethylenediamine   ** Cadoxene = cadmium ethylenediamine

References page IV-150

Polymer	Solvent	T°C	$s_o \times 10^{13}$	k_s	$D_o \times 10^7$	k_D	f/f_o	$\bar{v}_2$	$M \times 10^{-4}$	Remarks	Ref.
Cellulose (Cont'd.) linters hydrol.	cadoxene	25	2.75	3.70	0.75				15.5		97
			3.17	4.65	0.64				21.0		
			3.80	7.10	0.58				27.5		
			4.53	10.0	0.44				43.5		
			5.49	14.1	0.31				74.5		
sulfite pulp	cadoxene	20	2.87	3.67	1.06				11.5	s_t; c.a.; D_A; $M_{s,A}$	97
	FeTNa*		1.75		0.89			0.654	11.1		235
			2.17		0.60				20.14		
			2.98		0.46				36.4		
			3.35		0.35				53.9		
Cellulose acetate	acetone	20	4.07	6	5.4	0			10	$D_{2,o}$; B+R	13
					20.7				1.035	s_t; c.a.[cc/g]; $D_{2,o}$; $M_{t,w}$	39
			7.5	56	7.7				5.1		
			10.9	143	4.0				14.3		
			12.5	191	3.4			0.68	19.4		39
Cellulose triacetate	sym-tetrachloroethane	21.9						0.744	25	M_v	148
Cellulose acetate-co-butyrate	sym-tetrachloroethane	22.7						0.777	9.7	M_v	148
Cellulose nitrate	acetone	20					1.7	0.51	0.62	$M_{s,D}$	223
							3.2		3.0	SE	
			12.0				4.6		8.02	SE	
							5.4		19.9	$M_{s,D}$	
			30.0				6.9		61.3	$M_{s,D}$	
			13.9		6.5		3.74		10	a; $M_{s,D}$	276

* FeTNa = Iron-Tartaric acid complex Na salt

Polymer	Solvent	T°C	$s_o \times 10^{13}$	k_s	$D_o \times 10^7$	k_D	f/f_o	$\bar{v}_2$	$M \times 10^{-4}$	Remarks	Ref.
Cellulose nitrate (Cont'd.) (N = 13.8%)	acetone	20					0.57				
			14.0		3.29				19.0	s_t; c.a.; $D_A=D_{2,o}$; $M_{t,w}$	64
			14.2		2.60				24.2		65
			6.5		20.9				1.38	s_w; $D_{2,o}$; $M_{w,w}$	259
			7.1		19.3			0.572	1.63		
			8.3		13.3			0.570	2.78		
			12.6		5.6			0.566	10.0		
			15.3		4.5				15.3		
			14.5		3.5				18.7		
			16.8		2.8				26.7		
			25.3		2.3				49.5		
			26.2		1.0				117.5		
cotton (N = 13.8%)			7.2		25.0				1.3	s_t; c.a.; $D_A=D_{2,c}$; $M_{t,w}$	64
			8.8		16.5				2.3		
			11.1		10.8				4.6		
			10.8		6.45				7.4		
			12.8		6.30				9		
			15.2		3.80				17.8		
			17.1		2.90				26.2		
			20.5		2.00				45.6		
			21.5		1.50				63.0		
			37.5		0.56				249.0		64, 58

Polymer	Solvent	T°C	$s_o \times 10^{13}$	k_s	$D_o \times 10^7$	k_D	f/f_o	$\bar{v}_2$	$M \times 10^{-4}$	Remarks	Ref.
Cellulose nitrate from cotton (N=13.5-14%)	acetone	20	10.8		6.45				7.4	s_t; $D_A=D_{2,o}$; $M_{t,w}$	49, 58
			15.2		3.80				17.8		58
			17.1		2.90				26.2		
			20.5		2.00				45.6		
			20.0		1.50				59.3		
			30.5		1.20				113.0		
holo cellulose (spruce)			21.6	4.2	2.57	1.75	6.3	0.51	34	s_t; c.a.; $D_{2,o}$; a; $M_{t,w}$	14
			13.4	2.1	2.4	0.65			78		14
holo cellulose (α-cellulose)							7.7	0.51	23	s_t; c.a.; $D_{2,o}$; a; $M_{t,w}$	14
from linters			16		2.8				25	s_t; c.a.; $D_A=D_{2,o}$; $M_{t,w}$	65
			15.8		2.05				34.4		
			19.0	4.2	1.0	2.1	12.2	0.510	78	s_t; c.a.; $D_{2,o}$; a; $M_{t,w}$	14
-- , bleached			14.0	2.8	1.44	1.2	10.6	0.510	40	s_t; c.a.; a; $M_{t,w}$	14
			19.0	4.2	1.11	2.25	11.5	0.510	60		14
									68		
linters, bleached and unbleached			5.2		35				0.6	$M_{s,D}$	223
			8.7						3.0	SE	
			12.0						8.0	SE	
			18.0		3.7				19.9	$M_{s,D}$	
			30.0		2.0				61.3	$M_{s,D}$	
rayon pulp			17.6	4.8	3.01	2.35	6.0	0.51	24	s_t, c.a.[100 cc/g]; $M_{t,w}$ $D_{2,o}$; $M_{t,w}$	14

Polymer	Solvent	T°C	$s_0 \times 10^{13}$	k_s	$D_0 \times 10^7$	k_D	f/f_0	$\bar{v}_2$	$M \times 10^{-4}$	Remarks	Ref.
Cellulose nitrate (Cont'd.)											
rayon pulp	acetone	20	15.5	2.6	2.15	1.0	7.9	0.51	30		14
			16.7	3.6	1.94		8.2	0.51	35		
			18.3	4.8	1.48		9.6	0.51	51		
			23.3	11.5	1.66		8.2	0.51	57		
sulfate pulp			16.2	3.5	1.56	2.8	9.6	0.51	42	s_t, c.a.[100 cc/g]; $D_{2,0}$; a; $M_{t,w}$	14
sulfite pulp			16.4	3.6	1.56	2.65	9.6	0.51	43	s_t, c.a.[100 cc/g]; $D_{2,0}$; a; $M_{t,w}$	14
Cellulose nitrate	butyl acetate							0.584			259
	cyclohexanone		1.1					0.59	8.02	SE; [s_0] given	223
			2.0						61.3	$M_{s,D}$	
	ethyl acetate	21.3						0.556	35	M_v	148
from chemical cotton		20	11.4		1.49				37	s_t; $D_{2,0}$; $M_{t,w}$	91
			13.1		0.91				69		
from raw cotton (Delfos variety)					0.47				150		91
from linters			9.3		2.40				19.5	s_t, c.a.; $D_A = D_{2,0}$; $M_{t,w}$	65
from viscose rayon			9.26		4.77				9.3	s_t; $D_{2,0}$; $M_{t,w}$	91
									1.75	M_n	91
	methanol	20						0.545	8.02	SE	223
	pentyl acetate	20			13.3			0.54	2.7	$M_{w,w}$	259
					5.8				9.1		
					5.6				10		
					4.5				15.5		
					3.5				18.6		
					2.9				28.2		

References page IV-150

Polymer	Solvent	T°C	$s_o \times 10^{13}$	k_s	$D_o \times 10^7$	k_D	f/f_o	$\bar{v}_2$	$M \times 10^{-4}$	Remarks	Ref.
Cellulose nitrate (Cont'd.)											
from viscose rayon	pentyl acetate	20	4.0					0.55	8.02	SE	223
			6.5						61.3	$M_{s,D}$	
Cellulose trinitrate											
from purified chemical linters	ethyl acetate	30	6.34						4.13	M_w; $M_n = 3.46 \times 10^4$	90
			7.10						7.6	M_w; $M_n = 6.06 \times 10^4$	
			8.65						12.8	M_w; $M_n = 8.9 \times 10^4$	
from purified cotton linters			9.62						11.0	M_n; $s_o = 0.304 \times 10^{-13}$	90
			11.13						24.8	M_w $_o \times M_w^{0.29}$	
			12.66						57.3	M_w; $M_n = 25.7$	
Ethyl cellulose	acetone	20			3.46				2.0	D_o; $c = 6.1$ g/1	21
					1.43				5.3	$c = 5.0$ g/1	
					1.05				9.0	$c = 5.16$ g/1	
	sym-tetrachloroethane	21.9						0.864	19.0	M_v	148
Ethyl hydroxyethyl cellulose											
ca. 18% ethoxyl ca. 30% ethoxyl + hydroxyethyl	water	20	2.0		1.9	0.3	3.8	0.721	9.2	s_t; $D_{2,o}$; D_A given in ref.;b;	94
			2.32		1.4	0.3	4.1	0.711	14.0	$M_{t,w}$	
			2.63		1.1	0.3	5.1	0.703	20.0	$s = 3.1 \times 10^{-15} \times M^{0.36}$	
			3.0		0.8	0.3	6.0	0.705	30.0	$D_{2,o} = 10^{-4} \times M^{-0.7}$	
Hydroxyethyl cellulose	water	19.2						0.678	47.0	M_v	148
		25	2.82	3.85	1.86		3.96	0.701	12.5	s_t, c.a.; b; $\bar{v}_2$ at 20°C; $M_{t,w}$	98
			4.45	10.2	1.11		4.78		33.0		
			4.90	11.9	0.96		5.12		42	$s = 1.0 \times 10^{-15} M_{t,w}^{0.46}$	
			5.65	5.8	0.85		5.29		54.5	$D = 8.2 \times 10^{-5} M^{-0.54}$	

Polymer	Solvent	T°C	$s_o \times 10^{13}$	k_s	$D_o \times 10^7$	k_D	f/f_o	$\bar{v}_2$	$M \times 10^{-4}$	Remarks	Ref.
Methyl cellulose											
22.6% methoxyl	water	20	0.83				3.0	0.68	1.4	M_w; SE	222
27.05 "			1.29		1.49				7.06	s_t; c.a.; D_A; $M_{t,A}$	19
27.44 "			1.57		0.92			0.704	15.1		
28.45 "			2.50		0.71			0.710	30.2		
28.8 "			0.79		3.05			0.683	2.26		19, 20
			0.79				3.9	0.717	2.43	M_w; SE	222
31.7 "			0.89		2.34			0.720	3.43	s_t; c.a.; D_A; $M_{t,A}$	19, 20
31.8 "			0.89				4.5	0.73	3.81	M_w; SE	222
ca. 28 "			$s_o=0.85 \times 10^{-15}$ $\times M_{t,A}^{0.45}$		$D_o=0.79 \times 10^{-4}$ $\times M_{t,A}^{0.56}$			$\bar{v}_2=0.560+0.0542$ $\times$ (% OCH_3)			19, 20
	0.2 M NaCl	20			4.45				1.41	D_o; av. of M not specified	21
					3.05				2.43	D_o; c=5.0 g/l	
					2.47				3.81	D_o	
Sodium carboxymethyl cellulose	0.01 M NaOH; pH=12.0	20.6						0.505	70	M_v	148
cellulose	0.001 M NaCl	25	2.40						4.47	$M_{t,w}$	314
			2.30						4.6		
			2.50						9.06		
			2.58						9.42		
			2.65						16.3		
			2.62						19.4		
			2.85						28.0		
			2.96						34.6		
	0.005 M NaCl		2.54						7	M_n	277, 278
			3.00						10.4		

Polymer	Solvent	T°C	$s_o \times 10^{13}$	k_s	$D_o \times 10^7$	k_D	f/f_o	$\bar{v}_2$	$M \times 10^{-4}$	Remarks	Ref.
Sodium carboxymethyl cellulose (Cont'd.)											
	0.005 M NaCl		3.14						17.5		277, 278
			3.97						29.0		
	0.01 M NaCl		2.76						7	M_n	277, 278
			3.18						10.4		
			4.25						17.5		
			4.28						29		
			2.70						4.47		314
			3.11						16.3		
			4.53						34.6		
Sodium cellulose glycolate											
	0.2 M NaCl	20			3.08	1.85			5.5	$D_{2,o}$ [100 cc/g]; $M_{t,w}$	14
	0.5 M NaCl				3.30	2.15				$D_{2,o}$	14
	1.0 M NaCl		3.4	1.3	3.22		3.2	0.53	5.5	c.a.[100 cc/g]; s_t; $D_{2,o}$; a; $M_{t,w}$	14
Sodium cellulose xanthate											
	0.2 M NaOH+1.0 M NaCl		2.30	0.9	3.35	0.20	3.5	0.530	3.5	$D_{2,o}$; a; $M_{t,w}$	14
			2.40	0.7	3.40	0	3.4		3.7		
			2.80	1.0	2.98	0	3.5		4.8		
			2.80	0.9	2.84	0.08	3.7		5.2		
			2.70	0.8	2.28	0	4.3		6.1		
			4.4	2.8	1.83		4.3		12.6		

6 - POLYSACCHARIDES
(other than Cellulose and Cellulose Derivatives)

Polymer	Solvent	T°C	$s_o \times 10^{13}$	k_s	$D_o \times 10^7$	k_D	f/f_o	$\bar{v}_2$	$M \times 10^{-4}$	Remarks	Ref.
Amylopectin	water	20	44.8						310	s_t; M_w, LS; c=1.5 g/l	137
			8.8						4100	c=1.4 g/l	
Amylopectin acetate	methyl acetate				0.42	3.6			700	$D_{2,o}$, B+R;[100 cc/g]	13
Amylose acetate											
potato	methyl acetate				8.0	0			6.9	$D_{2,o}$, B+R;[100 cc/g]	13
corn					6.8	0			10.8		
tapioca					4.2	0.6			15.1		
potato					2.2	2.2			35.0		
Dextran	water	20	1.1-6.0						1-20	s_t vs M diagram	23
			2.02						2	s_t; M determ. by Ogston Method (ref. 24,25)	24
			3.04						4.4		
			3.47						6.5		
			5.47						15.0		
			9.6						46.0		
		20.9						0.60	16.0	M_v	148
		20	$s_o=2.45 \times 10^{-16} \times M_w^{0.44}$						1.8-40		26
			$s_o=2.36 \times 10^{-16} \times M_n^{0.45}$						1.3-20		26
	0.025 M Na_2HPO_4 + 0.025 M NaH_2PO_4	20	1.64		7.50		1.88		1.4	s_t; D_A; a; $M_{t,A}$	92
			2.64		4.69		2.19		3.6		
			4.1		3.12		2.49	0.62	8.4		
			5.3		2.40		2.79		14.1		
			6.55		1.73		3.15		24		
			23.3		0.75		3.61		199		
			26.4		0.55		4.25		305		
			150		0.25		4.03		3800		

References page IV-150

Polymer	Solvent	T°C	$s_o \times 10^{13}$	k_s	$D_o \times 10^7$	k_D	f/f_o	$\bar{v}_2$	$M \times 10^{-4}$	Remarks	Ref.
Dextran (cont'd.) from leuconostoc mesenteroides ca. 5% branched	0.05 Na$_2$H PO$_4$ + 0.05 M NaH$_2$PO$_4$	20	1.57		8.80		1.74	0.611	1.12	s_t; D_A; $M_{t,A}$	167
			1.96		6.20		2.08		1.98		
			2.44		5.58		2.03		2.74	$s_t = 1.45 \times 10^{-15}$	
			2.76		4.91		2.12		3.52	$\times M_{t,A}^{0.50}$	
			3.52		4.24		2.16		5.2		
			4.27		2.89		2.61		9.25		
			5.0		2.84		2.51		11.0		
			5.45		2.57		2.60		13.3		
			5.62		2.22		2.84		15.9		
			6.35		2.20		2.75		18.1		
			6.75		2.11		2.77		20.0		
			9.82		1.40		3.22		43.7		
highly branched	0.05 M Na$_2$HPO$_4$ + 0.05 M NaH$_2$PO$_4$	20	2.55		5.40		2.07	0.603	2.88	s_t; D_A; $M_{t,A}$	167
			3.21		3.95		2.36		4.96		
			3.47		3.52		2.48		6.02	$s_t = 3.43 \times 10^{-15} M_{t,A}^{0.42}$	
			4.05		2.95		2.66		8.40		
			4.73		2.30		2.98		12.5		
β-Dextrin	water	20	0.48					0.627	0.1134	c=1.0 g/l	171
Polyfructosan	water	25						0.639	0.148	M_w	265
								0.633	0.205		
								0.628	0.240		
Polyglucose A (synthetic)	water		0.80								138
Glycogen (different sources)	1 M NaCl	18-63			1.80-1.50			0.64-0.66	70-290	D_o; $M_{t,\sigma}$; $\bar{v}_2$ determ. in water; c=10 g/l	100
		20						0.62			138

Polymer	Solvent	T°C	$s_o \times 10^{13}$	k_s	$D_o \times 10^7$	k_D	f/f_o	$\bar{v}_2$	$M \times 10^{-4}$	Remarks	Ref.
Levan.											
from B-mesentericus	water	20	1.39					0.659	0.828	M_w; c=10.27 g/l	265
from living cultures			191		0.71				1730	$M_{s,D}$	260
(enzyme-sucrose synt.)			399		0.38				6700		
Levulan		20									
from levans			1.8		15.8				0.735	$M_{s,D}$	260
			3.3		6.9				3.07		
Polysaccharide from larchwood											
α-component			1.54		6.8				1.58	D_A; $M_{s,D}$	269
			5.25		3.4				9.88		
β-component			4.5								
from larch, heart wood											261
--, sap wood, α-comp.			4.5								
β-comp.			1.2								
Sodium alginate	acetate buffer	40	4.3		7.4				7.4		136
	pH 5.5; I.S. 0.05*		7.4		29.0				29.0		
	phosphate buffer pH 6.6	25	2.76					0.54		v_2 by diff. sedim.	152
								0.481		v_2 by pycnomet.	
	pH 6.6 (D$_2$O)		2.02								
Sodium carrageenate	acetate buffer	40	8						29		136
	pH 5.5 I.S.* 0.2		11.8						63		
			13.8						79		
Starch, acid treated	water				11.5	0.5			0.5	B+R;[100 cc/g]:$D_{2,o}$	13
					10.0	0.2			1.0		
Starch acetate	methyl acetate				15.3	0			3.2	B+R;[100 cc/g];$D_{2,o}$	13

* I.S. = Ionic strength

References page IV-150

7 - PROTEINS AND POLYPEPTIDES*

Polymer	Solvent	$T°C$	$s_o \times 10^{13}$	k_s	$D_o \times 10^7$	k_D	f/f_o	$\bar{v}_2$	$M \times 10^{-4}$	Remarks	Ref.
Actin active		20	64						7.6	c=1.0 g/1	255
Actomyosin		20	93–280		0.5				1400	$M_{s,D}$	255
Albumin											
bovine, serum, cryst.	water	25						0.7343			161
human, cryst.	0.15 M NaCl	20	4.6		6.1		1.28	0.733	6.9		120
bovine, cryst.	0.2 M NaCl	15	3.79	-0.24				0.727		c.b.; s_t	147
		20	4.36	-0.28				0.727	6.454		147
bovine, plasma, cryst.			4.73	-0.25				0.731		s_t; c.b.	156
bovine, cryst.		25	4.96	-0.31				0.731			147
bovine, plasma, cryst.			4.78					0.74		c.a.	152
	(D$_2$O)		2.97								
bovine, cryst.								0.730			146
porcine								0.731			146
bovine, cryst.		30	5.51	-0.34				0.736			147
bovine, serum	0.5 M KCl pH 5.14	1			3.261						244
	acetate buffer pH 4.6	1			3.066					c=2.5 g/1	252
		25			6.577						
bovine, plasma	acetate buffer	20	4.46		6.45					s_t; c=1.0 g/1	38
horse, serum			4.50		6.22			0.748	6.71	D_o; $M_{t,\sigma}$	108
serum										D_σ; c=7.0 g/1	67
bovine, serum	phosphate buffer pH 7.0	20.2	4.44		5.7				7.35		213
		21						0.733	6.6		148
	citrate buffer pH 4.0	22.2						0.738			148
serum	not given		4.5					0.734			121
human, plasma			4.6		6.1				6.9	$M_{s,D}$; cited in ref. 257	258

* Additional data may be found in H. M. Rauen, "Biochemisches Taschenbuch," Springer-Verlag, Berlin, 1964.

Polymer	Solvent	T°C	$s_o \times 10^{13}$	k_s	$D_o \times 10^7$	k_D	f'/f_o	$\bar v_2$	$M \times 10^{-4}$	Remarks	Ref.
Alcohol dehydrogenase from liver	phosphate buffer	20	5.1								241
					5.9				8.4		213
from horse liver	phosphate buffer pH 7.2		4.38		6.5			0.751	7.3	D_A; $M_{s,D}$	226
Aldolase			7						15	c=60 g/l	173
Arachin	phosphate buffer pH 5.5	21			3.62					D_σ; c=3.7 g/l	67
	not given				3.45					average of 15 meas.	68
					3.62				32.9		69, 70
Apomyoglobin I	phosphate buffer pH 7.0		1.89		10.4				1.72		213
Azachin	phosphate-NaCl buffer pH 7.5	20	13.2							main component	345
Bence-Jones protein	phosphate buffer pH 7.0				7.35					c=10 g/l	67
S-Carboxymethyl keratine 2	varying phosphate buffer		1.95-5.00								204
α-Chymotrypsin								0.736			182
Clupein (Hoffmann-LaRoche)	0.22 M acetate	20	0.46							c=1 g/l	171
(Carlsberg Lab)			0.69								
Collagen	2 M KCNS	20	3.48						12.5	M_n ⎫ same sample	301
	citrate buffer		3.77						14.7	M_w ⎭	
Cytochrome C	0.05 M borax buffer pH 8.7	20	1.83		11.5		1.21	0.702-0.707	1.36	b; $M_{s,D}$	225
	0.02 M phosphate buffer pH 7	20	1.89		10.1			0.71	1.56	D_σ	67, 73
beef, 0.42% Fe	0.05 M phosphate buffer pH 6.8	20	1.64				1.25				228

References page IV-150

Polymer	Solvent	T°C	$s_0 \times 10^{13}$	k_s	$D_0 \times 10^7$	k_D	f/f_0	$\bar{v}_2$	$M \times 10^{-4}$	Remarks	Ref.
Cytochrome C (Cont'd.)											
horse 0.31% Fe	0.05 M phosphate buffer pH 6.8	20	1.61				1.41				228
0.36% Fe			1.58				1.42				
0.41% Fe			1.89		9.5		1.34				
salmon 0.27% Fe			1.48		10.7		1.26	0.75			
0.41% Fe			2.33		10.2		1.19				
0.48% Fe			1.76				1.31				
chicken 0.37% Fe			1.63		11.3		1.23	0.72			
beef heart	0.05 M phosphate buffer pH 7.0	21.7	1.71		11.4			0.728	1.33	$\bar{v}_2$ measured in water	213
hemopeptide from peptic degradation of beef cytochrome C	0.03 M citrate pH 2.3	20	0.6		24.0		1.08	0.7	0.2		225
	0.05 M borax pH 8.7		1.57		11.8		1.25		1.0	$M_{s,D}$ } same sample	
	0.05 NaAc pH 4.0		2.53		56				0.38		68
Edestin	1.726 M NaCl phosphate-NaCl-buffer pH 7.5	20	13.3		3.19				33.4	$D_{2,0}$ main component	345
Erythrocruorin from different sources	buffer, see ref.	20	1.9						1.9	M_w, SE	76
			2.3						2.31		
			2.6						2.36		
			2.0						3.14		
			2.1						3.64		
			60.9						273		78
			57.4						285		
from daphnia	0.02 M phosphate buffer or acetate buffer		16.3					0.745	3.4		76
from lampetra								0.751			67

Polymer	Solvent	T°C	$s_o \times 10^{13}$	k_s	$D_o \times 10^7$	k_D	f/f_o	$\bar{v}_2$	$M \times 10^{-4}$	Remarks	Ref.
Erythrocruorin (Cont'd.)											
from lumbricus	0.01 M phosphate buffer pH 6.57	20			1.81					D_σ	67
from planorbis corneus	0.05 M phosphate buffer pH 6.67	20	33.7		1.96			0.745	163.4	$M_{t,\sigma}$	168
			33.7						134.1	s_t; M_w, SE	76
from petromyzon								0.751	1.91		76
Excelsin	0.826 M NaCl	20			4.26					D_σ; c=5.0 g/l	67
	1.024 M NaCl				4.32						
Fibrinogen	0.15 M NaCl						1.98		40		120
bovine	0.2 M NaCl	20						0.706			146
			8.62	-0.65						s_t; c.b.[100 cc/g];	156
			7.66	-0.74						measured at 30°C	155
			7.48	-0.56						25°C	
			7.87	-0.66						20°C	
			7.92	-0.67							
		25	8.46	-0.63						s_t, c.b.[100 cc/g]	154
		30	9.64	-0.93							
		15	6.64	-0.56							154
	0.1 M Na$_2$HPO$_4$	20	7.71	-0.72							154
			7.28	-0.66						measured at 30°C	155
			7.60	-0.65				0.715		25°C	
			7.57	-0.65						20°C	
			7.27	-0.62						15°C	
		25	8.74	-0.77				0.715			154
		30	9.37	-0.87				0.715			154
	0.05 M phosphate buffer pH 6.2	20	7.95		1.85	-5.9		2.34	33	b; $M_{t,A}$	42
	pH 5.57	20	7.95	11.1				2.388	0.71	39.0	s_t; c.a.[100 cc/g]; D_A; b; $M_{t,A}$	41, 42

References page IV-150

SEDIMENTATION AND DIFFUSION CONSTANTS

Polymer	Solvent	T°C	$s_o \times 10^{13}$	k_s	$D_o \times 10^7$	k_D	f/f_o	$\bar{v}_2$	$M \times 10^{-4}$	Remarks	Ref.
Fibrinogen (Cont'd.)											
bovine	0.05 M phosphate buffer pH 6.66 pH 7.66	20	8.03 8.10	11.3 21.8	1.82 1.90	-15.9 -22.0	2.410 2.362		39.7 39.9		41, 42
human	phosphate buffer pH 6.9 I.S.* 0.4	20	8.5		1.1		3.0	0.75	70	D_m; b; $M_{t,w}$	145
	I.S. 0.3		8.37								
	I.S. 0.2		8.34								
	I.S. 0.1		8.58								
	0.05 M citrate buffer pH 6.4	20	9.0						40		120
	not given		7.0						50	M_η cited in ref. 257	258
Gelatin	acetate buffer	20						0.685		c=10 g/l	339
	phosphate-KCNS-buffer	30	5.08 6.50				3.47 4.22		38.3 59.6	M_w	338
	17.51% KCNS	25						0.680			340
	various buffers	20	3.42- 2.46		1.45- 2.00		4.0- 3.6		17.8- 9.3	c= ca. 4 g/l	341
	water	20-30						0.682		c=10-20 g/l	339
Gliadin, from wheat	ethyl alcohol (64%)	20	2.1		6.72			0.722	2.74		67, 114
	ethyl alcohol (60 vol %) + 0.1 M NaCl	20	2.1		6.72			0.722	2.75	$M_{t,\sigma}$	168
α_2-Globulin, human	0.15 M NaCl	20	5.0 9.0				1.58 1.58	0.693 0.693	20 30		120
β_1-Globulin, human	0.15 M NaCl	20	5.5 7.0 20.0				1.37	0.725 0.724 0.74	9.0 15.0 50.0-100		120
β_2-Blobulin, human	0.15 M NaCl	20	2.9 7.0				1.7	0.95	130.0 15		120

*I.S. = Ionic Strength

Polymer	Solvent	T°C	$s_0 \times 10^{13}$	k_s	$D_0 \times 10^7$	k_D	f/f_0	$\bar{v}_2$	$M \times 10^{-4}$	Remarks	Ref.
γ-Globulin	0.15 M NaCl	20	7.2 10.0				1.38	0.739	15.6 30.0		120
α-Globulin	0.2 M NaCl						0.722				146
β-Globulin											
bovine, plasma	0.2 M NaCl	20	7.31	-0.25						s_t, c.b. [100 cc/g]	156
bovine								0.714			146
porcine								0.765			
γ-Globulin											
bovine, plasma	0.2 M NaCl	20	7.37	-0.24						s_t, c.b. [100 cc/g]	156
bovine								0.725			146
porcine								0.744			
Globulin, serum	0.2 M NaCl	20			4.1					c=10 g/l	67
γ-Globulin											
bovine	0.4726 M KCl	25					0.72				161
not specif.	phosphate buffer	20	7.3		3.81				17	D_A; $D_{2,0}$=3.57	170
Globulin, serum different sources	not given		7.1						13.8	SE	121
Glucose dehydrogenase from aspergillus niger	phosphate buffer pH 5.60	20	8.81		4.47		1.24	0.75	19.2	a	51
Glucose oxidase (Notatin)	phosphate buffer	20	8.27		5.13		1.16	0.75	15.2	$M_{s,D}$; c=3.6 g/l	47
Elutamine	water	25			76.23					c=6.76 g/l	251
Eenocyanin from various sources	various buffers	20			1.05-3.39						67
	various buffers		17.4-130.4		3.4-1.17				37.96-998		175
CO-Hemoglobin, human	0.008 phosphate buffer pH 6.5	20			7.54					D_σ; c=2.0 g/l	67
			4.5		6.90			0.749	6.3	D_σ; $M_{t,\sigma}$	168
	0.01 M phosphate buffer pH 6.8	20			14.7				6.8	c=1.7 g/l	158

References page IV-150

Polymer	Solvent	T°C	$s_0 \times 10^{13}$	k_s	$D_0 \times 10^7$	k_D	f/f_0	$\bar{v}_2$	$M \times 10^{-4}$	Remarks	Ref.
CO-Hemoglobin (Cont'd.)											
human	0.0286 M phosphate buffer pH 7.07	20	4.35							from Fresnel diffract. patt. c=1.2 g/l	38
	0.02 M phosphate buffer pH 6.7	20			10.65					D_σ	67
different samples	0.02 M-0.066 M phosphate buffer	20	4.48-4.60	given in ref.						c.b. [100 cc/g]	227
	NaCl		4.78	0.0439						c.b. [100 cc/g]	227
horse	0.034 M phosphate buffer pH 7.5	20			7.81					D_σ; c=3.8 g/l	67
Heparin	1 M KCl	25	3.06	13.8	9.8	14		0.479	1.55	s_t[cc/g]; $M_{s,D}$	190
			3.20	26.6	11.6	23		0.479	1.37		
Hexokinase monomer	phosphate buffer pH 8	2	3.7								173
dimer	acetate buffer pH 4.9		5.9								
Insulin	phosphate buffer pH 6.8	20			8.12					D_σ ; c=2.0 g/l	67
	pH 7.3				8.28 8.19					c = 2.0 g/l	
oxidized	phosphate buffer pH 6.8	20			7.16					c = 2.5 g/l	67
	pH 7.3				7.10					c = 3.0 g/l	
Insulin A	0.2 M K_2HPO_4	20	0.56						0.3	c = 0.6 g/l	171
Lactalbumin	acetate buffer pH 4.8	20			10.57					c = 7.0 g/l	67
Lactic dehydrogenase from hog heart	phosphate buffer pH 7.11	20	7.29							c = 2.5 g/l	38
Lactoglobulin	acetate buffer pH 5.0	20	2.95		7.18			0.751	4	D_σ; $M_{t,\sigma}$	168
	borate buffer pH 9.5	20	2.76		6.78			0.751	3.96		168

Polymer	Solvent	T°C	$s_o \times 10^{13}$	k_s	$D_o \times 10^7$	k_D	f/f_o	$\bar{v}_2$	$M \times 10^{-4}$	Remarks	Ref.
Lactoglobulin (Cont'd.)											
palmer	acetate buffer pH 5.0	20	2.95		7.27				3.97	$M_{t,D}$; c=1 g/1	159
	borate buffer		2.76		6.88				3.92	c=1 g/1	
	phosphate buffer pH 5.4		3.12		7.19				4.15	c=1 g/1	
	pH 6.1		3.12		7.32				4.24		
Legumin	phosphate buffer pH 7.61	20	12.1						38.8	main component	345
L-poprotein, human serum	various buffers pH 6.7		5.9						277	M_w, LS	306
			6.4						280		
			8.1						308		
Meromyosin (light)	0.05 M phosphate buffer, pH 6.3	20	3.0						ca. 12.8		347
(heavy)			7.2						32.0		
Mieloperoxidase	0.05 M borate buffer pH 9.9				4.9				14.5		213
	pH 7.0	20	7.93	-0.0429	4.81	1.26			14.5	c.b.,[ml/mg]; $D_{2,0}$; $M_{s,w}$	242
	water							0.731			242
Myoglobin	phosphate buffer pH 7.1	20			11.24					D_σ; c=3.5 g/1	67
CO-Myoglobin I	phosphate buffer pH 7.0		2.01		10.3				1.85		213
Myosin	0.5 M KCl pH 6.8		6.7						2500	s_t	79, 82
			7.2								80
	0.6 M KCl pH 6.7	1	6.40						49.3	M_w, LS	305
		25	6.75								
crystallized	veronal-acetate buffer pH 6.8	15			0.5		5.5	0.74	150	b; $M_{s,D}$	256
		20	7.2								

References page IV-150

Polymer	Solvent	T°C	$s_o \times 10^{13}$	k_s	$D_o \times 10^7$	k_D	f/f_o	$\bar{v}_2$	$M \times 10^{-4}$	Remarks	Ref.
Proteins, globular	various buffers	20	\multicolumn{4}{c}{$s_o = 7.95 \times 10^{-16} \times M^{0.563}$}				1.74–36.0	values for s_o taken from ref. 2	143
Rhodanese	phosphate buffer pH 7.44	20	3.0		7.5		1.28	0.742	3.71	D_A; $M_{s,A}$	224
	pH 7.0		3.03		8.2				5.56		213
Salmine	0.22 M acetate buffer pH 4.3	20	0.32								171
Polysarcosine	water	25	0.72		9.6				0.67		141
			0.80		7.7				0.97		
			0.87		7.0				1.39		
			0.92		6.2			0.736	1.61		
			0.98		5.7				1.62		
Sulfatase	veronal buffer pH 5.0	20	14.1					0.73	41.1	s_t; M_w, A, SE; $\bar{v}_2$ at 25°C	142
	pH 7.5		6.03					0.72	10.7		
Thyroglobulin human & hog	different buffers	20	19.2		2.39		1.50	0.72	70	s_t	123
Tropomyosin	phosphate buffer pH 6.7	20			2.65					D_o; c=7.0 g/l	67
	not given		2.6		2.35				10.4	$M_{s,D}$; c=6.0 g/l	272
Virus rabbit papilloma	phosphate buffer	20			0.59		1.49		4700	a; c=0.2 g/l	63
different samples			284							c = 2.1 g/l	174
southern bean mosaic	phosphate buffer	20	114		1.4		1.25	0.696	663	s_t; D_A; a; $M_{t,w}$ for $\bar{v}_2$ see ref.; c=5.0g/l	81
tobacco mosaic	phosphate buffer	20	188		0.53			0.788	4190	unhydrated;ref. 32	37
									4190	s_t	32, 34,36
	0.1 M phosphate buffer pH 7.0	26.8–28.7						0.725–0.712	4190		32, 33

References page IV-150

Polymer	Solvent	T°C	$s_o \times 10^{13}$	k_s	$D_o \times 10^7$	k_D	f/f_o	$\bar{v}_2$	$M \times 10^{-4}$	Remarks	Ref.
Virus (Cont't.)											
tobacco mosaic	0.1 M phosphate buffer pH 7.0		170-180							s_t	101
			174		0.3		3.12		5900	component 1	102
							3.0		6400	2	
								0.73			103, 104
bushy stunt			188						3900	M_w, LS	304
			132		1.26			0.712	9000	M_w	173
tomato bushy stunt		20	132								83,87
								0.739			83,87
								0.724			83,88
		20			1.2		1.27		1060	a; c=0.2 g/1	72
Yellow enzyme (old)	phosphate buffer pH 7.0		5.82		5.54			0.753	10.2		213, 230
Yellow respiratory enzyme	different buffers	20	5.76		6.28			0.731	7.75	s_t; M_w and M_z	122
Yellow ferment	phosphate buffer pH 5.86	20			6.28					D_σ; c=10.0 g/1	67
Zein	60 wt. % ethyl alcohol 0.1 M KCl	20			5.28					c= 8.8 g/1	67

8 – NUCLEIC ACIDS*

Polymer	Solvent	T°C	$s_o \times 10^{13}$	k_s	$D_o \times 10^7$	k_D	f/f_o	$\bar{v}_2$	$M \times 10^{-4}$	Remarks	Ref.
Barium thymate	1% BaCl$_2$(aqu. sol.)	25			31.1						72
Deoxyribonucleic acid	0.2 M NaCl; pH 6.5	25	29.4					0.55	575-1330		117, 118
Pancreas polynucleotide	1% NaCl(aqu. sol.)	25	2.4		19.0		1.2	0.52	0.67	c=5.0 g/l	72
Sodium thymonucleate	1% NaCl (aqu. sol.)	25	17.1				8.0	0.55	58	s_t; M calc. with s=6.4 x 10^{-13}; a;	72
			6.4		0.61					c=2.9 g/l	
			8.7				5.3	0.55	43	M calc. with s=8.0 x 10^{-13}; c=0.55 g/l	72
			8.0		1.0					c=1.1 g/l	
			9.3				5.6	0.55	45	M calc. w.s.=7.8 x 10^{-13}; c=0.7 g/l	72
			8.0		0.96					c=1.7 g/l	
			7.8		0.95					c=2.6 g/l	
Thymonucleic acid (DNA)	1% NaCl (aqu. sol.)	25			21.5		1.1	0.57	0.48	s_t; a; c=5.0 g/l	72
					22.3					c=5.0 g/l	
Thymus deoxypentose nucleic acid (DNA)	cacodylate buffer; pH 7	20	9.0							s_t; c.a.; in presence of degraded DNA;	118
			6.5							c=1.56 g/l	
Yeast nucleic acid (RNA)	1% NaCl (aqu. sol.)	25			26.3					c=5.0 g/l	72
					22.5					c=10.0 g/l	

* Additional data may be found in H. M. Rauen, "Biochemisches Taschenbuch," Springer Verlag, Berlin, 1964.

References page IV-150

II. SECOND VIRIAL COEFFICIENTS OF POLYMERS IN SOLUTION

A. Introduction

The osmotic pressure π of polymer solutions cannot be described by
van't Hoff's Law except in a θ-solvent. Thus, the expression:

$$\pi/c = RT/M \quad \text{(van't Hoff's Law)} \tag{1}$$

where c, R, T and M are the solute concentration, the gas constant, the
absolute temperature and the molecular weight of the solute, respectively,
only holds under theta conditions, or at infinite dilution, i.e. $\lim c = 0$.
The deviation from ideality is strongly dependent on the polymer concentration.
The osmotic pressure is thus conveniently developed in a power series of c such
that in the limit of zero polymer concentration, Equation (1) results. The
forms which are most frequently encountered are those as in Equations (2),
(3), and (4).

$$\pi/c = RT[A_1 + A_2 c + A_3 c^2 + ...] \tag{2}$$

$$A_1 = 1/M$$

$$\pi/c = (\pi/c)_{c=0} [1 + \Gamma_2 c + \Gamma_3 c^2 + ...] \tag{3}$$

$$\pi/c = \frac{RT}{M} + Bc + Cc^2 + ... \tag{4}$$

The parameters A_2, Γ_2, and B are the so-called second virial coefficients,
A_3, Γ_3, and C the third virial coefficients, and so on. With certain
assumptions it is possible to express the third virial coefficient in terms
of the second virial coefficient (Ref. 379-381). Especially when the second
second virial coefficient is small it is found (Ref. 382) that, for example,
Equation (3) can be approximately expressed as:

$$\pi/c = (\pi/c)_{c=0} [1 + (\Gamma_2/2)c]^2 \tag{5}$$

a form particularly convenient in plots of $(\pi/c)^{1/2}$ versus c.

The second virial coefficients defined by Equations (2), (3), and (4) are
related to each other through Equation (6).

$$B = RTA_2 = (RT/M)\Gamma_2 \tag{6}$$

The dimensions of the virial coefficients follow from Equations (2), (3),
and (4). Depending on whether the dimensions [g/mole] or just [g] are
accepted for M, A_2 has the dimensions [mole cc./g^2], when c is expressed
in g/cc. For Γ_2 the dimension depends only on that of c; frequently one
finds [cc/g]. A large variety of dimensions are found for B since its
dimension depends on those of R, c, and M. In this case, for example,
[erg. cc/g^2], [Joule cc/g^2], [l^2 atm./g^2], etc. are found in the literature.
Table II.B. lists the second virial coefficients in the dimension [mole cc./g^2]
unless otherwise indicated under "Remarks" and by an asterisk.

Based on the fluctuation theory of v. Smoluchowski (Ref. 383) and of
Einstein (Ref. 384), which links osmotic pressure with light scattering,
Debye (Ref. 385) established the fundamental equation for the light
scattering of polymers in solution

$$\frac{Kc}{R_\theta} RT = \frac{RT}{M} + 2Bc + 3Cc^2 + ... \tag{7}$$

which makes it possible to determine the second virial coefficient (and the third virial coefficient) from light scattering measurements.

In Equation (7), K is a constant and R_θ is the intensity of the (excess) scattered light at angle θ at unit distance when the primary intensity is unity. Variants of Equation (7), corresponding to those of Equations (2) and (3) are also frequent. The determination of second virial coefficients, usually as a "by-product" of molecular weight measurements, by both osmotic pressure and light scattering, is the most common practice today. It should, however, be mentioned that according to Schulz (Ref. 386), the second virial coefficient can also be related to the coefficients of the concentration dependence, k_D and k_s, of the diffusion and sedimentation constants

$$B = \frac{RT}{M} (k_D + k_s) \tag{8}$$

Later Flory (Ref. 387) established an equation, by means of which the separate determination of k_D and k_s becomes unnecessary:

$$(D/s) \ (1-\bar{v}_2 \rho) = \frac{RT}{M} + 2Bc + 3Cc^2 + \ldots \tag{9}$$

Equation (9) is based on previous considerations of Flory and Mandelkern (Ref. 388).

In the early 1940's the first attempts were made to find theoretical explanations for the nonideal behavior of polymer solutions. Since then the literature on polymer solution theory has increased vastly. It would go far beyond the frame of the "Polymer Handbook" to go into this subject, especially since numerous excellent books and review articles are available (Refs. 387,389-398).

The following table gives second virial coefficients for different polymer solutions. The polymers are divided into certain classes and arranged alphabetically keeping similar polymers together. The tremendous amount of data reported in the literature for homologous series of polymers prevented a listing of the second virial coefficients for every molecular weight. Following the suggestion of the Editors, only ranges of values for the second virial coefficients are reported here, taking the lowest and the highest values from the reference cited. If no trend was apparent in the data reported, an average value is given. In order to indicate the number of values reported in the original reference, a number, e.g. 5V, is given in the "Remarks" column. Values for solvent mixtures of different ratios, data for different pH etc. are treated similarly. The reader is asked to refer to the original reference to find the detailed data and conditions.

Polymer	Solvent	Temp. [°C]	$M \times 10^{-4}$	Sec. Virial Coeff. $\times 10^4$ [mole cc/g^2]	Remarks	Ref.
1 - POLYOLEFINS AND POLYDIENES						
Polybutadiene						
1,4-cis	benzene	28.6	6.0-29.3	ca. 15.3	11V; OS	297
			13.8	27.9	OS	297
unfractionated	cyclohexane	28.6	84-435	ca. 2.92	11V; LS	297
fractionated		28.6	14.3-164	7.50 to -1.63	7V; LS	297
1,4-trans (69%)	cyclohexane	28.6	107	1.67	LS	297
(60-70%) unfractionated		25	540-1900	ca. 0.52	7V; LS	288
fractionated		25	340-1800	2.6 to -0.4	12V; LS	288
			230-1100	ca. 2.67	5V; LS	288
Poly(butadiene-co-styrene)						
25-30% styrene	benzene	28.6	5.8-11.2	ca. 13.5	4V; OS	297
25-30%	cyclohexane	28.6	80-2670	ca. 0.9	4V; LS	297
24%		30	4.9-51.4	1.7 to 1.0	8V; OS	344
Poly(1-butene)						
atactic	n-nonane	35	4.41-130	2.4	LS	109
isotactic		80	10.5-93.5	6.05 to 1.05		109
atactic	toluene	45	2.63-55.8	10.8 to 4.10	OS	109
isotactic		45	9.01-77.5	6.57 to 3.73		
atactic	toluene	45		M -0.32	OS	316
isotactic				M -0.25		
Polyethylene	1-chloronaphthalene	125	11.5-216	*(12.0 to 0.78) $\times 10^4$	9V; LS; [cc/g]	291
low pressure			12.1-52.6	ca. 10.5	8V; LS	296
Marlex			31	11.6	LS	296
			62.5	10.6		

Polymer	Solvent	Temp. [°C]	$M \times 10^{-4}$	Sec. Virial Coeff $\times 10^4$ [mole cc/g^2]	Remarks	Ref.
Polyethylene (Cont'd.) high pressure linear, fractions	1-chloronaphthalene	125	14.4-72.0	5.2 to 9.2	14V; LS; M_n given in Ref.	231
		135	2-100	$6.3 \times 10^{-3} \times M_v^{-0.15}$		231a
	n-decane	115	14.5-70.0	5.9 to 1.6	2V; LS; M_n given in Ref.	231
	1,2,3,4-tetrahydro-naphthalene	105	14.5-69.0	21.8 to 6.6	2V; LS; M_n given in Ref.	231
		125	10.5-219	$*26.8\text{-}1.68 \times 10^4$	8V; LS [cc/g]	
branched (varying degree)		81	3.8-73.5	3.6 to 0.9	6V; LS	292
			260-610	ca. 0		292
high pressure		81	57.3	0.92	LS	293
			198	0.82		
low pressure		105	12.5-46.5	23.1 to 15.9	3V; LS	293
high pressure (fractionated)	p-xylene	81	0.9-21.5	27.8 to 6.54	12V; OS	292
low pressure (fractionated)		105	1.12-16	33.5 to 26.1	4V; OS	292
		105		$26.2 \times 10^{-3} \times M^{-0.24}$		292a
Polyisobutene	benzene	24-30	126	*78.1	$(1\text{-}(298/T))$ LS; M_v [cc/g^2] T=°K	308, 311
		30	55.6	$*0.45 \times 10^4$	[100 cc/g]	160
			72.2	$*0.52 \times 10^4$		
		40		$0.75 \times 10^{-3} M^{-0.12}$	OS	317
	cyclohexane	25	113	$*2.6 \times 10^4$	LS; [100 cc/g^2]	202
		30	3.79-72	$*\Gamma_2 = 3.581 \times 10^{-5} M^{0.85}$	7V [100 cc/g]; $\Gamma_3 = 1/4 \; \Gamma_2^2$	160
	ethyl caprylate	25	80	$*0.41 \times 10^4$	LS [100 cc/g^2]	202
	heptane	25	40 -190	2.85 to 2.75	3V; LS	56
		60	190	1.75		
	heptane/propyl alcohol 90/10	25	190	1.95	LS	56
	80/20	25	190	0		56

References page IV-150

Polymer	Solvent	Temp. [°C]	$M \times 10^{-4}$	Sec. Virial Coeff. $\times 10^4$ [mole cc/g^2]	Remarks	Ref.
Polyisobutene (Cont'd.)						
	heptane/propyl alcohol 80/20	60	190	0.85		56
	72/28	60	190	-0.25		56
Polyisoprene	cyclohexane	20	160	*6.5 $\times 10^4$	SD [atm cm^6/g^2] $C = 8$ [atm cm^6/g^3]	29
natural rubber		7	170	*14.2 $\times 10^4$	LS [atm cm^6/g^2]	30
		27		*14.3 $\times 10^4$		
	cyclohexene	7	130	*11.7 $\times 10^4$	LS [atm cm^6/g^2]	28
		27	130	*12.7 $\times 10^4$		
brominated						
0% bromine	cyclohexane	20	180	*14.3 $\times 10^4$	LS; [atm cc/g^2]	31
5.8% "			185	*9 $\times 10^4$		
7.3% "			190	*4.5 $\times 10^4$		
25.8% "			290	*2.6 $\times 10^4$		
41.5% "			310	*0.4 $\times 10^4$		
43.8% "			380	*0		
Polypropylene						
atactic	benzene	25		3.2 $\times 10^{-3}$M$^{-0.20}$	LS	318
	cyclohexane	25		20 $\times 10^{-3}$ M$^{-0.26}$		318
	1-chloronaphthalene	135		16.5 $\times 10^{-3}$M$^{-0.27}$	LS	318
		125		4.3 $\times 10^{-3}$ M$^{-0.16}$	LS	318
isotactic		140	10.7-111	ca. 3.9	4V; LS	315

2 - VINYL POLYMERS

Polymer	Solvent	Temp. [°C]	$M \times 10^{-4}$	Sec. Virial. Coeff. $\times 10^4$ [mole cc/g^2]	Remarks	Ref.
Polyacrylonitrile	dimethylformamide	25-40	3.3-10.1	ca. 19.1	13V; OS *	74
		20	0.9-6.9	*32.2 to 7.0	5V; OS [cm^4/g]	248
		25	4.3-29.8	*ca. 21	7V; OS [cc/g^2]	199
			2.7-15.9	16 to 20	OS	200
		35	2.8-57.5	$2.74 \times 10^{-2} M^{-0.24}$	9V; M$_\eta$	201
		20	9.1-76.2	$2.43 \times 10^{-2} \times M^{-0.22}$	LS	95
Polystyrene	benzene		7.9	6.2	OS (IUPAC sample)	11
			23.3	5.0	OS (IUPAC sample)	11
			63	5.1	OS (IUPAC sample)	11
		40	400	3.2	LS	172
branched		r.t.	17	4.9	LS	312
linear				5.7		
branched			25.7	3.3		
linear				5.4		
		25	10.9-500	ca. 3.83	8V; LS	56
		60		2.30		
	benzene/ethyl alcohol 80/20	25	175	1.75	LS	56
		60		1.55		
	70/30	25		0		
		60		1.1		
	benzene/hexane 50/50	25		1.0		
		60		0.9		
	40/60	25		0		
		60		0.65		
	30/70	60		0		

* Varying methods of solvent purification

Polymer	Solvent	Temp. [°C]	$M \times 10^{-4}$	Sec. Virial Coeff. $\times 10^4$ [mole cc/g^2]	Remarks	Ref.
Polystyrene (Cont'd.)	carbon tetrachloride	25	92	2.6	LS	294
	chloroform	20	37.2-280	8.0 to 6.6	4V; LS	176
	chloroform/methyl alcohol 100/0	25	33	7.5	LS	176
	90/10			5.4		
	80/20			1.9		
isotactic	1-chloro-4-methyl benzene	r.t.	41.0-105	ca. 2.4	2V; LS	328
atactic	1-chloro-n-undecane	27.96-43.99	40.6	*(-6.0 to 9.0) $\times 10^4$	9V; LS [cc/g] M_n given in Ref.	133
	cyclohexane	27-41.5	161	-0.37 to 0.258	5V; LS	166
		23-45	6.87	*(-0.098 to 0.054) $\times 10^4$	6V; LS [cal. cc/g^2]	105
		30	5-20.3	-0.276 to -0.445	4V; OS	106
		40	5-20.3	0.634 to 0.445	4V	
		50	5-20.3	1.33 to 0.901	4V	
		32.5-55	[η]=1.06 -2.10	-0.153 to 0.538	5V; LS	329
		35-55	320	0 to 0.54	3V; LS	334
			400	0 to 0.88	3V; LS	172
		31.94-43.99	40.6	*(-131 to 23.1) $\times 10^4$	5V; LS [cc/g]	133
		29.92-44.03	40.6	*(-16.3 to 22.7) $\times 10^4$	5V; OS [cc/g]	133
isotactic	o-dichlorobenzene	r.t.	19.6-26.4	2.9 to 1.9	3V; OS	328
atactic	dichloroethane	22	0.3-1.7	7 to 2.54	6V; LS	166
		25	0.3	6.8		
		67	1.6	2.7		

Polymer	Solvent	Temp. [°C]	$M \times 10^{-4}$	Sec. Virial Coeff. $\times 10^4$ [mole cc/g^2]	Remarks	Ref.
Polystyrene (Cont'd.)						
	dichloroethane/cyclohexane 65/35	22	161	3.98	LS	166
		67		3.32		
	35/65	22	161	2.76		
		67		2.70		
	6/94	22		0.78		
		67		1.27		
	diethyl malonate	27.95-43.99	40.6	*(-13.6 to 7.4) $\times 10^4$	6V; LS [cc/g]; M_n given in Ref.	133
	dioxane	25	90-92	2.9 to 2.8	2V; LS	294
	ethyl acetate	25	24.3	0.7	OS	196
	methyl ethyl ketone	7.5-45	6.87	*0.14 $\times 10^4$	LS [cal cc/g^2]	105
		r.t.	103	1.29	LS (IUPAC sample)	253
		25	24.5-54	1.2 to 1.0	2V; OS	196
			9.63-78.5	156 to 5.3	5V; OS	176
		20	11.5-280	2.2 to 0.72	8V; LS	
		see ref.	46	1.3±0.7	7V; OS (IUPAC sample)	4
			56.5	1.34±0.32	9V; LS	
			56.5	1.31±0.28	6V; LS	
		see ref.	8.6	1.3	OS (IUPAC sample)	11
			23.5	0.9	OS	
			68.0	1.25	OS	
			72.0	1.3	OS	
		22	0.2-17?	4.3 to 0.86	9V; LS	166
		25	0.32-98	3.5 to 1.05	8V; LS	
		67	51.7-98	0.89 to 0.81	3V; LS	

Polymer	Solvent	Temp. [°C]	$M \times 10^{-4}$	Sec. Virial Coeff. $\times 10^4$ [mole cc/g^2]	Remarks	Ref.
Polystyrene (Cont'd.) branched		25	17-25.7	1.9	2V; LS and OS	312
			90	1.3	LS	294
	methyl ethyl ketone/ isopropyl alcohol 87/13	22	1.63-1.74	(-0.2 to -0.3)	2V; LS	166
		67	1.63-1.74	0	2V; LS	
	toluene	see ref.	45.5	4.7±0.6	8V; OS (IUPAC sample)	4
			55.7	4.2±0.8	6V; LS	
			58.0	3.8±0.5	7V; LS	
		see ref.	7.9	6.2	OS (IUPAC sample)	11
			23.3	5.0	OS	
			63.0	5.1	OS	
			100	4.8	OS	
		25	9.9 -95.2	6.5 to 3.5	7V; LS and OS	176
			23.7	$*12.3 \times 10^{10}$	see Ref. [erg cm^3/g^2]	56
		25	7.2 -180	$*(11$ to $7.0)10^7$	10V; LS [cm^4/g]	245
		30	3.09-61.2	$*\Gamma_2=7.41 \times 10^{-5} \times M^{0.75}$	[100 cc/g] $\Gamma_3=1/4\ \Gamma_2^2$	160
		22	161	3.12	same sample; LS	166
		67	161	2.43		
isotactic		30	15.5 -71.0	4.17 to 1.56	4V; LS	290
atactic		28-67	98	$*20.4 \times ((79/T)-1)$	M_v; LS; [cc/g^2];T=°K	308, 310
		30		$M_n^{-0.22}$	OS	317
atactic		30		$4.6 \times 10^{-3} M_n^{-0.22}$	OS	319
isotactic		30		$2.1 \times 10^{-3} M_n^{-0.146}$	OS	319

Polymer	Solvent	Temp. [°C]	$M \times 10^{-4}$	Sec. Virial Coeff. $\times 10^4$ [mole cc/g^2]	Remarks	Ref.
Polystyrene (Cont'd.)	toluene	30.27	5.6-42.0	*(29 to 145) $\times 10^2$	5V; OS; [cc/g]	327
Poly(styrene-co-methyl methacrylate)						
ca. 50/50	carbon tetrachloride	25	133-190	2.3 to 2.4	2V; LS	294
	dioxane		133-190	3.8 to 3.6	2V; LS	294
fractionated	methyl ethyl ketone	25	4.9-227	3.2 to 1.45	11V; LS	294
unfractionated			97	1.55		294
	nitroethane		133-190	1.5 to 1.2	2V; LS	294
Poly(styrene-p-sulfonic acid) potassium salt	aqu. KCl	27.5	48	4.68	LS	320
Poly(p-chlorostyrene)	methyl ethyl ketone	21	48-422	1.29 to 0.752	10V; LS	300
Poly(2,5-dichlorostyrene)	dioxane	20	59.0-1960	0.88 to 0.20	7V; LS	250
Poly(vinyl acetate)	acetone	ca. 30	2.7-84.5	8.80 to 3.34	9V; LS	330
			34.3-72.2	3.66 to 3.50	LS	331
			7.8-66	6.5 to 2.5	8V; LS	289
	methanol	ca. 30	37.0-62.0	ca. 3.5	2V; LS	331
(linear)		ca. 36	162-190	1.14 to 1.3	2V; LS	333
(branched)		ca. 36	292	0.99	3V; LS	333
		ca. 36	358	1.06		333
	methyl ethyl ketone	25	87-342	3.51 to 2.43	11V; LS	111
		25	5.8-36.7	*ca. 10×10^4	8V; OS [atm cm^6/g^2]	112
			9.3-110	*ca. 12.4×10^4	LS; [atm cm^6/g^2]	112
		30	4.0-126.8	7.00 to 2.95	12V; LS	330
			30.0-77.2	3.93 to 2.90	LS	331
(linear)	methyl ethyl ketone	ca. 36	44-358	3.2 to 2.74	10V; LS	333
(branched)		ca. 36	43-1,260	2.99 to 0.66	9V; LS	333
(linear)	trichlorobenzene	ca. 36	138-376	2.29 to 1.75	12V; LS	333
				$5.94 \times 10^{-3} \times M^{-0.230}$		333

References page IV-150

Polymer	Solvent	Temp. [°C]	$M \times 10^{-4}$	Sec. Virial Coeff. $\times 10^4$ [mole cc/g^2]	Remarks	Ref.
Poly(vinyl acetate) (Cont'd.) (branched)	trichlorobenzene	ca. 36	161-411	1.69 to 1.18	19V; LS	333
Poly(vinyl alcohol)	water	30	18-19.6	*3.9 to 5.2	2V; LS [cc/g^2]	282, 283
		73.5	24.5	*1.119		
		80	10-45.8	*2.189 to 0.775	5V; LS; [cc/g^2]	
Poly(vinyl bromide)	tetrahydrofuran	r.t.	0.6-7.6	6 to 0	14V; LS	287
			10.4-27	2.7 to 2.0	2V; LS	
Poly(vinyl chloride)	cyclohexanone	30-70	9.0	*3.9 $\times$ (1 + (1613/T))	LS; M_V; [cc/g^2]; T=$^\circ$K	308, 309
		30	3.23-9.74	*3.7 $\times$ 10^6	OS; [cm^4/g]	108
	tetrahydrofuran	25	2.48	*6.85 $\times$ 10^{11}	OS; [erg cc/g^2]	75
		25	3.7-11.0	*ca. 2.5 $\times$ 10^{11}	5V; OS [erg cc/g^2]	75
Poly(vinyl ether):						
Poly(vinyl n-butyl ether)	methyl ethyl ketone	25	21.5-86.1	2.3 to 0.7	2V; LS	149
Poly(vinyl ethyl ether)	methyl ethyl ketone	25	34.7-40.9	3.4 to 2.3	2V; LS	149
Poly(vinyl isopropyl ether)	methyl ethyl ketone	25	53.6-89.4	1.9 to 1.7	2V; LS	149
Poly(vinyl methyl ether)	methyl ethyl ketone	25	1.3-45	ca. 3.89	12V; LS	149
Poly(4-vinylpyridine)	ethyl alcohol	r.t.	10.2-185	ca. 4.13	10V; LS	286
Poly(vinylpyrrolidone)	cyclohexanone	25	2.45-3.79	*ca. 2.6 $\times$ 10^{-3}	3V; OS [1/g^2]	191
	methanol	30?	0.7-12	31 to 5.9	12V; LS	164
	water	25	1.16-7.54	*ca. 3.39 $\times$ 10^{-3}	12V; OS [1/g^2]	191
			1.95-93.3	*64.7 to 2.52 $\times$ 10^{-3}	6V; LS [1/g^2]	191

3 - ACRYLIC AND METHACRYLIC POLYMERS

Polymer	Solvent	Temp. [°C]	$M \times 10^{-4}$	Sec. Virial Coeff. $\times 10^4$ [mole cc/g²]	Remarks	Ref.
Polyacrylamide	water	25-60	39	$*217 \times (1-(235/T))$	LS; [cc/g²] T=°K	308
		25	470	$*6.4 \times 10^{10}$	LS; [erg cm⁶/g²]	93
Poly(acrylic acid)	aqu. NaCl IS* 0.102-0.394	27.5	77	5.95 to 196	6V; LS	320
	1,4-dioxane	25	13.4-122	$*(0.28 \text{ to } 0.18) \times 10^4$	5V; LS; [100 cc/g]	202
	hydrogen chloride 0.2M	20-68	110	$*49.9 \times (1-(287/T))$	LS; [cc/g²]	308
sodium salt	aqu. NaCl 0.01M	25	6.4	*7.98	OS; [atm 1²/g²]	254
	0.05M		5.87	*1.22		
	0.01M		3.0-64.4	*ca. 0.68	6V	
	1.0M		5.8	*0.07		
Poly(acrylic acid esters):						
Poly(1,1-dihydroperfluorobutyl acrylate)	benzotrifluoride	25	200-3800	ca. 0.2	10V; LS	203
	methyl perfluoro-butyrate		520-1410	0.5	2V; LS	
Poly(ethyl acrylate)	acetone	28	32-800	*ca. 10.52	10V; OS; [atm dl²/g²]	208
		30	14.5-69.1	*ca. 14.6	13V; OS; [atm dl²/g²]	233
			13.2-69.1	*18.1 to 14.1	7V; OS [atm dl²/g²]	271
			14.5-71.1	*ca. 13.3	5V; OS [atm dl²/g²]	270
Poly(methyl acrylate)	acetone	25	28-250	4.2 to 2.4	17V; LS	246, 247
	methyl ethyl ketone/ isopropyl alcohol (58/42)					
Polymethacrylamides:						
<u>Polymethacrylamide</u>		20	29-272	0.1 to -0.06	8V; LS	246
	water	22-56	32	$*4.49 \times (1-(279/T))$	LS; [cc/g²]; T=°K	308

* IS = degree of ionization

References page IV-150

Polymer	Solvent	Temp. [°C]	$M \times 10^{-4}$	Sec. Virial Coeff. $\times 10^4$ [mole cc/g^2]	Remarks	Ref.
Poly(N-phenylmethacrylamide)	acetone		10-320	*4.1 to 3.2	LS; [cc/g^2]	229
Poly(p-carbethoxyphenylmeth- acrylamide)	dimethylformamide (DMF)		99.5	2.2	LS	267
	DMF/formamide (90/10)			1.2		
	ethyl acetate			6.2		
Poly(methacrylic acid)	hydrochloric acid 0.02M	27-53	59	*14.8 x ((329/T)-1)	LS; [cc/g^2] T=°K	308
	0.1	25	14.6-68.2	ca. 1.76	3V; OS	240
	0.114M		20-42.7	ca. 16.9	5V; LS	240
	1.0M		8.4-16.9	2.0 to 0.4	3V; OS	240
	LiBr in ethanol 0.125M	25	4.2-38.3	5.2 to 2.3	4V; LS	249
		30	3.4-42.1	4.9 to 1.8	5V; OS	249
	methanol	20-40	ca. 51.7	*ca. 2.42	3V; LS [cc/g^2]	346
	0.5M NaCl	20-60	ca. 50.5	*1.465 to 0	4V; LS; [cc/g^2]	346
	0.5M NaCl	20-40	51.0	*0.96 to 0.1	3V; LS	
	water + x M NaCl x = 0.18 to 0.0007	25	19.6	0 to 780	5V; LS	335
Poly(methacrylic acid esters):						
Poly(benzyl methacrylate)	benzene	25	25.1-134	*(0.8 to 1.82) x 10^4	4V; OS; [100 cc/g]	
Poly(n-butyl methacrylate)	acetone	r.t.	10.8-58.2	3.61 to 1.69	5V; OS	280
			11.6-61.3	3.04 to 1.33	5V; LS^x	
	isopropyl alcohol	20	10.8-50.6	-0.7 to -0.39	4V; LS	279
		23.7	10.7-65	-0.15 to 0.1	5V	
		25.0	10.7-65.3	+0.03 to 0.2	5V	
		31.0	10.7-65.3	ca. 0.54	5V	
		45.0	10.9-26.2	ca. 1.44	3V	

x third virial coefficient reported

Polymer	Solvent	Temp. [°]	$M \times 10^{-4}$	Sec. Virial Coeff. $\times 10^4$ [mole cc/g^2]	Remarks	Ref.
Poly(n-butyl methacrylate)(Cont'd.)	methyl ethyl ketone	23	25-258	2.08 to 1.69	7V; LS	165, 205
			11.7-66.6	3.65 to 1.95	5V; LS[x]	280
Poly(p-tert-butyl phenyl methacrylate)	acetone	r.t.	6-352	1.4 to 0.48	15V; LS	307
Poly(cetyl methacrylate)	heptane	25	20-107	3.38 to 1.9	9V; LS	253
Poly(ethyl methacrylate)	methyl ethyl ketone	23	20-263	4.9 to 1.83	9V; LS	152
Poly(n-hexyl methacrylate)	methyl ethyl ketone	23	64-405	1.77 to 1.17	8V; LS	295
Poly(n-lauryl methacrylate)	n-butyl acetate	23	26-360	1.10 to 0.47	8V; LS	205
Poly(methyl methacrylate)	acetone	20	2.3-530	*(12.2 to 1.55) $\times 10^{-2}$	10V; SD; [atm l^2/g^2]	52
			20-655	*2.25 to 0.68	3V; SD; [cc/g^2]	15
		25		$2.9 \times 10^{-3} M^{-0.22}$	LS	273
			6.8-137	*(7.1 to 3.5) $\times 10^7$	7V; LS; [981 cc^4/g]	232
			24-447	2.3 to 1.1	5V; LS	264
			2.77-780	*(9.75 to 2.9) $\times 10^{13}$	12V; LS; [erg cc/g^2]	99
			76	*1.9 $\times 10^4$	LS[100 cc/g^2]	202
			2.69-250	*(0.0097 to 3.90) $\times 10^4$	13V; LS; [cc/g]	275
			8.6-105	2.90 to 1.58	7V; OS	202
			9.2-79.8	1.89 to 1.52	9V; LS	202
			48.6-662	*2.38 to 0.82	4V; LS; [cc/g^2]	55
		30		* 2.63 $\times 10^{-3} M^{-0.22}$	OS; [dl/g]	274
unfractionated		30.5	16.2-64.7	*(28.8 to 88) $\times 10^4$	12V; OS; [cc/g]	274
fractionated			6.4-72.6	*(12.3 to 95) $\times 10^4$	5V; OS; [cc/g]	274
		r.t.	7.0-635	2.67 to 0.96	13V; LS	243
	butyl acetate	25	48.6-662	*0.96 to 0.36	4V; LS; [cc/g^2]	55
		-18 to 60	21	*0 to 1.20	6V; LS; [cc/g^2]	210, 215

x third virial coefficient reported

Polymer	Solvent	Temp. [°C]	M × 10^{-4}	Sec. Virial Coeff. × 10^4 [mole cc/g^2]	Remarks	Ref.
Poly(methyl methacrylate) (Cont'd.)						
	chlorobutane	4 to 43	3	*-1.6 to 0.365	12V; LS; [cc/g^2]	210, 215
		28 to 43	110	*-0.3 to 0.325	7V	15
		28 to 43	460	*-0.23 to 0.31	7V	
	chloroform	35.6	20-655	*-0.24 to 0.07	3V; SD; [cc/g^2]	232
	dioxane	25	83-137	*(12 to 10)10^7	2V; LS; [981 cc^4/g]	55
		25	48.6-662	*3.24 to 1.43	4V; LS; [cc/g^2]	294
			122-200	3.1 to 3.0	2V; LS	
	ethyl acetate	25	17.2-310	1.9 to 1.2	3V; OS	196
	4-heptanone	16 to 62	210	*-0.76 to 0.52	10V; LS; [cc/g^2]	210, 215
	isopentyl acetate	20 to 60	210	*-1.13 to 0.055	12V; LS; [cc/g^2]	210, 215
unfractionated	methyl ethyl ketone	25	2.0-173	*(4.02 to 1.39)10^{-2}	7V; LS; [cc/g^2]^x	273
fractionated			12.2-276	*(2.82 to 1.07)10^{-2}	4V	232
			76-140	*(5.4 to 4.2)10^7	4V; LS; [981 cc^4/g]	294
			122	1.6	LS	253
			3.4-980	2.78 to 1.46	10V; LS	163
			41-326	1.92 to 1.66	7V; LS;	163
	methyl ethyl ketone/ isopropyl alcohol (55/45)	23	41-326	0.08 to 0.02	6V; LS	163
	(58.2/41.8 vol)	4-36	21	*0.005 to 1.44	9V; LS; [cc/g^2]	210, 215
	(55/45)	4-36	21	*-0.57 to 1.14	10V;	
	(50/50)	8-50	21	*-1.56 to 0.91	10V;	
	(46.8/53.2)	8-40	21	*-1.02 to 0.68	8V;	

^{x} third virial coefficient reported

Polymer	Solvent	Temp. [°C]	$M \times 10^{-4}$	Sec. Virial Coeff. $\times 10^4$ [mole cc/g²]	Remarks	Ref.
Poly(methyl methacrylate) (Cont'd.)						
unfractionated	nitroethane	25	2.2 to 171	*5.51 to 1.68	6V; LS; [cc/g²]^x	273
fractionated			11.4 to 56.4	*3.38 to 1.73	2V	294
	nitromethane	25	122 to 200	ca. 2.6	2V; LS;	273
	toluene			$0.67 \times 10^{-3} M^{-0257}$	LS	274
Poly(n-octyl methacrylate)		30.5	1.2 to 2.0	$*(5.7 \text{ to } 8.5) \times 10^4$	3V; OS; [cc/g]	
	methyl ethyl ketone	23	326-1252	0.77 to 0.35	7V; LS	209

4 - CONDENSATION POLYMERS

Polymer	Solvent	Temp. [°C]	$M \times 10^{-4}$	Sec. Virial Coeff. $\times 10^4$ [mole cc/g²]	Remarks	Ref.
Poly(dimethyl siloxane)	bromobenzene	59.1-110.8	8	*-2.025 to 1.750	9V; LS [cc/g²]	216
		70-108.3	34	*-0.587 to 0.890	8V; LS	
		73.7-111.1	106	*-0.272 to 0.772	7V; LS	
	bromocyclohexane	16.7-60.2	3.3	*-1.5 to 2.260	8V; LS; [cc/g²]	216
		18.2-60.2	8.5	*-0.782 to 2.012	8V; LS	
		29.2-60.2	34	*-0.136 to 1.329	7V; LS	
		24.1-90.3	78	*-0.257 to 1.985	10V; LS	
		25.5-60.2	106	*-0.190 to -0.985	6V; LS	
	bromocyclohexane/ phenetol (6/7)	23.9-88.8	8	*-1.23 to 2.14	10V; LS; [cc/g²]	216
		26.8-93.9	34	*-0.536 to 1.490	10V; LS	
		31.8-90	106	*-0.239 to 1.280	8V; LS	

x third virial coefficient reported

References page IV-150

Polymer	Solvent	Temp. [°C]	$M \times 10^{-4}$	Sec. Virial Coeff. $\times 10^4$ [mole cc/g^2]	Remarks	Ref.
Poly(dimethyl siloxane) (Cont'd.)	phenetol	80.8-122.8	4.5	* -2.15 to 3.823	8V; LS; [cc/g]	216
		81.7-123.1	8.0	* -0.93 to 3.23	7V;	
		79.5-122.8	34	* -0.54 to 1.796	7V	
		90-112.8	106	* 0.015 to 1.466	6V	
Poly(ethylene oxide)	dimethylformamide	25-120	ca. 0.35	*(37 to 47) $\times 10^4$	4V; OS; [atm cc^2/g^2]	188
	methanol	25	0.1-3.1	*(102.5 to 39) $\times 10^4$	11V; LS; [atm cc^2/g^2]	192
			0.1-1.0	*(84.5 to 47.5) $\times 10^4$	4V; LS; [atm cc^2/g^2]	193
			0.4-2.3	*(87 to 46) $\times 10^4$	3V; LS; [atm cc^2/g^2]	184
			0.3-4.8	*(48 to 27.5) $\times 10^4$	2V; LS [atm cc^2/g^2]	185
	water	25	1.09-80	*(116 to 30.4) $\times 10^4$	5V; [atm cc^2/g^2]	189
			1.01	*62 $\times 10^4$	LS [atm cc^2/g^2]	184
Polyformaldehyde, diacetate	hexafluoroacetone	25	2.3-18.5	56-25	5V; LS	236
Poly(heptamethylene urea)	dichloroacetic acid	45	0.31-1.78	*(32 to 6.2) $\times 10^4$	6V; LS; [atm cc^2/g^2]	183
	dichloroacetic acid	73	0.26-2.35	*(82 to 8.0) $\times 10^4$	6V; LS; [atm cc^2/g^2]	183
		25-98	ca. 1.75	*(0 to 52) $\times 10^4$	4V; LS; [atm cc^2/g^2]	183
	formic acid 98%/KCl[x] 96/4	45	0.05	*5 $\times 10^4$	LS; [atm cc^2/g^2]	183
			0.3-1.39	*(104 to 59) $\times 10^4$	6V; LS [atm cc^2/g^2]	183
	98/2	73	0.46-1.62	*(105 to 64) $\times 10^4$	3V; LS [atm cc^2/g^2]	183
Poly(hexamethylene adipamide)	m-cresol	60	1.8	*183 $\times 10^4$	OS; [atm cc^2/g^2]	217
	formic acid (90%)	25	1.8	*840 $\times 10^4$	OS; [atm cc^2/g^2]	217
	formic acid (90%)/KCl 0.2-2.5M KCl	25	3.1	*(59.2 to -7.0) $\times 10^4$	7V; LS; [atm cc^2/g^2]	219

x several other combinations of formic acid and KCl reported in reference

Polymer	Solvent	Temp. [°C]	M x 10^{-4}	Sec. Virial Coeff. x 10^4 [mole cc/g^2]	Remarks	Ref.
Poly(hexamethylene adipamide) (Cont'd.)						
	formic acid (90%)/KCl 2.3M KCl	25	3.1	*0		219
	formic acid/2M KCl 82.5-98% acid	25	3.1	*(-9.4 to 36.5) x 10^4	5V; LS; [atm cc^2/g^2]	219
	formic acid (90%)/ 2M KCl	25	0.2-5.2	*(312 to 10.1) x 10^4	10V; LS; [atm cc^2/g^2]	218
	0.1M sodium trifluoro-acetate/ 2,2,3,3-tetra-fluoropropanol	25	6.2	*57.1 x 10^4	LS; [atm cc^2/g^2]	220, 221
Poly(4,4'-isopropylidene-diphenylene carbonate)	methylene chloride	25	6.1-12.2	*(3.6 to 2.5) x 10^{11}	2V; LS [erg cc/g^2]	45
		27	2.3-18.2	*(3.9 to 2.9) x 10^{11}	5V; OS [erg cc/g^2]	45
	tetrahydrofuran	20	0.8-26.6	*(4 to 1.29) x 10^{11}	5V; SD [erg cc/g^2]	45
		27	2.3-9.2	*(2.5 to 1.7) x 10^{11}	5V; OS [erg cc/g^2]	45
Poly(phosphoric acid) sodium salt	0.1-0.4M NaBr	25	ca. 69	10.2 to 0.4	4V; LS	303
	0.35M NaBr	25	1.1-125	2.1 to 0.9	12V; LS	303
Poly(propylene oxide)	hexane	46	3.42-441	3.16 to 0.523	16V; LS	207

5 - CELLULOSE AND CELLULOSE DERIVATIVES

Polymer	Solvent	Temp. [°C]	$M \times 10^{-4}$	Sec. Virial Coeff. $\times 10^4$ [mole cc/g^2]	Remarks	Ref.
Cellulose						
hydrolized linters	cadoxene^x	25	22.5-94.5	ca. 16.1	5V; LS	97
sulfite pulp			21.5	12.1	LS	
Cellulose acetate	acetone	r.t.	6.0-17.3	9.4 to 5.8	4V; LS	302
Cellulose nitrate %N = ca. 13.55	acetone	r.t.	6.16-248.2	*ca. 0.24	14V; OS; [atm l^2/g^2]	61
	acetone	25	7.7-264	ca. 6.10	11V; LS	22
from raw cotton %N = ca. 13.66	acetone	15	2.28-41.7	*ca. 0.24	8V; OS; [atm l^2/g^2]	195
from cotton	acetone	20	3.1-66.1	*ca. 0.28	11V; OS; [atm l^2/g^2]	194
	butyl acetate	20	15-40	*(1.0 to 0.5) $\times 10^{-2}$	LS; [atm l^2/g^2]	239
		25	3.0-36	*(3.5 tg 0.3) $\times 10^{-2}$	OS; [atm l^2/g^2]	239
from viscose rayon	ethyl acetate	29.7	7.15	*4.41 $\times 10^4$	OS; [100 cc/g]	91
from chemical cotton		29.5-45	*(2.85 to 2.57) $\times 10^4$	2V; OS [100 cc/g]	91
%N = 12.4	methyl ethyl ketone	25	13	10.8	OS	196

^{x} Cadmium ethylenediamine

Polymer	Solvent	Temp. [°C]	M x 10^{-4}	Sec. Virial Coeff. x 10^4 [mole cc/g^2]	Remarks	Ref.
Cellulose tricaproate	1-chloronaphthalene	24	6.25-131	6.5 to 1.1	4V; LS	334
	dimethylformamide	30-53.5	3.2	-0.58 to 0.65	3V; OS	334
	dioxane/water (1C0/7)	37.1-49.4	20.6	-0.19 to 0.37	3V; OS	334
		43-61	131	0 to 1.2	3V; LS	334
		63	19.5-148	7.0 to 3.0	3V; LS	334
Cellulose tricarbanilate %N = 8.19-8.41	acetone	7	6.7-267	*3.14 to 1.36	16V; LS; [cc/g^2]	281
		17	6.7-267	*3.16 to 1.32	16V; LS; [cc/g^2]	281
		27	6.7-267	*3.16 to 1.27	16V; LS; [cc/g^2]	281
	acetone/water 0-7.8% water	20	84	*2.02 to 0	7V; LS; [cc/g^2]	197
	diethyl ketone/methanol 0-52% methanol	20	84	*4.26 to 0	7V; LS; [cc/g^2]	197
	dioxane/methanol 0-57.5% methanol	20	84	*6.18 to 0	7V; LS; [cc/g^2]	197
	methyl ethyl ketore/methanol 0-57% methanol	20	84	*3.65 to 0	8V; LS; [cc/g^2]	197
Cellulose trinitrate from cotton linters; %N = 13.58	acetone	25	ca. 7.5	7.3 to 7.4	2V; LS	39
from purified chemical linters			ca. 6	*(23 to 79) x 10^4	3V; OS; [cc/g^2]	90
from bleached ramie; %N = ca. 13.8			9.9-22.8	ca. 4.1	5V; LS	89
from unbleached raw ramie; %N = ca. 13.7			ca. 24.5	5.1 to 3.8	2V; LS	89

References page IV-15C

Polymer	Solvent	Temp. [°C]	$M \times 10^{-4}$	Sec. Virial Coeff. $\times 10^4$ [mole cc/g^2]	Remarks	Ref.
Cellulose trinitrate (Cont'd.)						
from linters	ethyl acetate	25	4.1-57.3	*(32 to 367) $\times 10^4$	5V; LS; [cc/g]	90
			6.8	7.3	LS	89
from bleached ramie %N = 13.83		25	9.8-23.2	3.1 to 4.8	4V; LS	89
from unbleached ramie %N = 13.76		25	25	3.6	LS	89
from purified cotton linters	methyl ethyl ketone	r.t.	11-25.7	*(92 to 177) $\times 10^4$	2V; OS; [cc/g]	90
Ethyl hydroxyethyl cellulose ca. 18.0% ethoxyl; ca. 30% ethoxyl + hydroxyethyl	water	25	7.7-17.6	9.8 to 5.45	7V; LS and OS	94
Hydroxyethyl cellulose	cadoxene^x	25	7.8-60.5	14.2 to 12.5	4V; LS	285
	water	25	8.0-62.5	10.3 to 4.7	3V; LS	285
		3-58	57	3.9 to 1.8	5V; LS	285
		25	12.5-38.0	11.3	4V; OS	98
		25	19-62.5	5.43	4V; LS	98
	0.5M HCl	25	57	8.2	LS	285
	0.5M NaCl			4.3		
	0.5M NaOH			11.3		
Sodium carboxylmethyl cellulose						
DS ~ 0.21	cadoxene^x	25	4.9-47	14.4 to 13.3	4V; LS	284
DS ~ 0.44			6.8-66	16.9 to 12.5	5V	
DS ~ 0.94			6.7-105.5	14.6 to 9.8	5V	
	0.005M NaCl solution	25	7-29	ca. 68	4V; OS	277, 278
	0.01M			ca. 57.5	3V; OS	
	0.05M			ca. 25.1	4V; OS	
	0.2M			ca. 16.2	4V; OS	
	aqu. NaCl IS^xx = 0.5-0.005	r.t.	44.0	15.1 to 260	4V; LS	336

x Cadmium ethylenediamine
xx IS = Ionic strength

6 - POLYSACCHARIDES
(Other than Cellulose and Cellulose Derivatives)

Polymer	Solvent	Temp. [°C]	M × 10^{-4}	Sec. Virial Coeff. × 10^4 [mole cc/g^2]	Remarks	Ref.
Amylopectin	water		700-7300	0.06 to 0.44	LS	137
	aqu. KCl (0-5) × 10^{-3}M		1360	0.52 to 0	7V; LS	137
Amylose	dimethyl sulfoxide/ acetone 0-43.5%	20	59.2	*5.35 to 0	8V; LS; [cc/g^2]	198
	ethylenediamine (hydrate)			*5.64		
	formamide			*2.19		
	0.5M NaOH			*4.88		
	water	20	13.6-68.1	*0.02 to 1.8	10V; LS; [cc/g^2]	198
			68.1-175	*1.8 to 0.47	6V	198
Amylose carbanilate $\bar{x}_N$ = ca. 18.5	acetone	7	3.65-490	*1.67 to 0.124	25V; LS; [cc/g^2]	281
		17	3.65-490	*1.67 to 0.134	25V	
		27	5.63-490	*1.46 to 0.145	24V	
Amylose tricarbanilate	diethyl ketone/ methanol 0-34% methanol	20	218	*3.13 to -0.01	5V; LS; [cc/g^2]	197
	dioxane/methanol 0-51% methanol	20	218	*4.24 to 0	7V; LS; [cc/g^2]	197
	methyl ethyl ketone 0-33% methanol	20	218	*2.54 to 0	7V; LS; [cc/g^2]	197
Dextran	water	r.t.	3050-6000	0.42 to 0.1	9V; LS	342
		ca. 20	1.77-950	14.8 to 0.7	23V; LS	26
Guaran triacetate	acetonitrile	22.5	7.4-534	4.7 to 0.38	9V; LS	313

References page IV-150

7 - PROTEINS AND POLYPEPTIDES

Polymer	Solvent	Temp. [°C]	M x 10^{-4}	Sec. Virial Coeff. x 10^4 [mole cc/g^2]	Remarks	Ref.
Albumin (bovine, serum)	0.15M acetate buffer	r.t.	7.25	0.361	LS	348
Poly(γ-benzyl-L-glutamate)	chloroform	25	13-35.8	5.0 to 4.7	4V; LS	299
	dichloroacetic acid	25	2.14-33.6	15.7 to 7.5	3V; LS	299
$\alpha_{s1,2}$-Casein	phosphate buffers pH = 12.0 × IS varying betw. 0.2 to 1.2	r.t.	2.7	(17-17 × IS)	LS	298
Collagen	2M KCNS	25	12.5	3.0	OS	301
Fibrinogen (bovine)	phosphate buffer pH 5.57 - 7.77	20	ca. 39.0	*(0.16 to -0.005) x 10^4	3V; SD; [atm cc^2/g^2]	41
	pH ca. 6	7-27	ca. 38.7	*-6.15 to 3.1	7V; LS [cc/g^2]	48
Gelatin	water; pH = 5.1	40	9.2	ca.-30	LS	343
	0.05M phosphate buffer	30	27	2.4	LS	338
	KCNS-phosphate buffer	30	30.2-59.6	ca. 2.76	3V; LS	338
	2M KCNS; pH = 7.1	25	9.5	4.8	LS	343
	pH = 5.1		9.6	3.9		
	1M KCNS; pH = 6.3		9.7	5.0		
	pH = 5.1	40	9.0	2.6		
	0.15M NaCl pH = 3.1	40	8.8	6.0	LS	343
	pH = 5.1		ca. 9.4	ca. 2.5	3V	
	1.0M NaCl pH = 5.1		9.9	1.3		
Heparin	1M KCl	25	157	*21.0 x 10^4	A; [atm. cc^2/g^2]	189
				*21.6 x 10^4	SD	
			138	*35.0 x 10^4	A	
				*44.0 x 10^4	SD	

× IS = ionic strength

Polymer	Solvent	Temp. [°C]	$M \times 10^{-4}$	Sec. Virial Coeff. $\times 10^4$ [mole cc/g^2]	Remarks	Ref.
Pepsin different preparations	0.2M NaAc	25.6	4.20	1.46×10^{-4}		348
			3.28–4.27	0.85 to 1.41	8V; LS; scattering data	348
3-Phospho-D-glyceraldehyde-dehydrogenase	glycine-NaCH-NaCl-buffer	20	11.7	$*-1.7 \times 10^4$	A; [atm. cc^2/g^2]	189
				$*-0.36 \times 10^4$	SD	

1. G. Meyerhoff, Z. Electrochem. 61, 1250 (1957).
2. T. Svedberg and K. O. Pedersen, "Die Ultrazentrifuge," Th. Steinkopf, Dresden und Leipzig, 1940.
3. G. Meyerhoff, Makromol. Chem. 37, 97 (1960).
4. H. P. Frank and H. F. Mark, J. Polymer Sci. 17, 1 (1955).
5. G. Meyerhoff, in "Conference on the Ultracentrifuge," Academic Press, New York, 1963.
6. G. Meyerhoff, Makromol. Chem. 72, 214 (1964).
7. J. G. Kirkwood and J. Riseman, J. Chem. Phys. 16, 565 (1948).
8. J. Riseman and J. G. Kirkwood, in F. R. Eirich, "Rheology, Theory and Application," Vol. I, Academic Press, New York, 1956.
9. M. Kurata and H. Yamakawa, J. Chem. Phys. 29, 311 (1958).
10. H. Kuhn, W. Kuhn, and A. Silberberg, J. Polymer Sci. 14, 193 (1954).
11. International Union of Pure and Applied Chemistry, J. Polymer Sci. 10, 129 (1953).
12. A. F. Schick and S. J. Singer, J. Phys. Chem. 54, 1028 (1950).
13. C. O. Beckmann and J. Rosenberg, Ann. N. Y. Acad. Sci. 46, 209 (1945).
14. N. Gralén, Dissertation, Uppsala, 1944.
15. H. Lütge and G. Meyerhoff, Makromol. Chem. 68, 180 (1963).
16. K. Nachtigall and G. Meyerhoff, Z. Physik. Chem., (Frankfurt) 30, 35 (1961).
17. G. Meyerhoff, Makromol. Chem. 15, 68 (1955).
18. G. Meyerhoff, Makromol. Chem. 12, 45 (1954).
19. K. Uda and G. Meyerhoff, Makromol. Chem. 67, 168 (1961).
20. R. Signer and J. Liecht, Helv. Chim. Acta 21, 530 (1938).
21. A. Polson, Kolloid-Z. 83, 172 (1938).
22. A. M. Holtzer, H. Benoit, and M. Doty, J. Phys. Chem. 58 624 (1954).
23. J. W. Williams and W. M. Saunders, J. Phys. Chem. 58, 854 (1954).
24. A. G. Ogston and E. F. Woods, Trans. Faraday Soc. 50, 635 (1954).
25. A. G. Ogston, Trans. Faraday Soc. 49, 1481 (1953).
26. F. R. Senti, N. N. Hellman, N. H. Ludwig, G. E. Babcock, R. Tobin, C. A. Glass, and B. L. Lamberts, J. Polymer Sci. 17, 527 (1955).
27. L. D. Moore, Jr., G. R. Greear, and J. O. Sharp, J. Polymer Sci. 59, 339 (1962).
28. G. V. Schulz, K. Altgelt, and H.-J. Cantow, Makromol. Chem. 21, 13 (1956).
29. K. Altgelt and G. V. Schulz, Makromol. Chem. 32, 66 (1959).
30. K. Altgelt and G. V. Schulz, Makromol. Chem. 36, 209 (1960).
31. G. V. Schulz and A. Mula, Proc. Nat. Rubber Res. Conf., Kuala Lumpur, 1960, pp. 602-610.
32. L. Mandelkern, W. R. Krigbaum, H. A. Scheraga, and P. J. Flory, J. Chem. Phys. 20, 1392 (1952).
33. K. H. Schachman and M. A. Lauffer, J. Am. Chem. Soc, 71, 536 (1949).
34. M. A. Lauffer, J. Am. Chem. Soc. 66, 1188 (1944).
35. H. Neurath, Chem. Rev. 30, 357 (1942).
36. M. A. Lauffer, J. Am. Chem. Soc. 66, 1195 (1944).
37. H. K. Schachman and W. J. Kauzman, J. Phys. Chem. 53, 150 (1949).
38. H. W. McCormick, J. Polymer Sci. A1, 103 (1963).
39. S. J. Singer, J. Chem. Phys. 15, 341 (1947).
40. L. E. Miller and F. A. Hamm, J. Phys. Chem. 57, 110 (1953).
41. H. Ende, G. Meyerhoff, and G. V. Schulz, Z. Naturforsch. 13b, 713 (1958).
42. S. Shulman, J. Am. Chem. Soc. 75, 5846 (1953).
43. G. Meyerhoff, Z. Physik, Chem. (Frankfurt) 4, 335 (1955).
44. G. Meyerhoff, Z. Physik. Chem. (Frankfurt) 23, 100 (1960).
45. G. V. Schulz and A. Horbach, Makromol. Chem. 29, 93 (1959).
46. G. V. Schulz, D. Laue, and O. Bodmann, Makromol. Chem. 31, 75 (1959).
47. R. Cecil and A. G. Ogston, Biochem.J. 42, 229 (1948).
48. G. V. Schulz and H. A. Ende, Z. Physik. Chem. (Frankfurt) 36, 82 (1963).
49. G. V. Schulz and M. Marx, Makromol. Chem. 14, 52 (1954).
50. M. Cantow, G. Meyerhoff, and G. V. Schulz, Makromol. Chem. 49, 1 (1961).
51. O. Bodmann, D. Kranz, and G. V. Schulz, Makromol. Chem. 41, 225 (1960).
52. G. V. Schulz and G. Meyerhoff, Z. Elektrochem. 56, 545 (1952).
53. K. J. Ivin, H. A. Ende and G. Meyerhoff, Polymer 3, 129 (1962).
54. K. J. Ivin, J. Polymer Sci. 25, 228 (1957).
55. G. V. Schulz and H. Doll, Z. Elektrochem. 63, 301 (1959).
56. E. D. Kunst, Dissertation, Groningen, 1950.
57. G. V. Schulz, K. V. Günner, and H. Gerrens, Z. Physik. Chem. (Frankfurt) 4, 192 (1955).
58. G. Meyerhoff, Naturwissenschaften 41, 13 (1954).
59. G. Meyerhoff, and G. V. Schulz, Makromol. Chem. 7, 294 (1951).
60. G. V. Browning and J. D. Ferry, J. Chem. Phys. 17, 1107 (1949).
61. A. Münster, J. Polymer Sci. 8, 633 (1952).
62. J. Stamm, J. Am. Chem. Soc. 52, 3047 (1930).
63. J. Stamm, J. Am. Chem. Soc. 52, 3062 (1930).
64. G. Meyerhoff, J. Polymer Sci. 29, 399 (1958).
65. G. Meyerhoff, Makromol. Chem. 32, 249 (1959).
66. J. Hengstenberg and G. V. Schulz, Makromol. Chem. 2, 5 (1948).
67. A. Polson, Kolloid-Z 87, 149 (1939).
68. E. M. Bevilacqua, E. B. Bevilacqua, M. M. Bender and J. W. Williams, Ann. N. Y. Acad. Sci. 46, 309 (1945).

69. T. Svedberg and K. O. Pedersen, The Ultracentrifuge, The Clarendon Press, Oxford, 1940.
70. A. G. Polson, Dissertation, University of Stellenbosch, 1937, South Africa.
71. R. O. Carter, J. Am. Chem. Soc. 63, 1960 (1941).
72. H. G. Tennent and C. F. Vilbrandt, J. Am. Chem. Soc. 65, 424 (1943).
73. K. O. Pedersen and K. J. I. Andersson, unpubl. results, cit. i. ef. 67.
74. W. R. Kirgbaum, and A. M. Kotliar, J. Polymer Sci. 32, 323 (1958).
75. A. Oth, Ind. Chim. Belge 20, 423 (1955).
76. T. Svedberg, and I.-B. Eriksson-Quensel, J. Am. Chem. Soc. 56, 1700 (1934).
77. L. Krejci and T. Svedberg, J. Am. Chem. Soc. 56, 1706 (1934)
78. T. Svedberg and I.-B. Eriksson, J. Am. Chem. Soc. 55, 2834 (1933).
79. W. F. H. M. Mommaertz and R. G. Parrish, J. Biol. Chem. 188, 545 (1951).
80. P. Johnson and R. Landolt, Nature 165, 430 (1950).
81. G. L. Miller and W. C. Price, Arch. Biochem. Biophys. 10, 467 (1946).
82. W. F. H. M. Mommaertz, Arkiv Kemi Mineral. Geol. 19A, No. 17 (1945).
83. N. W. Pirie, Advan. Enzymol. 5, 1 (1945).
84. M. A. Lauffer, J. Phys. Chem. 44, 1137 (1940).
85. M. A. Lauffer and W. M. Stanley, J. Biol. Chem. 135, 463 (1940).
86. A. C. Ogston, Biochem. J. 37, 78 (1943).
87. A. E. McFarlane and R A Kekwick, Biochem. J. 32, 1607 (1938).
88. F. C. Bawden and N. W. Pirie, unpublished (cit. in Ref. 83).
89. M. M. Huque, D. A. Goring and S. G. Mason, Can. J. Chem. 36, 952 (1958).
90. M. L. Hunt, S. Newman, H. A. Scheraga, and P. J. Flory, J. Phys. Chem. 60, 1278 (1956).
91. S. Newman, L. Loeb, and C. M. Conrad, J. Polymer Sci. 10, 463 (1953).
92. B. Ingelman and M. S. Halling, Arkiv Kemi 1, 61 (1949).
93. H.-J. Cantow, Z. Naturforsch. 7b, 485 (1952).
94. R. S. J. Manley, Arkiv Kemi 9, 519 (1956).
95. Y. Fujisaki and H. Kobayashi, Chem. High Polymer (Japan) 19, 81 (1962).
96. H.-J. Cantow, Makromol. Chem. 30, 169 (1959).
97. D. Henley, Arkiv Kemi 18, 327 (1961).
98. W. Brown, Arkiv Kemi 18, 227 (1961).
99. H.-J. Cantow and G. V. Schulz, Z. Physik. Chem. (Frankfurt) 2, 117 (1954).
100. D. J. Bell, H. Gutfreund, R. Cecil, and A. G. Ogston, Biochem. J. 42, 405 (1945).
101. R. W. G. Wyckoff, J. Biol. Chem. 121, 219 (1937).
102. H. Neurath and A. M. Saum, J. Biol. Chem. 126, 435 (1938).
103. F. C. Bawden and N. W. Pirie, Proc. Roy. Soc. (London), Ser. B, 123, 274 (1937).
104. W. M. Stanley, J. Phys. Chem. 42, 55 (1938).
105. H.-J. Cantow, Z. Physik. Chem. (Frankfurt) 7, 58 (1956).
106. W. R. Krigbaum, J. Am. Chem. Soc. 76, 3758 (1954).
107. H. W. McCormick, J. Polymer Sci. 36, 341 (1959).
108. J. W. Breitenbach, E. L. Forster, and A. J. Renner, Kolloid-Z. 127, 1 (1952).
109. W. R. Krigbaum, J. E. Kurz, and P. Smith, J. Phys. Chem. 65, 1984 (1961).
110. H.-G. Elias and F. Patat, J. Polymer Sci. 29, 141 (1958).
111. A. R. Shultz, J. Am. Chem. Soc. 76, 3422 (1954).
112. H.-G. Elias, and F. Patat, Makromol. Chem. 25, 13 (1958).
113. T. Svedberg and I.-B. Eriksson, J. Am. Chem. Soc. 54, 3998 (1933).
114. L. Krejci and T. Svedberg, J. Am. Chem. Soc. 57, 946 (1935).
115. J. Bisschops, J. Polymer Sci. 17, 81 (1955).
116. K. Dialer and R. Kerber, Makromol. Chem. 17, 56 (1955).
117. A. Oth, Bull. Soc. Chim. Belges 64, 484 (1955).
118. A. R. Peacocke and H. R. Schachmann, Biochim. Biophys. Acta 15, 198 (1954).
119. K. Dialer, K. Vogler, and F. Patat, Helv. Chim. Acta 35, 869 (1952).
120. J. L. Oncley, G. Scatchard, and A. Brown, J. Phys. Chem. 51, 184 (1947).
121. P.   v. Mutzenbecher, Biochem. Z. 266, 250 (1933).
122. R. A. Kekwick and K. O. Pedersen, Biochem. J. 30, 2201 (1936).
123. M. Heidelberger and K. O. Pedersen, J. Gen. Physiol. 19, 95 (1935).
124. C. J. Howard and D. O. Jordan, J. Polymer Sci. 12, 209 (1954).
125. S. Newman and F. Eirich, J. Colloid Sci. 5, 541 (1950).
126. N. Gralén and G. Lagermalm, J. Phys. Chem. 56, 514 (1952).
127. J. A. V. Butler, A. B. Robins, and K. V. Shooter, Proc. Roy. Soc. (London), Ser. A 241, 299 (1951).
128. L. Mandelkern and P. J. Flory, J. Chem. Phys. 20, 212 (1952).
129. H. A. Dieu, J. Polymer Sci. 12, 417 (1957).
130. L. Freund and M. Daune, J. Polymer Sci. 29, 161 (1958).
131. D. O. Jordan, A. R. Mathieson, and M. R. Porter, J. Polymer Sci. 21, 463 (1956).
132. D. O. Jordan, A. R. Mathieson, and M. R. Porter, J. Polymer Sci. 21, 473 (1956).
133. T. A. Orofino and J. W. Mickey, Jr., J. Chem. Phys. 38, 2512 (1963).
134. M. Wales and K. E. Van Holde, J. Polymer Sci. 14, 81 (1954).
135. B. Rosen, P. Kamath and F. Eirich, Discussions Faraday Soc. 11, 135 (1951).
136. D. A. I. Goring and C. Chepeswick, J. Colloid Sci. 10, 440 (1955).
137. L. P. Witnauer, F. R. Senti, and M. D. Stern, J. Polymer Sci. 16, 1 (1955).
138. R. L. Baldwin, Biochem. J. 55, 644 (1953).
139. H. Malmgren, Acta Chem. Scand. 6, 1 (1952).
140. R. Gehm, Acta Chem. Scand. 5, 270 (1951).
141. J. H. Fessler and A. G. Ogston, Trans. Faraday Soc. 47, 667 (1951).

142. L. W. Nichol and A. B. Roy, Biochemistry 4, 386 (1965).
143. W. Scholtan, Makromol. Chem. 36, 162 (1960).
144. W. Scholtan, Makromol. Chem. 7, 209 (1952).
145. C. G. Holmberg, Arkiv Kemi, Mineral. Geol. 17A, No. 28 (1944).
146. V. L. Koenig, Arch. Biochem. 25, 241 (1950).
147. V. L. Koenig and J. D. Perrings, Arch. Biochem. Biophys. 41, 367 (1952).
148. G. R. Andersson, Arkiv Kemi 20, 513 (1963).
149. J. A. Manson and G. J. Arquette, Makromol. Chem. 37, 187 (1960).
150. H.-G. Elias, Makromol. Chem. 50, 1 (1961).
151. K. Nakanishi and M. Kurata, Bull. Chem. Soc. Japan 33, 152 (1960).
152. W. G. Martin, W. H. Cook, and C. A. Winkler, Can. J. Chem. 34, 809 (1956).
153. W. Scholtan, Makromol. Chem. 23, 128 (1957).
154. V. L. Koenig and J. D. Perrings, Arch. Biochem. Biophys. 36, 147 (1952).
155. V. L. Koenig and J. D. Perrings, Arch. Biochem. Biophys. 40, 218 (1952).
156. V. L. Koenig and K. O. Pedersen. Arch. Biochem. 25, 97 (1950).
157. I. B. Eriksson-Quensel, Biochem. J. 32, 585 (1938).
158. A. Tiselius and D. Gross, Kolloid-Z. 66, 11 (1934).
159. K. O. Pedersen, Biochem. J. 30, 961 (1936).
160. W. R. Krigbaum and P. J. Flory, J. Am. Chem. Soc. 75, 1775 (1953).
161. M. D. Dayhoff, G. E. Perlmann, and D. A. MacInnes, J. Am. Chem. Soc. 74, 2515 (1952).
162. S. N. Chinai and R. J. Samuels, J. Polymer Sci. 19, 463 (1956).
163. S. N. Chinai, J. D. Matlack, A. L. Resnick, and R. J. Samuels, J. Polymer Sci. 17, 391 (1955).
164. H. P. Frank and G. B.Levy, J. Polymer Sci. 10, 371 (1953).
165. S. N. Chinai and R. A. Guzzi, J. Polymer Sci. 21, 417 (1956).
166. P. Outer, C. I. Carr, and B. H. Zimm, J. Chem. Phys. 18, 830 (1950).
167. K. A. Granath, J. Colloid Sci. 13, 308 (1958).
168. O. Lamm and A. Polson, Biochem. J. 30, 528 (1936).
169. J. Oth and V. Desreux, Bull. Soc. Chem. Belges 66, 303 (1957).
170. W. B. Bridgman, J. Am. Chem. Soc. 68, 857 (1946).
171. H. K. Schachman and W. F. Harrington, J. Polymer Sci. 12, 379 (1954).
172. D. McIntyre, A. Wims, L. C. Williams and L. Mandelkern, J. Phys. Chem. 66, 1932 (1962).
173. H. K. Schachman, Protein and Function, Brookhaven Symposia in Biology: No. 13, 49 (1960).
174. H. K. Schachman, J. Am. Chem. Soc. 73, 4453 (1951).
175. I.-B. Eriksson-Quensel and T. Svedberg, Biol. Bull. 71, 498 (1936).
176. J. Oth and V. Desreux, Bull. Soc. Chem. Belges 63, 285 (1954).
177. P. J. Rempp, J. Chim. Phys. 54, 432 (1957).
178. K. Dialer and K. Vogler, Makromol. Chem. 6, 191 (1951).
179. V. N. Tsvetkov and S. I. Klenin, J.Polymer Sci. 30, 187 (1958).
180. O. Russl, U. Bianchi, and V. Magnasco, J. Polymer Sci. 30, 175 (1958).
181. G. Kegeles, S. M. Klainer, and W. J. Salem, J. Phys. Chem. 61, 1286 (1957).
182. G. W. Schwert and S. Kaufman, J. Biol. Chem. 179, 655 (1949).
183. J. Feisst and H.-G. Elias, Makromol. Chem. 82, 78 (1965).
184. H.-G. Elias, Z. Physik. Chem. (Frankfurt) 28, 303 (1961).
185. H.-G. Elias, Chem. Ingr.-Tech. 33, 359 (1961).
186. K. Frömbling and F. Patat, Makromol. Chem. 25, 41 (1958).
187. H.-G.Elias, Makromol. Chem. 27, 192 (1958).
188. H.-G. Elias and E. Männer, Makromol. Chem. 40, 207 (1960).
189. H.-G. Elias, Angew. Chem. 73, 209 (1961).
190. F. Patat and H.-G. Elias, Naturwissenschaften 46, 322 (1959).
191. J. Hengstenberg and E. Schuch, Makromol. Chem. 7, 236 (1952).
192. T. A. Ritscher and H.-G. Elias, Makromol. Chem. 30, 48 (1959).
193. C. Sadron, C., and P. Rempp, J.Polymer Sci. 29, 127 (1958).
194. A. Münster, Z. Physik. Chem. (Leipzig) 197, 17 (1951).
195. H. Diener and A. Münster, Z. Physik. Chem. (Frankfurt) 13, 202 (1957).
196. G. Jacobsson, Acta Chem. Scand. 8, 1843 (1954).
197. W. Burchard, Z. Physik. Chem. (Frankfurt) 42, 293 (1964).
198. W. Burchard, Makromol. Chem. 59, 16 (1963).
199. P. E. Onyon, J.Polymer Sci. 37, 315 (1959).
200. P. E. Onyon, J.Polymer Sci. 22, 13 (1956).
201. H. Kobayashi, J. Polymer Sci. 39, 369 (1959).
202. S. Newman, W. R. Krigbaum, C. Laugier, and P. J. Flory, J. Polymer Sci. 14, 451 (1954).
203. G. B. Rathmann, and F. A. Bovey, J. Polymer Sci. 15, 544 (1955).
204. I. J. O'Donnell, and E. F. Woods, J. Polymer Sci. 21, 397 (1956).
205. S. N. Chinai and R. A. Guzzi, J. Polymer Sci. 41, 475 (1956).
206. H. Kobayashi, J. Polymer Sci. 26, 230 (1957).
207. G. Allen, C. Booth, and M. N. Jones, Polymer (London) 5, 195 (1964).
208. J. E. Hansen, M. G. McCarthy, and T. J. Dietz, J. Polymer Sci. 7, 77 (1951).
209. S. N. Chinai, A. L. Resnick, and H. T. Lee, J. Polymer Sci. 33, 471 (1958).
210. R. Kirste, and G. V. Schulz, Z. Physik. Chem. (Frankfurt) 27, 301 (1961).
211. A. F. V. Eriksson, Acta Chem. Scand. 7, 623 (1953).
212. A. F. V. Eriksson, Acta Chem. Scand. 10, 378 (1956).
213. A. Ehrenberg, Acta Chem. Scand. 11, 1257 (1957).
214. R. V. Webber, J. Am. Chem. Soc. 78, 536 (1956).
215. G. V. Schulz and R. Kirste, Z. Physik. Chem. (Frankfurt) 30, 171 (1961).

216. G. V. Schulz, A. Haug, and R. Kirste, Z. Physik. Chem. 38, 1 (1963).
217. R. Schumacher and H.-G. Elias, Makromol. Chem. 76, 12 (1964).
218. H.-G. Elias and R. Schumacher, Makromol. Chem. 76, 23 (1964).
219. P. R. Saunders, J. Polymer Sci. 57, 131 (1961).
220. D. W. Carlson, Dissertation, University Delaware, June, 1959.
221. H. C. Beachell and D. W. Carlson, J. Polymer Sci. 40, 543 (1959).
222. R. Signer and P. v. Tavel, Helv. Chim. Acta 21, 535 (1938).
223. H. Moisimann, Helv. Chim. Acta 26, 61 (1943).
224. B. H. Sörbo, Acta Chem. Scand. 7, 1129 (1953).
225. A. Ehrenberg, and H. Theorell, Acta Chem. Scand. 9, 1193 (1949).
226. H. Theorell and R. Bonnichsen, Acta Chem. Scand. 5, 1105 (1951).
227. H. G. Boman, Acta Chem. Scand. 5, 1311 (1951).
228. A. Ehrenberg and S. Paléus, Acta Chem. Scand. 9, 538 (1955).
229. V. N. Tsvetkov and V. G. Aldoshin, Zh. Fiz. Khim. 33, 2767 (1959) (Russ. J. Phys. Chem. 33, 619 (1959)).
230. R. Chiang, J. Phys. Chem. 69, 1645 (1965).
231. V. Kokle, F. W. Billmeyer, Jr., L. T. Muus, and E. J. Newitt, J. Polymer Sci. 62, 251 (1962).
232. J. Bischoff and V. Desreux, Bull. Soc. Chim. Belges 61, 10 (1952).
233. Y. Hachihama and H. Sumitomo, Technol. Rept. Osaka Univ. 3, 385 (1953).
234. H. Vink, Arkiv Kemi 14, 29 (1957).
235. S. Claesson, W. Bergmann, and C. Jayme, Svensk Papperstid 62, 141 (1959).
236. W. H. Stockmayer and L.-L. Chan, ACS Meeting, Detroit, 1965, Polymer Preprints 6, 333 (1965).
237. M. J. R. Cantow, R. S. Porter and J. F. Johnson, ACS Meeting, Detroit, 1965, Polymer Preprints 6, 338 (1965).
238. G. M. Guzman, Anales Real Soc. Espan. Fis. Quim. (Madrid) 52B, 377 (1956).
239. J. Schurz, Papier 15, 530 (1961).
240. R. Arnold and S. R. Caplan, Trans. Faraday Soc. 51, 857 (1955).
241. A. Ehrenberg and K. Dalziel, Acta Chem. Scand. 11, 398 (1957).
242. A. Ehrenberg and K. Agner, Acta Chem. Scand. 12, 95 (1958).
243. K. Z. Fattakhov, V. N. Tsvetkov, and O. V. Kallistov, Zh. Eksperim. i. Teor. Fiz. 26, 351 (1954).
244. M. L. Wagner and H. A. Scheraga, J. Phys. Chem. 60, 1066 (1956).
245. C. E. H. Bawn, R. F. Freeman and A. R. Kamaliddin, Trans. Faraday Soc. 46, 862 (1950).
246. L. Trossarelli and G. Saini, Atti Accad. Sci. Torino: Classe Sci. Fis. Mat. Nat. 90, 419 (1955-56).
247. G. Saini and L. Trossarelli, Atti Accad. Sci. Torino: Classe Sci. Fis. Mat. Nat. 90, 431 (1955-56).
248. H. Frind. Faserforsch. Textiltech. 5, 540 (1954).
249. Q. A. Trementozzi, J. Am. Chem. Soc. 76, 5273 (1954).
250. V. E. Eskin and T. I. Volkov, Vysokomolekul. Soedin. 5, 614 (1963).
251. L. G. Longsworth, J. Am. Chem. Soc. 75, 5705 (1953).
252. L. G. Longsworth, J. Phys. Chem. 58, 770 (1954).
253. F. W. Billmeyer, Jr. and C. B. DeThan, J. Am. Chem. Soc. 77, 4763 (1955).
254. A. Takahashi, J. Hayashi, and I. Kagawa, Kogyo Kagaku Zasshi 60, 1059 (1957).
255. H. H. Weber, Biochim. Biophys. Acta 4, 12 (1950).
256. O. Snellman and T. Erdös, Biochim. Biophys. Acta 2, 650 (1948).
257. E. J. Cohn, J. L. Oncley, L. E. Strong, W. L. Hughes, Jr., and S. H. Armstrong, Jr., J. Clin, Invest. 23, 417 (1944).
258. J. L. Oncley, unpublished, (cited in Ref. 257).
259. I. Jullander, Arkiv Kemi 21A, 8 (1945).
260. D. S. Feingold and M. Gohatia, J. Polymer Sci. 22, 783 (1957).
261. G. L. Burgin, J. Am. Chem. Soc. 71, 2247 (1949).
262. J. Y. Chien, L. H. Shih, and S. C. Yu, J. Polymer Sci. 29, 117 (1958).
263. J. Y. Chien and L. H. Shih, Z. Physik. Chem. 207, 60 (1957).
264. J. Y. Chien, L. H. Shih, and K. I. Shih, Hua Hsueh Hsueh Pao 23, 215 (1957).
265. H.-G. Elias and H. H. Schlubach, Ann. Chem. 627, 126 (1959).
266. W. Scholtan, Makromol. Chem. 14, 169 (1954).
267. G. M. Chetyrkina, V. G. Aldoshin, and S. Y. Frenkel, Vysokomolekul. Soedin. 1, 1133 (1959).
268. G. V. Schulz and M. Hoffmann, Makromol. Chem. 23, 220 (1957).
269. H. Mosiman and T. Svedberg, Kolloid-Z. 100, 99 (1942).
270. H. Sumitomo and Y. Hachihama, Chem. High Polymers (Japan) 10, 544 (1953).
271. H. Sumitomo and Y. Yatsuhama, Chem. High Polymers (Japan) 11, 65 (1954).
272. K. Bailey, Nature 157, 368 (1946).
273. E. F. Casassa and W. H. Stockmayer, Polymer 3, 53 (1962).
274. T. G. Fox, J. B. Kinsinger, H. F. Mason, and E. M. Schuele, Polymer 3, 71 (1962).
275. E. Cohn-Ginsberg, T. G. Fox, and H. F. Mason, Polymer 3, 97 (1962).
276. H. Campbell and P. Johnson, Trans. Faraday Soc. 40, 221 (1944).
277. W. Brown and D. Henley, Makromol. Chem. 79, 68 (1964).
278. W. Brown, D. Henley and J. Ohman, Arkiv Kemi 22, 189 (1964).
279. R. Van Leemput and R. Stein, J. Polymer Sci. A2, 4039 (1964).
280. R. Van Leemput and R. Stein, J. Polymer Sci. A1, 985 (1963).
281. W. Burchard and E. Husemann, Makromol. Chem. 44-46, 358 (1961).
282. T. Matsuo and H. Inagaki, Makromol. Chem. 55, 150 (1962).
283. T. Matsuo and H. Inagaki, Makromol. Chem. 53, 130 (1962).

284. W. Brown, D. Henley and J. Öhman, Makromol. Chem. 62, 164 (1963).
285. W. Brown, D. Henley and J. Öhman, Makromol. Chem. 64, 49 (1963).
286. J. B. Berkowitz, M. Yamin, and R. M. Fuoss, J. Polymer Sci. 28, 69 (1958).
287. A. Ciferri, M. Kryszewski, and G. Weill, J. Polymer Sci. 27, 167 (1958).
288. R. L. Cleland, J. Polymer Sci. 27, 349 (1958).
289. S. N. Chinai, P. C. Scherer, and D. W. Lewi, J. Polymer Sci. 17, 117 (1955).
290. L. Trossarelli, E. Campi and G. Saini, J. Polymer Sci. 35, 205 (1959).
291. L. H. Tung, J. Polymer Sci. A2, 4875 (1964).
292. Q. A. Trementozzi, J. Polymer Sci. 23, 887 (1957).
292a. W. R. Krigbaum and Q. A. Trementozzi, J. Polymer Sci. 28, 295 (1958).
293. Q. A. Trementozzi, J. Polymer Sci. 36, 113 (1959).
294. W. H. Stockmayer, L. D. Moore, Jr., M. Fixman, and B. N. Epstein, J. Polymer Sci. 16, 517 (1955).
295. S. N. Chinai, J. Polymer Sci. 25, 413 (1957).
296. L. H. Tung, J. Polymer Sci. 36, 287 (1959).
297. W. Cooper, G. Vaughan, D. E. Eaves, and R. W. Madden, J. Polymer Sci. 50, 159 (1961).
298. P. Dreizehn, R. W. Noble, and D. F. Waugh, J. Am. Chem. Soc. 84, 4938 (1962).
299. P. Doty, J. H. Bradburg, and A. M. Holtzer, J. Am. Chem. Soc. 78, 947 (1956).
300. S. Mao and E. V. Frisman, Vysokomolekul. Soedin.4, 1839 (1962).
301. H.Boedtker and P. Doty, J. Am. Chem. Soc. 78, 4267 (1956).
302. R. S. Stein and P. Doty, J. Am. Chem. Soc. 68, 159 (1946).
303. U. P. Strauss, and P. L. Wineman, J. Am. Chem. Soc. 80, 2366 (1958).
304. H. Boedtker, and S. Simmons, J. Am. Chem. Soc. 80, 2550 (1958).
305. A. Holtzer and S. Lowey, J. Am. Chem. Soc. 81, 1370 (1959).
306. R. Bjorklund and S. Katz, J. Am. Chem. Soc. 78, 2123 (1956).
307. V. N. Tsvetkov and O. V. Kalistov, Zh. Fiz. Khim. 33, 710 (1959).
308. A. Silberberg, J. Eliassaf, and A. K. Katschalsky, J. Polymer Sci. 23, 259 (1957).
309. P. Doty and E. Mishuck, J. Am. Chem. Soc. 69, 1631 (1947).
310. P. Doty, M. Brownstein and W. Schlener, J. Phys. Colloid. Chem. 53, 213 (1949).
311. W. R. Krigbaum and P. J. Flory, J. Am. Chem. Soc. 75, 5254 (1953).
312. M. Morton, T. E. Helminiak, S. D. Gadkary and F. Bueche, J. Polymer Sci. 57, 471 (1962).
313. J. V. Koleske and S. F. Kurath, J. Polymer Sci. A2, 4123 (1964).
314. G. Sitaramaiah and D. A. I. Goring, J. Polymer Sci. 58, 1107 (1962).
315. R. Chiang, J. Polymer Sci. 28, 235 (1958).
316. W. R. Krigbaum, J. E. Kurz, and P. Smith, J. Phys. Chem. 65, 1984 (1961).
317. P. J. Flory, J. Am. Chem. Soc. 65, 372 (1943).
318. J. B. Kinsinger and R. E. Hughes, J. Phys. Chem. 63, 2002 (1959). From R. Chaing, Chapter in "Newer Methods of Polymer Characterization," ed. B. Ke Interscience Publ., New York, 1964, p 471
319. F. Danusso and G. Moraglio, Makromol. Chem. 28, 250 (1958).
320. T. A. Orofino and P. J. Flory, J. Phys. Chem. 63, 283 (1959).
321. H. W. McCormick, J. Polymer Sci. 41, 327 (1959).
322. I. Y. Poddubnyi, V. A. Grechanovskii, and M. I. Mosevitskii, Vysokomolekul. Soedin 5, 1042 (1964).
323. I. Y. Poddubnyi, V. A. Grechanovskii and M. I. Mosevitskii, Vysokomolekul. Soedin. 5, 1049 (1964).
324. I. Y. Poddubnyi, V. A. Grechanovskii and A. V. Podalinskii, Vysokomolekul. Soedin. 5, 1588 (1964).
325. W. Buchard, Makromol. Chem. 67, 182 (1963).
326. A. von Haug, and G. Meyerhoff, Makromol. Chem. 53, 91 (1962).
327. J. M. G. Cowie, D. J. Worsfold, and S. Bywater, Trans. Faraday Soc. 57, 705 (1961).
328. W. R. Krigbaum, D. K. Carpenter and S. Newman, J. Phys. Chem. 62, 1586 (1958).
329. W. R. Krigbaum and D. K. Carpenter, J. Phys. Chem. 59, 1166 (1955).
330. M. Matsumoto and Y. Ohyanagi, J. Polymer Sci. 46, 441 (1960).
331. Y. Ohyanagi and M. Matsumoto, Chem. High Polymer (Japan) 16, 296 (1959).
332. J. Moacanin, J. Appl. Polymer Sci. 1, 272 (1959).
333. G. C. Berry, L. M. Hobbs, and V. C. Long, Polymer (London) 5, 31 (1964).
334. W. R. Krigbaum and L. H. Sperling, J. Phys. Chem. 64, 99 (1960).
335. H. J. L. Trap, and J. J. Hermans, J. Phys. Chem. 58, 757 (1954).
336. N. S. Schneider and P. Doty, J. Phys. Chem. 58, 762 (1954).
337. S. Bywater and P. Johnson, Trans. Faraday Soc. 47, 195 (1951).
338. E. V. Gouinlock, Jr., P. J. Flory, and H. A. Scheraga, J. Polymer Sci. 16, 383 (1955).
339. K. Krishnamurti and T. Svedberg, J. Am. Chem. Soc. 52, 2897 (1930).
340. E. O. Kraemer, J. Phys. Chem. 45, 660 (1941).
341. E. O. Kraemer, J. Phys. Chem. 46, 177 (1942).
342. L. H. Arond and H. P. Frank, J. Phys. Chem. 58, 953 (1954).
343. H. Boedtker and P. Doty, J. Phys. Chem. 58 968 (1954).
344. T. Homma and H. Fujita, J. Appl. Polymer Sci. 9, 1701 (1965).
345. B. P. Brand, D. A. I. Goring, and P. Johnson, Trans. Faraday Soc. 51, 872 (1955).
346. E. A. Kanevskaya, P. I. Zubov, L. V. Ivanova, and Yu. S. Lipatov, Vysokomolekul. Soedin. 6, 981 (1964).
347. S. Lowey and C. Cohen, J. Mol. Biol. 4, 293 (1962).
348. M. J. Kronman and M. D. Stern, J. Phys. Chem. 59, 969 (1955).

349. G. Meyerhoff, "Bestimmung des Molekulargewichtes durch Diffusions - und Sedimentationsmessungen (Ultrazentrifuge)." In: Houben-Weyl: "Methoden der organischem Chemie." Vol. III, Part 1, pp. 390-408; Georg Thieme Verlag, Stuttgart, 1955.

350. J. Hengstenberg, "Sedimentation und Diffussion von Makromolekülen." In: H. A. Stuart: Physik der Hochpolymeren, Vol. II, pp. 411-494; Springer Verlag, Berlin, Göttingen, Heidelberg, 1953.

351. A. L. Geddes, "Determination of Diffusivity," In: A. Weissberger: Technique of Organic Chemistry, Vol. I, Part 1, pp. 551-619; Interscience Publishers, New York, N.Y., 1949.

352. J. B. Nichols and E. D. Bailey, "Determinations with the Ultracentrifuge," In: A. Weissberger: Technique of Organic Chemistry, Vol. I. Part 1, pp. 621-730, Interscience Publishers, New York, N.Y., 1949.

353. P. O. Kinell and B. G. Rånby, Advan. Colloid. Sci. $\underline{3}$, 182 (1950).

354. H. K. Schachman, "Ultracentrifugation in Biochemistry." Academic Press, New York and London; 1959.

355. R. L. Baldwin and K. E. Van Holde, Fortschr. Hochpolymer-Forsch. $\underline{1}$, 451 (1960).

356. H. Fujita, "Mathematical Theory of Sedimentation Analysis." Academic Press, New York, 1962.

357. J. W. Williams, "Ultracentrifugal Analysis in Theory and Experiment," Academic Press, New York, London, 1963.

358. M. Gehatia, J. Polymer Sci. $\underline{57}$, 241 (1962).

359. M. Gehatia, Naturwissenschaften $\underline{48}$, 598 (1961).

360. T. Svedberg and H. Rinde, J. Am. Chem. Soc. 46, 2677 (1924).

361. H. Mosimann and R. Signer, Helv. Chim. Acta $\underline{27}$, 1123 (1944).

362. P. W. Bridgman, Proc. Am. Acad. Arts Sci. $\underline{61}$, 57 (1926).

363. J. Orb and V. Desreux, Bull Soc. Chim. Belges $\underline{63}$, 133 (1954).

364. M. Wales, J. Am. Chem. Soc. $\underline{81}$, 4758 (1959).

365. H. Fujita, J. Chem. Phys. $\underline{24}$, 1084 (1956).

366. H.-G. Elias, Makromol. Chem. $\underline{29}$, 30 (1959).

367. H. Mark, In: Sänger, R., "Der feste Körper," pp. 65-104; Hirzel Verlag, Zürich, 1938.

368. Houwink, R. R.,J. Prakt. Chem. $\underline{157}$, 15 (1940).

369. I. Jullander, Arkiv Kemi. Mineral, Geol. $\underline{19B}$, No. 4 (1944).

370. I. Jullander, "Über die Berechnung von Molekulargewichten aus Messungen von Sedimentationsgeschwindigkeit und Diffusion." In: "The Svedberg," Jubilee Volume, Almquist and Wiksells Boktryckerei AB, Uppsala, 1944.

371. S. J. Singer, J.Polymer Sci. $\underline{1}$, 445 (1946).

372. N. Bauer, "Determination of Density," In: A. Weissberger. Techniques of Organic Chemistry, Vol. I. Part 1; Interscience Publishers, New York, N.Y., pp. 253-296, 1949.

373. H. Kienitz, "Bestimmung der Dichte." In: Houben-Weyl: Methoden der organischen Chemie. Vol III, Part 1, Georg Thieme Verlag, Stuttgart; pp. 163-217, 1955.

374. W. Geffcken, C. Beckmann and A. Kruis, Z. Physik. Chem.(B)$\underline{20}$, 398 (1933).

375. A. B. Lamb and R. E. Lee, J. Am. Chem. Soc. $\underline{35}$, 1666 (1913).

376. D. A. MacInnes, M. O. Dayhoff, and B. R. Ray, Rev. Sci. Instr. $\underline{22}$, 642 (1951).

377. D. A. MacInnes and M. O. Dayhoff, J. Am. Chem. Soc. $\underline{74}$, 1017 (1952).

378. J. Stauff and G. Rümmler, Kolloid-Z. $\underline{166}$, 152 (1959).

379. P. J. Flory and W. R. Krigbaum, J. Chem. Phys. $\underline{18}$, 1086 (1950).

380. P. J. Flory, J. Chem. Phys. $\underline{17}$, 1347 (1949).

381. W. H. Stockmayer and E. F. Casassa, J. Chem. Phys. $\underline{20}$, 1560 (1952).

382. W. R. Krigbaum and P. J. Flory, J. Polymer Sci. $\underline{9}$, 503 (1952).

383. M. v. Smoluchowski, Ann. Physik. $\underline{25}$, 205 (1908).

384. A. Einstein, Ann. Physik. $\underline{33}$, 1275 (1910).

385. P. Debye, J. Appl. Physics $\underline{15}$, 338 (1944).

386. G. V. Schulz, Z. Physik. Chem. $\underline{193}$, 168 (1944).

387. P. J. Flory, "Principles of Polymer Chemistry," Cornell University Press, Ithaca, New York, 1953.

388. L. Mandelkern and P. J. Flory, J. Chem. Phys. $\underline{19}$, 984 (1951).

389. C. Tanford, "Physical Chemistry of Macromolecules," John Wiley and Sons, New York, N.Y., 1961.

390. M. V. Volkenstein, "Configurational Statistics of Polymeric Chains," Interscience Publishers, New York-London, 1963.

391. P. J. Flory and W. R. Krigbaum, Ann. Rev. Phys. Chem. $\underline{2}$, 383 (1951).

392. F. T. Wall and L. A. Hiller, Jr., Ann. Rev. Phys. Chem. $\underline{5}$, 267 (1954).

393. J. J. Hermans, Ann. Rev. Phys. Chem. $\underline{8}$, 179 (1957).

394. E. F. Casassa, Ann. Rev. Phys. Chem. $\underline{11}$, 477 (1960).

395. W. H. Stockmayer, Makromol. Chem. $\underline{35}$, 54 (1960).

396. T. B. Grimley, "The Theory of High Polymer Solutions," in "Progress in High Polymers," Vol. I, Eds. J. C. Robb and F. W. Peaker; Academic Press, Inc., New York, N.Y., 1961.

397. R. E. Hughes and C. A. v. Frankenberg, Ann. Rev. Phys. Chem. $\underline{14}$, 291 (1963).

398. H. Morawetz, "Macromolecules in Solution," Interscience Publishing Co., New York, N.Y., 1965.

399. V. N. Tsvetkov and S. I. Klenin, Zh. Tekh. Fiz., $\underline{29}$,1393 (1959).

POLYMER-SOLVENT INTERACTION PARAMETER

(Table of Literature References)*

J. Rehner, Jr.

Chemicals Research Division
Esso Research & Engineering Company
Linden, New Jersey

The polymer-solvent interaction parameter is a semiempirical "constant" which provides a measure of the solvent power of a given liquid for a polymer. It continues to play a valuable role in the quantitative description of properties of polymer solutions and gels, even though its numerical value in a given polymer-solvent system usually depends on the ratio of the two components and on temperature. It is customarily denoted by the symbol μ (earlier) or x_1 (more recent), and was originally introduced (with still different notation) in Huggins' and Flory's independent studies of the statistical thermodynamics of polymer solutions. The following equation is one of several that have been employed to define this parameter: $x_1 = BV_1/RT$ where $B = z\Delta w_{12}/V_s$. Here, z is a lattice coordination number (the numerical value of which is expected to be in the range of six to twelve, but the actual value of which is considered to be of little importance), Δw_{12} is the interaction energy between the polymer and a solvent molecule, V_1 is the molecular volume of a polymer segment, R is the gas constant, and T is the absolute temperature. Accordingly, x_1 is a dimensionless quantity which characterizes the polymer-solvent interaction energy per solvent molecule, divided by kT, where k is Boltzmann's constant.

The parameter finds extensive use in a large variety of theoretical equations that have been derived to interpret experimental results on free energy, entropy, osmotic pressure, freezing point and vapor pressure changes, configurations of dissolved polymer molecules, phase equilibria in polymer solutions, stress-strain behavior of swollen polymer networks, cohesive energy in bulk polymers, and equilibrium swelling and crosslink concentration in polymer networks. The parameter is also encountered, explicit or implicitly, in some equations which are used to describe certain non-equilibrium properties of dissolved polymer molecules, such as their intrinsic viscosities.

Values of x_1 are generally determined by incorporating the appropriate experimental measurements into one or another of the various theoretical equations in which this parameter appears. No single equation is universally employed for this purpose, and it should be recognized that the various theoretical relationships thus employed have continued to undergo, in the course of time, modification and revision as new experimental data have become available. Many of the references cited below describe the particular equations and experimental procedures that are useful for this purpose, and may be consulted for further details.

The Table, which is taken from J. Polymer Sci. 46, 550 (1960), contains the literature references to values of the polymer-solvent interaction parameter for an alphabetically arranged list of polymers. Multiple references, where given, indicate either independently determined values for a particular polymer-solvent system, or values for different solvents, solvent mixtures, temperatures, degrees of swelling, solution concentrations, or methods of determination. A few of the references pertain to three-component systems. References for polymer fractions and for copolymers of varying comonomer ratio are listed under the general names of the parent materials.

---

* Some typical polymer-solvent interaction parameter values follow this table.

Polymer or Copolymer	Reference
Polybutadiene	36,67
Poly(butadiene-co-acrylonitrile)	14,67,73
Poly(butadiene-co-2-methyl-5-vinylpyridine)	44
Poly(butadiene-co-styrene)	10,14,28,44,67,68,80
Cellulose	40,70
Cellulose acetate	1,35,39,50
Cellulose nitrate	35,37,50,72
Polychloroprene (Neoprene GN, WRT)	14,67,73
Poly(chlorotrifluoroethylene)	16,32,38
Collagen	70
Poly(dimethyl siloxane)	17,34,43,60,71
Ethyl cellulose	50
Polyethylene	33,51,54,69,74,75
Poly(ethylene-co-propylene)	19
Poly(ethylene oxide)	35
Poly(hexamethylene adipamide)	70,76
Poly(hexamethylene sebacamide)	70
Polyindene, hydrogenated	35
Polyisobutene	3,15,24,25,36,46,48,58,59
Poly(isobutene-co-isoprene), (Butyl rubber)	10,14,15,44
Poly(isobutene-co-styrene)	61
Polyisoprene	
1,4-cis	20
Hevea rubber	5,6,10-14,26,29,31,35,44,45,47,52,53,67,79
Gutta Percha, Balata	35
cyclized	35
hydrogenated	35
Poly(methyl methacrylate)	12,15,59
Polymethylene	33
Polypropylene	41,51
Serum albumin	70
Silk	70
Polystyrene	2,4,7-9,15,21,27,35,39,48,49,58,59,63-66
Poly(styrene-co-divinylbenzene)	8
Poly(vinyl acetate)	18,39,42,46,57,59,70,77,78
Poly(vinyl alcohol)	39,56,62
Poly(vinyl chloride)	15,22,23,35,46
chlorinated	35
Poly(vinyl chloride-co-acrylonitrile)	82
Poly(vinyl chloride-co-vinyl acetate)	35
Poly(vinyl isobutyl ether)	55
Poly(vinylidene cyanide-co-vinyl acetate)	81
Viscose	70
Wool	70

REFERENCES

1. W. J. Badgley and H. Mark, J. Phys. Colloid Chem., 51, 58 (1947).
2. C. E. H. Bawn, R. F. J. Freeman, and A. R. Kammaliddin, Trans. Faraday Soc., 46, 677 (1950).
3. C. E. H. Bawn and R. D. Patel, Trans. Faraday Soc., 52, 1664 (1956).
4. C. E. H. Bawn and M. A. Wajid, Trans. Faraday Soc., 52, 1658 (1956).
5. A. F. Blanchard and P. M. Wootten, J. Polymer Sci. 34, 627 (1959).
6. C. Booth, G. Gee, and G. R. Williamson, J. Polymer Sci., 23, 3 (1957).
7. R. H. Boundy and R. F. Boyer, "Styrene, Its Polymers, Copolymers, and Derivatives," Reinhold, New York, 1952, p. 345.
8. R. F. Boyer and R. S. Spencer, J. Polymer Sci., 3, 97 (1948).
9. J. W. Breitenbach and H. P. Frank, Monatsh. Chem., 79, 531 (1948).
10. G. M. Bristow, Trans. Faraday Soc., 55, 1246 (1959).
11. G. M. Bristow, J. Polymer Sci., 36, 526 (1959).
12. G. M. Bristow, J. Appl. Polymer Sci., 2, 120 (1959).
13. G. M. Bristow and W. F. Watson, Trans. Faraday Soc., 54, 1567 (1958).
14. G. M. Bristow and W. F. Watson, Trans. Faraday Soc., 54, 1731 (1958).
15. G. M. Bristow and W. F. Watson, Trans. Faraday Soc., 54, 1742 (1958).
16. A. M. Bueche, J. Am. Chem. Soc., 74, 65 (1952).
17. A. M. Bueche, J. Polymer Sci. 15, 97 (1955).
18. G. R. Cotten, A. F. Sirianni, and I. E. Puddington, J. Polymer Sci., 32, 115 (1958).
19. G. Crespi and M. Bruzzone, Chim. Ind. (Milan) 41, 741 (1959).
20. R. E. Cunningham, J. Polymer Sci., 42, 571 (1960).
21. P. Doty, M. Brownstein, and W. Schlener, J. Phys. Colloid Chem., 53, 213 (1949).
22. P. Doty and E. Mishuck, J. Am. Chem. Soc., 69, 1631 (1947).
23. P. Doty and H. S. Zable, J. Polymer Sci. 1, 90 (1946).
24. P. J. Flory, J. Am. Chem. Soc., 65, 375 (1943).
25. P. J. Flory and H. Daoust, J. Polymer Sci., 25, 429 (1957).
26. P. J. Flory, N. Rabjohn, and M. C. Schaffer, J. Polymer Sci., 4, 225 (1949).
27. H. P. Frank and H. Mark, J. Polymer Sci., 6, 243 (1951).
28. D. M. French and R. H. Ewart, Anal. Chem., 19, 165 (1947).
29. G. Gee and W. J. C. Orr, Trans. Faraday Soc., 42, 507 (1946).
30. A. I. Goldberg, W. P. Hohenstein, and H. Mark, J. Polymer Sci., 2, 503 (1947).
31. S. L. Gumbrell and R. S. Rivlin, Trans. Faraday Soc., 49, 1945 (1953).
32. H. T. Hall, J. Am. Chem. Soc., 74, 68 (1952).
33. I. Harris, J. Polymer Sci., 8, 353 (1952).
34. R. L. Hauser, C. A. Walker, and F. L. Kilbourne, Jr., Ind. Eng. Chem., 48, 1202 (1956).
35. M. L. Huggins, Ann. N. Y. Acad. Sci., 44, 431 (1943).
36. R. S. Jessup, J. Res. Natl. Bur. Standards, 60, 47 (1958).
37. A. L. Jones, Trans. Faraday Soc., 52, 1408 (1956).
38. H. S. Kaufman and M. S. Muthana, J. Polymer Sci., 6, 251 (1951).
39. T. Kawai, J. Polymer Sci., 32, 425 (1958).
40. T. Kawai, J. Polymer Sci., 37, 181 (1959).
41. J. B. Kinsinger and R. E. Hughes, J. Phys. Chem., 63, 2002 (1959).
42. R. J. Kokes, A. R. Di Pietro, and F. A. Long, J. Am. Chem. Soc., 75, 6319 (1953).
43. A. Y. Korolev, K. A. Andrianov, L. S. Utesheva, and T. E. Vvedenskaya, Dokl. Akad. Nauk SSSR, 89, 65 (1953).
44. G. Kraus, "Rubber World," 135, No. 1, 67 (1956).
45. W. R. Krigbaum and D. K. Carpenter, J. Polymer Sci., 14, 241 (1954).
46. H. Mark and A. V. Tobolsky, "Physical Chemistry of High Polymeric Systems," 2nd ed., Interscience, New York, 1950, p. 265.
47. S. H. Maron and N. Nakajima, J. Polymer Sci., 40, 59 (1959).
48. S. H. Maron and N. Nakajima, J. Polymer Sci., 42, 327 (1960).
49. E. H. Merz and R. W. Raetz, J. Polymer Sci., 5, 587 (1950).
50. W. R. Moore, J. A. Epstein, A. M. Brown, and B. M. Tidswell, J. Polymer Sci. 23, 23 (1957).
51. G. Moraglio, Chim. Ind. (Milan), 41, 984 (1959).
52. L. Mullins, J. Polymer Sci., 19, 225 (1956).
53. L. Mullins, J. Appl. Polymer Sci., 2, 1 (1959).
54. M. S. Muthana and H. Mark, J. Polymer Sci., 4, 527 (1949).
55. M. S. Muthana and H. Mark, J. Polymer Sci., 4, 531 (1949).
56. A. Nakajima and K. Furutachi, Kobunshi Kagaku, 6, 460 (1949).
57. A. Nakajima, H. Yamakawa, and I. Sakurada, J. Polymer Sci., 35, 489 (1959).
58. R. Noel, D. Patterson, and T. Somcynsky, J. Polymer Sci., 42, 561 (1960).
59. T. A. Orofino and P. J. Flory, J. Chem. Phys., 26, 1067 (1957).
60. F. P. Price, S. G. Martin, and J. P. Bianchi, J. Polymer Sci., 22, 49 (1956).
61. J. Rehner, Jr., R. L. Zapp and W. J. Sparks, J. Polymer Sci., 11, 21 (1953).

62. I. Sakurada, A. Nakajima, and H. Fujiwara, J. Polymer Sci., $\underline{35}$, 497 (1959).
63. M. J. Schick, Ph.D. Thesis, Polytechnic Institute of Brooklyn, 1948.
64. M. J. Schick, P. Doty, and B. H. Zimm, J. Am. Chem. Soc., $\underline{72}$, 530 (1950).
65. A. R. Schulz and P. J. Flory, J. Am. Chem. Soc., $\underline{75}$, 3888 (1953).
66. A. R. Schulz and P. J. Flory, J. Polymer Sci., $\underline{15}$, 231 (1955).
67. R. L. Scott and M. Magat, J. Polymer Sci., $\underline{4}$, 555 (1949).
68. A. G. Shvarts, Kolloidn. Zh., $\underline{19}$, 376 (1957).
69. I. Sobolev, J. A. Meyer, V. Stannett, and M. Szwarc, Ind. Eng. Chem., $\underline{49}$, 441 (1957).
70. H. W. Starkweather, Jr., J. Appl. Polymer Sci., $\underline{2}$, 129 (1959).
71. L. E. St. Pierre, H. A. Dewhurst, and A. M. Bueche, J. Polymer Sci., $\underline{36}$, 105 (1959).
72. H. Takenaka, J. Polymer Sci., $\underline{24}$, 321 (1957).
73. A. V. Tobolsky, I. B. Prettyman, and J. H. Dillon, J. Appl. Phys., $\underline{15}$, 380 (1944).
74. Q. A. Trementozzi, J. Polymer Sci., $\underline{23}$, 887 (1957).
75. L. H. Tung, J. Polymer Sci., 24, 333 (1957).
76. L. Valentine, J. Polymer Sci., $\underline{23}$, 297 (1957).
77. V. V. Varadaiah, J. Polymer Sci., $\underline{19}$, 477 (1956).
78. R. H. Wagner, J. Polymer Sci., $\underline{2}$, 21 (1947).
79. G. S. Whitby, A. B. A. Evans, and D. S. Pasternack, Trans. Faraday Soc., $\underline{38}$, 269 (1942).
80. J. A. Yanko, J. Polymer Sci. $\underline{3}$, 576 (1948).
81. J. A. Yanko, J. Polymer Sci. $\underline{22}$, 153, (1956).
82. S. G. Zelikman and N. V. Mikhailov, Kolloidn, Zh. $\underline{19}$, 35 (1957).

SOME TYPICAL POLYMER-SOLVENT INTERACTION PARAMETER VALUES*

Polymer	Solvent	Temp. °C	μ	Ref.
Cellulose acetate	acetone	25	0.45	1
	methyl acetate	25	0.46	1
	pyridine	25	0.28	1
	α-picoline	25	0.36	1
	nitromethane	25	0.44	1
	aniline	25	0.38	1
	dioxane	25	0.38	1
Cellulose nitrate	acetone	25	0.27	1
	methyl ethyl ketone	25	0.21	1
	methyl n-propyl ketone	25	0.15	1
	methyl n-amyl ketone	25	0.02	1
	methyl acetate	25	0.30	1
	ethyl acetate	25	0.22	1
	n-amyl acetate	25	0.02	1
Ethyl cellulose	acetone	25	0.46	1
	methyl ethyl ketone	25	0.42	1
	methyl n-propyl ketone	25	0.37	1
	methyl n-amyl ketone	25	0.38	1
	methyl acetate	25	0.41	1
	ethyl acetate	25	0.40	1
	n-amyl acetate	25	0.28	1
	chloroform	25	0.34	1
	carbon tetrachloride	25	0.46	1
	benzene	25	0.48	1
Poly(ethylene oxide)	water	27	0.45	2
Polyisobutene	benzene	27	0.50	3
	cyclohexane	27	0.44	3
Polystyrene	toluene	27	0.44	2
	ethyl laurate	25	0.47	2
	n-propyl laurate	25	0.62	2
	isopropyl laurate	25	0.71	2
	n-butyl laurate	25	0.74	2
	isobutyl laurate	25	0.85	2
	isoamyl laurate	25	0.91	2
Poly(vinyl chloride)	tetrahydrofuran	27	0.14	2
	dioxane	27	0.52	2
	tributyl phosphate	53	-0.65	4
		76	-0.53	4
	nitrobenzene	53	0.29	4
		76	0.29	4

* Taken from "Physical Chemistry of High Polymers" by M. L. Huggins,
Wiley, New York, 1958, p. 48.

Polymer	Solvent	Temp. °C	μ	Ref.
Poly(vinyl chloride)	nitropropane	53	0.44	4
		76	0.42	4
	acetone	27	0.63	4
		53	0.60	4
	butanol	53	1.74	4
		76	1.58	4
Rubber	benzene	25	0.44	2
	carbon tetrachloride	15-20	0.28	2
	chloroform	15-20	0.37	2
	carbon disulfide	25	0.49	2
	amyl acetate	25	0.49	2

REFERENCES

1. W. R. Moore, J. A. Epstein, A. M. Brown, and B. M. Tidswell, J. Polymer Sci., 23, 23 (1957).
2. M. L. Huggins, Annals N. Y. Acad. Sci., 44, 431 (1943).
3. P. J. Flory, J. Am. Chem. Soc., 65, 372 (1943).
4. P. Doty and H. S. Zable, J. Polymer Sci., 1, 90 (1946).

THETA-SOLVENTS

H.-G. Elias, G. Adank, Hj. Dietschy, O. Etter, U. Gruber and F. W. Ibrahim

Swiss Federal Institute of Technology
Dept. of Industrial and Engineering Chemistry
Zurich, Switzerland

Contents

A. INTRODUCTION

Theta-solvents (θ-solvents) are solvents in which, at a given temperature, a polymer molecule is in the so-called theta-state, where it behaves like an ideal statistical coil (but see below). The theta-temperature may be phenomenologically defined as the critical miscibility temperature at the limit of infinite molecular weight (44). Since P. J. Flory was the first to show the importance of the theta-state for a better understanding of molecular and technological properties of polymers, theta-temperatures are also called "Flory-temperatures". (The name "van't Hoff-temperature" has been suggested (51), but is not accepted internationally).

The precise definition of a theta-temperature is given thermodynamically. The chemical potential of the solvent, $\Delta \mu_1$, can be split into an ideal and an excess term:

$$\Delta \mu_1 \equiv \Delta \mu_1^{id} + \Delta \mu_1^{exc} \qquad [1]$$

where the excess chemical potential is given by the enthalpy of dilution ΔH_1 and the excess entropy of dilution ΔS_1^{exc}:

$$\Delta \mu_1^{exc} \equiv \Delta H_1 - T \Delta S_1^{exc} \qquad [2]$$

At the theta-temperature, the excess chemical potential $\Delta \mu_1^{exc}$ and, correspondingly, the excess free enthalpy of dilution are zero. This does not imply, however, that both the enthalpy of dilution and the excess entropy of dilution are zero. It means only that both terms on the right-hand side of eq. [2] compensate each other.

The chemical potential itself is not a measurable quantity. However, it may be replaced for instance by the product of the osmotic pressure Π and the partial molar volume of the solvent $\bar{v}_1$:

$$- \Delta \mu_1 = \Pi \bar{v}_1 \qquad [3]$$

The concentration dependence of the osmotic pressure of solutions of non-electrolytes can be written as a power series

$$\Pi = \frac{RT}{\overline{M}_n} c_2 + A_2 \cdot c_2^2 + A_3 \cdot c_2^3 + \ldots \ldots \qquad [4]$$

where c_2 = concentration of the solute (polymer), R = gas constant, $\overline{M}_n$ = number average molecular weight of the polymer, and A_2, A_3 .... are the second, third, ... virial coefficients. At low polymer concentrations, the third term of the right-hand side of eq. [4] is negligible. Comparison of equations [1], [3] and [4] then gives

$$A_2 = - \frac{\Delta \mu_1^{exc}}{\overline{v}_1 c_2^2} \qquad [5]$$

Since by definition the excess chemical potential is zero at the theta-temperature, the second virial coefficient is zero, too. With respect to the concentration dependence of the osmotic pressure, the solution will consequently behave as pseudo-ideal at the theta-temperature. To avoid confusion with true ideal solutions (where both enthalpy of dilution and excess entropy of dilution are zero), it was proposed that solutions in the theta-state should be termed pseudo-ideal (99).

The thermodynamic behavior described above results from the fact that long-range interactions are not present in the theta-state. Long-range interactions are intra-molecular interactions between groups of one and the same polymer molecule separated by many chemical bonds. They correspond to van der Waals forces between different molecules in low molecular chemistry. At the theta-temperature, the polymer molecule thus exhibits its unperturbed dimensions, i.e. dimensions influenced only by short-range interactions between neighboring groups and by skeletal effects (bond distances, valence angles).

The suitability of a solvent as a theta-solvent thus depends on the polymer (consti-tution, configuration), on the solvent (constitution) and on temperature, because all these factors influence long-range interactions (interactions with solvent and ex-cluded volume effect). A molecular weight dependence of the theta-temperature is scarcely detectable for single solvents in the high molecular weight range of polymer (see however ref. 79). Not enough measurements are available at present for the low molecular weight range. With suitable mixed solvents at constant temperature, a small variation of the theta composition with molecular weight is measurable (35). This corresponds to a small variation of the theta-temperature with molecular weight at a given solvent composition.

The thermodynamic conditions for the theta-state are fulfilled for single as well as for mixed solvents. In the absence of large variations in temperature, the unperturbed dimensions of a given polymer are approximately the same in different single solvents. However, the dimensions can vary widely in mixed solvents (33), if solvent/non-solvent pairs are used. This behavior may be explained by the non-negligible interactions of non-solvent with polymer groups and interactions between solvent and non-solvent mole-cules. The observation of only small variations of the unperturbed dimensions with different single solvents at approximately equal theta-temperatures leads to the con-clusion that approximately equal interactions must be present in order to get theta conditions at equal temperatures.

Methods to Determine Theta-Solvents:

a) Phase equilibria (PE)

The temperature for phase separation, i.e. the critical miscibility temperature, is determined for a number of different concentrations of a polymer of known number-average molecular weight and the maximum critical miscibility temperature T_c is noted. The experiment is repeated for a series of polymers of the same constitution and configuration but of different molecular weights. For large molecular weights, the critical miscibility temperature T_c can be extrapolated to infinite molecular weight according to ref. (44):

$$(1/T_c) = (1/\theta) (1 + (b/\overline{M}_n^{0.5})) \qquad [6]$$

References page IV-183

where θ is the theta-temperature, and b a constant for the particular system. If
used with mixed solvents, the data must be extrapolated not only to infinite molecular
weight but, in addition, to infinite dilution (68). This is not a straightforward
procedure, however. The method can be used for separation in two liquid phases only.
Care must therefore be taken with crystalline polymers.

b) Second virial coefficient (A_2)

According to eq. [5] the second virial coefficient A_2 is zero for a θ-solvent and
consequently the slope of a Π/c vs c plot is also zero if the solvent is a θ-solvent.
The 3rd virial coefficient A_3 may be different from zero however, and measurements
should be made at sufficiently low concentrations. All absolute methods for the
determination of molecular weights may be used unless they depend on specific solvent
behavior, like ebullioscopy and cryoscopy. Methods normally used are osmotic pressure
(OP), light scattering (LS), sedimentation equilibrium (SE), and the approach to
sedimentation equilibrium [Archibalds method (Arch)].

The concentration dependence of reciprocal apparent molecular weights is determined
for a given polymer/solvent pair at different temperatures and the resulting 2nd
virial coefficients are plotted against temperature. The dependence of A_2 on temperature is linear only in the neighborhood of the theta-temperature. Care must be
taken, therefore, to work close to the theta-temperature.

Alternatively, the second virial coefficient for a given polymer may be measured at
a constant temperature using different solvent/nonsolvent ratios.

c) Concentration dependence of hydrodynamic parameters

The concentration dependence of the sedimentation coefficient (s) and of the diffusion
coefficient (D) is not only affected by thermodynamic effects but, in addition, by
frictional forces. The effect is more pronounced at higher molecular weights (82)
and even at theta-temperatures, therefore, a concentration dependence of s or D will
appear. As a result, this method is not very suitable to determine theta-temperatures
except for lower molecular weight polymers.

d) Cloud point titration (CT)

Polymer solutions of different concentrations are titrated with a non-solvent until
the first sign of cloudiness. The logarithm of the non-solvent concentration at the
cloud point is then plotted against the logarithm of the polymer concentration at
the cloud point and extrapolated to 100% polymer (28). The solvent/non-solvent
mixture at this point corresponds to a theta-mixture (29). A knowledge of the molecular weight is not necessary.

e) Viscosity-molecular weight relationship (VM)

The method makes use of the fact that the exponent, a, in the Staudinger-Mark-Houwink
equation

$$[\eta] = K \cdot M^a \qquad\qquad [7]$$

is equal to 0.5 for a random coil in a theta-solvent. A series of polymers of the
same type with widely different known molecular weights is used to determine intrinsic viscosities $[\eta]$ at different temperatures. The theta-temperature can be
determined either by direct experiment (VM(T-E), or, if it is not in the measurable
range by calculation (VM(T-C)) (See Ref. 44, Chapt. XIV).

An alternative method is to change the solvent/non-solvent ratio at a given temperature and to measure intrinsic viscosities of different polymers in different solvent
mixtures (6), however the exponent "a" does not depend linearly on solvent/non-sol-
vent composition.

The methods suitable for the determination of theta-solvents or theta-compositions
are compared below:

Method	Number of Polymer Samples Required	Conditions for Application of the Method		Determined Value*
		Knowledge of Polymer Molecular Weight Required	Type of Solvent	
Phase equilibrium (PE)	≥ 3	yes	preferably single	θ-temp.
Virial coefficient (A_2)	1	given by the applied method	single and mixed	θ-temp. or θ-comp.
Cloud point titration (CT)	1	no	mixed	θ-comp.
Viscosity-molecular-weight-relationship (VM)	≥ 3	yes	preferably mixed	θ-comp.

* temp. = temperature, comp. = composition.

In the following table, theta-solvents for various polymers have been compiled from the literature. They are subdivided into a number of polymer groups: Within each subgroup, the polymers are listed in alphabetical order. A compound like poly(p-bromostyrene) is therefore found in subgroup 2 (vinyl polymers), bromo- ..... and not under -styrene. The structural units of copolymers are also given in an alphabetical order. Poly(butadiene-co-styrene) is placed therefore after polybutadiene. Making use of this arrangement, the suffixes ortho (o), meta (m), para (p), normal (n), etc., were neglected. However, the suffices di-, tri- are used for alphabetical arrangement.

Within each group, the atactic polymers are followed by the isotactic and syndiotactic polymers. The microtacticity is expressed in diads. No data on triads could be found.

The theta-solvents are arranged in increasing order of their theta-temperatures. The components of mixed solvents are given in the order: solvent, followed by the non-solvent, or the worse solvent. The composition of mixed solvents is given on a volume/volume basis except as otherwise noted. Arrows ↑ or ↓ indicate different theta-temperatures reported for one given solvent. These additional temperatures may be found above (↑) or below (↓) the line where the arrow appears.

Polymer	θ-Solvent		θ-Temp.	Method	Ref.
	Name	Composition	(°C)		

1 - POLYOLEFINS

Polymer	Name	Composition	θ-Temp. (°C)	Method	Ref.
Poly(1-butene) atact.	anisole		86.2	PE	67
isotact.	anisole		89.1	PE	67
Polyethylene	diphenyl ether		161.4	PE	112
Poly(1-hexene sulfone)					
1:1 atact.	2-butanone/iso-propanol	41.5/58.5	4±5	A_2(LS);PE	57
	2-butanone/iso-propanol	37 /63	23.5±2	A_2(LS);PE	57
	n-hexyl chloride		13 ±2	A_2(LS);PE	57
Polyisobutene	ethylbenzene		-24.0	PE	48
	toluene		-13.0	PE	48
	chlorobenzene/ n-propanol	79.7/20.3	14.0	CT	37
	chloroform/ n-propanol	79.5/20.5	14.0	CT	37
	ethyl n-caprylate		22	PE	85
	benzene		24	VM	106
	benzene		24.0	PE,VM	48
	carbon tetrachloride/ 2-butanone	66.4/33.6	25.0	CT	37
	carbon tetrachloride/ dioxane	63.8/36.2	25.0	CT	37
	chlorobenzene/ n-propanol	76.0/24.0	25.0	CT	37
	chloroform/ n-propanol	77.1/22.9	25.0	CT	37
	cyclohexane/ 2-butanone	63.2/36.8	25.0	CT	37
	cyclohexane/dioxane	45.1/54.9	25.0	CT	37
	n-hexane/n-butanol	76.4/23.6	25.0	CT	37
	n-hexane/2-butanone	63.4/36.6	25.0	CT	37
	n-hexane/n-decanol	58.1/41.1	25.0	CT	37
	n-hexane/dioxane	51.8/48.2	25.0	CT	37
	n-hexane/n-heptanol	62.6/37.4	25.0	CT	37
	n-hexane/n-hexanol	68.3/31.7	25.0	CT	37
	n-hexane/3-methyl-2-butanone	57.6/42.4	25.0	CT	37

Polymer	θ-Solvent		θ-Temp.	Method	Ref.
	Name	Composition	(°C)		
Polyisobutene	(Cont'd.)				
	n-hexane/n-octanol	63.7/36.3	25.0	CT	37
	n-hexane/n-pentanol	71.7/28.3	25.0	CT	37
	n-hexane/n-propanol	80.3/19.7	25.0	CT	37
	methyl cyclohexanone/ n-butanol	70.8/29.2	25.0	CT	37
	methylcyclohexane/ n-decanol	52.5/47.5	25.0	CT	37
	methylcyclohexane/ dioxane	49.0/51.0	25.0	CT	37
	methylcyclohexane/ n-heptanol	60.5/39.5	25.0	CT	37
	methylcyclohexane/ n-octanol	56.0/44.0	25.0	CT	37
	methylcyclohexane/ n-pentanol	65.2/34.8	25.0	CT	37
	methylcyclohexane/ n-propanol	74.2/25.8	25.0	CT	37
	toluene/cyclohexanol	70.7/29.3	25.0	CT	37
	ethylbenzene/diphenyl ether	75 /25	26.8	PE	48
	ethyl heptanoate		33	PE	48
	chlorobenzene/ n-propanol	67.5/32.5	49.0	CT	37
	chloroform/ n-propanol	71.4/28.6	49.0	CT	37
	methylcyclohexane/ n-butanol	57.9/42.1	49.0	CT	37
	ethyl caproate		57	PE	48
	ethylbenzene/ diphenyl ether	50 /50	76.0	PE	48
	phenetole		86.0	PE, VM	48
	anisole		105.5	PE, VM	48
	diphenyl ether		148	PE	48
Poly(1-pentene) atact.	phenetole		48.3	A_2(OP)	69
isotact.	phenetole		55.8	A_2(OP)	69
	2-pentanol		62.4	PE	46
Polypropylene atact.	carbon tetrachloride/ n-propanol	74 /26	25.0	CT	32

References page IV-183

Polymer	θ-Solvent		θ-Temp.	Method	Ref.
	Name	Composition	(°C)		
Polypropylene (Cont'd.)					
atact.	carbon tetrachloride/ n-butanol	67 /33	25.0	CT	32
	n-hexane/n-butanol	68 /32	25.0	CT	32
	n-hexane/n-propanol	78 /22	25.0	CT	32
	methylcyclohexane/ n-propanol	69 /31	25.0	CT	32
	methylcyclohexane/ n-butanol	66 /34	25.0	CT	32
	isoamyl acetate		34	VM	23
	↓ 1-chloronaphthalene		68 ↓	A$_2$(LS)	103
	↑ 1-chloronaphthalene		74 ↑	PE	60
	cyclohexanone		92	PE	60
	↓ diphenyl ether		153 ↓	PE,VM	60
	↑ diphenyl ether		153.3 ↑	PE	61
isotact.	↓ diphenyl ether		145 ↓	PE;VM	60
	↑ diphenyl ether		146.2 ↑	PE	61
Poly(tetrafluoroethylene-co-trifluoronitrosomethane) 1:1					
atact.	trichlorotrifluoroethane (Freon 113)		35	VM	84

Polymer	θ-Solvent		θ-Temp.	Method	Ref.
	Name	Composition	(°C)		

2 - VINYL POLYMERS

Polymer	θ-Solvent Name	Composition	θ-Temp. (°C)	Method	Ref.
Poly(p-bromostyrene) atact.	benzene		20	VM(a=0.53	59
Poly(2,5-dichlorostyrene) atact.	ethyl acetate/ ethanol	93.7/6.3 (w/w)	30.5	A_2(LS)	40
Poly(3,4-dichlorostyrene) atact.	butyl acetate/ butanol	92.9/7.1 w/w	32.9	A_2(LS)	39
Poly(p-isopropylstyrene) atact.	dioxane/isopropanol	35 /65	20	CT	35
Poly(α-methylstyrene) atact.	benzene/methanol	79.4/20.6	30	?	86
Polystyrene atact	cyclohexane/toluene	86.9/13.1	15	PE	105
	2-butanone/iso-propanol	85.7/14.3	23	A_2(LS,OP)	15
	trans-decalin/ cis-decalin	76.9/23.1	19.3	PE	87
	benzene/n-hexane	39 /61	20	CT	52
	benzene/isopropanol	66 /34	20	CT	35
	dioxane/n-hexane	38 /62	20	CT	52
	dioxane/isopropanol	55 /45	20	CT	35
	3-methyl-2-butanone/ n-hexane	52 /48	20	CT	36
	benzene/cyclohexanol	38.4/61.6	25	CT;A_2(LS)	33
	benzene/n-hexane	34.7/65.3	25	CT;A_2(LS)	33
	benzene/methanol	77.8/22.2	25	CT;A_2(LS)	33
	benzene/isopropanol	64.2/35.8	25	CT;A_2(LS)	33
	2-butanone/methanol	88.7/11.3	25	CT;A_2(LS)	33
	2-butanone/methanol	89 /11	25	A_2(OP);VM	89
	carbon tetrachloride/ methanol	81.7/18.3	25	CT;A_2(LS)	33
	chlorobenzene/di-isopropyl ether	32 /68	25	CT;A_2(LS)	33
	chloroform/methanol	75.2/24.8	25	CT;A_2(LS)	33
	chloroform/methanol	74.7/25.3	25	A_2(OP);VM	89
	dioxane/methanol	71.4/28.6	25	CT;A_2(LS)	33

Polymer	θ-Solvent		θ-Temp.	Method	Ref.
	Name	Composition	(°C)		
Polystyrene (Cont'd.) atact.	tetrahydrofuran/ methanol	71.3/28.7	25	CT;A_2(LS)	33
	toluene/methanol	20 /80	25	A_2(OP);VM	89
	2-butanone/methanol	88.9/11.1	30	PE	105
	toluene/n-heptane	47.6/52.4	30	PE	105
	decalin		31	A_2(LS)	93
	benzene/methanol	74.0/26.0	34	VM	5
	2-butanone/iso- propanol	82.6/17.4	34	VM	5
	p-dioxane/methanol	65.1/34.9	34	VM	5
	toluene/methanol	75.2/24.8	34	VM	5
	↓ cyclohexane		34 ↓	PE	66
	↓ cyclohexane		34.4- 35.4 ↓	A_2(LS);VM	65
	↓ cyclohexane		35.0 ↓	A_2(LS)	88
	↓ cyclohexane		35 ↓	s, D	9
	↓ cyclohexane		35 ↓	D	81
	↓ cyclohexane		35 ↓	SE	78
	↑ cyclohexane		35 ↑	s	54
	2-butanone/ isopropanol	87 /13	67	A_2(LS)	88
	2-butanone/ isopropanol	87 /13	67	A_2(LS)	50
	ethylcyclohexane		70	PE	49
	methylcyclohexane		70.5	VM	27
Poly(styrene-co-p-iso- propylstyrene) atact.					
66.9% Styrene	dioxane/isopropanol	48 /52	20	CT	35
44 % Styrene	dioxane/isopropanol	44 /56	20	CT	35
12 % Styrene	dioxane/isopropanol	37 /63	20	CT	35
Poly(vinylidene chloride- co-n-butyl acrylate) atact.					
83.3/16.7	benzyl alcohol		44.0	PE	2

Polymer	θ-Solvent		θ-Temp.	Method	Ref.
	Name	Composition	(°C)		
Poly(vinylidene chloride-co-ethyl acrylate) atact.					
85.1/14.9	ethyl acetoacetate		49.6	PE	2
Poly(vinylidene chloride-co-n-hexyl acrylate) atact.					
85.5/14.5	benzyl alcohol		56.8	PE	2
Poly(vinylidene chloride-co-n-octyl acrylate) atact.					
84.4/15.6	benzyl alcohol		77.9	PE	2
Poly(vinyl acetate) atact.	2-butanone/iso-propanol	73.2/26.8	25	PE;A_2(LS)	104
	3-methyl-2-butanone/n-heptane	73.2/26.8	25	PE;A_2(LS)	104
	3-heptanone		29	PE;A_2(LS)	77
	3-methyl-2-butanone/n-heptane	72.7/27.3	30	PE;A_2(LS)	76
	6-methyl-3-heptanone		66	PE;A_2(LS)	77
Poly(vinyl benzoate) atact.	xylene		32.5	PE	96
Poly(vinyl bromide) atact.	tetrahydrofuran/methanol	83 /17	20	A_2(LS)	19
Poly(vinyl chloride) atact.	benzyl alcohol		155.4	PE	97
Poly(vinyl p-chloro-benzoate) atact.	2-butanone/n-butanol	53 /47	60	PE	94
Poly(β-vinylnaphthalene) atact.	toluene/decalin	43.5/56.5 w/w	30.2	A_2(LS);VM	41
Poly(vinyl pivalate) atact.	acetone/methanol	38.2/61.8	20	CT	26
	benzene/methanol	33.3/66.7	20	CT	26
	2-butanone/methanol	24.6/75.4	20	CT	26
Poly(2-vinylpyridine) atact.	heptane/propanol	59.6/40.4 w/w	25.0	PE	55
Poly(vinylpyrrolidone) atact.	water/acetone	33.2/66.8	25.0	CT;VM	29
Poly(vinyltriazole) atact.	dimethylformamide/dioxane	76.6/23.4	25	CT	30,73

References page IV-183

Polymer	θ-Solvent Name	Composition	θ-Temp. (°C)	Method	Ref.

3 - ACRYLIC POLYMERS

Polymer	θ-Solvent Name	Composition	θ-Temp. (°C)	Method	Ref.
Poly(acrylic acid) atact.	dioxane		30	PE;A_2(OP)	85
Poly(acrylonitrile-co-styrene) atact.					
ca. (1/2) = (mol/mol)	benzene/methanol	66.7/33.3	25	CT	30
ca. (1/2) = (mol/mol)	dimethylformamide/methanol	44.7/55.3	25	CT	30
Poly(n-butyl methacrylate) atact.	↓ isopropanol		21.5 ↓	A_2(LS);VM	12
	↑ isopropanol		23.7 ↑	PE;A_2(LS)	16
Poly(cyclohexyl methacrylate) atact.	n-butanol		23.0	VM	53
Poly(ethyl methacrylate) atact.	2-butanone/isopropanol	12.5/87.5	23	PE;A_2(LS)	14
	isopropanol		36.9	PE;A_2(LS)	16
Poly(2-ethylbutyl methacrylate) atact.	isopropanol		27.4	PE;A_2(LS)	25
Poly(n-hexyl methacrylate) atact.	isopropanol		32.6	PE;A_2(LS)	10
Poly(n-lauryl methacrylate) atact.	isopropyl acetate		13	PE;A_2(LS)	10a
	↓ n-pentanol		29.5 ↓	VM	72
	↑ n-pentanol		29.5 ↑	PE;A_2(LS)	71
Poly(methacrylic acid) atact.	0.002 M aqueous HCl		30	VM	58
Polymethacrylonitrile atact.	dimethylformamide		29.2	VM	90
Poly(methyl methacrylate) atact.	chloroform		-273 ± 50	VM(T-C)	47
	dichloroethane		-233 ± 50	VM(T-C)	47
	benzene		-223 ± 50	VM(T-C)	47
	methyl methacrylate		-163 ± 50	VM(T-C)	47
	2-butanone		∼-98	VM(T-C)	47
	ethyl acetate		∼-98	VM(T-C)	47
	toluene		-65 ± 10	VM(T-C)	47

Polymer	θ-Solvent		θ-Temp.	Method	Ref.
	Name	Composition	(°C)		

Poly(methyl methacrylate) (Cont'd.)

atact.	acetone		-55 ± 10	VM(T-C)	47
	methyl isobutyrate		-53 ± 10	VM(T-C)	47
	2-methyl-4-pentanone		-42	A_2(LS)	63
	methyl isovalerate		-37	A_2(LS)	63
	butyl acetate		-20	A_2(LS)	63
	2-butanone/ isopropanol	58.2/41.8	4	A_2(LS)(80% syn)	63
	2-butanone/ isopropanol	55 /45	7.0	A_2(LS)(80% syn)	102
	2-heptanone		∿11	VM(T-C)	47
	2-butanone/ isopropanol	55 /45	12.8	A_2(LS)	63
	benzene/n-hexane	70 /30	20	CT	52
	benzene/isopropanol	38 /62	20	CT	52
	dioxane/n-hexane	59 /41	20	CT	33
	3-methyl-2-butanone/ n-hexane	83 /17	20	CT	36
	2-ethylbutyraldehyde		22	PE	47
	2-butanone/isopropanol	50 /50	22.8	A_2(LS)	63
	acetone/ethanol	47.7/52.3	25	CT;A_2(LS)	34
	acetone/methanol	78.1/21.9	25	CT	34
	2-butanone/cyclohexane	59.5/40.5	25	CT;A_2(LS)	34
	2-butanone/n-hexane	70.7/29.3	25	CT;A_2(LS)	34
	2-butanone/isopropanol	50 /50	25.0	PE (7% isot.)	95
	2-butanone/isopropanol	50 /50	25	VM(T-E)	7
	2-butanone/isopropanol	50 /50	25	A_2(LS)	11
	2-butanone/isopropanol	58.2/41.8	25	A_2(LS)	34
	carbon tetrachloride/ n-hexane	99.4/ 0.6	25	CT	34
	carbon tetrachloride/ methanol	53.3/46.7	25	CT	34
	dioxane/cyclohexane	53.4/46.6	25	CT;A_2(LS)	34
	↓ 3-heptanone		∿25 ↓	VM(T-C)	47
	toluene/n-hexane	81.2/18.8	25	CT	34
	toluene/methanol	35.7/64.3	26.2	PE;A_2(LS)	16
	carbon tetrachloride		∿27	VM(T-C)	47

References page IV-183

Polymer	θ-Solvent		θ-Temp.	Method	Ref.
	Name	Composition	(°C)		

Poly(methyl methacrylate) (Cont'd.)

Polymer	Name	Composition	θ-Temp. (°C)	Method	Ref.
atact.	2-butanone/isopropanol	46.8/53.2	28.5	A_2(LS)	63
	↓ acetonitrile		30 ↓	VM;A_2(LS)	20
	↓ butyl chloride		32.6 ↓	A_2(LS)	62
	↑ 3-heptanone		33.7 ↑	PE (7% isot)	95
	↓ 4-heptanone		33.8 ↓	PE	47
	↓ 4-heptanone		34±10 ↓	VM(T-C)	47
	↑ n-butyl chloride		35.0 ↑	A_2(LS)(80% syn)	102
	2,2-dimethyl-4-pentanone		~35	PE	47
	↑ n-butyl chloride		35.4 ↑	A_2(LS)	63
	↑ 4-heptanone		40.4 ↑	A_2(LS)	63
	amyl acetate		~41	VM(T-C)	47
	2,4-dimethyl-3-pentanone		41	VM(T-E)	7
	↑ acetonitrile		45 ↑	PE;VM(T-C)	47
	2,4-dimethyl-3-pentanone		46	PE	47
	2-octanone		52	PE	47
	isoamyl acetate		57.5	A_2(LS)	63
	3-octanone		72	PE	47
7% i	n-propanol		84.4	PE	95
7% i	p-cymene		159.7	PE	95
94% i	2-butanone/ isopropanol	55 /45	25.0	A_2(LS)	102
94% i	n-butyl chloride		26.5	A_2(LS)	102
	acetonitrile		27.6	PE	64
90% i	2-butanone/ isopropanol	50 /50	30.3	PE	95
90% i	3-heptanone		40.0	PE	95
90% i	n-propanol		75.9	PE	95
90% i	p-cymene		152.1	PE	95
100% s	2-butanone/ isopropanol	55 /45	8.0	A_2(LS)	102
100% s	n-butyl chloride		26.5	A_2(LS)	102
100% s	n-propanol		85.2	PE	95

Polymer	θ-Solvent		θ-Temp.	Method	Ref.
	Name	Composition	(°C)		

Poly(methyl methacrylate-
co-styrene)
    atact.

%MMA = 73.9	benzene/n-hexane	62	/38	20	CT	36
= 57.7	benzene/n-hexane	59	/41	20	CT	36
= 41.9	benzene/n-hexane	51	/49	20	CT	36
= 23.7	benzene/n-hexane	44	/56	20	CT	36
= 73.9	benzene/isopropanol	41	/59	20	CT	36
= 57.7	benzene/isopropanol	48	/52	20	CT	36
= 41.9	benzene/isopropanol	51	/49	20	CT	36
= 23.7	benzene/isopropanol	57	/43	20	CT	36
= 73.9	3-methyl-2-butanone/ n-hexane	76	/24	20	CT	36
= 57.7	3-methyl-2-butanone/ n-hexane	71	/29	20	CT	36
= 41.9	3-methyl-2-butanone/ n-hexane	66	/34	20	CT	36
= 23.7	3-methyl-2-butanone/ n-hexane	60	/40	20	CT	36

Poly(n-octyl meth-
acrylate)
    atact.

	n-butanol		16.8	PE;A_2(LS)	13

Poly(isopropyl acrylate)
    atact.

	1,2-butanediol/ 1,3-butanediol	68.4/31.6 w/w	121.0	PE	75
	n-decane		166.6	PE	75
isotact.	1,2-butanediol/ 1,3-butanediol	68.4/31.6 w/w	123.5	PE	110
	n-decane		178.0	PE	110
syndiot.	n-decane		168.3	PE	75

Polymer	θ-Solvent		θ-Temp.	Method	Ref.
	Name	Composition	(°C)		

4 - POLYDIENES

Polymer	Name	Composition	θ-Temp. (°C)	Method	Ref.
Poly(1,4-butadiene) 90% cis					
90% 1.4	hexane/heptane	50 /50	5	PE,s	91
	3-pentanone		10.6	PE	1
	5-methyl-2-hexanone		12.6	PE	1
90% 1.4	hexane/heptane	75 /25	∿20	PE	91
	isobutyl acetate		20.5	VM;A_2(OP)	24
	2-pentanone		59.7	PE	1
Poly(butadiene-co-styrene) 70/30 (rad.)	n-octane		21	PE,VM,s,D	92
Poly(1,4-isoprene) cis[a]	2-pentanone		14.5	PE	109
96% cis	n-heptane/n-propanol	69.5/30.5 w/w	25	A_2(LS);CT; VM	18
trans[b]	n-propyl acetate		60	PE	109
Poly(1,2-co-3,4-iso-prene) 35% 1.2 65% 3.4	benzene/ isopropanol	55 /45	20	CT	35
Poly(bromo-1,4-isoprene) cis 30.2 double bonds subst.	cyclohexane		∿20	A_2(OP,LS)	101

a. natural rubber

b. gutta percha

Polymer	θ-Solvent		θ-Temp.	Method	Ref.
	Name	Composition	(°C)		

5 - POLYOXIDES

Polymer	θ-Solvent Name	Composition	θ-Temp. (°C)	Method	Ref.
Poly(ethylene oxide)	acetonitrile/isopropyl ether	45 /55	20	CT	35
	chloroform/n-hexane[a]	54 /46	20	CT	35
	chloroform/n-hexane[a]	47.4/52.6	20	CT;A_2(Arch); VM	29
	nitroethane/isopropyl ether	45 /55	20	CT	35
	0.45 M K_2SO_4 in water		35	PE	3
	0.39 M $MgSO_4$ in water		45	PE	3
Poly(tetrahydrofuran)	benzene/acetonitrile	38.5/61.5	25	CT	31
	2-butanone/acetonitrile	61.7/38.3	25	CT	31
	carbon tetrachloride/acetonitrile	49.8/50.2	25	CT	31
	chlorobenzene/acetonitrile	39.9/60.1	25	CT	31
	tetrahydrofuran/acetonitrile	41.3/58.7	25	CT	31
	toluene/acetonitrile	39 /61	25	CT	31

a. composition depends strongly on quality of n-hexane.

References page IV-183

Polymer	θ-Solvent		θ-Temp.	Method	Ref.
	Name	Composition	(°C)		

6 - POLYESTERS

Polymer	θ-Solvent		θ-Temp.	Method	Ref.
	Name	Composition	(°C)		
Poly(4,4'-isopropylidene-diphenylene carbonate)	chloroform		20	A_2(LS)	17
Poly (adipic acid-ethylene glycol)	cyclohexanol		114.5	PE	111
Poly (adipic acid hexamethylene glycol)	cyclohexanol		64	PE	111
Poly (adipic acid-polyethylene oxide)					
M_n of PEO = 150	chloroform/n-hexane	65 /35	20	CT	35
= 200	chloroform/n-hexane	63 /37	20	CT	35
= 300	chloroform/n-hexane	62 /38	20	CT	35
= 387	chloroform/n-hexane	60 /40	20	CT	35
= 600	chloroform/n-hexane	59 /41	20	CT	35
= 2580	chloroform/n-hexane	57 /43	20	CT	35
= 7000	chloroform/n-hexane	56 /44	20	CT	35
Poly (adipic acid-tetramethylene glycol)	cyclohexanol		77	PE	111
Poly (sebacic acid-ethylene glycol)	cyclohexanol		72	PE	111
Poly (sebacic acid-polyethylene oxide) M_n of PEO = 387	chloroform/n-hexane	56 /44	20	CT	35
	acetonitrile/iso-propyl ether	35.8/64.2	20	CT	35
Poly (suberic acid-ethylene glycol)	cyclohexanol		88	PE	111
Poly(suberic acid-polyethylene oxide) M_n of PEO = 387	chloroform/n-hexane	58 /42	20	CT	35
	acetonitrile/ isopropyl ether	38.6/61.4	20	CT	35
Poly (succinic acid-polyethylene oxide) M_n of PEO = 387	chloroform/n-hexane	61 /39	20	CT	35
	acetonitrile/iso-propyl ether	44.6/55.4	20	CT	35

Polymer	θ-Solvent		θ-Temp.	Method	Ref.
	Name	Composition	(°C)		

7 - POLYAMIDES

Polymer	θ-Solvent		θ-Temp.	Method	Ref.
Poly(adipic acid-hexamethylene diamine)	2.3 M KCl in 90% (vol) formic acid		25	A_2(LS)	98,38
	2.3 M KCl in 90% (vol) formic acid		25	VM	38

8 - POLYUREAS

Polymer	θ-Solvent		θ-Temp.	Method	Ref.
Poly(heptamethylene urea)	dichloroacetic acid		46	VM	43
	90% (vol) sulfuric acid		46	VM	43

9 - POLYSACCHARIDES

Polymer	θ-Solvent		θ-Temp.	Method	Ref.
Amylopectin	water		25.0	A_2(LS)	107
Amylose (potato)	dimethyl sulfoxide/acetone	56.6/43.5	20	VM	8
	dimethyl sulfoxide/methanol	49 /51	25.0	VM	21
	dimethyl sulfoxide/0.5 M KCl	25 /75	25.0	VM	21
	0.33 M KCl in water		25.0	VM	42
	sodium acetate buffer (0.5 N NaOH, 0.5 N acetic acid until pH = 5.0)		25.0	VM	21
Cellulose tributyrate	dodecane/tetralin	75 /25	122	PE	74
Cellulose tricaproate	dimethylformamide		41	A_2(OP)	68
Cellulose tricaprylate	dimethylformamide		140	PE	74
	3-phenylpropanol		48	PE	74

Polymer	θ-Solvent		θ-Temp.	Method	Ref.
	Name	Composition	(°C)		

10 - PROTEINS

Bovine serum albumin	water		10	A_2(Arch)	56

11 - POLYSILOXANES

Polymer	θ-Solvent Name	Composition	θ-Temp. (°C)	Method	Ref.
Poly(dimethyl siloxane)	cyclohexane		-81	A_2(OP)	70
	xylene		-47	A_2(OP)	70
	toluene		-30	A_2(OP)	70
	↓ benzene		-7 ↓	A_2(OP)	70
	↑ benzene		-3 ↑	A_2(LS)	70
	ethyl iodide		2.1	A_2(LS)	100
	ethyl acetate		18	A_2(OP)	70
	2-butanone		20	PE	45
	2-butanone		20	A_2(OP)	70
	$C_8F_{18}/C_2Cl_4F_2$	33.17/66.83 (w/w)	22.5	A_2(LS);PE	22
	carbon tetrachloride/ benzyl alcohol	78.8/21.2	25	CT	31
	chloroform/ benzyl alcohol	87.2/12.8	25	CT	31
	ethylbenzene/ benzyl alcohol	85.4/14.6	25	CT	31
	methylene chloride/ benzyl alcohol	77.3/22.7	25	CT	31
	toluene/cyclohexanol	66 /34	25	CT	31
	toluene/1-nitro- propane	64 /36	25	CT;A_2(LS)	31
	trichloroethylene/ benzyl alcohol	78.3/21.7	25	CT;A_2(LS)	31
	toluene/benzyl alcohol	83.8/16.2	25	CT	31
	toluene/nitroethane	74.1/25.9	25	CT	31
	toluene/nitromethane	81.1/18.9	25	CT	31
	bromocyclohexane		29.0	A_2(LS)	100

Polymer	θ-Solvent		θ-Temp.	Method	Ref.
	Name	Composition	(°C)		

Poly(dimethyl siloxane) (Cont'd.)

Polymer	Name	Composition	θ-Temp. (°C)	Method	Ref.
	bromocyclohexane/ phenetole	85.7/14.3	36.3	A_2(LS)	100
	chlorobenzene/ dimethyl phthalate	88.2/11.8	56.3	A_2(LS)	100
	chlorobenzene		68	A_2(OP)	70
	bromobenzene		78.7	A_2(LS)	100
	↓ phenetole		83.0 ↓	PE	45
	↓ phenetole		83 ↓	A_2(OP)	70
	↑ phenetole		89.5 ↑	A_2(LS)	100

12 - INORGANIC POLYMERS

Polymer	Name	Composition	θ-Temp. (°C)	Method	Ref.
Poly(metaphosphate)	0.415 M aqueous NaBr		25	A_2(LS)	108

1. M. Abe and H. Fujita, Rep. Prog. Polymer Phys. Japan 7, 42 (1964).
2. M. Asahina, M. Sato and T. Kobayashi, Bull. Chem. Soc. Japan 35, 630 (1962).
3. F. E. Bailey, Jr. and R.W. Callard, J. Appl. Polymer Sci. 1, 56 (1959).
4. U. Baumann, H. Schreiber and K. Tessmar, Makromol. Chem. 36, 81 (1960).
5. U. Bianchi, V. Magnasco and C. Rossi, Chim. Ind. (Milan) 40, 263 (1958).
6. U. Bianchi, V. Magnasco and C. Rossi, Ric. Sci. 28, 1412 (1958).
7. M. Bohdanecky, Collect. Czech. Chem. Commun. 29, 876 (1964).
8. W. Burchard, Makromol. Chem. 64, 110 (1963).
9. H. J. Cantow, Makromol. Chem. 30, 169 (1959).
10. S. N. Chinai, J. Polymer Sci. 25, 413 (1957).
     10a. S. N. Chinai, J. Polymer Sci. 44, 475 (1959).
11. S. N. Chinai and Ch. W. Bondurant, J. Polymer Sci. 22, 555 (1956).
12. S. N. Chinai, and R. A. Guzzi, J. Polymer Sci. 21, 417 (1956).
13. S. N. Chinai, A. L. Resnick and H. T. Lee, J. Polymer Sci. 33, 471 (1958).
14. S. N. Chinai and R. J. Samuels, J. Polymer Sci. 19, 463 (1956).
15. S. N. Chinai, P. C. Scherer, C. W. Bondurant and D. W. Levi, J. Polymer Sci.
     22, 527 (1956).
16. S. N. Chinai and R. J, Valles, J. Polymer Sci. 39, 363 (1959).
17. A. de Chirico, Chim. Ind. (Milan) 42, 248 (1960).
18. A. de Chirico, Chim. Ind. (Milan) 46, 53 (1964).
19. A. Ciferri and M. Lauretti, Ann. Chim. (Rome) 48, 198 (1958).
20. E. Cohn-Ginsberg, T. G. Fox and H. Maron, Polymer 3, 97 (1962).
21. J. M. G. Cowie, Makromol. Chem. 59, 189 (1963).
22. V. Cresenci and P. J. Flory, J. Amer. Chem. Soc. 86, 141 (1964).
23. F. Danusso and G. Moraglio, Rend. Accad. Naz. Lincei 25, 509 (1958).
24. F. Danusso, G. Moraglio and C. Cianotti, J. Polymer Sci. 51, 475 (1961).
25. F. E. Didot, S. N. Chinai and D. W. Levi, J. Polymer Sci. 43, 557 (1960).
26. J. Dohany, Thesis ETH Zürich, 1963.
27. E. T. Dumitru and L. H. Cragg, Cited in Ref. (44) p. 615.
28. H.-G. Elias, Makromol. Chem. 33, 140 (1959).
29. H.-G. Elias, Makromol. Chem. 50, 1 (1961).
30. H.-G. Elias, Makromol. Chem. 54, 78 (1962).
31. H.-G. Elias and G. Adank, unpublished data.
32. H.-G. Elias and Hj. Dietschy, unpublished data.
33. H.-G. Elias and O. Etter, Makromol. Chem. 66, 56 (1963).
34. H.-G. Elias and O. Etter, unpublished data.
35. H.-G. Elias and U. Gruber, Makromol. Chem. 78, 72 (1964).
36. H.-G. Elias and U. Gruber, unpublished data.
37. H.-G. Elias and F.W. Ibrahim, Makromol. Chem. in press.
38. H.-G. Elias and R. Schumacher, Makromol. Chem. 76, 23 (1964).
39. V. E. Eskin and L. N. Andreeva, Vysokomolekul. Soedin. 3, 435 (1961); ref. J.
     Polymer Sci. 56, S 39 (1962).
40. V. E. Eskin and K. Z. Gumargalieva, Vysokomolekul. Soedin. 2, 265 (1960).
41. V. E. Eskin and O. Z. Korothina, Vysokomolekul. Soedin. 2, 272 (1960); Polymer
     Sci. USSR 2, 247 (1961).
42. W. W. Everett and J. F. Foster, J. Amer. Chem. Soc. 81, 3464 (1959).
43. J. Feisst and H.-G. Elias, Makromol. Chem., in press.
44. P. J. Flory, "Principles of Polymer Chemistry," Cornell University Press,
     Ithaca, N. Y., 1953.
45. P. J. Flory, L. Mandelkern, J. B. Kinsinger and W. B. Shultz, J. Amer. Chem.
     Soc. 74, 3364 (1952).
46. P. J. Flory and J. E. Mark, to be published; priv. comm.
47. T. G. Fox, Polymer 3, 111 (1962).
48. T. G. Fox and P. J. Flory, J. Amer. Chem. Soc. 73, 1909 (1951).
49. T. G. Fox and P. J. Flory, J. Amer. Chem. Soc. 73, 1915 (1951).
50. T. G. Fox, J. B. Kinsinger, H. F. Mason and E. M. Schuele, Polymer 3, 71 (1962).
51. T. B. Grimley, Proc. Roy. Soc. (London) A212, 339 (1952).
52. U. Gruber, Thesis, ETH Zürich, 1964.
53. J. Hakozaki, J. Chem. Soc. Japan, Pure Chem. Sect. (Nippon Kagaku Zasshi) 82,
     158 (1961).
54. T. Homma, K. Kawahara, H. Fujita, and M. Ueda, Makromol. Chem. 67, 132 (1963).
55. A. J. Hyde and R. B. Taylor, Polymer 4, 1 (1963).
56. H. Inagaki, A. Nakazawa and T. Kotaka, J. Colloid Sci., in press; private comm.
57. K. J. Ivin, M. A. Ende and G. Meyerhoff, Polymer 3, 129 (1962).
58. A. Katchalsky and H. Eisenberg, J. Polymer Sci. 6, 145 (1951).
59. W. Kern and D. Braun, Makromol. Chem. 27, 23 (1958).
60. J. B. Kinsinger and R. E. Hughes, J. Phys. Chem. 67, 1922 (1963).
61. J. B. Kinsinger and R. A. Wessling, J. Amer. Chem. Soc. 81, 2908 (1959).
62. R. Kirste and G. V. Schulz, Z. Physik. Chem. (Frankfurt) 27, 301 (1960).
63. R. Kirste and G. V. Schulz, Z. Physik. Chem. (Frankfurt) 30, 171 (1961).
64. S. Krause and E. Cohn-Ginsberg, J. Phys. Chem. 67, 1479 (1963).

65. W. R. Krigbaum and D. K. Carpenter, J. Phys. Chem. $\underline{59}$, 1166 (1955).
66. W. R. Krigbaum and P. J. Flory, J. Polymer Sci. $\underline{11}$, 37 (1953).
67. W. R. Krigbaum, J. E. Kurz and P. Smith, J. Phys. Chem. $\underline{65}$, 1984 (1961).
68. W. R. Krigbaum and L. H. Sperling, J. Phys. Chem. $\underline{64}$, 99 (1960).
69. W. R. Krigbaum and J. D. Woods, J. Polymer Sci. $\underline{A2}$, 3075 (1964).
70. N. Kuwahara, Y. Miyake, M. Kaneko and J. Furuichi, Rep. Prog. Polymer Phys.
     (Japan) $\underline{5}$, 1 (1962).
71. H. T. Lee and D. W. Levi, J. Polymer Sci. $\underline{47}$, 449 (1960).
72. D. W. Levi, H. T. Lee, R. J. Valles, J. Polymer Sci. $\underline{62}$, S 163 (1962).
73. M. Lippay, Thesis ETH Zürich, 1963.
74. L. Mandelkern and P. J. Flory, J. Amer. Chem. Soc. $\underline{74}$, 2517 (1952).
75. J. E. Mark, Diss. Abstr. $\underline{23}$, 1205 (1962).
76. M. Matsumoto and Y. Ohyanagi, J. Polymer Sci. $\underline{46}$, 441 (1960).
77. M. Matsumoto and Y. Ohyanagi, J. Polymer Sci. $\underline{50}$, S 1 (1961).
78. H. W. McCormick, J. Polymer Sci. $\underline{36}$, 341 (1959).
79. D. McIntyre, J. H. O'Mara and B. C. Konouck, J. Amer. Chem. Soc. $\underline{81}$, 3498 (1959).
80. R. A. Mendelson, J. Polymer Sci. $\underline{46}$, 493 (1960).
81. G. Meyerhoff, Makromol. Chem. $\underline{37}$, 97 (1960).
82. G. Meyerhoff, in J. W. Williams, ed. "Ultracentrifugal Analysis in Theory and
     Praxis," Academic Press, New York, 1963.
83. J. Moacanin, J. Appl. Polymer Sci. $\underline{1}$, 272 (1959).
84. G. A. Morneau, P. I. Roth and A. R. Shultz, J. Polymer Sci. $\underline{55}$, 609 (1961).
85. S. Newman, W. R. Krigbaum, C. Laugier and P. J. Flory, J. Polymer Sci. $\underline{14}$,
     451 (1954).
86. S. Okamura, T. Higashimura and Y. Imanishi, Chem. High Polymers (Japan) $\underline{16}$,
     244 (1959).
87. R. Okada, Y. Toyoshima and H. Fujita, Makromol. Chem. $\underline{59}$, 137 (1963).
88. P. Outer, C. I. Carr and B. H. Zimm, J. Chem. Phys. $\underline{18}$, 830 (1950).
89. J. Oth and V. Desreux, Bull. Soc. Chim. Belges $\underline{63}$, 285 (1954).
90. C. G. Overberger, E. M. Pearce and N. Mayes, J. Polymer Sci. $\underline{34}$, 109 (1959).
91. I. Ya. Poddubnyi, V. A. Grechanovskii and M. I. Mosevitskii, Vysokomolekul.
     Soedin. $\underline{5}$, 1049 (1963); Polymer Sci. USSR $\underline{5}$, 105 (1964).
92. I. Ya. Poddubnyi, V. A. Grechanovskii, M. I. Mosevitskii and A. V. Podalinskii,
     Vysokomolekul. Soedin. $\underline{5}$, 1042 (1963); Polymer Sci. USSR $\underline{5}$, 97 (1964).
93. C. Reiss and H. Benoit, Compt. Rend. $\underline{253}$, 268 (1961).
94. Y. Sakaguchi, J. Nishino and K. Tsugawa, Chem. High Polymers (Japan) $\underline{20}$, 661
     (1963).
95. I. Sakurada, A. Nakajima, O. Yoshizaki and K. Nakamae, Kolloid-Z. $\underline{100}$, 41 (1962).
96. I. Sakurada, Y. Sakaguchi and S. Kokuryo, Chem. High Polymers (Kobunshi
     Kagaku) $\underline{17}$, 227 (1960).
97. M. Sato, Y. Koshiishi and M. Asahina, J. Polymer Sci. $\underline{B1}$, 233 (1963).
98. P. R. Saunders, J. Polymer Sci. $\underline{57}$, 131 (1961).
99. G. V. Schulz and H. J. Cantow, Z. Elektrochem. $\underline{60}$, 517 (1956).
100. G. V. Schulz and A. Haug, Z. Physikal. Chem. (Frankfurt) $\underline{34}$, 328 (1962).
101. G. V. Schulz and A. Mula, Makromol. Chem. $\underline{44/46}$, 479 (1961).
102. G. V. Schulz, W. Wunderlich and R. Kirste, Makromol. Chem. $\underline{75}$, 22 (1964).
103. Y. Shiokawa, H. Takeo, K. Takamizawa and T. Oyama, Rep. Prog. Polymer Phys.
     Japan $\underline{7}$, 49 (1964).
104. A. R. Shultz, J. Amer. Chem. Soc. $\underline{76}$, 3422 (1954).
105. A. R. Shultz, Thesis, Cornell University, cited in Ref. (44), p. 615.
106. V. S. Skazka, R. A. Zobov and A. Moshpauenko, Vysokomolekul. Soedin. $\underline{4}$, 1257
     (1962).
107. C. J. Stacy and J. F. Foster, J. Polymer Sci. $\underline{20}$, 56 (1956).
108. U. P. Strauss and P. L. Wineman, J. Amer. Chem. Soc. $\underline{80}$, 2366 (1958).
109. H. L. Wagner and P. J. Flory, J. Amer. Chem. Soc. $\underline{74}$, 195 (1952).
110. R. A. Wessling, Diss. Abstr. $\underline{23}$, 1536 (1962).
111. E. A. Zavaglia and F. W. Billmeyer, Jr. Official Digest $\underline{36}$, 221 (1964).
112. R. Chiang, private communication.

SOLVENTS AND NONSOLVENTS FOR POLYMERS

Klaus Meyersen

Mellon Institute
Pittsburgh, Pennsylvania

Contents

A. Introduction

The table contains qualitative data for a number of polymers. Since no standard definition for solvent-nonsolvent-systems has been used in most of the original sources, the recognition of a certain compound as a solvent or nonsolvent is to some extent influenced by personal interpretation. No attempt has been made to edit the original information. Division into only the two classes, solvents and nonsolvents, is dictated by the practical point of view, but it is more or less arbitrary and artificial. For more quantitative information the user is therefore referred to the tables of θ-solvents and fractionation of polymers in this Handbook.

The arrangement of polymers into nineteen classes is based on the chemical structure of their monomers.

The list of solvents and nonsolvents for each polymer follows a simple arrangement by functional groups (aliphatic, aromatic, chlorinated hydrocarbons; alcohols; ethers; amines; aldehydes, ketones; carboxylic acids; nitriles; nitro compounds; sulfur and phosphorus-containing organic compounds; water; acids; alkalies; salts).

The data refer to room temperature unless the temperature is given in a particular case. Some solution temperatures have been determined in sealed tubes. The temperature for some θ-solvents is given.

Since homologs and closely related compounds generally have similar properties, preference has been given to citing specific solvents or nonsolvents rather than general classes whenever possible (e.g., acetone, cyclohexanone instead of ketones) with the understanding that homologs and compounds with similar structures can be expected to exhibit similar properties. If class-names are used, they refer to the most common compounds. Less common compounds, although falling into a class already mentioned, are additionally cited.

Properties change gradually within a series of homologs of polymers as well as solvents. Solubility or dissolving power may increase, decrease, reach an optimum or minimum.

Solubility normally increases with rising temperature; however, negative temperature coefficients are observed. Increase in molecular weight reduces solubility. Enhanced branching increases the solubility compared to a linear polymer of the same molecular weight. Contradictory data found in the literature can be explained on the basis that some of the foregoing influences may have been neglected.

Certain combinations of two or more solvents may become nonsolvents. Conversely, mixtures of two or more nonsolvents may sometimes become solvents. These possibilities should be considered if new solvent-nonsolvent combinations are to be examined.

The classification of a certain compound as a nonsolvent does not necessarily imply ability to act as a precipitant since this is influenced also by the nature of the particular solvent of a solvent-nonsolvent pair. However, most nonsolvents combine both properties. Water is a nonsolvent for most polymers and is, therefore, only mentioned if similar polymers or derivatives are water-soluble.

Where formulae are given, they refer to the main structures present in the polymers.

Copolymers, with exception of polysulfones, have not been included in this table. In their behavior they resemble more or less the properties of the homopolymer of the dominating monomer, although they generally exhibit higher solubilities than the corresponding homopolymers.

Chemically modified polymers of commercial importance, e.g. cellulose derivatives, were considered only in those cases in which the reaction products were sufficiently well characterized.

The following abbreviations are used:

DMA	=	N,N-dimethylacetamide
DMF	=	N,N-dimethylformamide
DMS	=	dimethyl sulfoxide
TMS	=	tetramethylene sulfone
THF	=	tetrahydrofuran
sw	=	swelling
S.C.	=	substituent content
dil.	=	dilute
aqu.	=	aqueous
conc.	=	concentrated
elev.	=	elevated
D.S.	=	degree of substitution

References page IV-232

Polymer	Solvents	Nonsolvents	References

1 - OLEFIN POLYMERS

Polymer	Solvents	Nonsolvents	References
Polyethylene	above 60-70°C. aliphatic hydrocarbons; aromatic hydrocarbons; chlorinated hydrocarbons; higher aliphatic esters; higher ketones.	all common organic solvents at room temp.; mineral oils, chlorinated hydrocarbons (sw); more polar organic solvents even at elev. temps. (alcohols, acetone, water); alkalies; conc. acids (including hydrogen fluoride).	1,2,3,4,12
high pressure:	decalin (70°C), toluene; p-xylene (75°C).	n-propanol; acetone; methyl isobutyl ketone; nitromethane.	4
low pressure:	decalin (135°C); tetralin (120°C); p-xylene (100°C); α-chloronaphthalene (125°C).		
Poly(ethylene-sulfonic acid)	aqu. NaCl (0.5M).		
Polypropylene			
	above 80°C: hydrocarbons; chlorinated hydrocarbons; higher ketones; higher aliphatic esters.	all organic solvents at room temp.; more polar organic solvents even at elev. temp.	2
atactic:	cyclohexane; decalin (135°C); benzene; toluene; isoamyl acetate (θ,34°C).		4
isotactic:	decalin (135°C); tetralin (135°C); xylene (85°C); α-chloronaphthalene (139°C).		4
Poly(1-butene)			
	ethylcyclohexane (70°C).		4
Polyisobutene	sat. aliphatic hydrocarbons; n-pentene; diisobutylene; triisobutylene; aromatic and alkyl subst. aromatic hydrocarbons; benzene (θ,24°C); chlorinated aliphatic and aromatic hydrocarbons; tetradecanol; heptadecanol; n-butyl ether; n-amyl ether; isoamyl ether; β,β-dichloroethyl ether; mesityl oxide; THF; anisole (θ,105°C); phenetole (θ,86°C); isoamyl formate; butyl acetate; isoamyl butyrate; isoamyl caproate; methyl oleate; ethyl sulfide; carbon disulfide.	lower alcohols; ether(sw); lower ketones; lower acetic esters; conc. acids; conc. alkalies.	1,3,4,12, 121
Poly(pentenamer) (poly(cyclopentene))			
{CH = CH(CH$_2$)$_3$}$_n$	cycloaliphatic hydrocarbons; aromatic hydrocarbons;	alcohols; ethers;	131
	chlorinated hydrocarbons.	aliphatic ketones.	

Polymer	Solvents	Nonsolvents	References
Poly(cyclopentylethylene)			
	pentane (partially); toluene; chloroform;ether.	methanol	53
Poly(cyclohexylethylene)			
	pentane (partially); toluene; chloroform; ether (partially).	methanol	53
Poly(3-cyclohexyl-1-propene)			
	pentane (partially); toluene; chloroform;ether (partially).	methanol	53
Poly(4-cyclohexyl-1-butene)			
	pentane (partially); toluene; chloroform;ether (partially).	methanol	53
Poly(5-cyclohexyl-1-pentene)			
	pentane (partially); toluene; chloroform; ether (partially).	methanol	53

Halo-olefin Polymers (See also Vinyl Polymers)

Polymer	Solvents	Nonsolvents	References
Poly(chlorotrifluoroethylene)			
	cyclohexane (235°C); benzene (200°C); toluene (142°C); p-xylene (140°C); 1,1,1-trichloroethane (120°C); carbon tetrachloride (114°C); 1,2,3-trifluoro-pentachloro-propane; 1,2,3-trifluoro-pentachloro-pentane; 1,1,2,2-tetrafluoro-3,3,4,4-tetrachloro-cyclobutane; 1,2-dichloro-trifluorobenzene; 2,5-dinitro-trifluorobenzene (130°C); mesitylene (140°C); tri(dimethylamido)phosphate.	common organic solvents at room temp.	1,2,4,113, 124
Poly(tetrafluoroethylene)			
	no solvent known.		1,2

Polymer	Solvents	Nonsolvents	References

2 - DIENE POLYMERS (See also Natural Polymers)

1,2-Diene Polymers

Polyallene

	benzene; halogenated hydrocarbons.	hexane; methanol.	86

1,3-Diene Polymers

Polybutadiene

	chlorinated and nitrated hydrocarbons; higher ketones; higher aliphatic esters;	hydrocarbons*; alcohol water; dil. acids; dil. alkalies; hypochlorite solutions.	2,4,12

Stereoregular:
71% trans; 4%
cis, 25% 1,2:   cyclohexane;

79% trans; 21%
1,2:   cyclohexane;

3% trans; 92%
cis, 5% 1,2:   benzene; diisobutylene   isooctane, propanol

Polyisoprene

	hydrocarbons; chlorinated hydrocarbons; ether	alcohols; acetone; carboxylic acids.	2

Polychloroprene

	cyclohexane/toluene; petroleum ether/esters; benzene; chlorinated hydrocarbons; chlorobenzene; ethyl ether/ethyl acetate; dioxane; pyridine; cyclohexanone; ethyl acetate.	aliphatic hydrocarbons; mineral oils; aromatic hydrocarbons (sw); alcohols; ketones; water; non-oxidizing conc. acids, incl. hydrogen fluoride.	1,2,4,12

1,4-cis: hexane; benzene; chloroform; carbon tetrachloride; ether; THF.   methanol; ethanol; acetone.   49

Poly(1-methoxybutadiene)

crystalline: heptane; benzene; methanol; dioxane; acetone.   111

Poly(2-tert-butyl-1,3-butadiene)
   n-heptane; benzene; chloroform; carbon tetrachloride; ethyl ether; carbon disulfide.   acetone   51

Poly(cyclopentadiene)
   benzene; toluene; chloroform; carbon tetrachloride; THF; dioxane.   hexane; petroleum ether; methanol.   103

Poly(1,3-cyclohexadiene)
   benzene; xylene.   methanol   82

Poly(dimethylfulvene)
   n-hexane; benzene; halogenated hydrocarbons; ether; acetone.   alcohol   93

* Depending on structure.

Polymer	Solvents	Nonsolvents	References

Unconjugated Diene Polymers

Poly(4-vinyl-1-cyclohexene)

crystalline:	aromatic hydrocarbons; naphthenic hydrocarbons (partially); halogenated hydrocarbons (partially); carbon disulfide (partially);	aliphatic hydrocarbons ethers; alcohols; ketones.	91
amorphous:	petroleum ether.		

Poly(1,5-hexadiene)

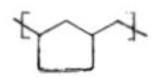

crystalline:	tetralin (125°C);	isopropanol; isopropanol/acetone; acetone.	
amorphous:	n-heptane; benzene.		

Poly(1,5-cyclooctadiene)

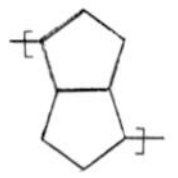

	aromatic hydrocarbons; chlorinated hydrocarbons; methanol (oligomers); ether (partially).	methanol	81

Poly(bicyclo-2.2.1-hepta-2,5-diene)(poly(norbornadiene))

low conversion:	benzene; chloroform; carbon tetrachloride; THF.	hexane.	57

Poly(5,7-dimethyl-1,6-octadiene)

	heptane; benzene; tetrachloroethylene.	methanol	52

Poly(diallyl phthalate)("pre-polymer," MW 14,000)

	toluene; chloroform; ether; acetone.		1

Poly(diallyldimethylsilane)

	benzene		106

Poly(diallylphenylphosphine oxide)

	ethanol; glacial acetic acid; DMF.		106

References page IV-232

Polymer	Solvents	Nonsolvents	References

3 - ACETYLENE POLYMERS

Polyacetylene

	isopropylamine; aniline; DMF	cyclohexane; benzene; toluene; methylene chloride; carbon tetra-chloride; methanol; pyridine; acetone; methyl ethyl ketone.	38

Poly(cyanoacetylene)(poly(α,β-dibromopropionitrile))

	conc. carboxylic acids.	common organic solvents.	63

Poly((hydroxymethyl)acetylene)(poly(α,β-dibromopropanol))

	conc. carboxylic acids.	common organic solvents.	63

Poly(butoxyacetylene)(poly(α,β-dibromoethylbutyl ether))

	conc. carboxylic acids.	common organic solvents.	63

Poly(phenylacetylene)

low mol. wt.:	methanol;		35,63
higher mol. wt.:	benzene.	methanol.	

Poly(diphenyldiacetylene)

	cyclohexane; chloroform; dioxane	methanol	64

Poly(pyridylacetylene)

	chloroform(partially); methanol; ethanol.	non-polar solvents, e.g. benzene.	105

Polymer	Solvents	Nonsolvents	References

4 - ALIPHATIC VINYL AND VINYLIDENE POLYMERS

Poly(vinyl alcohol) and Poly(allyl alcohol)

Poly(vinyl alcohol)

| | glycols (hot); glycerol (hot); piperazine; tri-ethylenediamine; diethylene-triamine; triethylenetetra-amine; formamide; DMF; DMS (hot); water; tri(dimethyl-amido)phosphate. | hydrocarbons; chlorinated hydrocarbons; lower alcohols; THF; dioxane; ethylene glycol formal; ketones; carboxylic acids; esters; ethyl lactate; conc. aqu. salt solutions. | 1,2,3,4, 12 |

Poly(vinyl alcohol) (12% acetyl)

| | water (cold). | hydrocarbons; halogenated hydrocarbons; ketones, carboxylic acids; esters; water (hot). | 2 |

Poly(vinyl alcohol) (35% acetyl)

| | water/alcohols. | water | |

Poly(allyl alcohol)

lower mol. wt.:

| | methanol; glycerol; cresol; dioxane; THF; pyridine; | | 1 |

high mol. wt.
(DP > 350):

| | mixtures of conc. hydro-chloric acid and dioxane, methanol, THF. | organic solvents; water. | |

Poly(vinyl aldals) and Poly(vinyl ketals)

Poly(vinyl formal) (medium viscosity)

| | benzene; benzene/ethanol (1:1); chloroform/metha-nol (9:1); carbon tetra-chloride; ethanol/diethyl ether (1:1); butanol; ace-tone; ethylene glycol; THF; benzyl acetate. | methanol (sw); ethanol (sw); ethylene glycol (sw) | 3 |

Poly(vinyl formal)

| | benzene/alcohol (70:30); toluene; xylene; methylene chloride; chloroform; carbon tetrachloride/ alcohol (70:30); dichloro-ethylene; dichloroethylene/ diacetone alcohol (50:50); 2-chloroethanol; benzyl alcohol; furfurol; THF; dioxane; cyclohexanone; formic acid; acetic acid; DMF. | aliphatic hydrocarbons; aromatic hydrocarbons (sw); methanol; ethanol; dioxane; pyridine (sw); esters; water; dilute acids; acetone (sw); | 2,3,12 |

Poly(vinyl acetal)

| | benzene; benzene/ethanol (1:1); toluene; chloroform; chloroform/methanol (9:1); carbon tetrachloride; di-chloroethylene; 2-chloro-ethanol; ethanol/ethyl ether (1:); butanol; THF; diox-ane; ethylene glycol; ace-tone; cyclohexanone; ethyl acetate; ethyl lactate; benzyl acetate. | aliphatic hydrocarbons; methanol (sw); ether (sw); pyridine (sw); water; dil. acids. | 3,12 |

References page IV-232

Polymer	Solvents	Nonsolvents	References
Poly(vinyl acetal)(high degree of acetalization)			
	ethylene dichloride; metha-nol; ethanol; dioxane; pyri-dine; acetic acid (glacial); nitromethane.	benzene; acetone;	2
Poly(vinyl butyral)			
	benzene; benzene/ethanol (1:1); toluene; chloroform; chloroform/methanol (9:1); carbon tetrachloride; di-chloroethylene; 2-chloro-ethanol; ethanol*; ethanol/ethyl ether (1:1); butanol*; THF, dioxane, ethylene gly-col; acetone; cyclohexanone; ethyl acetate; ethyl lac-tate; benzyl acetate*.	aliphatic hydrocarbons; methanol (sw); ethanol (sw)*; butanol (sw)*; ethylene glycol (sw); pyridine (sw); benzyl acetate (sw)*; water; dil. acids.	3,12
Poly(vinyl butyral)(high degree of acetalization)			
	benzene; ethylene di-chloride; ethanol; dioxane; acetone; acetic acid; DMF.	hydrocarbons; methanol; ether.	
Poly(vinyl isobutyral)			
	benzene/ethanol (1:1); chloroform/methanol (9:1); ethanol/ethyl ether (1:1); butanol; THF; cyclohexanone.	benzene (sw); carbon tetrachloride (sw); ethanol; ether (sw); ethylene glycol; ace-tone; ethyl acetate (sw); ethyl lactate (sw); benzyl acetate (sw).	3
Poly(vinyl cyclohexanone ketal)			
	chloroform; dichloro-ethylene; 2-chloroethanol.		
Vinyl Ester Polymers			
Poly(vinyl acetate)			
	benzene; toluene; chloro-form; carbon tetrachloride/ethanol; dichloroethylene/ethanol (29:80); methanol; ethanol/carbon tetra-chloride; ethanol/water; propanol/water; n-butanol/water; allyl alcohol; 2,4-dimethyl-3-pentanol; benzyl alcohol; tetrahydrofurfuryl alcohol; dimethyltetrahydro-furan; dioxane; glycol ethers; glycol ether esters; acetone; methyl ethyl ketone; methyl isopropyl ketone/n-heptane (73.2:26.8 vol.; θ, 25°C); ethyl n-butyl ke-tone (θ, 29°C); ethyl iso-amyl ketone (θ, 66°C); acetic acid; lower alipha-tic esters; vinyl acetate; acetals; acetonitrile; nitromethane.	saturated hydrocarbons; decalin; xylene (sw); mesitylene; carbon tetra-chloride (sw); ethanol (anhydrous, sw); anhydr. alcohols (C > 2); ethylene glycol; cyclo-hexanol; methylcyclo-hexanol; ether (anhydr. alcohol free); higher esters; nitromethane; car-bon disulfide; water (sw); dil. acids; dil. alkalies.	1,2,4,1

* Depending on mol. wt. and/or conversion.

Polymer	Solvents	Nonsolvents	References
Poly(vinyl chloroacetate)	chloroform; chlorobenzene; pyridine; dioxane; cyclo-hexanone; ethyl acetate.	satur. hydrocarbons.	2
Poly(vinyl n-butyrate)	benzene		4
Poly(vinyl isobutyrate)	benzene		4
Poly(vinyl pivalate)	benzene; toluene; acetone; butanone; ethyl acetate.	hexane; methanol; water.	28
Poly(vinyl n-caproate)	benzene.		4
Poly(vinyl caprylate)	aliphatic and aromatic hydrocarbons; acetone.	lower alcohols.	2
Poly(vinyl laurate)	aliphatic and aromatic hydrocarbons.	lower alcohols; acetone.	2
Poly(vinyl palmitate)	aliphatic and aromatic hydrocarbons.	lower alcohols; acetone.	2
Poly(vinyl benzoate)	xylene (θ, 32.5°C);dioxane; acetone.	petroleum ether.	4,33
Poly(vinyl sulfate)	aqu. NaCl (0.5M).		4

Vinyl and Vinylidene Halide Polymers (See also Halo-olefin Polymers)

Poly(vinyl chloride)

	Solvents	Nonsolvents	References
high mol. wt.:	THF; acetone/carbon disul-fide; methyl ethyl ketone;	aliphatic hydrocarbons; mineral oils; aromatic hydrocarbons (sw)*; vinyl chloride; alcohols; gly-cols; aniline (sw); acetone (sw); carboxylic acids; acetic anhydride (sw); esters; nitro-paraffins (sw); carbon disulfide; non-oxidizing acids; conc. alkalies.	1,2,3,4,12
lower mol. wt.:	toluene; xylene; methylene chloride; ethylene chloride; perchloroethylene/acetone; 1,2-dichlorobenzene; tetra-hydrofurfuryl alcohol; dioxane; acetone/carbon disulfide; cyclopentanone; cyclohexanone; diisopropyl ketone; mesityl oxide; iso-phorene; DMF; nitrobenzene; tri(dimethylamido)phosphate; tricresyl phosphate.		

Poly(vinyl chloride)(chlorinated)

	Solvents		References
	acetone; chlorinated hydrocarbons.		12

* Depending on mol. wt.

References page IV-232

Polymer	Solvents	Nonsolvents	References

Poly(vinylidene chloride)

high mol. wt.:   THF (hot);

medium and low
   mol. wt.:   (at elevated temp.) tetralin; trichloroethane; pentachloro-ethane; 1,2-dichlorobenzene; trichlorobenzene; tetrahydro-furfuryl alcohol; dioxane; cyclohexanone; DMA.

Nonsolvents: hydrocarbons; chloro-form; ethyl bromide; vinylidene chloride; alcohols; phenols; THF (sw); dioxane (sw); cyclohexanone (sw); car-bon disulfide; conc. and moderately conc. acids and alkalies (except ammonia).

References: 2,3,12

Poly(vinyl bromide)

THF; THF/methanol (83:17); θ, 20°C); cyclohexanone.

References: 4

Vinyl Ether Polymers

Poly(vinyl methyl ether)

Solvents: benzene; toluene; methylene chloride; chloroform; carbon tetrachloride; etha-nol; isopropanol; n-buta-nol; acetone; methyl ethyl ketone; cyclohexanone; ethyl acetate; butyl acetate.

Nonsolvents: aliphatic hydrocarbons; mineral oils; ethylene glycol; ethyl ether; water (hot).

References: 1,2,3,4, 110

amorphous: methanol; water.

crystalline: heptane; methanol; water.

Poly(vinyl ethyl ether)

Solvents: petroleum ether*; mineral oil; benzene; toluene; methylene chloride; chloro-form; carbon tetrachloride; methanol*; ethanol; iso-propanol; n-butanol; ace-tone; cyclohexanone; ethyl acetate; butyl acetate.

Nonsolvents: aliphatic hydrocarbons*;

References: 1,2,3,110

crystalline: heptane; methanol; ethyl ether; water.

Poly(vinyl n-propyl ether)

crystalline: heptane; acetone.   110

Poly(vinyl isopropyl ether)

crystalline: heptane; methanol;acetone.   110

Poly(vinyl n-butyl ether)

Solvents: cyclohexane; n-heptane*; benzene; methylene chloride; chloroform; carbon tetra-chloride; n-butanol; ethyl ether; bis(β-ethoxyethyl)-ether; methyl ethyl ketone; cyclohexanone; isopropyl acetate.

Nonsolvents: ethanol; β-ethoxyethanol.   110,123

crystalline: heptane.

---

* Depending on mol. wt. and structure.

Polymer	Solvents	Nonsolvents	References
Poly(vinyl isobutyl ether)			
amorphous and crystalline:	cyclohexane; n-heptane; benzene; toluene; methylene chloride; chloroform; carbon tetrachloride; ethyl ether; cyclohexanone; isopropyl acetate; carbon disulfide.	methanol; ethanol; β-ethoxyethanol.	1,2,3,22, 108, 110, 123
amorphous:	paraffins (60°C); aliphatic alcohols (C ≧ 3); bis(β-ethoxyethyl)ether; acetone*; methyl ethyl ketone;		
crystalline:	chloroform (50°C).	heptane*; benzene (20°C, sw); chloroform (20°C, sw); isopropanol (reflux);n-butanol; bis-β-ethoxyethyl)ether; methyl ethyl ketone.	
Poly(vinyl tert-butyl ether)			
amorphous:	acetone; methyl ethyl ketone		22, 110
crystalline:		heptane; benzene.	
Poly(vinyl neopentyl ether)			
crystalline:		heptane; benzene.	110
Poly(vinyl carbomethoxymethyl ether)	methylene chloride; chloroform	ethyl ether	118
Poly(vinyl 2-methoxyethyl ether)			
crystalline:	water.	ether.	110
Poly(vinyl 2-chloroethyl ether)			
crystalline:		acetone.	110
Poly(vinyl 2,2,2-trifluoroethyl ether)			
crystalline:		heptane; benzene; dioxane.	110
Poly(vinyl benzyl ether)			
crystalline:		acetone; ether	
Miscellaneous Vinyl Polymers			
Poly(vinyl methyl ketone)	chloroform; pyridine; THF; dioxane; acetone; methyl vinyl ketone; acetic acid; ethyl acetate; DMF.	alcohol; petroleum ether; carbon tetrachloride; ether; water.	1,2,12, 134
Poly(methyl isopropenyl ketone)	dioxane; acetone; ester.	petroleum ether; alcohol; water.	1,12, 134

* Depending on mol. wt. and structure.

References page IV-232

Polymer	Solvents	Nonsolvents	References
Poly(1-nitropropylene)			
	DMF (partially).		85
Poly(vinyl sulfofluoride)			
	THF; acetone; ethyl acetate; DMF.	ether.	1
Poly(vinylsulfonic acid)			
	methanol*; water.	hydrocarbons; methanol*; ketones; esters.	1,2
-- , sodium salt			
	water; aq. sodium chloride (0.5M).	methanol; acetone.	1
Poly(vinyldiphenylphosphine oxide)			
	benzene; toluene; methanol; ethanol.	hexane; water.	56,76
Poly(vinyldiphenylphosphine sulfide)			
	benzene; chloroform.	methanol.	76
Poly(dimethyl-2-cyano-2-propene-1-phosphonate)			
	acetone; DMF; acetonitrile.		99

$$\{CH_2-\underset{\underset{CH_2PO(OCH_3)_2}{|}}{C}(CN)\}_n$$

Polymer	Solvents	Nonsolvents	References
Poly(diethyl-2-cyano-2-propene-1-phosphonate)			
	acetone.		99
Poly(maleic anhydride)			
	lower aliphatic alcohols; ethers; ketones; nitro-paraffins; dioxane; buta-none; acetophenone; acetic anhydride; DMF; aceto-nitrile; nitroparaffines; water.	higher paraffins; most chlorinated hydrocarbons; aro-matic hydrocarbons.	83

* Depending on molecular weight and structure.

Polymer	Solvents	Nonsolvents	References

5 - AROMATIC VINYL POLYMERS

Styrene Polymers

Polystyrene

atactic: cyclohexane (θ, 34°C); cyclohexane/acetone; methylcyclohexane (θ,70°C); methylcyclohexane/acetone; ethylcyclohexane (θ,70°C); benzene; toluene; ethylbenzene; styrene; lower chlorinated aliphatic hydrocarbons; tetrahydrofurfuryl alcohol; phenol/acetone; THF; dimethyltetrahydrofuran; dioxane; methyl ethyl ketone; diisopropyl ketone; cyclohexanone; glycol formal; ethyl acetate; butyl acetate; methyl-, ethyl-, n-butyl phthalate; 1-nitro-propane; carbon disulfide; tributyl phosphate.

saturated hydrocarbons; alcohols; phenol; diols; ethylene chlorohydrin; ether; glycol ethers; acetone; acetic acid; isobutyl phthalate; (methyl)hexyl phthalate; tri(chloroethyl) phosphate tricresyl phosphate.

References for atactic: 1,2,3,4

isotactic: benzene; toluene.

Poly(α-methylstyrene)
benzene; benzene/methanol (79.4:20.6; θ, 30°C); toluene.
Reference: 4

Poly(4-chlorostyrene)
methyl ethyl ketone; toluene.
Reference: 4

Poly(4-bromostyrene)
benzene.
Reference: 4

Poly(dichlorostyrene)
toluene.
Reference: 4

Poly(4-methoxystyrene)
methyl ethyl ketone; toluene.
Reference: 4

Poly(2,5-dimethoxystyrene)
benzene; toluene; chloroform.
Nonsolvents: hexane; methanol.
Reference: 67

Miscellaneous Aromatic Vinyl Polymers

Poly(vinyl-bis(1-ethoxyethyl)hydroquinone)
benzene; chloroform.
Nonsolvents: methanol
Reference: 66

Poly(4-vinyl-phthalic acid)
methanol; DMF; water.
Nonsolvents: benzene; ether; methyl ethyl ketone.
Reference: 112

Poly(4-vinyl-phenyl boronic acid)
aqu. dioxane; aqu. acetone.
Nonsolvents: petroleum ether; benzene.
Reference: 47

Polymer	Solvents	Nonsolvents	References
Poly(diphenyl-4-styrylphosphine oxide)			
	benzene.	hexane.	77
Poly(diphenyl-4-styrylphosphine sulfide)			
	chloroform.	heptane; methanol.	77
Poly(4-vinyl-biphenyl)			
	benzene; toluene; dimethy- oxyethane; dimethoxyethane/ 2-methoxyethanol (70.6:29.4%v.).	methanol.	104
Poly(9-vinylanthracene)			
	methylene chloride.	methanol.	61
Poly(acenaphthylene)			
	benzene; toluene; chloro- form; carbon tetrachloride; 1,2-dichloroethane (θ,30°C).	alcohols; ethers; dimethoxyethane; acetone; carboxylic acids.	2
Polyindene			
	aromatic and chlorinated hydrocarbons; pyridine; ether; dioxane; ketones; drying oils.	aliphatic hydrocarbons (sw); lower alcohols; water; acids; alkalies.	12

Polymer	Solvents	Nonsolvents	References

6 - HETEROCYCLIC VINYL POLYMERS

N-Vinylcarbazole Polymers

Poly(N-vinylcarbazole)

| | benzene; toluene; xylene; methylene chloride; chloroform; tetrachloroethane; chlorobenzene; THF; dioxane; cyclohexanone; benzyl acetate; conc. nitric acid; conc. sulfuric acid. | aliphatic hydrocarbons; hydroaromatic hydrocarbons; carbon tetrachloride; trichloroethylene (sw); tetrachloroethylene; 1-chlorotoluene (sw); alcohols; chlorohydrin; diols; glycol monoether; ether; dimethyltetrahydrofuran; acetals; aliphatic ketones; dil. carboxylic acids; esters; water; dil. alkalies. | 1,2,3,12 |

Poly(9-Δ^5-pentenylcarbazole)

| | N-methylpyrrolidone (hot); acetone (partially). | methanol. | 32,99 |

Poly(9-Δ^5-hexenylcarbazole)

| | N-methylpyrrolidone (123°C); acetone (partially. | methanol. | 32,99 |

N-Vinylpyrrolidone Polymers

Poly(N-vinylpyrrolidone)

| | methylene chloride; chloroform; methanol; ethanol; aromatic alcohols; chlorohydrins; pyridine; acetone; glacial acetic acid; chloroacetic acid esters; lactic acid esters; nitromethane; water; dil. acids. | aliphatic and aromatic hydrocarbons; carbon tetrachloride; trichloroethylene; 1-chlorotoluene; diethyl ether; dipropyl ether; acetone; acetone/water; dipropyl ketone; acetic acid esters; methoxy-butyric acid esters; nitromethane/water. | 1,2,3,4,12 |

Vinylpyridine Polymers

Poly(2-vinylpyridine)

| | chloroform; alcohols/water; ethanol; pyridine; vinylpyridine; acetone; glacial acetic acid; aqu. mineral acids; | toluene; carbon tetrachloride; water (sw); | 1,2,116 |

| crystalline: | aromatic hydrocarbons (reflux); chlorinated solvents; methanol. | aliphatic hydrocarbons (reflux); ethyl ether; methyl ethyl ketone. | |

Poly(4-vinylpyridine)

| | methanol; ethanol; ethanol/water (92:8% wt); n-propanol; isopropanol/methyl ethyl ketone (86:14% wt); tert-butanol; cyclohexanol; benzyl alcohol; THF; dioxane/water (1:1); pyridine; acetone/water (1:1); nitromethane; aqu. mineral acids. | petroleum ether; diethyl ether; dioxane; acetone; methyl ethyl ketone; ethyl acetate; water. | 1,4 |

References page IV-232

Polymer	Solvents	Nonsolvents	References

Poly(2-methyl-5-vinylpyridine)
        methanol; DMF.   4

Miscellaneous Heterocyclic Vinyl Polymers

Poly(2,4-dimethyl-6-vinyl-s-triazine)

	benzene; alcohols; ketones; esters; water (cold); dil. alkali.	aliphatic hydrocarbons; water (ppt. below 73°C).	48

Poly(N-vinyl-1,2,4-triazole)

	glacial acetic acid; DMF; DMS; water.	hydrocarbons; chlorinated hydrocarbons; alcohols; ketones; esters.	21

Poly(N-vinylbenztriazole)

	chlorinated hydrocarbons; cyclohexanol; glacial acetic acid; DMF.	hydrocarbons; alcohols; ketones; esters; water.	21

Poly(N-vinylmorpholinone-(3))

	water.		126

Poly(coumarone)

	aromatic and chlorinated hydrocarbons; pyridine; ether; dioxane; ketones; drying oils.	water; lower alcohols; acids; alkalies; aliphatic hydrocarbons (sw).	12

Polymer	Solvents	Nonsolvents	References

7 - ACRYLIC AND METHACRYLIC POLYMERS

Poly(acrylic acids)

Poly(acrylic acid)

	alcohol; dioxane (θ, 30°C); formamide; water; dil. alkali solutions.	most organic solvents.	1,2,4,12

Poly(methacrylic acid)

	water; aqu. hydrogen chloride (0.002M; θ, 30°C); dil. aqu. sodium hydroxide.	hydrocarbons; alcohols; ketones; carboxylic acids; esters.	2,4

Poly(acrylates)

Poly(methyl acrylate)

	benzene; toluene; chlorinated hydrocarbons; THF; dimethyltetrahydrofuran; ketones; esters; glycolic ester ethers.	aliphatic hydrocarbons; hydrogenated napthalenes; carbon tetrachloride; alcohols; ether; 2-alkoxy-ethanols.	3,4

Poly(ethyl acrylate)

	benzene; toluene; chlorinated hydrocarbons; aliphatic alcohols ($C_1 \dots C_4$); ethyl ether; THF; dimethyltetrahydrofuran; glycol ether; glycolic ester ethers; ketones; esters.	aliphatic hydrocarbons; hydrogenated naphthalenes; aliphatic alcohols ($C \geqq 5$); cyclohexanol (also methylated); tetrahydrofurfuryl alcohol.	

Poly(butyl acrylate)

	aliphatic hydrocarbons, benzene; toluene; turpentine; chlorinated hydrocarbons; butanol; THF; dimethyltetrahydrofuran; glycolic ester ethers; ketones; esters.	methanol; ethanol; cyclohexyl acetate; ethyl lactate;	3

Poly(5-cyano-3-thia-pentyl acrylate)

	dioxane; pyridine; acetone; acetonitrile.	solvents of low C.E.D. value.	70

Poly(methacrylates)

Poly(methyl methacrylate)

	benzene; toluene; xylene (hot); methylene chloride; chloroform; ethylene dichloride; chlorobenzene; ethanol/water; ethanol/ carbon tetrachloride; isopropanol/methyl ethyl ketone (1:1; θ,25°C); allyl alcohol; isobutanol (hot); cyclohexanol (hot); β-ethoxyethanol; dioxane; acetone; methyl ethyl ketone; diisopropyl ketone (hot); cyclohexanone; formic acid; acetic acid; isobutyric acid; methyl formate; ethyl acetate; cyclohexyl acetate; isobutyl propionate; butyl lactate; nitroethane.	hexane; cyclohexane; gasoline; nujol; turpentine; castor oil; linseed oil; hydrogenated naphthalenes; carbon tetrachloride; methanol; ethanol (absolute); ethylene glycol; butylene glycol; glycerol; ethyl ether; isopropyl ether; higher esters; formamide.	1,2,3,4, 122

Polymer	Solvents	Nonsolvents	References
Poly(ethyl methacrylate)	benzene; toluene; xylene; tetralin; turpentine (hot); methylene chloride; chloroform; carbon tetrachloride; ethylene dichloride; chlorobenzene; ethanol (hot); isopropanol (θ,36.9°C); isobutanol (hot); cyclohexanol (hot); β-ethoxy ethanol; ethyl ether; dioxane; acetone; methyl ethyl ketone; methyl ethyl ketone/isopropanol (1:7, θ,23°C); diisopropyl ketone; cyclohexanone; formic acid (hot); acetic acid; isobutyric acid; methyl formate; ethyl acetate; cyclohexyl acetate; isobutyl propionate; butyl lactate.	hexane; cyclohexane; gasoline; nujol; castor oil; linseed oil; methanol; ethylene glycol; glycerol; isopropyl ether; formamide.	4,122
Poly(n-propyl methacrylate)	cyclohexane (hot); gasoline (hot); turpentine; castor oil (hot); linseed oil(hot); benzene; toluene; xylene; methylene chloride; chloroform; carbon tetrachloride; ethylene dichloride; chlorobenzene; ethanol; isobutanol; cyclohexanol; β-ethoxy ethanol; ethyl ether; isopropyl ether; dioxane; acetone; diisopropyl ketone; cyclohexanone; acetic acid; isobutyric aicd; methyl formate; ethyl acetate; cyclohexyl acetate; isobutyl propionate; butyl lactate.	hexane; nujol; methanol; ethylene glycol; glycerol; formic acid; formamide.	122
Poly(n-butyl methacrylate) and Poly(isobutyl methacrylate)	hexane; cyclohexane; gasoline; nujol (hot); turpentine; castor oil (hot); linseed oil (hot); benzene; toluene; xylene; methylene chloride; chloroform; carbon tetrachloride; ethylene chloride; chlorobenzene; ethanol (hot); isopropanol (θ,23.7°C); isobutanol; cyclohexanol; β-ethoxy ethanol; ethyl ether; isopropyl ether; dioxane; acetone; methyl ethyl ketone; diisopropyl ketone; cyclohexanone; acetic acid; isobutyric acid; methyl formate; ethyl acetate; cyclohexyl acetate; isobutyl propionate; butyl lactate.	methanol; ethylene glycol; glycerol; formic acid; formamide.	1,3,4,122

Polymer	Solvents	Nonsolvents	References
Poly(n-hexyl methacrylate)	isopropanol (θ,32.6°C); methyl ethyl ketone.		4
Poly(2-ethylbutyl methacrylate)	isopropanol (θ,27.4°C); methyl ethyl ketone.		4
Poly(n-octyl methacrylate)	n-butanol (θ,16.8°C); methyl ethyl ketone.		4
Poly(n-lauryl methacrylate)	n-pentanol (θ,29.5°C); isopropyl acetate (θ,13°C); n-butyl acetate.		4
Poly(4-(tert-butyl)phenyl methacrylate)	acetone.		4
Poly(bornyl methacrylate)	benzene.	methanol	78
Poly(β-(N-carbazyl)ethyl methacrylate)			
crystalline:	diphenylether (hot); aniline (hot; partially) nitrobenzene (hot).	methyl hexyl ketone.	29

Poly(crotonates)

Poly(tert-butyl crotonate)	heptane; chloroform.	methanol/water; acetone (sw).	54

Polyacrylonitriles

Polyacrylonitrile	o-,m-,p-phenylenediamine N-formylhexamethyleneimine; N-nitrosopiperidine; maleic anhydride; chloromaleic anhydride; succinic anhydride; acetic anhydride; citraconic anhydride; γ-butyrolactone; dioxanone; p-dioxanedione; ethylene oxalate; ethylene carbonate; propylene carbonate; 2-oxazolidone; 1-methyl-2-pyridone; 1,5-dimethyl-2-pyrrolidone; ϵ-caprolactam; DMF; dimethylthioformamide; N-methyl-β-cyanoethylformamide; cyanoacetic acid; α-cyanoacetamide; N-methylacetamide; N,N-diethylacetamide; N,N-dimethylacetamide; dimethylmethoxyacetamide; N,N-dimethyl-α,α,α-trifluoro-acetamide; N,N-dimethylpropionamide; N,N,N',N'-tetramethyloxamide; hydroxyacetonitrile; chloroacetonitrile/water;	hydrocarbons; chlorinated hydrocarbons; alcohols; ether; ketones; piperazinedione; 1,6-hexanediamine; propyl formate; formamide; methylformamide; n-butylformamide; diethylformamide; dipropylformamide; methoxyacetamide; N-methyldiacetamide; dimethyloxamide; ethylene urea; acetonitrile (sw); acrylonitrile; methoxyacetonitrile; 1-hydroxypropionitrile; 2-methoxypropionitrile; methylmalonitrile; dimethylmalonitrile; 1,1-dimethylsuccinonitrile; suberonitrile; methyl thiocyanate; hexamethylene dithiocyanate; aliphatic nitro-compounds; 1-nitrophenol; diethyl sulfoxide; n-butyl methyl sulfoxide; bis(2-hydroxyethyl) sulfoxide; diethyl sulfone (sw); diallyl-	1,4,12,119, 120

Polymer	Solvents	Nonsolvents	References
Polyacrylonitrile	(Cont'd.) β-hydroxypropionitrile; malonitrile; fumaronitrile; succinonitrile; adiponitrile; bis(2-cyanoethyl)ether; bis-(2-cyanoethyl)sulfide; bis(4-cyanobutyl)sulfone; 1,3,3,5-tetracyanopentane; nitromethane/water (94:6); 1,1,1-trichloro-3-nitro-2-propane; tri(2-cyano-ethyl)nitromethane; 3-,4 nitrophenol; methylene dithiocyanate; trimethylene dithiocyanate; DMS; tetra-methylene sulfoxide; di-methyl sulfone; ethyl methyl sulfone; 2-hydroxyethyl methyl sulfone; ethylene 1,2-bis(ethyl sulfone); di-methyl phosphite; diethyl phosphite; sulfuric acid; nitric acid; p-phenol sul-fonic acid; conc. aqu. lithium chloride; conc. aqu. zinc chloride; conc. aqu. aluminum perchlorate; conc. aqu. sodium thiocyanate; conc. aqu. calcium thio-cyanate; molten quaternary ammonium salts and their aqu. solutions.	sulfone; 3,4-dimethylsulfolane.	
Polymethacrylonitrile	methylene chloride; pyri-dine; acetone; cyclohexa-none; furfural; cyano-acetic acid; acetanhy-dride; ethylene carbonate; DMF (θ,20°C); benzonitrile; dinitriles; nitromethane; DMS; tri(dimethylamido)-phosphate.	aliphatic hydrocarbons; toluene; alcohols; esters; methacrylonitrile.	1,2,4

Polyacrylamides and Polymethacrylamides

Polymer	Solvents	Nonsolvents	References
Polyacrylamide	morpholine; water.	hydrocarbons; alcohols; glycols; ether; THF; esters; DMF; nitrobenzene.	1,2,4
Poly(N,N-dimethylacrylamide)	methanol; water (40°C).		4
Poly(N(1,1-dimethyl-3-oxobutyl)acrylamide)	toluene; butanol; methyl ethyl ketone.	water (sw).	13
Poly(acrylopiperidide)	DMF.		4
Poly(acrylomorpholide)	DMF.		4

Polymer	Solvents	Nonsolvents	References
Poly(9-acrylylcarbazole)			
atactic:	benzene (partially).	methanol.	45
tactic:	conc. or moderately conc. sulfuric acid; chloroform (partially).		
Polymethacrylamide	methanol; ethylene glycol; acetone; water.	hydrocarbons; ester.	1,2,4
<u>Polyacrolein</u>			
Polyacrolein (redoxpolymerization) Mixture of 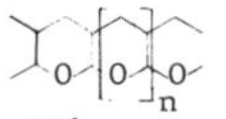 and $-[CH(CHO)-CH_2]_n-$	<u>above 60°C</u>: pyridine/water (55:45 to 90:10); <u>above 130°C</u>: nitrobenzene; DMS; sat. stannous chloride solution; γ-butyrolactone (160-170°C); ethylene carbonate (130-135°C); DMF (153°C); DMS (160-170°C); divinyl sulfone (150-155°C); TMS (160-165°C).	hydrocarbons; chlorinated hydrocarbons; lower alcohols; ether; aromatic ketones; esters.	95,96
Poly(α-methylacrolein)	aniline; pyridine; γ-butyrolactone; DMF; nitrobenzene.	hydrocarbons; alcohols.	1
<u>Poly(diacryl compounds)</u>			
Poly(diacrylylmethane) 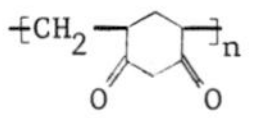	DMF; DMA; DMS; water.		79
Poly(acrylic anhydride) 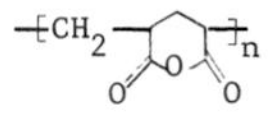	DMF; DMS.	benzene; alcohols; ether.	1
Poly(methacrylic anhydride)	DMF; DMS.	aliphatic hydrocarbons; methanol.	65

References page IV-232

Polymer	Solvents	Nonsolvents	References

8 - POLYETHERS

Aldehyde Polymers

Polyformaldehyde

	benzyl alcohol; phenol; chlorophenols; formamide; DMF; γ-butyrolactone; ethylene carbonate; bromobenzene; diphenyl ether; benzyl benzoate.	lower alcohols; lower esters; water.	2,135

Polyacetaldehyde

amorphous:	aromatic hydrocarbons; chloroform; alcohol; ketones; esters.		
crystalline:	chloroform (partially).	aromatic hydrocarbons; chloroform (partially); alcohols; ketones; esters.	

Poly(monochloroacetaldehyde)

amorphous:	chloroform.	methanol.	43
crystalline:		chloroform; methanol.	

Polychloral (poly(trichloroacetaldehyde))

crystalline:		chloroform; methanol; other common solvents.	117

Polypropionaldehyde

	DMF;		117
crystalline:	chloroform (partially).	common organic solvents.	

Polyacrolein (ionic polymerization)

$\text{-}[O - CH(CH{=}CH_2)]_n$

	benzene; carbon tetrachloride; THF; dioxane; acetone; DMF.	petroleum ether; methanol.	97

Poly(2-formyl-Δ^5-dihydropyran)

	aromatic hydrocarbons; chloroform; pyridine; THF.		39

Dialdehyde Polymers

Poly(trans-1,2-cyclohexanedicarboxaldehyde)

	hexane; benzene; chloroform.	methanol.	15

$\text{-}[O\text{-}CH\underset{}{\overset{O}{\diagup\hspace{-0.3em}\diagdown}}CH\text{-}]_n$

Poly(glutardialdehyde)

$[O\overset{O}{\diagup\hspace{-0.3em}\diagdown}]_n$

low mol. wt.:	benzene; chloroform; ethyl ether; THF; dioxane.	petroleum ether; water.	37,114,119, 127
high mol. wt.:	benzene (partially); methylene chloride; THF; pyridine.		

Polymer	Solvents	Nonsolvents	References

Poly(β-methylglutardialdehyde)

low mol. wt.: chloroform; ethyl ether; petroleum ether; water. 37
               THF; dioxane.

CH_3

Poly(β-phenylglutardialdehyde)

low mol. wt.: benzene; chloroform; ethyl petroleum ether; water. 37
               ether; THF; dioxane.

C_6H_5

Ketene and Ketone Polymers

Poly(dimethylketene)

$C(CH_3)_2$

low mol. wt.:   ether.   methanol.   24

higher mol. wt.: chloroform (partially).

Polyacetone
                 chloroform; carbon tetra-   6
                 chloride; acetone.

Poly(monobromoacetone)
                 acetone.

Poly(7-oxa-bicyclo[2.2.1]heptane)
                 phenol/carbon tetrachloride methanol.   77
                 (21.2:78.8 wt.%).

Aromatic Polyethers

Poly(3-phenoxylene)
                 benzene; biphenyl; 3-penta- methanol.   101
                 nol; phenyl ether; pyridine;
                 benzophenone; nitrobenzene;
                 DMF; DMS.

Poly(2,6-xylenol)

amorphous: α-pinene (hot).   α-pinene (cold);   128,129,
                                             methanol; ethanol.   130

crystalline: benzene; chloroform.   α-pinene (hot);
                                             methanol; ethanol.

1,2-Epoxide Polymers

Poly(ethylene oxide)
                 benzene; chloroform; car-   aliphatic hydrocarbons; 1,2,4
                 bon tetrachloride; alcohols; ethers; dioxane (sw);
                 cyclohexanone; esters; DMF; water (hot).
                 acetonitrile; water (cold);
                 aqu. K_2SO_4 (0.45M; θ, 35°C);
                 aqu. $MgSO_4$ (0.39M; θ, 45°C).

References page IV-232

Polymer	Solvents	Nonsolvents	References
Poly(propylene oxide)			
crystalline:	benzene; toluene; carbon tetrachloride; methanol (hot); ethanol; THF; dioxane; acetone; methyl ethyl ketone.	ether (sw); 2-amino-ethanol; ethyl acetate (sw); DMF.	1
Poly(cyclopentene oxide)	benzene; chloroform; carbon disulfide.	methanol.	80
Poly(cyclohexene oxide)	aliphatic hydrocarbons; paraffin (hot); toluene; methyl acetate; chinese wood oil.	ethanol; 2-ethoxy-ethanol; acetone.	1
Poly(phenylglycidyl ether)	xylene (hot);1,2-dichloro-benzene (hot); DMF (hot).	common organic solvents at room temperature.	30
Poly(1,2-di(epoxyethyl)benzene)	chloroform; THF.		34

$$\left[O - \underset{\underset{\langle - \rangle}{}}{\overset{O}{\diagup}} - CH_2 \right]_n$$

Higher Cyclic Ether Polymers

Poly(3,3-bis(chloromethyl)oxetane)	cyclohexanone.	methanol.	26
Poly(tetrahydrofuran)	benzene; methylene chloride; THF.	petroleum ether; hexane; methanol; water.	27

Polymer	Solvents	Nonsolvents	References

9 - POLYSULFIDES AND POLYSULFONES

<u>Polysulfides</u>

Poly(thiocarboxyl fluoride)
chloroform/methanol. — conc. nitric acid (reflux); aqu. sodium hydroxide (10%, reflux).

$\{S - CF_2\}_n$

Poly(ethylene dichloride-co-sodium tetrasulfide)
no solvent known. — gasoline; kerosine; turpentine; benzene (sw); carbon tetrachloride; alcohols; carbon disulfide; dil. acids; dil. alkalies. — 11,12

Poly(dichlorodiethylether-co-sodium disulfide)
1,1,2-trichloroethane (partially); other chlorinated hydrocarbons (partially); — gasoline (sw); kerosine (sw); turpentine (sw); benzene (sw); carbon tetrachloride (sw); alcohols; carbon disulfide; dil. acids; dil. alkalies. — 11,12

liquid polymers: benzene; ethylene dichloride.

Poly(dichlorodiethylether-co-sodium tetrasulfide)
1,1,2-trichloroethane (partially); other chlorinated hydrocarbons (partially); — gasoline (sw); kerosine; turpentine (sw); benzene (sw); carbon tetrachloride (sw); alcohols; carbon disulfide; dil. acids; dil. alkalies. — 11,12

liquid polymers: benzene; ethylene dichloride.

Poly(phenylene sulfide)
phenyl oxide (reflux: 1%); phenyl sulfide (reflux:1%); — <u>at reflux temperature:</u> toluene; pyridine; 2,4-lutidine. — 107

<u>Mono-olefin Polysulfones</u>

Poly(ethylene sulfone)
no solvent known. — common organic solvents. — 1,11

Poly(propylene sulfone)
conc. nitric acid; conc. sulfuric acid. — common organic solvents. — 1,11

Poly(1-butene sulfone)
acetone; cyclohexanone. — paraffins; cycloparaffins aromatic hydrocarbons. — 1

Poly(5-norbornene sulfone)
methylene chloride. — methanol. — 9

Poly(styrene sulfone)
benzene/acetone; chloroform; anisole; DMF; nitrobenzene; diisobutyl sulfone; sulfuric acid. — — 11

<u>Alkyne Polysulfones</u>

Poly(1-pentyne sulfone)
dioxane. — — 1

Poly(1-hexyne sulfone)
dioxane; acetone. — — 1

Polymer	Solvents	Nonsolvents	References
Poly(1-heptyne sulfone)	dioxane; acetone.		1

Diene Polysulfones

Polymer	Solvents	Nonsolvents	References
Poly(butadiene sulfone)	conc. nitric acid; conc. sulfuric acid.	common organic solvents.	1
Poly(isoprene sulfone)	conc. nitric acid; conc. sulfuric acid.	common organic solvents.	1
Poly(dimethylbutadiene sulfone)	conc. nitric acid; conc. sulfuric acid.	common organic solvents.	1

Poly(1,5-hexadiene sulfone)

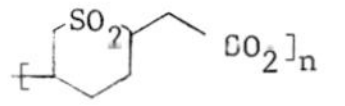

methyl ethyl ketone;
acetophenone; conc.
sulfuric acid.

Poly(cis,cis-cyclo-octadiene sulfone)

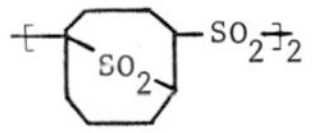

N-methylpyrrolidone;
DMF/lithium chloride (5%);
DMA/lithium chloride (5%);
DMS; TMS; sulfuric acid.

Poly(norbornadiene sulfone)

	Solvents	Nonsolvents	References
	DMF; DMS.	methanol; ethanol.	10

Polymer	Solvents	Nonsolvents	References

10 - MISCELLANEOUS ADDITION POLYMERS

<u>Poly(α,ω-polymethylene diisocyanates)</u>

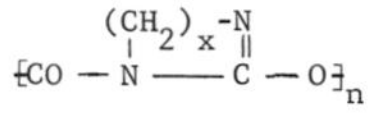

$$\left[CO - N \overset{(CH_2)_x}{\underset{|}{\rule{0pt}{0pt}}} \overset{-N}{\underset{|}{C}} - O \right]_n$$

Poly(methylene diisocyanate)
   x = 1   N-methylpyrrolidone/lithium   58
                           chloride; DMS; sulfuric acid.

Poly(ethylene diisocyanate)
   x = 2   DMS; sulfuric acid.

Poly(trimethylene diisocyanate)
   x = 3   m-cresol; sulfuric acid.

Poly(tetramethylene diisocyanate)
   x = 4   ethylene carbonate; sulfuric
                          acid.

Poly(5-iminohydantoins) (poly(diisocyanate-co-dicarbamoyl cyanide))
                            pyridine; N-methylpyroli-   46
                            done; DMF; DMS.

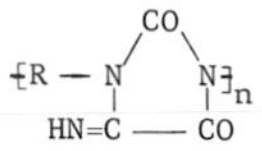

$$\left[R - N \overset{CO}{\underset{|}{\diagup \diagdown}} N \right]_n$$
$$HN=C \underset{|}{\rule{0pt}{0pt}} - CO$$

$R = (CH_2)_4;\ (CH_2)_6;$

$\quad C_6H_4;\ C_6H_4-CH_2-$

$\quad C_6H_4;\ C_6H_3(CH_3).$

Poly(perfluoroglutarodinitrile)

   DP < 10-12:   dioxane; acetonitrile.   14

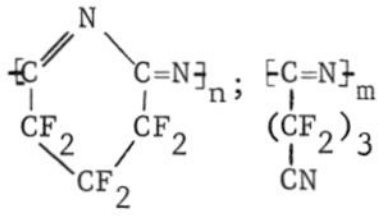

$$\left[C \overset{N}{\underset{|}{\diagup \diagdown}} C=N \right]_n;\ \left[C=N \right]_m$$

Poly(1-(perfluorobutyryl)aziridine)
                            acetone; 1,3-bis(trifluoro-   heptane; carbon tetra-   59
                            methyl)benzene; DMF.   chloride.

Polymer	Solvents	Nonsolvents	References

11 - FORMALDEHYDE RESINS

Phenol-formaldehyde resins

Polymer	Solvents	Nonsolvents	References
Novolaks and low mol. wt.:	hydrocarbons; ether; acetone; esters;		
4-tert-butylphenol and 4-phenylphenol polymers:	drying oils.		
Final resins:	molten phenols (with some decomposition).		
Fully cured resins:		most common organic compounds; alcohol; water (sw); dil. acids (sw); dil. alkalies (sw).	12

Melamine-formaldehyde resins

Polymer	Solvents	Nonsolvents	References
Very low mol.wt.:	alcohol; water		12
Intermediates:	pyridine; formalin; formic acids; dil. and conc. acids.		
Final resins; high mol. wt.:	no solvent known.		

Urea-formaldehyde resins   12

Polymer	Solvents	Nonsolvents	References
Very low mol.wt.:	alcohol; water.		
Intermediates:	pyridine; formalin; formic acid; dil. and conc. acids.		
Final resins; high mol. wt.:	no solvent known.		

Aniline-formaldehyde resins

Polymer	Solvents	Nonsolvents	References
Low mol. wt.:	chlorinated hydrocarbons; methylcyclohexanone.	hydrocarbons; alcohols; aniline (sw).	12
High mol. wt.:	no solvent known.	chlorinated hydrocarbons (sw); aniline (sw).	

p-Toluenesulfonamide-formaldehyde resins

Polymer	Solvents	Nonsolvents	References
	many organic solvents.	aliphatic hydrocarbons; alcohol; water.	12

Polymer	Solvents	Nonsolvents	References

12 - POLYESTERS

Aliphatic Polyesters

Poly(11-oxyundecanoate)

benzene; chloroform. — 4

Poly(hexamethylene succinate)

benzene; chloroform; THF. — 4

Poly(hexamethylene sebacate)

benzene; chloroform. — 4

Poly(hexadecamethylene sebacate)

chloroform. — 4

Poly(hexamethylene α,α'-dibutylsebacate)

benzene. — 4

Poly(octamethylene cis-hexahydroterephthalate)

chloroform. — 4

Poly(octamethylene trans-hexahydroterephthalate)

chloroform. — 4

Poly(hexamethylene maleate)

benzene; chloroform; THF. — 4

Poly(hexamethylene fumarate)

chloroform. — 4

Poly(hexamethylene acetylenedicarboxylate)

benzene; chloroform. — 4

Aromatic Polyesters

Poly(ethylene terephthalate)

chloral hydrate; phenol; phenol/tetrachloroethane (1:1 vol.); phenol/2,4,6-trichlorophenol (10:7 vol.); chlorophenol; nitrobenzene; halogenated aliphatic carboxylic acids. — hydrocarbons; chlorinated hydrocarbons; aliphatic alcohols; ketones; carboxylic esters; esters. — 2,4

Poly(p-phenylene isophthalate) and poly(4,4'-biphenylene isophthalate)

at elevated temp.: m-terphenyl; 2,4,6-trichlorophenol; halogenated biphenyls; halogenated diphenyl oxides; benzophenone; halogenated naphthalenes — common organic solvents. — 132

Polycarbonates

Poly(hexamethylene carbonate)

benzene; chloroform; acetone. — ethanol; ether — 1

Poly(p-phenylene carbonate)

— common organic solvents. — 1

Poly(m-phenylene carbonate)

— common organic solvents. — 1

Polymer	Solvents	Nonsolvents	References

Poly(4,4'-isopropylidenediphenylene carbonate)
        methylene chloride; chloro-   1
        form; dioxane; pyridine;
        DMF.

Poly(4,4'-(2-pentylidene)diphenylene carbonate)
        benzene; toluene; methylene   1
        chloride; chloroform; ethyl
        acetate; butyl acetate.

Boron, Sulfur, Phosphorus Containing Polyesters
_____

Poly(1,2-bis(hydroxymethyl)carborane-co-adipic acid)
        aromatic hydrocarbons; ace- aliphatic hydrocarbons.   60
        tone; isopropyl carborane;
        isopropenyl carborane.

$\{O-CH_2-C\underset{B_{10}H_{10}}{\diagdown_{\diagup}}CH_2O-CO-(CH_2)_4-CO\}_n$

Poly(aryl sulfonates)
        DMF.   methanol.   71

$\{SO_2-Ar-SO_2-O-Ar-O\}$

$Ar = C_6H_4;\ C_6H_4-C_6H_4$
    $C_6H_4-CH_2-C_6H_4;$
    $C_6H_4-O-C_6H_4;$
    $C_6H_4-SO_2-C_6H_4$

Poly(hydroquinone-co-aryloxy-phosphoryl dichloride) (phoryl resins)
        aromatic hydrocarbons; halo- aliphatic hydrocarbons;   99
$\{P(O)(OAr)-O-Ar'-O\}$ genated aliphatic hydro-   alcohols; esters; water.
        carbons; methanol or ethanol/
        butanol/toluene/xylene
        (8:4:65:23).

Poly(hydroquinone-co-(chloromethyl)phosphoryl dichloride)
        ethylene dichloride; DMF.   99

$\{P(O)(CH_2Cl)-O-C_6H_4-O\}$

Poly(hydroquinone-co-(N-dimethyl)phosphoramidic acid dichloride)
        DMF.   99

$\{P(O)[N(CH_3)_2]-O-C_6H_4-O\}_n$

Polymer	Solvents	Nonsolvents	References

13 - POLYAMIDES

Poly(isocyanates) (Nylon-1)

Poly(vinylisocyanate) (N-vinyl-nylon-1)

	pyridine; DMF; DMA; DMS.	chloroform; alcohols; dioxane; carbon disulfide.	31

Poly(butylisocyanate) (N-butyl-nylon-1)

	benzene; THF.		25

Aliphatic Polyamides

Poly(3-aminopropionic acid)

	glycerol (hot); phenol (hot); formic acid.		1

Poly(6-aminocaproic acid) (Nylon-6)

	m-cresol; chlorophenol; formic acid; acetic acid; trichloroacetic acid; ethylene carbonate; sulfuric acid; phosphoric acid; tri(dimethylamido) phosphate.	hydrocarbons; chloroform alcohols; ethers, ketones; esters.	2,4

Poly(11-aminoundecanoic acid)

	higher primary alcohols; DMF; DMS.		1

Poly(hexamethylene adipamide) and other Nylons of 6- and 6,6-type.

	room temperature: triflurooethanol; trichloroethanol; phenol; cresols; chloral-hydrate; formic acid; halogenated acetic acids; hydrogen fluoride; hydrogen chloride/methanol; liquid sulfur dioxide; sulfuric acid; phosphoric acid; saturated solutions of alcohol-soluble salts; e.g. calcium chloride, magnesium chloride in methanol;		1
	at 120-180°C: benzyl alcohol; ethylene chlorohydrin; 1,3-dichloropropanol; 2-butene-1,4-diol; diethylene glycol; acetic acid; formamide; N-acetylmorpholin; DMS.		2

Poly(decamethylene adipamide)

	chlorobenzene; diethyl succinate (79°C).		4

Poly(3,3'-(methylimino)bistrimethylene adipamide)

	chloroform; ethanol; C-7 fluoro alcohol; cresol; formic acid; DMF; water; aqu. hydrochloric acid (5%).	hexane; chlorobenzene; acetone; acetonitrile.	84

Polymer	Solvents	Nonsolvents	References

Aromatic Polyamides

Poly(benzidine-co-isophthalic acid)

| | conc. sulfuric acid. | methanol; m-cresol (sw); N-methylpyrrolidone (sw); formic acid (85%) (sw); glacial acetic acid (sw); DMF (sw); DMA (sw); DMS (sw). | 41 |

Poly(pyromellitic dianhydride-co-aromatic diamines) (polyamic-acids)

$$\text{HOOC} \overbrace{}^{} \text{COOH}$$
$$[\text{NH-CO} \text{CO-NII-R}]$$

$R = C_6H_4; \; C_6H_4-C_6H_4, C_6H_4-O-C_6H_4;$

$\quad C_6H_4-S-C_6H_4; \; C_6H_4-SO_2-C_6H_4;$

$\quad C_6H_4-CH_2-C_6H_4; \; C_6H_4-C(CH_3)_2-C_6H_4.$

| | DMF; DMA; DMS; tetramethyl urea. | | |

Sulfur and Phosphorous Containing Polyamides

Poly(1,6-hexamethylenediamine-co-bis(carboxyethyl) sulfide)

| | cresol; formic acid; DMF. | hexane; chloroform; chlorobenzene; ethanol; C-7 fluoro alcohol (sw); acetone; acetonitrile; water; aqu. hydrochloric acid (5%). | 84 |

Poly(1,6-hexamethylenediamine-co-benzene-1,3-bis-sulfonic acid chloride)

| | pyridine; DMF; aqu. sodium hydroxide. | ethanol; acetone; water. | 1 |

Poly(trans-2,5-dimethyl-piperazine-co-4,4'-sulfonyl-dibenzoyl chloride)

| | sym-tetrachloroethane/phenol (40:60); DMF. | methanol; water. | 1 |

Poly(bis(3-aminopropyl)phenyl phosphine-co-adipic acid)

| | ethanol; cresol; formic acid; DMF; aqu. hydrochloric acid (5%). | hexane (sw); chloroform; chlorobenzene; C-7 fluoro alcohol; acetone; acetonitrile; water. | 84 |

Poly(bis(3-aminopropyl)phenyl phosphine-co-terephthalic acid)

| | cresol; formic acid; DMF. | hexane; chloroform; chlorobenzene; ethanol (sw); acetone; acetonitrile; water; hydrochloric acid (5%; sw). | 84 |

Poly(bis(3-aminopropyl)methyl phosphine oxide-co-adipic acid)

| | ethanol; C-7 fluoro alcohol; cresol; formic acid; water; aqu. hydrochloric acid (5%). | hexane; chloroform; chlorobenzene; acetone; DMF; acetonitrile. | 84 |

Poly(bis(3-aminopropyl)n-octyl phosphine-co-adipic acid)

| | chloroform; C-7 fluoro alcohol; cresol; formic acid; DMF. | hexane; chlorobenzene (sw); ethanol; acetone; acetonitrile; water; aqu. hydrochloric acid (5%, sw). | 84 |

Polymer	Solvents	Nonsolvents	References
Poly(bis(3-aminopropyl)phenyl phosphine oxide-co-adipic acid)	ethanol; C-7 fluoro alcohol; cresol; formic acid; DMF; aqu. hydrochloric acid (5%).	hexane; chloroform (sw); chlorobenzene; acetone; acetonitrile; water.	84
Poly(hexamethylenediamine-co-bis(2-carboxyethyl)phenyl phosphine oxide)	ethanol; C-7 fluoro alcohol; cresol; formic acid; DMF.	hexane; chloroform (sw); chlorobenzene; acetone; acetonitrile; water (sw); aqu. hydrochloric acid (5%; sw).	
Poly(hexamethylenediamine-co-bis(p-carboxyphenyl)phenyl phosphine oxide)	C-7 fluoro alcohol; cresol; formic acid; DMF.	hexane; chloroform; chlorobenzene; ethanol (sw); acetone; acetonitrile; water; aqu. hydrochloric acid (5%).	84
Poly(piperazine-co-bis(2-carboxyethyl)-phenyl phosphine oxide)	chloroform; ethanol; C-7 fluoro alcohol; cresol; formic acid; DMF; aqu. hydrochloric acid (5%).	hexane; chlorobenzene; acetone; acetonitrile (sw); water (sw).	84

14 - POLYUREAS AND POLYURETHANS

Polymer	Solvents	Nonsolvents	References
Poly(ureas) (general)	phenol; m-cresol; formic acid; sulfuric acid.	alcohols; ether.	3
Poly(1,10-decamethylenediamine-co-1,6-hexamethylene-bis-ethylurethan)	phenol; formic acid.		1
Poly(diphenylmethane-4,4'-diisocyanate-co-4,4'-diaminodiphenylmethane)	DMF + 5% lithium chloride.		1
Poly(toluene-2,4-diisocyanate-co-N,N'bis(trimethylsilyl)-p,p'-diaminodiphenyl ether)	benzene; toluene; THF; DMF; DMS.	n-hexane.	87
Polyurethans (general)	phenol; m-cresol; formic acid; sulfuric acid.	saturated hydrocarbons; alcohols; ether.	2
Polyurethan (poly(propylene oxide) basis)	benzene; toluene/iso-octane (5:7 vol; θ, 39.5°C).		

Polymer	Solvents	Nonsolvents	References

15 - MISCELLANEOUS LINEAR CONDENSATION POLYMERS

Poly(carbodiimides)

Poly(diethylcarbodiimide)
    formic acid; aqu. mineral   55
    acids.

Poly(diallylcarbodiimide)
    formic acid.   55

Poly(di-n-butylcarbodiimide)
    formic acid.   55

Poly(methylisopropylcarbodiimide)
    formic acid.   55

Poly(di-n-hexylcarbodiimide)
    formic acid; n-heptane.   55

Poly(diphenylcarbodiimide)
    formic acid.   55

Poly(4,4'-diphenylenemethane-carbodiimide)
       m-cresol; trichloro-   23
       phenol/phenol (7:10).

Poly(hexamethylenecarbodiimide)   23
       no solvent known.   xylene; chloroform;
                                trichlorethylene;
Poly(1,3-xylylenecarbodiimide)   chlorobenzene; ethylene   23
       no solvent known.   chlorohydrin; cyclo-
                                hexanone; formic acid;
Poly(3-methyl-1,4-phenylenecarbodiimide) DMF; DMS.   23
       no solvent known.

Poly(2,2'-dimethyl-biphenylenecarbodiimide)   23
       no solvent known.

Poly(2,2'-dimethoxy-biphenylenecarbodiimide)   23
       no solvent known.

Poly(1,5-naphthylenecarbodiimide)   23
       no solvent known.

Poly(hydrazides)
  aliphatic:

Poly(adipyl dihydrazide-co-succinoyl chloride)
                            DMS (sw)   72

  aromatic-aliphatic:

Poly(adipyl dihydrazide-co-isophthaloyl chloride)
         tri(dimethylamido) phosphate   72
         DMS.

  fully aromatic, e.g.:

Poly(isophthalic dihydrazide-co-terephthaloyl chloride)
         N-methylpyrrolidone; formic   chloroform; trichloro-   73
         acid (degrad.); dichloro-   ethane (sw); trifluoro-
         acetic acid (degrad.); tri-   propanol; m-cresol;
         fluoroacetic acid (degrad.); nitrobenzene; water.
         DMA; DMS (cold); sulfuric
         acid (degrad.).

Polymer	Solvents	Nonsolvents	References

Aromatic Condensation Polymers

Poly(2,5-dimethylbenzylene)

			16
Low mol. wt.:	1,2- and 1,4-dichloro-benzene (hot).		

Poly(p-xylylene)

	biphenyl; chlorinated bi-phenyls; phenyl ether; ben-zoyl benzoate; nitrobenzene.		109,114

Poly(2,5-dimethylxylylene)

Low mol. wt.:	1,2- and 1,4-dichlorobenzene; chloroform.		16

Poly(2,5-dimethoxy-p-xylylene)

	chloroform.	common organic solvents.	94

Poly(p-xylylidene)

	no solvent known.		88

Poly(α-cyano-m-xylylidene) (poly(m-xylylidenedicyanide-co-isophthaldialdehyde))

	chloroform; DMF; nitro-benzene.		36

Poly(α-cyano-p-xylylidene) (poly(p-xylylenedicyanide-co-terephthaldialdehyde))

	no solvent known.		36

Poly(nitrophenylene)

		all common organic compounds.	42

Poly(tetramethyl-p-phenylenedimethylene)

		benzene; 1-chloronaph-thalene (sw); ethanol; benzyl benzoate (sw).	114

Poly(2,5-dihydroxy-p-phenylenedimethylene)

		common organic solvents; aqu. potassium hydroxide.	114

Poly(4,4'-oxydiphenylene dimethylene)

	benzene; naphthalene; other aromatic hydro-carbons; chloroform; bromoform.	petroleum ether; carbon tetrachloride (sw); alco-hols; cyclohexanol (sw); acids.	114

Poly(2,5-dimethoxy-p-phenylenedimethylene)

	aromatic hydrocarbons; bromoform.	water; methanol.	114

Polymer	Solvents	Nonsolvents	References

16 - HETEROCYCLIC CONDENSATION POLYMERS

Poly(benzimidazoles)

R = (-CH$_2$-)$_4$	formic acid; DMS (partially solvent).	DMF.	18
R = p-phenylene	formic acid.	DMF; DMS.	18
R = m-phenylene	formic acid.	DMF. DMS.	18

Poly(alkylene-5,5'-dibenzimidazoles)

n = 4,7,8,11,20	N-methylpyrrolidene; m-cresol; formic acid (85%); DMA; DMS; conc. sulfuric acid.	glacial acetic acid; DMF (sw).	40

Poly(arylene-5,5'-dibenzimidazoles)

Ar = m-phenylene	N-methylpyrrolidone; formic acid; DMF (partially)*; DMA; DMS; conc. sulfuric acid.	m-cresol; formic acid (85% (sw)); glacial acetic acid; DMF*.	18,40
Ar = p-phenylene	formic acid (2-3% soluble); DMS (0.5-1% soluble).	DMF.	
Ar = o-biphenylene	formic acid; DMF; DMS.		
Ar = p-biphenylene	formic acid (partially).	DMF; DMS.	
Ar = 3,5-pyridylene	formic acid (partially); DMF (partially); DMS.		
Ar = 2,5-furylidene	formic acid (partially); DMF; DMS.		

Ar = p-C$_6$H$_4$-NHCO-R-CONH-p-C$_6$H$_4$

R = (CH$_2$)$_8$; p-C$_6$H$_4$; m-C$_6$H$_4$

	N-methylpyrrolidone; DMF; DMA; DMS; conc. sulfuric acid.	methanol; m-cresol (sw); formic acid (sw); glacial acetic acid (sw).	

---

* Depending on mol. wt. and structure.

Polymer	Solvents	Nonsolvents	References

Poly(pyromellitimides)

R = $(CH_2)_9$	m-cresol.	common organic solvents.	1,20
R = $m-C_6H_4$; $p-C_6H_4$;	conc. sulfuric acid.	common organic solvents.	
R = $p-C_6H_4-p-C_6H_4$	fuming nitric acid.	common organic solvents.	
R = $p-C_6H_4-CH_2-p-C_6H_4$; $p-C_6H_4-C(CH_3)_2-p-C_6H_4$	conc. sulfuric acid.	common organic solvents.	
R = $p-C_6H_4-O-p-C_6H_4$	DMA; N-methylcaprolactame; fuming nitric acid.	common organic solvents.	
R = $p-C_6H_4-S-p-C_6H_4$	fuming nitric acid.	common organic solvents.	
R = $p-C_6H_4-SO_2-p-C_6H_4$; $m-C_6H_4-SO_2-m-C_6H_4$	conc. sulfuric acid.	common organic solvents.	

Poly(benzoxazoles)

R = $m-C_6H_4$	N-methyl-2-pyrrolidone; DMF; DMA; DMS; sulfuric acid; aqu. solutions of lithium hydroxide, potassium hy- droxide, sodium hydroxide.		90

Poly(oxadiazoles)

R = $(CH_2)_8$	benzene; chloroform; dichloroethylene; m-cresol; DMF; sulfuric acid.		74,92
R = $m-C_6H_4$	trifluoroacetic acid; sulfuric acid.	chloroform; tetra- fluoropropanol; m- cresol; DMF; nitrobenzene.	

Poly(oxadiazolidines)

R = $m-C_6H_4$	DMS.	methanol.	75

References page IV-232

Polymer	Solvents	Nonsolvents	References

Poly(dithiazoles)

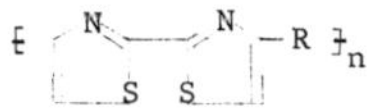

$R = p\text{-}C_6H_4$ sulfuric acid (cold).   ethanol; ether; DMF.   102
diphenylmethane; phenyl
ether; quinoline; formic
acid; DMA; DMS.

$R = p\text{-}C_6H_4\text{-}(CH_2)_6\text{-}p\text{-}C_6H_4$ sulfuric acid (cold);

average mol. wt.
11,000:   DMF (cold);

average mol. wt.
12,000:   DMF (hot);

average mol. wt.
27,000:   DMF (hot).

Poly(benzothiazoles)

$R = m\text{-}C_6H_4$;   conc. sulfuric acid.   19
3,5-pyridylene;
$p\text{-}C_6H_4\text{-}O\text{-}p\text{-}C_6H_4$;
$p\text{-}C_6H_4\text{-}CO\text{-}p\text{-}C_6H_4$.

Poly(piperazines)

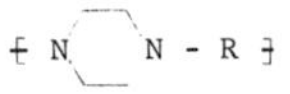

Poly((1,4-xylylenyl)-2-methylpiperazine)
           chloroform; sym-   ethanol.   62
           tetrachlorethane.

Poly(quinoxalines)

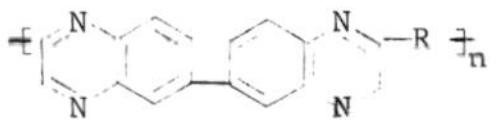

$R = p\text{-}C_6H_4$ formic acid; trifluoroacetic
acid; DMF; DMS; tri(dimethyl-
amino) phosphate; sulfuric
acid.

Poly(s-triazinyleneimides)

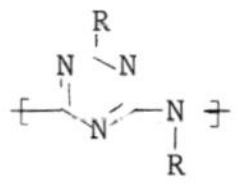

$R = CH_3$;   benzene; phenol; m-cresol.   50
   C_6H_5

Polymer	Solvents	Nonsolvents	References

17 - NATURAL POLYMERS AND MODIFIED NATURAL POLYMERS

Natural Rubber and Derivatives (See also Diene Polymers)

Natural rubber

	hydrocarbons; benzene; toluene; chlorinated hydrocarbons; n-propyl ketone (θ, 14.5°C).	alcohols; acetone; carboxylic acids.	2,4

Cyclized rubber

	aromatic and chlorinated hydrocarbons.	aliphatic hydrocarbons; oils (sw); alcohol; ether; acetone; water; acids; alkalies.	12

Hydrochlorinated rubber

	chlorinated hydrocarbons.	alcohol; water	12

Chlorinated rubber

	hydrogenated naphthas; aromatic and chlorinated hydrocarbons; ketones (limited solubility in acetone); esters; glyceryl esters.	aliphatic hydrocarbons; alcohol; ether (sw); acetone (sw); water; conc. acids; oxidizing acids; moderately conc. alkalies.	12

Gutta-percha

	hot petroleum ether; benzene; chloroform.	alcohol; water.	12

Cellulose and Derivatives *

Cellulose

	aqu. solutions of: cupriethylenediamine; sodium xanthate; tetramethylammonium hydroxide; calcium thiocyanate; alkalies (ice-cold); cupriamonium hydroxide; beryllium perchlorate; zinc chloride (hot); zinc chloride/hydrochloric acid (cold); conc. sulfuric acid; conc. phosphoric acid; for more solvents see table on Cellulose.	hydrocarbons; mineral oils; water (sw); dil. aqu. alkalies.	2,4,12, 134

Cellulose Ethers

Methyl cellulose

S.C. = 3 - 10%	alkali; water (cold); chloroform; alcohol/ benzene; pyridine; acetone; acetone/benzene; esters.	water (hot).	2,5,12
S.C. = 22 - 32%			
S.C. = > 40			

Ethyl cellulose

D.S. = 0.5-0.7		water (cold).	3,4,5,12
D.S. = 1.0-1.5	pyridine; formic acid; acetic acid; water (cold); cuoxam.	ethanol.	

* See also table on "Properties of Cellulose Materials".

References page IV-232

Polymer	Solvents	Nonsolvents	References

Ethyl cellulose (Cont'd.)

Polymer	Solvents	Nonsolvents	References
D.S. = 2	methylene chloride; chloroform; dichloroethylene; chlorohydrins; ethanol; THF.	hydrocarbons; carbon tetrachloride; trichloroethylene; alcohols; ether; ketones; esters; water.	
D.S. = 2.3	benzene; toluene; alkyl halogenids; alcohols; furan derivatives; ketones; acetic esters; carbon disulfide; nitromethane.	ethylene glycol; acetone (cold).	
D.S. = 3	benzene; toluene; methylene chloride; alcohols; esters.	hydrocarbons; decalin; xylene; carbon tetrachloride; tetrahydrofurfuryl alcohol; diols; n-propyl ether.	

Propyl cellulose

Polymer	Solvents	Nonsolvents	References
D.S. = 2.5	benzene; chloroform; dichloroethane; butanol; THF; dioxane; glycol formal; acetone; cyclohexanone; methyl cyclohexanone; methyl acetate.	hydrocarbons; methanol; ethanol; ethanol/ether (1:3); propanol.	3

Butyl cellulose

Polymer	Solvents	Nonsolvents	References
	ethanol.	water.	5

Allyl cellulose

Polymer	Solvents	Nonsolvents	References
D.S. = 3	benzene; carbon tetrachloride; ethanol.		3

Benzyl cellulose

Polymer	Solvents	Nonsolvents	References
D.S. = 2	tetralin; benzene/alcohol; benzene/acetone; methylene chloride; dichloroethylene; trichloroethylene; chlorobenzene; chlorohydrins; ethanol/carbon tetrachloride (1:1); tetrahydrofurfuryl alcohol; pyridine; acetone; methyl ethyl ketone; acetates ($<C_5$).	hydrocarbons; carbon tetrachloride; o-chlorotoluene; alcohols ($>C_5$); ether; dioxane; dipropyl ketone.	3,12

Hydroxyethyl cellulose

Polymer	Solvents	Nonsolvents	References
S.C. < 30%	alkali;		1,2,12
S.C. = 35-55%:	water;		
S.C. > 55%:	benzene/alcohol; benzene/acetone; chloroform; pyridine; acetone; esters.	benzene; methanol (sw)*; THF; acetone*; methyl acetate.	

Carboxymethyl cellulose

Polymer	Solvents	Nonsolvents	References
S.C. = 5-10%	alkali;		12
S.C. = 15-30%	water (sodium salt);		

* Depending on degree of conversion.

Polymer	Solvents	Nonsolvents	References

Carboxymethyl cellulose (Cont'd.)

    D.S. = high   benzene/alcohol; benzene/
acetone; chloroform;
pyridine; acetone; esters

Cyanoethyl cellulose

    S.C. = 8-12   alkali;   12

    S.C. = 24-32%   water;

    S.C. > 50%   chloroform; benzene/
alcohol; benzene/acetone;
pyridine; acetone; esters.

Cellulose esters

Cellulose triformate

                              pyridine; formic acid.   3

Cellulose acetate

    D.S. = 2-2.3   methylene chloride/metha-   hydrocarbons;   2,12
nol (80:20); chloroform/   aliphatic ethers;
methanol; benzyl alcohol;   weak mineral acids.
phenols; ethylene glycol
ethers; dioxane; dietha-
nolamine; pyridine; aniline;
acetone; cyclohexanone;
formic acid; acetic acid
(glacial); methyl acetate;
ethyl acetate/nitrobenzene;
glycol monoethyl ether
acetate; nitromethane.

Cellulose triacetate

                              methylene chloride; methy-   aliphatic hydrocarbons;   2,3,4,12
lene chloride/ethanol   benzene; dichloroethane;
(8:2); chloroform; chloro-   chlorobenzene; o-chloro-
form/alcohol; trichloro-   toluene; ethanol (abso-
ethane; THF; dioxane; ace-   lute); aliphatic ethers;
tone; acetone/water (8:2);   acetone; weak mineral
methyl acetate; ethyl   acids.
acetate; ethylene glycol
ether acetates; ethylene
carbonate.

Cellulose tripropionate

                              benzene; dichloroethane;   hydrocarbons; ethanol;   3
chlorobenzene; acetone;   o-chlorotoluene.
ethyl acetate.

Cellulose tributyrate

                              dodecane/tetralin (75:25   4
vol) (θ, 130°C); methyl
ethyl ketone.

Cellulose tricaproate

                              dioxane; DMF (θ, 41°C).

Celluluse tricaprylate

                              toluene; 3-phenylpropanol   4
(θ, 48°C); DMF (θ, 140°C).

Cellulose tricarbanilate

                              dioxane; pyridine; acetone.

References page IV-232

Polymer	Solvents	Nonsolvents	References

Cellulose nitrate

Cellulose nitrate,
N 10.5-12%:

	alcohols (lower); alcohol/ ether; acetone; amyl acetate; ethylene glycol esters; acetic acid (glacial).	higher alcohols; higher carboxylic acids; ethers; higher ketones.	2,12

N 12-14%:

	alcohol/ether; esters; ketones.	alcohol; ether.	12

Cellulose trinitrate,
N 14.14%;

	halogenated hydrocarbons; ethanol/ethyl ether; acetone; methyl amyl ketone; cyclohexanone; methyl acetate; ethyl acetate; ethyl butyrate; ethyl lactate; ethylene glycol ether acetates, ethylene carbonate; furan derivatives; nitrobenzene.	aliphatic hydrocarbons; aromatic hydrocarbons (sw); lower alcohols; higher alcohols (sw); ethylene glycol; ether; dil. carboxylic acids; water.	2,4,12

Starch and Derivatives

Starch

	fused chloral hydrate; cupriethylenediamine; water (hot; pressure); liquid ammonia.	water (sw); aqu. alkali (sw).	12,100

Amylose

	ethylenediamine; DMS; water (hot); aqu. KOH; aqu. KCL (0.33M; θ, 25°C).	n-butanol.	4,100

Amylose acetate

	chloroform; methyl acetate; nitromethane.	.	4

Amylose tricarbanilate

	dioxane; pyridine; acetone.		4

Amylopectin

	water; water/butanol.		

Other Polysaccharides

Alginic acid

	water (sparingly); aqu. alkalies; aqu. sodium carbonate.	hydrocarbons; hydrophobic organic compounds; hydrophilic organic compounds (sw); dil. acids; aqu. calcium salt solutions.	12,100

alkali and ammonium salts:	aqu. alkali; water	beryllium, beryllium-calcium, chromium, ferric salts: aqu. alkali; all salts: hydrocarbons; hydrophobic organic compounds in general.	4,12
magnesium and ferrous salts:	water		
calcium salt:	alkali (weak)		
copper, zinc, aluminum salts:	ammonium hydroxide		

Polymer	Solvents	Nonsolvents	References
Chitin			
	formic acid; conc. mineral acids (degrad.).	organic solvents; dil. acids.	100
Glycogen			
	dil. trichloroacetic acid.	alcohol.	100
Gum arabic			
	water (warm).	alcohol.	100
Gum tragacanth (Tragacanthin; tragacantic acid)			
	water.	alcohol; acetone.	100
Heparin			
	water; dil. alkali solution; alkaline solution of ammonium sulfate.	alcohol; acetone; acetic acid.	100
Pectin			
	water; dil. acids.	alcohol.	100
Natural Resins			
Colophony			
	hydrocarbons (~90%*; benzene; chloroform; carbon tetrachloride; methanol; ethanol; ether; acetone; ethyl acetate.		3
Copal			
	hydrocarbons (10-55%)*; benzene (35-60%)*; chloroform (30-90%)*; carbon tetrachloride (15-40%)*; methanol (20-70%)*; ethanol (20-100%)*; ether (10-90%)*; acetone (25-90%)*.		3
Shellac			
	benzene (10-20%)*; chloroform (25-40%)*; carbon tetrachloride (5-15%)*; methanol (100%); ethanol (85-98%)*; ether (10-25%)*; acetone (50-80%)*.	hydrocarbons.	3
Proteins			
Casein			
	formic acid; acetic acid/ aniline; acetic acid/phenol; lactic acid; aqu. formamide (55-95%); dil. acids (hot); aqu. alkali (1%; hot); various aqu. salt solutions: e.g., sodium carbonate; sodium chlorate; sodium nitrate; sodium thiocyanate.	glacial acetic acid; most organic solvents; hydrophilic liquids (sw); water (sw); cold dil. acids (sw); cold alkali solutions (sw).	3,12
Collagen (calf-skin)			
	citrate buffer (0.15M; pH 3.7).		4

* Percentage soluble; depending on source.

Polymer	Solvents	Nonsolvents	References
Collagen (ichthyocol)	cold citrate buffer (ph 4.3).		100
Gelatin	formic acid; glacial acetic acid; lactic acid; acetate buffer (0.17M; ph 4.75); various inorganic salt solutions: e.g., sodium carbonate; sodium chlorate; sodium nitrate; sodium thiocyanate.		3,4
Peanut protein; Soya-bean protein	aqu. urea.	most organic solvents; hydrophilic liquids (sw); water (sw); cold dil. acids (sw); cold dil. alkalies (sw).	
Nucleoprotein (calf thymus)	dil. salt solutions.		100
Nucleoprotein (sperm of sea urchin)	distilled water.	dil. salt solutions.	
Poly(sarcosine)	water.		4
Sericin	water (hot).		100
Silk	with little or no decomposition: cupraammonium hydroxide; cupriethylenediamine; related nickel complex. slight or medium decomposition: conc. aqu. solutions of halides and thiocyanates of lithium, sodium, calcium.	organic solvents; water (sw); dil. alkalies and acids at room temp. for short periods (sw).	12,100
Wool	with decomposition: thioglycolate solution; hot concentrated acids or alkalies; sodium sulfide solution.	water (sw); alkali solution (sw).	12
Zein	alcohol/xylene; aliphatic alcohols/water (70/30-90/10); phenols; dioxane (hot); aqu. acetone.	cold dil. acids (sw); cold dil. alkalies (sw)	12
Nucleic Acids			
Poly(adenylic acid)	citrate buffer (0.015M, pH 7.1); aqu. sodium chloride (0.15M).		4
Desoxyribonucleic acid (denatured: D. Pneumoniae; E. Coli)	aqu. phosphate (0.01M).		4
Ribonucleic acid	aqu. phosphate (0.12M).		4

Polymer	Solvents	Nonsolvents	References

18 - POLY(SILOXANES)

Poly(siloxanes) (general)

fluids and greases: aromatic and chlorinated hydrocarbons; esters.

lower alcohols; water; moderately conc. acids; and alkalies;

12

rubbers:

aromatic and chlorinated hydrocarbons (sw); esters (sw).

Poly(dimethylsiloxane)

cyclohexane; aliphatic hydrocarbons; cyclohexene; hydrogenated xylene; benzene; toluene; mesitylene; triethylbenzene; methylene chloride; chloroform; carbon tetrachloride; ethyl bromide; trichloroethylene; n-butyl chloride; chlorobenzene; o-fluorotoluene; 1,2-dimethoxyethane; phenetol (θ, 13°C) 4-chlorotoluene; 1,2-dichlorobenzene; octylamine; methyl ethyl ketone (θ, 20°C); diethyl ketone; ethyl acetate; isopropyl acetate; amyl acetate; cyclohexyl acetate.

dimethylnaphthalene; 1,2-dichloroethane; 1,4-dibromobutane; lauryl bromide; bromobenzene; dichlorobenzene; 4-bromotoluene; methanol; ethanol; 2-ethoxyethanol; 2-isopropoxyethanol; 2-butoxyethanol; n-decyl alcohol; cyclohexanol; benzyl alcohol; ethylene glycol; chloroethyl ether; p-dioxane; "Carbitol"; diphenyl oxide; aniline; acetone; cyclohexanone; γ-butyrolactone; mesityl oxide; acetophenone; methylacetophenone; ethyl formate; isobutylphenyl acetate; benzyl acetate; ethyl lactate; ethyl benzoate; diethyl phthalate; dibutyl phthalate; acetonitrile; 1-nitropropane; nitrobenzene; 1-nitrotoluene.

2,4,133

Polymer	Solvents	Nonsolvents	Reference

19 - METALORGANIC POLYMERS

Poly(bis(imidazolato)-metal(II))

$M = Cu(II); Zn(II);$ common organic 69
$Co(II).$ solvents.

Poly(aluminum triisopropylate-co-ethylenediamine)

chlorobenzene.   ether; halogenated   44
hydrocarbons.

$$\left[\underset{OR}{\overset{R}{\underset{|}{\leftarrow O - Al \leftarrow}}}\right]_x \left[- O - Al -\right]_y \left[- NHCH_2CH_2NH-\right]_z$$

$x:y = 3:2; (x + y):z \sim 13:1$

no solvent known.

$$\left[\underset{OR}{\overset{R \quad OH}{\underset{|}{\leftarrow O - Al \leftarrow}}}\right]_m \left[- NHCH_2CH_2NH -\right]_n$$

  $m:n \sim 60:1$ hexane; cyclohexane; benzene.

$$\left[\left[\underset{OH}{\overset{R \quad OH}{\underset{|}{\leftarrow O - Al \leftarrow}}}\right]_9 \left[- NHCH_2CH_2NH -\right]_2\right]$$

no solvent known.

$$\left[\left[\underset{OH}{\overset{R \quad OR}{\underset{|}{\leftarrow O - Al \leftarrow}}}\right]_7 \left[\underset{OR}{\overset{R \quad OR}{\underset{|}{\leftarrow O - Al \leftarrow}}}\right]_3 \left[- NHCH_2CH_2NH -\right]_3\right]_n$$

hydrocarbons.

REFERENCES

1. Houben-Weyl, "Methoden der Organischen Chemie," Band XIV/1 and 2, 4. Auflage, Thieme Verlag, Stuttgart 1961, 1963.
2. H. Dexheimer and O. Fuchs in R. Nitsche and K. A. Wolf, "Struktur und Physikalisches Verhalten der Kunststoffe," Springer Verlag, Berlin-Göttingen-Heidelberg 1961.
3. K. Thinius, "Analytische Chemie der Plaste," Springer Verlag, Berlin-Göttingen-Heidelberg 1952.
4. M. Kurata and W. H. Stockmayer,"Advances in Polymer Science," Vol. 3, p. 196, Springer Verlag, Berlin-Göttingen-Heidelberg 1963.
5. A. Münster, "Löslichkeit und Quellung" in H. A. Stuart, "Physik der Hochpolymeren," Vol. II, p. 193, Springer Verlag, Berlin-Göttingen-Heidelberg 1953.
6. J. Furukawa and T. Saegusa, "Polymerisation of Aldehydes and Oxides," Polymer Reviews, Vol. 3, Interscience, New York 1963.
7. J. K. Stille and D. W. Thomson, J. Polymer Sci. $\underline{62}$, S120 (1962).
8. A. H. Frazer and W. P. O'Neill, J. Amer. Chem. Soc. $\underline{85}$, 2613 (1963).
9. E. H. Hill and J. R. Caldwell, J. Polymer Sci. $\underline{A2}$, 1251 (1964).
10. R. J. Alexander and J. R. Doyle, J. Polymer Sci. $\underline{B3}$, 625 (1963).
11. N. Gaylord, "Polyethers," Part III, "Polyalkylene Sulfides and Other Polythioethers," High Polymers, Vol. XIII, Part III, Interscience, New York-London 1962.
12. W. J. Roff, "Fibers, Plastics, and Rubbers," Academic Press, New York 1956.
13. L. E. Coleman, J. F. Bork, and D. P. Wyman, ACS Division of Polymer Chemistry, Polymer Preprints $\underline{5}$, no. 1, 250 (1964).
14. I. B. Johns, ACS Division of Polymer Chemistry, Polymer Preprints $\underline{5}$, no. 1, 239 (1964).
15. C. G. Overberger and S. Ishida, ACS Division of Polymer Chemistry, Polymer Preprints $\underline{5}$, no. 1, 210 (1964).
16. J. E. Moore, ACS Division of Polymer Chemistry, Polymer Preprints $\underline{5}$, no. 1, 203 (1964).
17. J. K. Stille and J. R. Williamson, ACS Division of Polymer Chemistry, Polymer Preprints $\underline{5}$, no. 1, 185 (1964).
18. H. H. Levine, C. G. Delano, and K. J. Kjoller, ACS Division of Polymer Chemistry, Polymer Preprints $\underline{5}$, no. 1, 160 (1964).
19. P. Hergenrother, W. Wrasidlo, and H. H. Levine, ACS Division of Polymer Chemistry, Polymer Preprints $\underline{5}$, no. 1, 153 (1964).
20. C. E. Sroog, S. V. Abramo, C. E. Berr, W. M. Edwards, A. L. Endry, and K. L. Oliver, ACS Division of Polymer Chemistry, Polymer Preprints $\underline{5}$, no. 1, 132 (1964).
21. H. Hopff and M. Lippay, Makromol. Chem. $\underline{66}$, 157 (1963).
22. R. J. Kern, J. J. Hawkins, and J. D. Calfee, Makromol. Chem. $\underline{66}$, 127 (1963).
23. D. J. Lyman and N. Sadri, Makromol. Chem. $\underline{67}$, 1 (1963).
24. G. F. Pregaglia, M. Binaghi, and M. Cambini, Makromol. Chem. $\underline{67}$, 10 (1963).
25. W. Burchard, Makromol. Chem. $\underline{67}$, 182 (1963).
26. I. Penczek and S. Penzcek, Makromol. Chem. $\underline{67}$, 203 (1963).
27. K. Weissermel and E. Nölken, Makromol. Chem. $\underline{68}$, 140 (1963).
28. H. Hopff and J. Dohany, Makromol. Chemie $\underline{69}$, 131 (1963).
29. G. Natta, P. Longi, and E. Pellino, Makromol. Chem. $\underline{71}$, 212 (1964).
30. A. Takahashi and S. Kambara, Makromol. Chem. $\underline{72}$, 92 (1964).
31. R. C. Schulz and R. Stenner, Makromol. Chem. $\underline{72}$, 202 (1964).
32. J. Heller, D. J. Lyman, and W. A. Hewett, Makromol. Chemie $\underline{73}$, 48 (1964).
33. G. F. Santee, R. H. Marchessault, H. G. Clark, J. J. Kearny, and V. Stannett, Makromol. Chem. $\underline{73}$, 177 (1964).
34. C. Aso and Y. Aito, Makromol. Chem. $\underline{73}$, 141 (1964).
35. S. Kambara and H. Noguchi, Makromol. Chem. $\underline{73}$, 244 (1964).
36. W. Funke and E. C. Schütze, Makromol. Chem. $\underline{74}$, 71 (1964).
37. K. Meyersen, R. C. Schulz, and W. Kern, Makromol. Chem. $\underline{58}$, 204 (1962).
38. Y. Tabata, B. Saito, H. Sobue, and K. Oshima, Makromol. Chem. $\underline{76}$, 89 (1964).
39. H. Ohse, H. Cherdron, and F. Korte, Makromol. Chem. $\underline{76}$, 147 (1964).
40. Y. Iwakura, K. Uno, and Y. Imai, Makromol. Chem. $\underline{77}$, 33 (1964).
41. Y. Iwakura, K. Uno, Y. Imai, and M. Fukui, Makromol. Chem. $\underline{77}$, 41 (1964).
42. H. O. Wirth, R. Müller, and W. Kern, Makromol. Chem. $\underline{77}$, 91 (1964).
43. T. Iwata, G. Wasai, T. Saegusa, and J. Furukawa, Makromol. Chem. $\underline{77}$, 229 (1964).
44. R. F. Lang, Makromol. Chem. $\underline{78}$, 1 (1964).
45. J. Heller and C. B. Kingsley, Makromol. Chem. $\underline{78}$, 47 (1964).
46. A. Oku, M. Okano, and R. Oda, Makromol. Chem. $\underline{78}$, 186 (1964).
47. J. Pellon, L. H. Schwind, M. J. Guinard, and W. M. Thomas, J. Polymer Sci. $\underline{55}$, 161 (1961).
48. A. T. Coscia, R. L. Kugel, and J. Pellon, J. Polymer Sci. $\underline{55}$, 303 (1961).

49. C. A. Aufdermarsch, Jr. and R. Pariser, J. Polymer Sci. A2, 4727 (1964).
50. G. F. L. Ehlers, J. Polymer Sci. A2, 4989 (1964).
51. W. Marcony, A. Mazzei, S. Cucinella, and M. Cesari, J. Polymer Sci. A2, 4261 (1964).
52. J. M. Wilbur, Jr. and C. S. Marvel, J. Polymer Sci. A2, 4415 (1964).
53. A. D. Ketley and R. J. Ehrig, J. Polymer Sci. A2, 4461 (1964).
54. M. L. Miller and J. Skogman, J. Polymer Sci. A2, 4551 (1964).
55. G. C. Robinson, J. Polymer Sci. A2, 3901 (1964).
56. H. R. Allcock, J. Polymer Sci. A2, 4087 (1964).
57. J. Pellon, R. L. Kugel, and R. Marcus, J. Polymer Sci. A2, 4105 (1964).
58. Y. Iwakura, K. Uno, and K. Ichikawa, J. Polymer Sci. A2, 3387 (1964).
59. A. G. Pittman, and R. E. Lundin, J. Polymer Sci. A2, 3803 (1964).
60. J. Green, N. Mayes, and M. S. Cohen, J. Polymer Sci. A2, 3113 (1964).
61. R. H. Michel, J. Polymer Sci. A2, 2533 (1964).
62. J. F. Klebe, J. Polymer Sci. A2, 2673 (1964).
63. I. M. Paushkin and S. A. Nizova, J. Polymer Sci. A2, 2783 (1964).
64. P. Teyssie and A. C. Korn-Girard, J. Polymer Sci. A2, 2849 (1964).
65. J.C.L. Hwa, W. A. Fleming, and L. Miller, J. Polymer Sci. A2, 2383.
66. R. E. Moser, H. Kamogawa, H. Hartmann, and H. G. Cassidy, J. Polymer Sci. A2, 2401 (1964).
67. H. Kamogawa and H. G. Cassidy, J. Polymer Sci. A2, 2409 (1964).
68. H. S. Makowski, B. K. C. Shim, and Z. W. Wilchinsky, J. Polymer Sci. A2, 1549 (1964).
69. G. P. Brown and S. Aftergut, J. Polymer Sci. A2, 1839 (1964).
70. J. Prager, R. M. McCurdy and G. B. Rathmann, J. Polymer Sci. A2, 1941 (1964).
71. D. W. Thomson, and G. F. L. Ehlers, J. Polymer Sci. A2, 1051 (1964).
72. A. H. Frazer and F. T. Wallenberger, J. Polymer Sci. A2, 1137 (1964).
73. H. A. Frazer and F. T. Wallenberger, J. Polymer Sci. A2, 1147 (1964).
74. A. H. Frazer, W. Sweeny, and F. T. Wallenberger, J. Polymer Sci. A2, 1157 (1964).
75. A. H. Frazer and F. T. Wallenberger, J. Polymer Sci. A2, 1181 (1964).
76. R. Rabinowitz, R. Marcus, and J. Pellon, J. Polymer Sci. A2, 1233 (1964).
77. R. Rabinowitz, R. Marcus, and J. Pellon, J. Polymer Sci. A2, 1241 (1964).
78. M. Imoto, T. Otsu, and K. Tsuda, J. Polymer Sci. A2, 1407 (1964).
79. W. DeWinter, C. S. Marvel, and A. Abdul-Karim, J. Polymer Sci. A1, 3261 (1963).
80. R. Bacskai, J. Polymer Sci. A1, 2777 (1963).
81. R. Reichel and C. S. Marvel, J. Polymer Sci. A1, 2935 (1963).
82. D. A. Frey, M. Hasegawa, and C. S. Marvel, J. Polymer Sci. A1, 2057 (1963).
83. J. L. Lang, W. A. Pavelich, and H. D. Clarey, J. Polymer Sci. A1, 1123 (1963).
84. J. Pellon and W. G. Carpenter, J. Polymer Sci. A1, 863 (1963).
85. A. V. Topchiev and V. P. Alaniya, J. Polymer Sci. A1, 599 (1963).
86. W. P. Baker, J. Polymer Sci. A1, 655 (1963).
87. J. F. Klebe, J. Polymer Sci. B2, 1079 (1964).
88. D. F. Hoeg, D. I. Lusk, and E. P. Goldberg, J. Polymer Sci. B2, 697 (1964).
89. C. G. Overberger, S. Ozaki, and H. Makimal, J. Polymer Sci. B2, 627 (1964).
90. T. Kubota and R. Nakanishi, J. Polymer Sci. B2, 655 (1964).
91. W. Marconi, S. Cesca, and G. Della Fortuna, J. Polymer Sci. B2, 301 (1964).
92. M. Hasegawa and T. Unishi, J. Polymer Sci. B2, 237 (1964).
93. H. Mains and J. H. Day, J. Polymer Sci. B1, 347 (1963).
94. L. D. Taylor and H. S. Kolesinski, J. Polymer Sci. B1, 117 (1963).
95. R. C. Schulz, J. Kovacs, and W. Kern, Makromol. Chem. 52, 236 (1962).
96. R. Hank, Makromol. Chem. 52, 108 (1962).
97. R. C. Schulz and W. Passmann, Makromol. Chem. 60, 139 (1963).
98. H. S. Makowski, D. C. K. Shim, and Z. Wilchinski, J. Polymer Sci. A2, 1549 (1964).
99. Y. L. Gefter, International Series of Monographs on Organic Chemistry, Vol. 6, "Organophosphorus Monomers and Polymers," Pergamon Press, MacMillan Company, New York (1962).
100. B. Jirgensons, "Natural Organic Polymers," Pergamon Press, New York 1962.
101. G. P. Brown and A. Goldman, ACS Division of Polymer Chemistry, Polymer Preprints 4, no. 2, 39 (1963).
102. D. T. Longone and H. H. Un, ACS Division of Polymer Chemistry, Polymer Preprints 4, no. 2, 49 (1963).
103. S.-P. S. Yen, ACS Division of Polymer Chemistry, Polymer Preprints 4, no. 2, 82 (1963).
104. J. Moacanin, A. Rembaum, and R. K. Laudenslager, ACS Division of Polymer Chemistry, Polymer Preprints 4, no. 2, 179 (1964).
105. Y. Okamoto, W. Brenner, and D. A. Alia, ACS Division of Polymer Chemistry, Polymer Prints 4, no. 2, 575 (1964).
106. G. B. Butler, Proceedings of Conference on High Temperature Polymer and Fluid Research, p. 53, Dayton, Ohio, 1962.
107. H. A. Smith and C. E. Handlovits, Proceedings of Conference on High Temperature Polymer and Fluid Research, p. 123, Dayton, Ohio 1962.

108. J. Lal, J. Polymer Sci. 31, 181 (1958).
109. J. R. Schaefgen, J. Polymer Sci. 41, 133 (1959).
110. E. J. Vandenberg, R. F. Heck, and D. S. Breslow, J. Polymer Sci. 41, 520
      (1959).
111. R. F. Heck, and D. S. Breslow, J. Polymer Sci. 41, 522 (1959).
112. E. C. Winslow and A. Laferriere, J. Polymer Sci. 60, 74 (1962).
113. H. T. Hall, J. Amer. Chem. Soc. 74, 68 (1952).
114. C. Aso and Y. Aito, Makromol. Chem. 58, 195 (1962).
115. J. Furukawa, T. Saegusa, H. Fujii, A. Kawasaki, H. Imai, and Y. Fujii, Makromol.
      Chem. 37, 149 (1960).
116. G. Natta, G. Mazzanti, G. Dall'Asta, and P. Longi, Makromol. Chem. 37, 160
      (1960).
117. J. Furukawa, T. Saegusa, and H. Fujii, Makromol. Chem. 44/46, 398 (1961).
118. D. D. Coffman, E. H. Valk, A. B. Ness, J. Org. Chem. 13, 223 (1948).
119. W. W. Meyer, Jr. and D. A. Grev, J. Polymer Sci. B1, 29 (1963).
120. G. E. Ham, Ind. Eng. Chem. 46, 390 (1954).
121. H. C. Evans, and D. W. Young, Ind. Eng. Chem. 34, 461 (1942).
122. D. E. Strain, R. G. Kennelly, and H. R. Dittmar, Ind. Eng. Chem. 31, 382 (1939).
123. C. E. Schildknecht, S. T. Gross, H. R. Davidson, J. M. Lambert, and A. O. Zoss,
      Ind. Eng. Chem. 40, 2104 (1948).
124. DBP 926,163; 928,793; 929,931; 929,932 (1955), Farbwerke. Hoechst; O. Fuchs
      et al. Chem. Z. 1956, 1169; 1958, 3756.
125. Brit. P. 857,649 (1961), E. I. du Pont de Nemours and Company, C.A. 55, 11918
      (1961).
126. Brit. P. 849,038 (1960), Dow Chemical Company, C.A. 55, 12432 (1961).
127. C. G. Overberger, S. Ishida, and H. Ringsdorf, J. Polymer Sci. 62, S1 (1962).
129. W. A. Butte, C. C. Price, and R. L. Hughes, J. Polymer Sci. 61, S28 (1962).
130. G. F. Endres, A. S. Hay, and J. W. Eustance, J. Org. Chem. 28, 1300 (1963).
131. G. Dall'Asta, G. Natta, and G. Mazzanti, Chem. Engng. News 42, no. 14, 42
      (1964).
132. USP 3,036,990; 3,036,991 (1962), S. W. Kantor and F. F. Holub, General Electric
      Company.
133. D. Plazek, Mellon Institute, Pittsburgh, Pa., U.S.A., Private communication.
134. J. Brandrup, Chemstrand Research Center, Durham, N. C., U.S.A.; Private
      communication.
135. N. G. Gaylord, "Polyethers," Interscience, New York, 1963, Part I, p. 46.

FRACTIONATION OF POLYMERS

G. M. Guzmán

Departamento de Plásticos
del Patronato "Juan de la Cierva" (C.S.I.C.)
Madrid, Spain

Contents

A. PRINCIPLES OF POLYMER FRACTIONATION

As a general rule, the composition of a polymeric substance is not homogeneous. The differences between the macromolecules of such a substance may be classified according to three main properties: a) molecular weight, b) chemical composition and c) molecular configuration and structure. The fractionation of a polymeric substance means the separation of that substance into its different molecular species, using a suitable experimental technique, in order to obtain homogeneous fractions.

The molecular weight dispersity is a general feature for practically all synthetic polymers, as a consequence of the particular nature of the polymerization process by which they are made. Natural polymers usually present molecular weight dispersity as a consequence of the degradation processes suffered by the substance during isolation from the living tissues. Additional reasons, such as more or less accidental degradation during processing, improper handling, or routine use, may contribute substantially to an increase in the natural molecular weight dispersity already present in the sample.

The existence of molecular weight heterogeneity in macromolecular substances is therefore quite general. It is one of their fundamental properties and is directly responsible for the necessity of using several molecular weight averages for their description. It also exerts a permanent influence on all the properties of the substance, both in solution and in the solid state.

Conditions for chemical composition dispersity in polymers originate from those reactions which offer several possibilities of substitution along the backbone of the macromolecule, for instance, the synthesis of random, block and graft copolymers, and the many partial chemical transformations to which the substance can be subjected.

The third kind of heterogeneity mentioned above refers to differences in the physical configuration of the macromolecules, such as those arising between linear and branched polymers, and also to differences in the tacticity of the several molecular species present in the mixture, which usually is reflected in varying amounts of amorphous and crystalline portions in the substance.

Most of the experimental techniques developed so far to fractionate polymers refer to fractionation according to molecular weight. Chemical composition and physical structure dispersities are handled by more or less sophisticated modifications of the solubility methods, such as varying the nature of the solvent/nonsolvent mixture or the temperature of extraction.

Those experimental techniques referred to in this table are usually based on the variation of some property directly related to the molecular size. It is common to classify the fractionation methods according to their preparative or analytical character. The latter methods do not isolate fractions; they are mainly intended to explore the molecular weight distribution of the polymer.

The classification of fractionation methods, together with the basic idea of each experimental technique is briefly described below.

Reviews of polymer fractionation have been published by Cragg and Hammerschlag (1), Desreux and Oth (2), Schulz (3), Conrad (4), Hall (5), Channen (6), Guzmán (7), Fuchs (8), Käsbauer and Schuch (9) and Screaton (10).

B. FRACTIONATION METHODS

I. Fractionation by Solubility

(1) Fractional Precipitation

   Addition of nonsolvent. Successive precipitation of polymer species from a solution by addition of a miscible nonsolvent. The larger molecules precipitate first.

   Lowering the temperature. Successive precipitation of polymer species from a solution by controlled cooling. The larger molecules precipitate first.

   Solvent volatilization. Successive precipitation of polymer species from a solution of the polymer in a solvent/nonsolvent mixture by controlled evaporation of the more volatile solvent. The larger molecules precipitate first.

(2) Turbidimetric Titration

   Continuous precipitation of polymer species from a very dilute solution by progressive addition of nonsolvent. In the absence of coagulation the amount of polymer precipitated can be measured by the increase in optical density of the solution. The larger molecules precipitate first. This is an analytical method. The method can also be reversed i.e. the polymer is precipitated first completely and then redissolved by progressive addition of solvent.

(3) Summative Precipitation

   Simultaneous precipitation of polymer species from several solutions of the same sample by addition of increasing amounts of nonsolvent to the solutions. The sum of all the precipitates constitutes a cumulative weight distribution. This is an analytical method.

(4) Cumulative Volume of Precipitate

   Successive precipitation of polymer species from a solution by addition of increasing amounts of nonsolvent. Fractions are not isolated and the cumulative volume of precipitate is observed and determined after each nonsolvent increment. This is an analytical method.

(5) Fractional Solution

   Direct extraction. Direct and successive extraction of polymer with a liquid of increasing solvent power; smaller molecules are extracted first.

References page IV-272

Film extraction. A metal foil is coated thinly with polymer; the foil is cut into strips and extracted successively with solvent/nonsolvent mixtures of increasing solvent power. Smaller molecules are extracted first.

Column extraction. The polymer is distributed on an inert support packed in a column. Successive elution then takes place with a liquid of improving solvent power.

Extraction of a coacervate. Successive extraction of polymer species from a coacervate. Smaller molecules are extracted first.

(6) Distribution Between Immiscible Solvents

Polymer species are distributed according to molecular size between two immiscible liquids of different solvent power. Countercurrent extraction is particularly suitable for this method.

II. Fractionation by Chromatography

(1) Adsorption Chromatography (Chromatography on an active support)

The adsorption of polymer species on an active support depends on the molecular weight.

Frontal analysis. The active support is packed in a column; a solution of polymer passes down the column and is collected when leaving it. The concentration in the effluent changes with the volume collected, and presents successive fronts due to the different adsorbing power of molecular species.

Elution analysis. A small quantity of polymer is sorbed on the upper portion of the support packed in the column. Then elution with a suitable solvent takes place; each component moves down the column with different rate and is completely displaced at some time and collected in the effluent; in the gradient elution method the eluent is a liquid of increasing solvent power.

(2) "Precipitation" Chromatography (Baker-Williams-Method) (Chromatography on an
                                                          inactive support)

The support is an inert material packed in a column. On top of the column a small amount of polymer is placed, as in elution chromatography. A temperature gradient is set along the column, the upper part being at higher temperature than the bottom; then elution takes place with a solvent mixture of increasing solvent power. Polymer species move down the column being in a continuous exchange between a precipitated phase and a saturated solution. This distribution depends on the molecular size.

Precipitation chromatography can also be carried out in the absence of a temperature gradient. It then becomes essentially a continuous fractionation by fractional solution. (See above under Fractional Solution-Column Extraction)

(3) Gel Permeation Chromatography (Chromatography on a porous support)

Gel permeation chromatography is a new separation process based on differences in the depth to which molecules of different chain length are able to diffuse into the pores of an expanded and highly crosslinked polymer gel network. As a result of the restrictions imposed by the pore sizes on the larger molecules there is a greater pore volume available to the low molecular species giving them in effect a longer path length and they, therefore, are more strongly retarded during elution. Since polymer solubility and adsorption are not a part of the process the volume required for elution essentially depends only on the chain length and appears to be insensitive to structure.

(4) Partition Chromatography

Polymer species are distributed between two liquid phases, one of them mobile and the other fixed by absorption in a support. The immobile phase is packed in a column. The support consists of strips or sheets of porous paper.

(5) Ion-exchange Chromatography

The support is an ion-exchange resin, constituting an immobile phase, through which the solution of polymer is passed. This method is appropriate for polymer species bearing electric charges; the molecules are distributed between the liquid phase and the interface, according to their ionic adsorption forces, which depend on the electric charge and the size of the macromolecules.

III. Fractionation by Sedimentation

(1) Sedimentation Velocity

Sedimentation velocity of polymer species in a high centrifugal field is a function of molecular size. This is usually an analytical method unless a velocity ultracentrifuge of the preparative type is used.

(2) Sedimentation Equilibrium

At lower rotational speeds of the ultracentrifuge it becomes possible to create an equilibrium situation such that the rate of sedimentation is exactly equal to the rate of backdiffusion of the macromolecules. Larger polymer molecules are then found closer to the bottom of the cell than smaller ones.

(3) Density Gradient Technique

In a preformed or selfgenerated density gradient the polymer collects around the position of its own density in a band. The width of this band is dependent on the molecular weight of the polymer. A band of polydisperse macromolecules contains more high molecular weight polymer near its maximum than near its "tails". This technique is also capable of separating according to composition.

IV. Fractionation by Diffusion

(1) Thermal Diffusion

A polymer solution is placed between two surfaces, and a high temperature gradient is established between them. The solution is in contact with an upper and a lower reservoir. The temperature gradient gives rise to a thermal circulation of the molecules, producing a separation of polymer species, which migrate towards the lower reservoir. Thermal diffusion is more pronounced for the larger molecules than for the smaller.

(2) Brownian Diffusion

Polymer molecules diffuse at different rates from a solution into a solvent separated by a boundary, depending on their molecular weights. The translational diffusion constants can be determined by special optical means and related to the polydispersity of the sample. This is an analytical method.

V. Fractionation by Ultrafiltration Through Porous Membranes

A polymer solution is submitted to ultrafiltration through a series of membranes of different porosity. Rate of diffusion depends on the molecular size and the degree of permeability of the membranes. It is possible to isolate fractions with varying molecular weights at different times.

VI. Fractionation by Zone Melting

A solid solvent is packed in a column. A small amount of polymer is put on top of the solid solvent and dissolved by heating a narrow zone. After solidification, a lower zone is heated, melted, and resolidified. All the column is treated in this way. Polymer species move down the column at different rates depending on their molecular size during the molten stage. At the end, the polymer is distributed throughout the entire column and recovered by cutting the solid into several portions and subliming the solvent.

References page IV-272

Polymer	Method of Fractionation	Solvent or Solvent/ Nonsolvent Mixture	Remarks	Ref.

1 - OLEFIN POLYMERS

Poly(1-butene)

	Fractional precipitation	Cyclohexanone/cyclohexanol: glycol (3:1)	115°C	11

Polyethylene

	Fractional precipitation	Liquid ethylene at 130 atm. and 80°C	Releasing pressure	12
		Toluene/n-propanol	lowering temp.	13,14
		85% 2-Ethylhexanol/15% decalin	lowering temp.	15,16
		Xylene/n-propanol	90°C	17
		Xylene/triethylene glycol	130°C	18-20
		Xylene/poly(ethylene glycol)	Marlex 50, linear	21
		Xylene, toluene, benzene/ poly(ethylene glycol)	75°C	14
		Toluene/poly(ethylene glycol)	80°C	22
		85% 2-Ethylhexanol/15% decalin	Solvent volatilized	23
		Xylene/poly(ethylene glycol)	80°C	24
		Amyl acetate	133°C lowering temp. Alathon-14	25
	Fractional solution	Toluene	Column extraction	14,26
		Xylene	Column extraction	27
		Xylene/triethylene glycol	130°C	18
		Xylene/n-butanol	120°C film extraction	28
		Xylene/2-ethoxyethanol	127°C Column extraction	16,29, 30
	Coacervation	Xylene/poly(ethylene glycol)	125°C N₂ atm.	31
		Xylene/poly(ethylene glycol)	-	32
	Chromatography	Tetralin/2-butoxyethanol	"Precipitation" chrom. 160-110°C	33
	Sedimentation velocity	α-Bromonaphthalene at 110°C	Ultracentrifuge	34

Polymer	Method of Fractionation	Solvent or Solvent/ Nonsolvent Mixture	Remarks	Ref.
Polyisobutylene				
	Fractional precipitation	Liquid ethylene at 130 atm. and 80°C	Releasing pressure	12
		Benzene/acetone	Vistanex	37-39
		2,4,4-Trimethylpentene/ n-butanol	-	40
	Chromatography	2-Methylheptane	Charcoal and colloidal silica	40
		Toluene/methanol	Charcoal	41
		Benzene/acetone	"Precipitation" chrom. 50-28°C large scale, 80 ml/hr.	42
Poly(α-olefines) (General)				
	Chromatography	Benzene/ethanol	"Precipitation" Chrom.	43,44
Polypropylene				
	Fractional precipitation	Acetone/benzene	-	45
		Benzene/methanol	30°C Atactic	46
		Cyclohexane/acetone	-	46
		Cyclohexanone/ethylene glycol or dimethyl phthalate	130-135°C isotactic	46
		Xylene/poly(ethylene glycol)	112°C	47
	Fractional solution	Tetralin/2-ethoxyethanol	170°C column extraction	48
		Tetralin/diethylene glycol monoethyl ether with 25% ethylene glycol	180°C column extraction. Isotactic	49
		Tetralin/dimethyl phthalate	155°C-178°C column extraction	50
		o-Dichlorobenzene/diethylene glycol monomethyl ether	168°C-170°C column extraction	50,47
		Xylene/methanol	56°C atactic	51
		Kerosene/ethylene glycol (10%) in 2-butoxyethanol	156°C column extraction. Isotactic	51
		Xylene/poly(ethylene glycol)	134°C extraction of coacervate	47
		o-Dichlorobenzene/diethylene glycol monomethyl ether	172°C column extraction. Glass beads	52
		Kerosene/diethylene glycol monobutyl ether	150°C column extraction	53,54

Polymer	Method of Fractionation	Solvent or Solvent/ Nonsolvent Mixture	Remarks	Ref.
Polypropylene		Tetralin/diethylene glycol monoethyl ether	176°C column extraction. Isotactic	55
		Ethyl ether/acetone	Room temp. Column extraction. Atactic	55
	Extraction	Ethyl ether, heptane	Amorphous-crystalline	56
		Acetone, ether, n-hexane, n-heptane	Boiling. Amorphous-crystalline	57
		Ethyl ether, n-heptane, methylcyclohexane	Boiling. Amorphous-crystalline	58
		Ethyl ether, n-heptane	Boiling. Amorphous-crystalline	59
	Coacervation	Tetralin/poly(ethylene glycol) (Carbowax 200)	140°C	60
	Chromatography	–	Silica gel	61
			Polypropylene of high M.W. and high crystallinity	62
Poly(vinylcyclohexane) Extraction		Benzene	–	63
Poly(vinylcyclopentane) Extraction		Ethyl ether	–	63
Poly(vinylcyclopropane) Extraction		Benzene	–	63

Polymer	Method of Fractionation	Solvent or Solvent/ Nonsolvent Mixture	Remarks	Ref.
		2 - VINYL POLYMERS AND SUBSTITUTED OLEFIN POLYMERS		
Poly(allylbenzene)				
	Extraction	Butanone, toluene	Hot	64
		Acetone, ether, benzene	-	65
Poly(chlorotrifluoroethylene)				
	Fractional precipitation	Dichlorobenzotrifluoride/ diethyl phthalate (3:1)	Solvent volatilization, 150°C, Kel-F	66,67
Poly(α-chlorovinyl acetic acid)				
	Fractional precipitation	Methanol/water	-	68
Polystyrene				
	Fractional precipitation	Butanone/methanol	Lowering temp.	69
		Butanone/butanol + 2% water	Solvent volatilization at 50°C	70-72
		Butanone/methanol	Anionic polymer	73
		Butanone/methanol; acetone/ water: methanol (1:1)	-	37
		Butanone/methanol	Large scale, 38°C	74
		Butanone/methanol	-	75,84, 85
		Liquid ethylene at 130 atm. and 80°C	Releasing pressure	12
		Toluene/petroleum ether	-	76
		Toluene/poly(ethylene glycol)	Isotactic	77,78
		Ethyl acetate/ethanol	-	79
		Benzene/methanol	Cumulative volume of precipitate	80
		Benzene/methanol	-	38
		Benzene/methanol	Isotactic	81
		Chloroform/methanol	-	82
		Toluene/methanol	-	83,84
		Butanone/ethanol	-	86
	Fractional solution	Carbon disulfide/petroleum ether	Film extraction	28
		Benzene/ethanol	Column extrac-	87
	Extraction	Butanone, cyclohexanone, tetrahydrofuran, dioxane, ethyl acetate	Hot	88

References page IV-272

Polymer	Method of Fractionation	Solvent or Solvent/ Nonsolvent Mixture	Remarks	Ref.
Polystyrene				
	Extraction	Butanone, ether, tetrahydro-furan, ethyl acetate, benzene, toluene	Cold	88
	Coacervation	Benzene/methanol; Toluene/butanol; Chloroform/butanol; Butanone/butanol	-	89
	Turbidimetric titration	Benzene/methanol	-	90,91
		Butanone/acetone + 1% water	-	92
		Benzene/isopropanol	-	93
		Butanone/isopropanol	-	94
		Butanone/water:methanol (3:1)	-	91
		Toluene/methanol	-	95
	Chromatography	Butanone/ethanol	"Precipitation" chrom.	96-98, 99,100, 101
			Charcoal	102
		Toluene	"Gel permeation" Polystyrene crosslinked gels	103, 104
			"Gel permeation". Poly(methyl methacrylate) crosslinked beads	105
		Benzene/ethanol	"Precipitation" chrom.	106
	Sedimentation velocity	-	Ultracentrifuge	107
		Cyclohexane	35°C, Ultra-centrifuge	108
		Ethyl acetate, butanone	Ultracentrifuge	109
	Sedimentation equilibrium	Cyclohexane and methyl-cyclohexane	35° and 75°C Lowering the temp.	110
	Membrane diffusion	Toluene	Maranyl	111
	Thermal diffusion	Toluene	-	112
		Toluene, butanone	Column	113

Polymer	Method of Fractionation	Solvent or Solvent/ Nonsolvent Mixture	Remarks	Ref.
Polystyrene				
	Zone melting	Naphthalene	-	114
		Benzene	-	115,116
		Cyclohexane	-	117
Poly(α-methylstyrene)				
	Coacervation	Toluene/methanol	-	118
	Chromatography	-	"Precipitation" chromatography	119
Poly(ammonium-p-styrene sulfonate)				
	Ion exchange	-	Duolite	121
Poly(sodium-p-styrene sulfonate)				
	Fractional precipitation	4 N aqueous sodium iodide/ 9 N aqueous sodium iodide	-	120
Poly(vinyl acetate)				
	Fractional precipitation	Acetone/methanol:water (1:1 followed by 1:2)	-	122
		Acetone/n-hexane	-	123
		Acetone/water	-	124,125, 126
		Dioxane/isopropanol; benzene/isopropanol	-	127
		Methyl acetate/petroleum ether	-	126
		Methanol/water	Branched,35°C	128
	Fractional solution	Methyl and ethyl acetate/ petroleum ether	Film extraction	28,129, 130
	Turbidimetric titration	Acetone/water	-	91,131
	Distribution between two immiscible liquids	Benzene:methanol:water	Countercurrent	132
	Chromatography	-	Activated carbon + Supercel	133
		Benzene/isopropanol	"Precipitation" chrom. Large scale, 80 ml/hr, 60-28°C	134

References page IV-272

Polymer	Method of Fractionation	Solvent or Solvent/ Nonsolvent Mixture	Remarks	Ref.
Poly(vinyl acetate)				
	Thermal diffusion	Toluene	-	112
	Selective adsorption	Acetone	Carbon	135
Poly(vinyl alcohol)				
	Fractional precipitation	Water/acetone	-	136
		Water/n-propanol	-	137
		Water/acetone:n-propanol	-	138
	Fractional solution	Water/methyl acetate: methanol (3:1)	Film extraction	139
		Water/n-propanol	65°C	140
	Thermal diffusion	-	-	141
	Brownian diffusion	-	-	142
	Foam method	-	Amorphous- crystalline	143
Poly(vinyl chloride)				
	Fractional precipitation	Liquid ethylene at 130 atm and 80°C	Releasing pressure	12
		Cyclohexanone/n-butanol	-	144
		Cyclohexanone/methanol	Countercurrent	145
		Chlorobenzene + cyclohexane + acetone/methanol	-	146
		Tetrahydrofuran/water	50°C	147
		Tetrahydrofuran/water	-	148,149, 150
	Fractional solution	Tetrahydrofuran/water	44°C	151
		Cyclohexanone/methanol	Film extraction	152
	Turbidimetric titration	Cyclohexanone/heptane:carbon tetrachloride (9:1)	-	153
	Chromatography	Cyclohexanone/methanol	"Precipitation" chrom. 60-25°C	154

Polymer	Method of Fractionation	Solvent or Solvent/ Nonsolvent Mixture	Remarks	Ref.
Poly(vinyl chloride)				
	Thermal diffusion	Cyclohexanone	-	155
Poly(vinyl isobutyl ether)				
	Fractional precipitation	Toluene:butanone (1:1)/ ethanol	Lowering temp. Oppanol C	156
Poly(vinyl methyl ether)				
	Fractional precipitation	Methanol	65°C, then cooling to 25°C and 3°C	157
		Benzene/hexane, heptane or decane	-	158
		Water	Raising temp.	158
Poly(vinylpyridine)				
	Fractional precipitation	Nitromethane/benzene	4-vinyl	159
		tert-Butanol/benzene	4-vinyl	159
		Benzene/hexane	2-vinyl	160
	Fractional solution	tert-Butanol/benzene	Column extraction	161
Poly(vinylpyrrolidone)				
	Fractional precipitation	Water/acetone	-	162-165
		Chloroform/ether; ethanol/ benzene	-	163
		Ethanol/petroleum ether	-	164
	Turbidimetric titration	Water/sodium sulfate solutions	-	92,165, 166
	Sedimentation velocity	-	Ultracentrifuge	167
	Thermal diffusion	Water and ethanol	-	112,141

References page IV-272

Polymer	Method of Fractionation	Solvent or Solvent/ Nonsolvent Mixture	Remarks	Ref.

3 - ACRYLIC AND METHACRYLIC POLYMERS

Polymer	Method of Fractionation	Solvent or Solvent/ Nonsolvent Mixture	Remarks	Ref.
Poly(acrylic acid)	Thermal diffusion	-	-	141
Polyacrylamide	Fractional precipitation	Water/methanol	-	168,169
Poly(1,1-dihydroperfluorobutyl acrylate)	Fractional precipitation	Benzotrifluoride/methanol	-	189
Poly(methyl acrylate)	Fractional precipitation	Liquid ethylene at 130 atm and 80 °C	Releasing pressure	12
		Acetone/water:methanol(7:3)	-	196
Polyacrylonitrile	Fractional precipitation	Dimethylformamide/heptane: ether (1:1)	-	170,181
		Dimethylformamide/ligroin	50-60 °C	171
		Dimethylformamide/heptane	Followed by 2% CaCl$_2$ solutions	146
		Dimethylformamide/heptane	60 °C	172-177
		Hydroxyacetonitrile + ethanol/ benzene or toluene	-	178
		Dimethylformamide/decalin	110° to 90 °C	179
		Dimethylformamide/ethanol	pH 6.0, ageing period	180
		Dimethyl sulfoxide/toluene	-	182-185
		60% Nitric acid/butanol	5 °C	175,176
	Fractional solution	Dimethylformamide/butyl acetate	Film extraction 90 °C	28
		Dimethylformamide/heptane	Extraction	187
	Thermal diffusion	Dimethylformamide	-	188
Poly(methacrylic acid)	Fractional precipitation	Methanol/ether	-	190
		Methanol/methyl isobutyl ketone	Solvent volatilized	191

Polymer	Method of Fractionation	Solvent or Solvent/ Nonsolvent Mixture	Remarks	Ref.
Poly(N-phenylmethacrylamide)	Fractional precipitation	Acetone/benzene	-	215
Poly(n-butylmethacrylate)	Fractional precipitation	Acetone/methanol	Lowering temp.	192
Poly(cyclohexyl methacrylate)	Fractional precipitation	Dioxane/methanol	Lowering temp.	193
Poly(ethyl methacrylate)	Fractional precipitation	Acetone/acetone:water (4:1)	Lowering temp.	194
Poly(n-hexyl methacrylate)	Fractional precipitation	Acetone/abs. ethanol	Lowering temp.	195
Poly(methyl methacrylate)	Fractional precipitation	Acetone/aq. acetone	-	197
		Aq. acetone solutions	Lowering temp.	197
		Benzene/cyclohexane	-	198,199
		Chloroform/petroleum ether	-	200
		Acetone/hexane	Summative method	201
		Chloroform/heptane	Lowering temp.	82
		Benzene:chloroform (3:1)/ petroleum ether	-	202
		Benzene/petroleum ether	Syndiotactic	203
		Benzene/n-hexane	Isotactic	203,204
		Benzene/Skellysolve B	-	205
		Butanone:ethanol/cyclohexane	-	206
		Toluene/petroleum ether	Cationic polymers	207
	Fractional solution	Chloroform/petroleum ether	Film extraction	28
		-	Column extraction	208
		Butanone/cyclohexane:ethanol	Column extraction	206
		Toluene/petroleum ether (b.p. 40-60°C)	Column extraction	209

Polymer	Method of Fractionation	Solvent or Solvent/ Nonsolvent Mixture	Remarks	Ref.
Poly(methyl methacrylate)				
	Turbidimetric titration	Acetone/water	-	91,210
		Butanone/water:methanol (3:1)	-	91
	Chromatography	-	Activated carbon + Supercel	133
		Butanone/butanone:70% ethanol	Gradient elution	206
		Acetone/methanol	"Precipitation" chrom. Periodic temp. changes	211
	Sedimentation velocity	-	Ultracentrifuge	198,212, 213
	Thermal diffusion	Benzene	Plate type apparatus	214

Polymer	Method of Fractionation	Solvent or Solvent/ Nonsolvent Mixture	Remarks	Ref.

4 - DIENE POLYMERS

Polymer	Method of Fractionation	Solvent or Solvent/ Nonsolvent Mixture	Remarks	Ref.
Polybutadiene	Fractional precipitation	Toluene/methanol	-	216
		Benzene/acetone:dioxane followed by acetone:methanol	-	217
		Benzene/methanol	-	218
		Benzene or toluene/n-butanol	-	219
		Benzene/acetone	-	220
		Benzene/acetone	Branched polymers	221
	Chromatography	Diisobutylene/isooctane	cis-1,4,stereo-regular. "Precipitation" chrom.	222
		Diisobutylene/n-propanol	-	
		Toluene/isooctane		
		Toluene/n-propanol		
		Benzene/ethanol	"Precipitation" chrom.	223,224
	Sedimentation velocity	Hexane:heptane (1:1)	Ultracentrifuge stereoregular	224
		-	Ultracentrifuge, cis-1,4	225
		-	Ultracentrifuge	226
Polychloroprene	Fractional precipitation	Benzene/methanol	Neoprene	227-229
		Benzene/acetone	-	230
	Thermal diffusion	Benzene	0°C	231
Polyisoprene	Fractional precipitation	Benzene or toluene/n-butanol	-	219
		Benzene/acetone	Hevea	230
		Benzene/methanol and benzene/ isopropanol	Lowering temp.	232
		Chloroform/acetone	Pale crepe	233
		Toluene/methanol	5°C, N_2 atm.	234
		Benzene/methanol	Gutta percha	234
		Benzene/ethanol	Gutta percha, balata, synthetic trans-polyisoprene	220

Polymer	Method of Fractionation	Solvent or Solvent/ Nonsolvent Mixture	Remarks	Ref.
Polyisoprene (Cont'd.)				
	Fractional precipitation	Toluene/boiling methanol	Chlorinated natural rubber	235
		Toluene/methanol	-	236
		Toluene/methanol	Lowering the temp. cis-1,4	237
	Fractional solution	n-Hexane, acetone	Guayule, extraction	238,239
		Acetone	Hevea, extraction	240

5 - COPOLYMERS

Poly(acrylonitrile-co-butadiene)				
	Chromatography	-	Perbunan, charcoal	41
Poly(acrylonitrile-co-methyl acrylate)				
	Fractional precipitation	Dimethylformamide/heptane: ether (1:1)	-	241
		Dimethylformamide/petroleum ether: methylcyclohexane: dioxane (6:4:1)	-	179
Poly(acrylonitrile-co-methyl methacrylate)				
	Fractional precipitation	Dimethylformamide/n-hexane: ether (2:1)	-	242
Poly(acrylonitrile-co-styrene)				
	Fractional precipitation	Chloroform/methanol	-	243
Poly(acrylonitrile-co-vinyl acetate-co-methylvinylpyridine)				
	Fractional precipitation	Dimethylformamide/n-hexane: ether (2:1)	-	242
Poly(acrylonitrile-co-vinyl chloride)				
	Fractional precipitation	Acetone/methanol	-	244
Poly(butadiene-co-propylene)				
	Fractional precipitation	Benzene/butanone, methanol	-	245

Polymer	Method of Fractionation	Solvent or Solvent/ Nonsolvent Mixture	Remarks	Ref.
Poly(butadiene-co-styrene)				
	Fractional precipitation	Toluene/ethanol	SBR	246
		Toluene/methanol	SBR	247,248, 249
		Benzene/methanol	-	250
		Benzene/methanol	SBR/1500	251
		Benzene/acetone	-	230
		Benzene/methanol	Summative method	252
	Chromatography	Toluene/methanol	Charcoal	41
		Benzene/ethanol	"Precipitation" chromatography	224
	Sedimentation velocity	-	Ultracentrifuge	226
	Selective adsorption	-	Carbon black	253
	Membrane diffusion	-	-	254
Poly(butadiene-co-vinyl isopropyl ether)				
	Fractional precipitation	Benzene/methanol	-	255
Poly(cumarone-co-indene)				
	Fractional precipitation	Benzene:ethyl acetate/methanol	-	256
Poly(ethylene-co-propylene)				
	Fractional precipitation	Benzene/butanone	-	35
		Xylene/dimethylformamide	85°C	36
		Butyl ether/butanol	120°C	36
Poly(isoprene-co-styrene)				
	Fractional precipitation	Benzene/methanol	-	257
Poly(maleic anhydride-co-styrene)				
	Fractional precipitation	Acetone/benzene	-	258

References page IV-272

Polymer	Method of Fractionation	Solvent or Solvent/ Nonsolvent Mixture	Remarks	Ref.
Poly(maleic anhydride-co-vinyl ethyl ether)				
	Fractional precipitation	Butanone/cyclohexane	-	258
Poly(methyl methacrylate-co-styrene)				
	Fractional precipitation	Butanone/diisopropyl ether	-	259
	Chromatography	Benzene/methanol	"Precipitation" chromatography 40-15°C	260
		Benzene/petroleum ether		260
Poly(styrene-co-divinylbenzene)				
	Fractional precipitation	Acetone:dioxane (1:1)/ methanol and butanone	-	261
Poly(styrene-co-p-fluorostyrene)				
	Fractional precipitation	Tetrahydrofuran/methanol	-	262
	Extraction	Heptane, butanone, tetrahydro- furan	Boiling	262
Poly(styrene-co-o-methylstyrene				
	Extraction	Toluene/methanol	-	263
Poly(styrene-co-p-tert-butylstyrene)				
	Extraction	Toluene/methanol	-	263
Poly(styrene-co-3-methyl-1-butene)				
	Fractional precipitation	Carbon tetrachloride/methanol	-	264
Poly(styrene-co-4-methyl-1-pentene)				
	Fractional precipitation	Carbon tetrachloride/methanol	-	264
Poly(styrene-co-m-vinyltoluene)				
	Fractional precipitation	Butanone/butanol	Solvent volatilization	265
Poly(tetrafluoroethylene-co-trifluoronitrosomethane)				
	Fractional precipitation	Freon 113/acetone	-	266
Poly(vinyl acetate-co-vinylidene cyanide)				
	Fractional precipitation	Nitromethane/methanol:water (1.1) methanol	50°C	267

Polymer	Method of Fractionation	Solvent or Solvent/ Nonsolvent Mixture	Remarks	Ref.
		6 - BLOCK COPOLYMERS		
Acrylamide: methyl methacrylate				
	Fractional precipitation	Water/methanol followed by water	-	268
Acrylonitrile: methyl cellulose				
	Extraction	Water	Hot	269
Acrylonitrile: methyl methacrylate				
	Extraction; precipitation	Chloroform; dimethylformamide/ methanol	-	270
		Chloroform; benzene/methanol	-	271
Epoxide resin: butadiene styrene rubber				
	Turbidimetric titration	Chloroform/methanol	-	272
Isoprene: styrene				
	Turbidimetric titration	Toluene/methanol	-	273
Methyl methacrylate: ethyl cellulose				
	Fractional precipitation	Acetone/methanol	-	269
Methyl methacrylate: starch				
	Extraction; precipitation	Benzene; aq. dimethylformamide/ methanol	-	269
Methyl methacrylate: styrene				
	Fractional precipitation	Chloroform/methanol	-	268
		Benzene:monochlorobenzene (1:1)/ methanol	-	274
		Benzene/methanol	-	275
		Benzene:acetone (1:1)/ petroleum ether	-	276
	Fractional solution	Benzene/methanol	Column extraction	277
	Extraction	Acetone, tetralin	-	275
		Cyclohexane, acetonitrile	-	276
	Turbidimetric titration	Acetone/water	-	90
		Butanone/water:methanol(3:1)	-	275
		Butanone/isopropanol	-	276

References page IV-272

Polymer	Method of Fractionation	Solvent or Solvent/ Nonsolvent Mixture	Remarks	Ref.
Methyl methacrylate: styrene				
	Chromatography	-	"Precipitation" chromatography	278
		Benzene/methanol	"Precipitation" chromatography	275
Methyl methacrylate: vinyl acetate				
	Turbidimetric titration	Acetone/water	-	90
Styrene: benzyl cellulose				
	Fractional precipitation	Benzene/methanol	-	269
Styrene: butadiene				
	Fractional solution	Benzene	Extraction	279
Styrene: dihydronaphthalene				
	Extraction	Ethyl acetate, methyl isobutyl ketone	-	280
Styrene: ethylene oxide				
	Fractional precipitation	Dimethoxyethane/water and chloroform/water	90°C	274
Styrene: α-methylstyrene				
	Fractional precipitation	Butanone: benzene (6:1)/ methanol + 0.01% $CaCl_2$	-	274
Vinyl acetate: cellulose acetate				
	Extraction; precipitation	Methanol; benzene/methanol	-	269

Polymer	Method of Fractionation	Solvent or Solvent/ Nonsolvent Mixture	Remarks	Ref.
		7 - GRAFT COPOLYMERS		
Acrylamide + cellulose				
	Extraction	Dimethylformamide, water, cuprammonium	Cellophane	281
Acrylamide + cellulose acetate				
	Extraction	Acetone	Hot	281
Acrylamide + ethyl cellulose				
	Extraction	Methanol	Hot	281
Acrylamide + poly(N-eosin vinylamine hydrochloride)				
	Fractional precipitation	Water/acetone	-	268
Acrylamide + poly(vinyl alcohol)				
	Turbidimetric titration	Formic acid/butanone	-	282
		Water/ethanol	-	282
Acrylic acid + poly(N-eosin vinylamine hydrochloride)				
	Fractional precipitation	Water/acetone	-	268
Acrylic acid + poly(β-alanine)				
	Turbidimetric titration	85% formic acid/ethanol	-	283
Acrylic acid + polyethylene				
	Fractional precipitation	Xylene/methanol	130°C	284
Acrylonitrile + cellulose				
	Extraction	Dimethylformamide, water, cuprammonium	Cellophane	281
Acrylonitrile + cellulose acetate				
	Extraction	Dimethylformamide, dimethyl-formamide + dioxane (3.5:2)	Acetylated cotton	285
	Fractional precipitation	Dimethylformamide/chloroform	-	285
Acrylonitrile + poly(N-eosin vinylamine hydrochloride)				
	Fractional precipitation	Water/acetone	-	268
Glycidyl methacrylate + poly(vinyl chloride)				
	Extraction; precipitation	Methyl isobutyl ketone; isopropanol	-	286

References page IV-272

Polymer	Method of Fractionation	Solvent or Solvent/ Nonsolvent Mixture	Remarks	Ref.
Isobutylene + poly(chloromethylstyrene)				
	Fractional precipitation	Benzene:butanone (1:4)/methanol	-	287
Isopropyl styrene + poly(methyl methacrylate)				
	Fractional precipitation	Benzene/isopropanol	-	93
Methyl, ethyl, butyl, acrylates + cellulose acetate				
	Extraction; precipitation	Benzene; acetone/water	-	288
	Turbidimetric titration	Acetone:methanol (6:4)/methanol	-	288
Methyl methacrylate + cellulose acetate				
	Fractional precipitation	95% Pyridine + 5% acetone/water	-	289
Methyl methacrylate + polystyrene				
	Fractional precipitation	Chloroform/methanol	-	290
		Butanone/methanol:water (1:1)	-	291
Methyl methacrylate + poly(p-isopropylstyrene)				
	Fractional precipitation	Benzene/methanol	-	292
Methyl methacrylate + polyisobutylene				
	Extraction	Butanone, cyclohexane	-	293
Methyl methacrylate + poly(vinyl acetate)				
	Fractional precipitation	Acetone/methanol:water (1:2)	-	290
Methyl methacrylate + poly(vinyl alcohol)				
	Fractional precipitation	Benzene/n-butanol	-	294
Methyl methacrylate + poly(vinyl benzoate)				
	Fractional precipitation	Acetone/methanol	-	295
Methyl methacrylate + poly(vinyl chloride)				
	Fractional precipitation	Dioxane/methanol	-	290
Styrene + cellulose acetate				
	Fractional precipitation	Pyridine/aq. HCl	-	289
		Chloroform/n-heptane	Triacetylated viscose	285

Polymer	Method of Fractionation	Solvent or Solvent/ Nonsolvent Mixture	Remarks	Ref.
Styrene + cellulose acetate				
	Extraction	Benzene, acetone, 2-ethoxy ethanol, water	-	289
Styrene + poly(N-eosin vinylamine hydrochloride)				
	Fractional precipitation	Water/acetic acid	-	268
Styrene + polyethylene				
	Fractional precipitation	Toluene/methanol	90°C	296
Styrene + polyisobutylene				
	Fractional precipitation	Cyclohexane/n-propanol	-	297
	Extraction	Hexane, cyclohexane	-	298
		Butanone, cyclohexane	-	293
	Turbidimetric titration	Toluene/methanol	-	299
	Chromatography	Cyclohexane/isopropanol	"Precipitation" chromatography	297
Styrene + poly(ethyl acrylate)				
	Extraction	Cyclohexane, ether, acetonitrile	-	300
Styrene + poly(methyl acrylate)				
	Fractional precipitation	Chloroform/methanol	-	301
Styrene + poly(methyl methacrylate)				
	Fractional precipitation	Chloroform/methanol	-	290,301
		Benzene:chlorobenzene(1:1)/ petroleum ether	-	302
	Extraction	Ether, acetonitrile, benzene	-	303
	Turbidimetirc titration	Benzene:chlorobenzene(1:1)/ petroleum ether	-	304
Styrene + poly(vinyl chloride)				
	Fractional precipitation	Benzene/methanol	-	302
(Styrene:maleic anhydride) + poly(vinyl chloride)				
	Extraction	Butanone; ammoniumhydroxide	-	305

Polymer	Method of Fractionation	Solvent or Solvent/ Nonsolvent Mixture	Remarks	Ref.
Vinyl acetate + poly(ethyl α-chloroacrylate)				
	Fractional precipitation	Acetone/ethanol Butanone/methanol:water (1:1)	-	291
Vinyl acetate + poly(methyl methacrylate)				
	Fractional precipitation	Acetone/methanol	-	290,291
	Fractional solution	Acetone/water	Column extraction	306
	Chromatography	Acetone/acetone:water	"Precipitation" chromatography 45-15°C	307
Vinyl acetate + polystyrene				
	Fractional precipitation	Butanone/methanol	-	290
Vinyl acetate + poly(vinyl benzoate)				
	Fractional precipitation	Acetone/methanol and water	-	295
Vinyl chloride + poly(methyl methacrylate)				
	Fractional precipitation	Dioxane/methanol	-	290

Polymer	Method of Fractionation	Solvent or Solvent/ Nonsolvent Mixture	Remarks	Ref.

8 - POLYOXIDES

Polyacetaldehyde

	Extraction	Methanol, chloroform	Amorphous-crystalline	308

Polyaldehydes (general) (Propion,butyr,isobutyr, isovaler-aldehyde)

	Extraction	Acetone (boiling), diisopropyl ether, benzene	Amorphous-crystalline	309

Poly(2,6-dimethyl-1,4-phenylene oxide)

	Fractional precipitation	Ethylene dichloride/nitromethane	-	310

Poly(epichlorohydrin)

	Extraction; precipitation	Acetone (cold); acetone/ methanol, methanol/water	Amorphous-crystalline	313

Poly(ethylene oxide)

	Turbidimetric titration	Chloroform/n-hexane	-	93
	Distribution between two immiscible liquids	Water/hexane	Countercurrent	311,312
		Water/chloroform:benzene	Countercurrent	312

Poly(propylene oxide)

	Fractional precipitation	Methanol/water	-	314
		Isopropanol/water	74°C	314
		Isooctane	60°C Cooling Amorphous-crystalline	315
	Extraction; precipitation	Acetone (cold); acetone/ methanol, methanol/water	Amorphous-crystalline	313
	Chromatography	Acetone/diisopropyl ether	Column elution Alumina	316
	Distribution between two immiscible liquids	Water/hexane	Countercurrent	311,312
		Water/chloroform:benzene	Countercurrent	312

Poly(hydroxy ethers) (general) $\{O-R-O-CH_2-CH-CH_2\}_n$
$$OH$$

	Fractional solution	Chloroform/hexane	Column extraction Sand.	317

Polymer	Method of Fractionation	Solvent or Solvent/ Nonsolvent Mixture	Remarks	Ref.
Poly(formaldehyde diacetate)				
	Chromatography	Phenol/ethyl cellosolve	Column elution Kieselite	318
Polyepoxide + poly(organosiloxanes)				
	Turbidimetric titration	Dioxane/water	-	319

9 - POLYESTERS

Poly(adipic acid-co-ethylene glycol)				
	Fractional precipitation	Benzene/petroleum ether	-	320
Poly(adipic acid-co-decamethylene glycol)				
	Fractional precipitation	Benzene/petroleum ether	-	320
Poly(adipic acid-co-poly(ethylene glycol))				
	Fractional precipitation	Chloroform/n-hexane Acetonitrile/isopropyl ether	-	93
Poly(adipic acid-co-glycerol)				
	Fractional precipitation	Benzene/petroleum ether	-	321
Polycarbonates (general)				
	Fractional precipitation	Methylene chloride/n-heptane	-	331
	Fractional solution	Methylene chloride/n-hexane	Film extraction	332
	Turbidimetric titration	Chloroform/methanol	-	333
Poly(11-hydroxyundecanoic acid)				
	Fractional precipitation	Benzene/methanol	55 °C	322
Poly(phthalic anhydride-co-glycerol)				
	Fractional precipitation	Acetone/water	Alkyds	329
		Butanone:acetone/methanol, methanol:water	-	330

Polymer	Method of Fractionation	Solvent or Solvent/ Nonsolvent Mixture	Remarks	Ref.
Poly(sebacic, adipic, tartaric acid-co-1,6-hexanediol, 1,10-decanediol)				
	Fractional solution and precipitation	Benzene/methanol	-	324,325
Poly(sebacid acid-co-hexanediol-co-hexanetriol)				
	Fractional precipitation	Benzene/methanol	-	326
Poly(α,α'-dibutylsebacic acid-co-hexanediol)				
	Fractional solution and precipitation	Benzene/methanol	-	325,327
Poly(succinic, pimelic acids-co-hexanediol)				
	Fractional precipitation	Benzene/methanol	-	326
Poly(tartaric acid-co-hexanediol)				
	Chromatography	-	Urea	328
Poly(terephthalic acid-co-ethylene glycol) [Poly(ethylene terephthalate)]				
	Fractional precipitation	Phenol:tetrachloroethane/ ligroin	Terylene, 65°C pH = 6	171
		Phenol/cyclohexane	70°C	334
		m-Cresol/ligroin (b.p. 100°C)	50°C	335
		Dimethylformamide	Lowering temp.	335
	Fractional solution	Phenol:tetrachloroethane (3:2)/nonane	Film extraction 95°C	28,336
	Distribution between two immiscible liquids	m-Cresol/petroleum ether	-	335
	Chromatography	-	Charcoal	337

References page IV-272

Polymer	Method of Fractionation	Solvent or Solvent/ Nonsolvent Mixture	Remarks	Ref.

10 - POLYAMIDES

Polymer	Method of Fractionation	Solvent or Solvent/ Nonsolvent Mixture	Remarks	Ref.
Polyamides (general)	Distribution between immiscible liquids	Phenol/water	Continuous	338
	Mechanical fractionation	-	Interfacial condensation	339
Poly(10-aminocapric acid)	Distribution between immiscible liquids	Phenol/water	70 °C	340
Poly(6-aminocaproic acid) (ε-caprolactam)	Fractional precipitation	m-Cresol/cyclohexane	Nylon, Perlon	341
		m-Cresol/petroleum ether	Nylon 6	342
		m-Cresol/ligroin	Perlon, 50°C	171
		Phenol/water	Perlon, 70 °C	343
	Fractional solution	Formic acid/propyl acetate	Film extraction	28
	Coacervation	Phenol/ethylene glycol/water	Nylon 6	344
Poly(6-aminocaproic acid-co-hexamethylenediamine-co-adipic acid)	Fractional precipitation	Phenol/water	70-90°C	345
Poly(hexamethylenediamine-co-adipic acid)	Fractional precipitation	Phenol/water	Nylon 66	346
		m-Cresol/cyclohexane	-	341,347
	Turbidimetric titration	m-Cresol/cyclohexane	Nylon 66	348
Poly(fumaric acid-co-N,N'-diethyl-4,4'-diamino-3,3'-dimethyldiphenylmethane)	Turbidimetric titration	Dimethylformamide/water	-	349

Polymer	Method of Fractionation	Solvent or Solvent/ Nonsolvent	Remarks	Ref.

11 - POLYURETHANS

Poly(hexamethylenediamine-co-1,4-butanediol-bis-chlorocarbonate)

	Fractional precipitation	m-Cresol/n-hexane	-	350

Poly(propylene glycol-co-toluene diisocyanate)

	Fractional solution	Benzene/isooctane	Column extraction 34°C	351

12 - MISCELLANEOUS ORGANIC POLYMERS

p-Cresol-formaldehyde

	Fractional precipitation	Benzene/petroleum ether	-	353
		Toluene/petroleum ether	-	353
		Tetrahydrofuran/petroleum ether	-	353
		Benzene/methanol	-	353
		Methanol:tetrahydrofuran (2:1)/water	-	353
		Dioxane, ethylene chloride, trichloroethylene/methanol, ethanol, n-propanol, n-butanol, ether, formamide	-	354

Phenol-formaldehyde

	Fractional precipitation	Dioxane, ethylene chloride, trichloroethylene/methanol, ethanol, n-propanol n-butanol, ether, formamide	-	354
		Acetone/petroleum ether	-	321
		Methanol/water	-	321
		Alkali/acid	-	321
		Acetone:methanol/petroleum ether	-	321
	Coacervation	Ethanol or dioxane/salts in water	-	355
		Methanol, ethanol, n-propanol, acetone, dioxane/carbon dioxide, water solutions	Novolak	356

Urea-formaldehyde

	Fractional precipitation	Ethanol:water (1:1)/methanol	-	357

References page IV-272

Polymer	Method of Fractionation	Solvent or Solvent/ Nonsolvent Mixture	Remarks	Ref.
Polybenzofuran				
	Fractional precipitation	Benzene/methanol	Optically active	358
Polydiketene				
	Extraction	Acetone, dioxane	-	359
Polydimethylketene				
	Extraction	Methanol, ether, benzene, acetone	Boiling	360
Polysulfide rubbers				
	Chromatography	Dioxane	Column elution Silica gel	352

13 - NATURAL POLYMERS

a. Polysaccharides

Polymer	Method of Fractionation	Solvent or Solvent/ Nonsolvent Mixture	Remarks	Ref.
Alginates				
	Fractional precipitation	Water/manganous chloride + calcium chloride	Sodium alginate	361
		Water/sodium chloride	Sodium alginate	362
	Centrifugation	-	Ethylene diammonium alginates	363
Amylose				
	Fractional precipitation	Acetone/acetone:water (1:1)	Acetate	364
		Acetone/water	Carbanilate	365
		Dimethyl sulfoxide/ethanol	4 °C	366
		Dimethyl sulfoxide/abs. ethanol	-	367
		Dimethylformamide/methanol: 10% CaCl$_2$	Carbanilate	368
		Nitromethane/methanol	Acetate	369
		Water/ethanol	Glucoamido- ethyl	370

Polymer	Method of Fractionation	Solvent or Solvent/ Nonsolvent Mixture	Remarks	Ref.
		a. Polysaccharides (Cont'd.)		
Cellulose				
	Fractional precipitation	2N sodium hydroxide/methanol	Rayon, summative method	371
		Cupriethylenediamine (cuene) or cuprammonium hydroxide (cuoxam)/propanol	Varying temp.	372
		Acetone/acetone:water	Preripened, regenerated; alkali cellulose	373
		Acetone/acetone:water (3:1)	Tricarbanilate	374
	Fractional solution	Iron-sodium tartrate solution/NaOH, >5N	Summative method	375
	Extraction	Iron-sodium tartrate solution	Regenerated fibers	376
Cellulose acetate				
	Fractional precipitation	Acetone/ethanol	-	377
		Acetone/95% ethanol	Lowering temp.	378-381
		Aq. acetone/heptane: acetone (3:1)	-	382
		Acetone/ethanol	Solvent volatilized	381
		Acetone/water followed by acetone/pentane	"Cross" fractionation	383
		Acetone:water (3:1)/water	-	384
		Acetone/water	-	385
	Fractional solution	-	Column extraction	208
		Acetone/methanol	Column extraction	26
		Water/water:acetone	Summative Method	377
	Turbidimetric titration	Butanol:ethanol (4:1)/ 95% ethanol	-	386
	Thermal diffusion	Ethylene chloride	Triacetate	188
	Diffusion into porous charcoal	-	Countercurrent	387,388
Cellulose acetate-butyrate				
	Fractional precipitation	Acetone/water:acetone (1:1) + 2% salt, then water alone + 2% salt	-	389
		Acetone/isopropyl ether	-	390

References page IV-272

Polymer	Method of Fractionation	Solvent or Solvent/ Nonsolvent Mixture	Remarks	Ref.
	a.	Polysaccharides (Cont'd.)		
Cellulose acetate-butyrate	Turbidimetric titration	Acetone/ethanol:water (3:1)	-	391
Cellulose nitrate	Fractional precipitation	Acetone/n-hexane	-	393
		Acetone/ligroin		394
		Acetone/water	-	393,396
		Acetone/acetone:water (1:1)	-	397-399
		Acetone/petroleum ether	-	398
		Acetone + 9% water/water	-	401-403
		Acetone/acetone:water (1:4)	-	404
			"Triangle" method	405
		Acetone:n-hexane (1:1)/ n-hexane	-	406
		Acetone/water followed by acetone/heptane	"Cross" fractionation	407
		Acetone/acetone:water (4:1) until pure water	0°C, no light	408
		Acetone/heptane	Lowering temp.	82
		Ethyl acetate/n-heptane	-	409
	Fractional solution	Acetone/water:methanol	Column extraction	26
		Ethyl acetate/95% ethanol	-	400,410
	Sedimentation velocity	Acetone	Ultracentrifuge	411
	Chromatography	-	Starch	412
		-	Activated carbon	133
	Distribution between immiscible liquids	Cellulose triacetate gel in methyl acetate/water, ethanol, butyl acetate	-	412
	Turbidimetric titration	Acetone/methanol:water (9:1)	-	413
	Membrane diffusion	Acetone	-	414
	Diffusion into porous charcoal	-	Countercurrent	388
Cellulose tributyrate	Fractional precipitation	Acetone/water	-	392

Polymer	Method of Fractionation	Solvent or Solvent/ Nonsolvent Mixture	Remarks	Ref.
	a.	Polysaccharides (Cont'd.)		
Ethyl Cellylose	Fractional precipitation	Ethyl acetate:acetone (1:4)/ water	-	415
Dextran	Fractional precipitation	Aqueous solutions/95% ethanol	Acid hydrolyzed	416
		Water/methanol	-	417
		Aqueous solutions/methanol	Native, lowering temp.	418
	Chromatography	-	Activated carbon	133
		-	"Gel filtration" Packing cross-linked dextran	419
		-	"Precipitation" chromatography	420
	Sedimentation velocity	-	Ultracentrifuge	420
Pectins	Fractional precipitation	Dioxane/petroleum ether	Propionate Lowering temp.	421
	Membrane diffusion	-	-	254
	Fractional centrifugation	-	Amylopectin	422
Poly(arabinose)	Fractional precipitation	Acetone/petroleum ether	Araban acetate	423
	Chromatography	-	Charcoal	423
Poly(D-glucose)	Fractional precipitation	Water/abs. methanol	Lowering temp.	424
Starch	Precipitation	Thymol/n-butanol	-	425
	Centrifugation	Dilute alkali	-	426
	Aqueous leaching	-	-	427,428

Polymer	Method of Fractionation	Solvent or Solvent/ Nonsolvent Mixture	Remarks	Ref.

a. Polysaccharides (Cont'd.)

Polymer	Method of Fractionation	Solvent or Solvent/ Nonsolvent Mixture	Remarks	Ref.
Starch				
	Aqueous dispersion	-	-	428
	Alkaline leaching	-	-	428
Sodium ligno sulfonates				
	Fractional solution	NaCl solutions/95% ethanol	-	429
	Brownian diffusion	-	-	429
Xylan				
	Fractional precipitation	Dimethyl sulfoxide/ethanol	-	430

b. Poly(amino acids)

Polymer	Method of Fractionation	Solvent or Solvent/ Nonsolvent Mixture	Remarks	Ref.
Gelatin				
	Coacervation	Water/ethanol	-	431,432
Gramicidin-S				
	Distribution between immiscible liquids	-	Countercurrent	433
Insulin				
	Chromatography	-	Column elution Packing:diethyl- amino ethyl cellu- lose (DEAE)	434
Lactoglobulin				
	Salt fractionation	2.19 M ammonium sulfate solutions	-	435
Polypeptides from (L-, D-Lysine + L-Tyrosine)				
	Fractional precipitation	Water + 0.1 N HCl/0.1 M sodium citrate	-	436
Polysarcosine				
	Chromatography	Dioxane/water	Dimethylamide "Precipitation" chromatography	437

Polymer	Method of Fractionation	Solvent or Solvent/ Nonsolvent Mixture	Remarks	Ref.
	b.	Poly(amino acids) (Cont'd.)		
Poly(γ-benzyl-L-glutamates)				
	Fractional solution	Formic acid or hot ethanol	Extraction	438
	Dialysis	Dioxane	-	438
	Chromatography	-	Paper	438
Proteins				
	Fractional precipitation	Ethanol	Blood plasma. large scale, low temp.	439
Serum albumin				
	Diffusion convection	-	-	440
	Sedimentation velocity	-	Ultracentrifuge	167
	Brownian diffusion	-	-	441
Silk fibroin				
	Fractional precipitation	Lithium sulfocyanide solutions (d=1.20)/water	-	442

c.   Nucleic Acids

Polymer	Method of Fractionation	Solvent or Solvent/ Nonsolvent Mixture	Remarks	Ref.
Nucleic acids (general)				
	Chromatography	-	Paper DNA and RNA	443
		0.01 M sodium citrate	Column elution pH=6,5. ECTEOLA	444
Deoxyribonucleic acid				
	Ion exchange	-	Amberlite	445
	Chromatography	-	ECTEOLA	446
	Sedimentation velocity	-	Ultracentrifuge	447
Ribonucleic acid				
	Fractional solution	-	Column extraction ECTEOLA	448

References page IV-272

Polymer	Method of Fractionation	Solvent or Solvent/ Nonsolvent Mixture	Remarks	Ref.

14 - POLYSILOXANES

Silicones (general)

	Distribution be- tween two immis- cible liquids	Methanol/carbon tetrachloride/ cyclohexane	Countercurrent	449
	Chromatography	-	Carbon	449

IV-272   D. REFERENCES

1.   L. H. Cragg and H. Hammerschlag, Chem. Revs. 39, 79 (1946).
2.   V. Desreux and A. Oth, Chem. Weekbl. 48, 247 (1952).
3.   G. V. Schulz, "Die Physik der Hochpolymeren," Vol. 2. ed. H. A. Stuart, Springer,
     Berlin, 1953.
4.   C. M. Conrad, Ind. Eng. Chem. 45, 2511 (1953).
5.   R. W. Hall, "Techniques of Polymer Characterization," ed. P. W. Allen, Butterworths,
     London, 1959.
6.   E. W. Channen, Rev. Pure Appl. Chem., 9, 225 (1959).
7.   G. M. Guzmán, "Progress in High Polymers," ed. J. C. Robb, F. W. Peaker, Heywood,
     London, 1961.
8.   O. Fuchs and H. J. Leugering, "Kunststoffe," Vol. 1, ed. K. A. Wolf, Springer,
     Berlin, 1962.
9.   F. Käsbauer, E. Schuch, ibid.
10. R. M. Screaton, "Newer Methods of Polymer Characterization," ed. B. Ke,
     Interscience, New York, 1964.
11. S. S. Stivala, R. J. Valles, D. W. Levi, J. Appl. Polymer Sci., 7, 97 (1963).
12. U. S. Patent, 2,457,238 (1948).
13. K. Ueberreiter, H. J. Orthmann, G. Sorge, Makromol. Chem., 8, 21 (1952).
14. A. Nasini, C. Mussa, Makromol. Chem., 22, 59 (1957).
15. H. Wesslau, Makromol. Chem., 20, 111, (1956).
16. H. Wesslau, Makromol. Chem., 26, 96, 102 (1958).
17. R. S. Aries and A. P. Sachs, J. Polymer Sci., 21, 551 (1956).
18. L. H. Tung, J. Polymer Sci., 20, 495 (1956).
19. L. H. Tung, J. Polymer Sci., 24, 333 (1956).
20. L. H. Tung, S.P.E. Journal, 14, 25 (1958).
21. H. Okamoto, K. Sekikawa, J. Polymer Sci., 55, 597 (1961).
22. L. Nicolas, Makromol. Chem., 24, 173 (1957).
23. H. S. Kaufman and E. K. Walsh, J. Polymer Sci., 26, 124 (1957).
24. C. Mussa, J. Polymer Sci., 28, 587 (1958).
25. S. L. Aggarwal, L. Marker, and M. J. Carrano, J. Appl. Polymer Sci., 3, 78 (1960).
26. V. Desreux, Rec. Trav. Chim. Pays-Bas, 68, 789 (1949).
27. S. W. Hawkins, H. Smith, J. Polymer Sci., 28, 341 (1958).
28. O. Fuchs, Z. Elektrochem., 60, 229 (1956).
29. P. S. Francis, R. C. Cooke, Jr., and J. H. Elliott, J. Polymer Sci., 31, 453
     (1958).
30. P. M. Henry, J. Polymer Sci., 36, 3 (1959).
31. H. J. L. Schuurmans, J. Polymer Sci., 57, 557 (1962).
32. H. Okamoto, J. Polymer Sci., A2, 3451 (1964).
33. J. E. Guillett, R. L. Combs, D. F. Slonaker, and H. W. Coover, J. Polymer Sci.,
     47, 307 (1960).
34. H. W. McCormick, J. Polymer Sci., A1, 103 (1963).
35. T. Suminoe, N. Yamazoki, and S. Kambara, Chem. High Polymers (Japan) 20, 461
     (1963).
36. O. Fuchs, Makromol. Chem., 58, 65 (1962).
37. T. G. Fox, P. J. Flory, J. Am. Chem. Soc., 70, 2384 (1948).
38. W. R. Krigbaum and P. J. Flory, J. Am. Chem. Soc., 75, 1775 (1953).
39. T. G. Fox and P. J. Flory, J. Phys. Chem., 53, 197 (1949).
40. B. V. Losikov, N. I. Kaverina and A. A. Fedyantseva, Khim. Tekhnol. Topliva, 3,
     51 (1956).
41. I. Landler, Compt. Rend. 225, 629 (1947).
42. M. J. R. Cantow, R. S. Porter, and J. F. Johnson, J. Polymer Sci., C1, 187 (1963).
43. J. L. Jungnickel and F. T. Weiss, J. Polymer Sci., 49, 437 (1961).
44. D. L. Flowers, W. A. Hewett, R. D. Mullineaux, J. Polymer Sci., A2, 2305 (1964).
45. C. M. Fontana, J. Phys. Chem., 63, 1167 (1959).
46. J. B. Kinsinger, R. E. Hughes, J. Phys. Chem., 63, 2002 (1959).
47. T. E. Davis, R. L. Tobias, J. Polymer Sci., 50, 227 (1961).
48. P. Parrini, F. Sebastiano, and G. Messina, Makromol. Chem., 38, 27 (1960).
49. M. Hirooka, H. Kanda, and K. Nakaguchi, J. Polymer Sci., B1, 701 (1963).
50. R. A. Mendelson, J. Polymer Sci., A1, 2361 (1963).
51. S. Shyluk, J. Polymer Sci., 62, 317 (1962).
52. A. S. Hoffman, B. A. Fries, P. C. Condit, J. Polymer Sci., C4, 109 (1963).
53. P. W. O. Wijga, J. van Schooten, and J. Boerma, Makromol. Chem., 36, 115 (1960).
54. J. van Schooten, P. W. O. Wijga, Makromol. Chem., 43, 23 (1961).
55. M. Pegoraro, Chim. Ind. (Milan), 44, 18 (1962).
56. C. A. Russell, J. Appl. Polymer Sci., 4, 219 (1960).
57. J. Furukawa, et al., Makromol. Chem., 41, 17 (1960).
58. J. van Schooten, H. van Hoorn, and J. Boerma, Polymer 2, 161 (1961).
59. P. Longi and A. Roggero, Ann. Chim. (Rome), 51, 1013 (1961).
60. O. Redlich, A. L. Jacobson, and W. H. McFadden, J. Polymer Sci., A1, 393 (1963).
61. G. Geiseler, and H. P. Baumann, Z. Elektrochem., 62, 209 (1958).
62. G. Natta, M. Pegoraro, and M. Peraldo, Ricerca Sci., 28, 1473 (1958).

63. C. G. Overberger, A. E. Borchert, and A. Katchman, J. Polymer Sci., 44, 491 (1960).
64. G. F. D'Alelio, A. B. Finestone, L. Taft, and T. J. Miranda, J. Polymer Sci., 45, 83 (1960).
65. A. V. Topchiev, G. I. Chernyi, and V. N. Andronov, Dokl. Akad. Nauk. S.S.S.R., 143, 879 (1962).
66. H. S. Kaufman, E. Solomon, Ind. Eng. Chem., 45, 1779 (1953).
67. H. Okamoto, J. Polymer Sci., 37, 173 (1959).
68. R. Kocher, C. Sadron, Makromol. Chem., 10, 172 (1953).
69. I. Valyi, A. G. Janssen, and H. Mark, J. Phys. Chem., 49, 461 (1945).
70. A. I. Goldberg, W. P. Hohenstein, and H. Mark, J. Polymer Sci., 2, 503 (1947).
71. D. Cleverdon, and D. Laker, J. Appl. Chem., 1, 6 (1951).
72. N. Gralen and G. Lagermalm, J. Phys. Chem., 56, 514 (1952).
73. F. Wenger and S-P. S. Yen, Makromol. Chem., 43, 1 (1961).
74. E. H. Merz and R. W. Raetz, J. Polymer Sci., 5, 587 (1950).
75. F. Wenger, Makromol. Chem., 64, 151 (1963).
76. J. Hannus, G. Smets, Bull. Soc. Chim. Belg., 60, 76 (1951).
77. K. Kawahara, R. Okada, J. Polymer Sci., 56, 57 (1962).
78. K. Kawahara, Chem. High Polymer (Japan) 18, 687 (1961).
79. H. P. Frank and J. W. Breitenbach, J. Polymer Sci., 6, 609 (1951).
80. R. F. Boyer, J. Polymer Sci., 8, 73, 197 (1952).
81. V. N. Tsvetkov, N. N. Boitsova, Vysokomolekul. Soedin., 5, 1263 (1963).
82. H. Sihtola, E. Kaila, and N. Virkola, Makromol. Chem., 11, 70 (1953).
83. G. Natta, F. Danusso, and G. Moraglio, Makromol. Chem, 20, 37 (1956).
84. W. Hahn, W. Müller, and R. W. Webber, Makromol. Chem., 21, 131 (1956).
85. G. M. Guzmán, J. Polymer Sci., 19, 519 (1956).
86. J. P. Bianchi, F. P. Price, and B. H. Zimm, J. Polymer Sci., 25, 27 (1957).
87. A. Albert and D. C. Pepper, Proc. Roy. Soc. (London), A263, 75 (1961).
88. A. Yamada, Y. Yamamuro, and M. Yanagita, Bull. Chem. Soc. Japan, 35, 609 (1962).
89. J. H. S. Green and M. F. Vaughan, Chem. & Ind. 1958, 829.
90. H. W. Melville and B. D. Stead, J. Polymer Sci., 16, 505 (1956).
91. P. E. M. Allen, et al., Makromol. Chem., 39, 52 (1960).
92. J. Hengstenberg, Z. Elektrochem., 60, 236 (1956).
93. H.-G. Elias, and V. Gruber, Makromol. Chem., 78, 72 (1964).
94. J. R. Urwin, et al., Makromol. Chem., 72, 53 (1964).
95. A. R. Mathieson, J. Colloid Sci., 15, 387 (1960).
96. C. A. Baker, R. J. P. Williams, J. Chem. Soc., 1956, 2352.
97. N. S. Schneider, et al., J. Polymer Sci., 37, 551 (1959).
98. N. S. Schneider, L. G. Holmes, J. Polymer Sci., 38, 552 (1959).
99. J. L. Jungnickel, F. T. Weiss, J. Polymer Sci., 49, 437 (1961).
100. J. W. Breitenbach, H. G. Burger, Makromol. Chem., 54, 60 (1962).
101. I. Homma, et al., Makromol. Chem., 67, 132 (1963).
102. S. J. Yeh and H. L. Frisch, J. Polymer Sci., 27, 149 (1958).
103. J. C. Moore, J. Polymer Sci., A2, 835 (1964).
104. G. Langhammer, K. Quitzsch, Makromol. Chem., 43, 160 (1961).
105. H. Determann, G. Lüben, and T. Wieland, Makromol. Chem., 73, 168 (1964).
106. G. V. Schulz, A. Scholz, R. V. Figini, Makromol. Chem. 57, 220 (1962).
107. H. W. McCormick, J. Polymer Sci., 36, 341 (1959).
108. F. M. Brower and H. W. McCormick, J. Polymer Sci., A1, 1749 (1963).
109. K. Kawahara, Makromol. Chem., 73, 1 (1964).
110. H. J. Cantow, Makromol. Chem., 30, 81 (1959).
111. J. H. S. Green, H. T. Hookway, and M. F. Vaughan, Chem. & Ind. 1958, 862.
112. G. Langhammer, J. Polymer Sci., 29, 505 (1958).
113. D. L. Taylor, J. Polymer Sci., A2, 611 (1964).
114. F. W. Peaker and J. C. Robb, Nature, 182, 1591 (1958).
115. J. D. Loconti and J. W. Cahill, J. Polymer Sci., 49, S2 (1961).
116. J. D. Loconti and J. W. Cahill, J. Polymer Sci., A1, 3163 (1963).
117. A. M. Ruskin and G. Parravano, J. Appl. Polymer Sci., 8, 565 (1964).
118. D. E. Burge and D. B. Bruss, J. Polymer Sci., A1, 1927 (1963).
119. A. F. Sirianni, D. J. Worsfold, and S. Bywater, Trans. Faraday. Soc., 55, 2124 (1959).
120. C. A. Marshall, R. A. Mock, J. Polymer Sci., 17, 591 (1955).
121. N. Hartler, Acta Chem. Scand., 11, 1162 (1957).
122. R. H. Wagner, J. Polymer Sci., 2, 21 (1947).
123. A. R. Schultz, J. Am. Chem. Soc., 76, 3422 (1954).
124. A. Nakajima, I. Sakurada, Chem. High. Polymers (Japan) 11, 110 (1954).
125. J. C. Bevington, G. M. Guzmán, and H. W. Melville, Proc. Roy. Soc. (London), A221, 437 (1954).
126. O. Fuchs, Makromol. Chem., 58, 65 (1962).
127. H.-G. Elias and F. Patat, Makromol. Chem., 25, 13 (1957).
128. G. C. Berry and R. G. Craig, Polymer 5, 19 (1964).

129. A. Beresniewicz, J. Polymer Sci., 35, 321 (1959).
130. O. Fuchs, Makromol. Chem., 5, 245 (1951).
131. D. R. Morey, E. W. Taylor, and G. P. Waugh, J. Colloid Sci., 6, 470 (1951).
132. R. Rigamonti and E. Meda, Ricerca Sci., 25, 457 (1955).
133. S. Claesson, Discussions Faraday Soc., 7, 321 (1949).
134. M. J. R. Cantow, R. S. Porter, and J. F. Johnson, J. Polymer Sci., C1, 187 (1963).
135. P. J. Kangle and E. Pacsu, J. Polymer Sci., 54, 301 (1961).
136. H. A. Dieu, J. Polymer Sci., 12, 417 (1954).
137. T. Matsuo and H. Inagaki, Makromol. Chem., 55, 150 (1962).
138. A. H. Traaen, J. Appl. Polymer Sci., 7, 581 (1963).
139. O. Fuchs, Makromol. Chem., 7, 259 (1952).
140. A. Beresniewicz, J. Polymer Sci., 35, 321 (1959).
141. G. Langhammer, Naturwiss, 41, 552 (1954).
142. L. Freund and M. Daune, J. Polymer Sci., 29, 161 (1958).
143. K. Imai and M. Matsumoto, Bull. Chem. Soc. Japan, 36, 455 (1963).
144. P. Doty, H. Wagner, S. Singer, J. Phys. Coll. Chem., 51, 32 (1947).
145. L. de Brouckere, E. Bidaine, and A. van der Heyden, Bull. Soc. Chim. Belge, 58, 418 (1949).
146. N. V. Mikhailov and S. G. Zelikman, Kolloidn. Zh. 18, 717 (1956);
147. H. Batzer and A. Nisch, Makromol. Chem., 22, 131 (1957).
148. A. Takahaschi, M. Obara, and I. Kagawa, Kogyo Kagaku Zasshi, 66, 960 (1963).
149. G. Pezzin, G. Talamini, and G. Vidotto, Makromol. Chem., 43, 12 (1961).
150. T. Kobayashi, Bull. Chem. Soc. Japan, 35, 726 (1962).
151. H. Staudinger, M. Häberle, Makromol. Chem., 9, 48 (1952).
152. G. M. Guzman and J. M. G. Fatou, Anales. Real Soc. Espan. Fis. Quim., 54(B), 263 (1958).
153. A. Oth and V. Desreux, Bull. Soc. Chim. Belge, 63, 261 (1954).
154. M. A. Crook, F. S. Walker, Nature, 198, 1163 (1963).
155. G. M. Guzman and J. M. G. Fatou, Anales. Real Soc. Espan. Fis. Quim., 54(B), 609 (1958).
156. C. Schildknecht, S. Gross, and H. Davidson, Ind. Eng. Chem., 40, 2104 (1948).
157. E. J. Vandenberg, J. Polymer Sci., C1, 207 (1963).
158. J. A. Manson and G. J. Arquelte, Makromol. Chem., 37, 187 (1960).
159. E. B. Fitzgerald, and R. M. Fuoss, Ind. Eng. Chem., 42, 1603 (1950).
160. A. J. Hyde and R. B. Taylor, Polymer, 4, 1 (1963).
161. P. P. Spiegelman, and G. Parravano, J. Polymer Sci., A2, 2245 (1964).
162. K. Dialer and K. Vogler, Makromol. Chem., 6, 191 (1951).
163. B. Jirgensons, J. Polymer Sci., 8, 519 (1952).
164. W. Scholtan, Makromol. Chem., 24, 83 (1957).
165. L. C. Cerny, T. E. Helminiak, and J. F. Meier, J. Polymer Sci., 44, 539 (1960).
166. W. Scholtan, Makromol. Chem., 24, 104 (1957).
167. W. Scholtan, Makromol. Chem., 36, 162 (1960).
168. R. Schulz, G. Renner, A. Henglein, and W. Kern, Makromol. Chem., 12, 20 (1954).
169. B. Baysal, J. Polymer Sci., C4, 935 (1963).
170. P. Herrent, J. Polymer Sci., 8, 346 (1952).
171. A. Gordienko, Faserforsch. Textiltech., 4, 499 (1953).
172. R. C. Houtz, Textile Res. J., 20, 786 (1950).
173. J. Bisschops, J. Polymer Sci., 17, 81 (1955).
174. G. Ciampa, H. Schwindt, Chim. Ind., 37, 169 (1955).
175. Y. Fujisaki, Chem. High Polymers (Japan), 19, 64 (1962).
176. Y. Fujisaki and H. Kobayashi, Chem. High Polymers (Japan), 18, 305 (1961).
177. C. Booth and L. R. Beason, J. Polymer Sci., 42, 108 (1960).
178. H. Kobayashi, J. Polymer Sci., 26, 230 (1957).
179. W. Scholtan and H. Marzolph, Makromol. Chem., 55, 52 (1962).
180. M. L. Miller, J. Polymer Sci., 56, 203 (1962).
181. M. Takahaschi and M. Watanabe, Sen-i-Gakkaishi, 17, 122 (1961).
182. H. Kobayashi and Y. Fujisaki, J. Polymer Sci., B1, 16 (1963).
183. Y. Fujisaki and H. Kobayashi, Chem. High Polymer (Japan) 19, 49 (1962).
184. Y. Fujisaki and H. Kobayashi, Chem. High Polymer (Japan) 19, 73 (1962).
185. H. Kobayashi, K. Sasaguri, Y. Fujisaki, and T. Amano, J. Polymer Sci., A2, 313 (1964).
186. Y. Fujisaki, H. Kobayashi, Chem. High Polymers (Japan), 18, 305 (1961).
187. W. R. Krigbaum and A. M. Kotliar, J. Polymer Sci., 32, 323 (1958).
188. G. Langhammer, Makromol. Chem., 21, 74 (1956).
189. G. B. Rathmann and F. A. Bovey, J. Polymer Sci., 15, 544 (1955).
190. A. Katchalsky and H. Eisenberg, J. Polymer Sci., 6, 145 (1951).
191. N. M. Wiederhorn and A. R. Brown, J. Polymer Sci., 8, 651 (1952).
192. S. N. Chinai and R. A. Guzzi, J. Polymer Sci., 21, 417 (1956).
193. E. H. Merz, J. Polymer Sci., 3, 790 (1948).
194. S. N. Chinai and R. J. Samuels, J. Polymer Sci., 19, 463 (1956).
195. S. N. Chinai, J. Polymer Sci., 25, 413 (1957).

196. G. M. Guzmán, Anales Real. Soc. Espan. Fis. Quim., 50(B), 631 (1954).
197. J. H. Baxendale, S. Bywater, and M. G. Evans, Trans. Faraday Soc., 42, 675 (1946).
198. P. O. Kinell, Acta Chem. Scand., 1, 832 (1947).
199. A. V. Eriksson, Acta Chem. Scand., 3, 1 (1949).
200. E. Trommsdorff, H. Köhle, and P. Lagally, Makromol. Chem., 1, 169 (1948).
201. F. W. Billmeyer and W. H. Stockmayer, J. Polymer Sci., 5, 121 (1950).
202. G. Meyerhoff, Makromol. Chem., 12, 45 (1954).
203. V. N. Tsvetkov, V. S. Skazka, and N. M. Krivoruchko, Vysokomolekul Soedin., 2, 1045 (1960).
204. S. Krause and E. Cohn-Ginsberg, Polymer, 3, 566 (1962).
205. S. Krause and E. Cohn-Ginsberg, J. Polymer Sci., A2, 1393 (1964).
206. T. J. R. Weakley, R. J. P. Williams, and J. D. Wilson, J. Chem. Soc., 1960, 3963.
207. B. J. Cottam, D. M. Wiles, and S. Bywater, Can. J. Chem., 41, 1905 (1963).
208. V. Desreux, Bull. Soc. Chim. Belge, 57, 416 (1948).
209. E. J. Elgood, et al., J. Appl. Polymer Sci., 8, 882 (1964).
210. I. Harris and R. G. J. Miller, J. Polymer Sci., 7, 377 (1951).
211. J. Polacek, Collection Czech. Chem. Commun., 28, 1838 (1963).
212. P. O. Kinell, Acta Chem. Scand., 1, 335 (1947).
213. A. V. Eriksson, Acta Chem. Scand., 10, 360, 378 (1956).
214. I. Kössler and J. Krejsa, J. Polymer Sci., 57, 509 (1962).
215. M. I. Savitskaya and S. Ya. Frenkel, Zh. Fiz. Khim., 32, 1063 (1958).
216. K. C. Eberly and B. L. Johnson, J. Polymer Sci., 3, 283 (1948).
217. V. Garten and W. Becker, Makromol. Chem., 3, 78 (1949).
218. S. E. Bresler, I. Ya. Poddubnyi, and S. Ya. Frenkel, Zh. Tekhn. Fiz., 23, 1521 (1953).
219. D. J. Pollock, L. J. Elyash, and T. W. DeWitt, J. Polymer Sci., 15, 87, 336 (1955).
220. W. Cooper, D. E. Eaves, and G. Vaughan, J. Polymer Sci., 59, 241 (1962).
221. G. Vaughan, D. E. Eaves, and W. Cooper, Polymer, 2, 235 (1961).
222. J. M. Hulme and I. A. McLeod, Polymer, 3, 153 (1962).
223. W. Cooper, G. Vaughan, and J. Yardley, J. Polymer Sci., 59, 82 (1962).
224. W. Cooper, G. Vaughan, D. E. Eaves, R. W. Madden, J. Polymer Sci., 50, 159 (1961).
225. G. Moraglio, Chim. Ind. (Milan), 44, 352 (1962).
226. S. E. Bresler and S. Ya. Frenkel, Zh. Tekhn. Fiz., 23, 1502 (1953).
227. W. E. Mochel, J. B. Nichols, and C. J. Mighton, J. Am. Chem. Soc., 70, 2185 (1948).
228. W. E. Mochel and J. B. Nichols, J. Am. Chem. Soc., 71, 3435 (1949).
229. W. E. Mochel and J. B. Nichols, Ind. Eng. Chem., 43, 154 (1951).
230. E. A. Hauser and D. S. LeBeau, J. Phys. Chem., 54, 256 (1950).
231. I. Kössler and M. Stolka, J. Polymer Sci., 44, 213 (1960).
232. G. F. Bloomfield, Rubber Chem. & Tech., 24, 737 (1951).
233. S. Bywater and P. Johnson, Trans. Faraday Soc., 47, 195 (1951).
234. J. Moacanin, et. al., J. Am. Chem. Soc., 81, 2054 (1959).
235. R. Allirot, Compt. Rend., 231, 1065 (1950).
236. C. Booth, Polymer, 4, 471 (1963).
237. W. H. Beattie and C. Booth, J. Appl. Polymer Sci., 7, 508 (1963).
238. E. A. Hauser and D. S. LeBeau, India Rubber J., 110, 601 (1946); Rubber Chem. Techn., 20, 70 (1947).
239. J. W. Meeks, T. F. Banigan, and R. W. Planck, India Rubber World, 122, 301 (1950).
240. B. L. Johnson, Ind. Eng. Chem., 40, 351 (1948).
241. M. Takahashi and M. Watanabe, Sen-i-Gakkaishi, 17, 111 (1961).
242. G. R. Cotton and W. C. Schneider, J. Appl. Polymer Sci., 7, 1243 (1963).
243. J. Shimura, I. Mita, and H. Kambe, J. Polymer Sci., B2, 403 (1964).
244. J. Schurz, Th. Steiner, and H. Streitzig, Makromol. Chem., 23, 141 (1957).
245. T. Suminol, N. Yamazoki, and S. Kambara, Chem. High Polymers (Japan) 20, 461 (1963).
246. G. Mdme. Gavoret and M. Magat, J. Chim. Phys., 44, 90 (1947).
247. B. L. Johnson, Ind. Eng. Chem., 40, 351 (1948).
248. C. Booth and L. R. Beason, J. Polymer Sci., 42, 99 (1960).
249. A. D. Delman, B. B. Simms, and A. E. Ruff, J. Polymer Sci., 45, 415 (1960).
250. J. A. Yanko, J. Polymer Sci., 3, 576 (1948).
251. R. Endo, Chem. High Polymer (Japan), 19, 39 (1962).
252. M. A. Golub, J. Polymer Sci., 11, 281 (1953).
253. M. A. Golub, J. Polymer Sci., 11, 583 (1953).
254. J. L. Rosenberg and C. O. Beckmann, J. Colloid Sci., 3, 483 (1948).
255. S. N. Ushakov, S. P. Mitsengendler, and V. N. Krasulina, Izv. Akad. Nauk. S.S.S.R., 3, 366 (1957).
256. A. C. Zettlemoyer and E. T. Pieski, Ind. Eng. Chem., 45, 165 (1953).
257. N. Yamazaki, et. al., Kôgyô Kagaku Zasshi, 64, 1687 (1961).
258. J. D. Ferry, et. al., J. Colloid Sci., 6, 429 (1951).

259. W. H. Stockmayer, et al., J. Polymer Sci., 16, 517 (1955).
260. G. J. K. Acres and F. L. Dalton, J. Polymer Sci., A1, 2419 (1963).
261. C. D. Thurmond and B. H. Zimm, J. Polymer Sci., 8, 477 (1952).
262. C. G. Overberger and S. Nozakura, J. Polymer Sci., A1, 1445 (1963).
263. C. G. Overberger and S. Nozakura, J. Polymer Sci., A1, 1444 (1963).
264. C. G. Overberger and K. Mizamichi, J. Polymer Sci., A1, 2023 (1963).
265. R. A. Mock, et al., J. Polymer Sci., 11, 447 (1953).
266. G. A. Morneau, P. I. Roth, A. R. Schultz, J. Polymer Sci., 55, 609 (1961).
267. J. A. Yanko, J. Polymer Sci., 22, 153 (1956).
268. G. Smets, W. deWinter and G. Delzenne, J. Polymer Sci., 55, 767 (1961).
269. R. J. Ceresa, Polymer 2, 213 (1961).
270. R. J. Ceresa, Polymer 1, 480 (1960).
271. R. J. Ceresa, Polymer 1, 488 (1960).
272. V. A. Kargin, N. A. Plate, and A. S. Dobrynina, Kolloidn. Zh., 20, 332 (1958).
273. S. Schlick and M. Levy, J. Phys. Chem., 64, 883 (1960).
274. M. Baer, J. Polymer Sci., A2, 417 (1964).
275. P. Molyneux, Makromol. Chem., 43, 31 (1961).
276. J. R. Urwin and J. M. Stearne, Makromol. Chem., 78, 194 (1964).
277. G. M. Burnett, P. Meares, C. Paton, Trans. Faraday. Soc., 58, 723 (1962).
278. J. W. Breitenbach, O. F. Olaj, and A. Schindler, Monatsh. Chem., 91, 205 (1960).
279. R. J. Orr and H. L. Williams, J. Am. Chem. Soc., 79, 3137 (1957).
280. G. Champetier, et al., J. Polymer Sci., 58, 911 (1962).
281. N. Geacintov, et al., J. Appl. Polymer Sci., 3, 54 (1960).
282. G. M. Guzmán and F. Arranz, Anales. Real. Soc. Espan. Fis. Quim., 59(B), 455
      (1963).
283. G. M. Guzman and F. Arranz, Anales. Real. Soc. Espan. Fis. Quim., 59(B), 445
      (1963).
284. J. K. Rieke and G. M. Hart, J. Polymer Sci., C1, 117 (1963).
285. G. N. Richards, J. Appl. Polymer Sci., 5, 540 (1961).
286. A. Ravve and J. T. Khamis, J. Polymer Sci., 61, 185 (1962).
287. G. Kockelbergh and G. Smets, J. Polymer Sci., 33, 227 (1958).
288. F. Ide, R. Handa, and K. Nakatsuka, Chem. High Polymer (Japan), 21, 57 (1964).
289. H. Yasuda, J. A. Wray, and V. Stannett, J. Polymer Sci., C2, 387 (1963).
290. G. Smets and M. Claesen, J. Polymer Sci., 8, 289 (1952).
291. G. Smets, J. Roovers and W. van Humbeek, J. Appl. Polymer Sci., 5, 149 (1961).
292. J. D. Matlack, et al., J. Polymer Sci., 49, 353 (1961).
293. P. Borrell, G. Riess, and A. Banderet, Bull. Soc. Chim. France, 2, 354 (1961).
294. I. Sakurada, S. Matuzawa, and Y. Kubota, Makromol. Chem., 68, 115 (1963).
295. G. Smets and A. Hertoghe, Makromol. Chem., 17, 189 (1956).
296. W. K. W. Chen and H. Z. Friedlander, J. Polymer Sci., C4, 1195 (1963).
297. A. Chapiro, et al., J. Polymer Sci., C4, 491 (1963).
298. J. Sebban-Danon, J. Polymer Sci., 48, 121 (1960).
299. P. V. Kozlov, et al., Vysokomolekul. Soedin. 2, 1575 (1960).
300. L. J. Hughes and G. L. Brown, J. Appl. Polymer Sci., 7, 59 (1963).
301. G. Smets, A. Poot, and G. L. Duncan, J. Polymer Sci., 54, 65 (1961).
302. J. Gallot, P. Rempp, and J. Parrod, J. Polymer Sci., B1, 329 (1963).
303. S. P. Mitsengendler, et al., Vysokomolekul. Soedin., 4, 1366 (1962).
304. I. Mita, J. Chim. Phys., 59, 530 (1962).
305. P. Lebel and C. Job, J. Polymer Sci., C4, 649 (1963).
306. P. E. M. Allen, G. M. Burnett, J. M. Downer and H. W. Melville, Makromol. Chem.,
      38, 72 (1960).
307. R. Hardy and P. E. M. Allen, Makromol. Chem., 42, 38 (1960).
308. H. Fujii, J. Furukawa, T. Saegusa, and A. Kawasaki, Makromol. Chem., 40, 226 (1960).
309. G. Natta, et al., Atti Accad. Nazl. Lincei, 28, 18 (1960).
310. G. D. Staffin and C. C. Price, J. Am. Chem. Soc., 82, 3632 (1960).
311. L. C. Case, Makromol. Chem., 41, 61 (1960).
312. L. C. Case, J. Phys. Chem., 62, 895 (1958).
313. S. Ishida, Bull. Chem. Soc. Japan, 33, 727 (1960).
314. G. Allen, C. Booth, and M. N. Jones, Polymer, 5, 195 (1964).
315. G. Allen, C. Booth, and M. N. Jones, Polymer, 5, 257 (1964).
316. R. J. Morris and H. E. Persinger, J. Polymer Sci., A1, 1041 (1963).
317. G. E. Myers and J. R. Dagon, J. Polymer Sci., A2, 2631 (1964).
318. H. Kakiuchi and W. Fukuda, Kogyo Kagaku Zasshi, 66, 964 (1963).
319. K. A. Andrianov, et al., Vysokomolekul. Soedin., 3, 1692 (1961).
320. S. R. Rafikov, V. V. Korshak, and G. N. Chelnokova, Izv. Akad. Nauk. S.S.S.R., 642
      (1948).
321. J. Cepelák, Chem. Prumysl, 6, 106 (1956).
322. F. Lombard, Makromol. Chem., 8, 201 (1952).
324. H. Batzer, Makromol. Chem., 5, 66 (1950).
325. F. Wiloth, Makromol. Chem., 8, 111 (1952).

326. H. Batzer, Makromol. Chem., 12, 145 (1954).
327. H. Batzer and F. Wiloth, Makromol. Chem., 8, 55, 111 (1952).
328. W. Kern, H. Schmidt, and H. S. von Steinwehr, Makromol. Chem., 16, 74 (1955).
329. J. R. Fletcher, L. Polgar, and D. H. Solomon, J. Appl. Polymer Sci., 8, 663 (1964).
330. E. G. Bobalek, et al., J. Appl. Polymer Sci., 8, 632 (1964).
331. M. Tomikawa, Chem. High Polymer (Japan) 20, 11 (1963).
332. G. F. Bauman and S. Steingiser, J. Polymer Sci., A1, 3396 (1963).
333. S. Krozer, M. Vainryb, and L. Silina, Vysokomolekul Soedin., 2, 1876 (1960).
334. H. M. Koepp and H. Werrer, Makromol. Chem., 32, 309 (1959).
335. K. Ueberreiter and R. Götze, Makromol. Chem., 29, 61 (1959).
336. E. A. Haseley, J. Polymer Sci., 35, 309 (1959).
337. S. D. Bruck, J. Polymer Sci., 32, 519 (1958).
338. N. Duveau and A. Piguet, J. Polymer Sci., 57, 357 (1962).
339. P. W. Morgan and S. L. Kwolek, J. Polymer Sci., 62, 33 (1962).
340. K. Hoshino and M. Watanabe, J. Am. Chem. Soc., 73, 4816 (1951).
341. J. Juilfs, Kolloid Z,, 141, 88 (1955).
342. W. Griehl and H. Lückert, J. Polymer Sci., 30, 399 (1950).
343. F. Wiloth, Makromol. Chem., 14, 156 (1954).
344. E. Turska and M. Laczkowski, J. Polymer Sci., 23, 285 (1957).
345. H. Batzer and A. Müschle, Makromol. Chem., 22, 195 (1957).
346. G. B. Taylor, J. Am. Chem. Soc., 69, 638 (1947).
347. G. J. Howard, J. Polymer Sci., 37, 310 (1959).
348. G. J. Howard, J. Polymer Sci., A1, 2667 (1963).
349. O. Ya. Fedotova, et al., Vysokomolekul. Soedin., 5, 900 (1963).
350. M. Nishide and M. Sera, Kogyo Kagaku Zasshi, 64, 1145 (1961).
351. N. S. Rapp and J. D. Ingham, J. Polymer Sci., A2, 689 (1964).
352. A. N. Ceukin, et al., Vysokomolekul. Soedin., 4, 1088 (1962).
353. W. Kern, et al., Makromol. Chem., 6, 206 (1951).
354. R. E. Vogel, Kunststoffe, 42, 17 (1952).
355. A. Buzágh, K. Udvarhelyi, and F. Horkay, Kolloid Z., 154, 130 (1957).
356. A. Buzagh, K. Udvarhelyi, and F. Horkay, Kolloid Z., 157, 53 (1958).
357. R. E. Vogel, Kunststoffe, 44, 335 (1954).
358. M. Farina and G. Bressan, Makromol. Cjem., 61, 79 (1963).
359. J. Furukawa, et al., Makromol. Chem., 39, 243 (1960).
360. Y. Yamashita, S. Miura, and M. Nakamura, Makromol. Chem., 68, 31 (1963).
361. R. H. McDowell, Chem. & Ind. 1958, 1401.
362. A. Haugh, Acta Chem. Scand., 13, 601 (1959).
363. R. E. Cooper, J. Upadhyay, and A. Wassermann, J. Polymer Sci., 60, S46 (1962).
364. E. Huseman, Makromol. Chem., 26, 181, 199 (1958).
365. W. Burchard, B. Fritz, R. Lippert, B. Pfannemuller, and E. Husemann, Makromol. Chem., 44-46, 358 (1961).
366. W. Banks and C. T. Greenwood, Makromol. Chem., 67, 49 (1963).
367. J. M. G. Cowie, Makromol. Chem., 42, 230 (1960).
368. E. Husemann and B. Pfannemuller, Makromol. Chem., 49, 214 (1961).
369. J. M. B. Cowie, J. Polymer Sci., 49, 455 (1961).
370. R. L. Whistler and H. J. Roberts, J. Org. Chem., 26, 2458 (1961).
371. S. Coppick, O. A. Battista, and M. R. Lytton, Ind. Eng. Chem., 42, 2533 (1950).
372. H. Sihtola, E. Kaila, and L. Laamanen, J. Polymer Sci., 23, 809 (1957).
373. V. J. Masura, Faserforsch. Textiltech., 13, 517 (1962).
374. E. Husemann and R. Werner, Makromol. Chem., 59, 43 (1963).
375. G. Jayme, P. Kleppe, and A. Kunschner, Makromol. Chem., 48, 144 (1961).
376. P. Paulusma and D. Vermaas, J. Polymer Sci., C2, 488 (1963).
377. H. Konishi, Sen-i-Gakkaishi, 17, 1170 (1961).
378. A. M. Sookne and M. Harris, Ind. Eng. Chem., 37, 475, 478 (1945).
379. W. J. Badgley and H. Mark, J. Phys. Chem., 51, 58 (1947).
380. D. L. Swanson and J. W. Williams, J. Appl. Phys., 26, 810 (1955).
381. H. J. Phillipp and C. F. Bjork, J. Polymer Sci., 6, 383, 549 (1951).
382. P. C. Scherer and R. B. Thimpson, Rayon & Synth. Text., 31, 51 (1950).
383. A. J. Rosenthal and B. B. White, Ind. Eng. Chem., 44, 2693 (1952).
384. H. Staudinger and T. Eiche, Makromol. Chem., 10, 235 (1953).
385. G. M. Guzmán and J. M. G. Fatou, Anales, Real Soc. Espan. Fis. Quim., 53(B), 669 (1957).
386. J. Bischoff and V. Desreux, Bull. Soc. Chim. Belg., 60, 137 (1951).
387. H. A. Swenson, Acta Chem. Scand., 9, 572 (1955).
388. H. A. Swenson and A. Rosenberg, Acta Chem. Scand., 10, 1393 (1956).
389. J. W. Tamblyn, D. R. Morey, and R. H. Wagner, Ind. Eng. Chem., 37, 573 (1945).
390. D. R. Morey and J. W. Tamblyn, J. Phys. Chem., 51, 721 (1947).
391. D. R. Morey and J. W. Tamblyn, J. Appl. Phys. 16, 419 (1945).
392. R. F. Landel and J. D. Ferry, J. Phys. Chem., 59, 658 (1955).

393. W. E. Davis, J. Am. Chem. Soc., 69, 1453 (1947).
394. H. Asaoka and A. Suzuki, J. Soc. Text. Cell. Ind. (Japan), 11, 32 (1955).
395. H. A. Wannow, Fr. Thormann, Kolloid Z., 112, 94 (1949).
396. J. C. Aggarwala and J. L. McCarthy, J. Indian Chem. Soc., 26, 11 (1949).
397. F. Zapf, Makromol. Chem., 3, 164 (1949).
398. H. Nakahara and M. Shihanda, J. Soc. Text. Cell. Ind. (Japan), 8, 438 (1952).
399. F. Zapf, Makromol. Chem., 10, 61 (1953).
400. C. Emery and W. E. Cohen, Austr. J. Appl. Sci., 2, 473 (1951).
401. R. L. Mitchell, Ind. Eng. Chem., 45, 2526 (1953).
402. W. E. Roseveare and L. Poore, Ind. Eng. Chem., 45, 2518 (1953).
403. B. B. Thomas and W. J. Alexander, J. Polymer Sci., 15, 361 (1955).
404. G. V. Schulz and M. Marx, Makromol. Chem., 14, 52 (1954).
405. A. M. Meffroy-Bigget, Compt. Rend., 240, 1707 (1955).
406. W. G. Harland, J. Textile Inst., 46, 483 (1955).
407. K. Aejmelaeus, Ann. Acad. Sci. Fennicae, Ser. A., 2, 63 (1950).
408. M. Marx-Figini, Makromol. Chem., 32, 233 (1959).
409. P. C. Scherer and B. P. Rouse, Rayon & Synthetic Text., 29, 55, 85 (1948).
410. E. Heuser, Wm. Shockley, and R. Kjellgreen, Tappi, 33, 92 (1950).
411. J. Oth and V. Desreux, Ricerca Sci., 25, 447 (1955).
412. M. C. Brooks and R. M. Badger, J. Am. Chem. Soc., 72,1705, 4384 (1950).
413. A. Oth, Bull. Soc. Chim. Belg., 58, 285 (1949).
414. H. Vink and R. Wikstrom, Svensk Papperstid, 66, 55 (1963).
415. P. C. Scherer and R. D. McNeer, Rayon & Synth. Text., 30, 56 (1949).
416. F. R. Senti, et al., J. Polymer Sci., 17, 527 (1955).
417. M. Zief, G. Brunner, and J. Metzendorff, Ind. Eng. Chem., 48, 119 (1956).
418. L. H. Arond and H. P. Frank, J. Phys. Chem., 58, 953 (1954).
419. K. A. Granath and P. Flodin, Makromol. Chem., 48, 160 (1961).
420. K. H. Ebert, M. Brosche, and K. F. Elgert, Makromol. Chem., 72, 191 (1964).
421. H. S. Owens, J. C. Miers, and W. D. Maclay, J. Colloid Sci., 3, 277 (1948).
422. C. J. Stacy and J. F. Foster, J. Polymer Sci., 25, 39 (1957).
423. A. E. Goodban and H. S. Owens, J. Polymer Sci., 23, 825 (1957).
424. F. Michel, A. Bockmann, W. Mockstroth, Makromol. Chem. 48, 15 (1961).
425. J. M. G. Cowie and C. T. Greenwood, J. Chem. Soc., 1957, 4640.
426. H. Baum and G. A. Gilbert, J. Colloid Sci., 11, 428 (1956).
427. J. M. G. Cowie and C. T. Greenwood, J. Chem. Soc., 2862 (1957); C. T. Greenwood,
      Adv. Carbohydr. Chem., 11, 335 (1956).
428. W. Banks, C. T. Greenwood, and J. Thomson, Makromol. Chem., 31, 197 (1959).
429. J. Moacanin, N. Nelson, E. Back, V. F. Felicetta, and J. L. McCarthy, J. Am.
      Chem. Soc., 81, 2054 (1959).
430. R. G. LeBel and D. A. I. Goring, J. Polymer Sci., C2, 29 (1963).
431. G. Stainsby, Discussions Faraday Soc., 18, 288 (1954).
432. J. Pouradier and A. M. Venet, J. Chim. Phys., 47, 11 (1950).
433. A. R. Battersby and L. C. Craig, J. Am. Chem. Soc., 73, 1887 (1951).
434. M. Volini and M. A. Mitz, J. Am. Chem. Soc., 82, 4572 (1960).
435. M. P. Tombs, Biochem. J., 67, 517 (1957).
436. F. Micheel and W. Meckstroth, Makromol. Chem., 51, 107 (1962).
437. S. R. Caplan, J. Polymer Sci., 35, 409 (1959).
438. J. C. Mitchell, A. E. Woodard, and P. Doty, J. Am. Chem. Soc., 79, 3955 (1957).
439. J. B. Lesh, K. Schultz, and J. D. Porsche, Ind. Eng. Chem., 42, 1376 (1950).
440. J. G. Kirkwood and R. A. Brown, J. Am. Chem. Soc., 74, 1056 (1952).
441. M. Daune, H. Benoit, and C. Sadron, J. Polymer Sci., 16, 483 (1955).
442. R. Signer and R. Glanzmann, Makromol. Chem., 5, 257 (1951).
443. C. Singh, J. Sci. Ind. Res. India, 19C, 78 (1960).
444. D. N. Ward and J. D. Putch, Makromol. Chem., 38, 230 (1960).
445. A. Bendich, J. R. Fresco, H. S. Rosenkranz, and S. M. Beiser, J. Am. Chem. Soc.,
      77, 3671 (1955).
446. D. N. Ward and J. D. Putch, Makromol. Chem., 55, 121 (1962).
447. K. V. Shooter and J. A. V. Butler, J. Polymer Sci., 23, 705 (1957).
448. D. F. Bradley and A. Rich, J. Am. Chem. Soc., 78, 5898 (1956).
449. D. W. Bannister, C. S. G. Phillips, and R. J. P. Williams, Anal. Chem., 26, 1451
      (1954).

SPECIFIC REFRACTIVE INDEX INCREMENTS OF POLYMERS IN DILUTE SOLUTIONS

R. Chiang

Chemstrand Research Center
Durham, North Carolina

Contents

A. INTRODUCTION

This section presents a compilation of the specific refractive index increments, dn/dc, of polymers in solutions. This quantity is needed to calculate molecular weights, shapes and dimensions of polymers in solution using the light scattering equation:

$$\frac{K\,c}{R_\theta} = \frac{1}{\langle M\rangle_w P(\theta)} + 2A_2\,c \tag{1}$$

where

$$K = (2\pi^2/N\lambda^4)(n_o\,dn/dc)^2, \tag{2}$$

c is the concentration of the polymer in g/ml, R_θ is the reduced intensity at angle θ, $\langle M\rangle_w$ is the weight-average molecular weight, $P(\theta)$ is the particle scattering factor (see following section), A_2 is the second virial coefficient, N is Avogadro's number, λ is the wavelength of the light in <u>vacuo</u>, and n_o the refractive index of the solvent. Since dn/dc appears as a squared term in the light scattering equation, an error of 3% in dn/dc, for instance, will result in an error of about 6% in the molecular weight. Therefore this quantity must be determined accurately. The equation for K reduces to

$$K = 3.69 \times 10^{-6}\,n_o^2\,(dn/dc)^2 \text{ for } \lambda = 5461 \text{ Å}$$

$$= 9.09 \times 10^{-6}\,n_o^2\,(dn/dc)^2 \text{ for } \lambda = 4358 \text{ Å}.$$

Frequently, the light scattering equation is expressed in the form:

$$\frac{H\,c}{\tau} = \frac{1}{\langle M\rangle_w P(90)} + 2A_2\,c \tag{3}$$

where τ is the turbidity of the solution in excess of that of solvent, and

$$H = (32\pi^3/3N \ \lambda^4)(n_0 \ dn/dc)^2 \hspace{2cm} (4)$$

$$= 6.18 \times 10^{-5} \ n_0^2 (dn/dc)^2 \ \text{for} \ \lambda = 5461 \ \text{Å}$$

$$= 15.2 \times 10^{-5} \ n_0^2 (dn/dc)^2 \ \text{for} \ \lambda = 4358 \ \text{Å}.$$

Description of Common Methods of Measurement

Differential Refractometers: Values of dn/dc of polymers in dilute solutions are commonly determined by means of a differential refractometer, an interferometer, or a differential prism cell used in conjunction with the optical equipment of a schlieren apparatus[1,9,2]. Ordinary refractometers do not give satisfactory precision for this purpose; even precision refractometers such as Bausch and Lomb instruments and Pulfrich refractometers require solutions of high concentrations.

Differential refractometers are more often used because of their accuracy and ease of operation. Various types of differential refractometers have been described by Debye[1], by Brice and Halwer[2], by Bodmann[3], by Schulz, Bodmann and Cantow[4], and others. Interferometers measure the difference in refractive index between the solution and the solvent with a precision of 10^{-8}. Interferometers such as Hilger-Rayleigh and Zeiss interferometers are often employed.

Frequently it is necessary to determine the dn/dc of polymers at elevated temperatures because there are no solvents available at room temperatures. Differential refractometers modified for use at elevated temperatures with a heating block have been described by Ehl, Loucheux, Reiss, and Benoit[5] and by Drott and Mendelson[6]. Circulating hot paraffin oils of low heat capacity through the jacketed housing in the Brice Phoenix differential refractometer is less satisfactory because of the large temperature gradient occurring between the regulating bath and the cell. For use at moderately high temperatures, a low melting metal such as mercury or Wood's alloy placed in the space between the differential cell and the heated housing provides adequate heat transfer without additional modifications of the instrument[7].

Calibration: The differential refractometers are usually calibrated with standard solutions of known refractive index. The most common standards used are potassium chloride, sodium chloride and sucrose solutions, the refractive index of which have been accurately determined. These values are given at the end of the table for reference. It should be emphasized, however, that reagent-grade potassium chloride, sodium chloride as well as sucrose are contaminated with atmospheric moisture and should be dried prior to use. If the refractive index values of potassium chloride and sodium chloride solutions obtained by Kruis[8] are used for calibration, the specific drying procedure used by that author, namely 300°C under vacuum[9], should be followed. (Bodmann[3] reported that drying of sodium chloride and potassium chloride for 48 hrs. at either 220 or 300°C gives identical results). It should be taken into account that the values of dn/dc of potassium chloride, sodium chloride and sucrose change slightly with concentration as shown in the table.

Use of the Table

In the following table, the first column lists the name of the polymer, the second column, the solvent. The solvent mixtures are given in vol % unless otherwise indicated. The third column lists the temperatures at which the measurements were carried out; where the temperatures are not reported, the measurements were presumably carried out at 25°C or at room temperatures. The 4th and 5th columns give the dn/dc values obtained at 5461 and 4358 Å, respectively. The results obtained at other wavelengths as well as those for which wavelengths were not specified are listed in column 6.

The unit of dn/dc, unless otherwise specified, is ml/g.

The polymers are divided into several subgroups and are arranged alphabetically within these groups.

It is gratifying to see from the table that the agreements among the results obtained by independent workers are remarkably good. As an illustration, the average value of dn/dc of polystyrene in butanone measured at 25°C and 5461Å reported by 25 laboratories was 0.219 with a standard deviation of ±0.0024; this certainly reflects an excellent agreement. Although this case is exceptional, there are many other systems in which the accuracy of dn/dc is at least as good as, and often exceeds, the accuracy of the light scattering data obtainable under even the most careful conditions.

The data compiled here cover a period from the time when light scattering techniques were first applied to the characterization of high polymers to the end of the year 1964.

Suggested References

N. Bauer, K. Fajans, and S. Z. Lewis: "Refractometry," Chapter XVIII in Weissberger, "Technique of Organic Chemistry," Interscience Publishers, Inc., New York, 1960, Part II, Vol. I.

P. Doty and J. T. Edsall, "Advances in Protein Chemistry," Vol. VI., Academic Press, New York, 1951.

M. M. Fishman, "Light Scattering by Colloidal Systems--An Annotated Bibliography," Technical Service Laboratories, River Edge, N. J., 1957; with Supplement, 1958.

E. P. Geiduschek and A. Holtzer: "Application of Light Scattering to Biological Systems: Deoxyribonucleic Acid and the Muscle Proteins," in "Advances in Biological and Medical Physics," ed. by C. A. Tobias and J. H. Lawrence, Academic Press, New York, 1958, Vol. VI.

J. P. Kratohvil, Anal. Chem., 36, 458R-472R (1964).

M. Kurata and W. H. Stockmayer, Fortschr. Hochpolymer Forsch., 3, 196-312 (1963).

G. Meyerhoff, Fortschr. Hochpolymer Forsch., 3, 59-105 (1961).

K. A. Stacey, "Light Scattering in Physical Chemistry," Academic Press, New York, 1956.

B. Table of Specific Refractive Index Increments of Polymer Solutions

Name	Solvent	Temp, °C	dn/dc 5461Å	dn/dc 4358Å	dn/dc Others	Ref.
		1 - POLYOLEFINS				
Polyethylene	Chlorobenzene	81.0	...	0.0630	...	55
	1-Chloronaphtha-lene	135	-0.190	...	...	56,57
		90	-0.199	...	...	58,59
		125	-0.191	...	...	58,59
		140	-0.191	...	...	6
		99.5	-0.1924	...	...	60
		104.5	-0.1927	...	...	
		109	-0.1934	...		
		114	-0.1927	...		
		120	-0.1917	...		
		125	-0.1911	...		

$$\frac{d}{dT}(\frac{dn}{dc}) \cong 0.3 \times 10^{-4}$$

Name	Solvent	Temp, °C	dn/dc 5461Å	dn/dc 4358Å	dn/dc Others	Ref.
		114	-0.1957	...	...	5
		127	-0.1967	...		
		128	-0.1955	...		
		139	-0.1956	...		
		140	-0.1961	...		
		145	-0.1967	...	...	
		151	-0.1943	...		
		105	-0.188	...	...	61
		90	-0.183	...	...	62
		90	-0.198	...	...	63
		125	-0.195	...	...	63
	1,2,3,4-Tetra-hydronaphthalene	99.5	-0.0779	...	...	60
		104.5	-0.0773	...		
		109	-0.0766	...		
		114	-0.0759	..	...	
		120	-0.0745	...	...	
		125	-0.0736	...	...	

$$\frac{d}{dT}(\frac{dn}{dc}) = 1.8 \times 10^{-4}$$

Name	Solvent	Temp, °C	dn/dc 5461Å	dn/dc 4358Å	dn/dc Others	Ref.
-- , low mol. wt.[g]	1-Chloronaphtha-lene	65	-0.1951	...	...	7
		70	-0.1947	...	...	
		75	-0.1954	...	...	
		80	-0.1949	...	...	
	1,2,3,4-Tetra-hydronaphthalene	81.5	-0.0807	-0.0904	...	6

Name	Solvent	Temp, °C	dn/dc			Ref.
			5461Å	4358Å	Others	
Polyethylene (Cont'd.)						
-- , low mol. wt.[g]	1,2,3,4-Tetra- hydronaphthalene	50	-0.0840	...	...	7
		55	-0.0837	...	...	
		60	-0.0832	...	...	
		65	-0.0826	...	...	
		70	-0.0821	...	...	
		75	-0.0816	...	...	
		80	-0.0812	...	...	
		$\frac{d}{dT}(\frac{dn}{dc}) = 0.96 \times 10^{-4}$				
Poly(ethylene-co-propylene) (70/30)	1-Chloronaphthalene	135	-0.190	...	...	64
Poly(1-butene)[f]	n-Nonane	35	...	0.092	...	53
		80	...	0.108	..	
Polypropylene, isotactic	1-Chloronaphthalene	140	-0.188	...	...	56
		125	-0.189 ±0.005	...	...	70
		140	-0.195	...	...	6
atactic		50	-0.190	...	...	70a
		60	-0.188	...	...	
Poly(trifluoro-chloroethylene)	Mesitylene	145	0.027	...	...	65

SPECIFIC REFRACTIVE INDEX INCREMENTS

Name	Solvent	Temp,°C	dn/dc 5461Å	dn/dc 4358Å	dn/dc Others	Ref.
			2 - POLYDIENES			
Polybutadiene[d]	Carbon disulfide	25	-0.126[e]	...	...	48
	Cyclohexane	25	0.1174	...	...	49
	n-Hexane	25	0.152	...	...	48
cis	Cyclohexane		...	0.114	...	50
1,4-trans/1,2-79/21	Cyclohexane	25	0.118	0.126	...	51
	Heptane	25	0.141	0.151	...	51
Poly(butadiene-co-styrene (70/30)	Cyclohexane	-	...	0.124	...	50
Polyisoprene, 1,4-cis	n-Heptane/n-propanol (78/22)	25	0.162	...	...	69
Crêperubber	Chloroform	25	0.095	0.100	...	148
	Cyclohexane	25	0.1238	0.1305	...	148
	Cyclohexene	25	0.0943	0.0988	...	148
	Decalin	25	0.0605	0.0669	...	148
	n-Hexane	25	0.1802	0.1886	...	148
Rubber	Chloroform	-	0.105	...	...	149
	Hexane	-	0.189	...	...	149
GR-S rubber	Carbon tetrachloride	25	...	...	0.120	150
	Ethylene chloride	25	...	...	0.166	150
	Toluene	25	...	...	0.056	150
Poly(trichlorobuta-diene),	Benzene	25	...	...	0.06	52

$-(CH_2CH=CClCCl_2)_n-$

Name	Solvent	Temp, °C	dn/dc 5461Å	4358Å	Others	Ref.

3 - VINYL POLYMERS

Name	Solvent	Temp, °C	5461Å	4358Å	Others	Ref.
Poly(acrylic acid)	Dioxane	25	...	0.088	...	231
	Water	-	0.140	...	...	232
	0.2N HCl	-	0.146	...	...	224
Deg. of ionization	NaCl solution Ionic strength					
0.102	0.100	30	...	0.158	...	233
0.105	0.010		...	0.156	...	
0.335	0.100		...	0.179	...	
0.344	0.010		...	0.186	...	
0.947	1.00		...	0.253	...	
0.959	0.100		...	0.253	...	
0.994	0.0 0		...	0.261	...	

Polyacrylamides

Name	Solvent	Temp, °C	5461Å	4358Å	Others	Ref.
Poly(acrylamide)	Water	-	0.149	...	...	224
		30	...	...	0.195[w]	224a
		25	0.163	...	...	225
Poly(N-tert-butyl-acrylamide)	Methanol	-	0.234	0.249	...	226

Polyacrylates

Name	Solvent	Temp, °C	5461Å	4358Å	Others	Ref.
Poly(1,1-dihydroper-fluorobutyl acrylate)	Benzotrifluoride	25	...	...	0.0303[w]	10
					0.0311	
					0.0311	
					0.0305	
Poly(ethyl acrylate)	Acetone	25	0.106	0.109	...	11
Poly(methyl acrylate-co-2-vinylpyridine-co-dichlorostyrene) (37/47/16 mole %)						
	Acetic acid	30	...	0.171	...	12
	Butanone	30	...	0.153	...	12
Polyacrylonitrile	γ-Butyrolactone	25	0.079	...	...	42
	Dimethylformamide	25	0.083	...	...	42
		25			0.083	43
		25	...	0.080	...	44
		20	...	0.0797	...	45
		40	...	0.0842	...	45
		20	0.087	...	...	46
		50	0.099	...	...	46
		25	0.089	...	...	47
Poly(methacrylic acid)	Methanol	25	0.134	...	...	170
		-	0.134	...	...	234
	Dil. acid	-	...	0.1594	...	235
	0.001M HCl	25	...	0.159	...	236
		25	0.140	...	...	170
	0.002N HCl	30	...	...	0.138[r]	237

Name	Solvent	Temp,°C	dn/dc 5461Å	dn/dc 4358Å	Others	Ref.
Poly(methacrylic acid) (Cont'd.)						
	0.02N HCl	-	0.158	...	...	224
	0.05M HCl	25	0.137	...	...	170
	0.114N HCl	25	$(n^2-n_o^2)/c = 0.414$		...	239
	Alc. LiBr	-	...	0.154	...	240
	0.05N NaCl	-	0.168	...	...	234
	0.5N NaCl	-	0.183	...	...	234
	Aq. NaOH	-	0.243	...	...	234
	0.5M aq. urea	-	0.152	...	...	234
	Water	-	0.159	...	...	232
		25	0.142	...	...	170
Poly(methacrylic acid-co-2-dimethylaminoethyl methacrylate) (53.7 MMA)						
	5.86M NaCl, pH 5.48	-	...	0.189	...	241
	Water, pH 4.02-5.61	-	...	0.187	...	241
Poly(methacrylamide)	Water	-	0.209	...	...	224
Polymethacrylates						
Poly(n-butyl methacrylate)	Butanone	23	0.104	...	...	13
	Isopropanol	20.0	...	0.1059	...	14
		23.7		0.1066		
		25.0(θ)		0.1068		
		31.0		0.1076		
		45.0		0.1097		
		23(θ)	0.102	0.102	...	13
Poly(cetyl methacrylate)	n-Heptane	25	...	0.116	...	15
Poly(ethyl methacrylate)	Butanone	23	0.104	...	...	16
	Butanone/isopropanol (1/7)	23(θ)	0.107	...	...	16
Poly(2-ethylbutyl methacrylate)	Butanone	25	0.102	0.104	...	17
	Isopropanol	25	0.105	0.109	...	17
Poly(n-hexyl methacrylate)	Butanone	23	0.105	0.105	...	18
	Isopropanol	32.6(θ)	0.106	0.108	...	18
Poly(n-lauryl methacrylate)	n-Amyl alcohol	29.5(θ)	0.0718	0.0744	...	19
	n-Butyl acetate	23	0.090	0.092	...	20
	Isopropyl acetate	13(θ)	0.104	0.107	...	20
Poly(methyl methacrylate)	Acetone	25	0.134	0.136	...	21
		25	0.134	0.136	...	22
		23	0.134	0.137	...	23
		26-28	...	0.139	...	24
		25	...	0.1295	...	25
		25	0.1293	0.1313	0.134[t]	26,27
		28	...	...	0.131[a] ±0.002	28

Remarks and References page IV-309

Name	Solvent	Temp, °C	dn/dc			Ref.
			5461Å	4358Å	Others	
Poly(methyl methacrylate) (Cont'd.)						
	Acetonitrile	25	0.137	0.140	...	21
	Benzene	25	...	0.0398	...	24
		25	-0.010	...	...	29
	Bromobenzene	25	...	...	-0.0363^b	30
		25	-0.058	...	...	29
	Bromobenzene-methanol	25	...	-0.054 $+1.06(1.568-n_o)^u$		31
	1-Bromonaphthalene	25	-0.147	...	...	29
	Butanone	25	0.111	...	...	24,32, 33
		28	...	...	0.111 ± 0.002^a	28
		23	0.111	0.113	...	23
		25	0.112	...	...	34
		25	0.113	0.114	...	35
		-	0.109	...	...	36
		25	0.114	...	...	37
		25	...	0.117	...	38
	Butanone/isopropanol (55/45)	$23(\theta)$	...	0.117	...	38
		10	0.1075	0.1090	...	39
		20	0.114	0.1130	...	
		30	0.1153	0.1167	...	
		40	0.1192	0.1208	...	
	Butyl acetate	-	0.0970	0.0987		26
	Butyl chloride	20	0.0898	0.0913	...	39
		30	0.0934	0.0948	...	
		40	0.0970	0.0984	...	
	Carbon tetrachloride	25	0.023	...	...	29
	Chlorobenzene	25	...	...	-0.0106^b	30
		25	-0.026	...	...	29
	Chloroform	28	...	...	0.056 ± 0.002^a	28
			0.055	...	...	36
			0.0629	0.0631	0.0635^t	26
		25	...	...	0.0494^b	30
	Dioxane	-	0.0707	0.0720	0.074^t	26
	p-Dioxane	25	0.068	...	...	29
		25	...	...	0.0521^b	30
	Ethyl acetate	-	0.1180	0.1200	0.123^t	26
	Isoamyl acetate	20	0.0911	0.0931	...	39
		30	0.0926	0.0945	...	
		40	0.0942	0.0959	...	
		50	0.0957	0.0974	...	

Name	Solvent	Temp., °C	dn/dc			Ref.
			5461Å	4358Å	Others	

Poly(methyl methacrylate) (Cont'd.)

Name	Solvent	Temp., °C	5461Å	4358Å	Others	Ref.
	Nitromethane	25	0.094^c	...	...	32
	Tetrahydrofuran	-	0.0871	0.0887	0.091^t	26
	1,1,2-Trichloro-ethane	-	...	...	0.0245^b	30
Poly(octadecyl methacrylate)	Tetrahydrofuran	-	0.0855	...	...	40
Poly(n-octyl methacrylate)	n-Butanol	16.8(θ)	0.080	0.083	...	41
	Butanone	23	0.107	0.107	...	41

Polystyrenes

Name	Solvent	Temp., °C	5461Å	4358Å	Others	Ref.
Polystyrene	Benzene	40	0.1106	0.1160	...	77
		25	0.106	...	...	29
		25	0.1064	...	...	78
		r.t.	0.107 0.107	0.111	...	79
		25	0.110	...	...	67
		-	...	0.1151	...	80,81
		-	...	0.115	...	82
		-	...	0.118	...	83
	Benzene/cyclohexane					
	1.00/ 0	25	0.108	...	...	84
	75/25		0.129	...	...	
	65/35		0.137	...	...	
	50/50		0.149	...	...	
	35/65		0.160	...	...	
	25/75		0.167	...	...	
	Benzene/cyclohexanol (38.4/61.6)	25(θ)	0.108	...	...	85
	Benzene/isopropanol (65/35)	25	0.154	...	...	31
	(64.2/35.8)	25(θ)	0.159	...	...	85
	Benzene/methanol	25	$0.108+0.1447(1-\psi)^V$			31
	(80/20)	25	0.137	...	...	31
	(77.8/22.2)	25(θ)	0.145	...	...	85
	(3.27/1)	25	0.1222	...	...	67
	$C_6H_6/(CH_2Cl)_2CHOH$ (33/67)	-	0.112	...	...	31
	Bromobenzene	25	0.042	...	...	29
		-	...	0.066	...	83
	1-Bromonaphthalene	25	-0.051	...	...	29
	Butanone	25	0.220	...	...	29,33, 78,86
		25	0.220	0.231	...	87

Remarks and References page IV-309

Name	Solvent	Temp. °C	dn/dc			Ref.
			5461Å	4358Å	Others	
Polystyrene (Cont'd.)						
	Butanone	25	0.221	...	...	88
		20	0.221	...	...	89
		-	...	0.239	...	83
		r.t.	0.220	0.220	...	79
			0.221	0.231	...	
				0.229	...	
				0.229	...	
				0.222	...	
		25	0.218[i] ±0.002	0.231[j] ±0.004	...	90
		25	0.219	0.232	...	91
			0.214	0.231	...	
				0.231	...	
				0.229	...	
		20	0.219	0.228	...	91
			0.225	0.234	...	
				0.230	...	
				0.230	...	
		7.5	0.2138	0.2258	...	92
		15	0.2155	0.2275	...	
		20	0.2167	0.2287	...	
		25	0.2178	0.2298	...	
		30	0.2189	0.2309	...	
		35	0.2201	0.2321	...	
		40	0.2213	0.2333	...	
		45	0.2225	0.2345	...	
		30	...	0.228	...	6
		-	...	0.223	...	93
		25	...	0.222	...	94
		20	0.214	...	...	95
		-	...	...	0.216[a]	96
		20	...	0.229	...	97
		-	0.219	0.229	...	98
		25	0.218	0.231	...	35
	Butanone/isopropanol (6/1)	23(θ)	0.204	...	...	99
	(88.6/11.4)	25(θ)	0.211	...	...	85
	(87/13)	20	0.221	...	...	89
	(85/15)	25	0.219	...	...	31
	(50/50)	20(θ)	...	0.207	...	91
	(50/50)	26(θ)	0.217	0.228	...	91

Name	Solvent	Temp., °C	dn/dc 5461Å	dn/dc 4358Å	dn/dc Others	Ref.
Polystyrene (Cont'd.)						
	Butanone/methanol	25	0.219	...	...	31
		25(θ)	0.214	...	...	85
	(88.7/11.3)	25(θ)	0.214	...	...	85
	Butanone/ $(CH_2Cl)_2CHOH$	25	0.165	...	...	31
	Carbon tetrachloride	25	0.146	...	...	29
	Carbon tetrachloride/ methanol (81.7/18.3)	25(θ)	0.162	...	...	85
	Cyclohexane	28.9	0.1689	0.1798	...	100
		30.0	0.1693	0.1800	...	
		34.0	0.1705	0.1810	...	
		38.6	0.1719	0.1823	...	
		53.5	0.1765	0.1884	...	

$$\frac{d}{dT}\left(\frac{dn}{dc}\right) = 3.08\times10^{-4}\ 3.58\times10^{-4}$$

Name	Solvent	Temp., °C	dn/dc 5461Å	dn/dc 4358Å	dn/dc Others	Ref.
		35	0.1705	0.1814	...	77,100
		45	0.1739	0.1849	...	
		55	0.1772	0.1884	...	
		30	...	...	0.191^k ±0.008	102
		60	0.185	0.197	...	6
		20	0.1682	0.1795	...	92
		21	0.1685	0.1798	...	
		22	0.1687	0.1801	...	
		23	0.1690	0.1804	...	
		25	0.1695	0.1810	...	
		30	0.1709	0.1825	...	
		35	0.1723	0.1840	...	
		40	0.1738	0.1855	...	
		45	0.1752	0.1870	...	
		33.8-41.9	0.173	0.183	...	101
		35(θ)	...	0.181	...	101a
		35(θ)	0.171	...	...	85
		35(θ)	0.172	...	...	103
		34	...	0.181^e	...	104
		43	...	0.186^e	...	
		57	...	0.189^e	...	
		25	0.1503	...	...	78
	Chlorobenzene	-	...	0.099	...	83
	Chlorobenzene/iso- propyl ether (32.0/68.0)	25(θ)	0.192	...	...	85

Remarks and References page IV-309

Name	Solvent	Temp., °C	dn/dc			Ref.
			5461Å	4358Å	Others	
Polystyrene (Cont d.)						
	Chloroform	20	...	0.195	...	97
	p-Chlorotoluene	25	...	0.0925	...	105
		33	...	0.157[c]	...	101a
	Decalin	24	0.129	...	...	5
		52	0.137	...	...	
		60	0.138	...	...	
		87	0.143	...	...	
		104	0.147			
		123	0.152	...	...	
		139	0.155	...	...	
		$\frac{d}{dT}\left(\frac{dn}{dc}\right) = 2.2 \times 10^{-4}$				
	Dichloroethane	20	0.161	...	...	106
	Diethyl fumarate/ CH$_2$ClCH$_2$OH (80/20)	25	0.152	...	...	31
	Diethyl malonate	36	...	0.193[c]	...	101a
	Dioxane	25	0.171	...	...	33
		25	0.1723	...	...	78
		25	0.176	...	...	88
	p-Dioxane	25	0.168	...	...	29
	Dioxane/methanol (71.4/28.6)	25(θ)	0.191	...	...	85
	Tetrahydrofuran/me- thanol (71.3/28.7)	25(θ)	0.179	...	...	85
	Toluene	21.2	0.1068	0.1109	...	100
		28.9	0.1089	0.1126	...	
		30.0	0.1096	0.1134	...	
		38.6	0.1122	0.1168	...	
		58.0	0.1185	0.1242	...	
		79.4	0.1226	0.1280	...	
		$\frac{d}{dT}\left(\frac{dn}{dc}\right) = 2.89 \times 10^{-4} \quad 3.21 \times 10^{-4}$				
		30	0.109	0.114	...	6
		60	0.118	0.121	...	
		25	0.1076	...	...	7
		35	0.1111	...	...	
		50	0.1160	...	...	
		60	0.1178	...	...	
		70	0.1196	...	...	
		$\frac{d}{dT}\left(\frac{dn}{dc}\right) = 2.8 \times 10^{-4}$				

Name	Solvent	Temp., °C	dn/dc 5461Å	dn/dc 4358Å	Others	Ref.
Polystyrene (Cont'd.)						
	Toluene	25	...	0.112	...	86,107
		-	0.108	0.112	...	98
		25	...	0.112	...	107
		-	...	0.113	...	108
		20	0.108	...	...	89
		20	0.104	...	...	95
		25	0.1091^l	0.1129^l	...	109
		25	0.109	...	...	88
		20	0.110	...	...	110
		-	...	0.118	...	93
		30	...	...	0.108^k ±0.004	102
		-	...	...	0.106^a	96
		25	0.104, 0.108	0.108, 0.112	...	79
		30	...	0.111	...	111
		25	0.110	0.114	...	112
		r.t.	0.109^i	0.111^j ±0.001	...	90
		25	0.109	0.114	...	91
Polystyrene latex	Water		...	0.257	...	113
Polystyrene-polyiso-butylene mixture	Chloroform					
0 vol.% styrene		20-21	0.073	...	...	114
23			0.092	...	...	
47			0.117	...	...	
59			0.124	...	...	
72			0.137	...	...	
100			0.160	...	...	
Poly(styrene-co-acrylonitrile) 61.7 mole % styrene)	Butanone	30	...	0.203	...	115a
Poly(styrene-co-methyl methacrylate)						
random copolymer						
100 mole % styrene	Benzene	25	0.1086	...	...	115
76.1			0.0770	...	...	
65.5			0.0683	...	...	
39.3			0.0554	...	...	
32.1			0.1447	...	...	
19.6			0.0378	...	...	
0			0.0098	...	...	

Remarks and References page IV-309

Name	Solvent	Temp., °C	dn/dc			Ref.
			5461Å	4358Å	Others	

Poly(styrene-co-methyl methacrylate) (Cont'd.)

random copolymer

100 mole % styrene	Butanone	25	0.250	...	...	115
76.1			0.215	...	...	
65.6			0.181	...	...	
39.3			0.177	...	...	
32.1			0.161	...	...	
0			0.121	...	...	
100 mole % styrene	Ethyl acetate	25	0.226	...	...	115
76.1			0.193	...	...	
65.5			0.178	...	...	
39.3			0.172	...	...	
32.1			0.158	...	...	
19.6			0.149	...	...	
0			0.120	...	...	
50%	Butanone	25	0.172	...	...	33
	Nitroethane	25	0.148	...	...	33
70%	Benzene	25	0.068	...	...	29
	Bromobenzene	25	0.010[e]	...	...	29
	Butanone	25	0.185	...	...	29
	Carbon tetrachloride	25	0.103	...	...	29
	Chlorobenzene	25	0.045	...	...	29
	p-Dioxane	25	0.136	...	...	29
block copolymer (unfractionated)	Butanone	25	0.178	0.184	...	35
	Bromoform	25	-0.023	-0.025	...	35
	1-Chloronaphthalene	25	-0.053	-0.075	...	35
	o-Dichlorobenzene	25	0.019	0.018	...	35
	1,2-Dichloroethane	25	0.126	0.135	...	35
	Toluene	25	0.075	0.075	...	35
block copolymer (fractions)						
7% styrene	Butanone	25	0.119	0.123	...	35
19			0.132	0.137	...	
25			0.139	0.144	...	
33			0.148	0.153	...	
40			0.154	0.161	...	
44			0.158	0.166	...	
60			0.176	0.184	...	
74			0.190	0.202	...	
75			0.193	0.202	...	
77			0.194	0.205	...	

Name	Solvent	Temp., °C	dn/dc 5461Å	dn/dc 4358Å	Others	Ref.

Poly(styrene-co-methyl methacrylate) (Cont'd.)

block copolymer (fractions)

Name	Solvent	Temp., °C	5461Å	4358Å	Others	Ref.
83% styrene	Butanone	25	0.200	0.211	...	35
76			0.193	0.203	...	
77			0.194	0.204	...	
73			0.190	0.200	...	
80			0.198	0.208	...	
72			0.190	0.198	...	
70% styrene	Benzene	25	0.074	...	...	29
	Bromobenzene	25	0.015	...	...	29
	1-Bromonaphthalene	25	-0.096	...	...	29
	Butanone	25	0.195	...	...	29
	Carbon tetrachloride	25	0.116	...	...	29
	Chlorobenzene	25	0.051	...	...	29
	p-Dioxane	25	0.139	...	...	29
Polystyrene-poly-(methyl methacrylate) mixture (65/35)	Benzene	25	0.065	...	...	29
	Bromobenzene	25	0.007	...	...	29
	1-Bromonaphthalene	25	-0.088	...	...	29
	Butanone	25	0.180	...	...	29
	Chlorobenzene	25	0.044	...	...	29
	p-Dioxane	25	0.133	...	...	29
Poly(styrene-p-sulfonic acid) (K salt)	Aq. solution (I.S. 0.100)^x	30	...	0.197	...	233
Poly(p-chlorostyrene)	Butanone	-	0.188	...	...	116
Poly(2,5-dichloro-styrene)	Dioxane	20	0.188	...	...	117
	Ethyl acetate/ethanol (15/1 w/w)	30.5(θ)	0.226	...	...	117a
Poly(3,4-dichloro-styrene)	Butyl acetate/butanol (13/1 w/w)	32.9(θ)	0.169	...	...	118
Poly(α-methylstyrene)	Toluene	25	...	0.137	...	119
Poly(vinyl alcohol)	Water	60	0.1645	0.1695	...	130
		25	0.170	...	...	131
		20	0.150	...	...	132
		30	0.164	0.168	0.164^n	133
		20	0.144	...	...	134
Poly(vinyl bromide)	Cyclohexanone	35	0.075	...	...	135
	Tetrahydrofuran	20	0.112	...	0.110^p	136
Poly(vinyl chloride)	Cyclohexanone	-	...	...	0.070	137
		25	...	...	0.0781	43
	Dimethylformamide	25	...	...	0.084	43
	Dioxane	-	0.0850 0.0865	...	...	138
	Tetrahydrofuran	20	...	0.1124 ±0.00044	...	139
		25	...	...	0.102	43

Remarks and References page IV-309

Name	Solvent	Temp., °C	dn/dc			Ref.
			5461Å	4358Å	Others	
Poly(vinyl chloride) (Cont'd.)						
-- , latex	Water	-	0.200	...	...	140
Poly(vinyl esters)						
Poly(vinyl acetate)	Acetone	30	...	0.104	...	122,123
	Benzene	25	...	...	-0.0257[b]	30
		-	...	...	0.027	124
		25	...	0.030	...	125
	Butanone	25	0.080	0.080	...	125,126, 127
		30		0.080	...	123
	Butanone/n-heptane (73.2/26.8)	25(θ)	0.0753[m]	0.0753[m]	...	125,126
	Chlorobenzene	25	...	...	-0.0397[b]	30
	p-Dioxane	25	...	...	0.325[b]	30
	Methanol	-	...	0.1319	...	128
	Toluene	25	...	...	-0.0198[b]	30
	Trichlorobenzene	-	...	0.1030	...	129
Poly(vinyl laurate)	2,2-dimethylbutane	25	0.114	0.118	...	11
Poly(vinyl palmitate)	2,2-dimethylbutane	25	0.120	0.122	...	11
Poly(vinyl ethers)						
Poly(vinyl n-butyl ether)	Butanone	25	...	0.0792	...	141
Poly(vinyl ethyl ether)	Butanone	25	...	0.0736	...	141
Poly(vinyl isopropyl ether)	Butanone	25	...	0.0827	...	141
Poly(vinyl methyl ether)	Butanone	25	...	0.0944	...	141
Poly(vinyl octadecyl ether)	Tetrahydrofuran	-	0.0674	...	...	40
Poly(4-vinylpyridine)	Ethanol	-	...	0.231	...	142
		25	0.183	...	...	143
	95% ethanol	-	...	0.231	...	142
	Methanol	25	0.224	...	...	143
Poly(vinylpyridine-co-acrylic acid) (56.4 mole % VP)						
Na-salt	0.4M KCl	25	0.257	...	...	144
Hydrochloride	0.4M KCl	26	0.277	...	...	144
		26	0.239[y]	...	...	144

SPECIFIC REFRACTIVE INDEX INCREMENTS

Name	Solvent	Temp., °C	dn/dc			Ref.
			5461Å	4358Å	Others	
Poly(vinylpyridine-co-methyl acrylate) (55.8 mole % VP)						
	Benzene	27	0.066	...	...	144
	Butanone	27	0.178	...	...	144
Poly(4-vinyl-N-n-butylpyridinium bromide)	Water	25	0.188	...	...	143
Poly(vinylpyrroli-done)	Chloroform	25	0.108	0.108	...	145
	Methanol	25	0.1765	...	...	67
	Water	25	...	0.175	...	146
		25	...	0.178	...	147
		25	0.185	0.185	...	145
		25	0.135(?)	...	...	67
Poly(vinylsulfonic acid):						
K-salt	0.5M KCl	25	16.41×10^{-3} l./eq.		...	243
NH_4-salt	0.5M NH_4Cl	25	17.48×10^{-3} l./eq.		...	243

4 - CONDENSATION POLYMERS

Name	Solvent	Temp., °C	5461Å	4358Å	Others	Ref.
Poly(6-aminocaproic acid)	85% Formic acid	-	...	0.141	...	227
Poly(1,4-cyclohexy-lenedimethylene terephthalate)	Trifluoroacetic acid	25	0.268	...	...	120a
Poly(ethylene terephthalate)	Trifluoroacetic acid	25	0.268	...	...	120a
Poly(hexamethylene adipamide)	m-Cresol	25	-0.016	...	...	228
	Dichloroacetic acid	25	0.098	...	...	228
		50	0.099	...	...	
		80	0.104	...	...	
	90% Formic acid	25	...	0.145	...	229
		25	0.145	...	...	228
	90% Formic acid + 0.2M KCl	25	...	0.143	...	229

Remarks and References page IV-309

Name	Solvent	Temp., °C	dn/dc			Ref.
			5461Å	4358Å	Others	

Poly(hexamethylene adipamide) (Cont'd.)

Name	Solvent	Temp., °C	5461Å	4358Å	Others	Ref.
	90% Formic acid + 0.5M KCl	25	...	.140	...	229
	90% Formic acid + 1.0M KCl	25	...	0.136	...	229
	90% Formic acid + 1.5M KCl	25	...	0.131	...	229
	90% Formic acid + 2.0M KCl	25	...	0.126	...	229
		25	0.126	...	...	?88
			0.122	...	...	
			0.123	...	...	
	90% Formic acid + 2.5M KCl	25	...	0.122	...	229
	Formic acid/2.0M KCl (98/2)	25	...	0.137	...	229
	(95/5)	25	...	0.129	...	229
	(90/10)	25	...	0.126	...	229
	(85/15)	25	...	0.124	...	229
	(82.5/17.5)	25	...	0.123	...	229
	Octafluoropentanol	25	0.192	...	...	228
	95% H_2SO_4	25	0.0815	...	...	228
	2,2,3,3-Tetrafluoro-propanol with 0.1 N CF_3COONa	25	...	0.190	...	230
Poly(4,4'-isopropylidenediphenylene carbonate)						
	Chloroform	20(θ)	...	0.165	...	54
Polyurethan	Methanol	22	0.150 0.145	0.152 0.148	...	121

SPECIFIC REFRACTIVE INDEX INCREMENTS

Name	Solvent	Temp., °C	dn/dc 5461Å	dn/dc 4358Å	dn/dc Others	Ref.
			5 - POLYOXIDES			
Poly(ethylene oxide)	Butanone		0.094 0.097	...	...	66
	Chloroform/n-hexane (0.474/1)	20(θ)	0.0915	...	...	67
	Dioxane		0.045	...	...	66
	Methanol		0.149 0.150 0.149	...		66
		25	0.143	...	...	67
	Water		0.139	0.141	...	66
			...	0.145	...	
			...	0.142	...	
Polyformaldehyde	Benzyl alcohol	130	...	0.017	...	68
	p-Chlorophenol	90	...	0.003	...	68
	Dimethylformamide	150	...	0.075	...	68
	Phenol	100	...	0.027	...	68
Poly(propylene oxide)	Benzene	25	-0.0448	-0.0530	...	71
	Chlorobenzene	25	-0.0638	-0.0658	...	71
	Heptane	40	0.0460	0.0460	...	71
	Hexane	25	0.0775	0.0775	...	71
		46	0.0887	0.0887	...	
		46	0.0895	0.0895	...	
		57	0.101	0.101	...	
		57	0.104	0.104		
	Isceon 113 ($CCl_2F \cdot CClF_2$)	25	0.115	0.118	...	71
	Isooctane	35	0.0655	0.0655	...	71

Remarks and References page IV-309

Name	Solvent	Temp., °C	dn/dc 5461Å	dn/dc 4358Å	dn/dc Others	Ref.
6 - POLYSULFONES						
Poly(1-butene sulfone)	Chloroform	20	...	0.0970	0.0949^n	120
Poly(cyclohexene sulfone)	Chloroform	20	...	0.1133	0.1104^n	120
Poly(1-dodecene sulfone)	Chloroform	20	...	0.0695	0.0581^n	120
Poly(1-hexene sulfone)	Butanone	20	...	0.1229	...	120
	Butanone/isopropanol (37/63)	27	...	0.1242	...	120
		37	...	0.1261	...	
	(41.5/58.5)	7	...	0.1208	...	120
		20	...	0.1233	...	
	Chloroform	20	...	0.0790	0.0782^n	120
	n Hexyl chloride	7	...	0.0796	...	120
		20	...	0.0834	...	120
Poly(1-octene sulfone)	Chloroform	20	...	0.0732	0.0718^n	120

7 - SEMIORGANIC AND INORGANIC POLYMERS

Name	Solvent	Temp., °C	dn/dc 5461Å	dn/dc 4358Å	dn/dc Others	Ref.
Poly(dimethyl siloxane)	Benzene	20	0.0993	...	...	72
D.P. = 1,060,000	Bromocyclohexane	25	0.0783		...	73
= 780,000			0.0792		...	
= 340,000			0.0814		...	
= 84,600			0.090		...	
= 33,000			0.090		...	
	Toluene	25	0.094 ±0.003	0.103 ±0.005	... ...	74
		14.6	$-0.0947+0.099c$	$-0.1042+0.104c$		75
		19.9	$-0.0941+0.099c$	$-0.1037+0.104c$		
		25.4	$-0.0933+0.099c$	$-0.1029+0.104c$		
		29.9	$-0.0933+0.099c$	$-0.1027+0.104c$		
		34.8	$-0.0927+0.099c$	$-0.1023+0.104c$		
		$\frac{d}{dT}(\frac{dn}{dc}) =$	0.96×10^{-4}	0.95×10^{-4}		
Poly(phenyl siloxane)	Benzene	-	...	...	0.067^h	76
Poly(silicic acid)	Aq. solution	-	0.65	...	...	244
Poly(sodium phosphate)	0.10M NaBr	25	0.109	0.109	...	256
	0.25M NaBr		0.105	0.105	...	
	0.35M NaBr		0.102	0.102	...	
	0.40M NaBr		0.101	0.101	...	

Name	Solvent	Temp., °C	dn/dc 5461Å	dn/dc 4358Å	Others	Ref.
			5461Å	4358Å	Others	

8 - CELLULOSE AND DERIVATIVES

Name	Solvent	Temp., °C	5461Å	4358Å	Others	Ref.
Cellulose	Cadoxen (Triethy-lenediamine cadmium hydroxide)	25	0.182	0.185	...	166
Cellulose acetate	Acetone	-	0.115 0.115 0.116	...	...	151
D.S. = 2.5	Acetone	-	...	0.137	...	152
	Tetrachloroethane	25	...	...	0.060	150
Cellulose nitrate						
N content, %	Acetone					
10.98		-	0.0988^q	0.1022^q	...	156
11.89			0.0985	0.1010	...	
12.55			0.0950	0.0968	...	
13.94			0.0903	0.0930	...	
13.96			0.0900	-	...	
Cellulose trinitrate	Acetone	25	...	0.105	...	153,154, 155
	Ethyl acetate	30	...	0.102 ±0.002	...	153
		25	0.103	...	...	43
		25	...	0.104	...	155
Cellulose tricarb-anilate	Acetone	27	0.2033	0.2176	...	157
		7	0.1966	0.2069	...	
Cellulose trica-proate	1-Chloronaphthalene	24	0.147	...	...	158
	Dimethylformamide	41(θ)	0.0478	0.0442	...	158
	Dioxane / water (100/7)	63	0.104	...	...	158
Cellulose xanthate	NaOH solution	-	0.20	...	...	159
	-	-	0.212	...	...	160
	-	-	0.230	...	...	161
Carboxymethyl cellulose:						
	0.001 to 0.05 M NaCl	25	...	0.136^z	...	170
D.S. = 1.05	0.005 M NaCl	25	...	0.138	...	165
	0.2 M NaCl	25	...	0.134	...	165
D.S. = 1.15	0.5 M NaCl	25	...	0.154	...	171
	0.1 M NaCl	25	0.147 ±0.0007	...	...	172
Na-salt:	Cadoxen					
D.S. = 0.94		25	0.145	0.147	...	173
			0.145	0.148	...	
D.S. = 0.44			0.162	0.164	...	
			0.161	0.162	...	
D.S. = 0.21			0.171	0.175	...	
			0.168	0.171	...	

Name	Solvent	Temp., °C	dn/dc			Ref.
			5461Å	4358Å	Others	
Ramie Crystallites	Phosphate buffer	-	0.148	...	...	174
	Water	-	0.148	...	...	174
Diethylacetamide cellulose xanthate						
D.S. = 0.40	Dimethyl Sulfoxide/	24	0.144	...	...	162
0.49	water (90/10)		0.098	...	...	
0.60			0.144	...	...	
0.80			0.144	...	...	
0.92			0.098	...		
1.00			0.096	...	...	
1.22			0.079	...	...	
Ethyl cellulose	Methanol	25	...	0.130	...	163
Ethyl hydroxyethyl cellulose	Water	25	0.146	...	...	168
			0.146			
			0.151			
			0.148			
	Water	25	0.146	...	...	169
Hydroxyethyl cellulose	Cadoxen	25	0.130	0.132	...	164
			0.131	0.134		
	0.5M NaCl	25	0.131	0.133	...	164
	Water	25	0.139	0.141	...	164,167

SPECIFIC REFRACTIVE INDEX INCREMENTS

Name	Solvent	Temp., °C	dn/dc 5461Å	4358Å	Others	Ref.
\multicolumn 9 - POLYSACCHARIDES						
Amylose	KCl solution (pH 5)	-	...	0.146	...	175
	1 M KOH	-	...	0.146	...	175
	0.2N NaOH	-	...	0.142	...	176
	Water	-	0.154	0.156	...	177
		25	0.154	0.151	...	178
	Dimethyl sulfoxide	25	0.0659	0.0676	...	179
	1N KOH	25	...	0.146	...	179
	0.5N KCl	25	...	0.156	...	179
Amylose tricarb-anilate	Acetone	27	0.2164	0.2279	...	157
		7	0.2094	0.2218	...	
Araban		-	...	0.147	...	180
Araban acetate	Butanone	-	0.0886	...	...	181
	1% Dimethylformamide in water	-	...	0.142	...	180,181
	2M NaCl	-	...	0.130	...	180,181
Arabinose		-	...	0.144	...	180
Dextran	Water	25	0.150	...	...	184
		-	0.151	...	...	185
		-	...	0.151	...	186
		-	0.148	...	...	187
Dextrose	Water	-	...	0.147	...	180
Polyglucoside	Water	25	0.154	0.151	...	190
Guaran triacetate	Acetonitrile	22.5	0.1200 ±0.0004	...	...	182
Poly(levoglucosan)	Water	25	...	$K=3.43\times10^{-7}$	...	189
			...	0.1445	...	188
4-O-Methylglu-curonoxylan	Dimethyl sulfoxide with 2% water	25	0.064 ±0.006	...	...	191
Sodium carrageenate	Sodium acetate buffer (pH 5.5, I.S. 0.05)[x]	-	...	...	0.131	183

Name	Solvent	Temp., °C	dn/dc 5461Å	dn/dc 4358Å	dn/dc Others	Ref.

10 - PEPTIDES AND PROTEINS

Most of the measurements on dn/dc of proteins were carried out in dil. salt solutions with adjusted ionic strength and pH. The effect of wavelength on dn/dc of most proteins can be adequately represented by the relation

$$(dn/dc) = (dn/dc)_{5780} (0.940 + 2.00 \times 10^6/\lambda^2)$$

where λ is in Å (192).

The effect of charge, e, can be expressed by the equation

$$(dn/dc)_e = (dn/dc)_o (1 + a\ e)$$

where $\underline{a}$ is a proportionality constant, which is the same for both ovalbumin and serum albumin. Casassa and Eisenberg[255] pointed out that the change in dn/dc with the concentration of the salt can be represented by

$$(dn/dc)_m - (dn/dc)_o = -\bar{v}_2 (n_m - n_o)$$

where $(dn/dc)_m$ = measured dn/dc in a solvent containing salt with refractive index n_m

$(dn/dc)_o$ = measured dn/dc in the absence of salt

$\bar{v}_2$ = partial specific volume of the polymer.

For the effect of temperature on dn/dc, see ref. 192.

Albumins

Name	Solvent	Temp., °C	dn/dc 5461Å	dn/dc 4358Å	dn/dc Others	Ref.
Ovalbumin	Water	25	0.1865	0.1935	0.1851^n	192
		0	...	...	0.1876^n	192
	Aq. solution (pH 4.95)	0.5	...	...	0.1876^n	192
	0.1M NaCl (pH 4.8)	25	0.1820	0.1883	...	193
	0.1N HCl	25	0.185	...	...	194
Serum albumin		25	...	0.195	...	195
	Water	25	...	...	0.187	78
	Phosphate buffer	-	...	...	0.1875	196
Beef serum albumin	Phosphate buffer (pH 7.8, I.S. 0.18)^x	25	...	0.1884	...	197
Bovine serum albumin	Water	25	0.1883	0.1954	0.1869^n	192,192a
		0	...	...	0.1901^n	192
	Aq. solution (pH 5.05)	0.5	...	...	0.1901^n	192
	0.1M NaCl (pH 5.2)	25	0.1854	0.1924	...	193
	Acetate buffer 0.2M (pH 4.50)	25	...	0.1929 ±0.0011	...	198
Horse serum albumin	Acetate buffer 0.1M (pH 4.8)	25	0.1844	0.1912	...	193
Human serum albumin	Water	25	0.1868	0.1938	0.1854^n	192
		0	...	...	0.1887^n	192
	Aq. solution (pH 4.85)	0.5	...	...	0.1887^n	192

SPECIFIC REFRACTIVE INDEX INCREMENTS

Name	Solvent	Temp., °C	dn/dc 5461Å	dn/dc 4358Å	dn/dc Others	Ref.
Arachin (18.2% N)	Phosphate buffer	-	...	...	0.192	196,200
Poly(γ-benzyl-L-glutamate)	Chloroform	25	0.115	0.126	...	242
	Chloroform sat'd with formamide	25	0.115	0.126	...	242
	Dichloroacetic acid	25	...	0.100	...	242
	Dimethylformamide	25	...	0.118	...	242
$\alpha_{s1,2}$-Caseins	Aq. solution (pH 12)	-	0.181	...	...	201
Chymotrypsinogen	Phosphate buffer (pH 2.5, I.S. 0.15)[x]	25	...	0.1853	...	197
Collagen	Citrate buffer	25	...	0.187	...	202
Edestin (18.65% N)	Phosphate buffer	-	...	...	0.198	196,200
Fibrinogen	Phosphate buffer (pH 5.57)	7	0.1909	0.1970	...	205
		27	0.1951	0.2014	...	
	(pH 6.66)	6	0.1911	0.1976	...	205
		16	0.1907	0.1972	...	
		26	0.1906	0.1971	...	
	NaCl solution (pH 6.60)	7	...	0.1986	...	205
		27	...	0.1983	...	
Bovine fibrinogen	0.40M NaCl (pH adjusted)	-	...	0.197	...	206
		-	...	0.195	...	207
		-	...	0.199	...	208
Gelatin	Citrate buffer	25	...	0.187	...	202
	Water (pH 5.1)	25	...	0.194	...	209
	0.15M NaCl (pH 5.1)	25	...	0.1925	...	209
	1.0M NaCl (pH 5.1)	25	...	0.186	...	209
	1.0M KCNS	25	...	0.185	...	209
		30		0.172±0.004		210
	2.0M KCNS	25	...	0.173	...	209,202
	0.05M Phosphate	30	...	0.188 ±0.001	...	210
Globulins						
Human γ-globulin		25	0.1890	0.1960	0.1875[n]	192
		0	...	...	0.1875[n]	192
		25	...	...	0.186	199
		25	0.1890	0.1960	...	212
β-Lactoglobulin	0.5M NaCl	25	0.1818	0.1892	...	213
		25	0.1856	0.1926	0.1842[n]	192
		0	...	...	0.1865[n]	192
	0.1M NaCl (pH 5.2)	25	0.1822	0.1890	...	193,214

Remarks and References page IV-309

Name	Solvent	Temp.,°C	dn/dc 5461Å	4358Å	Others	Ref.
Glutamic dehydrogenase (beef liver)	0.05M phosphate buffer (pH 6.5)	11.5-33	...	0.193	...	204
D-glyceraldehyde-3-phosphate dehydrogenase	Potassium phosphate (pH 6.55-7.6; I.S. 0.10-0.135)[x]	-	0.185	0.190	...	203
Insulin	0.1M KCl (pH 1.96)	-	...	0.202	...	211
	Phosphate buffer (pH 2.6; I.S. 0.10)[x]	25	...	0.1919	...	197
Legumin	Phosphate buffer	-	...	...	0.197	196
		-	...	...	0.192	200
Lipoprotein	pH 3	25	...	0.175	...	215'
	pH 4.9		...	0.177	...	
	pH 6.7		...	0.177	...	
	pH 9.6		...	0.162	...	
β_1-Lipoprotein		25	...	...	0.171[w]	199
Lysozyme	0.1M NaCl (pH 6.2)	-	0.1888	0.1955	...	193
Myosin	Adenosine triphosphate	25	...	0.209	...	216
	0.5N KCl (pH 6.8; I.S. 0.5)[x]	-	0.1887	0.1910	...	217
	0.5M KCl (pH 7)	3	...	0.192 ±0.002	...	218
	0.6M KCl	25	...	0.208 ±0.2%	...	219
		-	...	...	0.181 ±0.002	220
Heavy meromyosin		-	...	...	0.186 ±0.002	220
Light meromyosin		-	...	...	0.176 ±0.002	220
Actomyosin	0.6M KCl+0.006M MgCl$_2$ (pH 7.0)	23	... K=6.50x10^{-7}		...	221
		20	0.193	0.195	0.191[n]	222
	KCl (I.S. 0.500)[x] K$_2$HPO$_4$(I.S. 0.0206)[x] KH$_2$PO$_4$(I.S. 0.0161)[x]	20	...	...	0.193[n]	222
	KCl (I.S. 0.500)[x] KHCO$_3$ (I.S. 0.0400)[x]	20	0.205	0.208	0.203[n]	222
Mann pepsin	Acetate buffer, 0.2M (pH 4.50)	25	...	0.1905 ±0.0040	...	198
	0.2M (pH 5.00)	25	...	0.1863 ±0.0018	...	198
Armour pepsin	Acetate buffer, 0.2M (pH 4.50)	25	...	0.1928 ±0.0021	...	198
Alcohol pepsin	Acetate buffer, 0.2M (pH 5.00)	25	...	0.1825 ±0.0021	...	198
Tobacco mosaic virus	0.1M Phosphate buffer	25	...	0.176	...	94
	Water	25	...	0.194 ±0.001	...	223
Turnip yellow virus	Phosphate buffer	-	...	...	0.196	196

Name	Solvent	Temp., °C	dn/dc			Ref.
			5461Å	4358Å	Others	
11 - DEOXYRIBONUCLEIC ACID*						
DNA (Varin sample)	Water	25	...	0.185	...	245
DNA (Simmons sample)	Water	25	...	0.191	...	245
DNA	0.20 M NaCl		...	0.191	...	246
DNA			0.185	...	...	247
DNA: sample No.						
C V 49			0.167	...	...	248
S VIII			0.179	...	...	
C V 3			0.169	...	...	
C V 42			0.164	...	...	
SV			0.177	...	...	
S XII			0.167	...	...	
C V 51			0.180	...	...	
C V 9			0.163	...	...	
C V 5			0.167	...	...	

---

* For additional data, see C. Sadron: "Proc. Intern. Congr.Biochem.," 3rd Congr.,
   Brussels, 1955, p. 125; E. P. Geiduschek and A. Holtzer: "Application of
   Light Scattering to Biological Systems: Deoxyribonucleic Acid and the Muscle
   Proteins" in"Advances in Biological and Medical Physics," ed. by C. A. Tobias
   and J. H. Lawrence, Academic Press, New York, 1958, Vol. VI.

Remarks and References page IV-309

Name	Solvent	Temp., °C	dn/dc 5461Å	dn/dc 4358Å	Others	Ref.
12 - COMMON STANDARDS AND MISCELLANEOUS COMPOUNDS							
Ludox (30% colloidal silica sol. in water)	Water	25	0.0745	...	...	86
		27	0.076	...	...	249
	0.05 M NaCl	23	0.0587	0.0592	0.0585^n 0.0593^s 0.0595^t	250
	Water	23	0.0608	0.0620	0.0606	250
Sucrose	Water	20	0.1439 ±0.0002	...	...	252
			0.1437 ±0.0001	...	...	252
			...	...	0.1436^w	2
		25	0.14292	0.14485	...	3
			0.1429	0.1448		109
		25	0.1430	...	...	253

c in g/ml

0.0352		25	0.1429	0.1451	...	254
0.0614			0.1427	0.1450	...	
0.106			0.1425	0.1447	...	
0.163			0.1422	0.1445	...	
0.251			0.1418	0.1440	....	
0.314			0.1414	0.1437	...	
0.353			0.1413	0.1435	...	
0.434			0.1409	0.1430	...	
0.587			0.1401	0.1423	...	
			dn/dc 0.1431 -0.0050c	0.1453 -0.0053c		
Sucrose octaacetate	Methanol	25	0.114	0.1165	...	87

	c in g solute/kg water	$\Delta n \times 10^3$		$\Delta n/c$ in g/g	
		5460.74Å (air)	4358.35Å (air)	5460.74Å (air)	4358.35Å (air)
Potassium chloride	0.69855	(0.09643)	(0.09976)	0.13804	0.14281
	1.0702	0.14758	0.15272	0.13790	0.14270
	10.8691	(1.4682)	(1.5204)	0.13508	0.13988
	23.7792*	(3.1582)	(3.2720)	0.13281	0.13760
	40.7030	(5.3103)	(5.4975)	0.13046	0.13506
Sodium chloride	0.9412	(0.16618)	(0.17236)	0.17656	0.18313
	1.0371	0.18338	0.19016	0.17676	0.18336
	3.3750	(0.59252)	(0.61402)	0.17556	0.18193
	5.6274	(0.9820)	(1.0192)	0.17450	0.18111
	6.9003	(1.2017)	(1.2465)	0.17415	0.17977
	11.3107	(1.9554)	(2.0300)	0.17288	0.17947
	20.5128	(3.5047)	(3.6337)	0.17085	0.17714
	37.8543	(6.345)	(6.582)	0.1676	0.1739
Sodium sulfate	2.2055	0.34414	0.34902	0.15604	0.15825
	(5.3887)	(0.82780)		0.15362	

Values of Δn in parentheses are interpolated or extrapolated by Stamm[251] from data given by Kruis[8].

* Data taken from ref. 3.

Remarks and References page IV-309

C. REMARKS

a. Measured at 4880Å.

b. Measured at 5600Å.

c. Values calculated from $(c/R_\theta)_{c=0, \; \theta=0}$ and the molecular weight of the sample.

d. Polymer structure has no effect on the value of dn/dc.

e. Calculated value.

f. The atactic and isotactic polymers exhibited the same dn/dc value in n-nonane.

g. The molecular weight of the sample was so low that it was soluble in tetralin at 50°C and in 1-chloronaphthalene at 65°C (6,7). The effect of molecular weight on the value of dn/dc is discussed in ref. 60.

h. Calculated from the slope of the plot of Δn vs. c in Fig. 1 (ref. 76).

i. Average of six different sources.

j. Average of eight different sources.

k. Measured at 3130Å.

l. For purification of the sample, see original article.

m. Change in dn/dc with wavelength between 4358 and 5461Å was less than 0.5%.

n. Measured at 5780Å.

p. Measured at 6437Å.

q. c is expressed in weight fraction.

r. Measured at 5470Å.

s. Measured at 4050Å.

t. Measured at 3660Å.

u. n_0 = refractive index of the mixture.

v. ψ = vol. fraction of benzene.

w. Measured at 5893Å.

x. I.S. = ionic strength

y. 1.39×10^{-3} eq. of HCl/g polymer

z. 2.2×10^{-3} eq/g polymer, M_n = 64,000

θ = θ-Temperature

D. REFERENCES

1. P. P. Debye, J. Appl. Phys., 17, 392 (1946).
2. B. A. Brice and M. Halwer, J. Opt. Soc. Am., 41, 1033 (1951).
3. O. Bodmann, Chem. Ing.-Tech., 29, 486 (1957).
4. G. V. Schulz, O. Bodmann, and H.-J. Cantow, Z. Naturforsch. 7a, 760 (1952).
5. J. Ehl, C. Loucheux, C. Reiss, and H. Benoit, Makromol. Chem., 75, 35 (1964)
6. E. E. Drott and R. A. Mendelson, Polymer Letters, 2, 187 (1964).
7. R. Chiang, ACS Meeting, Chicago, Polymer Preprint 5, 747 (1964); J. Polymer Sci. in press.
8. A. Kruis, Z. Physik. Chem., B34, 13 (1936).
9. A. Kruis, ibid, B34, 1 (1936).
10. G. B. Rathmann and F. A. Bovey, J. Polymer Sci., 15, 544 (1955).
11. J. E. Hansen; through ref. 2.
12. S. L. Aggarwal and F. A. Long, J. Polymer Sci., 11, 127 (1953).
13. S. N. Chinai and R. A. Guzzi, J. Polymer Sci., 21, 417 (1956).
14. R. Van Leemput and R. Stein, J. Polymer Sci., A2, 4039 (1964).
15. Jên-Yüan Ch'ien and Liang-ho Shih, Z. Physik. Chem., 207, 60 (1957).
16. S. N. Chinai and R. J. Samuels, J. Polymer Sci., 19, 463 (1956).

17. F. E. Didot, S. N. Chinai, and D. W. Levi, J. Polymer Sci., 43, 557 (1960).
18. S. N. Chinai, J. Polymer Sci., 25, 413 (1957).
19. H. T. Lee and D. W. Levi, J. Polymer Sci., 47, 449 (1960).
20. S. N. Chinai and R. A. Guzzi, J. Polymer Sci., 41, 475 (1959).
21. E. Cohn-Ginsberg, T. G. Fox, and H. F. Mason, Polymer (London), 3, 97 (1962).
22. S. Krause and E. Cohn-Ginsberg, Polymer (London), 3, 565 (1962).
23. E. S. Cohn and E. M. Schuele, J. Polymer Sci., 14, 309 (1954).
24. H. L. Bhatnagar and A. B. Biswas, J. Polymer Sci., 13, 461 (1954).
25. J. Y. Chien, S. P. Shen, L. H. Shih, J. C. Wu, and T. H. Chang, Sci. Sinica, (Peking) 6, 303 (1957); J. Y. Chien, L. H. Shih, and S. C. Yu, J. Polymer Sci., 29, 117 (1958).
26. H.-J. Cantow and O. Bodmann, Z. Physik. Chem. (Frankfurt), 3, 65 (1955).
27. H.-J. Cantow and G. V. Schulz, Z. Physik. Chem. (Frankfurt), 2, 117 (1954).
28. J. Bischoff and V. Desreux, Bull. Soc. Chim. Belges, 61, 10 (1952).
29. W. Bushuk and H. Benoit, Can. J. Chem., 36, 1616 (1958).
30. H. Daoust and M. Rinfret, J. Colloid Sci., 7, 11 (1952).
31. R. H. Ewart, C. P. Roe, P. Debye, and J. R. McCartney, J. Chem. Phys., 14, 687 (1946).
32. E. F. Casassa and W. H. Stockmayer, Polymer (London), 3, 53 (1962).
33. W. H. Stockmayer, L. D. Moore, Jr., M. Fixman and B. N. Epstein, J. Polymer Sci., 16, 517 (1955).
34. F. W. Billmeyer, Jr., and C. B. deThan, J. Am. Chem. Soc., 77, 4763 (1955).
35. S. Krause, ACS Meeting, New York, Polymer Preprint 1, 144 (1960).
36. C. I. Jose and A. B. Biswas, J. Polymer Sci., 27, 575 (1958).
37. W. H. Stockmayer and H. E. Stanley, J. Chem. Phys., 18, 153 (1950).
38. S. N. Chinai, J. D. Matlack, A. L. Resnick, and R. J. Samuels, J. Polymer Sci., 17, 391 (1955).
39. R. Kirste and G. V. Schulz, Z. Physik. Chem. (Frankfurt), 27, 301 (1961).
40. J. G. Fee, W. S. Port and L. P. Witnauer, J. Polymer Sci., 33, 95 (1958).
41. S. N. Chinai, A. L. Resnick, and H. T. Lee, J. Polymer Sci., 33, 471 (1958).
42. R. L. Cleland and W. H. Stockmayer, J. Polymer Sci., 17, 473 (1955).
43. C. Wippler, through SOFICA Photo-Gonio-Diffusométre (Societe Francaise D'Instruments de Control et D'Analysis, Strasbourg, France) instruction manual, 1962.
44. L. H. Peebles, Jr. private communication, 1958.
45. W. L. Hunter, private communication, 1962.
46. Y. Fujisaki and H. Kobayashi, Chem. High Polymer (Japan), 19, 81 (1962).
47. W. R. Krigbaum and A. M. Kotliar, J. Polymer Sci., 32, 323 (1958).
48. R. L. Cleland, J. Polymer Sci., 27, 349 (1958).
49. D. J. Harmon, ACS Meeting, Chicago, Polymer Preprint, 5, 712 (1964).
50. W. Cooper, G. Vaughan, D. E. Eaves, and R. W. Madden, J. Polymer Sci., 50, 159 (1961).
51. Ph. Ribeyrolles, A. Guyot, and H. Benoit, J. Chem. Phys., 56, 377 (1959).
52. S. A. Pavlova, T. A. Soboleva, and A. P. Suprun, Vysokomolekul.Soedin., 6, 122 (1964).
53. W. R. Krigbaum, J. E. Kurtz, and P. Smith, J. Phys. Chem., 65, 1984 (1961).
54. A. De. Chirico, Chim. Ind. (Milan), 42, 248 (1960).
55. Q. A. Trementozzi, J. Polymer Sci., 23, 887 (1957).
56. R. Chiang, J. Polymer Sci., 28, 235 (1958).
57. R. Chiang, J. Polymer Sci., 36, 91 (1959).
58. F. W. Billmeyer, Jr., J. Am. Chem. Soc., 75, 6118 (1953).
59. V. Kokle, F. W. Billmeyer, Jr., L. T. Muus, and E. J. Newitt, J. Polymer Sci., 62, 251 (1962).
60. R. Chiang and J. H. Rhodes, to be published.
61. Q. A. Trementozzi, J. Polymer Sci., 23, 887 (1957); 36, 113 (1959).
62. T. Kobayashi, A. Chitale, and H. P. Frank, J. Polymer Sci., 24, 156 (1957).
63. L. H. Tung, J. Polymer Sci., 36, 287 (1959); ibid A2, 4875 (1964).
64. R. Chiang, unpublished work, 1964.
65. A. M. Bueche, quoted by H. T. Hall, J. Polymer Sci., 7, 443 (1951).
66. P. Rempp, J. Chim. Phys., 54, 421, 432 (1957).
67. H.-G. Elias, Makromol. Chem., 50, 1 (1961).
68. I. M. Bel'govskii, N. S. Enikolopyan, and L. S. Sakhonenko, Vysokomolekul. Soedin., 4, 1197 (1962); Polymer Sci. (USSR), 4, 367 (1963).
69. W. H. Beattie and C. Booth, J. Appl. Polymer Sci., 7, 507 (1963).
70. N. E. Weston and F. W. Billmeyer, Jr., J. Phys. Chem., 65, 567 (1961).
70a. Y. Shiokawa, H. Takeo, K. Takamizawa, and T. Oyama, Rept. Prog. Polymer Phys. (Japan), 7, 49 (1964).
71. G. Allen, C. Booth, and M. N. Jones, Polymer (London), 5, 195 (1964).
72. V. Crescenzi and P. J. Flory, J. Am. Chem. Soc., 86, 141 (1964).
73. G. V. Schulz and A. Haug, Z. Physik. Chem. (Frankfurt), 34, 328 (1962).

74. H. H. Takimoto, C. T. Forbes, and R. K. Laudenslager, J. Appl. Polymer Sci., 5, 153 (1961).
75. R. Nilsson and L.-O. Sundelöf, Makromol. Chem., 66, 11 (1963).
76. S. A. Pavlova, V. I. Pakhomov, and I. I. Tverdokhlebova, Vysokomolekul. Soedin., 6, 1281 (1964).
77. D. McIntyre, A. Wims, L. C. Williams, and L. Mandelkern, J. Phys. Chem., 66, 1932 (1962).
78. C. Wippler and G. Scheibling, J. Chim. Phys., 51, 201 (1954).
79. H. P. Frank and H. F. Mark, J. Polymer Sci., 10, 129 (1953).
80. A. M. Bueche, J. Am. Chem. Soc., 71, 1452 (1949).
81. M. Morton, T. E. Helminiak, S. D. Gadkary, and F. Bueche, J. Polymer Sci., 57, 471 (1962).
82. V. V. Varadaiah, J. Polymer Sci., 19, 477 (1956).
83. P. Debye and W. M. Cashin, J. Chem. Phys., 19, 510 (1951).
84. B. E. Read, Trans. Faraday Soc., 56, 382 (1960).
85. H.-G. Elias, Makromol. Chem., 66, 56 (1963).
86. H. J. I. Trap and J. J. Hermans, Rec. Trav. Chim., 73, 167 (1954).
87. B. A. Brice, M. Halwer, and R. Speciser, J. Opt. Soc. Am., 40, 768 (1950), also ref. 2.
88. Q. A. Trementozzi, R. F. Steiner, and P. Doty, J. Am. Chem. Soc., 74, 2070 (1952).
89. B. H. Zimm, J. Chem. Phys., 16, 1099 (1948).
90. H. P. Frank and H. F. Mark, J. Polymer Sci., 17, 1 (1955).
91. The Committee on Molecular Weight and Molecular Weight Distribution of the Society of Polymer Science, Japan, Rept. Prog. Polymer Phys. (Japan), 7 (1964), supplement, p. 5-28.
92. H.-J. Cantow, Z. Physik. Chem. (Frankfurt), 7, 58 (1956).
93. D. K. Carpenter and W. R. Krigbaum, J. Chem. Phys., 24, 1041 (1956).
94. P. Doty and R. F. Steiner, J. Chem. Phys., 18, 1211 (1950).
95. P. M. Doty, B. Zimm, and H. Mark, J. Chem. Phys., 12, 144 (1944); through ref. 106.
96. J. Bischoff and V. Desreux, Bull. Soc. Chim. Belges, 59, 536 (1950).
97. J. Oth and V. Desreux, Bull. Soc. Chim. Belges, 63, 285 (1954).
98. S. H. Maron and R. L. H. Lou, J. Polymer Sci., 14, 29 (1954).
99. S. N. Chinai, P. C. Scherer, C. N. Bondurant, and D. W. Levi, J. Polymer Sci., 22, 527 (1956).
100. J. H. O'Mara and D. McIntyre, J. Phys. Chem., 63, 1435 (1959).
101. W. R. Krigbaum and D. K. Carpenter, J. Phys. Chem., 59, 1166 (1955).
101a. T. A. Orofino, private communication; T. A. Orofino and J. W. Mickey, Jr., J. Chem. Phys., 38, 2512 (1963).
102. W. R. Krigbaum, P Smith, and F. G. Mark, J. Appl. Phys., 34, 3218 (1963).
103. H.-J. Cantow, Z. Electrochem., 60, 209 (1956); through S. G. Weissberg, S. Rothman, and M. Wales: "Molecular Weights and Sizes," in "Analytical Chemistry of High Polymers" ed. by G. M. Kline, Interscience Publishers, Inc., N. Y., 1961.
104. N. T. Notley and P. J. W. Debye, J. Polymer Sci., 17, 99 (1955).
105. W. R. Krigbaum, D. K. Carpenter, and S. Newman, J. Phys. Chem., 62, 1586 (1958).
106. P. Outer, C. I. Carr, and B. H. Zimm, J. Chem. Phys., 18, 830 (1950).
107. J. M. G. Cowie, D. J. Worsfold, and S. Bywater, Trans. Faraday Soc., 57, 705 (1961).
108. L. De Brouckere and C. A. Anspach, Bull. Soc. Chim. Belges, 61, 622 (1952).
109. P. H. Norberg and L.-O. Sundelöf, Makromol. Chem., 77, 77 (1964).
110. O. Bodmann, Dissertation, Mainz, 1955; through ref. 109.
111. L. Trossarelli, E. Campi, and G. Saini, J. Polymer Sci., 35, 205 (1959).
112. J. Hengstenberg, Makromol. Chem., 6, 127 (1951).
113. W. B. Dandliker, J. Am. Chem. Soc., 72, 5110 (1950).
114. V. N. Kuleznev and V. M. Andreeva, Vysokomolekul. Soedin., 4, 1851 (1962).
115. J. B. Kinsinger, J. S. Bartlett, and W. H. Rauscher, J. Appl. Polymer Sci., 6, 529 (1962).
115a. Y. Shimura, I. Mita, and H. Kambe, Rept. Prog. Polymer Phys. (Japan), 7, 25 (1964).
116. S. Mao and E. V. Frisman, Vysokomolekul. Soedin., 4, 1839 (1962).
117. V. E. Eskin and T. I. Volkov, Vysokomolekul. Soedin., 5, 614 (1963).
117a. V. E. Eskin and K. Z. Gumargalieva, Vysokomolekul. Soedin., 2, 265 (1960).
118. V. E. Eskin and L. N. Andreeva, Vysokomolekul. Soedin., 3, 435 (1961).
119. A. F. Sirianni, D. J. Worsfold, and S. Bywater, Trans. Faraday Soc., 55, 2124 (1959).
120. K. J. Ivin, H. A. Ende, and G. Meyerhoff, Polymer (London), 3, 129 (1962).
120a. L. D. Moore, ACS Meeting, Cleveland, Polymer Preprint 1, 234 (1960).
121. J. Moacanin, J. Appl. Polymer Sci., 1, 272 (1959).

122. S. N. Chinai, P. C. Scherer, and D. W. Levi, J. Polymer Sci., 17, 117 (1955).
123. Y. Ohyanagi and M. Matsumoto, Chem. High Polymer (Japan), 16, 296 (1959);
     J. Polymer Sci., 46, 441 (1960).
124. M. R. Rao and V. Kalpagam, J. Polymer Sci., 49, S14 (1961).
125. R. O. Howard, Dissertation, Massachusetts Institute of Technology, 1952; through
     ref. 126.
126. A. R. Shultz, J. Am. Chem. Soc., 76, 3422 (1954).
127. H.-G. Elias and F. Patat, Makromol. Chem., 25, 13 (1957).
128. F. W. Billmeyer, Jr., through G. C. Berry, L. M. Hobbs, and V. C. Long, Polymer
     (London), 5, 31 (1964).
129. W. W. Graessley; through G. C. Berry, L. M. Hobbs and V. C. Long, Polymer
     (london), 5, 31 (1964).
130. T. Tatsuo and H. Inagaki, Makromol. Chem., 55, 150 (1962).
131. Y. Ohyanagi, Dissertation, Kyoto Univ., 1960; T. Matsuo and H. Inagaki,
     Makromol. Chem., 53, 130 (1962); T. Matsuo, Chem. High Polymer (Japan), 16,
     603 (1959).
132. H. Inagaki and T. Oyama, Chem. High Polymer (Japan), 1, 20 (1952); through
     ref. 133.
133. M. Matsumoto and Y. Ohyanagi, J. Polymer Sci., 31, 225 (1958).
134. H. A. Dieu, J. Polymer Sci., 12, 417 (1954). This value was also used by
     K. A. Stacey and P. Alexander, "International Symposium on Macromolecular
     Chemistry," (Milan-Turin), Interscience, New York, 1954, p. 889.
135. G. Blauer, M. Shenblat, and A. Katchalsky, J. Polymer Sci., 38, 189 (1959).
136. A. Ciferri, M. Kryszewski, and G. Weill, J. Polymer Sci., 27, 167 (1958).
137. A. Oth and V. Desreux, Bull Soc. Chim. Belges, 63, 261 (1954).
138. P. Doty, H. Wagner, and S. Singer, J. Phys. & Colloid Chem., 51, 32 (1947).
139. M. Freeman and P. P. Manning, J. Polymer Sci., A2, 2017 (1964).
140. H. Benoit, R. Ullman, A. J. De Vries and C. Wippler, J. Chim. Phys. 59, 889
     (1962).
141. J. A. Manson and G. J. Arquette, Makromol. Chem., 37, 187 (1960).
142. J. B. Berkowitz, M. Yamin, and R. M. Fuoss, J. Polymer Sci., 28, 69 (1958).
143. R. M. Fuoss and D. Edelson, J. Polymer Sci., 6, 767 (1951).
144. H. L. Wagner and F. A. Long, J. Phys. Colloid Chem., 55, 1512 (1951).
145. G. B. Levy and H. P. Frank, J. Polymer Sci., 17, 247 (1955).
146. J. Hengstenberg and E. Schuch, Makromol. Chem., 7, 236 (1952).
147. H. Mark, through ref. 146.
148. K. Altgelt and G. V. Schulz, Makromol. Chem., 36, 209 (1960).
149. S. Bywater and P. Johnson, Trans. Faraday Soc., 47, 195 (1951).
150. R. Rivest and M. Rinfret, J. Chem. Phys., 18, 1513 (1950).
151. R. S. Stein and P. Doty, J. Am. Chem. Soc., 68, 159 (1946).
152. L. H. Sperling and M. Easterwood, J. Appl. Polymer Sci., 4, 25 (1960).
153. M. L. Hunt, S. Newman, H. A. Scheraga, and P. J. Flory, J. Phys. Chem., 60,
     1278 (1956).
154. A. M. Holtzer, H. Benoit, and P. Doty, J. Phys. Chem., 58, 624 (1954).
155. M. M. Huque, D. A. I. Goring, and S. G. Mason, Can. J. Chem., 36, 952 (1958).
156. R. M. Badger and R. H. Blaker, J. Phys. Colloid Chem., 53, 1056 (1949).
157. W. Burchard and E. Husemann, Makromol. Chem., 44-46, 358 (1961).
158. W. R. Krigbaum and L. H. Sperling, J. Phys. Chem., 64, 99 (1960).
159. P. F. Onyon, J. Polymer Sci., 37, 295 (1959).
160. C. W. Tait, R. J. Vetter, J. M. Swanson, and P. Debye, J. Polymer Sci., 7, 261
     (1951).
161. S. Claesson, and H. H. Bruun, Svensk Papperstid ., 60, 336 (1957); through
     ref. 159.
162. R. H. Cornell and H. A. Swenson, J. Appl. Polymer Sci., 5, 641 (1961).
163. P. C. Scherer, A. Tanenbaum, and D. W. Levi, J. Polymer Sci., 43, 531 (1960).
164. W. Brown, D. Henley, and J. Öhman, Makromol. Chem., 64, 49 (1963).
165. W. Brown and D. Henley, Makromol. Chem., 79, 68 (1964).
166. D. Henley, Arkiv Kemi, 18, 327 (1961).
167. W. Brown, Arkiv Kemi, 18, 227 (1961).
168. R. St. J. Manley, Arkiv Kemi, 9, 519 (1956).
169. I. Jullander, Svensk Papperstid ., as quoted by Manley in ref. 168.
170. H. J. L. Trap and J. J. Hermans, J. Phys. Chem., 58, 757 (1954).
171. N. S. Schneider and P. Doty, J. Phys. Chem., 58, 762 (1954).
172. G. Sitaramaiah and D. A. I. Goring, J. Polymer Sci., 58, 1107 (1962).
173. W. Brown, D. Henley, and J. Öhman, Makromol. Chem., 62, 164 (1963).
174. R. H. Marchessault, M. Joan Koch, and J. T. Yang, J. Colloid Sci., 16, 345 (1961).
175. E. F. Paschall and J. F. Foster, J. Polymer Sci., 9, 85 (1952).
176. L. P. Witnauer, F. R. Senti, and M. D. Stern, J. Polymer Sci., 16, 1 (1955).
177. L. P. Witnauer, through ref. 2.
178. W. Burchard, Makromol. Chem., 59, 16 (1963).

179. W. W. Everett and J. F. Foster, J. Am. Chem. Soc., <u>81</u>, 3459 (1959).
180. Y. Tominatsu, K. J. Palmer, A. E. Goodban, and W. H. Ward, J. Polymer Sci., <u>36</u>,
      129 (1959).
181. Y. Tominatsu and K. J. Palmer, J. Polymer Sci., <u>A1</u>, 1005 (1963).
182. J. V. Koleske and S. F. Kurath, J. Polymer Sci., <u>A2</u>, 4123 (1964).
183. D. A. I. Goring, Can. J. Chem., <u>31</u>, 1078 (1953).
184. K. Frömbling and F. Patat, Makromol. Chem., <u>25</u>, 41 (1957); H. G. Elias,
      Makromol. Chem., <u>27</u>, 192 (1958).
185. L. H. Arond and H. P. Frank, J. Phys. Chem., <u>58</u>, 953 (1954).
186. Nat'l. Bur. Standards, U. S., Report, 1952, p. 72; K. A. Granath, J. Colloid
      Sci., <u>13</u>, 308 (1958).
187. B. Ingelman and M. S. Halling, Arkiv Kemi, <u>1</u>, 61 (1949); through G. C. Booth
      and V. Gold, J. Chem. Soc. (1956) 3380.
188. J. Da. Silva Carvalho, W. Prins, and C. Schuerch, J. Am. Chem. Soc., <u>81</u>, 4054
      (1959).
189. H. Abe and W. Prins, Makromol. Chem., <u>42</u>, 216 (1961).
190. F. R. Senti, N. N. Hellman, N. H. Ludwig, G. E. Babcock, R. Tobin, C. A. Glass,
      and B. L. Lamberts, J. Polymer Sci., <u>17</u>, 527 (1955)
191. D. A. I. Goring and T. E. Timell, J. Phys. Chem., <u>64</u>, 1426 (1960).
192. G. E. Perlmann and L. G. Longsworth, J. Am. Chem. Soc., <u>70</u>, 2719 (1948).
192a. G. Scatchard and J. Bregman, J. Am. Chem. Soc., <u>81</u>, 6095 (1959).
193. M. Halwer, G. C. Nutting, and B. A. Brice, J. Am. Chem. Soc., <u>73</u>, 2786 (1951).
194. G. F. Hanna and J. F. Foster, J. Phys. Chem., <u>57</u>, 614 (1953).
195. J. Edsall, H. Edelhoch, R. Lontie, and P. R. Morrison, J. Am. Chem. Soc., <u>72</u>,
      4641 (1950).
196. D. A. I. Goring and P. Johnson, Trans. Faraday Soc., <u>48</u>, 367 (1952).
197. F. Tietze and H. Neurath, J. Biol. Chem., <u>194</u>, 1 (1952).
198. M. J. Kronman and M. D. Stein, J. Phys. Chem., <u>59</u>, 969 (1955).
199. S. H. Armstrong, Jr., M. J. E. Budka, K. C. Morrison, and M. Hasson, J. Am. Chem.
      Soc., <u>69</u>, 1747 (1947).
200. B. P. Brand, D. A. I. Goring, and P. Johnson, Trans. Faraday Soc., <u>51</u>, 872 (1955).
201. P. Dreizen, R. W. Noble, and D. F. Waugh, J. Am. Chem. Soc., <u>84</u>, 4938 (1962).
202. H. Boedtker and P. Doty, J. Am. Chem. Soc., <u>78</u>, 4267 (1956).
203. W. B. Dandliker and J. B. Fox, Jr., J. Biol. Chem., <u>214</u>, 275 (1955).
204. C. Frieden, J. Biol. Chem., <u>237</u>, 2396 (1962).
205. G. V. Schulz and H. A. Ende, Z. Physik. Chem. (Frankfurt), <u>36</u>, 82 (1963).
206. Estimated by W. B. Dandliker as quoted by Katz, Gutfreund, Shulman, and Ferry
      in ref. 207.
207. R. F. Steiner and K. Laki, Arch. Biochem. Biophys., <u>34</u>, 24 (1951); S. Katz,
      K. Gutfreund, S. Shulman, and J. D. Ferry, J. Am. Chem. Soc., <u>74</u>, 5706 (1952).
208. C. S. Hocking, M. Laskowski, Jr., and H. A. Scheraga, J. Am. Chem. Soc., <u>74</u>,
      775 (1952).
209. H. Boedtker and P. Doty, J. Phys. Chem., <u>58</u>, 968 (1954).
210. E. Gouinlock, Jr., P. J. Flory, and H. A. Scheraga, J. Polymer Sci., <u>16</u>, 383 (1955).
211. P. Doty, M. Gellert, and B. Rabinovitch, J. Am. Chem. Soc., <u>74</u>, 2065 (1952).
212. "The Proteins" edited by H. Neurath and K. Bailey, Academic Press, New York,
      1953-1954; V. Ya. Chernyak, Vysokomolekul. Soedin., <u>2</u>, 1419 (1960).
213.   Pedersen, Biochem. J., <u>30</u>, 961 (1936); see also ref. 214.
214. M. Halwer and B. A. Brice, J. Colloid Sci., <u>4</u>, 439 (1949).
215. Calculated on basis of Armstrong's data (ref. 199); through R. Bjorklund and
      S. Katz, J. Am. Chem. Soc., <u>78</u>, 2122 (1956).
216. M. F. Gellert, P. H. Von Hippel, H. K. Schachman, and M. F. Morales, J. Am.
      Chem. Soc., <u>81</u>, 1384 (1959).
217. J. C. Rupp and W. F. H. M. Mommaerts, J. Biol. Chem., <u>224</u>, 277 (1957).
218. M. F. Gellert and S. W. Englander, Biochemistry, <u>2</u>, 39 (1963).
219. A. Holtzer and S. Lowey, J. Am. Chem. Soc., <u>81</u>, 1370 (1959).
220. A. Holtzer, S. Lowey, and T. M. Schuster, Symposium on the Molecular Basis of
      Neoplasia, Houston, Texas (1961); through S. Lowey and C. Cohn, J. Mol. Biol.
      <u>4</u>, 293 (1962).
221. J. Gergely, J. Biol. Chem., <u>220</u>, 917 (1956).
222. A. Wasserman and M. L. R. Harkness, Nature, <u>173</u>, 167 (1954); J. Chem. Soc., 1344
      (1954).
223. H. Boedtker and N. S. Simmons, J. Am. Chem. Soc., <u>80</u>, 2550 (1959).
224. A. Silberberg, J. Eliassaf, and A. Katchalsky, J. Polymer Sci., <u>23</u>, 259 (1957).
224a. T. A. Fadner and H. Morawetz, J. Polymer Sci., <u>45</u>, 475 (1960).
225. H.-J. Cantow, Z. Naturforsch., <u>7b</u>, 485 (1952).
226. E. A. S. Cavell, I. T. Gilson, B. R. Jennings, and H. G. Jerrard, J. Polymer
      Sci., <u>A2</u>, 3615 (1964).
227. H. G. Fendler and H. A. Stuart, Makromol. Chem., <u>25</u>, 159 (1957).
228. H.-G. Elias and R. Schumacher, Makromol. Chem., <u>76</u>, 23 (1964).

229. P. R. Saunders, J. Polymer Sci., 57, 131 (1962).
230. D. W. Carlson, Dissertation, University of Delaware, July, 1959; H. C. Beachell, and D. W. Carlson, J. Polymer Sci., 40, 543 (1959).
231. S. Newman, W. R. Krigbaum, C. Laugier, and P. J. Flory, J. Polymer Sci., 14, 451 (1954).
232. Z. Alexandrowicz, J. Polymer Sci., 40, 91 (1959).
233. T. A. Orofino and P. J. Flory, J. Phys. Chem., 63, 283 (1959).
234. E. A. Kanevskaya, P. I. Zubov, L. V. Ivanova, and Yu. S. Lipatov, Vysokomolekul. Soedin., 6, 981 (1964).
235. A. Oth and P. Doty, J. Phys. Chem., 56, 43 (1952).
236. P. Alexander and K. A. Stacey, Trans. Faraday Soc., 51, 299 (1955).
237. A. Katchalsky and H. Eisenberg, J. Polymer Sci., 6, 145 (1951).
239. R. Arnold and S. R. Caplan, Trans. Faraday Soc., 51, 857 (1955).
240. Q. A. Trementozzi, J. Am. Chem. Soc., 76, 5273 (1954).
241. G. Ehrlich and P. Doty, J. Am. Chem. Soc., 76, 3764 (1954).
242. P. Doty, J. H. Bradbury, and A. M. Holtzer, J. Am. Chem. Soc., 78, 947 (1956).
243. H. Eisenberg and E. F. Casassa, J. Polymer Sci., 47, 29 (1960).
244. A. Audsley and J. Aveston, J. Chem. Soc., 2320 (1962).
245. M. E. Reichmann, S. A. Rice, C. A. Thomas, and P. Doty, J. Am. Chem. Soc., 76, 3047 (1954).
246. L. F. Cavalieri, M. Rosoff, and B. H. Rosenberg, J. Am. Chem. Soc., 78, 5239 (1956).
247. K. A. Stacey. "Light Scattering in Physical Chemistry," Academic Press, New York, 1956; J. A. V. Butler, D. J. R. Laurence, A. B. Robins, and K. V. Shooter, Proc. Roy. Soc. (London), 250A, 1 (1959).
248. J. Pouyet and G. Weill, J. Polymer Sci., 23, 739 (1957).
249. G. B. Alexander and R. K. Iler, J. Phys. Chem., 57, 932 (1953).
250. Gj. Dezelic and J. P. Kratohvil, Kolloid-Z., 173, 38 (1960).
251. R. F. Stamm, J. Opt. Soc. Am., 40, 788 (1950).
252. G. V. Schulz, O. Bodmann, and H.-J. Cantow, J. Polymer Sci., 10, 73 (1952).
253. L. J. Gosting and M. S. Morris, J. Am. Chem. Soc., 71, 1998 (1949).
254. S. H. Maron and R. L. H. Lou, J. Phys. Chem., 59, 231 (1955).
255. E. F. Casassa and H. Eisenberg, J. Phys. Chem., 65, 427 (1961).
256. U. P. Strauss and P. L. Wineman, J. Am. Chem. Soc., 80, 2366 (1958).

DISSYMMETRIES AND PARTICLE SCATTERING FACTORS

R. Chiang

Chemstrand Research Center
Durham, North Carolina

Contents

A. INTRODUCTION

Scattering of light by macromolecules in dilute solutions has been shown to obey the following equation:

$$\frac{Kc}{R_\theta} = \frac{1}{\langle M \rangle_w \, P(\overline{\theta})} + 2 \, A_2 c \qquad (1)$$

where

$$K = (2\pi^2/N\lambda^4)(n_o \, dn/dc)^2,$$

c is the concentration of the polymer in g/ml, R_θ is the reduced intensity at angle θ, $\langle M \rangle_w$ is the weight-average molecular weight, $P(\theta)$ is the particle scattering factor, A_2 is the second virial coefficient, N is Avogadro's number, λ is the wavelength of the light in <u>vacuo</u>, and n_o the refractive index of the solvent.

For polymers whose dimensions are 1/20 or less of the wavelength of the incident light, the angular distribution is symmetrical about $\theta = 90°$; the intensities of the light scattered in the forward direction and in the backward direction are the same. For polymers with dimensions approaching the wavelength of the light, the scattering envelope is not symmetrical but is greater in the forward direction than in the backward direction because of the phase differences of the light scattered from different parts of the molecule (internal interference).

The particle scattering factor, $P(\theta)$, is defined as the ratio of the light intensity, $I(\theta)$, scattered by a polymer in solution at an angle θ to the light intensity, I_θ^o, in the absence of interference; thus,

$$P(\theta) = I_\theta / I_\theta^o = R_\theta / R_\theta^o$$

In practice, the light intensities scattered at an angle θ and its complementary angle $\pi - \theta$ are measured, the ratio of these intensities being referred to as the dissymmetry ratio and denoted by z_θ,

$$z_\theta = I_\theta / I_{\pi-\theta} = P(\theta)/P(\pi - \theta)$$

It has become standard practice to use 45 and 135° for measurements of dissymmetries, although angles other than 45 and 135° are occasionally used.

The Particle Scattering Factor

The particle scattering factor assumes different forms for different geometric shapes of the scattering particles. It may be calculated by the mathematical equations given below (1,2,3):

For monodisperse coils with mean-square end-to-end distance $\overline{r^2}$,

$$P(\theta) = (\frac{2}{x^2})\, [e^{-x}-(1-x)]; \quad x = \frac{k^2 v^2 \overline{r^2}}{6} = (2/3)(\frac{\overline{r^2}}{\lambda'^2})[2\pi\, \sin(\theta/2)]^2 \quad (2a)$$

For rods of length L,

$$P(\theta) = \frac{1}{x}\int_{o}^{2x}(\frac{\sin w}{w})dw - (\frac{\sin x}{x})^2; \quad x = \frac{kvL}{2} \quad (2b)$$

For discs of diameter D,

$$P(\theta) = \frac{x^o}{1} - \frac{x^2}{6} + \sum_{n=3}^{\infty}\frac{x^{2(n-1)}\cos(n+1)\pi}{(2n+b_{n-1}/b_{n-2})b_{n-1}} \quad ; \quad x = \frac{kvD}{2} \quad (2c)$$

b_n being the denominator of nth term; for example, $b_1 = 1$, $b_2 = 6$, etc.

For spheres of diameter D,

$$P(\theta) = [(\frac{3}{x^3})(\sin x - x \cos x)]^2; \quad x = \frac{kvD}{2} \quad (2d)$$

where $k = 2\pi/\lambda'$

$v = 2\, \sin(\theta/2)$

and λ' = the wavelength of light in solution (equal to the wavelength in vacuum divided by the refractive index of the solvent).

For the corresponding expressions for ellipsoids, cylinders and stiff chains, the literature on this subject should be consulted (4). Tables 2 and 3 give the calculated particle scattering factor for coils, rods and spheres for different values of x (5).

Regardless of the shape of the scattering particle, $P(\theta)$ can be directly determined by using the general equation

$$P(\theta) = 1 - (\overline{s^2}/3)\,(kv)^2 + \ldots\ldots \quad (3)$$

where $\overline{s^2}$ is the mean-square-radius of gyration, the first term following unity being always equal to 1/3 of $(kv)^2$ multiplied by the mean-square-radius of gyration. This quantity is directly determined by light scattering without any restriction to the shape of the molecule. $\overline{s^2} = \overline{r^2}/6$ for random coils, $\overline{s^2} = L^2/12$ for rods, and $\overline{s^2} = 3D^2/20$ for spheres, etc.

Furthermore it is clear from eq. (3) that $P(\theta)$ approaches unity when θ approaches zero or when the scattering center is small compared to the wavelength of the light (Rayleigh scattering or small particle scattering); otherwise, $P(\theta) < 1$.

Determination of Molecular Weight and Dimension

To obtain the molecular weights and dimensions of molecules from light scattering data, two methods are commonly used: the dissymmetry method and the method of Zimm (6).

References page IV-329

Dissymmetry Method. The dissymmetry method consists of the following steps:

1. The intensities of the scattered light at 45, 90, and 135° are measured for polymer solutions at different concentrations.

2. The dissymmetry ratios z_{45} are calculated for each concentration and extrapolated to zero concentration. The dissymmetry at zero concentration is referred to as the intrinsic dissymmetry $[z]$.

3. The correction factor P(90) is taken from Table 4 or 5 from the dissymmetry z_{45} after choosing the proper model.

4. The true molecular weight is obtained by substituting this correction factor P(90) into equation (1).

5. From $[z]$, the values of $\sqrt{\overline{r^2}}/\lambda'$, L/λ', and D/λ' for random coils, rods, and spheres, respectively, are calculated (Tables 4 and 6).

The dissymmetry method is conveniently used when the molecular weight, and hence the dissymmetry, is low; if the dissymmetry is high, extrapolation of the scattering data to zero concentration and zero angle is performed graphically by the method of Zimm.

Zimm Plot. Substituting eq. (3) into eq. (1) and averaging over all molecular weights we have

$$\frac{Kc}{R_\theta} = \frac{1}{\langle M \rangle_w} \left[1 + \frac{\langle s^2 \rangle_z}{3} \left(\frac{2\pi}{\lambda'}\right)^2 \left(2 \sin \frac{\theta}{2}\right)^2 \right] + \ \ldots\ldots \tag{4}$$

Note that the dimensions thus obtained are z-average quantities. In accordance with eq. (4), when Kc/R_θ is plotted against $\sin^2(\theta/2) + k'c$, where k' is an arbitrary constant, familes of straight lines or nearly straight lines are obtained at constant θ and constant c, thus forming a grid-like plot (Zimm plot). With the Zimm plot, it is possible to extrapolate the scattering data to $\theta = 0$ and $c = 0$ simultaneously. The two extrapolated lines intercept the ordinate at the same point $(Kc/R_\theta)_{c=0,\theta=0}$.

The weight-average molecular weight, second virial coefficient, and z-average mean square radius of gyration are calculated from the following equations:

$$\langle M \rangle_w = \frac{1}{\left(\frac{Kc}{R_\theta}\right)_{c=0,\theta=0}}$$

$$\overline{\langle s^2 \rangle_z} = \frac{3\lambda'^2}{16\pi^2} \left(\frac{\text{slope of the line } c=0}{\text{intercept}}\right)$$

$$A_2 = \frac{k' \ (\text{slope of the line } \theta=0)}{2}$$

Effect of Molecular Weight Distribution on $P(\theta)$

The scattering factors given in eq. (2) hold only for monodisperse samples. Significant deviations are encountered for broad molecular weight distributions. For coiled molecules having generalized exponential distribution

$$w\ (M) = \beta^{(\beta+1)}\ M^\beta\ \exp(-\beta M/\langle M \rangle_n)/\langle M \rangle_n^{(\beta+1)} \Gamma(\beta+1)$$

where β is the homogeneity parameter defined by

$$\langle M \rangle_z : \langle M \rangle_w : \langle M \rangle_n = (\beta+2) : (\beta+1) : \beta$$

and $w(M)$ is the weight fraction of a polymer having a molecular weight in the range of M and M + dM, the particle scattering factor will be according to Zimm (6)

$$P(\theta) = [2(1+\beta)^{(1+\beta)} - 2(1+\beta -\beta\langle x\rangle)(1+\beta + \langle x\rangle)^{\beta}]/\langle x\rangle^2\beta(1+\beta + \langle x\rangle)^{\beta},$$

where $\langle x\rangle$ is the weight average of x, x being defined in eq. (2a).

The effect of polydispersity on $P(\theta)$ as mentioned above has to be corrected using the correction factors given in Table 5 for different ratios of $\langle M\rangle_w/\langle M\rangle_n$.

Table 1

TRIGONOMETIC FUNCTIONS FREQUENTLY USED IN LIGHT SCATTERING MEASUREMENTS

θ	$\sin \theta$	$1 + \cos^2\theta$	$\dfrac{\sin \theta}{1 + \cos^2\theta}$	$\sin(\theta/2)$	$\sin^2(\theta/2)$
30°	0.500	1.750	0.286	0.259	0.0670
37.5°	0.609	1.628	0.374	0.322	0.104
45°	0.707	1.500	0.471	0.383	0.146
60°	0.866	1.250	0.693	0.500	0.250
75°	0.966	1.067	0.905	0.609	0.371
90°	1.000	1.000	1.000	0.707	0.500
105°	0.966	1.067	0.905	0.793	0.629
120°	0.866	1.250	0.693	0.866	0.750
135°	0.707	1.500	0.471	0.924	0.854
142.5°	0.609	1.628	0.374	0.947	0.897
150°	0.500	1.750	0.286	0.966	0.977

References page IV-329

Table 2

PARTICLE SCATTERING FACTOR FOR SPHERES AND RODS

[x is defined in eq. (2)](5)

| | $P(\theta)$ | | | $P(\theta)$ | |
x	sphere	rod	x	sphere	rod
0.1	0.998	0.999	2.6	0.219	0.543
0.2	0.998	0.996	2.7	0.191	0.524
0.3	0.978	0.990	2.8	0.165	0.506
0.4	0.968	0.983	2.9	0.141	0.409
0.5	0.949	0.973	3.0	0.120	0.473
0.6	0.929	0.961	3.1	0.0999	0.447
0.7	0.906	0.948	3.2	0.0824	0.443
0.8	0.818	0.933	3.3	0.0671	0.430
0.9	0.848	0.916	3.4	0.0534	0.417
1.0	0.817	0.897	3.5	0.0420	0.406
1.1	0.781	0.878	3.6	0.0320	0.395
1.2	0.745	0.857	3.7	0.0237	0.384
1.3	0.707	0.835	3.8	0.0172	0.375
1.4	0.667	0.813	3.9	0.0117	0.366
1.5	0.627	0.790	4.0	0.00757	0.358
1.6	0.587	0.767	4.1	0.00453	0.350
1.7	0.546	0.745	4.2	0.00231	0.343
1.8	0.506	0.720	4.3	0.000930	0.336
1.9	0.465	0.696	4.4	0.000199	0.329
2.0	0.426	0.673	4.5	0.0000196	0.323
2.1	0.388	0.650	4.6	0.000216	0.317
2.2	0.350	0.627	4.7	0.000740	0.311
2.3	0.316	0.605	4.8	0.00147	0.306
2.4	0.282	0.584	4.9	0.00233	0.300
2.5	0.249	0.563	5.0	0.00336	0.295

Table 3

PARTICLE SCATTERING FACTOR FOR MONODISPERSE COILS

[x is defined in eq. (2)](5)

$x^{\frac{1}{2}}$	$P(\theta)$	$x^{\frac{1}{2}}$	$P(\theta)$
0.1	0.996	2.6	0.228
0.2	0.987	2.7	0.215
0.3	0.971	2.8	0.203
0.4	0.949	2.9	0.192
0.5	0.922	3.0	0.182
0.6	0.891	3.1	0.172
0.7	0.855	3.2	0.163
0.8	0.817	3.3	0.155
0.9	0.776	3.4	0.147
1.0	0.736	3.5	0.140
1.1	0.694	3.6	0.134
1.2	0.652	3.7	0.127
1.3	0.613	3.8	0.122
1.4	0.573	3.9	0.116
1.5	0.536	4.0	0.111
1.6	0.499	4.1	0.106
1.7	0.466	4.2	0.102
1.8	0.434	4.3	0.0976
1.9	0.404	4.4	0.0936
2.0	0.377	4.5	0.0899
2.1	0.352	4.6	0.0864
2.2	0.328	4.7	0.0830
2.3	0.307	4.8	0.0799
2.4	0.287	4.9	0.0769
2.5	0.269	5.0	0.0741

Table 4

DISSYMMETRIES AND CORRECTION FACTORS FOR MONODISPERSE COILS (7)

	Discs		Spheres		Rods		Coils	
D/λ'	z_{45}	$\dfrac{1}{P(90)}$	z_{45}	$\dfrac{1}{P(90)}$	z_{45}	$\dfrac{1}{P(90)}$	z_{45}	$\dfrac{1}{P(90)}$
0.04	1.009	1.005	1.009	1.006	1.005	1.004	1.009	1.007
.06	1.017	1.012	1.020	1.014	1.011	1.008	1.022	1.016
.08	1.030	1.021	1.037	1.026	1.020	1.014	1.040	1.028
.10	1.048	1.033	1.058	1.040	1.031	1.022	1.063	1.044
.12	1.069	1.049	1.084	1.059	1.045	1.032	1.090	1.064
.14	1.095	1.067	1.117	1.081	1.061	1.043	1.124	1.088
.16	1.126	1.088	1.156	1.107	1.080	1.057	1.162	1.115
.18	1.163	1.112	1.202	1.138	1.102	1.072	1.206	1.147
.20	1.204	1.141	1.257	1.173	1.126	1.090	1.255	1.183
.22	1.252	1.173	1.320	1.214	1.153	1.109	1.310	1.223
.24	1.307	1.208	1.395	1.260	1.183	1.131	1.370	1.268
.26	1.368	1.249	1.481	1.313	1.216	1.154	1.436	1.317
.28	1.438	1.294	1.582	1.373	1.250	1.180	1.507	1.371
.30	1.516	1.344	1.700	1.440	1.288	1.207	1.583	1.430
.32	1.604	1.400	1.838	1.517	1.328	1.237	1.663	1.495
.34	1.703	1.461	2.000	1.604	1.370	1.269	1.748	1.564
.36	1.813	1.529	2.192	1.702	1.414	1.304	1.838	1.639
.38	1.936	1.605	2.420	1.814	1.460	1.341	1.931	1.720
.40	2.073	1.688	2.692	1.941	1.508	1.379	2.027	1.806
.42	2.224	1.780	3.021	2.086	1.556	1.421	2.126	1.898
.44	2.391	1.881	3.420	2.251	1.606	1.464	2.227	1.996
.46	2.574	1.992	3.912	2.441	1.656	1.510	2.329	2.100
.48	2.775	2.115	4.522	2.660	1.705	1.558	2.433	2.210
.50	2.991	2.249	5.292	2.912	1.754	1.608	2.538	2.325
.52	3.224	2.397	6.276	3.205	1.802	1.660	2.642	2.447
.54	3.472	2.560	7.559	3.548	1.848	1.714	2.747	2.575
.56	3.732	2.738	9.266	3.949	1.892	1.770	2.850	2.709
.58	4.000	2.932	11.59	4.423	1.933	1.827	2.953	2.849
.60	4.273	3.145			1.972	1.886	3.054	2.995
.62	4.544	3.376			2.007	1.946	3.154	3.148
.64	4.808	3.627			2.040	2.006	3.251	3.306
.66	5.059	3.899			2.069	2.068	3.347	3.469
.68	5.291	4.192			2.095	2.130	3.440	3.639
.70	5.498	4.506			2.118	2.193	3.530	3.815

	Discs		Spheres		Rods		Coils	
D/λ'	z_{45}	$\frac{1}{P(90)}$	z_{45}	$\frac{1}{P(90)}$	z_{45}	$\frac{1}{P(90)}$	z_{45}	$\frac{1}{P(90)}$
.72	5.678	4.841			2.139	2.256	3.618	3.996
.74	5.829	5.196			2.156	2.318	3.703	4.183
.76	5.951	5.570			2.172	2.380	3.785	4.376
.78	6.045	5.961			2.185	2.442	3.864	4.574
.80	6.114	6.366			2.197	2.503	3.940	4.778
.82	6.162	6.783			2.207	2.563	4.014	4.988
.84	6.195	7.208			2.216	2.622	4.084	5.203
.86	6.215	7.637			2.225	2.681	4.152	5.424
.88	6.227	8.066			2.232	2.738	4.217	5.650
.90	6.235	8.492			2.239	2.795	4.279	5.881
.92	6.243	8.911			2.246	2.850	4.338	6.118
.94	6.252	9.321			2.252	2.905	4.395	6.361
.96	6.265	9.719			2.258	2.958	4.449	6.609
.98	6.281	10.10			2.264	3.012	4.501	6.862
1.00	6.304	10.48			2.270	3.064	4.551	7.121

D = major dimension of scattering particle:
     diameter for discs and spheres; length for rods;
     root-mean-square end-to-end distance for coils.

References page IV-329

Table 5

CORRECTION FACTORS FOR POLYDISPERSE COILS
HAVING GENERALIZED EXPONENTIAL DISTRIBUTION (8)

| Monodisperse $\langle M_w \rangle/\langle M_n \rangle=1$ | | Deviations for Polydisperse Coils (added to monodisperse) | | | | | | | |
| | | $1.1 = \langle M_w \rangle/\langle M_n \rangle$ | $1.2 = \langle M_w \rangle/\langle M_n \rangle$ | $1.5 = \langle M_w \rangle/\langle M_n \rangle$ | $2.0 = \langle M_w \rangle/\langle M_n \rangle$ | $3.0 = \langle M_w \rangle/\langle M_n \rangle$ | $5.0 = \langle M_w \rangle/\langle M_n \rangle$ | $10.0 = \langle M_w \rangle/\langle M_n \rangle$ | $20.0 = \langle M_w \rangle/\langle M_n \rangle$ |
z_{45}	$\dfrac{1000}{P(\theta)}$								
1.02	1014	0	0	0	0	0	0	0	0
1.04	1028	0	0	0	0	0	0	0	1
1.06	1042	0	0	0	0	0	0	0	1
1.08	1056	0	0	0	0	0	0	1	1
1.10	1070	0	0	1	1	1	1	1	2
1.12	1085	0	0	1	1	2	2	2	3
1.14	1099	0	0	1	2	2	3	3	4
1.16	1113	0	1	2	3	3	3	4	4
1.18	1128	1	1	2	3	4	5	5	5
1.20	1142	1	1	3	4	5	6	6	7
1.22	1157	1	2	4	5	6	7	7	7
1.24	1171	1	2	5	6	8	9	9	9
1.26	1186	2	3	5	7	9	10	11	11
1.28	1201	2	3	6	9	11	12	13	13
1.30	1215	2	4	7	10	12	14	14	15
1.32	1230	2	5	8	11	14	15	16	17
1.34	1245	3	5	10	13	16	17	19	19
1.36	1260	3	6	11	14	18	19	21	22
1.38	1275	4	7	12	16	20	22	23	24
1.40	1290	4	7	13	18	22	24	26	27
1.42	1305	4	8	15	20	24	27	28	29
1.44	1320	5	9	16	22	26	29	31	32
1.46	1335	5	10	17	23	28	32	34	35
1.48	1350	6	11	19	26	31	35	37	38
1.50	1366	6	11	21	28	34	38	40	41
1.52	1381	7	12	22	30	36	41	43	45
1.54	1397	8	13	24	32	39	44	47	48
1.56	1412	8	14	26	35	42	47	50	52
1.58	1428	9	15	28	37	45	50	54	56
1.60	1444	9	16	29	40	48	54	58	60

		Deviations for Polydisperse Coils (added to monodisperse)							
Monodisperse $\langle M_w\rangle/\langle M_n\rangle=1$		$1.1 = \langle M_w\rangle/\langle M_n\rangle$	$1.2 = \langle M_w\rangle/\langle M_n\rangle$	$1.5 = \langle M_w\rangle/\langle M_n\rangle$	$2.0 = \langle M_w\rangle/\langle M_n\rangle$	$3.0 = \langle M_w\rangle/\langle M_n\rangle$	$5.0 = \langle M_w\rangle/\langle M_n\rangle$	$10.0 = \langle M_w\rangle/\langle M_n\rangle$	$20.0 = \langle M_w\rangle/\langle M_n\rangle$
z_{45}	$\dfrac{1000}{P(\theta)}$								
1.62	1460	10	18	31	43	51	58	62	64
1.64	1476	11	19	33	45	55	61	66	68
1.66	1492	11	20	35	48	58	65	70	72
1.68	1508	12	21	38	51	62	69	74	76
1.70	1524	13	22	40	54	66	73	79	81
1.72	1540	13	23	42	57	69	78	83	86
1.74	1557	14	25	44	60	73	82	88	91
1.76	1573	15	26	47	63	77	86	93	95
1.78	1590	16	27	49	67	81	91	98	101
1.80	1607	16	29	52	70	85	96	103	106
1.82	1624	17	30	54	74	90	101	108	111
1.84	1641	18	32	57	77	94	106	113	117
1.86	1658	19	33	60	81	99	111	119	123
1.88	1675	20	35	62	85	103	116	125	129
1.90	1693	21	36	65	89	108	122	131	135
1.92	1710	22	38	68	93	113	127	137	141
1.94	1728	23	39	71	97	118	133	143	147
1.96	1746	23	41	74	101	123	139	149	154
1.98	1763	24	43	77	105	129	145	156	161
2.00	1781	25	45	80	109	134	151	162	168
2.02	1799	26	46	83	114	140	157	169	175
2.04	1818	27	48	87	119	145	164	176	182
2.06	1836	28	50	90	123	151	170	183	189
2.08	1855	30	52	94	128	157	177	191	197
2.10	1874	30	53	97	133	163	184	198	205
2.12	1892	32	55	101	138	169	191	206	213
2.14	1911	33	57	104	143	176	198	214	221
2.16	1931	34	59	108	148	182	206	222	230
2.18	1950	35	62	112	153	189	214	230	238
2.20	1969	36	63	115	159	196	221	239	247
2.22	1989	37	66	120	164	203	229	247	256
2.24	2009	38	68	123	170	210	237	256	265
2.26	2029	40	70	128	176	217	246	265	275
2.28	2049	41	72	132	182	225	254	275	284
2.30	2069	42	74	136	188	232	263	284	294

References page IV-329

| Monodisperse $\langle M_w\rangle/\langle M_n\rangle=1$ | | Deviations for Polydisperse Coils (added to monodisperse) | | | | | | | |
| | | 1.1 $=$ $\langle M_w\rangle/\langle M_n\rangle$ | 1.2 $=$ $\langle M_w\rangle/\langle M_n\rangle$ | 1.5 $=$ $\langle M_w\rangle/\langle M_n\rangle$ | 2.0 $=$ $\langle M_w\rangle/\langle M_n\rangle$ | 3.0 $=$ $\langle M_w\rangle/\langle M_n\rangle$ | 5.0 $=$ $\langle M_w\rangle/\langle M_n\rangle$ | 10.0 $=$ $\langle M_w\rangle/\langle M_n\rangle$ | 20.0 $=$ $\langle M_w\rangle/\langle M_n\rangle$ |
z_{45}	$\dfrac{1000}{P(\theta)}$								
2.32	2090	43	77	140	194	240	272	294	304
2.34	2111	45	79	145	200	248	281	304	315
2.36	2131	46	81	149	206	256	290	314	325
2.38	2152	47	84	154	213	264	300	325	336
2.40	2174	49	86	158	219	272	310	335	347
2.42	2195	50	88	163	226	281	320	346	359
2.44	2217	51	91	168	233	290	330	358	370
2.46	2239	53	94	173	241	299	340	369	382
2.48	2260	54	96	178	248	308	351	381	395
2.50	2283	56	99	183	255	318	362	392	407
2.52	2305	57	102	188	263	327	373	405	420
2.54	2328	59	104	194	270	337	385	417	433
2.56	2351	60	107	199	278	347	396	430	446
2.58	2374	62	110	205	286	358	408	443	460
2.60	2397	64	113	210	294	368	420	457	474
2.62	2420	65	116	216	303	379	433	470	488
2.64	2444	67	119	222	311	390	446	485	503
2.66	2468	69	122	228	320	401	459	499	518
2.68	2492	70	125	234	329	412	472	514	533
2.70	2517	72	128	240	338	421	486	528	549
2.72	2542	74	131	246	347	436	499	544	565
2.74	2566	75	135	253	356	448	514	560	581
2.76	2592	77	138	259	366	460	528	576	598
2.78	2617	79	141	266	376	473	543	592	615
2.80	2643	81	145	273	386	486	559	609	633
2.82	2669	83	148	279	396	499	574	626	651
2.84	2695	85	152	287	406	513	590	644	670
2.86	2722	87	155	294	417	527	606	662	689
2.88	2749	89	159	301	428	541	623	680	708
2.90	2776	91	163	309	439	555	640	700	728
2.92	2803	93	166	316	450	570	657	719	748
2.94	2831	95	170	324	461	585	675	739	769
2.96	2859	97	174	332	473	601	694	759	790
2.98	2887	99	178	340	485	616	712	779	811
3.00	2916	102	183	348	498	633	732	801	834

Monodisperse $\langle M_w \rangle / \langle M_n \rangle = 1$		Deviations for Polydisperse Coils (added to monodisperse)							
		$1.1 = \langle M_w \rangle / \langle M_n \rangle$	$1.2 = \langle M_w \rangle / \langle M_n \rangle$	$1.5 = \langle M_w \rangle / \langle M_n \rangle$	$2.0 = \langle M_w \rangle / \langle M_n \rangle$	$3.0 = \langle M_w \rangle / \langle M_n \rangle$	$5.0 = \langle M_w \rangle / \langle M_n \rangle$	$10.0 = \langle M_w \rangle / \langle M_n \rangle$	$20.0 = \langle M_w \rangle / \langle M_n \rangle$
z_{45}	$\dfrac{1000}{P(\theta)}$								
3.02	2945	104	187	357	510	649	751	822	856
3.04	2974	106	191	365	523	666	771	845	880
3.06	3004	108	195	374	536	683	792	868	904
3.08	3034	111	200	383	549	704	812	891	928
3.10	3064	113	204	392	563	719	834	915	954
3.12	3095	115	209	401	577	737	856	939	979
3.14	3126	118	213	411	591	756	878	965	1006
3.16	3157	121	218	421	606	776	901	990	1033
3.18	3189	123	223	430	621	795	925	1016	1060
3.20	3221	126	228	441	636	816	949	1044	1089
3.22	3254	128	233	451	651	836	973	1071	1118
3.24	3287	131	238	461	667	858	999	1099	1147
3.26	3320	134	243	472	684	879	1025	1129	1178
3.28	3354	137	249	483	700	901	1051	1158	1209
3.30	3388	140	254	494	718	924	1079	1189	1241
3.32	3423	143	259	505	735	947	1106	1220	1274
3.34	3458	146	265	517	752	971	1135	1252	1308
3.36	3493	149	271	529	771	995	1164	1285	1343
3.38	3529	152	277	541	789	1020	1194	1319	1378
3.40	3565	155	283	554	808	1046	1225	1353	1415
3.42	3602	159	289	566	827	1072	1256	1388	1452
3.44	3640	162	296	580	848	1099	1289	1425	1491
3.46	3678	165	302	593	868	1126	1321	1462	1530
3.48	3716	169	308	607	889	1154	1356	1500	1570
3.50	3755	172	315	620	910	1183	1390	1539	1611
3.52	3795	176	322	634	932	1213	1426	1580	1654
3.54	3835	180	329	649	954	1243	1462	1621	1698
3.56	3876	183	336	663	977	1274	1500	1663	1742
3.58	3917	187	343	679	1000	1306	1539	1707	1789
3.60	3959	191	350	694	1024	1338	1578	1752	1836
3.62	4001	195	358	710	1049	1372	1619	1798	1885
3.64	4044	199	366	726	1074	1406	1660	1845	1934
3.66	4088	204	374	743	1100	1441	1704	1894	1986
3.68	4132	207	382	760	1126	1477	1747	1943	2038
3.70	4177	212	391	778	1153	1514	1792	1995	2093

References page IV-329

Monodisperse $\langle M_w\rangle/\langle M_n\rangle=1$		Deviations for Polydisperse Coils (added to monodisperse)							
		$1.1 = \langle M_w\rangle/\langle M_n\rangle$	$1.2 = \langle M_w\rangle/\langle M_n\rangle$	$1.5 = \langle M_w\rangle/\langle M_n\rangle$	$2.0 = \langle M_w\rangle/\langle M_n\rangle$	$3.0 = \langle M_w\rangle/\langle M_n\rangle$	$5.0 = \langle M_w\rangle/\langle M_n\rangle$	$10.0 = \langle M_w\rangle/\langle M_n\rangle$	$20.0 = \langle M_w\rangle/\langle M_n\rangle$
z_{45}	$\dfrac{1000}{P(\theta)}$								
3.72	4223	216	399	795	1181	1552	1839	2047	2148
3.74	4269	221	407	814	1210	1591	1886	2101	2205
3.76	4317	225	416	832	1238	1631	1935	2157	2264
3.78	4364	231	425	852	1260	1672	1985	2214	2325
3.80	4413	235	435	871	1299	1714	2037	2272	2387
3.82	4462	241	444	891	1331	1758	2089	2333	2452
3.84	4513	245	454	912	1363	1802	2144	2395	2517
3.86	4564	251	464	933	1396	1848	2200	2459	2586
3.88	4616	256	474	954	1430	1894	2258	2525	2655
3.90	4669	262	484	977	1465	1943	2318	2593	2727
3.92	4723	268	494	1000	1500	1993	2378	2662	2801
3.94	4777	273	506	1023	1538	2044	2442	2735	2878
3.96	4833	279	517	1047	1575	2096	2506	2808	2956
3.98	4890	285	528	1071	1614	2150	2572	2885	3037
4.00	4948	291	540	1096	1653	2205	2640	2963	3121

Table 6

AVERAGE DIMENSIONS OF POLYDISPERSE COILS
HAVING GENERALIZED EXPONENTIAL DISTRIBUTION (8)

z_{45}	$\langle M\rangle_w/\langle M\rangle_n = 1$ (monodisperse)	$(1000/\lambda')\langle r^2\rangle_w^{\frac{1}{2}}$							
		$\langle M\rangle_w/\langle M\rangle_n = 1.1$	$\langle M\rangle_w/\langle M\rangle_n = 1.2$	$\langle M\rangle_w/\langle M\rangle_n = 1.5$	$\langle M\rangle_w/\langle M\rangle_n = 2.0$	$\langle M\rangle_w/\langle M\rangle_n = 3.0$	$\langle M\rangle_w/\langle M\rangle_n = 5.0$	$\langle M\rangle_w/\langle M\rangle_n = 10.0$	$\langle M\rangle_w/\langle M\rangle_n = 20.0$
1.02	57	54	52	49	46	44	42	41	40
1.04	80	77	71	70	66	62	60	59	58
1.06	98	94	91	85	81	77	74	72	71
1.08	113	108	105	99	93	89	86	84	83
1.10	126	121	117	111	105	100	96	94	93
1.12	138	133	129	121	115	110	106	103	102
1.14	149	143	139	131	124	119	114	112	111
1.16	159	153	149	140	133	127	123	120	118
1.18	168	163	158	149	142	135	131	127	126
1.20	177	171	167	157	150	143	138	135	133
1.22	186	180	175	165	157	150	145	142	140
1.24	194	188	183	173	165	158	152	149	147
1.26	202	195	190	180	172	164	159	155	154
1.28	209	203	197	187	179	171	166	162	160
1.30	216	210	204	194	185	178	172	168	166
1.35	233	227	221	210	201	193	187	183	181
1.40	249	242	237	226	216	208	202	198	196
1.45	264	257	252	241	231	222	216	211	209
1.50	278	271	266	255	245	236	229	225	223
1.55	292	285	279	268	258	249	242	238	236
1.60	304	298	292	281	274	262	255	251	248
1.65	317	310	305	291	284	275	268	263	261
1.70	329	323	317	307	297	287	280	275	273
1.75	340	335	329	319	309	300	293	288	285
1.80	352	346	341	331	321	312	305	300	297
1.85	363	357	353	343	333	324	317	312	309
1.90	373	368	364	354	345	336	329	324	321
1.95	384	379	375	366	357	348	341	336	333
2.00	395	390	386	377	368	359	353	348	345

References page IV-329

z_{45}	$\langle M \rangle_w / \langle M \rangle_n = 1$ (monodisperse)	$(1000/\lambda')\langle r^2 \rangle_w^{\frac{1}{2}}$							
		$\langle M \rangle_w / \langle M \rangle_n = 1.1$	$\langle M \rangle_w / \langle M \rangle_n = 1.2$	$\langle M \rangle_w / \langle M \rangle_n = 1.5$	$\langle M \rangle_w / \langle M \rangle_n = 2.0$	$\langle M \rangle_w / \langle M \rangle_n = 3.0$	$\langle M \rangle_w / \langle M \rangle_n = 5.0$	$\langle M \rangle_w / \langle M \rangle_n = 10.0$	$\langle M \rangle_w / \langle M \rangle_n = 20.0$
2.10	415	411	408	400	391	383	376	372	369
2.20	435	432	429	422	414	406	400	395	393
2.30	454	452	450	444	437	430	424	420	418
2.40	474	472	471	466	460	454	448	444	442
2.50	493	493	492	488	484	478	473	469	467
2.60	512	513	513	511	507	502	498	495	493
2.70	531	533	534	533	531	527	524	521	519
2.80	550	553	555	556	555	553	550	548	547
2.90	570	574	576	579	580	579	578	576	575
3.00	589	595	598	603	606	606	606	605	604
3.10	609	616	620	627	632	634	635	635	635
3.20	629	637	643	652	659	663	665	666	666
3.30	650	659	666	678	687	693	697	699	699
3.40	671	682	690	705	716	725	730	733	734
3.50	693	706	715	732	746	757	765	769	771
3.60	716	730	740	761	778	792	801	807	810
3.70	739	755	767	791	811	828	840	848	851
3.80	764	781	795	823	846	867	881	891	895
3.90	789	809	824	856	883	908	925	937	942
4.00	816	838	855	891	923	951	972	986	993

REFERENCES

1. P. Debye, J. Phys. Coll. Chem., 51, 18 (1947).
2. P. Debye and E. W. Anacker, J. Phys. Coll. Chem., 55, 644 (1951)
3. B. H. Zimm, R. S. Stein, and P. Doty, Polymer Bulletin, 1, 90 (1945).
4. See, for example: (a) E. P. Geiduschek and A. Holtzer: "Application of Light Scattering to Biological Systems: Deoxyribonucleic Acid and the Muscle Proteins," in "Advances in Biological and Medical Physics," ed. by C. A. Tobias, and J. H. Lawrence, Academic Press, New York, 1958, Vol. VI.; (b) A. Peterlin, "Light Scattering by Non-Gaussian Macromolecular Coils," Proceedings of the Interdisciplinary Conference on Electromagnetic Scattering," Pergamon Press, New York, 1963, p. 357-357.
5. P. Doty and R. F. Steiner, J. Chem. Phys., 18, 1211 (1950).
6. B. H. Zimm, J. Chem. Phys., 16, 1099 (1948).
7. W. H. Beattie and C. Booth, J. Phys. Chem., 64, 696 (1960).
8. W. H. Beattie and C. Booth, J. Polymer Sci., 44, 81 (1960).

DIPOLE MOMENTS OF POLYMERS IN SOLUTION

W. R. Krigbaum and J. V. Dawkins

Department of Chemistry
Duke University
Durham, N. C.

Contents

A. INTRODUCTION

Each conformation of a polar polymer in solution will have a dipole moment μ, in Debye units D, equal to the vectorial sum of the moments of the N dipolar groups along the chain. The mean-square dipole moment $\overline{\mu^2}$ of a long chain molecule in solution is expressed by (1,2):

$$\overline{\mu^2} = \varphi N \mu_o^2$$

where μ_o is the dipole moment of the monomeric repeating unit and φ is a constant characterizing the average molecular conformation. Generally N is equal to the number-average degree of polymerization $\overline{P}_n$, but for poly(alkylene oxides):

$$N = \overline{P}_n + 1$$

since the chain molecule has two hydroxyl endgroups. Except in the case of short chains, the dipole moment per monomer unit $(\overline{\mu^2}/N)^{\frac{1}{2}}$ is usually independent of N. If φ is independent of $\overline{P}_n$, solvent, and temperature and, therefore, of the excluded volume effect, its value can be correlated with short range intramolecular inter-actions. Current theory (3) predicts that when the internal motion of the chain is restricted, φ is less than unity, and also that isotactic, atactic, and syndio-tactic forms of the same polymer should have different average moments, although theory cannot furnish a reliable estimate of the nature and magnitude of the difference.

The value of φ is readily determined since $\overline{\mu^2}$ and μ_o^2 can be obtained directly from
the experimental measurement of the dielectric constant of the polymer, and of a
polar molecule having a structure similar to the monomer unit, in the same solvent
at the same temperature (see the article of de Brouckère and Mandel (4) for references
to experimental techniques). The interpretation of the results is seriously handi-
capped because of the lack of an accepted theory of dielectric behavior. The calculation of the dipole moment from the dielectric constant was pioneered by Debye (5).
His theory of dilute solutions can be applied to polar polymers in non-polar solvents.
To obtain a correct absolute value for $\overline{\mu^2}$, the internal field must be evaluated by
taking into account the interactions of neighboring dipoles along the polymer
chain (3). When polar solvents are employed, the internal field problem is more
serious and will be influenced by polymer-solvent interactions and intermolecular
dipole interactions. Various theories have been proposed for calculating the interaction effects (4) and their application in calculating $\overline{\mu^2}$ is influenced by the extent
of solvent polarization.

Since the measured value of the dipole moment may be in considerable error, care
should be exercised in the use of $\overline{\mu^2}$ for elucidating polymer structure and conformation.
The table contains most of the data in the literature. Wherever possible, experimental conditions have been included and assumptions concerning the constant φ are
mentioned. The model compounds used for comparison are given under remarks.

References page IV-338

B. DIPOLE MOMENTS OF POLYMERS IN SOLUTION

1 - VINYL POLYMERS

Polymer	Solvent	Temperature (°C)	$(\overline{\mu^2/N})^{1/2}$ (D)	φ	Remarks	Reference
Polystyrene						
isotactic	toluene	38.4	0.44	0.53	μ_o taken as 0.60 D	6
atactic	toluene	38.4	0.36	0.35	μ_o taken as 0.60 D	6
	carbon tetrachloride	25.0	0.26	0.55	μ_o (ethyl benzene)=0.35 D	7
Poly(o-bromostyrene)	-	-	-	1.21		8
Poly(o-chlorostyrene)	-	-	-	0.50		8
	-	-	-	1.69		8
Poly(p-chlorostyrene)	benzene	30.0 and 50.0	1.45	0.56	μ_o (p-chlorotoluene)=1.93 D	1
	-	-	-	0.42-0.56		8
isotactic	benzene	30.0	1.22	-		9
atactic	benzene	30.0	1.22	-		9
Poly(p-iodostyrene)	-	-	-	0.50		8
Poly(vinyl acetate)	benzene and carbon tetrachloride	25.0	1.61-1.70	0.89-0.94	μ_o (ethyl acetate)=1.80 D	10
	benzene	20.0	1.70	0.84	μ_o (ethyl acetate)=1.86 D	11
	-	-	-	0.75-0.80		12
Poly(vinyl bromide)	dioxane	25.0	1.41-1.79	0.53-0.86	μ_o (ethyl bromide)=1.93 D. $\overline{\mu^2}$ varies non-linearly with N.	13

Polymer	Solvent	Temperature (°C)	$(\overline{\mu^2}/N)^{\frac{1}{2}}$ (D)	φ	Remarks	Reference
Poly(vinyl chloride)	dioxane	25.0	1.61-1.68	0.66-0.72	μ_o (ethyl chloride in carbon tetra-chloride)=1.98 D	14
atactic	tetrahydrofuran	20.0	1.31	0.64	μ_o (sec-butyl chloride in tetra-hydrofuran)=1.64 D	15
syndiot.	tetrahydrofuran	20.0	1.39	0.71	μ_o (sec-butyl chloride in tetra-hydrofuran)=1.64 D	15
atactic	tetrahydrofuran	40.0	1.31	0.62	μ_o (sec-butyl chloride in tetra-hydrofuran)=1.66 D	15
	dioxane	20.0 and 40.0	1.62	0.59	μ_o (sec-butyl chloride in dioxane)=2.12 D	15
	dioxane	20.0 - 65.0	1.67-1.75	0.70-0.75	μ_o (sec-butyl chloride)=2.00 D. φ independent of N and temperature	16
	-	-	-	0.75		1
Poly(vinyl isobutyl ether)						
isotactic	benzene	25.0	1.16	0.90	μ_o = 1.22 D. Isotactic form postulated to be in a helical conformation.	12
atactic	benzene	25.0	1.07	0.77	μ_o = 1.22 D	12
isotactic	benzene	50.0	1.21	0.98	μ_o = 1.22 D. Isotactic form postulated to be in a helical conformation.	12
atactic	benzene	50.0	1.11	0.83	μ_o = 1.22 D	12
isotactic	benzene	30.0	0.99	-		9
atactic	benzene	30.0	0.98	-		9

Polymer	Solvent	Temperature (°C)	$(\overline{\mu^2/N})^{\frac{1}{2}}$ (D)	φ	Remarks	Reference
			2 - ACRYLIC AND METHACRYLIC POLYMERS			
Poly(methyl acrylate)	benzene	25.0	1.41-1.44	0.64-0.67	μ_0 (methyl propionate in benzene)=1.76 D	17
Poly(ethyl acrylate) atactic	benzene	30.0	1.02	-		9
syndiot.	benzene	30.0	1.02	-		9
Poly(methyl methacrylate) isotactic	benzene	30.0	1.43	0.67	μ_0 (methyl propionate in benzene)=1.73 D (reference 20)	18
atactic	benzene	50.0	1.29-1.35	0.56-0.61	μ_0 (methyl propionate in benzene)=1.73 D (reference 20)	18
syndiot.	benzene	30.0	1.27	0.53	μ_0 (methyl propionate in benzene)=1.73 D (reference 20)	18
isotactic	benzene	25.0-65.0	1.40-1.44	0.77-0.81	μ_0 (monomer in benzene)=1.60 D. Isotactic form postulated to be in a helical conformation.	19
atactic	benzene	25.0-65.0	1.33-1.41	C.69-0.78	μ_0 (monomer in benzene)=1.60 D	19
syndiot.	benzene	25.0-55.0	1.34-1.41	C.70-0.78	μ_0 (monomer in benzene)=1.60 D	19
isotactic	toluene	30.0-90.0	1.29-1.39	0.65-0.75	μ_0 (monomer in benzene)=1.60 D	19
atactic	toluene	30.0-90.0	1.30-1.41	0.66-0.78	μ_0 (monomer in benzene)=1.60 D	19
syndiot.	toluene	30.0-90.0	1.31-1.42	0.67-0.79	μ_0 (monomer in benzene)=1.60 D	19
atactic	5 solvents	25.0	-	0.62	μ_0 (methyl propionate in each solvent) φ independent of solvent	20
	benzene	25.0	1.33-1.52	0.55-0.72	μ_0 (methyl isobutyrate in benzene)=1.80 D	21
	dioxane	23.0	1.50	-		4
	-	-	-	0.53-0.66		8,12

References page IV-338

Polymer	Solvent	Temperature (°C)	$(\overline{\mu^2/N})^{\frac{1}{2}}$ (D)	φ	Remarks	Reference
Poly(ethyl methacrylate)	-	-	-	0.59-0.62		8
Poly(propyl methacrylate)	-	-	-	0.56-0.59		8
Poly(isopropyl methacrylate)	-	-	-	0.61-0.66		8
Poly(butyl methacrylate)	-	-	-	0.55-0.59		8
	4 solvents	23.0	1.39-1.65	-	$(\overline{\mu^2/N})^{\frac{1}{2}}$ is temperature dependent	4
Poly(phenyl methacrylate)	-	-	-	0.55		8
Poly(p-chlorophenyl methacrylate)	-	-	-	0.35		8
Poly(dichlorophenyl methacrylate)	-	-	-	0.38		22

3 - POLYDIENES AND POLYOXIDES

Polymer	Solvent	Temperature (°C)	$\bar{P}_n$	$(\overline{\mu^2/N})^{\frac{1}{2}}$ (D)	ϑ	Remarks	Reference
Polyisoprene cis 1,4	benzene	25.0	13,762	0.28	0.70	μ_o (2-methyl-2-butene in benzene)=0.34 D	23
trans 1,4	benzene	25.0	3,125	0.31	C.82	μ_o (2-methyl-2-butene in benzene)=0.34 D	23
Polychloroprene	benzene	20.0	280	1.45	-		11
Poly(ethylene oxide)	dioxane	25.0	1-7	1.68-1.29	-		24
	benzene	20.0	1.0-33.6	1.41-1.09	-		25
	benzene	20.0	2-227	1.46-1.07	-		2
	benzene	25.0	4.1-153.0	1.61-1.13	-		26
	benzene	25.0	4.0-176.2	1.68-1.13	-		27
Diethoxy poly (ethylene oxide)	benzene	20.0	2 and 6	1.15 and 1.11	-		2
	benzene	25.0	1-6	1.14-1.07	-		28
	benzene	50.0	1-6	1.14-1.09	-		28
Poly(propylene oxide)	benzene	25.0	6.6-69.0	1.40-1.02	-		25

C. REFERENCES

1. P. Debye and F. Bueche, J. Chem. Phys., 19, 589 (1951).
2. J. Marchal and H. Benoit, J. Chim. Phys., 52, 818 (1955); J. Polymer Sci., 23,
    223 (1957).
3. M. V. Vol'kenstein, "Configurational Statistics of Polymeric Chains," (Trans-
    lated by S. N. and M. J. Timasheff) p. 331, Interscience: New York, 1963.
4. L. de Brouckère and M. Mandel, "Dielectric Properties of Dilute Polymer Solutions,"
    in Advances in Chemical Physics, ed. by I. Prigogine, 1, p. 77, Interscience:
    New York, 1958.
5. P. Debye, "Polar Molecules," Chemical Catalog Co.: New York, 1929.
6. W. R. Krigbaum and A. Roig, J. Chem. Phys., 31, 544 (1959).
7. C. G. Le Fèvre, R. J. W. Le Fèvre and G. M. Parkins, J. Chem. Soc.,(1958) 1468.
8. O. B. Ptitsyn, Soviet Phys.-Usp. (English transl.), 2, 797 (1960).
9. H. A. Pohl and H. H. Zabusky, J. Phys. Chem., 66, 1390 (1962).
10. C. G. Le Fèvre, R. J. W. Le Fèvre and G. M. Parkins, J. Chem. Soc., (1960) 1814.
11. I. Sakurada and S. Lee, Z. Phys. Chem., B43, 245 (1939).
12. M. Takeda, Y. Imamura, S. Okamura and T. Higashimura, J. Chem. Phys., 33, 631 (
    (1960).
13. R. J. W. Le Fèvre and K. M. S. Sundaram, J. Chem. Soc., 1962, 4003.
14. R. J. W. Le Fèvre and K. M. S. Sundaram, J. Chem. Soc., 1962, 1494.
15. A. Kotera, M. Shima, N. Fujisaki and T. Kobayashi, Bull. Chem. Soc. Japan, 35,
    1117 (1962).
16. Y. Imamura, J. Chem. Soc. Japan, 76, 217 (1955).
17. R. J. W. Le Fèvre and K. M. S. Sundaram, J. Chem. Soc., 1963 , 3188.
18. R. Bacskai and H. A. Pohl, J. Polymer Sci., 42, 151 (1960).
19. R. Salovey, J. Polymer Sci., 50, S7 (1961).
20. J. Marchal and C. Lapp, J. Polymer Sci., 27, 571 (1958).
21. R. J. W. Le Fèvre and K. M. S. Sundaram, J. Chem. Soc., 1963 , 1880.
22. G. P. Mikhailov, J. Polymer Sci., 30, 605 (1958).
23. R. J. W. Le Fèvre and K. M. S. Sundaram, J. Chem. Soc., 1963, 3547.
24. T. Uchida, Y. Kurita, N. Koizumi and M. Kubo, J. Polymer Sci., 21, 313 (1956).
25. G. D. Loveluck, J. Chem. Soc., 1961 , 4729.
26. M. Aroney, R. J. W. Le Fèvre and G. M. Parkins, J. Chem. Soc., 1960, 2890.
27. V. Magnasco, G. Dellepiane and C. Rossi, Makromol. Chem., 65, 16 (1963).
28. A. Kutera, K. Suzuki, K. Matsumura, T. Nakano, Y. Oyama and U. Kambayashi,
    Bull. Chem. Soc. Japan, 35, 797 (1962).

HEATS AND ENTROPIES OF DILUTION FOR NON-POLAR POLYMER-LIQUID SYSTEMS

C. Booth and M. N. Jones

University of Manchester
Department of Chemistry
Manchester, England

The entropy of dilution (Δs_1) and the heat of dilution (Δh_1) are defined by the following equations:

$$\Delta h_1 = \left(\frac{\partial(H_1 - H_1^{\circ})}{\partial n_1}\right)_{T,P,n_2}, \quad \Delta s_1 = \left(\frac{\partial(S_1 - S_1^{\circ})}{\partial n_1}\right)_{T,P,n_2}$$

where S_1 and H_1 are the entropy and enthalpy of the solvent in solution (no superscript) and in its standard state (superscript o). They are the change in entropy or enthalpy when one mole of solvent is added to an infinite amount of solute. Dimensions are (Δs_1) cal. deg^{-1}. mole^{-1}. and (Δh_1) cal. mole^{-1}. Smoothed values have been taken from those investigations judged to be reliable and discussed in detail, together with experimental procedures, in Polymer 5, 343, (1964).

Polymer	Solvent	Temp. Range, °C	Δs_1 or Δh_1	Volume Fraction of Polymer ($\emptyset_2$)					
				0.9	0.8	0.7	0.6	0.5	0.4
Polystyrene	acetone	25-50	Δs_1		0.57	0.24	0.11	0.04	
			Δh_1		24	14	8	4.5	
	propyl acetate	25-70	Δs_1		1.05	0.60	0.36	0.20	0.12
			Δh_1		98	68	52	39	29
	cyclohexane	34-44	Δs_1		1.92	1.21	0.71	0.49	0.20
			Δh_1		486	308	188	108	60
Polybutadiene	benzene	26.9	Δs_1	2.94	1.76	1.12	0.72	0.45	
			Δh_1	208	164	126	92	64	
	chloroform	0-25	Δs_1		0.93	0.50	0.26	0.13	
			Δh_1		-141	-106	-77	-54	
Polyisobutene	benzene	25-40	Δs_1		1.93	1.35	0.88	0.50	
			Δh_1		404	296	212	140	
	cyclohexane	15-50	Δs_1			1.18	0.77	0.48	0.28
			Δh_1			191	138	98	64
Polyisoprene (natural rubber)	benzene	16-70	Δs_1		1.70	1.07	0.67	0.40	0.22
			Δh_1	247	191	141	100	65	38
	ethyl acetate	25-50	Δs_1	2.45	1.13			0.20	0.07
			Δh_1	410	225			52	23
	methyl ethyl ketone	25-45	Δs_1	2.60	1.28	0.68	0.40		
			Δh_1	495	303	180	107		
	methyl acetate	25	Δs_1			0.36			
			Δh_1			104			
	methyl propyl ketone	25	Δs_1				0.24		
			Δh_1				60		
Polypropylene atactic	diethyl ketone	25-45	Δs_1	3.00	1.56	0.86	0.52	0.30	0.14
			Δh_1	670	400	230	140	85	43
	diisopropyl ketone	25-45	Δs_1			1.85	1.17		
			Δh_1			413	266		

SOLUBILITY PARAMETER VALUES

H. Burrell

Interchemical Corporation
Clifton, New Jersey

and

B. Immergut (in part)

Polytechnic Institute of Brooklyn
Brooklyn, New York

Contents

A. INTRODUCTION

The process of dissolving a polymer in a solvent is governed by the familiar free energy equation

$$\Delta F = \Delta H - T \Delta S$$

where ΔF the change in free energy, ΔH the heat of mixing, T the absolute temperature and ΔS the entropy of mixing.

Since the dissolution of a polymer always is connected with a large increase in entropy the magnitude of the heat term ΔH is the deciding factor in determining the sign of the free energy change. Many theoretical treatments of this factor have been made, but that proposed by Hildebrand (16a) is most useful. Hildebrand states that

$$\Delta H_M = V_M \left[\Delta E_1 / V_1 \right)^{1/2} - (\Delta E_2 / V_2)^{1/2} \right]^2 \phi_1 \phi_2 \qquad\qquad \text{I}$$

where ΔH_M = overall heat of mixing

V_M = total volume of the mixture

Δ_E = energy of vaporization of component 1 or 2

V = molar volume of component 1 or 2

ϕ = volume fraction of component 1 or 2 in the mixture

The expression $(\Delta E/V)$ is the energy of vaporization per cubic centimeter. This has been variously described as the "internal pressure" or the "cohesive energy density."

If this equation is rearranged as follows

$$\Delta H_M / V_M \phi_1 \phi_2 = \left[(\Delta E_1 / V_1)^{1/2} - (\Delta E_2 / V_2)^{1/2} \right]^2 \qquad\qquad \text{II}$$

it may be seen that the heat of mixing per cubic centimeter at a given concentration is equal to the square of the difference between the square roots of the cohesive energy densities of the components. It is, therefore, convenient to assign to this quantity the symbol δ. Expressed mathematically,

$$\delta = (\Delta E/V)^{1/2} \qquad\qquad \text{III}$$

where ΔE is the energy of vaporization to a gas at zero pressure (i.e. at infinite separation of the molecules).

The dimensions of δ are $(\text{cal.}/\text{cc.})^{1/2}$.

If we substitute δ in the right-hand side of equation II, we can easily see that the unit heat of mixing of two substances is dependent on $(\delta_1 - \delta_2)^2$. If the heat of mixing is not to be so large as to prevent mixing, then $(\delta_1 - \delta_2)^2$ has to be relatively small. In fact, if $(\delta_1 - \delta_2)^2 = 0$, solution is assured by the entropy factor. As the value approaches zero, $\delta_1 \rightarrow \delta_2$. This is mathematically equivalent to saying that if the δ values of two substances are nearly equal, the substances will be miscible. For this reason, Hildebrand has termed δ the solubility parameter.

No assumptions were made about polarity, solvation, or association in deriving the solubility parameter. The solubility parameter governs only the heat of mixing of liquids or amorphous polymers. A noncrystalline polymer will, therefore, dissolve in a solvent of similar δ without the necessity of solvation, chemical similarity, association or any specially directed intermolecular force. The high entropy change possible with polymers is sufficient reason for solution to occur.

The solubility parameter of a solvent, δ_s, is a readily calculable quantity. The solubility parameter, δ_p, of a polymer (or for that matter of any nonvolatile substance), cannot be determined directly because most polymers cannot be vaporized without decomposing. δ_p is, therefore, defined as the same as that of a solvent in which the polymer will mix (a) in all proportions, (b) without heat effect, (c) without volume change and (d) without reaction or any special association (35a).

CALCULATION OF δ FROM PHYSICAL CONSTANTS

From Heat of Vaporization - It can be shown that

$$\Delta E = \Delta H - RT$$

where ΔH is the latent heat of vaporization at temperature $T^\circ K$ and R is the gas constant (1.986), so that

$$\Delta E_{25^\circ C} = \Delta H_{25^\circ C} - 592.$$

Where ΔH at 25°C may be found in the literature, the value may be used to calculate ΔE. This is the most direct way to calculate δ and is also the most accurate. In fact, all other methods are approximations to a degree. However, it should be noted that the most accurate numerical values do not always correspond exactly to observed solubility behavior. Sometimes a shift of a few tenths of a unit seems to be required to describe actual behavior. The reason for this is not known.

For most solvents, direct measurements of the heat of vaporization at the desired temperature have not been made or cannot be found in the literature. In such cases, one must resort to one of the various known methods for estimating ΔH, as for example the Clausius-Clapeyron equation. Perhaps the most convenient of the estimations is Hildebrand's equation

$$\Delta H_{25^\circ C} = 23.7 T_b + 0.020 T_b^2 - 2950$$

where T_b is the boiling point in °K. This is given graphically in "The Solubility of Nonelectrolytes," (16a). Figure 1 is an adaptation of Hildebrand's curve, in which RT has already been subtracted from ΔH so that ΔE at 25°C may be read directly from the boiling point in °C at 760 millimeters. In each of these cases the data are reasonably accurate only for liquids which are not hydrogen bonded. They do not yield accurate data for esters, ketones, alcohols, etc. H. Burrell has found, however, that a final correction may be applied to the δ calculated from ΔE read from Figure 1, so that the estimate of the solubility parameter is sufficiently close for practical

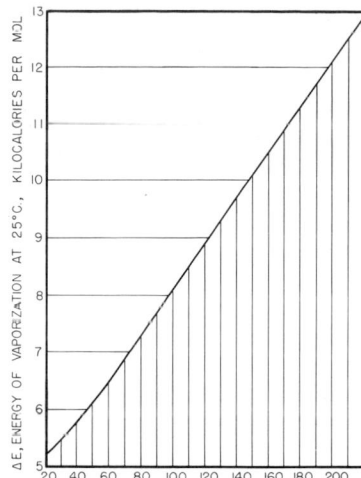

Figure 1 - The Solu-
bility parameter δ of
a solvent can be cal-
culated from its en-
ergy of vaporization.
In this curve ΔE at
25°C may be read di-
rectly from the
boiling point.

applications (7). These corrections are as follows:

    for alcohols, add 1.4 to calculated δ;
    for esters, add 0.6 to calculated δ;
    for ketones, add 0.5 to calculated δ if the boiling point is under 100°C.
      Otherwise nothing is added.

Figure 1, therefore, represents the most convenient source of data for calculating δ.

From Thermal Coefficients - The solubility parameter may be estimated at T°K from the
coefficient of thermal expansion α and the compressibility β by the equation

$$\delta \cong (\alpha T/\beta)^{1/2}$$

Since these thermal coefficients are not readily available for most liquids, the method
is mostly of theoretical interest.

This equation might provide a means for direct estimation of δ for polymers because α
and β should be measurable whereas ΔH, of course, is not.

From Relationship of Pressure to Temperature - δ may also be calculated from $(TdP/dT)^{1/2}$,
where dP/dT must be determined at constant volume. The data required here are the
same as for the Clausius-Clapeyron equation, and the calculation is somewhat simpler.

From van der Waals' Gas Constant - Tables are available in most handbooks for the
van der Waals correction constants to the Gas Law, a and b, where a must be in
$(liters)^2$ (atmospheres). For some liquids these values may be at hand where other
data are not available, or it might be desirable to check a δ value obtained from
other sources. In such cases the expression

$$\delta \cong 1.2a^{1/2}/V$$

may be useful.

From Critical Pressure - The solubility parameter is related to the critical pressure
P_c of a substance through the empirical equation

$$\delta \cong 1.25 \, P_c^{1/2}$$

where the critical pressure is expressed in atmospheres. This equation gives values
of poor accuracy. However, the calculation is quick and simple where a table of
critical pressures is at hand.

From Surface Tension - A rather interesting relationship is

$$\delta = 4.1 \; (\gamma/V^{1/3})^{0.43}$$

where γ is the surface tension in dynes per centimeter. The correlation with values calculated from ΔH is good.

From Strucutral Formula - Small (35) has published a table of "molar-attraction constants" which allows the estimation of the solubility parameter merely from the structural formula of the compound and its density. Small's data are reproduced in Table B. The molar-attraction constants, G, are additive over the formula and are related to the solubility parameter by the equation

$$\delta = d\Sigma G/M$$

where ΣG is the sum for all the atoms and groupings in the molecule, d is the density and M the molecular weight. The table should not be used for alcohols, amines, carboxylic acids or other strongly hydrogen bonded compounds unless such functional groups constitute only a small part of the molecule so that the proportional error is not great. In general, the accuracy is quite good to the first decimal place, which is adequate for practical purposes.

The real value of Small's method lies in its application to polymers. The methods mentioned previously are suitable only for volatile solvents where some physical property, such as the boiling point, can be measured. In this case, however, if the G values are added for the structural configuration of the repeating unit in the polymer chain, the solubility parameter may be calculated.

EXPERIMENTAL DETERMINATIONS OF δ

As mentioned above, except for Small's method, δ_p cannot be calculated from the physical constants of polymers because of their nonvolatility. A direct estimation is, therefore, the only recourse when the structural formula for the polymer is not accurately known.

From Solubility - A list of solvents of gradually increasing δ can be arranged such that a given polymer is soluble in all of the solvents grouped within a certain range in the list. Gee (13) indicates that it may not be exactly correct to assume that the solubility parameter of the polymer is actually the midpoint of the soluble range. However, for practical purposes this provides an adequate estimation. (see below)

From Swelling Values - Another way of determing δ for polymers is to prepare a sparsely cross-linked form (for example, by copolymerizing about 1 per cent divinyl benzene with styrene) and to immerse samples in a series of liquids of varying solubility parameter. Being cross-linked, the material will not dissolve but will swell to varying degrees. The amount of swelling will be greatest in the liquid which has the same δ as the polymer. By inference, the soluble, uncross-linked polymer also has the same value.

Other Methods - Scatchard (31a) suggested using refractive index measurements, and Small (35) described an osmotic pressure or vapor pressure calculation.

Method for Determining Solubility Parameter Ranges of Commercial Polymers - For practical commercial purposes it has been found expedient to determine experimentally a solubility parameter range for each H-bonded class of solvents. The midpoints of these ranges may be taken as single-valued quantities for some purposes, but such midpoints will not necessarily agree with single-values obtained by other methods (13). The value-ranges given in the table of commercial polymers were determined with the intention of developing a practical system for use in paint laboratories; therefore commercial grades of solvents and polymers were used.

A gram or two of solid polymer is placed in a test tube and an approximate amount of a selected solvent is added such that the final solution would have about the correct solids content for the expected commercial use, e.g. 50% for alkyds, 20% for vinyls, etc. The exact amount is often unimportant except for poor solvents; it should be kept in mind that polymers are usually miscible in concentrated solutions although they may form two phases in dilute solution. The mixture may be warmed and stirred to speed up solution, but it should be cooled and observed at room temperature. The resulting mixture should be a single phase, clear and free from gel particles or cloudiness or else the polymer is judged insoluble. The solvents to be used are selected from the Solvent Spectra shown below:

Poorly Hydrogen Bonded

Solvent	δ
n-pentane	7.0
n-heptane	7.4
Apco thinner	7.8
Solvesso 150	8.5
toluene	8.9
tetrahydronaphthalene	9.5
o-dichlorobenzene	10.0
1-bromonaphthalene	10.6
nitroethane	11.1
acetonitrile	11.8
nitromethane	12.7

Moderately Hydrogen Bonded

Solvent	δ
diethyl ether	7.4
diisobutyl ketone	7.8
n-butyl acetate	8.5
methyl propionate	8.9
dibutyl phthalate	9.3
dioxane	9.9
dimethyl phthalate	10.7
2,3-butylene carbonate	12.1
propylene carbonate	13.3
ethylene carbonate	14.7

Strongly Hydrogen Bonded

Solvent	δ
2-ethyl hexanol	9.5
methyl isobutyl carbinol	10.0
2-ethylbutanol	10.5
n-pentanol	10.9
n-butanol	11.4
n-propanol	11.9
ethanol	12.7
methanol	14.5

Here a group of solvents has been especially selected so that the δ values increase by reasonably constant steps within each H-bonded class. The object of using this solvent spectrum is to establish a solubility parameter range for a polymer rather than a single valued number. This has the advantage of automatically showing the allowable difference which can be tolerated between the absolute values of the polymer and solvent. In carrying out the procedure it is convenient to select the first trials about 1/3 and 2/3 of the way down any one column; for example, in the poorly H-bonded group toluene and nitroethane would be chosen. If the polymer is soluble in both, there is no need to try intermediate solvents because experience (as well as theory) have shown that the polymer will be soluble in every case; instead the solvents at the ends of the spectrum should be tried next. If the polymer was soluble in one but not both of the initial trials, the third trial should be about half way between the two. By successive choices sets of two adjacent solvents will be found, one of which dissolves the polymer and one of which does not. The parameter values of the solvents which do dissolve the polymer mark the ends of the range. The procedure is then repeated for the other two H-bonded classes.

The table of solubility parameters consists of four parts. The first two list values for low molecular weight compounds and proprietary mixtures which conceivably could serve as solvents. The first part is arranged alphabetically and the second numerically. The third part lists solubility parameter ranges for commercial polymers and the fourth solubility parameter for general polymers.

The successful practical use of the solubility parameter concept has depended on categorizing solvents into three broad groups relating to their tendency to hydrogen bond. The hydrogen-bonding group is indicated for each "solvent" by the designations

p = poorly H-bonded (hydrocarbons contg. halogen, nitrate, cyano groups)
m = moderately H-bonded (esters, ethers, ketones)
s = strongly H-bonded (alcohols, amines, amides, acids)

The values in the first two tables have been calculated from heats of vaporization where they were available from the literature. In most cases however, the heats were estimated from Hildebrand's equation as adapted by Burrell. Corrections were applied to values for esters and alcohols as described above. In the case of some proprietary hydrocarbon solvents which are mixtures with boiling ranges and unknown molecular weight, the solubility parameter was estimated from the Kauri-butanol value. The number of solvents listed is greatly expanded from the tables originally published in the "Official Digest;" the values for glycol ethers have also been corrected.

B. MOLAR-ATTRACTION CONSTANTS AT 25°C

Group		G		Group	G
$-CH_3$		214	CO	ketones	275
$-CH_2-$	single-bonded	133			
$-CH<$		28	COO	esters	310
$>C<$		-93			
			CN		410
$CH_2=$		190	Cl	(mean)	260
$-CH=$	double-bonded	111	Cl	single	270
$>C=$		19	Cl	twinned as in $>CCl_2$	260
			Cl	triple as in $-CCl_3$	250
$CH\equiv C-$		285	Br	single	340
$-C\equiv C-$		222	I	single	425
Phenyl		735	CF_2 } n-fluorocarbons only		130
Phenylene(o,m,p)		658	CF_3 }		274
Naphthyl		1146			
Ring, 5-membered		105-115	S	sulfides	225
Ring, 6-membered		95-105	SH	thiols	315
Conjugation		20- 30	ONO_2	nitrates	~440
			NO_2	(aliphatic nitro-compounds)	~440
H	(variable)	80-100	PO_4	(organic phosphates)	~500
O	ethers	70	Si	(in silicones)*	-38

---

* estimated by H. Burrell (6).

C. TABLE OF SOLUBILITY PARAMETERS

1 - Solubility Parameters of Solvents (alphabetical list)

δ (cal/cc)$^{1/2}$	Name	H-bonding Group
10.3	acetaldehyde	m
10.1	acetic acid	s
10.3	acetic anhydride	s
9.9	acetone	m
11.9	acetonitrile	p
9.5	acetyl chloride	m
11.6	acetylmorpholine (N)	m
11.2	acetylpiperidine (N-)	s
11.4	acetylpyrrolidine (N-)	s
12.0	acrylic acid	s
10.5	acrylonitrile	p
11.8	allyl alcohol	s
16.3	ammonia	s
7.8	amyl acetate (iso)	m
8.5	amyl acetate (normal)	m
8.3	amyl acetate (secondary)	m
10.0	amyl alcohol (iso)	s
10.9	amyl alcohol (normal)	s
8.7	amylamine (normal)	s
7.6	amyl bromide (normal)	m
8.3	amyl chloride (normal)	m
6.9	amylene	p
7.3	amyl ether (normal, di-)	m
8.0	amyl formate (iso)	m
8.5	amyl formate (normal)	m
8.4	amyl iodide (normal)	m
8.4	anethole (para)	m
10.3	aniline	s
9.9	anthracene	p
7.5	Apco #18 solvent	p
7.3	Apco #140 solvent	p
7.8	Apco thinner	p
8.8	Aroclor 1248	p
9.4	benzaldehyde	m
9.2	benzene	p
8.4	benzonitrile	p
12.1	benzyl alcohol	s
8.5	bicyclohexyl	p
10.6	bromonaphthalene	p
7.1	butadiene-1,3	p
6.8	butane (normal)	p
11.6	butanediol-1,3	s
12.1	butanediol-1,4	s
11.1	butanediol-2,3	s
8.3	butyl acetate (iso)	m
8.5	butyl acetate (normal)	m
8.2	butyl acetate (secondary)	m
8.8	butyl acrylate (normal)	m
10.5	butyl alcohol (iso)	s
11.4	butyl alcohol (normal)	s
10.8	butyl alcohol (secondary)	s
10.6	butyl alcohol (tert.)	s
8.7	butyl bromide (normal)	m
8.4	butyl bromide (secondary)	m
7.8	butyl (iso) butyrate (normal)	m
8.1	butyl (normal) butyrate (normal)	m
8.1	butyl chloride (iso)	m
12.1	butylene-2,3 carbonate	m
6.7	butylene (iso)	p
8.2	butyl formate (iso)	m
8.9	butyl formate (normal)	m

SOLUBILITY PARAMETER VALUES

Table 1 (Cont'd.)

δ (cal/cc)$^{1/2}$	Name	H-bonding Group
8.6	butyl iodide (normal)	m
9.4	butyl lactate (normal)	m
8.25	butyl methacrylate	m
7.5	butyl stearate	m
8.8	butyl propionate	m
9.0	butyraldehyde	m
10.3	butyric acid (iso)	s
10.5	butyric acid (normal)	s
12.6	butyrolactone	m
10.5	butyronitrile	p
12.7	caprolactam (epsilon)	m
10.1	caprolactone	m
9.4	capronitrile	p
10.0	carbon disulfide	p
8.6	carbon tetrachloride	p
9.2	Celanese solvent 601	p
12.6	chloroacetonitrile	p
9.5	chlorobenzene	p
9.7	chloroethyl acetate (beta)	m
9.3	chloroform	p
8.8	chlorotoluene (para)	p
10.2	cresol (meta)	s
11.0	cyclobutanedione	m
8.2	cyclohexane	p
11.4	cyclohexyl alcohol	s
9.9	cyclohexanone	m
8.7	cyclopentane	p
10.4	cyclopentanone	m
8.2	cymene (para)	p
8.8	decahydronaphthalene	p
6.6	decane (normal)	p
9.2	diacetone alcohol	m
8.2	diacetone alcohol methyl ether (Pentoxone)	m
13.7	diacetylpiperazine (N,N)	m
9.1	diamyl phthalate	m
10.4	dibromoethane-1,2	p
10.1	dibromoethylene-1,2	p
8.0	dibutoxyethyl phthalate (Kronisol)	m
8.7	dibutyl phenyl phosphate	m
9.3	dibutyl phthalate	m
9.2	dibutyl sebacate	m
11.0	dichloroacetic acid	s
10.0	dichlorobenzene (ortho)	p
9.8	dichloroethyl ether	m
9.1	dichloroethylene, cis-1,2	p
9.0	dichloroethylene, trans-1,2	p
9.0	dichloropropane-1,2	p
8.2	dichloropropane-2,2	p
9.9	diethylacetamide (N,N)	m
8.0	diethylamine	s
8.8	diethyl carbonate	m
12.1	diethylene glycol	s
9.5	diethylene glycol monobutyl (n) ether	m
10.2	diethylene glycol monoethyl ether	m
8.5	diethylene glycol monoethyl ether acetate	m
8.7	diethylene glycol monolaurate	m
7.4	diethyl ether	m
10.6	diethylformamide (N,N)	m
8.8	diethyl ketone	m
8.6	diethyl oxalate	m
10.0	diethyl phthalate	m
9.9	diethyl-2,2-propanediol-1,3 (heptylene glycol)	s
12.4	diethyl sulfone	m
5.5	difluoro-dichloromethane (Freon 12)	p
7.8	difluoro-tetrachloroethane (Freon 112)	p

Table 1 (Cont'd.)

δ (cal/cc)$^{1/2}$	Name	H-bonding Group
15.4	diformylpiperazine (N,N)	m
8.9	di-n-hexyl phthalate	m
7.7	diisobutylene	p
7.8	diisobutyl ketone	m
7.2	diisodecyl phthalate	m
6.9	diisopropyl ether	m
8.0	diisopropyl ketone	m
10.8	dimethylacetamide (N,N)	m
9.7	dimethylaniline	m
11.2	dimethyl-2,2-butanediol-1,2 (Isobutylene glycol)	s
10.0	dimethyl-2,2-butanediol-1,3	s
9.9	dimethyl carbonate	m
8.8	dimethyl ether	m
12.1	dimethylformamide (N,N)	m
11.0	dimethyl malonate	m
13.1	dimethylnitroamine (N,N)	s
11.0	dimethyl oxalate	m
12.5	dimethyl phosphite	m
10.7	dimethyl phthalate	m
4.9-5.9	dimethyl siloxanes	p
9.4	dimethyl sulfide	p
12	dimethyl sulfoxide	m
14.5	dimethyl sulfone	m
12.1	dimethyltetramethylene sulfone	m
8.7	dioctyl adipate	m
7.9	dioctyl phthalate	m
8.6	dioctyl sebacate	m
10.0	dioxane-1,4	m
10.2	dioxolane-1,3	m
8.5	dipentene	p
8.6	diphenyl 2-ethylhexyl phosphate	m
10.0	dipropylene glycol	s
9.3	dipropylene glycol mono-methyl ether	m
9.7	dipropyl phthalate	m
11.3	dipropyl sulfone	m
6.0	ethane	p
12.3	ethylacetamide	s
9.1	ethyl acetate	m
8.6	ethyl acrylate	m
12.7	ethyl alcohol	s
10.0	ethylamine	s
8.2	ethyl amyl ketone	m
8.8	ethylbenzene	p
8.2	ethyl benzoate	m
9.6	ethyl bromide	m
10.5	ethyl-2-butanol-1	s
8.5	ethyl n-butyrate	m
7.3	ethyl caprylate	m
9.2	ethyl chloride	m
11.0	ethyl cyanoacetate	m
9.7	ethylene bromide	p
14.7	ethylene carbonate	m
12.2	ethylene chlorohydrin	s
9.8	ethylene dichloride	p
14.6	ethylene glycol	s
10.0	ethylene glycol diacetate	m
9.2	ethylene glycol methyl ether acetate	m
9.5	ethylene glycol monobutyl ether	m
10.5	ethylene glycol monoethyl ether	m
8.7	ethylene glycol monoethyl ether acetate	m
11.4	ethylene glycol monomethyl ether	m
11.1	ethylene oxide	m
13.9	ethylformamide (N)	s
9.4	ethyl formate	m
9.4	ethyl-2-hexanediol-1,3 (octylene glycol)	s
9.5	ethyl hexanol	s

SOLUBILITY PARAMETER VALUES

δ (cal/cc)$^{1/2}$	Name	H-bonding Group
7.8	ethyl hexyl acrylate	m
8.9	ethylidene chloride	p
9.4	ethyl iodide	m
7.5	ethyl isobutyl ether	m
7.9	ethyl isobutyrate	m
10.0	ethyl lactate	m
9.2	ethyl mercaptan	p
8.3	ethyl methacrylate	m
8.3	ethyl orthoformate	m
8.4	ethyl propionate	m
5.5-6.2	fluorocarbons, aliphatic	p
7.5-8.2	fluorocarbons, aromatic	p
19.2	formamide	s
12.1	formic acid	s
13.0	formylmorpholine (N)	m
11.5	formylpiperidine (N)	m
9.4	furane	m
11.2	furfural	m
12.5	furfuryl alcohol	s
16.5	glycerol	s
7.4	heptane (normal)	p
10.6	heptyl alcohol (normal)	s
10.5	hexamethylphosphoramide	s
7.3	hexane (normal)	p
10.3	hexanediol-2,5	s
7.4	hexene-1	p
10.7	hexyl alcohol (normal)	s
3.0	hydrogen	p
9.0	hydrogenated terphenyl (Monsanto's HB-40)	p
12.1	hydrogen cyanide	s
9.1	isophorone	m
7.4	isoprene	p
8.1	lauryl alcohol	s
6.9	Low Odor Mineral Spirits	p
13.6	maleic anhydride	s
15.1	malononitrile	p
8.8	mesitylene	p
9.0	mesityl oxide	m
11.2	methacrylic acid	s
5.4	methane	p
14.6	methylacetamide	s
9.6	methyl acetate	m
8.9	methyl acrylate	m
14.5	methanol	s
11.2	methylamine	s
8.0	methyl amyl acetate	m
8.5	methyl amyl ketone	m
10.5	methyl benzoate	m
9.6	methyl bromide	m
8.3	methyl n-butyl ketone	m
8.9	methyl n-butyrate	m
9.9	methyl caprolactone	m
9.7	methyl chloride	m
7.8	methylcyclohexane	p
9.3	methylcyclohexanone	m
9.3	methyl ethyl ketone	m
13.4	methyl ethyl sulfone	m
16.1	methylformamide (N)	s
10.2	methyl formate	m
8.3	methyl n-hexyl ketone	m

Table 1 (Cont'd.)

δ (cal/cc)$^{1/2}$	Name	H-bonding Group
10.2	methyl iodide	m
8.4	methyl isoamyl ketone	m
10.0	methyl isobutyl carbinol	s
8.4	methyl isobutyl ketone	m
8.3	methyl isobutyrate	m
8.5	methyl isopropyl ketone	m
7.9	methyl isovalerate	m
8.8	methyl methacrylate	m
7.8	methyl nonyl ketone	m
10.3	methyl-2-pentanediol-1,3	s
9.7	methyl-2-pentanediol-2,4	s
8.5	methyl-2-pentanediol monoethyl ether (Pentoxol)	s
8.9	methyl propionate	m
8.7	methyl propyl ketone	m
12.5	methyl propyl sulfone	m
11.3	methyl pyrrolidone-2 (N)	m
10.6	methyl salicylate	m
12.9	methyltetramethylene sulfone	m
7.9	methyl n-valerate	m
9.7	methylene chloride	p
12.4	methylene glycolate	m
11.8	methylene iodide	p
8.3	monofluoro-dichloromethane (Freon 21)	p
7.6	monofluoro-trichloromethane (Freon 11)	p
9.9	naphthalene	p
6.3	neopentane	p
11.0	neopentyl glycol	s
10	nitrobenzene	p
11.1	nitroethane	p
12.7	nitromethane	p
7.0	nitro-n-octane	p
10.3	nitro-1-propane	p
9.9	nitro-2-propane	p
7.6	octane (normal)	p
10.3	octyl alcohol (normal)	s
9.4	pentachloroethane	p
7.0	pentane (normal)	p
11.5	pentanediol-1,5	s
10.8	pentanediol-2,4	s
5.8	perfluoroheptane	p
6.0	perfluoromethylcyclohexane	p
9.8	phenanthrene	p
8.6	pine oil	p
8.7	piperidine	s
13.6	piperidone	s
6.4	propane	p
13.3	propiolactone	m
9.9	propionic acid	s
10.0	propionic anhydride	s
10.8	propionitrile	p
8.4	propyl acetate (iso)	m
8.8	propyl acetate (normal)	m
11.5	propyl alcohol (iso)	s
11.9	propyl alcohol (normal)	s
8.6	propylbenzene (normal)	p
8.9	propyl bromide	m
8.4	propyl butyrate	m
7.9	propyl butyrate (iso, iso)	m
8.5	propyl chloride (normal)	m
13.3	propylene-1,2 carbonate	m
12.6	propylene glycol	s
10.1	propylene glycol methyl ether	m
9.2	propylene oxide	m
7.8	propyl ether (di-, normal)	m

SOLUBILITY PARAMETER VALUES

Table 1 (Cont'd.)

δ (cal/cc)$^{1/2}$	Name	H-bonding Group
9.2	propyl formate	m
8.5	propyl propionate	m
10.7	pyridine	s
13.4	pyrone (gamma)	m
14.7	pyrrolidone (alpha)	s
10.8	quinoline	s
11.9	Santicizer 8	m
7.2	Shell Sol 72	p
7.4	Shell TS28 Solvent	p
8.1	Socal Solvent No. 1	p
7.9	Socal Solvent No. 2	p
7.7	Socal Solvent No. 3	p
8.6	Solvesso 100	p
8.5	Solvesso 150	p
9.3	styrene	p
15.4	succinic anhydride	s
8.4	Terpene B	p
9.7	tetrachloroethane-1,1,2,2	p
9.3	tetrachloroethylene (perchloroethylene)	p
9.9	tetraethylene glycol	s
9.1	tetrahydrofuran	m
9.5	tetrahydronaphthalene	p
13.4	tetramethylene sulfone	m
11.4	tetramethyloxamide	m
8.9	toluene	p
9.6	trichloroethane-1,1,2	p
9.2	trichloroethylene	p
8.4	tricresyl phosphate	m
10.7	triethylene glycol	s
7.3	trifluoro-trichloroethane (Freon 113)	p
7.4	trimethyl-3,5,5-hexanol (nonyl alcohol)	s
8.6	triphenyl phosphate	m
9.3	triphenyl phosphite	m
9.2	tripropylene glycol	s
8.7	tripropylene glycol methyl ether	m
8.1	turpentine	p
9.8	valeric acid (normal)	s
9.6	valeronitrile (normal)	p
7.6	Varnolene (Varsol #2)	p
7.8	vinyl chloride	m
9.1	vinyltoluene	p
7.6	V M & P Naphtha	p
23.4	water	s
8.8	m-xylene	p

2 - Solubility Parameters of Solvents (numerical list)

δ (cal/cc)$^{1/2}$	Name	H-bonding Group
3.0	hydrogen	p
4.9-5.9	dimethyl siloxanes	p
5.4	methane	p
5.5	difluoro-dichloromethane (Freon 12)	p
5.5-6.2	fluorocarbons, aliphatic	p
5.8	perfluoroheptane	p
6.0	ethane	p
6.0	perfluoromethylcyclohexane	p
6.3	neopentane	p
6.4	propane	p
6.6	decane (normal)	p
6.7	butene (iso)	p
6.8	butane (normal)	p
6.9	amylene	p
6.9	diisopropyl ether	m
6.9	Low Odor Mineral Spirits	p
7.0	nitro-n-octane	p
7.0	pentane (normal)	p
7.1	butadiene-1,3	p
7.2	diisodecyl phthalate	m
7.2	Shell Sol 72	p
7.3	amyl ether (normal, di-)	m
7.3	Apco #140 Solvent	p
7.3	ethyl caprylate	m
7.3	hexane (normal)	p
7.3	trifluoro-trichloroethane (Freon 113)	p
7.4	diethyl ether	m
7.4	heptane (normal)	p
7.4	hexene-1	p
7.4	isoprene	p
7.4	Shell TS28 Solvent	p
7.5	Apco #18 Solvent	p
7.5	butyl stearate	m
7.5	ethyl isobutyl ether	m
7.5-8.2	fluorocarbons, aromatic	p
7.6	amyl bromide (normal)	m
7.6	monofluoro-trichloromethane (Freon 11)	p
7.6	octane (normal)	p
7.6	V M & P Naptha	p
7.6	Varnolene (Varsol #2)	p
7.7	diisobutylene	p
7.7	Socal Solvent No. 3	p
7.8	amyl acetate (iso)	m
7.8	Apco thinner	p
7.8	butyl (iso) butyrate (normal)	m
7.8	difluoro-tetrachloroethane (Freon 112)	p
7.8	diisobutyl ketone	m
7.8	ethyl hexyl acrylate	m
7.8	methylcyclohexane	p
7.8	methyl nonyl ketone	m
7.8	propyl ether (di-, normal)	m
7.8	vinyl chloride	m
7.9	dioctyl phthalate	m
7.9	ethyl butyrate (iso)	m
7.9	methyl valerate (iso)	m
7.9	methyl valerate (normal	m
7.9	propyl butyrate (iso, iso)	m
7.9	Socal Solvent No. 2	p
8.0	amyl formate (iso)	m
8.0	dibutoxyethyl phthalate (Kronisol)	m
8.0	diethylamine	s
8.0	diisopropyl ketone	m
8.0	methyl amyl acetate	m
8.1	butyl (normal) butyrate (normal)	m
8.1	butyl chloride (iso)	m

SOLUBILITY PARAMETER VALUES

Table 2 (Cont'd.)

$\delta \ (cal/cc)^{1/2}$	Name	H-bonding Group
8.1	lauryl alcohol	s
8.1	Socal Solvent No. 1	p
8.1	turpentine	p
8.2	butyl acetate (secondary)	m
8.2	butyl formate (iso)	m
8.2	cyclohexane	p
8.2	cymene (para)	p
8.2	diacetone alcohol methyl ether (Pentoxone)	m
8.2	dichloropropane-2,2	p
8.2	ethyl amyl ketone	m
8.2	ethyl benzoate	m
8.25	butyl methacrylate	m
8.3	amyl acetate (secondary)	m
8.3	amyl chloride (normal)	m
8.3	butyl acetate (iso)	m
8.3	ethyl methacrylate	m
8.3	ethyl orthoformate	m
8.3	methyl n-butyl ketone	m
8.3	methyl n-hexyl ketone	m
8.3	methyl butyrate (iso)	m
8.3	monofluoro-dichloromethane (Freon 21)	p
8.4	amyl iodide (normal)	m
8.4	anethole (para)	m
8.4	benzonitrile	p
8.4	butyl bromide (secondary)	m
8.4	ethyl propionate	m
8.4	methyl isoamyl ketone	m
8.4	methyl isobutyl ketone	m
8.4	propyl acetate (iso)	m
8.4	propyl butyrate	m
8.4	Terpene B	p
8.4	tricresyl phosphate	m
8.4	trimethyl-3,5,5-hexyl alcohol (nonyl alcohol)	s
8.5	amyl acetate (normal)	m
8.5	amyl formate (normal)	m
8.5	bicyclohexyl	p
8.5	butyl acetate (normal)	m
8.5	diethylene glycol monoethyl ether acetate	m
8.5	dipentene	p
8.5	ethyl n-butyrate	m
8.5	methyl amyl ketone	m
8.5	methyl isopropyl ketone	m
8.5	methyl-2-pentanediol monoethyl ether (Pentoxol)	s
8.5	propyl chloride (normal)	m
8.5	propyl propionate	m
8.5	Solvesso 150	p
8.6	butyl iodide (normal)	m
8.6	carbon tetrachloride	p
8.6	diethyl oxalate	m
8.6	dioctyl sebacate	m
8.6	diphenyl 2-ethylhexyl phosphate	m
8.6	ethyl acrylate	m
8.6	pine oil	p
8.6	propylbenzene (normal)	p
8.6	Solvesso 100	p
8.6	triphenyl phosphate	m
8.7	amylamine (normal)	s
8.7	butyl bromide (normal)	m
8.7	cyclopentane	p
8.7	dibutyl phenyl phosphate	m
8.7	diethylene glycol monolaurate	m
8.7	dioctyl adipate	m
8.7	ethylene glycol monoethyl ether acetate	m
8.7	methyl propyl ketone	m
8.7	piperidine	s
8.7	tripropylene glycol methyl ether	m
8.8	Aroclor 1248	p

Table 2 (Cont'd.)

δ (cal/cc)$^{1/2}$	Name	H-bonding Group
8.8	butyl acrylate (normal)	m
8.8	butyl propionate	m
8.8	chlorotoluene (para)	p
8.8	decahydronaphthalene	p
8.8	diethyl carbonate	m
8.8	diethyl ketone	m
8.8	dimethyl ether	m
8.8	ethylbenzene	p
8.8	mesitylene	p
8.8	methyl methacrylate	m
8.8	propyl acetate	m
8.8	xylene	p
8.9	butyl formate (normal)	m
8.9	di-n-hexyl phthalate	m
8.9	ethylidene chloride	p
8.9	methyl acrylate	m
8.9	methyl butyrate (normal)	m
8.9	methyl propionate	m
8.9	propyl bromide	m
8.9	toluene	p
9.0	butyraldehyde	m
9.0	dichloroethylene, trans-1,2	p
9.0	dichloropropane-1,2	p
9.0	hydrogenated terphenyl (Monsanto's HB-40)	p
9.0	mesityl oxide	m
9.1	diamyl phthalate	m
9.1	dichloroethylene, cis-1,2	p
9.1	ethyl acetate	m
9.1	isophorone	m
9.1	tetrahydrofuran	m
9.1	vinyltoluene	p
9.2	benzene	p
9.2	Celanese Solvent 601	m
9.2	diacetone alcohol	m
9.2	dibutyl sebacate	m
9.2	ethyl chloride	m
9.2	ethylene glycol methyl ether acetate	m
9.2	ethyl mercaptan	p
9.2	propylene oxide	m
9.2	propyl formate	m
9.2	trichloroethylene	p
9.2	tripropylene glycol	s
9.3	chloroform	p
9.3	dibutyl phthalate	m
9.3	dipropylene glycol mono-methyl ether	m
9.3	methylcyclohexanone	m
9.3	methyl ethyl ketone	m
9.3	styrene	p
9.3	tetrachloroethylene (perchloroethylene)	p
9.3	triphenyl phosphite	m
9.4	benzaldehyde	m
9.4	butyl lactate (normal)	m
9.4	capronitrile	p
9.4	dimethyl sulfide	p
9.4	ethyl formate	m
9.4	ethyl-2-hexanediol-1,3(octylene glycol)	s
9.4	ethyl iodide	m
9.4	furane	m
9.4	pentachloroethane	p
9.5	acetyl chloride	m
9.5	chlorobenzene	p
9.5	diethylene glycol monobutyl ether (normal)	m
9.5	ethylene glycol monobutyl ether	m
9.5	ethylhexanol	s
9.5	tetrahydronaphthalene	p
9.6	ethyl bromide	m
9.6	methyl acetate	m

SOLUBILITY PARAMETER VALUES

Table 2 (Cont'd.)

δ (cal/cc)$^{1/2}$	Name	H-bonding Group
9.6	methyl bromide	m
9.6	trichloroethane-1,1,2	p
9.6	valeronitrile (normal)	p
9.7	chloroethyl acetate (beta)	m
9.7	dimethylaniline	m
9.7	dipropyl phthalate	m
9.7	ethylene bromide	p
9.7	methyl chloride	m
9.7	methylene chloride	p
9.7	methyl-2-pentanediol-2,4 (hexylene glycol)	s
9.7	tetrachloroethane-1,1,2,2	p
9.8	dichloroethyl ether	m
9.8	ethylene dichloride	p
9.8	phenanthrene	p
9.8	valeric acid (normal)	s
9.9	acetone	m
9.9	anthracene	p
9.9	cyclohexanone	m
9.9	diethylacetamide (N,N)	m
9.9	diethyl-2,2-propanediol-1,3 (heptylene glycol)	s
9.9	dimethyl carbonate	m
9.9	methyl caprolactone	m
9.9	naphthalene	p
9.9	nitro-2-propane	p
9.9	propionic acid	s
9.9	tetraethylene glycol	s
10.0	amyl alcohol (iso)	s
10.0	carbon disulfide	p
10.0	dichlorobenzene (ortho)	p
10.0	diethyl phthalate	m
10.0	dimethyl-2,2-butanediol-1,3	s
10.0	dioxane-1,4	m
10.0	dipropylene glycol	s
10.0	ethylamine	s
10.0	ethylene glycol diacetate	m
10.0	ethyl lactate	m
10.0	methyl isobutyl carbinol	s
10.0	nitrobenzene	p
10.0	propionic anhydride	s
10.1	acetic acid	s
10.1	caprolactone	m
10.1	dibromoethylene-1,2	p
10.1	propylene glycol methyl ether	m
10.2	cresol (meta)	s
10.2	diethylene glycol monoethyl ether	m
10.2	dioxolane-1,3	m
10.2	methyl formate	m
10.2	methyl iodide	m
10.3	acetaldehyde	m
10.3	acetic anhydride	s
10.3	aniline	s
10.3	butyric acid (iso)	s
10.3	hexanediol-2,5	s
10.3	methyl-2-pentanediol-1,3	s
10.3	nitro-1-propane	p
10.3	octyl alcohol (normal)	s
10.4	cyclopentanone	m
10.4	dibromoethane-1,2	p
10.5	acrylonitrile	p
10.5	butyl alcohol (iso)	s
10.5	butyric acid (normal)	s
10.5	butyronitrile	p
10.5	ethyl-2-butanol-1	s
10.5	ethylene glycol monoethyl ether	m
10.5	hexamethylphosphoramide	s
10.5	methyl benzoate	m
10.6	bromonaphthalene	p

Table 2 (Cont'd.)

δ (cal/cc)$^{1/2}$	Name	H-bonding Group
10.6	butyl alcohol (tert.)	s
10.6	diethylformamide (N,N)	m
10.6	heptyl alcohol (normal)	s
10.6	methyl salicylate	m
10.7	dimethyl phthalate	m
10.7	hexyl alcohol (normal)	s
10.7	pyridine	s
10.7	triethylene glycol	s
10.8	butyl alcohol (secondary)	s
10.8	dimethylacetamide (N,N)	m
10.8	pentanediol-2,4	s
10.8	propionitrile	p
10.8	quinoline	s
10.9	amyl alcohol (normal)	s
11.0	cyclobutanedione	m
11.0	dichloroacetic acid	s
11.0	dimethyl malonate	m
11.0	dimethyl oxalate	m
11.0	ethyl cyanoacetate	m
11.0	neopentyl glycol	s
11.1	butanediol-2,3	s
11.1	ethylene oxide	m
11.1	nitroethane	p
11.2	acetylpiperidine (N)	s
11.2	dimethyl-2,2-butanediol-1,2 (Isobutylene glycol)	s
11.2	furfural	m
11.2	methacrylic acid	s
11.2	methylamine	s
11.3	dipropyl sulfone	m
11.3	methylpyrrolidone-2 (N)	m
11.4	acetylpyrrolidine (N)	s
11.4	butyl alcohol (normal)	s
11.4	cyclohexanol	s
11.4	ethylene glycol monomethyl ether	m
11.4	tetramethyloxamide	m
11.5	formylpiperidine (N)	m
11.5	pentanediol-1,5	s
11.5	propyl alcohol (iso)	s
11.6	acetylmorpholine (N)	m
11.6	butanediol-1,3	s
11.8	allyl alcohol	s
11.8	methylene iodide	p
11.9	acetonitrile	p
11.9	propyl alcohol (normal)	s
11.9	Santicizer 8	m
12.0	acrylic acid	s
12.0	dimethyl sulfoxide	m
12.1	benzyl alcohol	s
12.1	butanediol-1,4	s
12.1	butylene-2,3 carbonate	m
12.1	diethylene glycol	s
12.1	dimethylformamide (N,N)	m
12.1	dimethyltetramethylene sulfone	m
12.1	formic acid	s
12.1	hydrogen cyanide	s
12.2	ethylene chlorohydrin	s
12.3	ethylacetamide (N)	s
12.4	diethyl sulfone	m
12.4	methylene glycolate	m
12.5	dimethyl phosphite	m
12.5	furfuryl alcohol	s
12.5	methyl propyl sulfone	m
12.6	butyrolactone	m
12.6	chloroacetonitrile	p
12.6	propylene glycol	s
12.7	caprolactam (epsilon)	m
12.7	ethyl alcohol	s

Table 2 (Cont'd.)

δ (cal/cc)$^{1/2}$	Name	H-bonding Group
12.7	nitromethane	p
12.9	methyltetramethylene sulfone	m
13.0	formylmorpholine (N)	m
13.1	dimethylnitroamine (N,N)	s
13.3	propiolactone	m
13.3	propylene-1,2 carbonate	m
13.4	methyl ethyl sulfone	m
13.4	pyrone (gamma)	m
13.4	tetramethylene sulfone	m
13.6	maleic anhydride	s
13.6	piperidone	s
13.7	diacetylpiperazine (N,N)	m
13.9	ethylformamide (N)	s
14.5	methanol	s
14.5	dimethyl sulfone	m
14.6	ethylene glycol	s
14.6	methylacetamide (N)	s
14.7	ethylene carbonate	m
14.7	pyrrolidone (alpha)	s
15.1	malonylnitrile	p
15.4	diformylpiperazine (N,N)	m
15.4	succinic anhydride	s
16.1	methylformamide (N)	s
16.3	ammonia	s
16.5	glycerol	s
19.2	formamide	s
23.4	water	s

3 - Solubility Parameters of Commercial Polymers

Polymer	Solubility Parameter Ranges in Solvents which are Hydrogen Bonded:		
	Poorly	Moderately	Strongly
ACRYLICS			
Acryloid B-44	8.9-11.9	8.5-13.3	0
Acryloid B-66	8.5-11.1	7.8-12.1	0
Acryloid B-72	8.5-12.7	8.9-13.3	0
Acryloid B-82	8.5-11.1	8.9-12.1	0
Poly(butyl acrylate)	7.0-12.7	7.4-12.1	9.5-12.7
Poly(methacrylic acid)	0	9.9	12.7-14.5
Poly(methyl methacrylate) Lucite 2041	8.9-12.7	8.5-13.3	0
Poly(ethyl methacrylate) Lucite 2042	8.5-11.1	7.8-13.3	9.5-11.4
Poly(n-butyl methacrylate) Lucite 2044	7.4-11.1	7.4- 9.9	9.5-11.4
Poly(isobutyl methacrylate) Lucite 2045	8.5-11.1	8.5- 9.9	9.5-11.4
ALKYDS			
30% Soy, Glycerol Phthalate	8.5-12.7	8.5-14.7	0
45% Soy, Glycerol Phthalate	7.0-11.1	7.4-10.8	9.5-11.9
45% Soy, Pentaerythritol Phthalate	7.0-11.1	7.4-10.8	9.5-11.9
45% Linseed, Glycerol Phthalate	7.0-11.9	7.4-10.8	9.5-11.9

Table 3 (Cont'd.)

Polymer	Solubility Parameter Ranges in Solvents which are Hydrogen Bonded:		
	Poorly	Moderately	Strongly

EPOXY RESINS

Polymer	Poorly	Moderately	Strongly
Epon E-72	8.5-10.6	7.4- 9.9	9.5-11.4
Epon 812	8.9-12.7	7.8-14.7	10.0-14.5
Epon 864	9.5-12.7	8.5-14.7	0
Epon 1001	10.6-11.1	8.5-13.3	0
Epon 1004	0	8.5-13.3	0
Epon 1007	0	8.5-13.3	0
Epon 1009	0	8.5- 9.9	0

HYDROCARBON RESINS

Polymer	Poorly	Moderately	Strongly
Alpex Cyclized Rubber	7.4-10.6	7.8	0
Gilsonite Brilliant Black	7.8-10.6	7.8- 8.5	0
Gilsonite Selects	7.8- 9.5	7.8- 8.5	9.5
Nebony 100	8.5-10.6	7.8- 9.9	0
Neville LX685	7.4-10.6	9.3- 9.9	0
Panarez 3-210	8.5-10.6	0	0
Petrolatum 125 HMP	8.5- 8.9	0	0
Pliolite NR	8.5-10.6	0	0
Pliolite P-1230	9.5-10.6	0	0

PHENOLICS

Polymer	Poorly	Moderately	Strongly
Bakelite CKR-5254	8.5-10.0	7.8-13.3	9.5-10.8
Bakelite CKR-5360	8.5-11.1	7.8-13.3	9.5-11.4
Bakelite CKR-2400	8.9-11.9	7.8-13.3	9.5-14.5
Bakelite BKR-2620	0	8.4-14.7	9.5-14.5
Durez 220	8.5-10.6	7.8- 9.8	9.5-11.4
Durez 550	7.0-11.9	7.4- 9.8	9.5-14.5
Methylon 75202	0	8.9-12.1	0

POLYESTERS

Polymer	Poorly	Moderately	Strongly
Goodyear "Vitel Resin PE100-X"	11.1	9.9	0
Soluble Mylars:			
49000	10.6-11.1	10.6-11.1	0
49001	8.9-10.6	9.3- 9.9	0
49002	9.5-10.6	9.3- 9.9	0

AMINE RESINS

Polymer	Poorly	Moderately	Strongly
Beckamine P-196	8.9-11.1	8.5-10.8	9.5-12.7
Beetle 227-8	0	0	8.9-11.4
Resimene 888	8.5-10.6	7.4-12.1	9.5-12.7
Uformite MX-61	8.5-11.1	7.4-11.1	9.5-11.1

CELLULOSE DERIVATIVES

Polymer	Poorly	Moderately	Strongly
Cellulose Acetate, LL-1	11.1-12.7	9.9-14.7	0
Cellulose Acetate-Butyrate	11.1-12.7	8.5-14.7	12.7-14.5
Cellulose Butyrate,	11.1-12.7	8.5-14.7	12.7-14.5
Cyanoethyl Cellulose	11.1-12.7	12.2-14.7	0
Ethyl Cellulose, K-200	0	8.5-10.8	9.5-11.4
Ethyl Cellulose, N-22	8.1-11.1	7.4-10.8	9.5-14.5
Ethyl Cellulose, T-10	8.5- 9.5	7.8- 9.8	9.5-11.4
Nitrocellulose, RS,	11.1-12.7	7.8-14.7	14.5
Nitrocellulose, SS,	11.1-12.7	7.8-14.7	12.7-14.5

Polymer	Solubility Parameter Ranges in Solvents which are Hydrogen Bonded:		
	Poorly	Moderately	Strongly

POLYAMIDES

Polymer	Poorly	Moderately	Strongly
Nylon, Type 8	0	0	11.9-14.5
Versamid 100	8.5-10.6	8.5- 8.9	9.5-11.4
Versamid 115	8.5-10.6	7.8- 9.9	9.5-12.7
Versamid 900	0	0	0
Versamid 930	0	0	9.5-11.4
Versamid 940	0	0	9.5-11.4
Versalon 1112	0	0	9.5-11.4
Versalon 1175	0	0	9.5-11.4

ROSIN DERIVATIVES

Polymer	Poorly	Moderately	Strongly
WW Gum Rosin	8.5-11.1	7.4-10.8	9.5-11.4
Wood Rosin M Grade	7.4-10.6	7.4-10.8	9.5-14.5
Ester Gum	7.0-10.6	7.4-10.8	9.5-10.9
Alkydol 160	9.5	8.5-10.8	9.5-12.7
Amberol F-7	8.5-10.6	7.8- 9.8	9.5-10.9
Amberol 750	0	8.9-10.8	9.5-12.7
Amberol 801	8.5-11.1	7.4- 9.9	0
Arochem 455	0	7.8-13.3	9.5-14.5
Arochem 462	9.5	8.5-10.8	9.5-14.5
Dymerex	7.4-10.6	7.8- 9.9	9.5-11.4
Nelio B952	9.5-10.6	7.4-10.8	9.5-12.7
Nelio VBR757	0	8.5-10.8	9.5-14.5
Neolyn 23	8.5-11.1	8.5-13.3	0
Newport V-40	8.5-11.1	7.4-12.1	9.5-14.5
Pentalyn A	8.5-10.6	7.4- 9.9	9.5-11.4
Pentalyn G	8.5-10.6	7.8- 9.9	9.5-10.9
Pentalyn K	8.5-10.6	7.8- 9.9	9.5
Pentalyn 830	8.5- 9.5	7.8-10.8	9.5-11.4
Pentalyn 856	8.5-11.1	7.4-10.8	9.5-11.4
Vinsol	10.6-11.9	7.8-13.3	9.5-12.7

STYRENE POLYMERS AND COPOLYMERS

Polymer	Poorly	Moderately	Strongly
Buton 100	7.0-10.6	7.4- 9.9	0
Buton 300	8.5-10.6	7.4- 9.9	9.5-10.5
Lytron 810	11.9	9.9-14.7	0
Lytron 820	9.5	8.9-14.7	10.9-14.5
Marbon 9200	8.5-10.6	9.3- 9.9	0
Piccoflex 120	8.5-11.1	7.8- 9.9	0
Styron 440M-27	8.5-10.6	9.3	0
Styron 475M-27	8.5-10.6	9.3	0
Styron 480-27	9.5-10.6	9.3	0
Lustrex "High Test 88"	8.5-10.6	9.3	0
Shell X-450	9.5-10.6	8.5-12.1	9.5-12.7
Bakelite RMD4511 (S/An)	10.6-11.1	9.3	0

VINYLS

Polymer	Poorly	Moderately	Strongly
Exon 470	8.5-11.1	7.8- 9.9	0
Exon 471	8.5-11.1	7.8-12.1	0
Exon 473	8.5-11.1	7.8- 9.9	0
Geon 121	10.6-11.1	9.3- 9.9	0
Poly(vinyl butyl ether)	7.8-10.6	7.4- 9.9	9.5-11.4
Poly(vinyl ethyl ether)	7.0-11.1	7.4-10.8	9.5-14.5
Poly(vinyl formal) (7/70E)	0	9.9-13.3	0
Poly(vinyl formal) (15/95E)	0	9.9-13.3	0
Poly(vinyl isobutyl ether)	7.0-10.6	7.4- 9.9	9.5-11.4
Saran F-120	9.5-11.1	12.1-14.7	0
Saran F-220	9.5-11.1	10.8-14.7	0
Vinylite AYAA	8.9-12.7	8.5-14.7	14.5
Vinylite VAGH	10.6-11.1	7.8- 9.9	0

Table 3 (Cont'd.)

Polymer	Solubility Parameter Ranges in Solvents which are Hydrogen Bonded:		
	Poorly	Moderately	Strongly

VINYLS (Cont'd.)

Vinylite VMCH	10.6-11.1	7.8-12.1	0
Vinylite VYHH	9.3-11.1	7.8-13.3	0
Vinylite XYHL	0	8.9-10.8	9.5-14.5
Vinylite XYSG	0	8.9-10.8	9.5-14.5
Vinylite VXCC	9.5-11.1	7.8-13.2	0
Vinylite VYLF	9.5-11.1	7.8-13.2	0
Elvax 150 (PVAc/E)	7.8-10.6	0	0
Elvax 250 (PVAc/E)	8.5- 9.5	0	0
Elvax EOD 3602-1	7.0-10.6	7.8- 8.5	0

MISCELLANEOUS

Beckolin #27 (Modified Oil)	7.0-11.1	7.4- 9.9	9.5-11.4
Carbowax 4000	8.9-12.7	8.5-14.7	9.5-14.5
Chlorinated Rubber	8.5-10.6	7.8-10.8	0
Conoco H-35	7.0-11.1	7.4- 9.9	9.5-11.4
Dammar Gum (Dewaxed)	8.5-10.6	7.8- 9.9	9.5-10.9
Hypalon 20	8.1- 9.8	8.4- 8.8	0
Hypalon 30	8.5-10.6	7.8- 8.5	0
Lexan 100 Polycarbonate Resin	9.5-10.6	9.3- 9.9	0
Lexan 105 Polycarbonate Resin	9.5-10.6	9.3- 9.9	0
Santolite MHP	10.6-12.7	7.8-14.7	9.5
Shellac (Pale-Pale)	0	9.9-10.8	9.5-14.5
Silicone DC-23	7.4-8.5	7.4- 7.8	9.5-10.0
Silicone DC-1107	7.0- 9.5	9.3-10.8	9.5-11.4
Sylkyd 50	7.0-12.7	7.9-12.9	9.5-14.5
Silicone Intermediate Z6018	8.5-11.1	7.9-12.2	10.0-11.4
Soy Oil	7.0-11.1	7.4-10.8	9.5-11.9
Soy Oil, Blown	7.0-11.1	7.4-10.8	9.5-12.7

SOLUBILITY PARAMETER VALUES

4 - Solubility Parameter of General Polymers

Polymer	$\delta(\text{cal/cc})^{1/2}$	Method	T°C	Ref.
Poly(acrylic acid)				
-- , butyl ester	8.8		35	24
	8.80	av.		24
	9.05	swelling		24
	8.5	calc.		24
	9.1	swelling		26
	9.05			26
-- , ethyl ester				
	9.35	av.		24
	9.4	swelling		24
	9.7	calc.		24
	9.4	swelling		26
	9.35			26
	9.38			14
	9.2	calc.		17
-- , isobornyl ester	8.2	calc.		17
-- , methyl ester				
	10.1	av.		24
	10.15	swelling		24
	9.8	calc.		24
	10.15	swelling		26
	10.4			26
	10.1	swelling		26
-- , propyl ester				
	9.05			24
	9.00	av.		24
	9.0	calc.		24
Polyacrylonitrile	12.5			20
	12.75	calc.	25	35
	15.4			36
Alkyd, medium oil length	9.4			6
Benzyl cellulose	12.33			34
Polybutadiene	7.16	calc.		8
	8.40			20
	8.35			34
	8.38	calc.		35
	8.4-8.6	obs.		35
	8.1			36
	8.6			21
(emulsion)	8.40			28
(sodium)	8.60			28
	8.1	calc.		17
	8.35			33
hydrogenated	8.1	swelling		24
	8.05			24
	8.1	av.		24
Poly(butadiene-co-acrylonitrile)				
BUNA N (82/18)				
	8.75-8.66			5
(80/20)	9.0	calc.		20
	9.5	obs.		20

References page IV-368

Table 4 (Cont'd.)

Polymer	$\delta(cal/cc)^{1/2}$	Method	T°C	Ref.
Poly(butadiene-co-acrylonitrile) (Cont'd.)				
BUNA N (75/25)	9.25	calc.	25	35
	9.38	obs.		12
	9.5	obs.		33
	8.9			36
	9.5			28
(70/30)				
	9.90-9.83			5
	9.38			13
(61/39)	10.3			5
	10.45-10.40			5
Poly(butadiene-co-styrene)				
BUNA S (96/4)				
	8.13-8.04			5
(90/10)	8.37			34
(87.5/12.5)				
	8.10-8.01			5
	8.09			13
	8.6			33
	8.46			35
(85/15)	8.40			34
	8.48	calc.		35
	8.5	obs.		35
	8.50			28
	8.51	calc.		20
	8.50	obs.		20
	8.55			33
(75/25)	8.45			34
	8.54	calc.		35
	8.09	obs. (lit)		35
	8.6	obs. (lit)		35
	8.1			36
	8.55			28
	8.58	calc.		20
	8.55	obs.		20
	8.60			33
(71.5/28.5)				
	8.17-8.09			5
	8.56			35
(70/30)	8.48			34
(60/40)	8.55			34
	8.65	calc.		35
	8.67	obs.		35
	8.67			28
	8.68	calc.		20
	8.67	obs.		20
	8.70			33
Poly(butadiene-co-vinylpyridine)				
(75/25)	9.35			28
Cellulose	15.65			34
Cellulose acetate (56% ac. groups)	13.60			34
(48% ac. groups)	13.29			34
Cellulose diacetate	11.35	calc.		35
	10.9			36
	10.9			21
Cellulose nitrate (11.83% N)	14.85			34
	10.48	calc.		35
	10.6			21
	11.5			6
(11.4% N)	10.72			21

SOLUBILITY PARAMETER VALUES

Polymer	$\delta(cal/cc)^{1/2}$	Method	T°C	Ref.
Polychloroprene	9.00		25	34
	8.11	calc.		8
	9.38	calc.		35
	8.18	obs.		12
	9.25	obs.		33
	8.6			36
	8.2			11
	9.2			21
	9.2			28
	8.19	swelling		13
	8.6			5
	8.67-8.57			5
Poly(α-chloroacrylic acid)				
-- , methyl ester	10.1	calc.		35
Poly(α-cyanoacrylic acid)				
-- , methyl ester	14.0	obs.		18
Poly(dimethyl siloxane)	7.35			34
	7.3	obs.		7
	7.55	swelling		25
	7.6	av.		25
	7.3			36
	7.62			14
Epoxy resin	10.9			36
Ethyl cellulose	10.3			6
Polyethylene	7.70			34
	8.1	calc.		35
	7.8			16
	7.9			31
	8.35			2
	8.0	calc.		38
	7.9			36
	7.9			21
	8.2	calc.		31
	7.9	obs.		22
Poly(ethylene sulfide)	9.40			34
	9.38	swelling		13
	9.0	swelling		13
Poly(ethylene terephthalate)	10.7			36
	10.7	calc.		35
Poly(hexamethylene adipamide)	13.6			36
Polyisobutene	7.1	calc.		8
	7.85	av.	35	23
	7.8	swelling		23
	8.05	"		23
	7.94			5,33
	7.85		25	34
	7.70	calc.		35
	8.05	obs.		35
	8.0			16
	8.05			33
	8.1			7
	7.8			5
	8.3	calc.		38
	8.05			21
	8.05			28

References page IV-368

Table 4 (Cont'd.)

Polymer	$\delta(cal/cc)^{1/2}$	Method	T°C	Ref.
Poly(isobutene-co-isoprene)				
butyl rubber				
	7.85-7.77			5
	8.05			33
	7.70			35
Polyisoprene,				
-- , 1,4-cis-	7.42	calc.	25	8
	8.13			12
	8.15		35	23
	8.10		"	23
	10.	swelling	"	23
	8.10	av.	"	23
	8.05	swelling	"	23
	8.10	swelling	"	23
	8.15	calc.	"	23
	8.1	swelling		25
	8.0			25
	8.05	av.		25
	8.22		25	34
	8.15	calc.	25	35
	7.9	obs.		35
	7.98	"		35
	8.35	"		35
	7.9			21
-- , natural rubber	7.9			13
	8.1			5
	8.15			35
	8.35			33
	8.3			38
	8.1			36
	8.0			5,33
	8.35			28
	7.98			13
	8.1			5
	8.06-8.12			5
-- , Gutta Percha	8.1	calc.		22
-- , chlorinated	9.4			6
Poly(methacrylic acid)				
-- , butyl ester	8.75	swelling		26
	8.7			26
	8.80	swelling		26
	8.75			26
	8.3	calc.		22
-- , ethoxyethyl ester	9.0	swelling		26
	9.9			26
-- , ethyl ester	8.95	swelling		26
	8.9			26
	9.1	calc.		22
-- , n-hexyl ester	8.6	calc.		22
-- , isobornyl ester	8.1			17
-- , lauryl ester	8.2	calc.		22

Polymer	$\delta(cal/cc)^{1/2}$	Method	T°C	Ref.
Poly(methacrylic acid)(Cont'd.)				
-- , methyl ester	9.08		25	5
	9.12-9.05			5
	9.5	swelling		26
	9.45			26
	12.84			34
	9.25	calc.		35
	9-9.5			1
	9.08			36
-- , octyl ester	8.4	calc.		22
-- , propyl ester	8.8	calc.		22
-- , stearyl ester	7.8	calc.		22
Polymethacrylonitrile	10.7	calc.		35
	10.7			36
Polymethylene	7.0	extrap.	20	14
Polypropylene	9.2		25	16
	9.4	calc.		38
Polystyrene	8.56			5
	8.59-8.53			5
	9.85	calc.		8
	8.73 or 8.76			15
	9.1			20
	9.15		35	23
	9.10	av.		23
	9.10	swelling		23
	9.12	calc.		23
	9.33		25	34
	9.12	calc.		35
	9.1	obs. (lit)		35
	8.6-9.7	" "		35
	8.5			4
	8.6			5
	9.0			16
	10.3	calc.		38
	8.56			36
	8.72			31,5
	9.1			33
	8.6-8.7			21
	9.1			28
Poly(styrene-co-divinylbenzene)	9.1	obs. (lit)		35
	8.50			4
Poly(styrene sulfide)	9.3±0.5			30
Poly(tetrafluoroethylene) (Teflon)	6.2	calc.		35
	6.2			36
Polyurethan (unknown composition)	10.0	swelling		25
	10.0	av.		25

References page IV-368

Table 4 (Cont'd.)

Polymer	$\delta(cal/cc)^{1/2}$	Method	T°C	Ref.
Poly(vinyl acetate)	9.59	calc.	25	8
	9.35		35	27
	9.40	Small's Method		27
	8.80	lit.		27
	11.05		25	34
	9.4	calc.		35
	9.4			36
Poly(vinyl alcohol)	12.60			34
Poly(vinyl bromide)	9.49			9
	9.6	calc.		35
Poly(vinyl chloride)				
	9.45-9.38			5
	9.42	calc.		8
	10.10			34
	9.55	calc.		35
	9.7	obs.		21
	9.4			5
	9.7			7
	10.8			16
	9.8			38
	9.53			36
	9.7			21
Poly(vinyl chloride-co-vinyl acetate) (87/13)	10.6	calc.		8
	10.4			6
Poly(vinylidene chloride)	12.2			7
Poly(vinylidene cyanide-co-vinyl acetate)	11.08	calc.		39
Poly(vinyl propionate)	8.80		35	27
	9.05	Small's Method		27

D. REFERENCES

1. J. Alfrey, A. O. Goldberg and J. A. Price, J. Colloid Sci., $\underline{5}$, 251 (1950).
2. G. Allen, G. Gee, D. Mangaraj, D. Sims and G. J. Wilson, Polymer, $\underline{1}$, 467 (1960).
3. R. F. Boyer and R. S. Spencer, J. Polymer Sci., $\underline{3}$, 97 (1948).
4. R. F. Boyer and R. S. Spencer, in "High Polymer Physics," Paper 5, Part III, Remoen Press, N. Y., 1948.
5. G. M. Briston and W. F. Watson, Trans. Faraday Soc., $\underline{54}$, 1731, 1742 (1958).
6. H. Burrell, Official Digest of the Federation of Societies for Paint Technology, $\underline{27}$, 726 (1955) $\underline{29}$, 1069, 1159 (1957).
7. H. Burrell , Interchemical Review, $\underline{14}$, No. 1, No. 2, (1955).
8. A. T. DiBenedetto, J. Polymer Sci., $\underline{A1}$, 3459 (1963).
9. D. Edelson and R. M. Fuoss, J. Am. Chem. Soc., $\underline{71}$, 3548 (1949).
10. H.-G. Elias and O. Etter, Makromol. Chem., $\underline{66}$, 56 (1963).
11. G. Gee, Trans. Faraday Soc. $\underline{40}$, 468 (1944).
12. G. Gee, Trans. Faraday Soc., $\underline{38}$, 418 (1942), see also ref. 13.
13. G. Gee, Trans. Inst. Rubber Ind., $\underline{18}$, 266 (1943).
14. G. Gee, G. Allen and G. Wilson, Polymer (London), $\underline{1}$, 456 (1960).
15. J. H. S. Green, Nature $\underline{183}$, 818 (1959).
16. R. A. Hayes, J. Appl. Polymer Sci., $\underline{5}$, 318 (1961).
16a. J. Hildebrand and R. Scott, "The Solubility of Nonelectrolytes," 3rd Edition, Reinhold Publishing Corporation, New York, 1949.
17. L. J. Hughes, private communication.
18. J. B. Kinsinger, private communication.
19. W. R. Krigbaum, private communication.
20. M. Lautout and M. Magat, Z. Physik. Chem. (Frankfurt), $\underline{16}$, 292 (1958).
21. M. Magat, J. Chem. Phys., $\underline{46}$, 344 (1949).
22. L. Mandelkern, private communication.
23. D. Mangaraj, S. K. Bhatnagar, and S. B. Rath, Makromol. Chem., $\underline{67}$, 75 (1963).
24. D. Mangaraj, S. Patra, and S. B. Rath, Makromol. Chem. $\underline{67}$, 84 (1963).
25. D. Mangaraj, Makromol. Chem., $\underline{65}$, 29 (1963).
26. D. Mangaraj, S. Patra and S. Rashid, Makromol. Chem., $\underline{65}$, 39 (1963).
27. D. Mangaraj, S. Patra, P. C. Roy, and S. K. Bhatnagar, Makromol. Chem., $\underline{84}$, 225 (1965).
28. H. Mark, A. V. Tobolsky, "Physical Chemistry of High Polymers," Interscience, New York, 1950, p. 263.
29. W. R. Moore, J. Polymer Sci., $\underline{5}$, 91 (1950).
30. A. Noshay and C. C. Price, J. Polymer Sci., $\underline{54}$, 533 (1961).
31. R. B. Richards, Trans. Faraday Soc., $\underline{42}$, 10 (1946).
31a. G. Scatchard, Chem. Revs., $\underline{44}$, 7 (1949).
32. C. Schuerch, J. Am. Chem. Soc., $\underline{74}$, 5061 (1952).
33. R. L. Scott and M. Magat, J. Polymer Sci., $\underline{4}$, 555 (1949).
34. A. G. Shvarts, Kolloidn. Zh. $\underline{18}$, 755 (1956), Colloid. J., $\underline{18}$, 753 (1956).
35. P. A. Small, J. Appl. Chem., $\underline{3}$, 71 (1953).
35a. H. M. Spurlin, J. Polymer Sci., $\underline{3}$, 714 (1948).
36. A. V. Tobolsky, "Properties and Structure of Polymers," Wiley, New York, 1960 p. 64, 66.
37. E. E. Walker, J. Appl. Chem. , $\underline{2}$, 470 (1952).
38. F. Vocks, J. Polymer Sci., $\underline{A2}$, 5319 (1964).
39. J. A. Yanko, J. Polymer Sci., $\underline{22}$, 153 (1956).

V.
MISCELLANEOUS PROPERTIES

ENERGIES OF ACTIVATION FOR THE THERMAL DEGRADATION OF POLYMERS

N. Grassie

Chemistry Department
The University
Glasgow, Scotland

The rate constant of a chemical reaction, k, is given by the Arrhenius equation, $k = A \exp(-E/RT)$ in which A is a constant, R and T are the gas constant and the absolute temperature respectively and E is the energy of activation of the reaction, expressed in kcal/mole. Since $\log k = \log A - 2.303\, E/RT$, E is obtained from the slope of the log k vs. 1/T plot. The rate of a reaction is given quite generally by, $kC_A{}^a\, C_B{}^b\, C_C{}^c \ldots\ldots$ in which C_A, C_B, C_C, $\ldots\ldots$ are the concentrations of the reactants and a, b, c, $\ldots\ldots$ are constants. Thus provided rate measurements at different temperatures are made under the same concentration conditions, the energy of activation may be obtained simply from the slope of the plot of log rate vs 1/T.

The majority of the data presented refers to the rate of production of volatile material as measured by the loss in weight of the polymer. Other less common methods of rate measurement are referred to in column 4 of the table.

Polymer	Temp. Range °C	Energy of Activation kcal/mole	Type of Measurement and Remarks	Ref.
Poly(acrylic acid)				
-- , methyl ester	271-286	34		1
-- , tert-butyl ester	261-222	39	initially	2
		29	crystalline	2
		31	amorphous	2
Polyacrylonitrile	218-260	31		3
Poly(6-aminocaproic acid)	355-365	34-43	increases with purification of monomer	43
Polybenzyl	386-416	50		4
Polybutadiene	380-395	62		3
Cellulose	251-291	50	cotton	6,7
		49	viscose	6,7
		47	hydrocellulose	6,7
		46	fortisan	6,7
Cellulose triacetate	283-306	45		7
Polyethylene	375-436	46	MW = 11,000	8
		52.6	MW = 16,000	8
		66.1	MW = 23,000	8
	360-392	63	MW = 20,000	5,9,10
	350.9-372.6	64	branched	5,9,10
	345-396	72	polymethylene	5,9,10
-- , chlorotrifluoro-	331-371	56		11

Polymer	Temp. Range °C	Energy of Activation kcal/mole	Type of Measurement and Remarks	Ref.
Polyethylene (Cont'd.)				
-- , tetrafluoro-	423.5-513	80.5	loss in weight and pressure of volatile products	12
	480.5-508.5	76		13
	450-550	75±4		14
Poly(chlorotrifluoro-ethylene-co-vinylidene fluoride)	340-380	53	volatile material produced	15
Poly(ethylene oxide)	320-335	46		16
Poly(ethylene terephthalate)	336-356	38		17
Polyformaldehyde				
hydroxyl end groups	100-120	27.1	pressure of volatile product	18
" " "	170-285	26	" "	19
" "	135-190	20	" "	20
			E initial - increases to 52 after 20% volatilization.	
acetate end groups	240-340	32	pressure of volatile product	19
	178-190	56	" "	20
Polyisobutene	306-326	49		5
Polyisoprene (natural rubber)	291-311	56-63		23
	60-100	25.8	chain scission in cyclohexane and trans-decalin solution measured by decrease in M_W.	24
Poly(methacrylic acid)	153-192	37±3	water produced	28
-- , methyl ester	220-280	32-42	monomer produced	25
			E increasing from 32 to 42 with extent of degradation from 0-100% (benzoyl peroxide initiated polymer)	
	170-210	29.5±1	rate of production of volatile material measured mass spectrometrically	26
	240-270	30	benzoyl peroxide initiated polymer	1
	310-325	52	thermally polymerized at room temperature	1
	110-180		increase of pressure in a closed system	27
		48	MW = 10^4	
		31	MW = 10^6	

References page V-4

Polymer	Temp. Range °C	Energy of Activation kcal/mole	Type of Measurement and Remarks	Ref.
Poly(perfluoroglutaro-diamidine)	491-513	39		21
Poly(perfluoroglutaro-diamidine-co-perfluoro-butyrodiamidine) (1/1)	491-513	43		21
Poly(perfluoro-4-chloro-1,6-heptadiene)	-	56.6		22
Poly(perfluoroheptene)	-	63		22
Polypropylene	336-366	58		5
	320-341	55	volatile material produced	29
	250-300	65	rate of random bond scission	30
-- , perfluoro-	-	56.6		22
Poly(propylene oxide)	265-285	20	atactic	16
	285-300	45	isotactic	16
Poly(pyromellitimide) (H film)	521-660	74	in vacuum	31
	435-485	33	in air	31
Polystyrene	299-348	55		32
-- , (cross-linked)	330-390	53-58	E increases from 53 to 58 with divinyl benzene content increasing from 2% to 56%	33,34
	360-390	65	containing 25% trivinyl benzene	33,34
-- , (divinyl benzene)	360-390	65		33,34
-- , (trivinyl benzene)	394-440	73		33,34
-- , α-deutero-	321-341	55		1,5
-- , β-deutero-	326-346	56		1,5
-- , α-methyl-	228.8-275-5	55		1,10
	214-240	62.2	rate of monomer production	35
	253-289	65		36
-- , 3-methyl-	318-338	56		1
-- , 2,3,4,5,6-pentafluoro-	395-415	65		37
-- , α,β,β-trifluoro-	311-326	64		11
Poly(vinyl acetate)	242-264	53.6	production of acetic acid	38
Poly(vinyl chloride)	150-190	20	production of HCl	39
	200-250	33	production of HCl in nitrogen	40
		24	in oxygen	
	235-260	26-32		41
Poly(vinylcyclohexane)	321-336	49		1
Poly(vinylidene fluoride)	371-420	48		33
	340.5-368	71		13
Poly(p-xylylene)	401-411	73		4
	-	58	rate of random bond scission	42

REFERENCES

1. S. L. Madorsky, J. Polymer Sci., 11, 491 (1953).
2. J. R. Schaefgen and I. M. Sarasohn, J. Polymer Sci., 58, 1049 (1962).
3. S. Straus and S. L. Madorsky, J. Res. Natl. Bur. Std., 61, 77 (1958).
4. L. A. Wall and R. E. Florin, J. Res. Natl. Bur. Std., 60, 451 (1958).
5. S. L. Madorsky and S. Straus, J. Res. Natl. Bur. Std., 53, 361 (1954).
6. S. L. Madorsky, V. E. Hart, and S. Straus, J. Res. Natl. Bur. Std., 56, 343 (1956).
7. S. L. Madorsky, V. E. Hart and S. Straus, J. Res. Natl. Bur. Std., 60, 343, (1958).
8. H. H. G. Jellinek, J. Polymer Sci., 4, 13 (1949).
9. S. L. Madorsky, J. Polymer Sci., 9, 133 (1952).
10. S. L. Madorsky, J. Res. Natl. Bur. Std., 62, 219 (1959).
11. S. L. Madorsky and S. Straus, J. Res. Natl. Bur. Std., 55, 223 (1955).
12. S. L. Madorsky, V. E. Hart, S. Straus and V. A. Sedlek, J. Res. Natl. Bur. Std., 51, 327 (1953).
13. J. M. Cox, B. A. Wright, and W. W. Wright, J. Appl. Polymer Sci., 8, 2935 (1964).
14. H. C. Anderson, Makromol. Chem., 51, 233 (1962).
15. T. G. Degteva, I. M. Sedova and A. S. Kuz'minskii, Polymer Sci. U.S.S.R. 4, 1036 (1963).
16. S. L. Madorsky and S. Straus, J. Polymer Sci., 36, 183 (1959).
17. S. Straus and L. A. Wall, J. Res. Natl. Bur.Std., 60, 39 (1958).
18. Y. Iwasa and T. Imoto, Nippon Kagaku Zasshi, 84, 31 (1963).
19. L. A. Dudina and N. S. Enikolopyan, Polymer Sci. U.S.S.R., 5, 36 (1964).
20. N. Grassie and R. S. Roche, unpublished.
21. L. A. Wall and S. Straus, J. Res. Natl. Bur. Std., 65A, 227 (1961).
22. S. Straus and L. A. Wall, Soc. Plastics Engrs. J., 56 (January, 1964).
23. S. Straus and S. L. Madorsky, Ind. Eng. Chem., 48, 1212 (1956).
24. P. S. Sarfare, H. L. Bhatnagar and A. B. Biswas, J. Appl. Polymer Sci., 7, 2199 (1963).
25. N. Grassie and H. W. Melville, Proc. Roy. Soc. A. 190, 1 (1949).
26. P. D. Zemany, Nature, 171, 391 (1953).
27. S. Bywater, J. Phys. Chem., 57, 879 (1953).
28. D. H. Grant and N. Grassie, Polymer, 1, 125 (1960).
29. V. D. Moiseev, M. B. Neiman and A. I. Kriukova, Polymer Sci. U.S.S.R., 2, 55 (1961).
30. T. E. Davis, R. L. Tobias and E. B. Peterli, J. Polymer Sci., 56, 485 (1962).
31. S. D. Bruck, Polymer 5, 435 (1964).
32. S. L. Madorsky, D. McIntyre, J. H. O'Mara and S. Straus, J. Res. Natl. Bur. Std., 66A, 307 (1962).
33. S. L. Madorsky and S. Straus, J. Res. Natl. Bur. Std., 63A, 261 (1959).
34. S. Straus and S. L. Madorsky, J. Res. Natl. Bur. Std., 65A, 243 (1961).
35. D. H. Grant, E. Vance and S. Bywater, Trans. Faraday Soc., 56, 1697 (1960).
36. D. W. Brown and L. A. Wall, J. Phys. Chem., 62, 848 (1958).
37. L. A. Wall, J. M. Antonucci, S. Straus and M. Tryon, Soc. Chem. Ind. (London), Monograph 13, 295 (1961).
38. N. Grassie, Trans. Faraday Soc., 49, 835 (1953).
39. A. Guyot, J. P. Benevise and Y. Trambouze, J. Appl. Polymer Sci., 6, 103 (1962).
40. G. Talamini and G. Pezzin, Makromol. Chem., 39, 26 (1960).
41. R. R. Stromberg, S. Straus and B. G. Achhammer, J. Polymer Sci., 35, 355 (1959).
42. J. R. Schaefgen, J. Polymer Sci., 41, 133 (1959).
43. S. Straus and L. A. Wall, J. Res. Natl. Bur. Std. 63A, 269 (1959).

PRODUCTS OF THERMAL DEGRADATION OF POLYMERS

N. Grassie

Chemistry Department
The University
Glasgow, Scotland

The chemical nature of the thermal decomposition of polymers varies widely from one material to another. At its simplest it may consist of complete breakdown to a single, and readily identifiable product which is often monomer. On the other hand, a complex mixture of products may be obtained together with a relatively stable intractible residue.

From the point of view of identification there are three types of products of thermal degradation. Firstly, substances of the molecular dimensions of monomer or less, of which a detailed analysis can usually be made. Secondly, substances are often produced which are volatile at the degradation temperatures but involatile at ordinary temperatures. These are usually polymer chain fragments which are larger than monomer. Although they may be referred to as dimeric, trimeric, etc., their precise chemical structures have usually not been determined. Finally, the involatile residue which often remains is frequently insoluble although a knowledge of the mechanism of the degradation reaction combined with spectral data can often give some information about its structure. The relative amounts of these three kinds of products can vary with the temperature of degradation although not a great deal of information of this kind is available. However, the temperature ranges in which the experiments have been carried out are quoted in the table since they give some idea of the relative stability of the polymers.

Most of the data are concerned with the volatile small molecular products of degradation. Information about larger chain fragments and involatile residues is given where it is available and relevant.

Polymer	Temp. Range (°C)	Degradation Products	Ref.
Poly(acrylic acid)			
-- , methyl ester	292-399	26% of products are volatile at 25°C, mainly methyl alcohol and carbon dioxide with traces of monomer and methyl methacrylate and C_4-C_6 oxygenated compounds. 74% of products are larger chain fragments involatile at 25°C.	1,2
-- , tert-butyl ester	>160	86% isobutylene, 11% water, 3% carbon dioxide	3
-- , α-bromo-, methyl ester	110-150	methyl bromide, hydrogen bromide	4
-- , α-cyano-, methyl ester	>180	yellows and some monomer formed	5
-- , α-chloro-, sec-butyl ester	190	sec-butyl chloride, butylene, hydrogen chloride	6

Polymer	Temp. Range (°C)	Degradation Products	Ref.
Polyacrylonitrile	<200	colors through yellow, orange, red and black	7
	250-280	12% of products are volatile at 25°C, consisting of hydrogen cyanide, acrylonitrile and vinyl acetonitrile. 88% of products are involatile at room temperature	8,9
Polybenzyl	386-416	7.4% of products are volatile at 25°C - 5.9% toluene, 1.4% benzene, 0.1% xylene	10,11
Polybutadiene	325-475	14.1% of products are volatile at 25°C including 1.5% of monomer among other saturated and unsaturated hydrocarbons. 85.9% of products are larger fragments involatile at 25°C.	12
Poly(butadiene-co-acrylonitrile) (70/30)	310-400	14.5% of products are volatile at 25°C, consisting of saturated and unsaturated hydrocarbons	8
Poly(butadiene-co-styrene)(75/25)	327-430	11.8% of products are volatile at 25°C - 1.91% butadiene with other saturated and unsaturated hydrocarbons.	8,12
Cellulose	250-397	H_2O with smaller amounts of CO_2 and CO and a tar containing principally levoglucosan.	14,15
Cellulose (oxidized)	180-331	mainly H_2O and CO_2, smaller amounts of CO, formaldehyde, methanol, acetic acid, ethanol and acetaldehyde, and very little tar.	
Cellulose triacetate	250-310	product fraction volatile at 25°C contains acetic acid, CO_2, CO, CH_4, H_2, acetaldehyde and acetone. Heavier fractions do not contain levoglucosan acetate.	15
Polychloroprene	377	hydrogen chloride	16
Polyethylene	335-450	continuous spectrum of saturated and unsaturated hydrocarbons from C_2-C_{90}- lower temperature favor larger fragments.	10,12
-- , chlorotrifluoro- (KEL-F)	347-418	25% of products volatile at 25°C- monomer with traces of C_3F_5Cl and $C_3F_4Cl_2$. 72.1% of larger chain fragments involatile at 25°C.	11
-- , tetrafluoro-	504-538	>95% monomer, 2-3% C_3F_6, no larger fragments (in vacuum)	
	1200	monomer yield drops, larger fragments appear (in vacuum)	17
	600-700	at 5 mm. pressure, pure monomer; at 760 mm. pressure, 15.9% monomer, 25.7% C_3F_6, 58.4% C_4H_8.	18
-- , trifluoro -	380-800	high yields of HF and products involatile at 25°C.	17

References page V-11

Polymer	Temp. Range °C	Degradation Products	Ref.
Poly(ethylene oxide)	324-363	9.7% of products volatile at 25°C - 3.9% monomer with smaller amounts of CO_2, formaldehyde, ethanol and saturated and unsaturated C_1 - C_7 compounds.	19
Poly(ethylene terephthalate)	283-306	acetaldehyde major gaseous product with CO_2, CO, C_2H_4, H_2O, CH_4, benzene, 2-methyl-dioxolane, terephthalic acid and more complex chain fragments.	20
Polyformaldehyde	222	100% monomer	21
Polyisobutene	288-425	18.1% monomer together with methane, isobutane and C_5 and higher saturated and unsaturated hydrocarbons.	12
	up to 1200	as temperature is increased the yields of fragments smaller than monomer increase at the expense of larger fragments.	13
Polyisoprene, synthetic	287-400	3.4% isoprene, 8.8% dipentene, small amounts of p-menthene	1,12, 24
-- , natural rubber	287-400	3.9% isoprene, 13.2% dipentene, small amounts of p-menthene	1,12, 24
	450-800	dipentene main product at 450°C, optimum yields of isoprene in range 675-800°C, e.g. 58% at 750°C and 10 mm. Hg.	25
-- , gutta percha	287-400	3.0% isoprene, 15.6% dipentene, small amounts of p-menthene	1,12, 24
Poly(methacrylic acid)	200	almost quantitative yields of H_2O, traces of monomer, residue of poly(methacrylic anhydride)	32
-- , methyl ester	170-300	100% monomer	26,27
	246-1200	as temperature is raised fragmentation increases to give complex series of products and monomer yield correspondingly decreases.	1
	160	100% monomer under 2537 Å radiation	28
-- , ethyl ester	250	monomer	29
-- , n-propyl ester	250	monomer	29
-- , i-propyl ester	250	monomer	29
-- , n-butyl ester	250	40% monomer and traces of 1-butene	30
	170	100% monomer under 2537 Å radiation	30
-- , i-butyl ester	250	monomer	29
-- , sec-butyl ester	250	monomer and small amount of olefin by cracking of side chain	29
-- , tert-butyl ester	180-200	high yields of isobutylene and water, 1% monomer, trace of methacrylic acid, residue of poly(methacrylic anhydride).	31

Polymer	Temp. Range (°C)	Degradation Products	Ref.
Poly(methacrylic acid) (Cont'd.)			
-- , tert-butyl ester			
	<180	100% monomer under 2537 Å	
-- , n-amyl ester	250	monomer	29
-- , i-amyl ester	250	monomer	29
-- , 1,2-dimethylpropyl ester	250	monomer and small amount of olefin by side chain cracking	29
-- , neopentyl ester	250	monomer	29
-- , 3,3-dimethylbutyl ester	250	monomer	29
-- , 1,3-dimethylbutyl ester	250	monomer and small amount of olefin by side chain cracking	29
Polymethacrylonitrile	<200	no volatile material, coloration through yellow, orange and red	33
	220-270	50-100% monomer depending upon pretreatment and purity of polymer.	33
Poly(methyl isopropenyl ketone)	270-360	H_2O	34
	150-190	monomer under 3130 Å	35
Poly(methyl vinyl ketone)	270-360	H_2O, 3-methyl-2-cyclohexene-1-one and other six membered ring ketones.	36
Nylon 6 and 66		see "Note added in proof"	
Poly(perfluoroglutarodiamidine)	430-503	C_2F_4 with traces of CF_4, C_3F_6 and larger chain fragments.	22
Poly(perfluoroglutarodiamidine-co-perfluorobutyrodiamidine) (1:1)	415-505	C_2F_4, CF_4, C_2F_6 and smaller amounts of C_3F_6 and C_3F_8 and larger chain fragments.	22
Poly(perfluoro-4-chloro-1,6-heptadiene)	320-400	completely volatilized - products unknown	23
Polyperfluoroheptene	210-270	100% monomer	23
Polypropylene	328-410	saturated and unsaturated hydrocarbons from C_2 upwards, monomer yield 0.17%.	10
	400-1200	as temperature is raised, yield of small fragments increases at expense of large fragments.	13
-- , perfluoro-	280-400	100% monomer	23
Poly(propylene oxide)			
-- , atactic	270-330	12.8% of products at 25°C including 4.00% acetaldehyde, 2.22% acetone, 1.43% dipropyl ether and 0.75% propylene.	19
-- , isotactic	275-355	20% of products volatile at 25°C including 6.34% acetaldehyde, 2.39% acetone, 2.19% dipropyl ether and 2.22% propylene.	19
Polystyrene	300-400	40.6% monomer, 2.0% toluene, 0.1% CO, remainder dimer, trimer, and tetramer - monomer yield increases with pressure of nitrogen - 62% at 760 mm.	37,38

References page V-11

Polymer	Temp. Range (°C)	Degradation Products	Ref.
Polystyrene (Cont'd.)			
	500-1200	small hydrocarbon fragments appear (C_1-C_6) - fragmentation is greater the higher the temperature and the greater the pressure of inert gas.	13
-- , (cross-linked)	346-450	cross-linking with increasing quantities of divinyl or trivinylbenzene progressively decreases the styrene yield - the yield of larger chain fragments and the amount of carbonization also increase.	9,39
-- , (poly(divinylbenzene))	385-450	volatile products include toluene, benzene, styrene and xylene	9,39
-- , (poly(trivinylbenzene))	470-500	mixture of aliphatic and aromatic hydrocarbons	9,39
-- , α-deutero-	334-387	68.4% monomer, 1.5% α-deutero styrene, 0.6% α-methylstyrene, 29.5% larger chain fragments	1,10
-- , β-deutero-	345-384	39.7% monomer, 1.2% toluene, 0.1% deuterotoluene, 59% larger chain fragments	1,10
-- , 3-methyl-	309-399	44.4% monomer, 7.3% xylene, 48.3% larger chain fragments.	2
-- , α-methyl-	200-500	95-100% monomer	13
	500-1200	fragments both larger and smaller than monomer appear in increasing amounts the higher the temperature, particularly CH_4, C_2H_4 and C_6H_6 until at 1200°C the monomer yield is only 33.9%.	13
-- , 2,3,4,5,6-pentafluoro-	390-446	63% of the products are volatile at 25°C - contains some monomer.	40
-- , α,β,β-trifluoro-	333-382	72% monomer, 28% larger chain fragments	11
Poly(vinyl acetate)	213-235	quantitative yields of acetic acid.	41
	300	small amounts of aromatics including benzene	41
Poly(vinyl alcohol)	250	quantitative yields of H_2O	42
Poly(vinyl butyrate)	300-325	butyric acid	43
Poly(vinyl chloride)	200-300	quantitative yields of HCl	44
	400	saturated and unsaturated, aliphatic and aromatic hydrocarbons are produced with benzene and toluene in high yield.	44
Poly(vinylcyclohexane)	335-391	small amounts of cyclohexene, cyclohexane, methylcyclohexene, methylcyclohexane, vinylcyclohexene, vinylcyclohexane, ethylcyclohexane with larger chain fragments.	1,2

Polymer	Temp. Range (°C)	Degradation Products	Ref.
Poly(vinyl fluoride)	372-480	high yields of HF and products involatile at 25°C - little carbonization	17
Poly(trifluorovinylphenyl ether)	275-500	maximum of 75% volatilization - products unknown.	23
Poly(vinylidene chloride)	225-275	high yields of HCl	
Poly(vinylidene cyanide)	>160	high yields of monomer	46
Poly(vinylidene fluoride)	400-475	5.3-8.0% HF and high yields of products involatile at 25°C - some carbonization	
Poly(p-xylylene)	420-465	3.6% of products are volatile at 25°C and consist of 2.83% xylene, 0.29% toluene, 0.28% methylethylbenzene, 0.14% methyl-styrene, 0.06% benzene - products involatile at 25°C consist of dimeric - octameric fragments.	10,11 47

"Note added in Proof"

Nylon 6 and 66	310-380	H_2O, CO_2, cyclopentanone, traces of saturated and unsaturated hydro-carbons. Purification from water and acid polymerization catalysts increases stability and decreases yield of CO_2.	48,49

References page V-11

REFERENCES

1. S. Straus and S. L. Madorsky, J. Res. Natl. Bur. Std., 50, 165 (1953).
2. S. L. Madorsky, J. Polymer Sci., 11, 491 (1953).
3. J. R. Schaefgen and I. M. Sarasohn, J. Polymer Sci., 58, 1049 (1962).
4. C. S. Marvel and J. C. Cowan, J. Am. Chem. Soc., 61, 3156 (1939).
5. A. J. Canale, W. E. Goode, J. B. Kinsinger, J. R. Panchak, R. L. Kelso and R. K. Graham, J. Appl. Polymer Sci., 4, 231 (1960).
6. J. W. C. Crawford and D. Plant, J. Chem. Soc., 1952, 4492.
7. W. J. Burlant and J. L. Parsons, J. Polymer Sci., 22, 249 (1956).
8. S. Straus and S. L. Madorsky, J. Res. Natl. Bur. Std., 61, 77 (1958).
9. S. L. Madorsky and S. Straus, J. Res. Natl. Bur. Std., 63A, 261 (1959).
10. S. L. Madorsky and S. Straus, J. Res. Natl. Bur. Std., 53, 361 (1954).
11. S. L. Madorsky and S. Straus, J. Res. Natl. Bur. Std., 55, 223 (1955).
12. S. L. Madorsky, S. Straus, D. Thompson and L. Williamson, J. Res. Natl. Bur. Std., 42, 499 (1949).
13. S. Straus and S. L. Madorsky, J. Res. Natl. Bur. Std., 66A, 401 (1962).
14. S. L. Madorsky, V. E. Hart, and S. Straus, J. Res. Natl. Bur. Std., 56, 343 (1956).
15. S. L. Madorsky, V. E. Hart and S. Straus, J. Res. Natl. Bur. Std., 60, 343 (1958).
16. R. F. Schwenker, Jr., and L. R. Beck, Textile Research J., 624 (August, 1960).
17. S. L. Madorsky, V. E. Hart, S. Straus and V. A. Sedlek, J. Res. Natl. Bur. Std., 51, 327 (1953).
18. E. E. Lewis and M. A. Naylor, J. Am. Chem. Soc., 69, 1968 (1947).
19. S. L. Madorsky and S. Straus, J. Polymer Sci., 36, 183 (1959).
20. E. P. Goodings, Soc. Chem. Ind. (London), Monograph, 13, 211 (1961).
21. C. E. Schweitzer, R. N. MacDonald and J. O. Punderson, J. Appl. Polymer Sci., 1, 158 (1959).
22. L. A. Wall and S. Straus, J. Res. Natl. Bur. Std., 65A, 227 (1961).
23. S. Straus and L. A. Wall, Soc. Plastics Engrs. J., 56 (January, 1964).
24. S. Straus and S. L. Madorsky, Ind. Eng. Chem., 48, 1212 (1956).
25. B. S. T. Boonstra and G. J. Van Amerongen, Ind. Eng. Chem., 41, 161 (1949).
26. N. Grassie and H. W. Melville, Proc. Roy. Soc. A190, 1 (1949).
27. P. D. Zemany, Nature, 171, 391 (1953).
28. P. R. E. J. Cowley and H. W. Melville, Proc. Roy. Soc. A210, 461 (1952).
29. J. W. C. Crawford, J. Soc. Chem. Ind., 68, 201 (1949).
30. N. Grassie and J. R. MacCallum, J. Polymer Sci., 2, 983 (1964).
31. D. H. Grant and N. Grassie, Polymer, 1, 445 (1960).
32. D. H. Grant and N. Grassie, Polymer, 1, 125 (1960).
33. N. Grassie and I. C. McNeill, J. Chem. Soc. 1956, 3929.
34. C. S. Marvel, E. H. Riddle and J. O. Corner, J. Am. Chem. Soc., 64, 92 (1942).
35. K. F. Wissbrun, J. Am. Chem. Soc., 81, 58 (1959).
36. C. S. Marvel and G. L. Levesque, J. Am. Chem. Soc., 60, 280 (1938).
37. S. L. Madorsky and S. Straus, J. Res. Natl. Bur. Std., 40, 417 (1948).
38. S. L. Madorsky, "Thermal Degradation of Organic Polymers," Wiley, New York, 1964.
39. S. Straus and S. L. Madorsky, J. Res. Natl. Bur. Std., 65A, 243 (1961).
40. L. A. Wall, J. M. Antonucci, S. Straus and M. Tryon, Soc. Chem. Ind. (London), Monograph, 13, 295 (1961).
41. N. Grassie, Trans. Faraday Soc., 48, 379 (1952).
42. J. B. Gilbert and J. J. Kipling, Fuel 12, 249 (1962).
43. J. B. Gilbert, J. J. Kipling, B. McEnaney and J. N. Sherwood, Polymer, 3, 1 (1962).
44. R. R. Stromberg, S. Straus and B. G. Achhammer, J. Polymer Sci., 35, 355 (1959).
45. F. H. Winslow, W. O. Baker and W. A. Yager, quoted in ref. 38, Chapter V.
46. H. Gilbert, F. F. Miller, S. J. Averill, R. F. Schmidt, F. D. Stewart and H. L. Trumbull, J. Am. Chem. Soc., 76, 1074 (1954).
47. P. Bradt, V. H. Dibeler and F. L. Mohler, J. Res. Natl. Bur. Std., 50, 201 (1953).
48. S. Straus and L. A. Wall, J. Res. Natl. Bur. Std., 60, 39 (1958).
49. S. Straus and L. A. Wall, J. Res. Natl. Bur. Std., 63A, 269 (1959).

PERMEABILITY CONSTANTS

H. Yasuda

Cedar-Sinai Medical Center
Eye Research Laboratory
Los Angeles, California

Contents

A. INTRODUCTION

When small molecules permeate through a polymer membrane, the rate of permeation can be expressed by parameters which may be characteristic of the polymer. The general concept of the ease with which a permeant passes through a barrier is often referred to as "permeability." However, this general term "permeability" does not refer to the mechanism of the permeation process and in the literature, the rates of transmission in several different units are often cited as permeability. For example, the total rate of transmission, (amount of penetrant)/(time); the rate of transmission per unit area, (amount of penetrant)/(area)(time); the rate of transmission per unit area and unit film thickness, (amount of penetrant)(film thickness)/(area)(time); and also the rate of transmission per unit area, unit thickness, unit time and unit pressure-(or concentration)-drop across the film, (amount of penetrant)(film thickness)/ (area)(time)(pressure-drop), all appear under the general term "permeability."

The coefficient which has the dimensions

$$P = \frac{(\text{amount of permeant})(\text{film thickness})}{(\text{area})(\text{time})(\text{pressure-drop across the film})}$$

or in the more general form,

$$P = \frac{(\text{amount of permeant})}{(\text{area})(\text{time})(\text{driving force gradient across the film})}$$

may be defined as the permeability coefficient P.

When a permeant does not interact with the polymer, this permeability constant P is usually characteristic for the permeant-polymer system. Permeation of many gases, such as H_2, He, N_2, O_2 and CO_2, through many polymers belong to his case. On the other hand, if a permeant interacts with polymer molecules, P is no longer a constant, and depends on pressure, thickness and other environmental conditions. In such cases, a single value of P does not represent the characteristic permeability of the polymer membrane and it is necessary to know the dependency of P on all possible variables in order to obtain the complete profile of the permeability of the polymer. In these cases, the transmission rate Q, which has the dimensions

$$Q = (\text{amount of permeant})(\text{film thickness})/(\text{area})(\text{time})$$

is often used for practical purposes, provided that the saturated vapor pressure of the permeant at a specified temperature is applied across the film. Permeabilities of films to water and organic compounds are often presented in this way.

The amount of permeant, in both P and Q, can be expressed by weight, moles or gaseous volume at standard temperature and pressure. These can readily be converted from one unit into another. The preferred metric units of the permeability constant used in this handbook are;

$$(\text{cm}^3 \text{ STP})(\text{cm})/(\text{cm}^2)(\text{sec})(\text{cm Hg})$$

This composite unit sometimes appears in literature as

$$(\text{cm}^2)(\text{sec}^{-1})(\text{cm Hg}^{-1})$$

or

$$(\text{cm}^3 \text{ STP})/\text{cm}^2/\text{cm}/\text{sec}/\text{cm Hg}$$

Since permeability constants given in this composite unit are often in the range of 10^{-6} -- 10^{-13} for many polymers and permeants, many other larger composite units are used in the literature. Some of those composite units and their conversion factors are listed in Table 1. A number of different composite units for Q are also used in the literature and some of them are listed in Table 2 together with their conversion factors.

Since the transmission rate Q is not a real constant which is characteristic for a polymer, it should only be used as a means of comparing orders of magnitude. In the following tables, the parameter Q is presented in the units of

$$(\text{g})(\text{mil})/(\text{m}^2)(24 \text{ hr})$$

since most of the hydrophobic polymers, such as polyolefins and fluorocarbon polymers, have water transmission rates near unity at around room temperature when expressed in these units. This offers a convenient reference point for relative comparison of permeabilities of vapors in various polymers.

The temperature dependence of the permeability constant can be represented by an Arrhenius type expression

$$P = P_o \exp(-E_p/RT)$$

Consequently, the permeability constant at temperature T_2 can be calculated from the value at temperature T_1, if the activation energy of permeation, E_p, is known. The activation energy of permeation is usually different at above and below the glass transition temperature (1,2).

Although permeability constants are listed for many polymers in the following tables, the permeability constant, in a strict sense, is not only a function of the chemical structure of polymers. In other words, the permeability constant varies with the morphology of polymers and depends on many other physical factors such as density, degree of crystallinity, degree of orientation, etc. However, the chemical structure of a polymer can be considered as the predominant factor which controls the magnitude of the permeability constant.

References page V-24

Since the pressure of the gas or vapor is used as the unit of the driving force in the composite units of the permeability constant, the permeability constant P is not the diffusion constant D, but the product of the diffusion constant D, and the solubility constant of the gas in the polymer, S, i.e.,

$$P = D \cdot S$$

Therefore, a high permeability constant does not always mean a high diffusivity of the permeant. Only if the amount of permeant and the driving force can be expressed by the concentration of the penetrant inside the polymer, the permeability constant defined previously becomes essentially equal to the diffusion constant.

Since the transmission rate Q includes neither pressure nor concentration of permeant in its dimensions, it is necessary to know either the vapor pressure at saturation or the concentration of permeant under the conditions of the measurement in order to correlate Q to P or D of the permeant in the polymer. Knowledge of the following general trends in permeability as related to some influencing factors may be useful for the proper interpretation of the tables:

Density can be regarded as a measure of "looseness" of the polymer structure and, in general, the lower the density the higher the permeability.

Molecular weight of a polymer has been found to have little effect on the permeability of polymer, except in the very low range of molecular weights.

Crystallinity of a semi-crystalline polymer reduces the permeability significantly from the value of the corresponding amorphous polymer, i.e., the higher the degree of crystallinity, the lower the permeability. (3,4,5,6,7,8,9,10,11,12)

Orientation of polymer molecules reduces the permeability. (10,13,14,15,16,17,18, 19,20)

Crosslinking decreases the permeability, especially for large molecular size permeants. (3,21,22,23,24,25,26)

Plasticizers usually, but not always, increase the permeability. (27,28,29,30,31, 32,33,34,35)

Humidity increases the permeability of some hydrophilic polymers. (36,37,38)

Liquid permeants have slightly higher permeabilities than the corresponding saturated vapor under many practical conditions. (39,40,41,42,43)

Solution-cast films have variable permeabilities depending upon the kind of solvent and the drying technique. Poor solvents tend to yield films of higher permeability. (40,44)

The method of vulcanization has a significant effect on the permeability of elastomers.

Fillers generally decrease the permeability; however, the effect is complicated by the type, shape and amount of filler, and its interaction with the permeant. (4,35)

B. DIMENSIONS OF PERMEABILITY CONSTANT P

Multiplication Factors to Obtain P in

From	$\dfrac{(cm^3)(cm)}{(sec)(cm^2)(cm\ Hg)}$	$\dfrac{(cm^3)(mm)}{(sec)(cm^2)(cm\ Hg)}$	$\dfrac{(cm^3)(cm)}{(sec)(cm^2)(atm)}$	$\dfrac{(cm^3)(mil)}{(24\ hr)(m^2)(atm)}$	$\dfrac{(in^3)(mil)}{(24\ hr)(100\ in^2)(atm)}$
$\dfrac{(cm^3)(cm)}{(sec)(cm^2)(cm\ Hg)}$	1	10	7.6×10	2.59×10^{13}	1.02×10^{11}
$\dfrac{(cm^3)(mm)}{(sec)(cm^2)(cm\ Hg)}$	10^{-1}	1	7.6	2.59×10^{12}	1.02×10^{10}
$\dfrac{(cm^3)(cm)}{(sec)(cm^2)(atm)}$	1.32×10^{-2}	1.32×10^{-1}	1	3.40×10^{11}	1.34×10^{9}
$\dfrac{(cm^3)(mil)}{(24\ hr)(m^2)(atm)}$	3.86×10^{-14}	3.86×10^{-13}	2.94×10^{-12}	1	3.93×10^{-3}
$\dfrac{(in^3)(mil)}{(24\ hr)(100\ in^2)(atm)}$	9.80×10^{-12}	9.80×10^{-11}	7.46×10^{-10}	2.54×10^{2}	1

C. DIMENSIONS OF TRANSMISSION RATE Q

Multiplication Factors to Obtain Q in

From	$\dfrac{(g)(cm)}{(m^2)(24\ hr)}$	$\dfrac{(g)(mil)}{(m^2)(24\ hr)}$	$\dfrac{(g)(mil)}{(100\ m^2)(hr)}$	$\dfrac{(g)(mil)}{(100\ in^2)(hr)}$
$\dfrac{(g)(cm)}{(m^2)(24\ hr)}$	1	3.94×10^{2}	1.64×10^{3}	1.06
$\dfrac{(g)(mil)}{(m^2)(24\ hr)}$	2.54×10^{-3}	1	4.17	2.69×10^{-3}
$\dfrac{(g)(mil)}{(100\ m^2)(hr)}$	6.10×10^{-4}	2.40×10^{-1}	1	6.45×10^{-4}
$\dfrac{(g)(mil)}{(100\ in^2)(hr)}$	9.43×10^{-1}	3.72×10^{2}	1.55×10^{3}	1

D. PERMEABILITY OF POLYMERS

1 - PERMEABILITY OF POLYMERS TO NITROGEN, OXYGEN AND CARBON DIOXIDE

Polymer	N_2				O_2				CO_2			
	°C	$P \times 10^{10}$	E_p	Ref.	°C	$P \times 10^{10}$	E_p	Ref.	°C	$P \times 10^{10}$	E_p	Ref.
Cellulose and Cellulose Derivatives												
Cellulose (Cellophane)	25	0.0032		(36)	25	0.0021		(35)	25	0.0047		(36)
Cellulose acetate	30	0.28*	6.5*	(45)	30	0.78*	5.0*	(45)	30	2.38*	4.3*	(45)
Cellulose nitrate	25	0.12		(46)	25	1.95		(46)	25	2.12		(46)
Ethyl cellulose	30	8.4*	4.2*	(45)	30	26.5*	4.2*	(45)	30	41.0*	1.3*	(45)
Elastomers												
Polybutadiene	25	6.5	8.2	(22)	25	19.2	7.1	(22)	25	139	5.2	(22)
Polychloroprene (Neoprene)	25	1.2	10.6	(22)	25	4.0	9.9	(22)	25	25.8	8.5	(22)
Poly(dialkyl siloxane) (Silicone rubber)					30	70		(44)	30	350		(44)
Poly(dimethylbutadiene) (Methyl rubber)	25	0.48	13.3	(22)	25	2.1	11.3	(22)	25	7.5	11.2	(22)
Polyisoprene (Natural rubber)	25	8.2	9.3	(22)	25	23.8	6.6	(22)	25	135	6.2	(22)
Fluorocarbon polymers												
Poly(tetrafluoroethylene) (Teflon)									20	4.7		
Poly(trifluorochloroethylene) (Kel-F) (Amorphous)	25	0.005	14.3	(47)	25	0.040	11.2	(47)	40	0.21	11.8	(47)
Poly(trifluorochloroethylene) (Kel-F) (Crystalline)	25	0.003	11.9	(47)	40	0.025	10.9	(47)	40	0.048	11.1	(47)
Polyamides and Polyesters												
Poly(6-aminocaproic acid) (Nylon 6)	30	0.0095	11.2	(45)	30	0.038	10.4	(45)	20	0.088	9.7	(45)
Poly(ethylene terephthalate) (Mylar)	30	0.011	7.5	(45)	30	0.045	6.4	(45)	30	0.15	6.2	(51)
Poly(4,4'-isopropylidene diphenylene carbonate) (Lexan)	25	0.3	6.0	(50)	25	1.4	4.6	(50)	25	8.0	3.8	(50)

References page V-24

Polymer	N_2				O_2				CO_2			
	°C	$P \times 10^{10}$	E_p	Ref.	°C	$P \times 10^{10}$	E_p	Ref.	°C	$P \times 10^{10}$	E_p	Ref.
Olefin Polymers												
Polyethylene, low density	30	1.36	11.2	(48)	30	3.95	9.8	(48)	30	16.7	8.7	(48)
high density	30	0.18	9.54	(48)	30	0.51	8.4	(48)	30	2.1	7.2	(48)
Polypropylene	30	0.44	13.3	(49)	30	2.3	11.4	(49)	30	9.2	9.1	(49)
Polyformaldehyde (Delrin)					30	0.38		(52)	30	1.9		(52)
Polystyrene	30	0.29		(47)	30	1.1		(47)	30	8.8		(47)
Poly(vinyl acetate)					30	0.5		(1)				
Poly(vinyl alcohol)					25	0.0089		(36)	25	0.012		(36)
Poly(vinyl chloride)	30	0.11	7.2	(44)	30	0.3	6.6	(44)	30	1.5	5.8	(44)
Poly(vinylidene chloride) (Saran)	30	0.00094	16.8	(45)	30	0.0053	15.9	(45)	30	0.03	12.3	(45)
Rubber hydrochloride (Pliofilm)	30	0.14*	10.0*	(45)	30	0.54*	8.4*	(45)	30	1.3*	8.6*	(45)

* plasticized polymer used

References page V-24

2 - PERMEABILITY OF POLYMERS TO HELIUM AND HYDROGEN

Polymer	He				H_2			
	°C	$P \times 10^{10}$	E_p	Ref.	°C	$P \times 10^{10}$	E_p	Ref.
Cellulose and Cellulose								
Cellulose	20	0.0005	9.9	(53)	25	0.0065		(36)
Cellulose acetate	20	13.6		(53)	20	3.5		(53)
Cellulose nitrate	25	6.9	5.2	(46)	20	2.0	5.7	(53)
Ethyl cellulose	30	400	3.2	(44)	20	87		(53)
Elastomers								
Polybutadiene					25	42	6.6	(22)
Polychloroprene	20	537		(53)	25	13.6	8.1	(22)
Poly(dimethylbutadiene)	25	15	6.6	(22)	25	17	8.0	(22)
Polyisoprene (Natural rubber)	25	30	6.5	(22)	25	52	6.9	(22)
Fluorocarbon Polymers								
Poly(tetrafluoroethylene)	20	15.7		(53)	20	20		(53)
Poly(trifluorochloroethylene)	20	6.8	5.6	(53)	20	0.94	7.2	(53)
Polyamides and Polyesters								
Poly(6-aminocaproic acid)(Nylon 6)	20	0.53	8.7	(53)				
Poly(ethylene terephthalate)	20	4.7	4.4	(54)	20	3.7	5.4	(54)
Poly(4,4'-isopropylidene-diphenylene carbonate)	25	10	4.8	(50)	25	12	5.4	(50)
Polyolefins								
Polyethylene, low density	30	6.5	8.4	(48)	30	12	8.3	(55)
high density	30	1.4	7.1	(48)	20	3.0		(53)
Polypropylene	20	38	7.7	(54)	20	41	9.2	(54)
Poly(vinyl acetate)	25	11		(53)	25	9.0		(53)
Poly(vinyl alcohol)	20	0.001		(53)	25	0.009		(36)
Poly(vinyl chloride)	30	4.0	6.3	(44)	20	2.4		(53)
Poly(vinylidene chloride)	34	0.31		(53)				
Rubber hydrochloride	20	1.3		(53)				

References page V 24

3 - PERMEABILITY OF POLYMERS TO WATER AND HYDROGEN SULFIDE

Polymer	H_2O				H_2S			
	°C	$P \times 10^{10}$	E_p	Ref.	°C	$P \times 10^{10}$	E_p	Ref.
Cellulose					45	0.006	21.4	(33)
Cellulose acetate	25	5,500	0	(56)	30	3.5	5.1	(33)
Cellulose nitrate	25	6,300		(46)				
Ethyl cellulose	20	12,000	0.4	(41)				
Polytrifluorochloroethylene, (amorphous)	25	0.29		(47)				
Poly(6-aminocaproic acid)	25	177		(47)	30	0.33	13.9	(33)
Poly(4,4'-isopropylidene-diphenylene carbonate)	25	1,400		(50)				
Poly(ethylene terephthalate)	25	130	0.7	(56)	30	0.072	7.4	(33)
Polyethylene, low density	25	90	8.0	(56)	30	43.3	10.0	(33)
high density	25	12		(56)				
Polypropylene	25	51	10.1	(56)	20	0.33		(57)
Polystyrene	25	1,200		(47)				
Poly(vinyl alcohol)					25	0.007		(36)
Poly(vinyl chloride)	25	156		(47)	20	0.19		(57)
Poly(vinylidene chloride)	25	0.5	11.0	(56)	30	0.03	17.8	(33)
Rubber hydrochloride	25	16	6.8	(41)	30	0.1	17.6	(33)

4 - PERMEABILITY OF POLYMERS TO AMMONIA AND SULFUR DIOXIDE

Polymer	NH_3				SO_2			
	°C	$P \times 10^{10}$	E_p	Ref.	°C	$P \times 10^{10}$	E_p	Ref.
Cellulose					25	0.0017		(36)
Cellulose nitrate	25	57.1		(46)	25	1.76		(46)
Ethyl cellulose	25	705		(46)	25	264		(46)
Poly(6-aminocaproic acid)(Nylon 6)	20	1.2		(57)				
Polyethylene, low density	20	32.6	8.0	(55)	30	39	10.6	(55)
Polypropylene	20	9.2		(57)				
Poly(vinyl chloride)	20	4.9		(57)				

References page V-24

5 - PERMEABILITY OF POLYMERS TO ETHYLENE OXIDE AND METHYL BROMIDE (45)

Polymer	Ethylene Oxide $P \times 10^{10}$ 0°C p = 33 cm Hg	Methyl Bromide $P \times 10^{10}$ 60°C p = 39.5 cm Hg
Cellylose acetate, (plasticized)	14	0.068
Ethyl cellulose, (plasticized)	4.2	-
Poly(trifluorochloroethylene)	0.012	0.046
Poly(ω-aminocaproic acid (Nylon 6)	-	0.084
Poly(ethylene terephthalate)	-	0.0008
Polyethylene, low density	0.49	4.72
Poly(vinyl alcohol)	0.00002	-
Poly(vinylidene chloride)	-	0.008
Rubber hydrochloride	7.3	0.34

E.   TRANSMISSION RATES THROUGH POLYMERS

1 - TRANSMISSION RATE OF WATER THROUGH POLYMERS

Polymer	Temp. °C	Q (g)(mil)/(m^2)(24 hr)	Ref.
Cellulose	35	1,600	(58)
Cellulose acetate	39.5	1,200	(59)
Cellulose nitrate	40	630	(35)
Polybutadiene	39.5	680	(60)
Polychloroprene	39.5	240	(60)
Polyisobutylene	39.5	18	(60)
Polyisoprene (Natural rubber)	39.5	270	(60)
Poly(tetrafluoroethylene)	39.5	4.8	(60)
Poly(trifluorochloroethylene)	39.5	4.8	(60)
Poly(vinyl fluoride)	40	46	(61)
Poly(hexamethylene adipate-co-sebacate)	39.5	180	(60)
Poly(ethylene terephthalate)	39.5	38	(59)

TRANSMISSION RATES OF WATER THROUGH POLYMERS (Cont'd.)

Polymer	Temp. °C	Q (g)(mil)/(m^2)(24 hr)	Ref.
Polyethylene, low density	39.5	17	(60)
Polyacrylonitrile	39.5	180	(60)
Poly(methyl methacrylate)	39.5	550	(60)
Polystyrene	39.5	170	(60)
Poly(vinyl alcohol)	35	1,500	(60)
Poly(vinylidene chloride)	39.5	4.8	(60)
Rubber hydrochloride	39.5	21	(60)

2 - TRANSMISSION RATES OF SOME ORGANIC SOLVENTS THROUGH POLYMERS (58)

Polymer	Q (g)(mil)/(m^2)(24 hr) at 35 °C				
	Benzene	n-Hexane	Carbon tetrachloride	Ethyl alcohol	Ethyl acetate
Cellulose	2.5	1.7	3.4	62	27
Cellulose acetate	900	5.5	15	2,200	7,200
Poly(hexamethylene adipate-co-sebacate-co-aminocaproate) (Nylon 66/610/6)	6.8	8.4	4.6	2,200	5.8
Polyethylene, low density	9,300	5,500	16,000	44	1,000
Polyacrylonitrile	4.6	3.0	6.0	0	2.7
Polystyrene	19,000	-	28,000	0	sol.
Poly(vinyl alcohol)	6.3	4.4	6.6	24	5.1

References page V-24

3 - TRANSMISSION RATES OF VARIOUS ORGANIC
COMPOUNDS THROUGH LOW DENSITY POLYETHYLENE (62)

Permeant	Q (g)(mil)/(m^2)(24 hr)		
	0°C	21.1°C	54.4°C
Acetic acid	5.43	48.1	1,020
Acetic anhydride	2.02	12.6	459
Acetone	21.7	105	2,850
Allyl alcohol	2.48	22.5	357
Amyl acetate	8.68	134	4,170
i-Amyl alcohol	-	3.10	-
Aniline	3.88	26.4	924
Benzaldehyde	5.74	105	3,190
Benzene	700	6,820	69,800
n-Butyl alcohol	1.55	7.13	316
sec-Butyl alcohol	1.86	9.61	58.3
t-Butyl alcohol	0.775	4.03	419
Butyaldehyde	13.9	155	9,050
Carbon tetrachloride	790	9,460	121,000
Chlorobenzene	896	7,050	68,400
p-Chlorotoluene	465	4,710	64,600
Cyclohexane	490	3,890	57,800
Decane	147	1,100	18,000
Diethyl ether	744	4,850	124,000
Ethanethiol	403	6,200	155,000
Ethyl acetate	29.5	256	5,860
Ethyl alcohol	-	10.9	-
Formaldehyde	-	82.2	-
n-Heptane	753	4,190	41,100
Formic acid	3.88	10.4	186
n-Hexane	744	5,430	140,000
Methyl alcohol	3.88	18.9	446
Methyl ethyl ketone	57.4	195	5.050
Nitrobenzene	5.74	75.9	1,550
Octyl alcohol	1.55	7.75	397
n-Pentane	1,500	8,150	233,000
i-Pentane	744	4,190	77,500
2-Pentene	2,790	10,800	248,000
Phenol	1.55	7.75	372
n-Propyl alcohol	1.09	7.75	34.7
i-Propylamine	35.7	632	10,900
Tetradecane	26.4	226	6,260
Toluene	899	7,830	89,500
o-Xylene	558	3,970	55,800
p-Xylene	1,330	7,530	74,400

F. REFERENCES

1. P. Meares, J. Am. Chem. Soc., 76, 3415 (1954).
2. P. Meares, Trans. Faraday Soc., 53, 101 (1957).
3. H. A. Bent, J. Polymer Sci., 24, 387 (1967).
4. K. Kammermeyer, Ind. Eng. Chem., 49, 1685 (1957).
5. A. W. Myers, C. E. Rogers, V. Stannett, and M. Szwarc, TAPPI, 41, 716 (1958).
6. A. S. Michaels and R. B. Parker, Jr., J. Polymer Sci., 41, 53 (1959).
7. A. S. Michaels and H. J. Bixler, J. Polymer Sci., 50, 393 (1961).
8. C. H. Klute, J. Appl. Polymer Sci., 1, 340 (1959).
9. C. H. Klute, J. Polymer Sci., 41, 307 (1959).
10. S. W. Lasoski, Jr., and W. H. Cobbs, Jr., J. Polymer Sci., 36, 21 (1959).
11. A. S. Michaels and H. J. Bixler, J. Polymer Sci., 50, 413 (1961).
12. Y. Ito, Kobunshi Kagaku, 18, 13 (1961).
13. G. S. Hartley, Trans. Faraday Soc., 42B, 6 (1946).
14. C. Robinson, Trans. Faraday Soc., 42B, 12 (1946).
15. G. S. Hartley, Trans. Faraday Soc., 45, 820 (1949).
16. J. Crank and C. Robinson, Proc. Roy. Soc. (London), A204, 549 (1951).
17. G. S. Park, J. Polymer Sci., 11, 97 (1953).
18. J. A. Barrie and B. Platt, J. Polymer Sci., 49, 479 (1961).
19. J. A. Barrie and B. Platt, J. Polymer Sci., 54, 261 (1961).
20. Y. Ito, Kobunshi Kagaku, 18, 6 (1961).
21. R. M. Barrer, Trans. Faraday Soc., 38, 322 (1942).
22. G. J. van Amerongen, J. Appl. Phys., 17, 972 (1946).
23. R. M. Barrer and G. Skirrow, J. Polymer Sci., 3, 549 (1948).
24. A. Aitken and R. M. Barrer, Trans. Faraday Soc., 51, 116 (1955).
25. I. Sobolev, J. A. Meyer, V. Stannett, and M. Szwarc, J. Polymer Sci., 17, 417
     (1955).
26. R. M. Barrer and R. R. Fergusson, Trans. Faraday Soc., 54, 989 (1958).
27. P. M. Doty, W. H. Aiken, and H. Mark, Ind. Eng. Chem., Anal. Ed., 16, 686 (1944).
28. G. Deeg and C. J. Frosch, Modern Plastics, 22, No. 3, 155 (1944).
29. P. M. Doty, J. Chem. Phys., 14, 244 (1946).
30. R. F. Boyer, J. Appl. Phys., 20, 540 (1949).
31. D. W. Brubaker and K. Kammermeyer, Ind. Eng. Chem., 44, 1465 (1952).
32. D. W. Brubaker and K. Kammermeyer, Ind. Eng. Chem., 45, 1148 (1953).
33. W. Heilman, V. Tammela, J. A. Meyer, V. Stannett, and M. Szwarc, Ind. Eng. Chem.,
     48, 821 (1956).
34. C. A. Kumins, C. J. Rolle, and J. Roteman, J. Phys. Chem., 61, 1290 (1957).
35. Y. Ito, Kobunshi Kagaku, 18, 285 (1961).
36. V. L. Simril and A. Hershberger, Modern Plastics, 27, No. 11, 95 (1950).
37. J. A. Meyer, C. E. Rogers, V. Stannett, and M. Szwarc, TAPPI, 40, 142 (1957).
38. Y. Ito, Kobunshi Kagaku, 18, 158 (1961).
39. E. R. Thornton, V. Stannett, and M. Swarc, J. Polymer Sci., 28, 465 (1958).
40. A. S. Michaels, R. F. Baddour, H. J. Bixler, and C. Y. Choo, Ind. Eng. Chem.
     Process Design and Development, 1, 14 (1962).
41. H. Yasuda and V. Stannett, J. Polymer Sci., 57, 907 (1962).
42. V. Stannett and H. Yasuda, J. Polymer Sci., 1, Part B, 289 (1963).
43. R. C. Binning, R. J. Lee, J. F. Jennings, and E. C. Martin, Ind. Eng. Chem., 53,
     47 (1961).
44. R. W. Roberts and K. Kammermeyer, J. Appl. Polymer Sci., 7, 2183 (1963).
45. R. Waack, N. H. Alex, H. L. Frisch, V. Stannett, and M. Szwarc, Ind. Eng. Chem.,
     47, 2524 (1955).
46. P. Y. Hsieh, J. Appl. Polymer Sci., 7, 1743 (1963).
47. A. W. Myers, V. Tammela, V. Stannett, and M. Szwarc, Modern Plastics, 37, No. 10,
     139 (1960).
48. H. J. Bixler, Dissertation, Massachusetts Institute of Technology, Cambridge,
     Mass.
49. A. W. Myers, V. Stannett, and M. Szwarc, J. Polymer Sci., 35, 285 (1959).
50. F. J. Norton, J. Appl. Polymer Sci., 7, 1649 (1963).
51. C. E. Rogers, J. A. Meyer, V. Stannett, and M. Szwarc, TAPPI, 39, 741 (1956).
52. C. J. Major and K. Kammermeyer, Modern Plastics, 39, No. 11, 135 (1962).
53. Y. Ito, Kobunshi Kagaku, 18, 124 (1961).
54. D. Jeschke and H. A. Stuart, Z. Naturforsch., 16a, 37 (1961).
55. D. V. Brubaker and K. Kammermeyer, Ind. Eng. Chem., 46, 733 (1954).
56. A. W. Meyers, J. A. Meyer, C. E. Rogers, V. Stannett, and M. Szwarc, TAPPI, 44,
     58 (1961).
57. H. Braunisch and H. Lenhart, Kolloid Z., 177, 24 (1961).
58. V. L. Simril and A. Hershberger, Modern Plastics, 27, No. 10, 97 (1950).
59. L. E. Amborski and D. W. Flierel, Ind. Eng. Chem., 45, 2290 (1953).
60. D. W. Morgan, Ind. Eng. Chem., 45, 2296 (1953).
61. V. L. Simril and B. A. Curry, J. Appl. Polymer Sci., 4, 62 (1960).
62. M. Salame, S. P. E. Trans., 1, 153 (1961).

RADIATION CHEMICAL YIELDS: "G-VALUES"

A. Chapiro

Laboratoire de Chimie des Radiations du C.N.R.S.
Bellevue, France

(Figures compiled from "Radiation Chemistry of Polymeric Systems"
Interscience Publishers, 1962 and "Selected Constants--Radiolytic
Yields," Tables des Constantes, Vol. 13, I.U.P.A.C. Pergamon
Press, 1963.)

This table lists G-Values which are defined as yields of molecules, free radicals or
products formed per 100 eV absorbed in the system.

Table I

YIELDS OF FREE RADICALS FOR DIFFERENT MONOMERS

Monomer	G (R$^{\cdot}$)
Styrene	0.66 - 0.69
Ethylene	4.4
Methyl methacrylate	5.5 - 11.5
Methyl acrylate	6.3 - 15
Vinyl acetate	9.6 - 12
Acrylonitrile	2.4 - 5.6
Ethyl acrylate	10.9
n-Butyl acrylate	17.4

Table II

YIELDS OF IONIC INITIATION FOR DIFFERENT MONOMERS

Monomer (and solvent)	G (init.)
Isobutylene	0.15 - 0.30
Butadiene	0.2
Styrene/CH$_2$Cl$_2$ (1/3)	0.5

Table III

YIELDS OF INITIATION FOR MONOMERS IN THE SOLID STATE

Monomer	G (init.)
Acrylamide	0.5
Styrene	0.6
Acrylonitrile	0.15
Methyl methacrylate/paraffin	0.4 - 1.3

Table IV

YIELDS OF CHEMICAL CHANGES IN POLYETHYLENE

Chemical Process	G at 20°C	below - 40°C
Crosslinking	2.0	1.0
Hydrogen evolution	4.1	3.2
Unsaturation	1.8	1.8

Table V

YIELD OF CROSSLINKING (c.l.) AND RATIO β/α OF DEGRADATION
TO CROSSLINKING FOR POLYMERS OF THE "CROSSLINKING TYPE"

Polymer	G(c.l.) at 20°C	β/α
Polypropylene	0.6	0.8 - 1.0
Polystyrene	0.04 - 0.06	0 - 0.2
Natural rubber	1.3	0.14
Polybutadiene	2.0	
Polyacrylonitrile	1.4	
Poly(methyl acrylate)	0.5 - 1.1	0.17
Poly(vinyl chloride)	0.2 - 0.5	
Poly(vinyl acetate)	0.28	0.1
Poly(dimethyl siloxane)	2.5	0
Poly(methylphenyl siloxane)	0.8	
Polyamides	0.3	

Table VI

YIELDS OF DEGRADATION FOR POLYMERS OF THE "DEGRADING TYPE"

Polymer	G (breaks) at 20°C
Polyisobutylene	3.0
Poly(methyl methacrylate)	1.9
Cellulose	10.0
Poly(α-methylstyrene)	0.25

HIGH RESOLUTION NUCLEAR MAGNETIC RESONANCE OF POLYMERS

F. A. Bovey
Bell Telephone Laboratories
Murray Hill, New Jersey

Contents

A. INTRODUCTION

Nuclear magnetic resonance spectroscopy has been applied to polymers in two ways:
(a) observation of the wide-line spectra of polymers in the solid state (1) and
(b) observation of the more highly resolved spectra which can be obtained when polymers are dissolved in suitable solvents. The width and detailed shape of the wide-line spectrum, particularly if known as a function of temperature, can be interpreted in terms of structure and molecular motion. In solution, polymers give spectra in which the resonance lines are only a small fraction (10^{-3} to 10^{-4}) of their width in the solid state. It is with these spectra that we are concerned in this tabulation. Such spectra can be interpreted to give valuable information concerning (a) polymer composition and structure, including "head-to-tail" and "head-to-head:tail-to-tail" bonding of monomer units, geometrical isomerism, monomer ratios in copolymers, etc.; (b) stereochemical configuration, i.e., whether the polymer is isotactic or syndiotactic, or, if "atactic", what the proportions of the stereochemical sequences are; and (c) miscellaneous useful data, including polymer-solvent interactions, conformational preferences, etc. It is principally with (a) and (b) that we shall deal here. There are other possible means of obtaining information concerning (a), but NMR is uniquely powerful in providing information concerning (b), and most published work has been undertaken with this in mind. A heavy stress on stereochemical configuration is accordingly evident in the tabulation below.

Users of this table who wish a more complete discussion of the nuclear magnetic resonance phenomenon, particularly as applied to polymers, than there is space to provide here, should consult the following sources:

I. L. M. Jackman, "Applications of Nuclear Magnetic Resonance Spectroscopy in Organic Chemistry," Pergamon Press (London), 1959.
II. F. A. Bovey and G. V. D. Tiers, Fortschr. Hochpolymer-Forsch., 3, 139-195 (1963).
III. D. W. McCall and W. P. Slichter, "Newer Methods of Polymer Characterization," Chap. VIII; Bacon Ke, Editor; Interscience Publishers, New York, 1964.

Proton Shielding Values

The values of τ for polymer proton spectra are based on the arbitrary assignment of the value $\tau = 10.000$ to tetramethylsilane, (2), dissolved in the polymer solution, usually to the extent of 1-2%. τ-values are given by the equation

$$\tau_x = 10 - \frac{v_x \times 10^6}{\text{rf oscillator frequency (cps)}} , \qquad (1)$$

where v_x represents the increase in frequency in cycles per second which would be required to cause the peak x to fall at the position (previously) occupied by the tetramethylsilane peak. This quantity is readily measured by means of low frequency modulation (usually 10^2 to 10^3 cps) of the NMR signal (via the magnetic field), which produces sidebands on either side of the main peak. Peak positions on the τ-scale may be obtained by graphical interpolation between the reference peak and one of its sidebands (of accurately known frequency), or between two reference sidebands, and application of Eq. 1. With instruments of the type of the Varian "A-60", such measurements are greatly facilitated, since τ-values may be directly read from the calibrated recorder paper once the tetramethylsilane peak has been adjusted to coincide with the "10.000 τ" bench-mark.

Increasing values of τ signify increasing shielding of the proton. Since τ-values are expressed in dimensionless units (i.e., parts per million of change of magnetic field strength), they are independent of the strength of the magnetic field employed, or (which is the same thing) the frequency of the rf oscillator, despite the well-known fact that magnetic shielding differences among nuclei ("chemical shifts") are proportional to the magnetic field employed. Most of the data tabulated have been obtained on instruments operating at 40 Mc/s (about 9400 gauss for protons) or 60 Mc/s (about 14,000 gauss for protons), but some data using 100 Mc/s (23,500 gauss) instruments (Varian "HR-100") have been reported, and use of stronger magnetic fields, with accompanying simplification of spectra, may be expected to increase.

In this tabulation, only those data are recorded which are reported by the authors using the τ-scale, or which can be converted to the τ-scale. There is a small residuum of data in which an external reference or no reference is employed; this is not included.

Fluorine Shielding Values

Fluorine shielding values are more sensitive to choice of solvent than proton shielding values. For this reason the definition of the φ scale for fluorine chemical shifts (3) specifies CCl_3F as both reference and solvent, and further specifies that the chemical shifts are extrapolated to infinite dilution. If this extrapolation is not performed (it commonly is not) the values obtained are termed φ* values. It is not possible to employ CCl_3F as a solvent for most polymers (particularly at elevated temperatures). In such cases, CCl_3F is employed in the same manner as tetramethylsilane, i.e., as a minor component of the system. The "φ" values reported for fluorine-containing polymers are thus only approximate. Comparison to small-molecule analogs, for example, is strictly valid only if the latter are measured in the same solvent as the polymer. With this reservation understood, the "φ" values for polymer fluorine resonances may be defined as for small molecules:

$$\varphi^*_x = \frac{v_x \times 10^6}{\text{rf oscillator frequency (cps)}}, \qquad (2)$$

the position of the CCl_3F resonance being thus taken as zero. For fluorine spectra at 14,100 gauss, the appropriate frequency is approximately 56.4 Mc/s. Most fluorine spectra are currently reported at this frequency.

Method of Representing Chemical Shifts and Other Spectral Characteristics

In polymer spectra, the resonances are almost invariably multiplets, often so poorly resolved as to appear as broad singlets. In those few instances where the resonance appears as a narrow "true" singlet, the designation of τ or φ value stands alone. More commonly, it will be followed by one of the following designations:

  b: broad, i.e., exceeding 2-3 cps in half-height width. This may be a result of dipolar broadening (conspicuous in many polymer spectra; see below), which in turn may contribute to failure to resolve a multiplet, resulting in even greater apparent broadening. If the latter is the case (as is common), the peak position will be additionally designated as "u.m.c." (unresolved multiplet center).

  d: doublet, the members of which may be broadened, indicated by "b"

  t: triplet

  q: quartet

Notes page V-60; References page V-66

p: pentuplet

s: sextuplet

h: septet

In general, these designations are reserved for multiplets which appear to be at least approximately "binomial" (i.e., 1:1 for t; 1:3:3:1 for q; 1:4:6:4:1 for p, etc.), as expected for nuclei or groups of equivalent nuclei which are equally or nearly equally coupled to all the nuclei in another group. The recorded τ or φ* value corresponds to the center of such a multiplet. For weakly coupled systems of nuclei, i.e., where the chemical shift difference (in cps) substantially exceeds the J coupling, the multiplet center represents the true chemical shift quite accurately. If the couplings to other nuclei were abolished, as can actually be done by the "spin decoupling" technique (4), the multiplet would shrink to a singlet located at this position.

Polymer NMR spectra are often quite complex. Those of vinyl polymers having only one α-substituent must be treated as systems of at least six spins. The complexity increases when the chemical shift differences are comparable to or do not greatly exceed the couplings. The multiplets may be so distorted from their "binomial" form that they are not recognizable; extra lines appear and overlap may become serious. Very few spectra of such strongly coupled polymer systems have been fully analyzed. Where such cases have been analyzed, the resonances will be designated "m" and the τ-value will be the true chemical shift. In cases not analyzed or only very approximately analyzed by first-order calculation, the chemical shift recorded will be the apparent center of the multiplet, usually the maximum rather than the center of gravity, and this will be followed by "m.c.", to indicate a multiplet center rather than a true chemical shift. Such multiplets may often consist of two or more nuclei having different chemical shifts.

Nature of Polymer Spectra

In addition to the complicating features just indicated, which can occur in the NMR spectra of small molecules as well, interpretation of polymer spectra is hampered by a special difficulty peculiar to large molecules. This is the phenomenon of dipolar broadening (see sources I and II, page 1 for a fuller explanation), which is always observed in the NMR spectra of molecules constrained to rotate slowly or not at all, as in solids or viscous liquids, particularly at low temperature. The local magnetic fields arising from neighboring nuclei give rise to an envelope of lines about each resonance so that peaks are greatly broadened and all fine structure is lost. In solution in solvents of normal viscosity, molecular motion is much more rapid. This has the effect of nearly abolishing these local field effects so that the resonance lines become very much narrower. For polymers, particularly those with stiff chains, motional narrowing may be considerably less than for small molecules, and even in solution at temperatures as high as 150-200° the lines may remain appreciably broadened. This is particularly true of backbone protons in vinyl polymers, which, because of their slower reorientation, generally give broader lines than side-chain protons.

Linewidths are not given in the tables below because they are seldom reported. Experience indicates that under "good" conditions, i.e., in solvents of moderate viscosity and at a temperature of 150-200°, backbone protons give spectra with an intrinsic linewidth of about 2.5 to 3.0 cps (somewhat less for very short chains), while side-chains give lines of about half this width. Not infrequently the apparent linewidth may be greater than this. In "strongly coupled" spectra (for example, the phenyl resonance in polystyrene) this width is due to the large number of very closely spaced lines, and would be observed even for small molecules. Apparent excess linewidth may also occur if the polymer is stereochemically irregular (see below), because of overlapping of a number of resonances differing only slightly in chemical shift.

Nuclear Magnetic Resonance and Stereochemical Configuration of Vinyl Polymers

Geometrical and positional isomerism (including head-to-head:tail-to-tail vs head-to-tail positioning of monomer units) in polymer chains require no special word, since the spectral interpretation is essentially the same as for small molecules. With regard to the use of NMR for the determination of stereochemical configuration (see sources II and III, page 1), the following explanation will define the terms employed in the tables. This terminology is now generally accepted for describing the results of such studies:

i: α-proton (or other observable α-substituent) of the center monomer unit of an isotactic triad of monomer units, i.e., a triad of units all of which have the same stereochemical configuration, ddd (or lll).

s: α-proton (or other observable α-substituent) of the center monomer unit of a syndiotactic triad of monomer units, dld (or ldl).

h: α-proton (or other observable α-substituent) of the center monomer unit of a heterotactic triad of monomer units, ddl (or lld, ldd, dll).

r: "racemic" methylene group (or CF_2 group), i.e., one between two monomer units having opposite configuration (syndiotactic sequence).

m: "meso" methylene group (or CF_2 group), i.e., one between two monomer units having the same configuration (isotactic sequence).

In the literature, these designations are commonly used not only to describe the type of group observed, but also to indicate the normalized probability of its occurrence, i.e., the proportion of the groups among all such groups in the polymer. For any polymer:

$$i + h + s = 1.0$$

$$r + m = 1.0$$

The purpose of these tables is to provide information concerning spectral positions (and couplings) of various groups in polymers, rather than to report the actual structures and composition of the rather large number of polymers which have now been measured. Therefore, the above terms are employed here only in the first sense, i.e., to indicate the stereochemical type.

If a polymer is reported as being largely or entirely of one stereochemical type (e.g., isotactic or syndiotactic), this fact will be indicated. Otherwise, the stereochemical composition will generally not be indicated, although there are occasional exceptions to this usage.

In certain instances, the assignment of resonances to specific nuclei has not been established. The peak position is followed by the designation "unassgd" in such cases. This is commonly the case for pairs of meso β-methylene protons.

Abbreviations

The following additional abbreviations will be employed:

TMS: tetramethylsilane

HMDS: hexamethyldisiloxane

DMF: N,N-dimethylformamide

DMA: N,N-dimethylacetamide

DMSO: dimethyl sulfoxide

DSS: sodium 2,2-dimethyl-2-silapentane-5-sulfonate, $(CH_3)_3SiCH_2CH_2CH_2SO_3Na$

TFA: trifluoroacetic acid

u.m.c.: unresolved multiplet center; see introduction above

"m": distorted multiplet of strongly coupled systems; see introduction above

m.c.: apparent multiplet center; see introduction above

1 - OLEFIN POLYMERS

Structure	Solvent; conc.	Ref. signal	Temp., °C	Freq. Mc/s	τ	J	Notes	Ref.
Polypropylene $-CH_{(2)}-\overset{\overset{\displaystyle H_{(1A)}}{\vert}}{\underset{\underset{\displaystyle CH_{3\,(3)}}{\vert}}{C}}-H_{(1B)}$	p-dichloro-benzene;	HMDS	175	60	$H_{(1)}, H_{(2)}$:ca.8.C-9.2, complex m (iso. and syndio.) $H_{(3)}$:9.09,d	$H_{(2)}-H_{(3)}$:ca. 6.0	1	5
	o-dichlorc-benzene; 0.28 mg in 0.35 ml.	HMDS	150	60 and 100	$H_{(1)}$(isotactic): $H_{(A)}, H_{(B)}$:ca.8.69,d. ca. 9.07,d,unassgd $H_{(1)}$(syndiotactic):ca. 8.95,m $H_{(2)}$:i:8.31,m s:8.33,m (h:8.32,m,assumed position) $H_{(3)}$:i:9.08,d h:9.10,d s:9.12,d	$H_{(1A)}-H_{(1B)}$:ca. 13 $H_{(2)}-H_{(3)}$:6.0 for i,s,and h	1 1 1	6
Poly(propylene-2-d_1) $-CD-\overset{\overset{\displaystyle H_{(1A)}}{\vert}}{\underset{\underset{\displaystyle CH_{3\,(3)}}{\vert}}{C}}-H_{(1B)}$	2-chloro-thiophene;	HMDS	110	60	$H_{(1)}$(isotactic): $H_{(A)}, H_{(B)}$:8.77,d; 9.15,d; unassgd $H_{(1)}$(syndiotactic):9.15 $H_{(3)}$(syndio and isc):9.15	$H_{(1A)}-H_{(1B)}$:13.2 $H_{(1)}-H_{(3)}$:0	1	5

Structure	Solvent; conc.	Ref. signal	Temp., °C	Freq. Mc/s	τ	J	Notes	Ref.
Poly(propylene-2,3,3,3-d_4) $\begin{array}{c} H\text{-}(1A) \\ \text{-CD}\text{---}\overset{\mid}{C}\text{-} \\ \overset{\mid}{CD_3} \quad H\text{-}(1B) \end{array}$	2-chloro-thiophene	HMDS	110	60	$H_{(1)}$(isotactic): $H_{(A)}, H_{(B)}$:8.77,d; 9.15,d; unassgd $H_{(1)}$(syndiotactic):9.05	$H_{(1A)}\text{-}H_{(1B)}$:13.2	1	5
Polyisobutene $\begin{array}{c} CH_3 \\ \mid \\ \text{-}C\text{-}CH_2\text{-} \\ \mid \\ CH_3 \end{array}$	CCl_4; <5%	TMS	32	60	CH_2:8.57 CH_3:8.88			7
Poly(3-methyl-1-butene) $\begin{array}{c} CH_3 \\ \mid \\ \text{-}CH_2CH_2C\text{-} \\ \mid \\ CH_3 \end{array}$	CCl_4; <5%	TMS	32	60	$\text{-}CH_2CH_2\text{-}$:8.88,b CH_3:9.16		2	7
Poly(4-methyl-1-pentene) $\begin{array}{c} CH_3 \\ \mid \\ \text{-}CH_2CH_2C\text{-} \\ \mid \\ CH_3 \end{array}$	CCl_4; <5%	TMS	32	60	$\text{-}CH_2CH_2CH_2\text{-}$:8.86,b CH_3:9.16		2	7
Poly(5-methyl-1-hexene) $\begin{array}{c} CH_3 \\ \mid \\ \text{-}CH_2CH_2CH_2C\text{-} \\ \mid \\ CH_3 \end{array}$	CCl_4; <5%	TMS	32	60	$\text{-}CH_2CH_2CH_2CH_2\text{-}$:8.82,b CH_3:9.16		2	7

2 - VINYL POLYMERS AND OTHER SUBSTITUTED OLEFINS

Structure	Solvent; conc.	Ref. signal	Temp. °C	Freq. Mc/s	τ	J	Notes	Ref.
Polyacrylates:								
Poly(acrylamide)								
$-CH_2-CH-$ $C=N$ $H_{(1)}$ $H_{(2)}$	H_2O; pH 4.5; 20 vol%	DSS	25	40	$H_{(1)}$:3.01,b; $H_{(2)}$:2.26,b; CH: ca. 7.9; CH_2:8.30	W ≈ 10 cps; W ≈ 10 cps	44	30
	H_2O; pH 4.5; 20 vol%	DSS	70	40	$H_{(1)},H_{(2)}$:3.20	$H_{(1)}-H_{(2)}$:prob < 1	45	
Poly(isopropyl acrylate) H_C H_A H_C $-C-C-C-$ CO_2 H_B $CO_2CH(CH_3)_2$ (1) (2)								
(isotactic)	chlorobenzene; 14.0%	TMS	150	60	isotactic: $H_{(1)}$:4.96,h; $H_{(2)}$:8.76,d; $H_{(A)}$:8.32,m; $H_{(B)}$:7.86,m; $H_{(C)}$:7.43,m	$H_{(1)}-H_{(2)}$:6.14 ± 0.02; $H_{(A)}-H_{(b)}$:-13.6; $H_{(A)}-H_{(C)}$:6.50; $H_{(B)}-H_{(C)}$:6.50	37; 34,37	25

Structure	Solvent; conc.	Ref. signal	Temp., °C	Freq. Mc/s	τ	J	Notes	Ref.
Poly(isopropyl acrylate) (Cont'd.)								
	chloro-benzene; ca. 10%	TMS	144	60	atactic: $H_{(1)}$:4.95,h $H_{(2)}$:8.73,d	$H_{(1)}-H_{(2)}$:6.14 ± 0.02	35,37	25
					CH_2: r:$H_{(A)}$,$H_{(B)}$:8.19,t $H_{(C)}$:7.44,p	$H_{(A)}-H_{(C)}$ = $H_{(B)}-H_{(C)}$:ca. 6.5	36,37	
					m: not accurately measurable, appears to be same as in isotactic polymer			
Poly(methyl acrylate), -CH$_3$-CH$_2$- CO$_2$CH$_3$	chloro-benzene; 15% w/v	TMS	150	60	OCH_3:6.22 CH:7.38,p CH_2:8.06,t (Note 38)	$CH-CH_2$:6.6		26
Poly(methyl acrylate), deuterated -CD— C — H CO$_2$CH$_3$ (D)	C$_6$H$_6$; 10%	TMS	r.t.	60	CO_2CH_3:6.59 CHD: m:$H_{(A)}$:8.57,b $H_{(B)}$:7.88,b r:8.16,b [$H_{(C)}$:7.39,b]		39,40 39,40 39,40 39,40, 41	27

Structure	Solvent; conc.	Ref. signal	Temp., °C	Freq. Mc/s	τ	J	Notes	Ref.
Polymethacrylates:								
Poly(methacrylic acid)								
$-C(CH_3)(CO_2H)-CH_2-$	DMSO; 10% w/v	TMS	95	40	CO_2H:2.66 ± 0.03 CH_3:8.99,b CH_2:masked		46	29
	formamide; 10% w/v	TMS	98	40	CO_2H:exchanges CH_3:8.82,b CH_2:8.01, very b		46	29
	pyridine; 10% w/v	TMS	95	40	CO_2H:ionized CH_3:8.15,b CH_2:7.44,very b		46	29
Poly(methacrylamide)								
$-CH_2-C(CH_3)(C(=O)-NH_{(1)}H_{(2)})-$	H_2O;pH 4.0; 20 vol %	DSS	25	40	$H_{(1)}$:ca. 3.0, very b $H_{(2)}$:ca. 2.3, very b		47	30
Poly(methyl methacrylate)								
$-C(CH_3)(CO_2)-CH_AH_B-C(CH_3)(CO_2CH_3)-$ (isotactic)	$CHCl_3$; 15% w/v	TMS	90	40	CO_2CH_3:6.40 (i,h, and s all ca. equiv.) α-CH:i:8.78 h:8.95 s:9.09 m:CH_2: (Note 42) $H_{(A)}$:8.44,d $H_{(B)}$:7.84,d r:8.14,b	$H_{(A)}-H_{(3)}$: -15.5	43	28

Notes page V-60; References page V-66

Structure	Solvent conc.	Ref. signal	Temp. °C	Freq. Mc/s	τ	J	Notes	Ref.
Poly(methyl methacrylate) (Cont'd.)								
	pyridine; 10% w/v	TMS	95	40	CO_2CH_3:6.32 α-CH_3:i:8.56 h:8.70 s:8.81 CH_2:7.88, very b, u.m.c.		43	29
	C_6H_6; 10% w/v	TMS	96	40	<u>isotactic polymer:</u> CO_2CH_3:6.47 α-CH_3:8.59 CH_2:$H_{(A)}$:7.58,d (Note 42) $H_{(B)}$:8.32,d <u>syndiotactic polymer:</u> CO_2CH_3:6.54 α-CH_3:8.77 CH_2:7.92,b	$H_{(A)}$-$H_{(B)}$:-14.4	43	29
	dioxane; ca. 5%	TMS	95	40	CO_2CH_3: masked by solvent α-CH_3:i:8.82 h:9.00 s:9.12 CH_2: partially masked by solvent C^{13}-satellite		43	29

Structure	Solvent conc.	Ref. signal	Temp. °C	Freq. Mc/s	τ	J	Notes	Ref.
Polystyrenes:								
Polystyrene								
$\begin{array}{c} H_A \quad H_B \\ -C-C- \\ H_C \end{array}$ (phenyl ring, positions 1–6)	tetra-chloro-ethylene; 20% w/v	TMS	128	60	isotactic polymer: $\underline{}$ H(2)(=H(6)):3.43$_0$ H(3)(=H(5)):3.06$_3$ H(4):3.09$_6$	H(2)-H(3), H(3)-H(4) (=H(4)-H(5), H(5)-H(6)): 6.0 ± 0.1 H(2)-H(4), H(3)-H(5) H(2)-H(6)(=H(4)-H(6)): 2.0 ± 0.1 H(2)-H(5), H(3)-H(6): 1.0 ± 0.2	3,6	8
	o-dichloro-benzene; 20% w/v	TMS	200	60	H(A):7.60$_7$ H(B) $\simeq$ H(C):8.34$_0$	H(A)-H(B) $\simeq$ H(A)-H(C) 7.00 ± 0.05 H(B)-H(C):-14.0 ± 0.2	3,5	8
	tetra-chloro-ethylene; 20% w/v	TMS	128	60	atactic polymer: $\underline{}$ H(2)(H(6)):3.50,b H(3),H(4),(H(5)):3.08,b		3,4,6	8
Poly(styrene-β-d$_2$) $\begin{array}{c} H_A \quad D \\ -C-C- \\ C_6H_5 \quad D \end{array}$	o-dichloro-benzene; 20% w/v	TMS	200	60	H(A):i:7.68,b h:7.78,b s:7.97,b		5	8

Structure	Solvent conc.	Ref. signal	Temp., °C	Freq. Mc/s	τ	J	Notes	Ref.
Poly(styrene-β-d_2) (Cont'd.)								
	C_6H_6; 15% w/v	C_6H_6 (2.84)	100	60	"atactic" polymer: $H(A)$: i:7.61,b h:7.73,b s:7.92,b		5	9
Poly(styrene-α-d_1)								
$\begin{array}{c} D\ H_B \\ \mid\ \mid^{,B} \\ -C-C- \\ \mid \\ C_6H_5HC \end{array}$	o-dichloro-benzene; 20% w/v	TMS	200	60	$H(B) \simeq H(C)$ (in both m and r): 8.39,b		5	8
	C_6H_6; 15% w/v	C_6H_6 (2.84)			isotactic polymer: $\underline{H(B)} \simeq H(C)$:8.36, m.c. "atactic" polymer: $\underline{H(B)} \simeq H(C)$:8.41, m.c.		5	9
Styrene telomers (stereochemistry unknown)								
$Cl-CH-CH_2\underset{A_1\ {}^2B_1}{-}(CH-CH_2)_n\underset{A_2\ {}^2B_2}{-}CH-CH_2\underset{A_3\ {}^2B_3}{-}CCl_3$ $n(=1,2,3,5)$	CS_2; 16-20% w/v	TMS	ca. 25	60	ring A:2.78-2.80, very narrow "m" ring B: $H(2)$,$H(6)$:3.45,b, u.m.c. $H(3)$,$H(4)$,$H(5)$):ca.2.96,b, u.m.c. ring C: ca. 2.90, very narrow "m" $H(A_1)$:ca.5.78,t $H(A_2)$:"m", ca. q; moves from 7.9 to 8.2, as n increases $H(A_3)$;"m", ca. 7.1-7.3			10

Structure	Solvent; conc.	Ref. signal	Temp. °C	Freq. Mc/s	τ	J	Notes	Ref.
Styrene telomers	(stereochemistry unknown) (Cont'd.)				$H_{(B_1)}$:ca. 7.1-7.2, complex m.c. $H_{(B_2)}$:"m", moves from 8.1 to 8.5 as n increases $H_{(B_3)}$:7.1$_5$,d			10
Poly(2-chlorostyrene) -CH - CH$_2$- Cl (ring numbered 1,2,3,4,5,6)	CCl$_4$, 10% w/v	TMS	80	40	ring: ca. 2.9, very b, u.m.c. CH: 7.2, very b, u.m.c. CH$_2$: 8.3, very b, u.m.c.			13
Poly(3-chlorostyrene) -CH-CH$_2$- Cl (ring numbered 1,2,3,4,5,6)	CCl$_4$, 10% w/v	TMS	30	40	ring: ca. 3.0, very b, u.m.c.; ca. 3.5, very b, u.m.c. CH, CH$_2$ ca. 8.3, very b, u.m.c.			13
Poly(4-chlorostyrene) -CH-CH$_2$- Cl (ring numbered 1,2,3,4,5,6)	CCl$_4$, 10% w/v	TMS	80	40	ring: $H_{(2)}$,$(H_{(6)})$: ca. 3.6,b,u.m.c. $H_{(3)}$,$(H_{(5)})$: 3.1, b, u.m.c. CH, CH$_2$: ca. 8.3 very b, u.m.c.		3	13

Structure	Solvent; conc.	Ref. signal	Temp. °C	Freq. Mc/s	τ	J	Notes	Ref.
Poly(4-iodostyrene) -CH-CH$_2$- (ring 6,2,5,3) I								
	CS$_2$; 9.6% w/v	TMS	65	60	isotactic polymer: H$_{(2)}$,(H$_{(6)}$):3.73,d H$_{(3)}$,(E$_{(5)}$):2.65,d CH:8.15,b,u.m.c. CH$_2$:8.66,b,u.m.c.	H$_{(2)}$-H$_{(3)}$(=H$_{(5)}$-H$_{(6)}$): 7.60	3	14
	o-dichloro-benzene; 12.1% w/v	TMS	100	60	isotactic polymer: H$_{(2)}$,(H$_{(6)}$):3.60,d H$_{(3)}$,(H$_{(5)}$):2.56,d CH:7.90,b,u.m.c. CH$_2$:8.46,b,u.m.c.	H$_{(2)}$-H$_{(3)}$(=H$_{(5)}$-H$_{(6)}$): 7.60	3	14
	CS$_2$; 16.7% w/v	TMS	25	60	"atactic" polymer: H$_{(2)}$,(H$_{(6)}$):3.82,b,u.m.c. H$_{(3)}$,(H$_{(5)}$):2.70,b, u.m.c. CH, CH$_2$:ca. 8.4, very b,u.m.c.		3	14
Poly(α-methylstyrene) CH$_3$ -C-CH$_2$- C$_6$H$_5$								

	CHCl$_3$, 20% w/v	TMS	80	56.4	ring: i:3.15
					        h:2.95
					        s:2.83
					 CH$_3$: i:9.18
					       h:9.65
					       s:9.86
							7	11

					CH$_2$:8.51, very b, u.m.c.		8	

	C$_6$H$_6$; 20% w/v	TMS	80	56.4	ring: masked by solvent
					 CH$_3$: i:9.04
					       h:9.46
					       s:9.67
								11

					CH$_2$:8.27, very b, u.m.c.		8	

Structure	Solvent; conc.	Ref. signal	Temp., °C	Freq. Mc/s	τ	J	Notes	Ref.
Poly(α-methylstyrene) (Cont'd.)								
	$CHCl_3$; 10% w/v	$CHCl_3$ (2.74)	80	60	ring: i:3.09 h:2.88 s:masked by solvent CH_3: s:9.07 h:9.57 i:9.79 CH_2: m:8.25,b r:8.42,b		7,9	12
Poly(trifluorochloroethylene)								
F F -C-C- Cl F	3,3'-bistrifluoromethyl-biphenyl; 100 mg in 0.5 ml of solvent	CCl_3F and solvent (Note 20)	150	40	CF: s and h: 125.6,b i: 127.8,b		21,23	19
					CF_2: meso: 104.2,b syndio: 106.0,b		22,23	20
Poly(trifluoroethylene)								
F F -C-C- H F	DMF or butanone	TFA	prob. r.t.	30	CF: 210 CF_2: 117		24,25	
Poly(vinyl ethers):								
Poly(vinyl methyl ether)								
$H_{(A)}$ $H_{(B)}$ -C — C- OCH_3 $H_{(C)}$	chlorobenzene; 10% w/v	TMS	150	60	$H_{(A)}$: ca. 6.42,p $H_{(B)}$,$H_{(C)}$: m: 8.07,d; 8.23,d; unassgd r: 8.23 OCH_3: 6.69	m and r: $H_{(A)}-H_{(B)}$; ≅ $H_{(A)}-H_{(C)}$: 5.80 m: $H_{(B)}-F_{(C)}$: 14.0	26,27	15

Poly(vinyl methyl ether) (Cont'd.)

Structure	Solvent conc.	Ref. signal	Temp., °C	Freq., Mc/s	τ	J	Notes	Ref.
	chloro-benzene: CH_2CH_2,1:3 mole ratio	TMS	37	100	$H_{(A)}$: s:6.43,p h:6.48,p i:6.54,p $H_{(B)}$,$H_{(C)}$: m:8.12,d; 8.34,d,unassgd r:8.29 OCH_3: s:5.70 h:6.72 i:6.74		26,27	21
	CCl_4	TMS	37	100	OCH_3: s:– h:6.70 i:6.72		27	21
	CH_2Cl_2	TMS	37	100	OCH_3: s:6.69 h:6.71 i:6.73		27	21
	CS_2	TMS	37	100	OCH_3: s:6.75 h:6.77 i:6.79		27	21
	chloro-benzene	TMS	37	100	OCH_3: s:– h:6.70 i:6.72		27	21

Poly(α-methylvinyl methyl ether)

Structure	Solvent conc.	Ref. signal	Temp., °C	Freq., Mc/s	τ	J	Notes	Ref.
CH_3 $-C-CH_2-$ OCH_3	benzene	TMS	175	60	OCH_3: 6.87 CH_2: 8.03 CH_3: 8.55		28	22

Poly(α-methylvinyl ether) (Cont'd.)

Structure	Solvent; conc.	Ref. signal	Temp. °C	Freq. Mc/s	τ	J	Notes	Ref.
chloro-benzene		—	140		OCH$_3$: 6.86 CH$_2$: 8.04 CH$_3$: 8.57		28	22
chloroform		—	9_		OCH$_3$: 6.86 CH$_2$: 8.15 CH$_3$: 8.64		28	22

Poly(vinyl acetate)

Structure	Solvent; conc.	Ref. signal	Temp. °C	Freq. Mc/s	τ	J	Notes	Ref.
-CH-CH$_2$- OCOCH$_3$	CCl$_4$; 10%	TMS	110	60	CH: 5.14,p CH$_2$: 8.22,t OCOCH$_3$: i(or s): 8.02 h : 8.04 s(or i): 8.06,d	CH-CH$_2$: ca. 6.2	29 29	15
	CH$_2$Cl$_2$	TMS	37	100	CH: i:5.03,p h:5.07,p s:5.10,p CH$_2$: 8.18, partially resolved m.c. OCOCH$_3$: s:7.98 h:8.00 i:8.02		30 31	2?

Notes page V-60; References page V-66

Structure	Solvent; conc.	Ref. signal	Temp., °C	Freq. Mc/s	τ	J	Notes	Ref.
Poly(vinyl alcohol)								
$-CH-CH_2-$ / OH	DMSO	TMS	37	100	CH: 6.15,b,u.m.c. CH$_2$: 8.53,b,u.m.c.		33	24
Poly(vinyl chloride)								
$H_A H_B$ / $-C-C-$ / ClH_C	chlorobenzene; 15.0% w/v	TMS	150	60	"atactic" polymer: H$_{(A)}$: s:5.48,p h:5.59,p i:5.71,p CH$_2$: m:H$_{(B)} \simeq$ H$_{(C)}$: 7.76,t r: 7.96,t	H$_{(A)}$-H$_{(B)}$: $\simeq$ H$_{(A)}$-H$_{(C)}$: 6.6 H$_{(B)}$-H$_{(C)}$:(ca. 14.0)	10,13 11,13	15
Poly(vinyl chloride-α-d$_1$)								
$D \; H_B$ / $-C-C-$ / ClH_C	chlorobenzene; 15% w/v	TMS	150	60	"atactic" polymer: CH$_2$: m:H$_{(B)} \simeq$ H$_{(C)}$: 7.76 r: 7.96, t	H$_{(B)}$-H$_{(C)}$: ca.-14.0	11,12, 13	16
Poly(vinyl fluoride) H^1 resonance: $-CH-CH_2-$ / F (duPont "Tedlar" type 20)	benzaldehyde; ca. 10%	TMS	180	60	CH: main resonance: 5.00,d,p smaller resonance: 5.18,d (Note 16) CH$_2$: 7.90,t each peak b (Note 17)	CH-F(gem): 47.0 CH$_2$-F (vic): 20.8 CH-CH$_2$ (vic): 4.7	14,15	15

Structure	Solvent; conc.	Ref. signal	Temp. °C	Freq. Mc/s	ϕ^* (see spectrum, Fig. 1)	J	Notes	Ref.
Poly(vinyl fluoride) (Cont'd.) F^{19} resonance:								
$\begin{array}{c} F \quad F_{(1)} \quad F_{(2)} \quad F_{(3)}F_{(4)} \quad F \\ -C-CH_2-C-CH_2-C-CH_2-CH_2-C-C-CH_2-C-CH_2- \\ -H \quad -H \quad H \quad H \quad H \quad H \quad -H \quad H \end{array}$								
$F_{(1)}, F_{(2)};$ "head-to-tail"	N,N-dimethyl-acetamide: hexamethyl-phosphoramide, 1:1 v/v	CCl_3F	85	56.4	180.2, b; 182.2, b unassgd		16	18,19
$F_{(3)},$ "tail-to-tail" 30% w/v					195.8, b; 198.2, b			
$F_{(4)},$ "head-to-head"					191.5, b; 189.3, b			

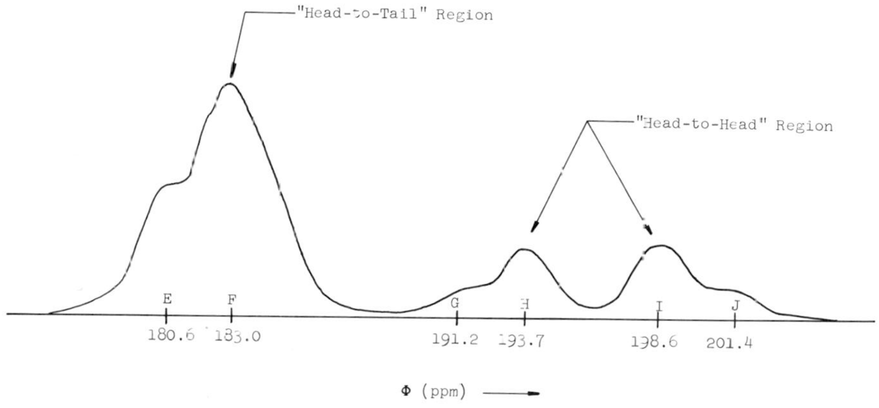

Fig. 1: F^{19} Resonance Spectrum of Poly(vinyl fluoride)

Notes page V-60; References page V-66

Structure	Solvent; conc.	Ref. signal	Temp. °C	Freq. Mc/s	φ* (see spectrum, Fig. 2)	J	Notes	Ref.

Poly(vinylidene fluoride) $-CH_2CF_{2(1)} - CH_2CF_2 - CF_2 - CH_2 - CH_2CF_2 - CH_2CF_2 - CH_2CF_2 -$ (2) (3) (4) (1) (1)

Poly(vinylidene fluoride)							18	18
$F_{(1)}$ "head-to-tail"	N,N-dimethyl-acetamide; 25% w/v	CCl_3F	"r.t."	56.4	91.6, b			
$F_{(2)}$ "head-to-head"					113.6, b			
$F_{(3)}$ "head-to-head"					115.9, b			
$F_{(4)}$ "tail-to-tail"					94.8, b			

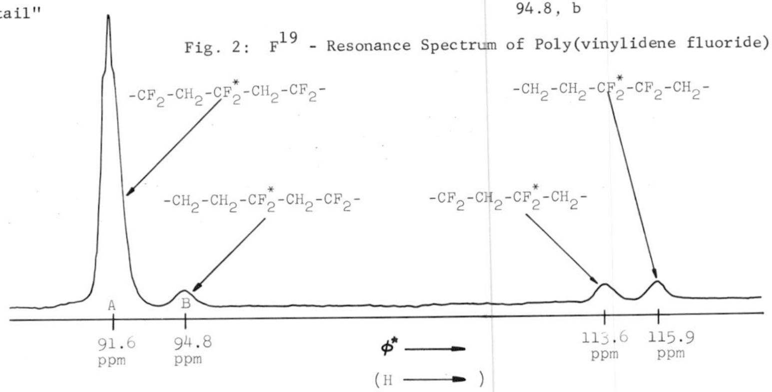

Fig. 2: F^{19} - Resonance Spectrum of Poly(vinylidene fluoride)

$-CF_2-CH_2-CF_2^*-CH_2-CF_2-$

$-CH_2-CH_2-CF_2^*-CH_2-CF_2-$

$-CF_2-CH_2-CF_2^*-CH_2-$

$-CH_2-CH_2-CF_2^*-CF_2-CH_2-$

91.6 ppm   94.8 ppm   113.6 ppm   115.9 ppm

A   B

φ*   (H)

Poly(vinyl trifluoroacetate)	acetone-d_6	TMS	37	100	τ		32	24
$-CH - CH_2 -$ $\quad\quad\mid$ $\quad OCOCF_3$					CH: i:4.63, q h:4.72, q s:4.78, q CH_2:7.61, b partially resolved t.			

3 - VINYL COPOLYMERS

Poly(methyl methacrylate-co-styrene) (MMA)

$$..-C\underset{\underset{CO_2CH_3\ (3)}{|}}{\overset{\overset{CH_3\ (1)}{|}}{|}}-CH_2\ (2)\ ..-CH\ (4)\ CH_2\ (5)$$
$$\underset{C_6H_5}{|}$$

Structure	Solvent conc.	Ref. signal	Temp. °C	Freq. Mc/s	τ	J	Notes	Ref.
10 mole % MMA	CCl₄ 20% w/v	TMS	90	40	H(1): 9.50, b; H(2),H(4),H(5): 8.4, v.b. H(3): 6.89, 7.17, 7.53 phenyl: meta-para: ca. 3.10; ortho: ca. 3.4		48	31
25 mole % MMA	CCl₄ 20% w/v	TMS	90	40	H(1): 9.45, b; H(2),H(4),H(5): 8.4, v.b. H(3): 6.75, 7.15, 7.60 phenyl: meta-para: ca. 3.10; ortho: ca. 3.4		48	31
50 mole % MMA	CHCl₃; CCl₄ 20% w/v	TMS	90	40	H(1): 9.38, b; H(2): 8.40; H(4),H(5): 8.50 H(3): 6.55, 6.70, 7.10, 7.62 phenyl: 3.10		48	31
75 mole % MMA	CHCl₃; CCl₄ 20% w/v	TMS	90	40	H(1): 9.25, b; H(2): 8.23; H(4),H(5): 8.42 H(3): 6.45, 7.02, 7.62 phenyl: 3.00		48	31

Structure	Solvent; conc.	Ref. signal	Temp. °C	Freq. Mc/s	τ	J	Notes	Ref.
Poly(methyl methacrylate-co-styrene)(MMA) (Cont'd.)								
90 mole % MMA	$CHCl_3$; CCl_4 20% w/v	TMS	90	40	$H_{(1)}$: 9.17,b; $H_{(2)}$: 8.23 $H_{(4)}$,$H_{(5)}$: 8.40 $H_{(3)}$: 6.45, 7.00 phenyl: 2.93		49 48	31
Poly(methyl methacrylate-co-α-methylstyrene) (MMA)					CH_3 $-\overset{CH_3}{\underset{CO_2CH_3}{C}}_{(1)}\cdot CH_2-\cdots-C_{(4)}^{(3)}CH_2-\cdots$ $(2)\quad C_6H_5$ (5)			
12 mole % MMA	CCl_4; 20% w/v	TMS	90	40	$H_{(1)}$: 9.45,b; $H_{(2)}$,$H_{(5)}$; 8.30,b $H_{(3)}$: 6.63, 6.95; $H_{(4)}$: 9.70 phenyl: 2.88		50	31
28 mole % MMA	CCl_4; 20% w/v	TMS	90	40	$H_{(1)}$: 8.92,b, 9.40,b; $H_{(2)}$,$H_{(5)}$: 8.27, b $H_{(3)}$: 6.60,6.93; $H_{(4)}$: 9.66 phenyl: 2.90		51 50	31
54 mole % MMA	$CHCl_3$; CCl_4 20% w/v	TMS	90	40	$H_{(1)}$: 8.83,b; 9.08,b; $H_{(2)}$: 8.17,b; $H_{(5)}$: 8.30,b $H_{(3)}$: 6.50, 6.80; $H_{(4)}$: 9.60 phenyl: 2.90		51 50	31
78 mole % MMA	$CHCl_3$; CCl_4 20% w/v	TMS	90	40	$H_{(1)}$: 8.83,b, 9.10,b; $H_{(2)}$: 8.17; $H_{(3)}$: 6.40, 6.80; $H_{(4)}$: 9.57; $H_{(5)}$:- phenyl: 2.90		51	31
91.5 mole % MMA	$CHCl_3$; CCl_4 20% w/v	T	90	40	$H_{(1)}$:8.80,b;9.00,b;9.15,b;$H_{(2)}$:8.17; $H_{(3)}$: 6.37,5.80;$H_{(4)}$:9.57;$H_{(5)}$:- phenyl: 2.90		51	31

Poly(styrene-co-butadiene) mainly: -CHCH$_2$CH$_2$CH = CHCH$_2$-
                                          $\overset{|}{\text{C}_6\text{H}_5}$

Solvent; conc.	Ref. signal	Temp., °C	Freq. Mc/s	% styrene charged, by wt.	% Conversion	Est. mole % copolymer styrene	$\bar{m}_1$, av. styrene sequence length	Aromatic (Note 52)	CH = (Note 53)	CH$_2$ (Note 53)	Width of aromatic peaks cps	Reference
CCl$_4$; ca. 15 ± 5%, w/v	TMS	25	40	0	47.0	0	-	-	4.63	8.01	-	13
				10	36.0	4.7	1.04	2.90	4.65	7.99	6.0	
				20	46.5	10	1.1	2.87	4.65	7.96	6.0	
				40	28.0	22	1.3	2.86	4.66	8.02	5.6	
				60	37.5	39	1.6	2.90	4.72	8.07	8.8	
				80	8.5	61	2.6	2.99	4.92	8.16 8.39	14.5	
				90	15.0	78	4.6	3.01	5.01	8.4 (broad)	19	
				95	50.0	88	8.7	3.94	5.01	8.48	19	
				100	100.0	100	-	3.03 3.48	-	8.46	19	

4 - DIENE POLYMERS

Structure	Solvent; conc.	Ref. signal	Temp., °C	Freq. Mc/s	τ	J	Notes	Ref.
Polyisoprene								
cis-1,4: $CH_3(2)$ $H(3)$ / $C=C$ / $-CH_2(1)$ $CH_2-(4)$	CCl_4; 1-5%	TMS	25 ± 1	60	$H(2)$: 8.33			32
	C_6H_6; 1-5%		"	"	$H(2)$: 8.21			32
	CS_2; 1-5%		"	"	$H(2)$: 8.38			32
	CS_2; 2-10%		r.t.	100	$H(1),H(4)$: ca. 8.0, "d" / $H(2)$: 8.33 / $H(3)$: 4.92, b, partially resolved m.c.			33
trans-1,4: $CH_3(2)$ $CH_2-(4)$ / $C=C$ / $-CH_2(1)$ $H(3)$	CCl_4; 1-5%	TMS	25 ± 1	60	$H(2)$: 8.41			32
	C_6H_6; 1-5%		"	"	$H(2)$: 8.35			32
	CS_2; 1-5%		"	"	$H(2)$: 8.46			32
	CS_2; 2-10%		r.t.	100	$H(1),H(4)$: 8.03,b / $H(2)$: 8.40 / $H(3)$: 4.92, b, partially resolved m.c.			33
3,4-: $-CH(3) CH_2-(4)$ / C / $CH_2=(1)$ $CH_3(2)$	CS_2; 2-10%	TMS	r.t.	100	$H(1)$: 5.33, "d"		54,55	33

Structure	Solvent; conc.	Ref. signal	Temp., °C	Freq., Mc/s	τ	J	Notes	Ref.
Polychloroprene								
cis-1,4: $Cl \backslash C=C / H_{(1)}$ $-CH_2 / \backslash CH_2^-$ (1)	CS_2	TMS	prob., 55	60, 100	$H_{(1)}$: 4.49, m.c. ca. t, incompletely resolved	$H_{(1)}-H_{(2)}$: 5-6		34
trans-1,4:	CS_2	TMS	prob., 35	60, 100	$H_{(1)}$: 4.56, m.c. ca. t, incompletely resolved	$H_{(1)}-H_{(2)}$: 5-6		34
5 - DIENE COPOLYMERS								
Poly(butadiene-co-isoprene)								
$-CH = CH_2$ (1) (2)	CCl_4	TMS	25 ± 1	60	$H_{(1)}$: 4.70 $H_{(2)}$: 4.97			35
$-CH = CH-$					4.70			
$-CH = C(1) - CH_3(2)$ $-C-$					$H_{(1)}$: 4.95 $H_{(2)}$: 8.42			
$CH_3(2)$ $-C(2) = CH_2(1)$					$H_{(1)}$: 5.35 $H_{(2)}$: 8.42			
$-CH-C-C$					8.02			
$-CH-C-C$					8.74			
CH_3-C-C-					9.08			

6 - POLYOXIDES

Structure	Solvent; conc.	Ref. signal	Temp., °C	Freq. Mc/s	τ	J	Notes	Ref.
Polyformaldehyde								
$-OCH_2-$ (1)	p-chlorophenol; 12% w/v	TMS	80	60	$H_{(1)}$: 5.06			36
end group:					$H_{(2)}$: 5.28			
CH_3-OCH_2-O- (3) (2)					$H_{(3)}$: 6.64			
$-OCH_2-CH_2-O-$ (4) (4)					$H_{(4)}$: 6.28			
(ethylene oxide copolymer unit)								
Polyacetaldehyde								
CH_3 (2), $-O-C-$, $H_{(1)}$	aniline, aromatic solvents	TMS	150	60	$H_{(1)}$: ca. 5.30, p; $H_{(2)}$: s:8.56 h:8.58 i:8.66		56, 58	37
	DMF, aliphatic solvents	TMS	150		$H_{(2)}$: h:8.69 i:8.72		57	

Structure	Solvent; conc.	Ref. signal	Temp., °C	Freq. Mc/s	τ	J	Notes	Ref.

7 - POLYURETHANS

Prepolymer (Mol. wt. ca. 1000) from Propylene Glycol and 4,4'-Methylenediphenylene Diisocyanate) (Note 59)

Structure: $-O_2C-NH-$⟨cyclohexyl⟩$-CH_2-$⟨cyclohexyl⟩$-NHCO_2-$ ...

| | DMSO, 40 mg/.4 ml | TMS | 60 | | NH: 0.59 | | | 38 |
| | DMA, 40 mg/.4 ml | | | | NH: 0.53 | | | |

Prepolymer from Propylene Glycol and 2,4-Tolylene Diisocyanate and 2,6-Tolylene Diisocyanate

| | DMSO, 40 mg/.4 ml | TMS | 40 | 60 | $H_{(1)}$ 0.49
$H_{(2)}$ 1.43
$H_{(3)}$ 0.67 | | | 38 |
| | DMA 40 mg/.4 ml | TMS | 40 | 60 | $H_{(4)}$ 1.08
$H_{(5)}$ 1.28 | | | 38 |

8 - PHENOL-FORMALDEHYDE RESINS

The following data are for model compounds of varying complexity representing reactants and intermediates occurring in phenol-formaldehyde condensations. They are presented in two tables: a. representing compounds with free hydroxyls and b. those with acetylated hydroxyls.

a. Nonacetylated Materials

Structure	Solvent conc.	Ref. signal	Temp., °C	Freq. Mc/s	τ, J (Note 60)	Notes	Ref.
$HOCH_2OH$	most data obtained for dil. sol. in dry acetone; exceptions indicated in footnotes	TMS	30	60	5.05 (ca. 1:2:1,t, partially exchange-averaged, J = 0.7 cps)	61	39
$HOCH_2(OCH_2)_xOCH_2OH$					5.10 (ca. 1:1,d, slightly exchange-averaged, J = 1.1 cps)	61	
$HOCH_2(OCH_2)_xOCH_2OH$					5.15	61	
$Ar(CH_2O)_2H$					5.05-5.23	62	
$o\text{-}HOC_6H_4CH_2OH$					4.87-5.12	63	
$4,6\text{-}(CH_3)_2\text{-}2\text{-}(HOCH_2)\text{-}C_6H_2OH$					4.87-5.22	63	
$4\text{-}(CH_3)\text{-}2,6\text{-}(HOCH_2)_2\text{-}C_6H_2OH$					5.37	63	
$2,6\text{-}(HOCH_2)_2\text{-}C_6H_3OH$					5.20	64	
$2\text{-}Cl\text{-}4,6\text{-}(HOCH_2)_2\text{-}C_6H_2OH$					6 = 5.37		
$2,4,6\text{-}(HOCH_2)_3\text{-}C_6H_2OH$					2,6 = 5.23,5.10 (Note 63) 5.43 (Note 64)		
$[3\text{-}(HOCH_2)\text{-}2\text{-}(HO)\text{-}C_6H_5]_2CH_2$					5.03 (Note 63) 5.35 (Note 64)		
$[3,5\text{-}(HOCH_2)_2\text{-}4\text{-}(HO)\text{-}C_6H_2]_2CH_2$					5.00		
$p\text{-}HOC_6H_4CH_2OH$					5.45,5.08	63	
$2,6\text{-}(CH_3)_2\text{-}4\text{-}(HOCH_2)\text{-}C_6H_2OH$					5.53,5.10	63	
$2\text{-}Cl\text{-}4,6\text{-}(HOCH_2)_2\text{-}C_6H_2OH$					4 = 5.47	63	
$2,4,6\text{-}(HOCH_2)_3\text{-}C_6H_2OH$					4 = 5.50,5.10 (Note 63), 5.43 (Note 64)		
$C_6H_5CH_2OH$					5.42-5.57	65	
$(C_6H_5CH_2)_2O$					5.53,5.52	65	
$[2\text{-}(HO)\text{-}C_6H_4CH_2]_2O$					5.28,4.88	65	

Structure	Solvent conc.	Ref. signal	Temp., °C	Freq. Mc/s	τ,J (Note 60)	Notes	Ref.
[4-(HO)-C$_6$H$_4$CH$_2$]$_2$O					5.60,5.42	63	39
[3,5-(CH$_3$)$_2$-2-(HO)-C$_6$H$_5$CH$_2$]$_2$O					5.53,5.45	65	
2-(HO)-C$_6$H$_4$]$_2$CH$_2$					6.02	66	
[2-(CH$_3$)-2-(HO)-C$_6$H$_3$]$_2$CH$_2$					6.05	66	
[3-(HOCH$_2$)-2-(HO)-C$_6$H$_3$]$_2$CH$_2$					6.17 (Note 63), 6.08 (Note 64)		
2,6-[2-(HO)-C$_6$H$_4$CH$_2$]$_2$-C$_6$H$_3$OH					6.03	66	
2,6-[5-Cl-2-(HO)-C$_6$H$_4$CH$_2$]$_2$-C$_6$H$_3$OH					6.05	66	
p-Chlorophenol-formaldehyde novolac; o,o'-methylene bridges					6.03	66	
[Dehalogenated p-chlorophenol-formaldehyde novolac; o,o'-methylene bridges					6.07	66	
c-Chlorophenol-formaldehyde novolac; o,o'-methylene bridges					6.00	66	
Dehalogenated o-chlorophenol-formaldehyde novolac; o,o'-methylene bridges					6.10	66	
[2-(HO)-C$_6$H$_4$]-CH$_2$-[4-(HO)-C$_6$H$_4$					6.10	66	
[3,5-Cl$_2$-2-(HO)-C$_6$H$_2$]-CH$_2$-··· ···[3-Cl-4-(HO)-C$_6$H$_3$]					2 = 6.17	66	
					6.15	66	
2,4-[4-(HO)-C$_6$H$_4$CH$_2$]$_2$-C$_6$H$_3$OH					6.15	66	
o-Chlorophenol-formaldehyde novolac; o,p'-methylene bridges					6.17	66	
Dehalogenated o-chlorophenol-formaldehyde novolac; o,p'-methylene bridges							
[4-(HO)-C$_6$H$_4$]$_2$CH$_2$					6.23	66	
[3-(CH$_3$)-4-(HO)-C$_6$H$_3$]$_2$CH$_2$					6.30	66	
[3,5-(HOCH$_2$)$_2$-4-(HO)-C$_6$H$_2$]$_2$CH$_2$					6.00	63	
[3,5-(CH$_3$)$_2$-4-(HO)-C$_6$H$_2$]$_2$CH$_2$					6.33		

Structure	Solvent conc.	Ref. signal	Temp., °C	Freq. Mc/s	τ,J (Note 60)	Notes	Ref.
2,4-[4-(HO)-$C_6H_4CH_2$]$_2$-C_6H_3OH					4 = 6.28	63	39
o-Chlorophenol-formaldehyde novolac; p,p'-methylene bridges					6.28	66	
Dehalogenated o-Chlorophenol-formaldehyde novolac; p,p'-methylene bridges					6.30	66	
Trioxane					5.00	65	
m-$HOC_6H_4CH_2OH$					5.37	63	
2,6-$(CH_3)_2$-4-$(HOCH_2)$-C_6H_2OH					7.55	63	
4-(CH_3)-2,6-$(HOCH_2)_2$-C_6H_2OH					7.78	64	
4,6-$(CH_3)_2$-2-$(HOCH_2)$-C_6H_2OH					4 = 7.78, 6 = 7.62	63	
[3,5-$(CH_3)_2$-2-(HO)-$C_6H_2CH_2$]$_2$O					7.83,7.82	63	
[3,5-$(CH_3)_2$-4-(HO)-C_6H_2]$_2CH_2$					7.82	65	

b. Acetylated Materials (Note 67)

Structure	Solvent conc.	Ref. signal	Temp., °C	Freq. Mc/s	τ	J	Notes	Ref.
$(AcO)_2CH_2$	CCl_4 or $CDCl_3$; ca. 5-22 vol. %	TMS	30	60	4.40		68	39
$AcOCH_2(OCH_2)_xOCH_2OAc$					4.58-4.70		68	
$AcOCH_2(OCH_2)_xOCH_2OAc$					5.10-5.15		68	
$A=CH_2OCH_2OAc$					5.72-5.83		69	
$C_6H_5CH_2OAc$					4.90-4.95			
$AcOC_6H_4CH_2OAc$								
ortho					4.97-4.98			
meta					4.92-4.97			
para					4.95-4.98			
$2,4-(CH_3)_2-6-(AcOCH_2)-C_6H_2OAc$					5.07			
$2,6-(CH_3)_2-4-(AcOCH_2)-C_6H_2OAc$					5.10			
$2,6-(AcOCH_2)_2-C_6H_3OAc$					4.98-5.02			
$2,4-(AcOCH_2)_2-C_6H_3OAc$					5.00			
$2,4-(AcOCH_2)_2-6-Cl-C_6H_2OAc$					$2,4 = 5.00$			
$2,4,6-(AcOCH_2)_3-C_6H_2OAc$					$2,6 = 5.00-5.03$			
					$4 = 4.93-5.97$			
$[3,5-(AcOCH_2)_2-4-(AcO)-C_6H_2]_2CH_2$					5.08		69	
$ArCH_2OCH_2OAc$					5.37-5.52			
$(C_6H_5CH_2)_2O$					5.47-5.52			
$[3,5-(CH_3)_2-2-(AcO)-C_6H_2CH_2]_2O$					5.73			
$[3,5-(CH_3)_2-2-(HO)-C_6H_2CH_2]_2O$					5.43			
$[2-(AcO)-C_6H_4CH_2]_2O$					5.60			
$[4-(AcO)-C_6H_4CH_2]_2O$					5.55			
$[5-Cl-2-(AcO)-C_6H_3]_2CH_2$					6.25			
Acetylated o,o'-bridged novolac: methylene bridges					6.27			

Structure	Solvent conc.	Ref. signal	Temp., °C	Freq. Mc/s	τ	J	Notes	Ref.
[4-(AcO)-C6H4]2CH2					6.13			39
[3,5-(AcOCH2)2-4-(AcO)-C6H2]2CH2					6.07			
AcOC6H5					7.87			
AcOC6H4CH2OAc:								
ortho					7.73-7.82			
meta					7.75-7.82			
para					7.75-7.85			
2,4-(CH3)2-6-(AcOCH2)-C6H2OAc					7.88			
2,6-(CH3)2-4-(AcOCH2)-C6H2OAc					7.80			
2,6-(AcOCH2)2-C6H3OAc					7.70-7.77			
2,4-(AcOCH2)2-C6H3OAc					7.67			
2,4-(AcOCH2)2-6-Cl-C6H2OAc					7.70			
2,4,6-(AcOCH2)3-C6H2OAc					7.70-7.75			
[5-Cl-2-(AcO)-C6H3]2CH2					7.80			
[4-(AcO)-C6H4]2CH2					7.95			
[3,5-(AcOCH2)2-4-(AcO)-C6H2]2CH2					7.73			
[4-(AcO)-C6H4CH2]2O					7.85			
[2-(AcO)-C6H4CH2]2O					7.90			
[3,5-(CH3)2-2-(AcO)-C6H2]2O					7.72			
Acetylated o,o'-bridged novolac, AcOAR					7.97			
C6H5CH2OAc					7.92-7.95			
AcOC6H4CH2OAc:								
ortho					8.00-8.05			
meta					8.00-8.05			
para					7.95-8.03			
					7.97-8.03			

Structure	Solvent conc.	Ref. signal	Temp., °C	Freq. Mc/s	τ	J	Notes	Ref.
2,6-$(CH_3)_2$-4-$(AcOCH_2)$-C_6H_2OAc					8.03			39
2,5-$(AcOCH_2)_2$-C_6H_3OAc					7.98-8.05			
2,4-$(AcOCH_2)_2$-C_6H_3OAc					2 = 8.03, 4 = 8.00			
2,4-$(AcOCH_2)_2$-6-Cl-C_6H_2OAc					2 = 8.03, 4 = 7.97			
2,4,6-$(AcOCH_2)_3$-C_6H_2OAc					2,6 = 8.00-8.03 4 = 7.93-8.00			
[3,5-$(AcOCH_2)_2$-4-(AcO)-$C_6H_2]_2CH_2$					8.07			
2,4-$(CH_3)_2$-6-$(AcOCH_2)$-C_6H_2OAc					8.08			
$Ar(CH_2O)_2Ac$					8.02-8.08		69	
$(AcO)_2CH_2$					7.95-7.97		68	
$(AcO)(CH_2O)_xAc, x > 1$					7.95-8.00		68	
2,6-$(CH_3)_2$-4-$(AcOCH_2)$-C_6H_2OAc					8.92			
[3,5-$(CH_3)_2$-2-(AcO)-$C_6H_2CH_2]_2O$					7.93-7.87			
2,4-$(CH_3)_2$-6-$(AcOCH_2)$-C_6H_2OAc					4 = 7.95, 2 = 7.77			
o-$(AcO)_2C_6H_4$					7.90			

C. NOTES

1. The chemical shifts reported for all polypropylene and deuteropolypropylene spectra are estimated from the published spectra, since no specific data are provided by the authors. The error is thus at least ± 0.02 ppm. For the data reported in Ref. 6, chemical shifts had to be estimated from the complex, strongly coupled spectra of the isotactic, syndiotactic, and atactic polymers by analogy to closely related analyzed spectra. The difference in chemical shift, $\tau_{H_{(1A)}} - \tau_{H_{(1B)}}$, is given by the author as 0.38 in Ref. 5; the same value is estimated from the spectra of Ref. 6.

   The chemical shifts for all polypropylene protons in 2-chlorothiophene (Ref. 5) are considerably higher than reported in Ref. 6. This must in part reflect an increased shielding arising from the presence of deuterium (this may be as large as ca. + 0.05 ppm) but is probably mainly a solvent effect. For comparison to other nondeuterated polypropylenes and related polymers, the data of Ref. 6 are preferable, although a complete and careful analysis of these spectra has not yet been reported. Further reference: S. Ohnishi and K. Nukada, J. Polymer Sci. B3, ("Polymer Letters") 179 (1965).

2. Isomerization of these monomers occurs during the $AlCl_3$-catalyzed polymerization.

3. Quantities necessarily equal by symmetry are in parentheses; others are not necessarily equal but appear equal within experimental uncertainty.

4. Peak centers used for $H_{(5)}$ and/or $H_{(6)}$.

5. The presence of deuterium is known to cause appreciable upfield shifts (0.02-0.05 τ), so these values are not directly comparable to those for isotactic polymer.

6. Most reported N.M.R. data for polystyrene give chemical shifts as centers of rather broad, poorly resolved or unresolved multiplets; these multiplet centers do not correspond exactly with the true chemical shifts. "Atactic" polystyrene (probably actually largely syndiotactic) does not give well-resolved spectra, and so true chemical shifts cannot be reliably reported and the couplings are likewise indeterminate. Isotactic polystyrene gives fairly well-resolved spectra under appropriate conditions, and these can be analyzed by matching to machine calculated spectra, (Ref. 8). Other references are:
   [a] F. A. Bovey, G. V. D. Tiers, and G. Filipovich, J. Polymer Sci. 38, 73 (1959).
   [b] R. J. Kern and J. V. Pustinger, Nature 185, 236 (1960).
   [c] T. Yoshino, H. Kyogoku, J. Komiyama, and Y. Manabe, J. Chem. Phys. 38, 1026 (1963).
   [d] W. P. Slichter and D. W. McCall in "Newer Methods of Polymer Characterization," B. Ke, Ed., Interscience Publishers, New York 1963, p. 343.

7. Unlike those of polystyrene, the aromatic rings of poly(α-methylstyrene) are observably sensitive to stereochemical configuration.

8. The polymers were predominantly syndiotactic and so this is probably closer to
    the r CH_2 position; but as the multiplet was too poorly resolved to analyze,
    this is uncertain.

9. Position of $CHCl_3$ in $CHCl_3$ with reference to TMS at ca 25°; as the temperature was
    actually 80°, the reported polymer τ-values are correspondingly less reliable than
    those of Ref. 11. They appear to be about 0.06-0.08 τ too low.

10. Spin decoupling was used to establish position of overlapping pentuplets; assign-
    ments of s and i resonances are dependent on meso and racemic CH_2 assignments,
    which are believed correct but not certain. The polymer measured was approxi-
    mately two-thirds syndiotactic.

11. Since the chemical shifts of H_B and H_C are coincidentally equal within experi-
    mental error (confirmed by poly(vinyl chloride-α-d_1) data), J_{BC} is not directly
    measurable; the value given is that for meso-2,4-dichloropentane, reported by
    Doskocilova, J. Polymer Sci. **B2**, 421 (1964).

12. Approximately two-thirds syndiotactic.

13. There is some disagreement as to the proper interpretation of the CH_2 resonance
    in poly(vinyl chloride); see Tincher, Ref. b below. The interpretation given
    above, i.e., that $H_B \simeq H_C$ in chemical shift is that given by Johnsen (Ref. a
    below) and is supported by spin-decoupling and deuterium substitution results.
    Other references:
    [a]U. Johnsen, J. Polymer Sci., **54**, S7 (1961).
    [b]W. C. Tincher, J. Polymer Sci. **62**, S148 (1962).
    [c]R. Chujo, S. Satoh, T. Ozeki, and E. Nagai, J. Polymer Sci. **61**, S12 (1962).

14. The structure probably contained a substantial number of head-to-head tail-to-tail
    monomer units; these were not definitely identifiable in the proton spectrum, but
    the smaller CH resonance and an asymmetry observable in the CH_2 triplet may be
    associated with them.

15. The polymer was treated with ultrasonic radiation to produce solution.

16. Observable only on decoupling from CH_2, hence d (still coupled to F).

17. Narrowed on CH decoupling but no finer structure observable.

18. Since CCl_3F was not used as solvent, the values recorded are not strictly φ^*
    values; see "introduction"

19. The fluorine peaks are broad and probably represent a number of overlapping reso-
    nances as well as unresolved spin-spin multiplicity. Not all the resolvable
    spectral structure can be assigned with confidence. The smaller shoulders in
    the "head-to-tail" and "head-to-head" regions may be attributable to

stereochemical irregularity, but it is not known which configuration predominates. The monomer units associated with head-to-head structures represent 32% of the area of the fluorine spectrum. Other references:

    R. E. Naylor, Jr., and S. W. Lasoski, Jr., J. Polymer Sci. <u>44</u>, 1 (1960).

20. CCl_3F was not present in the polymer solutions; instead, measurement of the solvent CF_3 resonance was observed in a 10% solution of CCl_3F in the solvent, and polymer peaks were then referred to the solvent CF_3, taken as 63.8 $\varphi*$. The values are not strictly $\varphi*$ values but should be close.

21. Assignments probable but not certain.

22. Assignments based on model compounds (see Note 23) and considered highly probable.

23. The polymer peaks are about 50 cps in half-height width, and therefore multiplicity from spin-spin coupling was obscured. From the well-resolved spectra of the closely related model compounds dl- and meso-$CF_2ClCFClCF_2CFClCF_2Cl$, observed under identical conditions, the following couplings to the central CF_2 group were observed: dl-compound: F-C-C-F: 5.1 cps; F-C-C-C-F; 17.1 cps; meso-compound: F-C-C-F: ca. 3.4 cps; F-C-C-C-F: 14.3 cps. Geminal F-F coupling was ca. 280 cps in the meso-compound, and this so far exceeds the probable $\varphi*$ between these nuclei in the polymer that the outer peaks resulting from this splitting cannot be seen; both meso-fluorines would appear in the same position in the polymer spectrum even if resolution were substantially greater. Other references:

    R. E. Naylor and S. W. Lasoski, Jr., J. Polymer Sci. <u>44</u>, 1 (1960).

24. Reference is probably external, but reporting of $\varphi*$ is independent of authors' reference. See note 25.

25. Data are based on these authors' reported values for the principal fluorine resonances of poly(vinyl fluoride) and poly(vinylidene fluoride) reported above and comparison to these data; in view of differing solvent, relatively poor resolution, and other variables, these values cannot be considered reliable within less than ±5 ppm.

26. Double resonance employed for $H_{(A)}$.

27. Brownstein and Wiles (Ref. (a) below) have observed the spectra of poly(vinyl methyl ether) in CCl_4, $CHCl_3$, and nitromethane, and have reported partial separation of i, h, and s for $H_{(A)}$. Separation was best in nitromethane. Only relative chemical shifts were reported. Other references:

    [a] S. Brownstein and D. M. Wiles, J. Polymer Sci. <u>A2</u>, 1901 (1964).

    [b] R. J. Kern, J. J. Hawkins, and J. D. Calfee, Makromol. Chem. <u>66</u>, 126 (1963).

28. Since all three resonances were singlets under all conditions of temperature and solvent, these polymers are believed to be entirely syndiotactic, presumably a requirement of the bulky α-substituents.

29. Remains a singlet, somewhat broadened on decoupling.

30. Polymer nearly random; h assignment assumed, i and s not assignable on evidence
     available; but see results in CH_2Cl_2.

31. Decoupling employed; assignments made by conversion to poly(vinyl methyl ether)
     of known stereochemistry.

32. Decoupling employed for CH.

33. Poly(vinyl alcohol) spectra in D_2O are also reported by these authors, but no
     reference was employed. The separation of chemical shifts of CH and CH_2 is
     essentially the same in both solvents. In D_2O, a decoupling experiment showed
     that the syndiotactic α-CH peak is 0.03 ppm downfield and the isotactic peak is
     0.06 ppm upfield from the central heterotactic peak. The β-CH_2 resonance showed
     m and l peaks separated by 0.08 ppm, the latter being at higher field.

34. This assignment is to be taken literally with reference to the structural formula,
     i.e., in the planar zigzag conformation, $H_{(A)}$ is on the side of the zigzag plane
     away from the ester group.

35. This polymer is probably predominantly (ca. 75%) syndiotactic.

36. Isotactic and heterotactic $H_{(C)}$ not distinguishable from the predominant
     syndiotactic $H_{(C)}$.

37. Isotactic poly(isopropyl α-cis-β-d_2-acrylate) was also reported in Ref. 25. Peak
     positions for $H_{(A)}$ and $H_{(B)}$ (both present) are in nearly the same position as
     determined by analysis of the spectrum of the undeuterated polymer, although
     some upfield shift due to deuterium might be expected. See also under poly(methyl
     acrylate).

38. Polymer is predominantly syndiotactic; isotactic resonances not clearly measurable.

39. Proton designations refer to structural formula given for poly(isopropyl acrylate).
     See also Note 37.

40. Peaks broadened by unresolved multiplicity arising from deuterium couplings.

41. $H_{(C)}$ arise from residual α-protons in polymer. Further reference:
        K. Matsuzaki, T. Uryu, A. Ishida and T. Ohki, J. Polymer Sci. B2, 1141 (1962).

42. It is believed that this assignment is correct in terms of the structural formula,
     i.e., with $H_{(A)}$ on the side of the zigzag plane away from ester group; this
     assignment is based on that for poly(isopropyl acrylate) and poly(methyl acrylate).
     Other references:
        F. A. Bovey, J. Polymer Sci. 46, 59 (1960); U. Johnsen and K. Tessmar, Kolloid.-Z

168, 160 (1960); A. Nishioka, Y. Kato, T. Uetake, and H. Watanabe, J. Polymer Sci. 61 S32 (1962); D. W. McCall and W. P. Slichter, in "Newer Methods of Polymer Characterization," B. Ke, editor, Interscience Publishers, New York, 1964; p. 321; T. G. Fox and H. W. Schnecko, Polymer 3, 575 (1962).

44. Under strongly acidic and basic conditions, the amide peaks disappear because of exchange with water.

45. $H_{(1)}$ and $H_{(2)}$ peaks coalesce to a singlet at 70° because of rotation about the C-N bond.

46. The polymer was probably predominantly syndiotactic, but stereochemical shifts could not be resolved.

47. No spectral peaks can be seen in aqueous poly(methacrylamide) solutions unless the molecular weight is very low.

48. The $H_{(3)}$ peaks correspond to MMA units with styrene units on one side (less shielded) and on both sides (more shielded); the positions of these peaks are also influenced by the stereochemistry of the flanking styrene units. Consult Ref. 31 for details.

49. CCl_4 used only for measurements of aromatic resonance. Other references:
     [a]H. J. Harwood, J. Polymer Sci. B3, ("Polymer Letters") 419 (1965).
     [b]A. Nishioka, Y. Kato, and N. Ashikari, J. Polymer Sci. 62, S10 (1962).

50. The $H_{(3)}$ peaks correspond to MMA units with α-methylstyrene units on one side (less shielded) and both sides (more shielded); see Note 48, and also consult Ref. 31.

51. Multiplicity is due to stereochemical configuration; see under poly(methyl methacrylate).

52. All aromatic peaks are broad, representing unresolved fine structure; they become broader and more asymmetric as styrene content is increased.

53. Values represent centers of broad, asymmetric peaks containing unresolved fine structure.

54. Reported as a minor component of a synthetic cis-polyisoprene; not present in natural cis- or trans-polyisoprene (i.e., rubber or balata, respectively).

55. The components of this "doublet" correspond to the two vinyl protons, not individually assigned. Other references:
     R. B. Bates and D. M. Gale, J. Am. Chem. Soc. 82, 5749 (1960).

56. Probably represents overlapping quartets of isotactic and heterotactic $H_{(1)}$.

57. Spectra taken in aromatic solvents differ from spectra taken in aliphatic solvents.

58. Syndiotactic peaks. Very small, detectable only at 100 Mc/s.

59. On addition of water, a peak at 1.47τ appears, corresponding to formation of urea linkage -NHCONH-.

60. The τ-values given are chemical shifts for the protons underlined. Chemical shifts for the aromatic ring protons were in the range from about 2.33-3.42τ. Sample concentrations were between 5 and 25 wt.-% model compound in dry acetone, except where designated to be otherwise.

61. Data obtained from a 10 vol.-% solution of 50 wt.-% formalin in acetone. The shifts and proton exchange rates were markedly dependent on temperature and the formaldehyde:water:acetone ratios.

62. Data obtained from dilute acetone solutions of products resulting from the heating of slightly basic excess benzyl alcohol with paraformaldehyde and from the freeze-drying of a slightly basic solution of saligenin in excess formalin.

63. Data taken from solutions which were 15 wt.-% model compound in dry pyridine.

64. Data taken from solutions which were 15 wt.-% model compound in dry DMSO.

65. Data taken from solutions which were 15 wt.-% model compound in carbon tetrachloride.

66. Results of R. C. Hirst, W. J. Burke, E. D. M. Grant, paper presented before the Pittsburgh Conference on Analytical Chemistry and Applied Spectroscopy, Pittsburgh, Pa., March, 1962. Their data have been converted from the low-field $C^{13}H_3$ line of acetone as their primary reference to internal TMS as the secondary reference.

67. Chemical shifts for the aromatic ring protons were in the range of 2.33-3.42τ. Sample concentrations were between 5 and 25 vol.-% model compound in carbon tetrachloride.

68. Data obtained from the products resulting from low-temperature acetylation of 50 wt.-% formalin in excess pyridine and excess acetic anhydride.

69. Data obtained from the acetates of products resulting from the heating of slightly basic, excess benzyl alcohol with paraformaldehyde and from the freeze-drying of slightly basic solutions of saligenin in excess formalin.

D. REFERENCES

1. W. P. Slichter, Fortschr. Hochpolymer. Forsch., 1, 35-74 (1958).
2. G. V. D. Tiers, J. Phys. Chem. 62, 1151 (1958).
3. G. Filipovich and G. V. D. Tiers, J. Phys. Chem. 63, 761 (1959).
4. J. D. Baldeschwieler and E. W. Randall, Chem. Rev. 63, 81 (1963).
5. F. C. Stehling, J. Polymer Sci. A2, 1815 (1964).
6. J. C. Woodbrey, J. Polymer Sci. B2, 315 (1964).
7. W. R. Edwards and N. F. Chamberlain, American Chemical Society Meeting, Atlantic City, September, 1962, preprint booklet, p. 105.*
8. F. A. Bovey, F. P. Hood, E. W. Anderson, and L. C. Snyder, J. Chem. Phys., (in press).
9. S. Brownstein, S. Bywater, and D. J. Worsfold, J. Phys. Chem. 66, 2067 (1962).
10. F. A. Bovey, F. P. Hood, and E. W. Anderson, unpublished observations.
11. S. Brownstein, S. Bywater, and D. J. Worsfold, Makromol. Chem. 48, 127 (1961).
12. Y. Sakurada, M. Matsumoto, K. Imai, A. Nishioka, Y. Kato, J. Polymer Sci. B1, 633 (1963).
13. F. A. Bovey, G. V. D. Tiers, and G. Filipovitch, J. Polymer Sci. 38, 73 (1959).
14. F. A. Bovey, R. Salovey, F. P. Hood, and E. W. Anderson, unpublished observations.
15. F. A. Bovey, E. W. Anderson, D. C. Douglass, and J. A. Manson, J. Chem. Phys. 39, 1199 (1963).
16. F. A. Bovey and G. V. D. Tiers, Chem. and Ind. 1962, 1826.
17. C. W. Wilson, III, paper presented to Polymer Div., 148th Meeting American Chemical Society meeting, Chicago, September, 1964.
18. C. W. Wilson, III, J. Polymer Sci. A1, 1305 (1963).
19. G. V. D. Tiers and F. A. Bovey, J. Polymer Sci. A1, 833 (1963).
20. R. E. Naylor and S. W. Lasoski, Jr., J. Polymer Sci. 44, 1 (1960).
21. K. C. Ramey, N. D. Field, and I. Hasegawa, J. Polymer Sci. B2, 865 (1964).
22. M. Goodman and Y. Fan, J. Am. Chem. Soc. 86, 4922 (1964).
23. K. C. Ramey and N. D. Field, J. Polymer Sci. B2, 69 (1964).
24. K. C. Ramey and N. D. Field, J. Polymer Sci. B2, 63 (1964).
25. C. Schuerch, W. Fowells, A. Yamada, F. A. Bovey, F. P. Hood, and E. W. Anderson, J. Am. Chem. Soc. 86, 4481 (1964).
26. F. A. Bovey, F. P. Hood, and E. W. Anderson, unpublished observations.
27. T. Yoshino, J. Komiyama, and M. Shinomiya, J. Am. Chem. Soc. 86, 4482 (1964).
28. F. A. Bovey and G. V. Tiers, J. Polymer Sci. 44, 173 (1960).
29. G. V. D. Tiers and F. A. Bovey, unpublished observations.
30. F. A. Bovey and G. V. D. Tiers, J. Polymer Sci. A1, 849 (1963).
31. F. A. Bovey, J. Polymer Sci. 62, 197 (1962).
32. H. Y. Chen, Anal. Chem. 34, 1793 (1962).
33. M. A. Golub, S. A. Fuqua, and N. S. Bhacca, J. Am. Chem. Soc. 84, 4981 (1962).
34. R. C. Ferguson, J. Polymer Sci. 2A, 4735 (1964).
35. H. Y. Chen, Anal. Chem. 34, 1134 (1962).
36. G. Allen, R. Warren, and K. J. Taylor, Chem. and Ind. 1964, 623.
37. J. Brandrup and M. Goodman, J. Polymer Sci. B2, 123 (1964); ACS Meeting, Chicago, Polymer Preprints, 5, 1119 (1964); J. Polymer Sci. A3, 327 (1965).
38. M. Sumi, Y. Chokki, Y. Nakai, M. Nakabayashi, and T. Kanzawa, Angew. Chem. 3, 146 (1964).
39. J. C. Woodbrey, H. P. Higginbottom, and H. M. Culbertson, J. Polymer Sci. A3, 1079 (1965).

OPTICALLY ACTIVE POLYMERS

M. Goodman, A. Abe* and Y. L. Fan

Polymer Research Institute
Polytechnic Institute of Brooklyn
Brooklyn, New York

Contents

The optical activity of polymers carrying asymmetric side chains and their low molecular weight analogs is given,

by definition:

$$[M]_D = [\alpha]_D \times \frac{\text{Mean Residue Weight}}{100}$$

Abbreviations used:

BPO = Benzoyl peroxide
AIBN = Azobisisobutyronitrile

* Present address: Department of Chemistry, Stanford University, Stanford, California

1 - Poly(α-olefins)

Polymers	Polymerization Systems			Polymer (P) Values		Monomer (M) or Model Compound (MC) Values		Optical Activity Measured		References
	Catalyst or Initiator	Solvent	T°C	$[\alpha]_D$	$[M]_D$	$[\alpha]_D$	$[M]_D$	Solvent	T°C	
Poly((S)(+)-5-methyl-1-heptene)	Al(i-C₄H₉)₃- TiCl₃	isooctane	R.T.	–	+ 27.4 – + 68.1	–	+ 11.7(MC)	benzene		1-3,12
Poly((S)(+)-4-methyl-1-hexene)	Al(i-C₄H₉)₃- TiCl₄	isooctane	R.T.	–	+205 – +288	–	+ 21.3(MC)	benzene(MC) toluene(P)	25	1-3,12
	Al(i-C₄H₉)₃- TiCl₃	"	"	–	+149 – +279	–	"	benzene	"	1-3,12
Poly((R)(-)-3,7-dimethyl-1-octene)	Al(i-C₄H₉)₃- TiCl₄			–	– 20 – –120	–	+ 14.4(MC)	toluene	"	4,3
	Al(i-C₄H₉)₃- TiCl₃			–	– 35.3 – –144	–	"		"	
	LiAlH₄-TiCl₄- monomer	benzene	30-40	–78.1	–111	+ 6.25	+ 8.88(MC)	CCl₄	"	
Poly((S)(+)-6-methyl-1-octene)	Al(i-C₄H₉)₃- TiCl₃	isooctane	R.T.	–	+ 16.0	–	+ 13.3(MC)	benzene	25	3
Poly((S)(+)-3-methyl-1-pentene)	Al(i-C₄H₉)₃- TiCl₄	–	20-25	–	+ 29.4 – +158	–	– 11.4(MC)	tetralin(P)	20(MC) 25(P)	1-3,5,6,12
	Al(i-C₄H₉)₃- TiCl₃	–	"	–	+ 75.8 – +157	–	"	"		

2 - Polyacrylate Derivatives and Analogs

Polymers	Polymerization Systems			Polymer (P) Values		Monomer (M) or Model Compound (MC) Values		Optical Activity Measured		References
	Catalyst or Initiator	Solvent	T°C	$[\alpha]_D$	$[M]_D$	$[\alpha]_D$	$[M]_D$	Solvent	T°C	
Poly(L-bornyl acrylate)	AIBN	-	65	-	- 46.1	-	- 56.4(M)	toluene	25	7
	"	benzene	60	-	- 47.2	-	"	"	"	
	"	toluene	35	-	- 47.4	-	"	"	"	
	C_6H_5MgBr	"	-70	-	- 43.0	-	"	"	"	
	U.V. benzoin	"	-78	-	- 47.2	-	"	"	"	
Poly(d-sec-butyl α-bromoacrylate)	BPO	dioxane	R.T.	-	+ 15.3	-	+ 37.4(M)	dioxane	30	9
Poly(d-sec-butyl α-chloroacrylate)	BPO	-	50-100	-	+ 23.4	-	+ 55.5(M)	M; chloroform (P)	22 (M) 21 (P)	8
	BPO	dioxane	R.T.	-	+ 17.9	-	+ 42.2(M)	dioxane	25	9
Poly(vinyl ℓ-β-phenyl-butyrate)	BPO	dioxane	100	-29.1	-	-20.4(M)	-	dioxane	"	9
Poly(diamyl itaconate)	-	-	R.T.	+ 4.92	-	+ 4.97(M)	-	-	-	10
	BPO	-	40-85	+ 4.75	-	+ 5.57(M)	-	heptane	20	11
Poly(L-bornyl methacrylate)	AIBN	benzene	55	-	- 70.8	-	- 50.1	toluene	"	7
Poly((+)-1,3-dimethyl-butyl methacrylate)	BPO AIBN	-	82-110	+ 18.2	+ 30.9	+23.4(MC)	+43.5(MC)	sym-tetra-chloroethane	"	13,14
Poly(ℓ-menthyl methacrylate)	AIBN	benzene	55	-	-193	-	-202(M)	benzene	25	15
	BPO	-	40-85	-	-256.3	-	-202(M)	chloroform	20	11
	C_6H_5MgBr	toluene	R.T.	-	-158.9	-	"	"	"	11

Polymers	Polymerization Systems			Polymer (P) Values		Monomer (M) or Model Compound (MC) Values		Optical Activity Measured		References
	Catalyst or Initiator	Solvent	T°C	$[\alpha]_D$	$[M]_D$	$[\alpha]_D$	$[M]_D$	Solvent	T°C	
Poly(ℓ-menthyl methacrylate) (Cont'd.)	C₆H₅MgBr	toluene	-75	-	-177.0	-	-202(M)	benzene	25	15
	γ-ray	-	"	-	-194.0	-	"	"	"	15
Poly(ℓ-α-methylbenzyl methacrylate)	U.V. AIBN	-	35	-79.5	-151	-54.4(M)	-103(M)	dioxane	25	17
	U.V. benzoin	-	-65	-72.5	-138	"	"	"	25	17
	n-butyl Li	toluene	-60	-100	-190	"	"	"	"	17
	AIBN	dioxane	35	-	-147	-	-78.8(M)	M;dioxane(P)	25	18,19
Poly(2-methylbutyl methacrylate)	BPO	-	100	-	+ 5.93	-	+ 6.99(M)	isooctane(M)	20	11,20
	C₆H₅MgBr	toluene	R.T.	-	+ 6.84	-	+ 6.99(M)	chloroform(P)	"	11,20
Poly(3-O-methacryloyl-1,2-5,6-diisopropylidene-D-glucofuranose)	BPO	benzene	80	- 49.0	-	-32.2(M)	-	ethanol(M); sym-tetra-chloroethane(P)	25	21,22
Poly(1-O-methacryloyl-2,3-4,5-diisopropylidene-L-sorbofuranose)	AIBN	"	40-50	- 48.4	-	-28.8(M)	-	benzene	20	23-25
	AIBN			- 84.5	-	- 8.6(M)	-	benzene		24

3 - Polyacrylamide Derivatives

Polymers	Catalyst or Initiator	Solvent	T°C	$[\alpha]_D$	$[M]_D$	$[\alpha]_D$	$[M]_D$	Solvent	T°C	References
Poly(methacrylyl-L-glutamic acid)	AIBN	dioxane	60	- 23.0	-	-26.0(MC)	-	dioxane	25	26
Poly(methacrylyl-D-alanine)	AIBN	dioxane	60	+ 42.0	-	+48.9(MC)	-	dioxane	25	26

Polymers	Polymerization Systems			Polymer (P) Values		Monomer (M) or Model Compound (MC) Values		Optical Activity Measured		References
	Catalyst or Initiator	Solvent	T°C	$[\alpha]_D$	$[M]_D$	$[\alpha]$	$[M]_D$	Solvent	T°C	
Poly(acrylyl-L-glutamic acid)	AIBN	dioxane	60	− 21.0	−	− 21.0 (MC)	−	dioxane	25	26
Poly((−)-N-propyl-N-α-methylbenzylacrylamide)	AIBN	toluene	70	−	−167	−	−444 (M)	benzene	25	27
	n-Butyl Li	"	22	−	−318	−	−444 (M)	"	25	
Poly((+)-N-methyl-N-α-methylbenzylacrylamide)	AIBN	−	60	−	278	−	504 (M)	benzene	25	27
	BPO	−	80	−		−	"	"	"	
	n-Butyl Li	toluene	22	−	397	−	"	"	"	
	"	"	−50	−	366	−	"	"	"	
	"	"	22	−	379	−	"	"	"	
	C_6H_5MgBr	toluene	"	−	337	−	"	"	"	
4 − Polyvinylamine Derivatives										
Poly(N-vinyl-N'-(ethyl L-aminoisocaproate)urea)	AIBN	benzene	60	+ 20.3	+ 46.3	+ 0.48 (M)	+ 1.1 (M)	benzene	25	28
Poly(N-vinyl-N'-(diethyl L-glutamate)urea)	AIBN	benzene	60	+ 7.83	+ 21.3	+ 21.6 (M)	+ 58.9 (M)	benzene	25	28
Poly(N-vinyl-N'-(diethyl L-asparagate)urea)	AIBN	"	"	+ 24.3 + 31.7	+ 65.1 + 82.0	+ 43.5 (M) −	+ 112.5 (M)	dioxane benzene	25	28
Poly(ℓ-menthyl N-vinyl carbamate)	AIBN	"	95	− 60.4		− 79.3 (M)	−179.7 (M)	benzene	25	28
	AIBN	benzene	60	− 60.4		"	"	"	"	
	γ-ray	"	22	− 58.5	−131.8	"	"	"	"	
	tert-butyl hydroperoxide	sulfur dioxide	−25	− 66.2		"	"	"	"	

References page V-74

5 - Poly(vinyl ethers) and Analogs

Polymers	Polymerization Systems			Polymer (P) Values		Monomer (M) or Model Compound (MC) Values		Optical Activity Measured		References
	Catalyst or Initiator	Solvent	T°C	$[\alpha]$	$[M]_D$	$[\alpha]$	$[M]_D$	Solvent	T°C	
Poly(ℓ-bornyl vinyl ether)	$BF_3 \cdot OEt_2$			-	-142	-	-122.4(M)	benzene	25	29
Poly((S)-sec-butyl vinyl ether)	$Al(i-C_4H_9)Cl_2$	propylene + toluene	-78	-	+246	-	+13.24(M)	M;toluene(P)	25	30
	$Al(i-C_4H_9)_3-$ H_2SO_4	diethyl ether	15-20	-	+206	-	+13.67(M)	"	"	30
Poly(ℓ-cholesteryl vinyl ether)				-	-93	-	-131.4(M)			29
Poly(ℓ-menthyl vinyl ether)	C_4H_9MgBr	toluene	80	-	-358	-	-121.9(M)	chloroform(M) benzene(P)	"	29
	$BF_3 \cdot OEt_2$	n-hexane	-78	-	-396	-	"	"	"	
	$SnCl_4$	petroleum ether	25	-	-373	-	"	"	"	
	$Mn-MoO_3$ H_2SO_4	n-hexane	-10	-	-357	-	-118.8(M)	n-hexane	"	33
	"	"	-30	-	-353	-	"	"	"	
Poly((S)-2-methylbutyl vinyl ether)	$Al(i-C_4H_9)Cl_2$	propylene + toluene	-78	-	+ 4.9	-	+ 1.1(MC) + 7.61(M)	(MCM); toluene(P)	25	31
	$Al(i-C_4H_9)_3-$ H_2SO_4	ether	15-20	-	+ 5.9	-	" "	"	"	
	$Al(i-OC_3H_7)_3-$ H_2SO_4	ethyl acetate	0-20	-	+ 6.4	-	" "	"	"	
Poly(ℓ-α-methylbenzyl vinyl ether)	$BF_3 \cdot OEt_2$	propane	-78	-	+ 68.6	-	- 71.9(M)	benzene	"	32

Polymers	Polymerization Systems			Polymer (P) Values		Monomer (M) or Model Compound (MC) Values		Optical Activity Measured		References
	Catalyst or Initiator	Solvent	T°C	$[\alpha]$	$[M]_D$	$[\alpha]$	$[M]_D$	Solvent	T°C	
Poly(3-O-vinyl-1,2-5,6-diisopropylidene-α-D-glucofuranose)	$BF_3 \cdot OEt_2$	n-hexane + methylene chloride	-78	—	+ 5.7	—	- 77.2(P)	ethanol(M)sym tetrachloro-ethane(P)	25	34 22
Poly(divinylacetal of (R)-(+)-3,7-dimethyloctanal)	AIBN			+ 3.18	+ 7.19	+ 2.48(MC)	+ 5.31(MC)	chloroform		35
	$BF_3 \cdot OEt_2$			- 6.78	- 15.32	+ 2.48(MC)	+ 5.31(MC)	chloroform		
6 - Polystyrene Derivatives										
Poly(d-sec-butyl-p-vinyl benzoate)	BPO	—	40	+ 22.9	—	+24.0(M)	—	benzene	50	36
Poly(p-vinylbenzyl-d-sec-butyl ether)	BPO	dioxane	55	+ 10.15	—	+12.07(M)	—	dioxane	"	37
Poly(o-vinylbenzyl d-sec-butyl sulfide)	AIBN	—	76	+ 9.57	—	+13.97(M)	—	(M);benzene (P)	24.7	16
7 - Polyaldehydes										
Poly((R)(+)-citronellal)	Al(i-C_4H_9)$_3$	ether	-78	- 82.7 - 90.1	-127 -139	—	+ 11.2(MC)	chloroform	25	38
	n-Butyl Li	n-hexane	"	- 91.1	-140	—	"	"	"	
	$BF_3 \cdot OEt_2$	ether	"	- 89.5	-138	—	"	"	"	
Poly((R)(+)-3,7-dimethyloctanal)	n-Butyl Li			- 94.3	-147	+ 10.0(M)	—	chloroform	25	39
Poly((R)(+)-6-methoxy-4-methylhexanal)	$ZnEt_2$	n-hexane	-78	+ 36.7	+ 52.8	—	+ 8.24(MC)	chloroform	25	38

References page V-74

8 - REFERENCES

1. P. Pino, G. P. Lorenzi and L. Lardicci, Chim. Ind. (Milan) 42, 712 (1960).
2. P. Pino and G. P. Lorenzi, J. Am. Chem. Soc., 82, 4745 (1960).
3. P. Pino, F. Ciardelli, G. P. Lorenzi, and G. Montagnoli, Makromol. Chem., 61, 207 (1963).
4. M. Goodman, K. J. Clark, M. A. Stake and A. Abe, Makromol. Chem., 72, 131 (1964).
5. W. J. Bailey and E. T. Yates, J. Org. Chem., 25, 1800 (1960).
6. S. Nozakura, S. Takeuchi, H. Yuki, and S. Murahashi, Bull. Chem. Soc. Japan, 34, 1673 (1961).
7. R. C. Schulz and H. Hilpert,   Makromol. Chem. 55, 132 (1962).
8. J. W. C. Crawford and D. Plant, J. Chem. Soc., 1952, 4492.
9. C. S. Marvel, J. Dec, and H. G. Cooke, Jr., J. Am. Chem. Soc., 62, 3499 (1940).
10. P. Walden, Z. Phys. Chem., 20, 383 (1896).
11. E. I. Klabunovskii, I. I. Petrov and M. I. Schvartmen, Vysokomolekul. Soedin. 6, 1487 (1964).
12. P. Pino, G. P. Lorenzi, L. Lardicci, and F. Ciardelli, Vysokomolekul. Soedin. 3, 1597 (1961).
13. C. L. Arcus and D. W. West, Chem. Ind. (London), 1958, 230.
14. C. L. Arcus and D. W. West, J. Chem. Soc., 1959, 2699.
15. R. C. Schulz, A. Naturforschung, 19b, 387 (1964).
16. C. G. Overberger and L. C. Palmer, J. Am. Chem. Soc., 78, 666 (1956).
17. K. J. Liu, J. S. Szuty and R. Ullman, ACS Meeting, Chicago, Polymer Preprint 5, No. 2, 761 (1964).
18. N. Beredjick and C. Schuerch, J. Am. Chem. Soc. 78, 2646 (1956).
19. N. Beredjick and C. Schuerch, 80, 1933 (1958).
20. E. I. Klabunovskii, M. I. Schvartmen, and I. I. Petrov, Vysokomolekul. Soedin. 6, 1579 (1964).
21. T. P. Bird, W. A. P. Blank, E. T. Dewar, and D. Rutherford, Chem. Ind. (London) 1960, 1331.
22. W. A. P. Black, E. T. Dewar, and D. Rutherford, J. Chem. Soc., 1963, 4433.
23. S. Kimura and M. Imoto, Makromol. Chem., 50, 155 (1961).
24. S. Kimura, K. Hirai, and M. Imoto, Kogyo Kagaku Zasshi, (Japan) 65, 688 (1962).
25. M. Imoto and S. Kimura, Makromol. Chem., 53, 210 (1962).
26. R. K. Kulkarni and H. Morawetz, J. Polymer Sci., 54, 491 (1961).
27. V. E. Kaiser and R. C. Schulz, Makromol. Chem., 81, 273 (1965).
28. R. C. Schulz , and H. Hartmann, Makromol. Chem., 65, 106 (1963).
29. G. Anzuino, V. Crescenzi, M. D'alagni, A. M. Liquori, F. Quadrifoglio and F. Ascoli, communication at the IX. Natl. Meeting of Italian Chem. Soc., Naples, 1962.
30. G. P. Lorenzi, E. Benedetti and E. Chiellini, Chim. Ind., (Milan), 46, 1474 (1964).
31. P. Pino and G. P. Lorenzi, Makromol. Chem., 47, 242 (1961).
32. G. J. Schmitt and C. Schuerch, J. Polymer Sci., 45, 313 (1960).
33. D. Basagni, A. M. Liquori and B. Pispe'sa, J. Polymer Sci., B2, 241 (1964).
34. W. A. P. Black, E. T. Dewar, and D. Rutherford, Chem. Ind. (London), 1962, 1624.
35. M. Goodman and A. Abe, J. Polymer Sci., A2, 3491 (1964).
36. C. S. Marvel and C. G. Overberger, J. Am. Chem. Soc., 68, 2106 (1946).
37. C. S. Marvel and C. G. Overberger, J. Am. Chem. Soc. 66, 475 (1944).
38. A. Abe and M. Goodman, J. Polymer Sci., A1, 2193 (1963).
39. A. Abe, Ph.D. Thesis, Polytechnic Institute of Brooklyn, Brooklyn, N. Y. (1963).

ANISOTROPY OF THE SEGMENTS AND MONOMER UNITS OF SELECTED POLYMER MOLECULES

V. N. Tsvetkov

Institute for Macromolecular Compounds
Academy of Science U.S.S.R.
Leningrad, U.S.S.R.

The table contains the values of intrinsic segmental anisotropy $\alpha_1 - \alpha_2$ of some chain molecules, as obtained by flow birefringence and viscosity measurements in solutions in absence of the shape effect (1).

They are calculated from Kuhn's (2) and Peterlin's (3) equation

$$\left[\frac{\Delta n}{g(\eta - \eta_o)} \right]_{g \to o} = \frac{4\pi}{45\ T} \cdot \frac{(n^2+2)^2}{n} \cdot (\alpha_1 - \alpha_2)$$

where Δn is the observed value of the flow birefringence of the solution, g is the velocity gradient, η is the viscosity of the solution, η_o and n are the viscosity and refraction index, respectively, of the solvent.

The segmental anisotropy of the chain $\alpha_1 - \alpha_2$ depends on the anisotropy of their monomer units $a_{\|} - a_{\perp}$ and the equilibrium rigidity of the chain $\overline{r^2}/L$. Here L is the full length of the extended chain and $\langle r^2 \rangle^{\frac{1}{2}}$ the root mean square end-to-end distance in a θ-solvent.

$a_{\|} - a_{\perp}$ is the difference in polarizabilities of the monomer unit in the direction parallel and perpendicular to the chain axis. The values $a_{\|} - a_{\perp}$ are calculated from the equation:

$$a_{\|} - a_{\perp} = \lambda L (\alpha_1 - \alpha_2)/\overline{r^2}$$

where λ is the length of the monomer unit along the chain axis.

Polymer	Solvent	$\alpha_1 - \alpha_2$ x $10^{25} cm^3$	$a_{\|} - a_{\perp}$ x $10^{25} cm^3$	Reference
Poly(acrylic acid)				
-- , n-butylester	benzene	-11	- 1.5	15
	toluene	- 6.5	- 0.9	15
-- , methylester	benzene	+17	+ 2.5	15
	toluene	+26	+ 3.6	15
Polyacrylonitrile	dimethyl-formamide	-23	- 1.8	30
Poly(γ-benzyl-l-glutamate)	dichloro-ethane	+25000	+20	28
Polybutadiene	benzene	+30	+ 4.3	7
Cellulose				
-- , cyanoethyldiacetyl	cyclohexanone	+15	+ 0.8	27

Polymer	Solvent	$\alpha_1 - \alpha_2$ $\times 10^{25} cm^3$	$a_{||} - a_{\perp}$ $\times 10^{25} cm^3$	Reference
Cellulose (Cont'd.)				
-- , tribenzoate	bromobenzene	-914	- 90	25
-- , triethyl	carbon tetrachloride	+430	+ 21	23
-- , trinitrate	cyclohexanone	-300	- 18	24
-- , triphenylmethylcyanoethyl	phenyl ethyl ether	+220	+ 10	26
Deoxyribonucleic acid (DNA)	0.2 N aqueous NaCl	ca. -100000	ca.-180	29
Poly(1,4-diisopropenylbenzene)	bromoform	+ 78		10
Poly(4,4'-diisopropenylphenylethane)	bromoform	+142		10
Polyethylene	xylene	+ 50	+ 7	4
Poly(ethylene terephthalate)	dichloroethane/phenol (1:1)	+ 70		9
Polyisobutene	benzene	+ 50	+ 8.2	6
Polyisoprene				
cis (Natural rubber)	benzene,toluene	+ 50		8
trans (Gutta-percha)	benzene	+ 85		8
Polymethacrylamide				
-- , N-phenyl-	o-toluidine	-103	- 13	22
-- , - , p-carbethoxy-	o-toluidine	-230	- 23	22
-- , - , p-chloro-	o-toluidine	-160	-20	22
Poly(methacrylic acid)				
-- , n-butyl ester				
atactic	benzene	- 14	- 2.1	17
isotactic	benzene	- 2	- 0.3	18
-- , tert-butyl ester				
atactic	benzene	+ 2.1	+ 0.3	19
isotactic	benzene	+ 19.3	+ 3.0	19
-- , methyl ester				
atactic	benzene	+ 2	+ 0.3	16
isotactic	benzene	+ 25	+ 3.5	16
-- , β-naphthyl ester	tetrabromoethane	- 60	- 8.5	29
-- , phenyl ester	bromobenzene	- 10.5	- 1.5	29
-- , - , p-tert-butyl-	bromobenzene	- 90	- 7.5	20,21
Polypropylene atactic, isotactic	carbon tetrachloride	+ 30	+ 3.5	5
Polysiloxane				
-- , dimethyl-	petroleum ether	+ 4.7	+ 0.96	11
-- , methylphenyl-	petroleum ether	- 66	- 13.5	11
Polystyrene				
atactic	bromoform	-145	- 18	12,14
isotactic	bromoform	-224	- 23	12
-- , p-chloro-	bromoform	-230	- 35	14

References page V-73

Polymer	Solvent	$\alpha_1 - \alpha_2$ $\times\ 10^{25} cm^3$	$a_{\parallel} - a_{\perp}$ $\times\ 10^{25} cm^3$	Reference
Polystyrene (Cont'd.)				
-- , 2,5-dichloro-	bromoform	-265	-30	14
-- , 3,4-dichloro-	tetrabromo-ethane	-300	- 25	6
-- , 2,5-dimethyl-	bromoform	-180	- 25	14
-- , p-methyl-				
atactic	bromoform	-147	- 20	13
isotactic	bromoform	-140	- 19	13
Poly(vinyl acetate)	benzene	+ 5.4	+ 0.8	15
	toluene	+ 13.5	+ 2.0	15
Poly(β-vinylnaphthalene)	tetrabromo-ethane	-430	- 30	29
Poly(vinylpyrrolidone)	benzyl alcohol	- 75	- 10	29

REFERENCES

1. V. N. Tsvetkov, Chapter XIV in Bacon Ke (Ed.), "Newer Methods of Polymer Characterization," Interscience, New York, 1964.
2. W. Kuhn and H. Kuhn, Helv. Chim. Acta 26, 1394 (1943).
3. A. Peterlin, J. Polymer Sci. 12, 45 (1954).
4. T. I. Garmonova, Leningrad. Universitet, Vestnik Ser. Fiz. Khim. N22, 4 (1962).
5. V. N. Tsvetkov, O. V. Kallistov, E. V. Korneeva, and I. K. Nekrasov, Vysokomolekul. Soedin, 5, 1538 (1963).
6. V. N. Tsvetkov, V. E. Bychkova, S. M. Savvon and I. K. Nekrasov, Vysokomolekul. Soedin, 1, 1407 (1959).
7. V. N. Tsvetkov, A. I. Petrova and I. J. Poddubny, J. Phys. Chem. (USSR) 24, 994 (1950).
8. V. N. Tsvetkov, S. M. Savvon and Gao-Yu-Shou, Vysokomolekul. Soedin. 5, 81 (1963).
9. S. M. Savvon and K. K. Turoverov, Vysokomolekul. Soedin 6, 205 (1964).
10. V. N. Tsvetkov and S. J. Magarik, Dokl. Akad. Nauk SSSR, 115, 911 (1957).
11. V. N. Tsvetkov, E. V. Frisman, and N. N. Boitzova, Vysokomolekul. Soedin.2, 1001 (1960).
12. V. N. Tsvetkov and S. J. Magarik, Dokl. Akad. Nauk SSSR, 127, 840 (1959).
13. V. N. Tsvetkov and N. N. Boitzova, Vysokomolekul. Soedin. 5, 1263 (1963).
14. E. V. Frisman, A. M. Martsinovsky and N. A. Domnitcheva, Vysokomolekul. Soedin. 2, 1148 (1960).
15. V. N. Tsvetkov, N. N. Boitzova, and M. G. Vitovskaja, Vysokomolekul. Soedin.6, 297 (1964).
16. V. N. Tsvetkov and N. N. Boitzova, Vysokomolekul. Soedin. 2, 1176 (1960).
17. V. N. Tsvetkov and S. J. Ljubina, Vysokomolekul. Soedin.1, 857 (1959).
18. V. N. Tsvetkov, M. G. Vitovskaja, and S. J. Ljubina, Vysokomolekul. Soedin.4, 577 (1962).
19. V. N. Tsvetkov, N. N. Boitzova, and M. G. Vitovskaja, Vysokomolekul. Soedin.6, 297 (1964).
20. V. N. Tsvetkov and S. J. Magarik, Dokl. Akad. Nauk SSSR 115, 911 (1957).
21. V. N. Tsvetkov,and I. N. Shtennikova, Zh. Tekhn. Fiz. 29, 885 (1959).
22. V. N. Tsvetkov and V. E. Bychkova, Vysokomolekul. Soedin. 6, 600 (1964).
23. V. N. Tsvetkov and I. N. Shtennikova, Vysokomolekul. Soedin.2, 808 (1960).
24. V. N. Tsvetkov, I. N. Shtennikova, N. A. Megeritzkaja, and L. S. Bolotnikova, Vysokomolekul. Soedin.5, 74 (1963).
25. V. N. Tsvetkov and I. N. Shtennikova, Vysokomolekul. Soedin.6, 1041 (1964).
26. V. N. Tsvetkov, A. E. Grischenko, O. P. Kosmina, and P. A. Slavetzkaja, Vysokomolekul. Soedin.7, 000 (1965).
27. V. N. Tsvetkov, A. E. Grischenko, and P. A. Slavetzkaja, Vysokomolekul. Soedin. 6, 856 (1964).
28. V. N. Tsvetkov, Y. V. Mitin, I. N. Shtennikova, V. R. Glushenkova, and G. I. Ohrimenko, Vysokomolekul. Soedin.6, 000 (1964).
29. V. N. Tsvetkov, V. E. Eskin, and S. J. Frenkel, "Structure of Molecules in Solution," Nauka,Moscow, 1964.

VI.
PHYSICAL CONSTANTS OF
SOME IMPORTANT POLYMERS*

*Additional values for these polymers may be found in
the tables of individual constants in this Handbook.

PROPERTIES OF CELLULOSE MATERIALS*

T. Lukanoff and B. Philipp

Deutsche Akademie der Wissenschaften zu Berlin
Institut für Faserstoff-Forschung
Teltow-Seehof, Germany

Contents

* For additional values see the tables of individual constants in this Handbook.

A. Unit Cell Dimensions*

Cellulose Modification	Crystal System	a[Å]	b[Å]	c[Å]	β	Space Group	Notes on Origin and Preparation of Sample	References
Cellulose I	Monoclinic	8.35	10.3	7.9	84°	P 2_1	ramie	34,35,45-47
		8.167	10.306	7.844	84° 5'	C_2^2 P 2_1	ramie	8,9
		8.26	10.30	7.83	85° 24'	C_2^2 P 2_1	comparison of two well-crystallized samples of ramie	10,11
		8.18	10.30	7.79	85°			
		10.8	10.4	11.8	85°		bacterial cellulose	7
		8.205 ±0.035+	not measured	7.908 ±0.011+	81° 51' ± 11'+		bacterial cellulose	1
		8.181 ±0.039+	"	7.873 ±0.025+	82° 96' ± 24'+		linen	1
		8.171 ±0.032+	"	7.846 ±0.019+	83° 37' ± 8'+		ramie	1
		8.174 ±0.007+	"	7.889 ±0.005+	83° 28' ± 0'+		cotton	1
		8.283	"	7.963	83° 33'		cladophora prolifera	1
		8.212	"	7.882	83° 21'		valonia	1
		8.203	10.295	7.836	84° 23'		mean value of measurements of different samples	12
Cellulose II	triclinic	10.85	10.3	12.08	93° 14'	P 1		15
	triclinic	2 x 8.20	10.34	2 x 7.84	82°	P 1	valonia; electron diffraction	13
	monoclinic	8.14	10.3	9.14	62°	P 2_1		25
		8.22	10.3	9.17	51° 8'		mercerized ramie	24
		8.14	10.3	9.14	52°		cellulose II, dry	2
		8.58	10.3	9.38	59°		cellulose II, hydrate I	2

* For critical comments on the different unit cells proposed for cellulose I and II, especially the "Meyer-Misch-cell", see references 22,23. Additional data may be found in references 26-48.

+ = standard deviation.

Cellulose Modification	Crystal System	Dimension of Unit Cell a[Å]	b[Å]	c[Å]	β	Space Group	Notes on Origin and Preparation of Sample	References
Cellulose II	monoclinic	10.03	10.3	9.98	52°		cellulose II, hydrate II, identical with "water cellulose," ref. 8.	2
		7.95	not measured	9.22	62° 18'		30% NaOH/60' - dried at 60°C, then completely dried at 110°C	10
		8.13	not measured	9.17	61° 48'		30% NaOH/60' - dried at 60°C, then exposed to water vapor at 60°C	10
		7.641	10.31	9.200	63.51°		bone dry cellulose II	3
		7.894	10.31	9.222	62.15°		dried but not bone dry	3
		8.033	10.31	9.303	61.22°		bone dried, then reswollen in water	3
		8.238	10.31	9.414	59.91°		swollen in water without previous drying	3
		7.917	10.292	9.150	62° 45'		mean value of different samples, dry	12
		8.251	10.3	9.254	61° 13'		mean value of different samples, moist	12
		8.014 ±0.041	not measured	9.149 ±0.022	62° 26' ± 5'		mercerized bacterial cellulose	1
		7.970 ±0.055	"	9.219 ±0.038	62° 14' ± 10'		mercerized ramie	1
		8.059 ±0.019	"	9.382 ±0.030	61° 45' ± 15'		mercerized liner	1
		7.902	"	9.185	62° 51'		viscose, samples of different origin	1
		7.955 ±0.024	"	9.167 ±0.109	63° 3' ± 5'		cuprammonium rayon	1
		7.917 ±0.027	"	9.083 ±0.040	62° 42' ± 9'		Fortisan	1
		8.001	"	9.061	63° 23'		cellopentaose	1

References page VI-34

+ = standard deviation.

Cellulose Modification	Crystal System	Dimension of Unit Cell a[Å]	b[Å]	c[Å]	β	Space Group	Notes on Origin and Preparation of Sample	References
Cellulose III	tetragonal	15.5	10.4	15.5	90°			16
IIIα	monoclinic	7.72-7.82	10.28	9.93-10.0	57°7'-58°6'		extreme limits of measurements with different samples obtained via NH_3-cellulose from native cellulose	4,17,18
IIIβ	monoclinic	7.63-7.72	10.28	9.80-9.89	58°8'-60°6'		extreme limits of measurements with different samples obtained via NH_3-cellulose from mercerized cellulose	4,17,18
Cellulose IV	tetragonal	7.95	10.2	7.95	90°			19
	orthorhombic	7.94-8.19	10.28	7.92-8.02	90°		extreme limits from measurements of different samples	18,20
Cellulose X	monoclinic	8.10	10.3	8.16	78°18'		obtained by treatment of cellulose I or II with 40% HCl	5,14,21
	orthorhombic	8.12	10.3	7.99	90°			6

B. State of Order, Crystallinity

Within the rather broad spectrum of results from various physical and chemical methods for determination of average "state of order" (so-called "crystallinity") of cellulose samples, only X-ray diffraction data are presented in this table. For comparing quantitatively samples of different origin with regard to state of order, the following terms are used:

Degree of Crystallinity after HERMANS and WEIDINGER (49-54)

$$D \; C = \frac{I_{cr}}{I_{cr} + I_{am}}$$

Crystallinity Index after ANT-WUORINEN (55)

$$Cr \; I = \frac{Am \; W}{Cr \; H}$$

Crystallinity Ratio (index of order) after ANT-WUORINEN and VISAPÄÄ (56,57)

$$Cr \; R \; (I \; O) = 1 - \frac{Am \; H}{Cr \; H} = 1 - \frac{Am \; H}{Tot.H-Am \; H}$$

I_{cr} = scattering intensity of ordered regions

I_{am} = scattering intensity of disordered regions

$Am \; W$ = half angular width in radians of the overlapping 101 and 002 reflections, measured in radians

$Cr \; H$ = ratio of crystalline height to total distance between zero-line and total blackness

$Am \; H$ = height of interference minimum at $2\theta = 18$-$19°$ for cellulose I and $2\theta = 13$-$15°$ for cellulose II

$Tot. \; H$ = height of interference maximum at $2\theta = 22$-$23°$ for cellulose I and $2\theta = 19$-$22°$ for cellulose II

Type of Cellulose	D C	References	Cr I	References	Cr R (I O)	References
Ramie	0.65-0.71	52,53,58				
Ramie, mercerized	0.49	59				
Flax, bleached	average 0.67 range 0.64-0.69	55	average 0.74 range 0.70-0.77	55	0.62-0.69	58
Cotton, different origins	0.69-0.71	53				
	average 0.70 range 0.66-0.74	55	average 0.70 range 0.66-0.74	55		
Cotton linters	0.70	53	average 0.72-0.73 range 0.69-0.76	55,60,61	0.82-0.86	56,57
Cotton linters, mercerized	average 0.48 range 0.41-0.55	55	average 0.43 range 0.32-0.50	55,62	0.56-0.59	57,62,63
Cellulose from Valonia ventricosa	average 0.68 range 0.65-0.70	52				
Bacterial cellulose (Acetobacter xylinum)	0.40	52				
Different wood pulps	0.62-0.70	52,53,55,58	0.61-0.68	55,60,61,62	0.58-0.72	56,57,53,63
Different wood pulps, mercerized	0.49	59	0.35-0.43	62	0.45-0.56	57,63
Viscose rayon, normal grade	0.38-0.40	52,53,54,64,65	0.27-0.79	55,61,62,65		
	average 0.27 range 0.13-0.36	55				
Viscose staple fibers, normal grade	0.30-0.39	52,53,65,66	0.30-0.79	55,65	0.34-0.38	56,57,63
	average 0.42 range 0.30-0.52	55				
Viscose fibers, mercerized	0.40-0.52	54,59,64	0.36-0.43	61,62	0.45-0.56	57,63
High tenacity viscose rayons	0.23-0.56	52,53,54,64,65,67	0.28-0.78	61,65,68		
High wet modulus (HWM) viscose fibers = Polynosics	0.27-0.44	52,53,64,65,66	0.30-0.76	61,65,68		
Cellophane	0.30-0.40	52,53,66				

Type of Cellulose	D C	References	Cr I	References	Cr R (I O)	References
Regenerated cellulose precipitated from viscose as flake	0.45-0.53	69				
Cuprammonium rayon	0.40-0.44	51,52,54				
Cuprammonium rayon, mercerized	0.49	59				
Saponified acetate fibers	average 0.38	53				
Fortisan	0.39-0.54	53,65,66,69	0.33-0.86	61,65,68		
"Amorphous" powder, obtained by dry-grinding viscose rayon	0.08	70,71				
"Amorphous" powder, obtained by dry-grinding viscose rayon, recrystallized	0.35-0.40	71				

C. X-Ray Orientation

For evaluation of x-ray orientation of cellulose (72,73) the "orientation factor" f_x (74,75,76) is used in the following table. As existing data are largely a function of the stretching conditions in the spinning process, only ranges of f_x are presented for regenerated cellulose fibers.

Nature of Material	Data	References
Ramie	0.97	76
Ramie, mercerized without tension	0.90	76
Ramie, mercerized and reorientated	0.98	76
Viscose rayon, normal grade	0.31-0.91	65,68,76,77
Viscose staple fibers, normal grade	0.30-0.67	65,78
Lilienfeld rayon	0.70-0.94	65,76,77
High-tenacity viscose cord rayon	0.39-0.998	54,65,67,77
High wet modulus (HWM) viscose fibers	0.45-0.993	65,67,68,77,78
Isotropic viscose model fibers, without stretching	0.06-0.15	79
Isotropic viscose model fibers, after intense stretching	up to 0.90	79
Cuprammonium rayon	0.86	76
Fortisan	0.7 -0.99	65,67,68,77,78

D. Density of Cellulose

Type of Cellulose	$d_t^4 [\text{g ml}^{-1}]$	References
Cellulose I	1.582-1.630[a]	3,12,18,30,89,81,82
Cellulose II	1.583-1.62[a]	12,30,80,81
Cellulose IV	1.61[a]	12
Cotton	1.545-1.585	83-87,96,97
Ramie	ca. 1.550	81,87
Flax	1.541	90
Hemp	1.541	90
Jute	1.532	90
Wood pulps	1.535-1.547	81,85,88,89,91,92,96
Cuprammonium fibers	1.519-1.531	85,86,97
Polynosics	1.489-1.528	93,98
Viscose fibers (and films) (rayon and staple)	1.508-1.548	85,86,91,94,99,99a
High tenacity viscose fibers	1.498-1.524	94,99b

[a] Calculated from x-ray data.

PROPERTIES OF CELLULOSE MATERIALS

E. Thermal Properties

Property	Type of Cellulose	Data	References
Specific heat $[\text{cal g}^{-1} \text{ deg}^{-1}]$	cotton	0.291; 0.317-0.324	100,101
	ramie	0.424	102
	rayon, staple fibers	0.324	101
	rayon	0.338-0.381	102
Thermal conductivity* $[\text{cal g}^{-1} \text{ cm}^{-1} \text{ deg}^{-1}]$	cotton		
	rayon, staple fibers	ca. 5×10^{-4}	101
Heat of crystallization $[\text{cal g}^{-1}]$	extrapolated to 100% crystallinity	25.3 ± 1.2	103
	cellulose I	29.1	104
Heat of combustion $[\text{cal g}^{-1}]$	linters	4165	105
	wood pulp	4173	105
Differential heat of absorption of liquid water (at zero regain) (cal/g of liquid water)	cotton	360; 295-317; 289; 285	106,107,108,109
	cotton	232-243; 230-240	110,111
	linters	273	112
	linters mercerized	317	112
	flax	298; 288	107,110
	wood pulps	280-300; 262	112,113
	Fortisan	295; 279	109,110
	cuprammonium fibers	290; 266	107,110
	normal viscose fibers	305; 290-280; 251; 235; 219-244	106,107,111,110
	high tenacity viscose fibers	330; 291; 240	107,109,110
Integral heat of wetting in water (at zero regain and 25°C) (cal/g of dry material)	cotton	8.1-13.4	107,109,111, 114-124
	linters	10.4-13.8	103,112,125,126
	cotton mercerized	14.8-18.8	109,112,118,122, 127,128
	cotton ball milled	21.6	120
	ramie	8.2-11.6	111,118,119,128
	flax	9.4-13.0	107,128
	wood pulps	11.8-17.0	112,116,118, 119,121
	Fortisan	18.2	109
	cuprammonium rayon	22.4	107
	normal viscose fibers (rayon and staple)	16.3-25.2	103,107,109,112, 118,119,123,129,130
	high tenacity viscose fibers	20.4-25.7	107,109,112
Heat of solution (cal/g of dry material)	cotton in Cuene‡	25.8	103
	cotton in Et_3PhNOH	34.0	120
	rayon in Cuene‡	22.8	103
	rayon in Et_3PhNOH	33.0-36.5	131
	ball milled cellulose in Et_3PhNOH	58.0	120
	cellulose II in Et_3PhNOH	43.6	120
Coefficient of expansion $[\text{deg}^{-1}]$ -30°C to +25°C	cotton linters	4×10^{-4}	95

* Approximate data only are presented as the thermal conductivity depends largely
  on relative humidity and packing density of the fiber material.
‡ Cuene = Cupriethylendiamine.

References page VI-34

F. Refractive Indices and Birefringence

Type of Cellulose	$n_{\parallel}$	$n_{\perp}$	$n_{\parallel} - n_{\perp}$	References*
Ideally oriented native cellulose fiber (cellulose I)	1.618	1.544	0.074	132
Ramie	1.595-1.601	1.525-1.534	0.061-0.071	133-138
Flax	1.571-1.595	1.517-1.532	0.054-0.067	136,138,139
Hemp	1.585-1.591	1.526-1.530	0.055-0.065	139,141
Cotton	1.576-1.595	1.527-1.534	0.045-0.062	134,136,138, 140,142,143
Jute	1.577	1.536	0.041	138
Ideally oriented regenerated cellulose fiber (cellulose II)	1.578	1.523	0.055[a] 0.043[b]	132 (144) 132
Fortisan			0.045	145
High tenacity rayon	1.542-1.553	1.509-1.513	0.029-0.043	142(136,146,147)
Polynosics	1.556-1.570	1.518-1.531	0.036-0.043	142,148(144)
Normal viscose fibers	1.529-1.547	1.512-1.520	0.013-0.034	152(136,142, 146-150)
Cuprammonium fibers	1.548-1.571	1.519-1.534	0.018-0.037	133,136,140, 145,(136,138)

* References in parenthesis give additional data

[a] bone dry   [b] conditioned

G. Infrared Spectrum of Cellulose

The following table gives selected data on position and - as far as possible - assignment of IR-absorption bands of cellulose I and cellulose II according to decreasing wave number. Data on cellulose III and cellulose IV were omitted, as the few references (153-156) available barely include assignments, and as it is generally agreed that the IR-spectra of cellulose III and cellulose IV resp. closely resemble those of cellulose II and cellulose I resp. Even between cellulose I and cellulose II the differences are rather small, the bands being generally more diffuse with cellulose II. Differences in intensity of absorption with conversion of cellulose I to cellulose II or between "Valonia type" and "ramie type" of cellulose I are marked in the following table by underlining (increase) or bracketing (decrease) of the wave number concerned.

Position of Absorption Bands in cm^{-1}			Assignment	References
Cellulose I		Cellulose II		
Valonia, Bacterial Cellulose	Ramie, Cotton			
	6770	6770	OH stretching, overtone	157
5190		5190	absorbed H_2O, overtone	157
4780		4780	OH and CH deformation + OH stretching	157
		4560	observed with cellophane only	157
4365		4365	C-O stretching + OH stretching or CH_2 bending + CH_2 stretching	157

| Position of Absorption Bands in cm^{-1} | | | Assignment | References |
Cellulose I Valonia, Bacterial Cellulose	Cellulose I Ramie, Cotton	Cellulose II		
	4235	4235	OH and CH deformation + CH and CH_2 stretching	157
	3990	3970	C-O stretching + CH and CH_2 stretching	157
	3125-3660		free OH and bonded OH stretching	158
		3484-3490 3444-3450	OH stretching of crystalline part of cellulose II after elimination of the amorphous part	153,154,156,159,160
	3200-3400	3200-3400	OH stretching, bands of H bonds	153,155
	3401-3405 ⊥		OH stretching	153,161,162
		3374-3394	OH stretching, maximum of absorption depending on origin of cellulose II	163
	3375		OH stretching	159,164
		3350-3360	broad band of OH stretching, obviously not resolved completely	154,165
3350 ‖		(3350) ‖	OH stretching	159,161,164
	3340-3345	(3340)	OH stretching	156,162,166
		3322	OH stretching	160
	3305⊥-3309 ⊥		OH stretching	153,159,162,164
	3300 ‖		OH stretching	161
	3275		OH stretching	153,159,164
3243-3245			OH stretching	153,162,164
		3163	OH stretching	160
	2970 ‖		CH stretching	159
	2967 ‖		antisym. CH_2 stretching	161
	2960		antisym. CH_2 stretching	167,168
	2945		antisym. CH_2 stretching	155,159
2914 ⊥	2910 ⊥		CH stretching	155,159,161,167
	2900	2900	broad band of CH stretching	156
2897 ⊥			CH stretching	155,159
	2880-2890		CH stretching	167,168
	2870 ⊥		CH stretching	155,159
	2853 ‖		sym. CH_2 stretching	159,161,169
	1760		C=O band from ester groups	158
	1730-1740		C=O stretching of carboxyl or lacton groups	158,170,171,172
	1635-1670		absorbed H_2O	155,158,161,166,168,170,173

References page VI-34

Position ob Absorption Bands in cm^{-1}			Assignment	References
Cellulose I		Cellulose II		
Valonia, Bacterial Cellulose	Ramie, Cotton			
	1550-1650		COO' stretching	168
	1590		COO' stretching	158
	1560		COO' stretching	174
	1530		COO' stretching	170
	1455 ⊥		OH in plane bending	173
	1446 ⊥		OH in plane bending, "crystallinity band" (17?)	161
	1440		OH in plane bending	155
	1426-1430 ‖	(1426-1430 ‖)	CH$_2$ bending	155,156,161, 164,167,169, 173,175-177
	1380	1380	CH bending, same intensity with cellulose I and II	156,173
	1350-1450	1350-1450	COO' stretching	168
	1370	1370	COO' stretching	168,174,175
	1374 ‖		CH bending	173
	1370		CH bending	155,158
	1365		CH bending	161
	1350-1355	1355		156,175
	1340	(1340)	OH in plane bending	167,175,177
1336			OH in plane bending	173
	1330-1335		OH in plane bending	155,158,161
	1328		OH in plane bending	173
	1320	(1320)	OH in plane bending or CH bending	158,167,168, 177,178
1317 ⊥			CH$_2$ wagging	173
	1315		CH$_2$ wagging	155
	1310		OH bending	161
	1290	1290		177
1282	(1282 ‖)	1280	CH bending	155,173
	1275 ⊥			173
	1250			173
	1240	1240		156,168
	1230-1235	1235	OH in plane bending ?	155,173,177
	1210	1210		156
	1205 ⊥	(1205)	OH in plane bending	155,173,177
	1170	(1170)		177
	1164	(1164)	stretching of C-O in ring or bending of C-OH	158,166
	1162 ‖		antisym. bridge oxygen stretching	155,173
	1125 ‖	(1125)		173
	1120		antisym. in phase ring wagging	155

Position of Absorption Bands in cm^{-1}

Cellulose I — Valonia, Bacterial Cellulose	Cellulose I — Ramie, Cotton	Cellulose II	Assignment	References
	1119		C-O-C stretching	158
	1115		1115	"association band"	156
	1110		(1110)	antisym. in phase ring stretching	173,176
	1060		~1065	OH bending	158,175
	1058 ||		C-O stretching	155
1040				175
	1035 ||		C-O stretching	173
	1025		C-O stretching	155
	1015 ||		C-O stretching	173
	(1005)		1005		177
	1000 ||		C-O stretching, or C-C stretching	158,173
	(985-990)		990	C-O stretching	155,176
		970		167
	(900-910)		900	CH bending or CH₂ stretching, "amorphous band"	166-168, 172, 177
	(893-895 ||)		895	antisym. out-of-phase stretching	155,173,175
~800			ring breathing	173
~740 ⊥			CH₂ rocking	173
~700 ⊥			OH out-of-plane bending	173
663 ⊥			OH out-of-plane bending	169,173
~650			OH out-of-plane bending	158,161
620	620			177
560				156,177
520	525			156,168
500				168
450	460			156,168
430	425			156,168

References page VI-34

H. Nonglucose Carbohydrates in Cellulosic Materials

Data were obtained by estimation of the "pentosan content" by destillative dehydra-
tation and subsequent determination of the furfural obtained by volumetry, gravimetry,
or colorimetry.

Because of the vaste of literature and the impossibility to discriminate between
xylose and arabinose units by this method, data are given as a short survey only,
omitting references to the original literature.

Nature of Material	Pentosan Content
Cotton linters, raw	1.5-2
" " , purified	0.1-0.5
Jute	9-11
Hemp	3-10
Flax	3-8
Wood pulps	
Coniferous sulfate, paper grade	5-10
" prehydrolysis sulfate, rayon grade	2-4
" " " , cord grade	1.5-2.5
" " " , acetate grade	0.2-0.5
" sulfite, paper grade	4-7
" " , rayon grade	2.5-5
" sulfite-soda, rayon grade	2-4
" sulfite, cord grade	1-2
Deciduous sulfate, paper grade	18-28
" prehydrolysis sulfate, rayon grade	3-6
" (gumwood) prehydrolysis sulfate, cord grade	1.5-2.5
" sulfite, paper grade	8-20
" " , rayon grade	3.5-7
Annual plants, sulfate, paper grade	18-31
" " , prehydrolysis sulfate, rayon grade	3-8
" " , sulfite, rayon grade	3-6

I. Permeability of Regenerated Cellulose Film to Oxygen

Nearly all published data available on gas permeability of cellulose film refer to
plasticized or coated films and are not typical for cellulose as a polymeric material.
Thus, only very few data are presented here on "pure cellulose film" for comparison
with other polymers. For further permeability values of plasticized or coated film
to various gases compare ref. (179) and (180) and the tables on "Permeability Constants"
in this Handbook.

Type of Film	Thickness	Relative Humidity	Permeability in $cm^3/100\ cm^2/24\ h/atm.$	Reference
Regenerated cellulose film	17.8 μm	48%	0.233	179
" " "	17.8 μm	87%	2.64	179
" " " (never dried)	(17.8 μm)	100%	279	179

K. Solvents for Cellulose

Dissolution of cellulose is always preceded by chemical reaction with the hydroxyl groups of the carbohydrate chain. The following table somewhat arbitrarily covers "one-step solution processes" in aqueous media only, where chemical reaction and dissolution occur simultaneously, and in most cases rather unstable addition-compounds are formed. "Two-step solution processes" via well defined cellulose derivatives (esters like cellulose nitrate, ethers like carboxymethyl-cellulose) are not included.

Solvent	Optimal Conditions for Dissolution	Remarks	Analytical and/or Technical Application	References
Mineral acids in aqueous solution				
HCl, HBr	40-42% HCl ~66% HBr	fast hydrolytic degradation	–	181
H_2SO_4	~66% H_2SO_4 (10.5M)	fast hydrolytic degradation	–	182
H_3PO_4	~83% H_3PO_4 (14.1M) 0°C	less hydrolytic degradation than with HCl and H_2SO_4, incomplete dissolution of high-DP native cellulose	approximate estimation of chain length distribution by fractional dissolution	182,183
Neutral salts in concentrated aqueous solution				
$ZnCl_2$	~65% $ZnCl_2$	strong swelling, dissolution accompanied by degradation	manufacture of vulcanized fiber	184,185
$Ca(SCN)_2$	~60% $Ca(SCN)_2$ ~125°C	dissolution accompanied by degradation, high-DP native cellulose is barely dissolved	analytical separation of cotton and rayon	186,187
LiSCN, NaSCN, LiI, NaI, KI	~10% of salt 100°C	low DP cellulose (β-cellulose) to about 50% dissolved	–	188
$K_2[HgI_4]$	–	–	–	187
Strong bases in aqueous solution				
LiOH	7% LiOH -5°C	degraded cotton cellulose nearly completely dissolved	–	189
NaOH	9-10% NaOH -5°C	cellulose of low and medium DP and high accessibility only is dissolved	characterization of pulp and rayon by alkali solubility	189

Solvent	Optimal Conditions for Dissolution	Remarks	Analytical and/or Technical Application	References
NaOH + ZnO	10% NaOH+4% ZnO; 0-10°C 12% NaOH+5% ZnO; ~10°C	nearly complete dissolution of rayon and hydrolytic degraded pulp, native wood pulp dissolved to about 50%	incomplete fractionation by dissolution	189,190
NaOH + BeO	10-12% NaOH+2.5% BeO; ~20°C	extraction of low DP cellulose from wood pulp	characterization of rayon pulp	190
Tetraethylammonium-hydroxide and some higher homologs	2.3 M TEOH; ambient temperature	complete dissolution of regenerated cellulose and of wood pulp up to DP 1500	viscosimetric estimation of DP	191-193
Trimethylbenzyl-ammoniumhydroxide ("Triton B"), Dimethyldibenzyl-ammoniumhydroxide ("Triton F")	Triton B: 3.5M;20°C ~2M;0°C Triton F: 2M;20°C >1.8M; 0°C	complete dissolution of native and regenerated cellulose	viscosimetric estimation of DP; production of filaments on an experimental scale	192,194
Tetraalkylphosphonium hydroxides	-	-	-	195
Tetraalkylarsonium hydroxides	-	-	-	195
Trialkylsulfonium hydroxides	-	-	-	196
Trialkylselonium hydroxides	-	-	-	185
Metal complex solutions				
[Cu(NH$_3$)$_4$](OH)$_2$ "Cuoxam", "Cuam"	for viscosimetric estimation of DP usually 15g/l Cu, 200 g/l NH$_3$; 20°C	complete and fast dissolution of even high DP native cellulose; considerable degradation by oxygen	viscosimetric estimation of DP, production of filaments on a technical scale; most widely used solvent for cellulose	199
[Cu(en)$_2$] (OH)$_2$ "Cupriethylenediamine", "Cuene", "CED"	for viscosimetric estimation of DP usually 0.5 mole/l Cu; 1 mole/l ethylenediamine 20°C	complete and fast dissolution of even high DP native cellulose; solution less sensitive to oxydative degradation than cellulose in cuoxam	viscosimetric determination of DP, investigation of physico-chemical properties of cellulose solutions	200,201
Cu:Biuret:Alkali	0.12-0.5 mole Cu + equivalent amount of biuret, in 1.6N KOH	solutions are sensitive against oxidative degradation	-	202

Metal complex solutions (Cont'd.)

Solvent	Optimal Conditions for Dissolution	Remarks	Analytical and/or Technical Application	References
$[Co(en)_3](OH)_2$ "Cooxene"	6.8% (by weight) Co, 26.6% ethylenediamine, 1.2% glycerol	6-8% cellulose of DP 650 are dissolved by the solvent specified	–	203
$[Ni(NH_3)_6](OH)_2$ "Nioxam"	3.76% Ni; 30.4% NH_3	4% cellulose of DP 620 are dissolved by the solvent specified	–	204
$[Ni(en)_3](OH)_2$ "Nioxene"	~8% Ni in 30 – 40% aqu. soln. of ethylenediamine	2% cellulose of DP 620 are dissolved	–	204
$[Zn(en)_3](OH)_2$ "Zincoxene"	4.1% Zn; 40.6% ethylenediamine	–	–	205
$[Cd(en)_3](OH)_2$ "Cadoxene"	~4.5% Cd in 30% aqu. soln. of ethylene-diamine	3% cellulose of DP 670 are dissolved rapidly to a colorless, clear solution	viscosimetric estimation of DP, investigation of physico-chemical properties of cellulose solutions, characterization of rayon pulps by turbidimetry and particle counting	206
	4.5-5.2% Cd in 30% aqu. soln. of ethylene-diamine + 0.2-0.5M NaOH	cotton cellulose of DP1200 is completely dissolved		207
complex solution of the Na-salt of Fe-tartaric acid in tartrate + NaOH. "FeTNa"	350 g/l complex (Fe: tartaric acid:NaOH= 1:3:6) + 2.75N NaOH + 40 g/l Na-tartrate	even native cellulose of high DP is completely dissolved; oxydative degradation is very small	estimation of DP; investigation of physico-chemical properties of cellulose solutions, characterization of pulps, morphological investigation of swelling and dissolution of cellulose	208,209

L. Viscosity-Molecular Weight Relationships*

The constants K_m and a of the Mark-Houwink equation $[\eta] = K_m M^a$ are given. The corresponding constants relating intrinsic viscosity and degree of polymerization are also given. The constants K_m and K'_m are related by the following equation:

$$K'_m = K_m M_o^a$$

M_o = molecular weight of the monomer unit

Abbreviations:
F   = Fractionated
U   = Unfractionated
Osm = Osmotic Measurement
S   = Measurement by Sedimentation
SD = Measurement by Sedimentation-Diffusion
LS = Measurement by Light Scattering
FeTNa = Na-salt of tartratoferric acid in complex solution
NC = Nitrocellulose

Constants of Mark-Houwink-Equation $[\eta] = K_m M^a$ and $[\eta] = K'_m DP^a$

$[\eta] = K'_m DP^a$		$[\eta] = K_m M^a$		Interval of $[\eta]$	Rate of Shear $\overline{G}$	Temp.	Nitrogen Content	Nature of Sample	Method of Calibration	System used for Calibration	References
K'_m	a	$K_m \cdot 10^2$	a	$[ml\ g^{-1}]$	$[sec^{-1}]$	$[°C]$	%				
Nitrocellulose-Acetone (NC-Acetone)											
0.7	1.0	0.258	1.0	73-770	-	-	12.5		Osm	NC-acetone	210
0.8	1.0	0.296	1.0	-	-	-	12.5		Osm	NC-acetone	211
1.1	1.0	0.406	1.0	150-1300	-	20	12.0-12.5	U	Osm	NC-acetone	212
0.95	1.0	0.35	1.0	150-1300	-	20	12.0-12.5	F	Osm	NC-acetone (reprecipi-tated cell)	212
1.02	1.0	0.356	1.0	182-365	-	20	~13.6	F	Osm	NC-acetone	213
0.82	1.0	0.304	1.0	47-1154	1200	20	~12.5	F	Osm	NC-acetone	214

* See also table on "Viscosity-Molecular Weight Relationships" in this Handbook.

References page VI-34

$[\eta] = K'_m DP^a$		$[\eta] = K_m M^a$		Interval of $[\eta]$	Rate of Shear G	Temp.	Nitrogen Content	Nature of Sample	Method of Calibration	System used for Calibration	References
K'_m	a	$K_m \cdot 10^2$	a	$[ml\ g^{-1}]$	$[sec^{-1}]$	$[°C]$	%				
Nitrocellulose-Acetone (Cont'd.)											
1.02	1.0	0.377	1.0	650-1460	1200	20	~12.5	F	Osm	NC-acetone	214
1.29	0.98	0.508	0.98	77-800	-	20	~13.4	F	Osm	NC-acetone	215
1.06	1.0	0.374	1.0	-	-	-	~13.4	F	Osm	NC-acetone	216
1.37	0.98	-	0.98	170-900	-	-	-	F	Osm	NC-acetone	217
1.54	0.98	0.614	0.98	162-1210	-	20	~13.1	cotton U	Osm	NC-acetone	218
1.81	0.98	0.722	0.98	176-1200	-	20	~13.1	pulp U	Osm	NC-acetone	218
3.09	0.83	2.82	0.83	80-750	-	20	13.3-	cotton F	Osm	NC-acetone	219
4.46	0.82	4.37	0.82	100-700	-	20	~13.5	pulp F	Osm	NC-acetone	220
1.93	0.91	1.1	0.91	112-3000	0	25	13.9	FU	Osm	NC-acetone	221,222
1.14	1.0	0.42	1.0	112-680	0	25	13.9	FU	Osm	NC-acetone	221,222
0.91	1.0	0.336	1.0	680-3000	0	25	13.9	FU	Osm	NC-acetone	221,222
19.5	0.516	105.0	0.516	350-650	0	-	13.8	F	Osm	NC-acetone	223
1.1	1.0	0.378	1.0	650-2450	-	25	13.8	F	Osm	NC-acetone	224
1.95	0.91	1.12	0.91	120-2850	-	20	13.8	-	Osm	NC-acetone	225
1.42	0.933	0.713	0.933	100-1500	-	25	14.1	F	Osm	NC-acetone	226,227
1.36	0.948	0.62	0.948	100-1800	-	20	13.8	F	Osm,SD	NC-acetone	228
2.10	0.795	2.53	0.795	-	-	25	12.1	F	Osm	NC-acetone	229
1.56	0.92	0.84	0.92	135-559	-	25	13.8	F	Osm	NC-acetone	230
1.33	0.81	1.43	0.81	94-568	-	25	12.5	F	Osm	NC-acetone	230
1.43	0.93	0.735	0.93	-	-	-	13.4	F	Osm	NC-acetone	216
1.5	0.91	0.863	0.91	390-5020	-	-	13.8	F	SD	NC-acetone	231
3.85	0.79	4.32	0.79	237-4550	1300	-	13.8	FU	SD	NC-acetone	232
1.8	0.9	1.085	0.9	237-4550	1300	-	13.8	FU	SD	NC-acetone	232
1.5	0.9	0.904	0.9	237-4550	1300	-	13.8	FU	SD	NC-acetone	233,234
0.727	1.0	0.250	1.0	300-4500	1300	-	13.8	FU	SD	NC-acetone	234
4.46	0.76	5.94	0.76	>1200	-	-	13.8	FU	SD	NC-acetone	236

$[\eta] = K'_m \, DP^a \qquad [\eta] = K_m \, M^a$

K'_m	a	$K_m \cdot 10^2$	a	Interval of [η] [ml g^{-1}]	Rate of Shear G [sec^{-1}]	Temp. [°C]	Nitrogen Content %	Nature of Sample	Method of Calibration	System used for Calibration	References
Nitrocellulose-Acetone (Cont'd.)											
0.82	1.0	0.282	1.0	<1200	-	-	13.8	FU	SD	NC-acetone	236
3.7	1.0	1.4	1.0	390-600	-	-	~12.0	U	S	NC-acetone	237
1.43	0.98	-	-	45-2200	-	-	-	FU	LS	NC-acetone	238
4.95	1.0	1.7	1.0	123-3030	0	-	13.8	F	LS	NC-acetone	223
0.83	0.95	0.377	0.95	90-1800	-	25	13.8	F	LS	NC-butyl acetate	239
2.19	0.86	1.66	0.86	170-520	-	-	13.8	F	LS	NC-acetone	240
Nitrocellulose-Ethyl Acetate (NC-Ethyl Acetate)											
1.33	1.0	-	-	-	-	-	-	-	-	-	241
2.13	0.92	1.22	0.92	100-5000	0	25	13.9	FU	Osm	NC-acetone	221,222
1.33	0.98	0.51	0.98	153-687	-	25	13.8	F	Osm	NC-acetone	230
1.80	0.82	1.83	0.82	125-716	-	25	12.5	F	Osm	NC-acetone	230
1.32	1.03	0.38	1.03	100-5000	0	25	15.9	FU	Osm	NC-acetone	242
1.25	1.0	0.437	1.0	430-6400	500	-	13.5	U	SD	NC-ethyl acetate	243
0.685	1.0	0.235	1.0	123-3530	0	-	13.8	F	LS	NC-acetone	223
0.755	1.01	0.25	1.01	107-1500	2500	30	13.5	F	LS	NC-ethyl acetate	244
0.276	1.37	0.063	1.37	107-1500	2500	30	13.5	F	Osm	NC-ethyl acetate	244
Nitrocellulose-Butyl Acetate (NC-Butyl Acetate)											
1.41	0.969	0.58	0.969	<700	-	25	14.1	F	Osm	NC-acetone	226,227
2.01	0.94	0.96	0.94	175-753	-	25	13.8	F	Osm	NC-acetone	230
2.49	0.79	3.00	0.79	147-788	-	25	12.5	F	Osm	NC-acetone	230
1.41	0.905	0.92	0.905	-	200-500	25	12.1	F	Osm	NC-acetone	229
1.52	1.0	0.525	1.0	212-1900	200-500	25	13.7	F	Osm	NC-butyl acetate	245
0.81	1.0	0.28	1.0	212-1900	-	25	13.7	F	LS	NC-butyl acetate	245
0.78	0.99	0.283	0.99	90-1800	-	25	13.8	F	LS	NC-butyl acetate	239

$[\eta] = K'_m DP^a$ $[\eta] = K_m M^a$

K'_m	a	$K_m \cdot 10^2$	a	Interval of $[\eta]$ [ml g^{-1}]	Rate of Shear G [sec^{-1}]	Temp. [°C]	Nitrogen Content %	Nature of Sample	Method of Calibration	System used for Calibration	References
Nitrocellulose-Ethyl Lactate											
1.2	1.03	0.38	1.03	119-1600	0	25	13.9	F U	Osm	NC-acetone	221,222
Nitrocellulose-n-Amyl Methyl Ketone											
2.74	0.780	3.61	0.780	-	-	25	12.1	F	Osm	NC-acetone	229
1.92	0.92	1.03	0.92	179-990	-	25	13.8	F	Osm	NC-acetone	230
1.85	0.82	1.95	0.82	134-776	-	25	12.5	F	Osm	NC-acetone	230
Nitrocellulose-Cyclohexanone											
2.00	0.81	2.24	0.81	-	-	25	12.1	F	Osm	NC-acetone	229
3.26	0.82	3.06	0.82	177-602	-	25	13.8	F	Osm	NC-acetone	230
2.61	0.75	3.96	0.75	125-612	-	25	12.5	F	Osm	NC-acetone	230
Cellulose-Cuprammonium Hydroxide (Cell.-Cuam)											
0.5	1.0	0.308	1.0	90-900	-	20		U	Osm	Cell.-acetate-m-cresol	246
0.55	1.0	0.339	1.0	100-1000	-	20		U	Osm	NC-acetone	246
3.19	0.657	11.3	0.657	20-400	-	25		F	Osm	Cell.-2.5-acetate-acetone	226
2.91	0.661	10.1	0.661	20-400	-	25		F	Osm	NC-acetone	226
8.08	0.523	56.4	0.523	470-1680	-	20		U	SD	Cell-Cuam	247
0.524	0.81	0.85	0.81	470-1680	-	20		U	SD	Cell-Cuam	248
0.85	0.77	1.70	0.77	470-1680	-	20		U	SD	Cell-Cuam	249
0.435	1.0	0.268	1.0	175-1970	500	-		U	SD	NC-ethyl acetate	243
0.68	0.9	0.70	0.9	480-2800	-	-		U	SD	NC-acetone	250
0.53	0.9	0.545	0.9	100-2800	-	-		U	SD	NC-acetone	233
1.14	1.15	0.33	1.15	470-1680	-	-		U	SD	Cell-Cuam	251

$[\eta] = K'_m DP^a$		$[\eta] = K_m M^a$		Interval of $[\eta]$	Rate of Shear $\dot{G}$	Temp.	Nature of Sample	Method of Calibration	System used for Calibration	References
$\bar{x}_m$	a	$K_m \cdot 10^2$	a	[ml g^{-1}]	[sec^{-1}]	[°C]				
Cellulose-Cuam (Cont'd.)										
0.16	1.0	0.099	1.0	-	-	-	FU	SD,LS	NC-acetone	252
1.58	0.76	3.3	0.76	>425	-	-	FU	SD	NC-acetone	236
0.29	1.0	0.18	1.0	<425	-	-	FU	SD	NC-acetone	236
0.384	1.0	0.237	1.0	120-505	-	-	U	S	Cell-Cuam	237
0.80	0.81	1.30	0.81	30-600	-	25	F	LS	NC-butyl acetate	239
Cellulose-Cupriethylenediamine (Cell.-Cuene)										
0.80	1.0	0.493	1.0	300-600	-	20	U	Osm	NC-acetone	253
1.33	0.905	1.33	0.905	100-2140	0	25	FU	Osm	NC-acetone	221,222
0.807	1.0	0.498	1.0	100-240	0	25	FU	Osm	NC-acetone	221,222
0.64	1.0	0.395	1.0	240-2140	0	25	FU	Osm	NC-acetone	221,222
0.77	1.0	0.475	1.0	<1000	-	-	U	Osm	NC-acetone	233
0.54	1.0	0.334	1.0	<1000	-	-	F	Osm	NC-acetone	233
0.98	0.9	1.01	0.9	-	-	25	U	Osm	NC-acetone	254
2.0	0.834	2.89	0.334	50-500	-	-	U	-	NC-ethyl acetate	255
1.7	0.8	2.88	0.8	140-550	980	25	U	Osm	Cell-Cuene	256
0.57	1.0	0.352	1.0	50-1000	-	25	U	-	NC-ethyl acetate	257
0.59	1.0	0.364	1.0	230-2720	500	-	U	SD	NC-ethyl acetate	243
0.98	0.9	1.01	0.9	190-2800	0	-	FU	SD	NC-acetone	250
0.82	0.9	0.85	0.9	190-2800	0	-	FU	SD	NC-acetone	233
0.58	1.0	0.358	1.0	600-1300	-	-	U	SD	Cell-FeTNa	258
0.248	1.0	0.153	1.0	-	-	-	U	SD	NC-acetone	252
2.44	0.76	5.10	0.76	>600	-	-	FU	SD	NC-acetone	236
0.448	1.0	0.277	1.0	<600	-	-	FU	SD	NC-acetone	236

References page VI-34

$[\eta] = K'_m DP^a$		$[\eta] = K_m M^a$		Interval of $[\eta]$	Rate of Shear	Temp.	Nature of Sample	Method of Calibration	System used for Calibration	References
K'_m	a	$K_m \cdot 10^2$	a	$[ml\ g^{-1}]$	$[sec^{-1}]$	$[°C]$				

Cellulose-Cadmiumethylenediamine (Cell.-Cadoxene)

K'_m	a	$K_m \cdot 10^2$	a	Interval	Rate	Temp.	Sample	Method	System	Ref.
1.38	1.0	0.850	1.0	143-1415	-	-	U	Osm	NC-acetone	207
1.4	0.8	2.39	0.8	143-1415	-	-	U	Osm	NC-acetone	207
0.56	1.0	0.346	1.0	<1200	-	-	U	Osm	NC-acetone	260
0.435	1.0	0.268	1.0	50-750	-	25	U	-	NC-ethyl acetate	257
2.5	0.75	5.47	0.75	<1800	500	25	U	SD	Cell-cadoxene	261
0.51	1.01	0.315	1.01	200-1100	-	20	U	SD	Cell-FeTNa	262
0.38	1.0	0.235	1.0	200-1100	-	20	U	SD	Cell-FeTNa	263
0.201	1.0	0.124	1.0	-	-	-	FU	SD,LS	NC-acetone	252
1.98	0.76	4.13	0.76	>530	-	-	FU	SD	NC-acetone	236
0.365	1.0	0.225	1.0	<530	-	-	FU	SD	NC-acetone	236
0.525	0.94	0.427	0.94	-	-	20	U	SD	NC-acetone	264
0.712	0.94	0.593	0.94	<1000	-	20	F	SD	NC-acetone	264
3.64	0.72	9.33	0.72	>1000	-	20	F	SD	NC-acetone	264
1.8	0.77	3.56	0.77	<1800	500	25	U	LS	Cell-cadoxene	261

Cellulose - FeTNa

K'_m	a	$K_m \cdot 10^2$	a	Interval	Rate	Temp.	Sample	Method	System	Ref.
0.998	1.0	0.615	1.0	800-1700	-	-	U	Osm	NC-acetone	265
0.74	1.0	0.457	1.0	50-1400	-	25	U	-	NC-ethyl acetate	257
0.84	1.0	0.519	1.0	300-1600	0	20	U	SD	Cell-FeTNa	266
0.925	1.0	0.571	1.0	300-1600	0	20	U	SD	Cell-FeTNa	266
0.814	1.0	0.502	1.0	300-1600	0	20	U	SD	Cell-FeTNa	266
0.66	1.01	0.407	1.01	660-2000	0	20	U	SD	Cell-FeTNa	258,266
0.575	1.0	0.355	1.0	<1300	-	20	U	SD	Cell-FeTNa	263
0.49	1.0	0.303	1.0	<1600	-	20	U	SD	Cell-FeTNa	263
0.325	1.0	0.201	1.0	<800	-	20	U	SD	Cell-FeTNa	263

$[\eta] = K'_m DP^a$		$[\eta] = K_m M^a$		Interval of $[\eta]$	Rate of Shear $\overline{G}$	Temp.	Nature of Sample	Method of Calibration	System used for Calibration	References
K'_m	a	$K_m \cdot 10^2$	a	[ml g^{-1}]	[sec^{-1}]	[°C]				
Cellulose-Zincethylenediamine (Cell-Zincoxene)										
0.767	0.936	0.585	0.936	-	-	20	U	Osm	NC-acetone	267
Cellulose-Tetraethylammonium Hydroxide										
0.42	1.0	0.26	1.0	-	-	20	U	Osm	NC-acetone	253
Cellulose- LiOH -Solution										
0.55	1.0	0.34	1.0	-	-	20	U	Osm	NC-acetone	253
Cellulose- Ca(SCN)$_2$ -Solution										
0.8	1.0	0.493	1.0	-	-	20	U	Osm	NC-acetone	253
Cellulose- H$_3$PO$_4$ -Solution										
2.0	1.0	1.23	1.0	-	-	20	U	Osm	NC-acetone	253
Cellulose- 10% NaOH -Solution										
0.7	1.0	0.43	1.0	-	-	20	U	Osm	NC-acetone	253

M. Ratio of Intrinsic Viscosities in Different Solvents
(only references are given for less important ratios)

$\frac{[\eta] \text{ NC*-Acetone}}{[\eta] \text{ Cell-Cuene}}$

Data	References
1.46	222
1.42	221
1.18-1.90	228
1.83	233
1.55	268
1.83	271
1.9	278

$\frac{[\eta] \text{ NC-Acetone}}{[\eta] \text{ Cell-Cuam}}$

Data	References
2.2	246
2.6	232
2.09-2.63	268
2.17	228
2.83	236
2.9	278

$\frac{[\eta] \text{ NC-Acetone}}{[\eta] \text{ Cell-FeTNa}}$

Data	References
1.27	258
1.6	278

$\frac{[\eta] \text{ NC-Acetone}}{[\eta] \text{ Cell-Cadoxene}}$

Data	References
2.25	236

$\frac{[\eta] \text{ NC-Acetone}}{[\eta] \text{ Ethyl Acetate}}$ (221,222,228, 230,235,274, 275)

$\frac{[\eta] \text{ NC-Acetone}}{[\eta] \text{ NC-Butyl Acetate}}$ (228,230, 275,276)

$\frac{[\eta]\text{-Cell-Cuene}}{[\eta]\text{-Cell-Cuam}}$

Data	References
1.34	243
1.05	269
1.51-1.70	272
1.25	270
1.37	271
1.54	233
1.39	228
1.53	278

$\frac{[\eta] \text{ Cell-Cuene}}{[\eta] \text{ Cell-FeTNa}}$

Data	References
0.88	209
0.91	278

$\frac{[\eta] \text{ Cell-Cuene}}{[\eta] \text{ Cell-Cadoxene}}$

Data	Reference
0.81	207

$\frac{[\eta] \text{ Cell-Cuam}}{[NC\text{-Ethyl Acetate}}$

Data	Reference
0.35	243

$\frac{[\eta] \text{ Cell-Cuam}}{[\eta] \text{ Cell-FeTNa}}$

Data	References
0.45	270
0.59	278

$\frac{[\eta] \text{ Cell-Cuam}}{[\eta] \text{ Cell-Cadoxene}}$

Data	References
0.89	252
0.80	260

$\frac{[\eta] \text{ Cell-Cuam}}{[\eta] \text{ Cell-10\% NaOH}}$

Data	Reference
0.72	277

$\frac{[\eta] \text{ Cell-Cadoxene}}{[\eta] \text{ Cell-FeTNa}}$ (252,262)

---

*NC = Nitrocellulose   Cell = Cellulose   Cuene, Cuam, FeTNa see under
Solvents for Cellulose

References page VI-34

N. Geometric Dimensions of Cellulose Molecules in Solution*

Data are given on KUHN-KUHN equivalent chain length A_m, the radius of gyration $\langle s^2 \rangle^{\frac{1}{2}}$, and the end-to-end distance $\langle r^2 \rangle^{\frac{1}{2}}$.

Molecular weight and in some cases values of A_m, $\langle s^2 \rangle^{\frac{1}{2}}$ and $\langle r^2 \rangle^{\frac{1}{2}}$ are designated according to the method used for the measurement.

Abbreviations: OS = osmotic measurement
                LS = light scattering
                SD = sedimentation-diffusion
                UC = equilibrium measurement in ultracentrifuge

Solvent System	Remarks on Sample	Temperature of Measurement [°C]	$\overline{M} \times 10^{-3}$		A_m [Å]	$\langle s^2 \rangle^{\frac{1}{2}}$ [Å]	$\langle r^2 \rangle^{\frac{1}{2}}$ [Å]	Ref.[≠]
Cellulose-Cuam			195.6		50			279(280)
Cellulose-Cadoxene					70			281(282)
	linters	25	–	(OS)		895 (LS)	2190 (LS)	261
			1415	(UC)				
			945	(LS)				
			745	(SD)				
			152	(OS)		485 (LS)	1190 (LS)	261
			430	(UC)				
			290	(LS)				
			210	(SD)				
Cellulose nitrate-acetone			13	(SD)			200[+]	252
			23.5	(SD)			280[+]	
			46	(SD)			550[+]	
			90	(SD)			750[+]	
			178	(SD)			1150[+]	
			262	(SD)			1300[+]	
			456	(SD)			1850[+]	
			630	(SD)			2050[+]	
			2490	(SD)			5300[+]	

* See also table on "Unperturbed Dimensions" in this Handbook.

≠ References in parenthesis give additional data.

+ Different methods of calculation.

PROPERTIES OF CELLULOSE MATERIALS

O. Second Virial Coefficients of Cellulose*

Some representative second virial coefficients A_2 are listed below as a function of sample molecular weight. The second virial coefficinet is obtained from the relation:

$$\pi \;=\; \frac{RT}{M}\, c + A_2 c^2 + \ldots\ldots$$

where π = osmotic pressure
R = gas constant
T = temperature
M = molecular weight
c = concentration

Degrees of polymerization of samples are designated according to method used for measurement:

OS = osmotic measurement

LS = light scattering

Solvent System	Sample	Degree of Polymerization		Temperature [°C]	$A_2 \times 10^{-7}$ [dyn cm^4 g^{-2}]	Ref.
Cellulose-Cadoxene	linters cellulose	940	(OS)	25	2.63	261
		610	(OS)		2.93	
	wood pulp	175	(OS)		3.45	
	linters cellulose	5820	(LS)		4.31	
		3570	(LS)		4.29	
		2290	(LS)		3.62	
		1780	(LS)		4.36	
		1400	(LS)		3.40	
	wood pulp	1310	(LS)		3.00	
Cellulose nitrate-acetone	linters cellulose	2250	(OS)		2.31	219
		1620	(OS)		2.36	
		1250	(OS)		2.44	
		924	(OS)		2.45	
		792	(OS)		2.41	
		671	(OS)		2.40	
		597	(OS)		2.56	
		439	(OS)		2.37	
		307	(OS)		2.61	
		251	(OS)		2.45	
		110	(OS)		3.58	

* See also table on "Second Virial Coefficients of Polymers" in this Handbook.

References page VI-34

P. Diffusion and Sedimentation Data*

Data are given on partial specific volume of solute v, coefficient of diffusion D, sedimentation coefficient s_o, sedimentation number $[s_o]$ and friction coefficient f/f_k. Molecular weights of samples are designated according to method used for measurement:

LS = light scattering

SD = measurement by sedimentation-diffusion

UC = equilibrium measurement in ultracentrifuge

Solvent System	Sample	Temperature [°C]	$\bar{M} \times 10^{-3}$	v [cm³ g⁻¹]	$D \times 10^7$ [cm² sec⁻¹]	$s_o \times 10^{13}$ [sec]	$[s_o] \times 10^{15}$ [cm²]	f/f_k	References
Cellulose-Cuam	aged alkali-cellulose	not given	62 (SD)	0.51	1.44	1.9	2.50	4.6	286
	spruce sulfite pulp	"	105 (SD)	0.51	1.16	2.6	3.92	4.8	286
	aged alkali-cellulose	"	210 (SD)	0.51	0.84	3.8	5.0	5.3	286
	pine sulfate pulp	"	320 (SD)	0.51	0.60	4.1	5.4	6.4	286
	sulfate pulp	"	560 (SD)	0.51	0.54	6.5	8.56	5.9	286
	sulfite pulp	"	700 (SD)	0.51	0.42	6.3	8.3	7.1	286
	α-cellulose from holocellulose	"	950 (SD)	0.51	0.32	6.5	8.56	8.4	286
		"	580 (SD)	0.66					
	linters cellulose, bleached with ClO₂	"	1700 (SD)	0.51	0.26	9.2	12.1	8.6	286
		"	1200 (SD)	0.66					
	cotton linters, not bleached	"	2100 (SD)	0.51	0.23	10.3	13.6	9.0	286
	Georgia cotton	"	2400 (SD)	0.51	0.20	10.4	13.7	9.8	286
	ramie fiber	"	2800 (SD)	0.51	0.18	10.8	14.2	10.4	286
	flax fiber	"	8200 (SD)	0.51	0.10	17.5	23.1	13.1	286
Cellulose-Cuene	acetylation grade wood pulp	25	175		1.2	5.5			287
	sulfite pulp, ClO₂-bleached, refined with 5% NaOH		333		0.95	8.3			287

* See also table on "Sedimentation and Diffusion Constants" in this Handbook.

Solvent System	Sample	Temperature [°C]	$\bar{M} \times 10^{-3}$	v [cm³g⁻¹]	$D \times 10^7$ [cm² sec⁻¹]	$s_o \times 10^{13}$ [sec]	$[s_o] \times 10^{15}$ [cm²]	f/f_k	References
Cellulose-Cadoxene	linters cellulose	25	745 (SD)		0.31	5.49			261
		25	435 (SD)		0.44	4.53			
		25	275 (SD)		0.58	3.80			
		25	210 (SD)		0.64	3.17			
		25	155 (SD)		0.75	2.75			
		25	43 (SD)		1.77	1.80			
Cellulose-FeTNa	bleached spruce sulfite pulp (DP ~ 1000)	20		0.654	0.60	2.17			258
	sample C, acid hydrolyzed (DP >1000)	20		0.654	0.89	1.75			258
	bleached spruce sulfite pulp (DP ~ 2000)	20		0.654	0.46	2.98			258
	bleached cotton linters (DP >3000)	20		0.654	0.35	3.35			258
Cellulose nitrate-acetone		not given	6.2 (SD)	0.51	35	5.2	1.35	1.7	286
		"	199 (SD)	0.51	3.7	18	4.67	5.4	286
		"	613 (SD)	0.51	2.0	30	7.78	6.9	286
	bleached cotton linters	"	400 (SD)	0.51	1.44	14	3.87	10.6	286
	sulfate pulp	"	420 (SD)	0.51	1.56	16.2	4.48	9.6	286
	sulfite pulp	"	455 (LS)	0.51	1.56	16.4	4.53	9.6	286
	rayon pulp	"	570 (SD)	0.51	1.66	23.3	6.45	8.2	286
	unbleached linters	"	620 (LS)	0.51	1.00	19.0	5.25	12.2	286

Q. First Order Rate Constants and Energy of Activation of Homogeneous Hydrolysis of Cellulose*

Hydrolyzing Acid	Medium Concentration [%]	Temperature [°C]	Concentration of Cellulose [%]	Rate Constant $\times 10^6$ [min^{-1}]	Energy of Activation [kcal mole^{-1}]	Origin and Preparation of Cellulose Sample	References
H_2SO_4	50	20.5	1	123		viscose rayon	292
		30	1	580			
		40	1	2850			
	51	18	0.5	30.5		cotton	293
		30	0.6	234			
	52	18	0.57	40	28.1	native ramie	294
		30	0.57	272			
		40	1.5	1850		cotton linters	295
	65	0.12	5.65	14		cotton	296
		20	1.27	400			
H_3PO_4	78	12	not given	0.329	29.6	purified cotton, partially degraded, reprecipitated after dissolution in H_3PO_4	297
		20		1.27			
		29		6.10			
		40		39.1			
	81.25	20	not given	0.85	35	acetate grade sulfite pulp	299
		30		7.1			
		40		37			
		20	not given	1.0	34	prehydrolyzed sulfate pulp	299
		30		8.9			
		40		38			
	86	0.12	0.07	0.083		purified cotton	296
		20	0.07	average 2.8 range 2.2 - 4			
	92.3	25	0.10	7.18		wood pulp, unbeaten	303

* Additional data may be found in references 289,290,291,298,301,302, and 303.

References page VI-34

R. Electrical Properties

As existing data are largely depending on the method of measurement as well as on moisture and electrolyte content of the material investigated, only some representative data are presented in this table. Further details are given in surveys of HEARLE (304) and in references in parenthesis.

Property	Nature of Material	Data	Remarks on Preparation of Sample and Method of Measurement	References
Specific resistance ρ (resistivity) [ohm·cm]	insulating paper	~ 5 · 10^{14}	air dry	304a
	cotton	~ 2 · 10^7	52% R.H., 30°C, single fiber[a]	305
		~ 1 · 10^7	62% R.H., 30°C	
		~ 7 · 10^5	75% R.H., 30°C	
		~ 3 · 10^5	85% R.H., 30°C	
	viscose rayon	~ 3 · 10^6	75% R.H., 30°C, single fiber	305
		~ 1 · 10^6	85% R.H., 30°C	
	viscose yarn	1.3–3.5 · 10^6	75% R.H., 30°C, nominal size 150/75	305
Mass specific resistance[b] Rs = ρ · d [ohm·g·cm^{-2}]	raw cotton	8 · 10^5	75% R.H., 25°C	306(307)
	ramie	1.8 · 10^6 resp. / 6 · 10^4	M[c] = 10%, 20°C	307
	hemp	1.05 · 10^7	M = 10%, 20°C	307
	jute, purified	2.5 - 10^8	M = 10%, 20°C	307
	flax, purified	6.6 · 10^6	M = 10%, 20°C	307
	viscose rayon	1.1 · 10^8	M = 10%, 20°C	307
	cuprammonium rayon	2.6 · 10^8	M = 10%, 20°C	307
	Fortisan	3.5 · 10^7	M = 10%, 20°C	307
	cotton	7 - 10^6	65% R.H., 20°C	308
Dielectric constant ε	regenerated cellulose	6.7 - 7.5	sheets regenerated from viscose 1 kc, 20°C-70°C	309(310)
	cellophane film dry	7.7	0.06 kc, 25°C	310(312,313,315)

[a] R.H. = Relative Humidity
[b] log Rs = -n log M + K   n and K = constants
[c] M = moisture content

Property	Nature of Material	Data	Remarks on Preparation of Sample and Method of Measurement	Reference
Dielectric constant ε (Cont'd.)	cellophane film dry	7.3	10 kc, 25°C	310
		6.7	10^3 kc, 25°C	
	cotton linters	6.1	1 kc, 30°C	311
	cotton	3.2	0% R.H., 1 kc	314(317)
		7.1	45% R.H., 1 kc	
		18.0	65% R.H., 1 kc	
		3.0	0% R.H., 100 kc	
		4.4	45% R.H., 100 kc	
		6.0	65% R.H., 100 kc	
	pure cellulose	7.5	bone dry, 0.1 kc, 20°C	316
		7.2	" , 1 kc, 20°C	
		7.0	" , 10 kc, 20°C	
		5.8	" , 10^4 kc, 20°C	
		5.6	" , 10^5 kc, 20°C	
	viscose rayon	3.5	0% R.H., 100 kc	314(317)
		4.7	45% R.H., 100 kc	
		5.3	65% R.H., 100 kc	
		3.6	0% R.H., 1 kc	
		5.4	45% R.H., 1 kc	
		8.4	65% R.H., 1 kc	
	alpha wood pulp	6.15	vacuum dried at 30°C, 1 kc, 30°C	315
Dissipation factor δ	viscose staple fibers	0.007	packing density, 50% 0% R.H., 1 kc	314(317)
		0.08	,45% R.H., 1 kc	
		0.40	,65% R.H., 1 kc	
		0.015	,0% R.H., 100 kc	
		0.02	,45% R.H., 100 kc	
		0.03	,55% R.H., 100-5000 kc	

References page VI-34

Property	Nature of Material	Data	Remarks on Preparation of Sample and Method of Measurement	References
Dissipation factor δ (Cont'd.)	pure cellulose	0.015	20°C, 0.1 kc	316
		0.02	20°C, 1 kc	
		0.03	20°C, 10 kc	
		0.045	20°C, 10^2 kc	
		0.065	20°C, 10^3 kc	
		0.08	20°C, 10^4 kc	
		0.07	20°C, 10^5 kc	

S. Physical and Mechanical Properties

Definitions:

1. Breaking strength is the maximum load required to break a fiber. Breaking length
is the length of the freely hanging fiber, which will cause the fiber to break
under its own weight.

Strength in kg/mm^2 = strength in g/den x 9 x sp. gr. of the fiber

Strength in $lb/inch^2$ = strength in g/den x sp. gr. x 12.861.

Strength in g/tex = breaking strength in kilometers = strength in g/den x 9.

2. Modulus of elasticity is the ratio of unit stress to unit strain.

3. Moisture regain is the percentage of water in the fiber at standard conditions
(20°C, 65 per cent R.H.) calculated for the constant oven dry weight of the fiber.

4. Water imbibition is the weight of water in per cent retained by the wet fiber after
centrifuging at standard conditions.

All data of dry fibers are given for standard conditions (65 per cent R.H. and 20°C).
Data are taken from references (65,319,320,321).

| | Cotton | Flax | Jute | Viscose rayon | | Viscose Staple Fibers | | |
				Normal	High Tenacity	Normal	High wet modulus (HWM) = Polynosics	Cross-linked
Breaking strength (g/den) dry	3.0-4.9	4.5-9.0	~3.4	1.6-2.5	4.0-6.1	1.8-3.0	3.0-6.0	2.0-2.3
Breaking length (km) dry	27-44	40.5-81.0	~30.6	14.5-22.5	36-54	16-27	27-54	18.0-20.7
wet/dry (%)	100-110	102-106	99-104	45-60	65-80	45-65	70-80	65-75
Breaking elongation dry (%)	8-10	2.5-3	1.7-1.9	15-30	9-20	14-30	7-15	12-16
Breaking elongation wet (%)	11	2.5-3	1.7-1.9	20-40	14-26	22-30	8-20	14-19
Modulus of elasticity (g/den)	42-82	200	195	33-77	69-100	48-68	30-90	35-42
Moisture regain (%)	7.1-8.5	10.0	12	12	14	13	12.1-12.7	13
Water of imbibition (%)	48			85-120	45-70	95-100	55-70	40-65

T. REFERENCES

1. H. J. Wellard, J. Polymer Sci., 13, 471 (1954).
2. P. H. Hermans and A. Weidinger, J. Colloid Sci., 1, 185 (1946).
3. W. Kast and R. Schwarz, Z. Elektrochem., 56, 228 (1952).
4. Ch. Legrand, J. Polymer Sci., 7, 333 (1951).
5. Ø. Ellefsen, J. Gjønnes and N. Norman, Acta Chem. Scand., 13, 853 (1959).
6. Ø. Ellefsen and N. Norman, J. Polymer Sci., 58, 769 (1962).
7. E. Sauter, Z. Physik. Chem. (Leipzig), B35, 83 (1937).
8. H. Kiessig, Z. Physik. Chem. (Leipzig), B43, 79 (1939).
9. H. Kiessig, Z. Elektrochem., 54, 320 (1950).
10. Ch. Legrand, Compt. Rend., 226, 1983 (1948); 227, 529 (1948).
11. Ch. Legrand, Acta Cryst., 5, 800 (1952).
12. E. Treiber in E. Treiber, Ed., "Die Chemie der Pflanzenzellwand," Springer,
    Berlin, 1957, p. 157.
13. D. G. Fisher and J. Mann, J. Polymer Sci., 42, 189 (1960).
14. Ø. Ellefsen, Norelco Reptr., 7, 104 (1960).
15. K. C. Ellis and J. O. Warwicker, J. Polymer Sci., 56, 339 (1962).
16. K. Hess and J. Gundermann, Chem. Ber. 70B, 1788 (1937).
17. Ch. Legrand, J. Chem. Phys., 48, 33 (1951).
18. Ch. Legrand, Dissertation, Paris, 1953.
19. K. Hutino and I. Sakurada, Naturwissenschaften, 28, 577 (1940).
20. Ch. Legrand, Compt. Rend., 233, 407 (1951).
21. Ø. Ellefsen, J. Gjønnes and N. Norman, Norsk Skogind., 13, 411 (1959).
22. D. W. Jones, J. Polymer Sci., 32, 371 (1958); 42, 173 (1960).
23. T. Petitpas, M. Oberlin and J. Mering, J. Polymer Sci., C2, 423 (1963).
24. T. Kubo, Z. Physik. Chem. (Leipzig), A187, 297 (1940).
25. K. R. Andress, Z. Physik. Chem. (Leipzig), B2, 380 (1929).
26. T. S. Gross and T. L. Clark, Z. Krist., 99, 357 (1938).
27. G. Honjo and M. Watanabe, Nature, 181, 326 (1958).
28. R. O. Herzog, J. Phys. Chem., 30, 460 (1926).
29. K. Weissenberg, A. Burgeni and O. Kratky, Naturwissenschaften, 17, 181 (1929).
30. A. Burgeni and O. Kratky, Z. Physik. Chem. (Leipzig), B4, 401 (1929).
31. E. Treiber, Monatsh. Chem., 80, 508 (1949).
32. A. I. Barry, C. F. Petersen and A. I. King, J. Am. Chem. Soc., 58, 333 (1936).
33. L. Loeb and L. Segal, J. Polymer Sci., 14, 121 (1954).
34. K. H. Meyer and H. Mark, Z. Physik. Chem. (Leipzig), B2, 115 (1929).
35. H. Mark and G. v. Susich, Z. Physik. Chem. (Leipzig), B4, 431 (1929).
36. H. Kiessig, Z. Elektrochem., 54, 320 (1950); Structure Reports, 13, 503 (1950).
37. I. Sakurada and K. Hutino, Kolloid-Z., 77, 347 (1936).
38. O. Kratky and E. Treiber, Z. Elektrochem., 55, 716 (1951).
39. K. Hess and H. Kiessig, Z. Physik. Chem. (Leipzig), B49, 235 (1941).
40. M. Polanyi, Naturwissenschaften, 9, 288 (1921).
41. O. L. Sponsler and W. H. Dore, 4th Colloid Symposium Monograph, 174 (1926).
42. O. L. Sponsler and W. H. Dore, Nature, 125, 633 (1930).
43. O. L. Sponsler and W. H. Dore, J. Am. Chem. Soc., 50, 1940 (1928).
44. K. H. Meyer and G. W. Paschow, Helv. Chim. Acta, 18, 589 (1935).
45. K. H. Meyer and L. Misch, Helv. Chim. Acta, 20, 232 (1937).
46. K. H. Meyer and L. Misch, Chem. Ber.,70B, 266 (1937).
47. A. v. d. Wyk and K. H. Meyer, J. Polymer Sci., 2, 583 (1946).
48. U. Yoshida and Ch. Park, Mem. Coll. Sci., Univ. Kyoto, Ser. A, 17, 443 (1934);
    through Structure Reports, 3, 828 (1933-35).
49. P. H. Hermans and A. Weidinger, J. Appl. Phys., 19, 491 (1948).
50. P. H. Hermans and A. Weidinger, Bull. Soc. Chim. Belges, 57, 123 (1948).
51. P. H. Hermans and A. Weidinger, Kolloid-Z., 115, 103 (1949); 120, 3 (1951).
52. P. H. Hermans and A. Weidinger, J. Polymer Sci., 4, 135 (1949).
53. P. H. Hermans, Makromol. Chem., 6, 25 (1951).
54. P. H. Hermans and A. Weidinger, Textile Res. J., 31, 558 (1961).
55. O. Ant-Wuorinen, Paperi Puu, 37, 335 (1955).
56. O. Ant-Wuorinen and A. Visapää, Paperi Puu, 43, 105, 207, 289, 343 (1961).
57. A. Visapää, Faserforsch. Textiltech., 15, 579 (1964).
58. G. Jayme and H. Knolle, Papier, 18, 249 (1964).
59. P. H. Hermans and A. Weidinger, J. Polymer Sci., 6, 533 (1951).
60. O. Ant-Wuorinen and A. Visapää, Paperi Puu, 38, 523 (1956).
61. H. L. Vosters, Svensk Papperstid., 65, 65 (1962).
62. O. Ant-Wuorinen and A. Visapää, Paperi Puu, 40, 313 (1958).
63. O. Ant-Wuorinen and A. Visapää, Paperi Puu, 44, 337 (1962).
64. A. Lude, Ann. Sci. Textiles Belges, 1961 (2), 36.
65. E. Treiber, Chemiefasern, 14, 25 (1964).
66. J. K. Smith, W. J. Kitchen and D. B. Mutton, J. Polymer Sci., C2, 499 (1963).
67. D. S. Jackson and A. Sandig, Textile Res. J., 31, 421 (1961).

68. H. Krässig and W. Kitchen, J. Polymer Sci., $\underline{51}$, 123 (1961).
69. P. H. Hermans and A. Weidinger, J. Polymer Sci., $\underline{5}$, 565 (1950).
70. P. H. Hermans and A. Weidinger, J. Am. Chem. Soc., $\underline{68}$, 2547 (1946).
71. P. H. Hermans, "Physics and Chemistry of Cellulose Fibers," Elsevier, New York, 1949, pp. 317-18.
72. J. A. Howsmon and W. A. Sisson in E. Ott, H. M. Spurlin and M. W. Grafflin, Eds., "Cellulose and Cellulose Derivatives," 2nd ed., Interscience, New York, 1954, pp. 291-316.
73. O. Kratky in H. A. Stuart, Ed., "Die Physik der Hochpolymeren," Springer, Berlin, 1955, Vol. III, pp. 288-305.
74. J. de Booys and P. H. Hermans, Kolloid-Z., $\underline{97}$, 229 (1941).
75. J. J. Hermans, P. H. Hermans, D. Vermaas and A. Weidinger, Rec. Trav. Chim., $\underline{65}$, 427 (1946).
76. P. H. Hermans, "Physics and Chemistry of Cellulose Fibers," Elsevier, New York, 1949, pp. 251-262.
77. H. Vosters, Svensk Papperstid., $\underline{65}$, 65 (1962).
78. T. K. Smith, W. J. Kitchen and D. B. Mutton, J. Polymer Sci. C2, 499 (1963).
79. P. H. Hermans, J. J. Hermans, D. Vermaas and A. Weidinger, J. Polymer Sci., $\underline{1}$, 393 (1946); $\underline{2}$, 632 (1947).
80. W. Kast, Z. Elektrochem., $\underline{57}$, 525 (1953).
81. P. H. Hermans, "Contribution to the Physics of Cellulose Fibers," Elsevier, New York, 1946, p, 64.
82. W. J. Lyons, J. Chem. Phys., $\underline{9}$, 377 (1941).
83. A. J. Stamm and L. A. Hansen, J. Phys. Chem., $\underline{41}$, 1007 (1937).
84. H. Wakeham, Textile Res. J., $\underline{19}$, 595 (1949).
85. W. Moll, Z. Ver.Deut. Chem., Beihefte, Nr. 47, 105 (1943).
86. G. F. Davidson, J. Textile Inst., $\underline{18}$, T 175 (1927).
87. J. M. Preston and M. V. Nimkar, J. Textile Inst., $\underline{41}$, T 446 (1950).
88. J. A. Howsmon, Textile Res. J., $\underline{19}$, 152 (1949).
89. N. V. Klenkova, O. M. Kulakova and L. A. Volkova, Zh. Prikl. Khim., $\underline{36}$, 166 (1963).
90. V. I. Sharkov and V. P. Levanova, Vysokomolekul. Soedin., $\underline{1}$, 1027 (1959).
91. K. Lauer and U. Westerman, Kolloid-Z., $\underline{107}$, 89 (1944).
92. F. C. Brenner, V. Frilette and H. Mark, J. Am. Chem. Soc., $\underline{70}$, 877 (1948).
93. E. Klein and K. Bosarge, J. Polymer Sci., C2, 515 (1963).
94. N. V. Mikhailov, E. Z. Fainberg and M. Kozler, Vysokomolekul. Soedin., $\underline{2}$, 1044 (1960).
95. M. V. Tsilipotkina, A. A. Tager, B. S. Petrov and G. Pustobaeva, Vysokomolekul. Soedin., $\underline{4}$, 1844 (1962).
96. B. Alince and L. Kuniak, Papir Celulosa, $\underline{19}$, 67 (1964).
97. P. H. Hermans, J. J. Hermans and D. Vermaas, Kolloid-Z, $\underline{109}$, 9 (1944); J. Polymer Sci. $\underline{1}$, 149, 156, 162 (1946).
98. Centre de Recherches des Industries Textiles de Rouen, Bull. Inst. Textile France, $\underline{1962}$, 945.
99. N. V. Mikhailov, M. N. Zav'yalova and V. O. Gorbacheva, Khim. Volokna, $\underline{1960}$, (1), 19.
99a. J. Juilfs, Forschungsber. Wirtsch. Verkehrsministeriums Nordrhein-Westfalen Nr. 381, 38, 44 (1957).
99b. J. Jacquemart, Bull. Inst. Textile France, $\underline{1962}$, 963.
100. F. C. Magne, H. I. Portas and H. Wakeham, J. Am. Chem. Soc., $\underline{69}$, 1896 (1947).
101. H. Sommer and F. Winkler in H. Sommer, Ed., "Handbuch der Werkstoffprüfung," Vol. V, Springer, Berlin, 1960, p. 1122.
102. N. V. Mikhailov and E. Z. Fainberg, Vysokomolekul. Soedin., $\underline{4}$, 230 (1962).
103. E. Calvet and P. H. Hermans, J. Polymer Sci., $\underline{6}$, 33 (1951).
104. W. Kast in H. A. Stuart, Ed., "Die Physik der Hochpolymeren," Vol. III, Springer, Berlin, 1955, p. 283.
105. R. S. Jessup and E. J. Proser, J. Res. Natl. Bur. Std., $\underline{44}$, 387 (1950).
106. J. B. Taylor, J. Textile Inst., $\underline{45}$, T 642 (1954).
107. J. C. Guthrie, J. Textile Inst., $\underline{40}$, T 489 (1949).
108. S. M. Neale and W. A. Stringfellow, Trans. Faraday Soc., $\underline{37}$, 525 (1941).
109. W. H. Rees, J. Textile Inst., $\underline{39}$, T 351 (1948).
110. D. K. Ashpole, Nature, $\underline{169}$, 37 (1952).
111. P. H. Hermans, "Contribution to the Physics of Cellulose Fibers," Elsevier, New York, 1946, pp. 33-37.
112. E. Balcerzyk and K. Hempel, Przeglad Papier., $\underline{20}$, 309 (1964).
113. W. Morrow, Tappi, $\underline{42}$, 167 (1959).
114. M. M. Chilikin, Zh. Prikl. Khim., $\underline{3}$, 221 (1930).
115. G. H. Argue and O. Maas, Can. J. Res., $\underline{B13}$, 564 (1935).
116. W. B. Campbell, Ind. Eng. Chem., $\underline{26}$, 218 (1934).
117. W. G. Macmillan, R. R. Mukherjee and M. K. Sen, J. Textile Inst., $\underline{37}$, T 13 (1946).

118. K. Lauer, R. Döderlein, C. Jäckel and O. Wilde, J. Makromol. Chem., 1, 76 (1943).
119. A. V. Dumanskii and E. F. Nekryach, Kolloidn. Zh., 17, 171 (1955).
120. S. M. Lipatov, D. V. Zharkovskii and J. M. Zagraevskaya, Kolloidn. Zh., 21, 526 (1959).
121. K. P. Mishchenko, S. L. Talmud and V. I. Yakimova, Vysokomolekul. Soedin., 1, 662 (1959).
122. D. V. Zharkovskii, Dokl. Akad. Nauk Belorussk. SSR, 3, 492 (1959), through Chem. Zentr., 1961, 17966.
123. Kh.U.Usmanov and I. Kh. Khakimov, Uzbeksk. Khim. Zh., 1959 (5), 30.
124. Kh. U. Usmanov, A. A. Yul'chibaev and Sh. Nadzhimutdinov, Vysokomolekul. Soedin., 3, 1217 (1961).
125. M. Wahba, J. Phys. Colloid Chem., 52, 1197 (1948).
126. E. F. Nekryach and F. Semchenko, Ukr. Khim. Zh., 26, 700 (1960).
127. J. L. Morrison, W. B. Campbell and O. Maas, Can. J. Research, B 18, 168 (1940).
128. I. Kh. Khakimov, U. T. Mat'yakubova and Kh. U. Usmanov in Kh. U. Usmanov, Ed., "Khimia i Physiko-Khimia Prirodnych i Sinteticheskich Polimerov," Nauka, Tashkent, 1964, p. 36.
129. M. Wahba, J. Phys. Colloid Chem., 54, 1148 (1950).
130. Ya. V. Pak and Kh. U. Usmanov, Kolloidn. Zh., 18, 233 (1956).
131. N. V. Mikhailov and E. Z. Fainberg, Dokl. Akad. Nauk SSSR 109, 1160 (1956); J. Polymer Sci., 30, 259 (1958).
132. P. H. Hermans, "Contribution to the Physics of Cellulose Fibers," Elsevier, New York, 1946, pp. 144-146.
133. P. H. Hermans, "Contribution to the Physics of Cellulose Fibers," Elsevier, New York, 1946, P. 113.
134. A. Frey-Wyssling, Helv. Chim. Acta, 19, 911, 981 (1936).
135. K. Kanamaru, Helv. Chim. Acta, 17, 1037, 1425 (1934).
136. J. M. Preston, Trans. Faraday Soc., 29, 65 (1933).
137. K. Atsuki and S. Okajima, J. Soc. Chem. Ind. Japan, 40, 360 B (1937).
138. A. Frey-Wyssling, Kolloidchem. Beihefte, 23, 40 (1927).
139. A. Herzog, Textile Forschg., 4, 58 (1922).
140. A. Herzog, "Die Unterscheidung von natürlichen und künstlichen Seiden," Th. Steinkopff, Dresden, 1910, p. 59. A. Herzog, "Die mikroskopische Untersuchung der Seide und Kunstseide," Springer, Berlin, 1924, pp. 66-69.
141. A. Frey-Wyssling, Jahrb. Wiss. Botanik, 65, 201 (1926).
142. J. Jacquemart, Bull. Inst. Text. France, 1962, 963.
143. R. Meredith, J. Textile Inst., 37, T 205 (1946).
144. B. E. Bingham, Makromol. Chem., 77, 139 (1964).
145. A. N. J. Heyn, Textile Res. J., 22, 513 (1952).
146. E. Treiber, Lecture at 2nd Intern. Man-Made Fiber Conference, Dornbirn, July 15, 1963.
147. V. A. Berestnev, N. I. Grechushkina, M. B. Lytkina, V. A. Kargin, Khim. Volokna, 1962 (3), 45.
148. E. Klein and K. Bosarge, J. Polymer Sci., C2, 515 (1963).
149. S. B. Newman in G. M. Kline, Ed., "Analytical Chemistry of Polymers," Part III, John Wiley, New York, 1962, pp. 286-287.
150. N. Barakat and A. M. Hindeleh, Textile Res. J. 34, 581 (1964).
151. J. M. Preston and R. V. Bhat, J. Textile Inst., 39, T 211 (1948).
152. L. Rose and J. D. Griffiths, J. Textile Inst., 39, P 265 (1948).
153. H. J. Marrinan and J. Mann, J. Polymer Sci., 21, 301 (1956).
154. H. J. Marrinan and J. Mann, J. Polymer Sci., 32, 357 (1958).
155. H. G. Higgins, C. M. Stewart and K. J. Harrington, J. Polymer Sci., 51, 59 (1961).
156. B. Schneider and J. Vodnanski, Collection Czech. Chem. Commun., 28, 2080 (1963).
157. K. H. Bassett, C. Y. Liang and R. H. Marchessault, J. Polymer Sci., A1, 1687 (1963).
158. F. G. Hurtubise, Can. Textile J., 76, 53 (1959).
159. C. Y. Liang and R. H. Marchessault, J. Polymer Sci., 35, 529 (1959); 37, 385 (1959).
160. H. J. Marrinan and J. Mann, J. Appl. Chem. (London), 4, 201 (1954).
161. M. Tsuboi, J. Polymer Sci., 25, 159 (1957).
162. H. J. Marrinan and J. Mann, J. Polymer Sci., 27, 595 (1958).
163. P. Bouriot, Bull. Inst. Textile France, 1962, 1197.
164. B. D. Saksena, K. C. Aggarwal and G. S. Jauhri, J. Polymer Sci., 62, 347 (1962).
165. J. Mann and H. J. Marrinan, Trans. Faraday Soc., 52, 481, 487, 492 (1956).
166. F. G. Hurtubise and H. Krässig, Anal. Chem., 32, 177 (1960).
167. B. I. Stepanov, R. G. Zhbankov and R. Marupov, Vysokomolekul. Soedin., 3, 1633 (1961).
168. B. I. Stepanov and R. G. Zhbankov, Zavodsk. Lab., 29, 696 (1963).
169. R. H. Marchessault, Pure Appl. Chem., 5, 107 (1962).
170. O. Ant-Wuorinen and A. Visapää, Paperi Puu, 42, 367 (1960).

171. O. Aut-Wuorinen and A. Visapää, Paperi Puu, 45, 35 (1963).
172. R. T. O'Connor, E. F. Du Pre and O. Mitcham, Textile Res. J., 28, 382 (1958).
173. C. Y. Liang and R. H. Marchessault, J. Polymer Sci., 39, 269 (1959).
174. H. G. Higgins, J. Polymer Sci., 28, 645 (1958).
175. F. H. Forziati and J. W. Rowen, J. Res. Natl. Bur. Std., 46, 38 (1951).
176. A. W. Mc. Kenzie and H. G. Higgins, Svensk Papperstid., 61, 893 (1958).
177. J. Vodnanski, M. Slabina and B. Schneider, Collection Czech. Chem. Commun.,
     28, 3245 (1963).
178. R. G. Zhbankov, V. I. Nepochatych, R. Marupov and Z. A. Rogovin, Vysokomolekul.
     Soedin., 4, 1696 (1962).
179. W. T. Koch, W. B. Kunz and J. T. Massengale, Tappi, 46, 569 (1963).
180. N. Buchner, Papier, 14, 126 (1960).
181. R. Willstätter and L. Zechmeister, Chem. Ber., 46, 2401 (1913).
182. A. Ekenstam, Chem. Ber., 69, 549, 553 (1936).
183. A. Ekenstam, Svensk Papperstid., 45, 81 (1942).
184. Th. Taylor, Brit. Pat. 787 (1859).
185. F Letters, Kolloid-Z., 58, 229 (1932).
186. P. P. v. Weimarn, Kolloid-Z., 11, 41 (1912).
187. H. Erbring and H. Geinitz, Kolloid-Z., 84, 25 (1938).
188. I. R. Katz and I. Seiberlich, Paper Trade J., 110 (7), 37 (1940).
189. G. F. Davidson, J. Textile Inst., 25, T 174 (1934); 27, T 112 (1936); 28, T 27
     (1937).
190. E. Treiber and B. Abrahamson, Papier, 13, 253 (1959).
191. A. Dehnert and W. König, Cellulosechemie, 6, 1 (1925).
192. Th. Lieser and E. Leckzyck, Ann. Chem., 522, 56 (1936).
193. Th. Lieser, Ann. Chem., 528, 276 (1937).
194. T. Brownsett and D. A. Clibbens, J. Textile Inst., 32, T 57 (1941).
195. Th. Lieser, "Kurzes Lehrbuch der Cellulosechemie," Gebrüder Borntraeger, Berlin-
     Nikolassee, 1953, p. 41.
196. R. S. Shutt, U. S. Pat. 2,371,359 (13/3/1945) through C. A. 39, 3667 (1945).
197. G. Jayme, Tappi, 44, 299 (1961).
198. W. Bergmann, K. K. Hasvold and J. Trüften, Papier, 18, 150 (1964).
199. E. Schweizer, J. Prakt. Chem., 72, 109 (1857).
200. W. Traube, Chem. Ber., 44, 3319 (1911).
201. F. L. Straus and R. M. Levy, Paper Trade J., 114, 23 (1942).
202. G. Jayme and F. Lang, Kolloid-Z., 150, 5 (1957).
203. G. Jayme, Papier, 5, 244 (1951).
204. G. Jayme and K. Neuschäffer, Papier, 9, 563 (1955).
205. G. Jayme and K. Neuschäffer, Papier, 11, 47 (1957).
206. G. Jayme and K. Neuschäffer, Makromol. Chem., 23, 71 (1957).
207. D. Henley, Svensk Papperstid., 63, 143 (1960).
208. G. Jayme and V. Verburg, Reyon, Zellwolle u. Chemiefasern, 32, 193; 275 (1954).
209. L. Valtasaari, Paperi Puu, 39, 243; 250; 252 (1957).
210. E. H. Büchner and H. E. Steutel, Proc. Acad. Sci. Amsterdam, 36, 671 (1933).
211. A. Dobry, J. Chim. Phys., 31, 568 (1934).
212. H. Staudinger and G. V. Schulz, Chem. Ber. 68, 2320 (1935).
213. H. A. Wannow and Fr. Thormann, Kolloid-Z., 108, 94 (1940).
214. E. Husemann and G. V. Schulz, Z. Physik. Chem. (Leipzig), B 52, 1 (1942).
215. H. A. Wannow, Kolloid-Z., 112, 103 (1944).
216. J. Jullander, Arkiv Kemi, A 21, 8 (1945).
217. R. H. Blaker, R. M. Badger and R. M. Noyes, J. Phys. Chem., 51, 574 (1947).
218. E. Heuser and L. Jörgensen, Tappi, 34, 450 (1951).
219. A. Münster, Z. Physik. Chem. (Leipzig), 197, 17 (1951).
220. A. Münster, J. Polymer Sci., 8, 633 (1952).
221. E. H. Immergut, J. Schurz and H. Mark, Monatsh. Chem., 84, 219 (1953).
222. E. H. Immergut, B. G. Ranby and H. Mark, Ind. Eng. Chem., 45, 2483 (1953).
223. A. M. Holtzer, H. Benoit and P. Doty, J. Phys. Chem., 58, 624 (1954).
224. A. M. Holtzer, H. Benoit and P. Doty, J. Phys. Chem., 58, 635 (1954).
225. T. Okawa, Sen-i Gakkaishi, 13, 305 (1957).
226. R. J. E. Cumberbirch and W. G. Harland, J. Textile Inst., 49, T 679 (1958).
227. W. G. Harland, J. Textile Inst., 49, T 478 (1958).
228. E. Treiber, B. Abrahamson and V. Holta, Svensk Papperstid., 62, 459 (1959).
229. W. R. Moore and G. D. Edge, J. Polymer Sci., 47, 469 (1960).
230. G. P. Pearson and W. R. Moore, Polymer 1, 144 (1960).
231. G. Meyerhoff, Naturwissenschaften, 41, 13 (1954).
232. G. V. Schulz and M. Marx, Makromol. Chem., 14, 52 (1954).
233. M. Marx, Papier, 10, 135 (1956).
234. G. Meyerhoff, Makromol. Chem., 32, 249 (1959).
235. M. Wandel, Dissertation, Stuttgart 1957.
236. M. Marx-Figini, Papier, 16, 551 (1962).

237. E. O. Kraemer, Ind. Eng. Chem., 30, 1200 (1938).
238. R. M. Badger and R. H. Blaker, J. Phys. Chem., 53, 1056 (1949).
239. R. J. C. Michie, Polymer, 2, 446 (1961).
240. M. M. Huque, D. A. J. Goring and S. G. Mason, Can. J. Chem., 36, 952 (1958).
241. W. J. Alexander and R. L. Mitchell, Anal. Chem., 21, 1497 (1947).
242. T. Kawai and K. Kamide, J. Polymer Sci., 54, 343 (1961).
243. S. Newman, L. Loeb and C. M. Conrad, J. Polymer Sci., 10, 463 (1953).
244. M. L. Hunt, S. Newman, H. A. Scheraga and P. J. Flory, J. Phys. Chem., 60, 1278 (1956).
245. J. Schurz, Papier, 15, 10 (1961).
246. H. Staudinger and G. Daumiller, Ann. Chem., 529, 219 (1937).
247. N. Gralén, Dissertation, Uppsala, 1944.
248. W. Badgley, B. I. Frilette and H. Mark, Ind. Eng. Chem., 37, 227 (1945).
249. P. H. Hermans, "Physics and Chemistry of Cellulose Fibers," Elsevier, New York, 1949, p. 119.
250. M. Marx, Makromol. Chem., 16, 157 (1955).
251. M. I. Arkhipov, Izv. Vysshykh Uchebn. Zavedenii, Khim. i Khim. Tekhnol., 3, 1109 (1960).
252. G. Meyerhoff, Fortschr. Hochpolymer. Forsch., 3, 59 (1961).
253. H. Staudinger and G. Daumiller, Chem. Ber., 70, 2508 (1937).
254. H. Vink, Arkiv Kemi, 11, 29 (1957).
255. W. J. Alexander, O. Goldschmid and R. L. Mitchell, Ind. Eng. Chem., 49, 1303 (1957).
256. H. Vink, Arkiv Kemi, 14, 195 (1959).
257. D. K. Smith, R. F. Bampton and W. J. Alexander, Ind. Eng. Chem., Proc. Des. Developm., 2, 57 (1963).
258. S. Claesson, W. Bergmann and G. Jayme, Svensk Papperstid., 62, 141 (1959).
260. H. Nadziakiewicz and H. Jedlinska, Polimery, 7, 85 (1962).
261. D. Henley, Arkiv Kemi, 18, 327 (1961).
262. G. Jayme and P. Kleppe, Papier, 15, 6 (1961).
263. G. Jayme and P. Kleppe, Papier, 15, 492 (1961).
264. L. S. Bolotnikova and T. I. Samsonova, Vysokomolekul. Soedin., 6, 533 (1964).
265. N. S. Nikolaeva, E. M. Mogilevskii and Z. K. Lin'kova, Khim. Volokna, 1960, (4), 20.
266. W. Bergmann, Dissertation, TH Darmstadt 1958.
267. V. P. Saxena, H. L. Bhatnagar and A. B. Biswas, J. Appl. Polymer Sci., 7, 181 (1963).
268. Ø. Ellefsen and F. A. Abadie-Maumert, Norsk Skogind., 10, 238 (1956).
269. W. E. Gloor and E. D. Klug in E. Ott, M.W.Grafflin and H.M. Spurlin, Eds., "Cellulose and Cellulose Derivatives," Part III, Interscience, New York, 1955, p. 1440.
270. N. Gralén and J. Linderot, Svensk Papperstid., 59, 14 (1956).
271. C. M. Conrad, V. W. Tripp and T. Mares, J. Phys. Coll. Chem., 55, 238 (1956).
272. B. L. Browning and L. O. Sell, Tappi, 39, 489 (1956).
273. W. E. Roseveare and L. Poore, Ind. Eng. Chem., 45, 2518 (1953).
274. M. Marx-Figini and G. V. Schulz, Makromol. Chem., 54, 102 (1962).
275. W. R. Moore, J. A. Epstein, A. M. Brown and B. M. Tidswell, J. Polymer Sci., 23, 23 (1957).
276. L. Nicolas, Bull. Assoc. Tech. Ind. Papetière, 5, 427 (1951).
277. W. Zimmermann, Melliand Textilber., 23, 73 (1942).
278. B. Philipp and K. J. Linow, to be published.
279. A. Peterlin in H. A. Stuart, Ed., "Die Physik der Hochpolymeren,"Vol. II, Springer Berlin, 1953, p. 556.
280. H. A. Stuart in H. A. Stuart, "Die Physik der Hochpolymeren,"Vol. II, Springer, Berlin, 1953, pp. 654-664.
281. S. Claesson, Polymer, 3, 471 (1962).
282. W. Burchard, Z. Physik. Chem. (Frankfurt), 42, 293 (1964).
286. J. Hengstenberg in H. A. Stuart, Ed., "Die Physik der Hochpolymeren,"Vol. II, Springer, Berlin, 1953, pp. 464-477.
287. H. Vink, Arkiv Kemi, 11, 29 (1957).
288. G. R. Andersson, Arkiv Kemi, 20, 513 (1963).
289. L. I. Novikova and A. A. Konkin, Zh. Prikl. Khim., 32, 1081 (1959).
290. A. A. Konkin, A. G. Yashunskaya and E. M. Bychkova, Nauchn. Issled. Tr., Vses, Nauch. —Issled. Inst. Iskusstvennogo Volokna, 1955,(2) 3 .
291. A. A. Konkin, N. I. Kaplan and Z. A. Rogovin, Zh. Prikl. Khim., 28, 729 (1955).
292. A. A. Konkin and L. I. Novikova, Nauchn. Issled. Tr. Vses. Nauchn. Issled. Inst. Iskusstvennogo Volokna, 1957, (3), 3.
293. K. Freudenberg and G. Blomquist, Chem. Ber., 68, 2070 (1935).
294. K. Freudenberg, W. Kuhn, W. Dürr, F. Bolz and G. Steinbrunn, Chem. Ber., 63, 1510 (1930).
295. A. A. Konkin, R. A. Krylova and Z. A. Rogovin, Kolloidn. Zh.,15, 246 (1953).
296. A. Ekenstam, Chem. Ber. 69, 553 (1936).

297. G. V. Schulz and H. J. Löhmann, J. Prakt. Chem., 157, 238 (1941).
298. G. V. Schulz and E. Husemann, Z. Physik. Chem., B52, 23 (1942).
299. R. H. Marchessault and B. G. Ranby, Svensk Papperstid., 62, 230 (1959).
300. B. G. Ranby, J. Polymer Sci., 53, 131 (1961).
301. L. Jörgenson, Dissertation, Trontheim 1950.
302. R. A. Martin and E. Pacsu, Textile Res. J., 26, 192 (1956).
303. A. J. Stamm and W. E. Cohen, J. Phys. Chem., 42, 921 (1938).
304. J. W. S. Hearle, J. Textile Inst., 43, P 194, (1952); J. W. S. Hearle in
      J. W. S. Hearle and R. H. Peters, Eds., "Moisture in Textiles," Butterworth,
      London, 1960, pp. 123-141.
304a. H. F. Church, J. Soc. Chem. Ind. (London), 66, 221 (1947).
305. S. P. Hersh and D. J. Montgomery, Textile Res. J., 22, 805 (1952).
306. A. C. Walker and M. H. Quell, J. Textile Inst., 24, T 123 (1933).
307. J. W. S. Hearle, J. Textile Inst., 44, T 117, 144, 155, 177 (1953).
308. J. W. S. Hearle, J. Textile Inst., 48, P 40 (1957).
309. A. Campbell, Proc. Roy. Soc. (London) A 78, 196 (1907); through G. E. Collins,
      J. Textile Inst., 13, T 204 (1922).
310. W. N. Stoops, J. Am. Chem. Soc., 56, 1480 (1934).
311. H. A. de Luca, W. B. Campbell and O. Maas, Can. J. Res. B16, 273 (1938).
312. T. M. Shaw and J. J. Windle, J. Appl. Phys., 21, 956 (1950).
313. H. W. Verseput, Tappi, 34, 572 (1951).
314. J. W. S. Hearle, Textile Res. J., 24, 307 (1954); 26, 108 (1956).
315. D. E. Kane, J. Polymer Sci., 18, 405 (1955).
316. W. Trapp and L. Pungs, Holzforschung, 10, 65 (1956).
317. I. S. Eifer and E. I. Berner, Khim. Volokna, 1963, (4) 45.
318. L. T. Muus, Tidsskr. Textiltek., 13, 139 (1955).
319. R. S. Govil, Man-Made Textiles, 41, (9), 45 (1964).
320. N. S. Wooding in I. W. S. Hearle, Ed., "Fibre Structure," Butterworth, London,
      1963, pp. 460, 466.
321. W. Wegener in H. Sommer, Ed., "Handbuch der Werkstoffprüfung," Vol. V, Springer,
      Berlin, 1960, pp. 394, 428.

PHYSICAL CONSTANTS OF POLYETHYLENE*

S. L. Aggarwal

Research and Development Center
The General Tire and Rubber Company
Akron, Ohio

Table I:	Property	Value	References
Bond Length (C-C) [Å]		1.53	1,2,3
Bond Angle (C∠C) [deg]		112	1,2,3

Chain Branching (short)

Effect on density and refractive index.   8

CH_3 groups per 1000 C atoms	Density [g cc^{-1}]	Refractive Index n_D^{25}
83	0.91	1.5060
48	0.917	1.5168
46	0.925	1.5152
26	0.929	1.5227
16	0.926	1.5260

Effect on expansion coefficient (mean) and crystalline specific volumes.   9

Methyl Groups per 1000 C atoms	$(1/V_{20})(\Delta V/\Delta T) \times 10^4$		V_{20}
	-150 to 100°C	0 to 100°C	
0.3	2.47	3.13	1.001
2	2.59	2.95	0.998
17.5	2.61	2.98	1.010
23	2.84	3.42	1.009
37	2.96	3.70	1.017

Effect on long period spacings and crystallinity of completely annealed samples.   10

Polyethylene	Methyl Groups per 1000 C atoms	Long Period Spacing, Å	% Crystallinity
Branched (High Pressure)	60	220	21
	45	200	48
	35	210	50
	28	220	53
	20	230	56
	15	250	59
	10	260	62
Linear (Ziegler Type Catalysts)	7	320	77
	5	360	79
Linear (Phillips Petroleum Process)	2	420	88

* Data for two basic types of polyethylenes: "High Pressure" and "Low Pressure," are tabulated for only those properties which are dependent on the short chain branching in the polymer chain. The "High Pressure" polyethylenes are more branched (8-40 CH_3 groups 1000 carbons), than the "Low Pressure" polyethylenes (~5 methyl groups/ 1000 C).

Table I (Cont'd.)

Property	Value	References

Chain Branching (short) (Cont'd.)

Effect on melting point. (Both the amount and randomness   11
of branching affect the melting point. Experimental conditions used for the following data were not adequate for
equilibrium crystallinity and accuracy of melting points).

Methyl Groups per 1000 C Atoms	Melting Point, [°C]
87	105
28	113
28	108
8	123
0	132 (?)

Coefficient of thermal expansion (branched polyethylene)   12

Temp. [°C]	Coefficient of expansion x 10^5		Specific Volume Ratio $(V_E/V_{25°C})$
	linear	cubical	
-35	10.0	30	0.969
20	13.7	41	0.975
0	18.3	55	0.986
20	23.7	71	0.997
25	24.8	74	1.000
40	29.0	87	1.012
60	33.7	101	1.031
80	40.3	121	1.055
100	46.6	140	1.094
110	51.0	153	1.130
115	25.0	75	1.140
115-150	25.0	75	-
150	25.0	75	1.168

Crystallinity (Depends upon short chain branching; the following are   13,14
some representative values of typical polyethylenes)

Polyethylene Type	Methyl Groups per 1000 C atoms	Melting Point [°C]	Percent Cryst.
Marlex 50 (Phillips, Linear)	0	135	91
Super-Dylan (Ziegler, Linear)	0	130	81
DYNH (Union Carbide/Branched)	25.6	112	52

Crystallization Kinetic Parameters*   15

(Isothermal crystallization data fitted to the equation:

$\theta = \exp(-Kt^4)$, where θ = fraction uncrystallized at time
t minutes; ΔT is the difference between the melting temperature and isothermal crystallization temperature.)

Linear Polyethylene, m.p. = 129°C

ΔT [°C]	K [Min.$^{-4}$]	$t_{1/2}$
10	9.11×10^{-5}	9.3
9	1.82×10^{-5}	14
7	5.71×10^{-8}	59
6	7.71×10^{-10}	170

* See also Table on "Rate of Crystallization of Polymers"

References page VI-51

Table I (Cont'd.)

Property	Value	References

Crystallographic Data and Crystallographic Modifications (See Table Ia)

Density, $[g \ cc^{-1}]$ (See also Table Ic)

(Unless otherwise stated, the values of density are given for 25°C)

Amorphous (from extrapolation of data above the melting point)	0.855	16
Commercial high pressure polyethylenes	0.915-0.935	17
Experimental high pressure polyethylenes	0.940-0.970	17
Ziegler process (18,19) polyethylenes	0.940- .965	17
Phillips process (20) polyethylenes	0.960-0.970	17
Crystal density (theoretical)	See Crystallographic Data and Crystallographic Modifications	

Dimensions of Linear Polyethylene Molecules (unperturbed) in tetralin at 105°C:
$\langle r_o^2 \rangle_w$ is the weight average mean-square end-to-end distance in Å, M_w is the
weight average molecular weight; D is the diameter of a spherical segment of
the lattice model chain; and $r_{max.}$ is the length of the fully extended chain.

$M_w \times 10^{-5}$	$(\langle r_o^2 \rangle_w / M_w)^{1/2}$	$(\langle r_o^2 \rangle_w / Dr_{max.})$	21
1.25	1.92	7.80	
2.69	2.15	9.86	
4.65	1.90	7.73	

Temperature dependence of $\langle r_o^2 \rangle$ (in long chain paraffinic   22
hydrocarbon solvents).

$$-d\ln\langle r_o^2 \rangle / dT = 1.2 \times 10^{-3}$$

Elastic Compliance $[cm^2 \ dyn^{-1}]$ See Table Ic

Electrical Properties

Dielectric constant, at 100 kc at 23°C	2.3	23
Dielectric Loss, tan δ	$1 \times 10^{-4} - 1 \times 10^{-3}$	24,25

The values of tan δ depend on temperature, and structure
of polyethylene (24).

Dielectric Strength, $[volts \ cm^{-1}]$ 26

-200 to 0°C	7×10^6	
50°C	5.3×10^6	
100°C	1.8×10^6	

Entropy of Fusion

ΔS_u, $[cal \ deg^{-1} \ mole^{-1}]$

	2.34	28
	2.29	27

at constant volume, $(\Delta S_u)_v$,
$[cal \ deg^{-1} \ mole^{-1}]$

	1.77	27
	1.84	29

Flash Ignition Temperature

(ASTM Method E136-58T):	340°C	30

Table I(Cont'd.)

Property	Value	References
Frictional Properties		31

Coefficient of Friction μ	Steel Sliding on Polymer		Polymer Sliding on Steel		Polymer Sliding on Polymer	
	Polished	Abraded	Polished	Abraded	Polished	Abraded
Static (μ_s)	0.60	0.33	0.60	0.33	0.60	0.33
Kinetic (μ_K)	0.60	0.33	0.60	0.33	0.60	0.33
	0.50	0.25				

Glass Transition Temperature	-125 °C	47,48
Heat Capacity	see Thermodynamic Properties	
Heat of Combustion		32

Density, [g cm^{-3}]	Methyl Groups per 1000 C Atoms	Heat of Combustion, ΔE, [cal g^{-1}]
0.9391	8.3	11,085
0.9220	24.7	11,104
0.9053	46.2	11,116

Heat of Fusion

From differential thermal analysis data:

Polyethylene Type	Melting Point, [°C]	Heat of Fusion [cal g^{-1}]	
Marlex 50 (Phillips, Linear)	135	58.6	13
Super-Dylan (Ziegler, Linear)	130	52.2	13
DYNH (Union Carbide, branched)	112	33.6	13
Linear Polyethylene From dilatometric measurements:		67	27
From calorimetric measurements:		66.2	33

Infrared Absorption Bands	see Table Ib
Infrared Functional Groups	see Table Ic
Intrinsic Viscosity [dl g^{-1}]	see Table Ic
Melt Index	see Table Ic

Melting Point, [°C]

Linear Polyethylene:	137.5	27
Linear Polyethylene, high molecular weight fraction:	138.5	41
From extrapolation of m.p. of n-paraffins:	141±2.4	42
(See also Table Ic)		
(See also chain branching, effect on melting point)		

Melt Viscosity	see Table Ic

Table I (Cont'd.)

Property	Value	References

Permeability and Diffusion Constants*

Permeability constant $\bar{P}, \left[\dfrac{cc\ (S.T.P.)}{cm\ sec\ (atm.)}\right]$; Diffusion constant D, $[cm^2\ sec^{-1}]$

Apparent activation energy for permeation $E_{\bar{P}}$ $[kcal\ g^{-1}\ mole^{-1}]$

Activation energy for diffusion E_D $[kcal\ g^{-1}\ mole^{-1}]$

To convert permeability constants to other units, see page 172 of reference 25 and table on "Permeability Constants of Polymers".

Component	$\bar{P} \times 10^7$	$E_{\bar{P}}$	D	E_D	
	High Density (0.964 g cc^{-1}) Polyethylene;				
	Volume Fraction Crystalline = 0.77. Data for P and D at 25°C				
He	0.087	7.1	30.7	5.6	43
O_2	0.0308	8.4	1.7	8.8	
A	0.129	9.0	1.16	9.3	
CO_2	0.0275	7.2	1.24	8.5	
CO	0.0147	9.4	0.96	8.8	
N_2	0.0109	9.5	0.93	9.0	
CH_4	0.0296	9.7	0.57	10.4	
C_2H_6	0.045	10.2	0.146	12.5	
C_2H_4	0.306	7.9	0.247	11.3	
C_3H_6	0.088	9.3	0.106	12.5	
C_3H_8	0.041	10.7	0.049	13.6	
SF_6	0.00064	13.2	0.016	15.0	
H_2O**	1.368	-	-	-	44
	Low Density (0.914 g cc^{-1}) Polyethylene; Volume				
	Fraction Crystalline = 0.43. Data for $\bar{P}$ and D at 25°C				
He	0.375	8.3	68.0	5.9	43
O_2	0.220	10.2	4.60	9.6	
A	0.208	10.8	3.60	10.1	
CO_2	0.96	9.3	3.72	9.2	
CO	0.113	11.1	3.32	9.5	
N_2	0.074	11.8	3.20	9.9	
CH_4	0.220	11.3	1.93	10.9	
C_2H_6	0.52	11.3	0.68	12.8	
C_2H_4	3.22	9.3	1.05	11.9	
C_3H_6	1.10	10.4	0.58	12.5	
C_3H_8	0.72	11.2	0.322	13.3	
SF_6	0.013	14.3	0.135	14.8	
H_2O***	9.42	8.0	-	-	44

Properties of a series of selected polyethylene samples   see Table Ic

Refractive Index

Amorphous, $[n^{25}_{5461}]$	1.49	45
Crystal, $\alpha \simeq \beta$	1.520	45
γ	1.582	

(α, β, and γ are refractive indices along the a, b, and c crystallographic directions of the crystal)

---

*   See also table on "Permeability Constants".

**   Data at 30°C, and polyethylene sample had density of 0.954 g cc^{-1}.

***   Data at 30°C, and polyethylene sample had density of 0.922 g cc^{-1}.

Table I (Cont'd.)

Property	Value	References

Refractive Index (Cont'd.)

Specific Refractivity, r, [cc g^{-1}]   46

$r = v(\dfrac{n^2-1}{n^2+1})$ where v and n are specific volume and
refractive index, respectively.

Temp. [°C]	v[cc g^{-1}]	n	r
Low Density Polyethylene (Alathon-10)			
90	1.159	1.4801	0.3293
100	1.178	1.4693	0.3283
108	1.209	1.4575	0.3297
113	1.239	1.4432	0.3286
118	1.250	1.4392	0.3289
124.4	1.256	1.4368	0.3288
			Av. 0.3290
High Density Polyethylene (Marlex 50)			
130	1.261	1.4327	0.3273
139.9	1.270	1.4297	0.3297
150.6	1.281	1.4261	0.3283
154.0	1.284	1.4246	0.3281

Solvent-Nonsolvent Systems for Fractionation*

Solvent	Nonsolvent	
xylene	triethylene glycol	49,50
p-xylene	ethylene glycol monoethyl ether	51
tetralin	2-butoxyethanol	52
xylene	poly(ethylene oxide) mol. wt. 200	53,54

Thermal Conductivity, [cal cm^{-1} sec^{-1} deg^{-1}]

Low density polyethylene: 8.3×10^{-4} 55,56

Temperature dependence of thermal conductivity   57

Temperature, [°C]	Thermal Conductivity $\times 10^4$	
	High Density	Low Density
50	8.7	7.0
0	10.0	8.4
-50	11.0	9.2
-100	11.7	9.2

* See also table on "Fractionation of Polymers".

References page VI-51

Table I (Cont'd.)

Property	Value	References

Thermodynamic Properties

Heat Capacity, C_p, Entropy, S, Enthalpy, H, and Gibbs' Free Energy, F, of "high pressure, low density" polyethylene.   58

Temp. [°K.]	Heat Capacity C_p [cal deg^{-1} g^{-1}]	S_T-S_0 °K. [cal deg^{-1} g^{-1}]	H_T-H_0 °K. [cal g^{-1}]	$-(F_T-F_0$ °K.) [cal g^{-1}]
10	(0.008)	0.0046	0.020	0.003
20	0.0173	0.0115	0.120	0.053
30	0.0384	0.0228	0.398	0.172
40	0.0597	0.0369	0.889	0.403
50	0.0806	0.0526	1.592	0.775
60	0.0999	0.0691	2.497	1.304
70	0.1185	0.0861	3.599	1.998
80	0.1340	0.1030	4.862	2.863
90	0.1480	0.1196	6.270	3.896
100	0.1615	0.1360	7.823	5.097
110	0.1739	0.1520	9.505	6.455
120	0.1858	0.1677	11.306	7.980
130	0.1972	0.1830	13.226	9.649
140	0.2081	0.1980	15.250	11.480
150	0.2210	0.2128	17.393	13.463
160	0.2319	0.2274	19.650	15.597
170	0.2438	0.2418	22.026	17.871
180	0.2552	0.2561	24.521	20.297
190	0.2660	0.2702	27.124	22.863
200	0.2790	0.2841	29.846	25.554
210	0.2919	0.2980	32.698	28.392
220	0.3069	0.3119	35.685	31.374
230	0.3235	0.3259	38.837	34.491
240	0.3426	0.3401	42.165	37.759
250	0.3644	0.3545	45.705	41.148
260	0.3887	0.3693	49.468	44.704
270	0.4151	0.3845	53.484	48.409
273.15	(0.430	0.3898	54.89	49.69
280	(0.455)	0.4012	57.84	52.48
290	(0.493)	0.4170	62.61	56.23
300	(0.540	0.4349	67.88	60.41
310	(0.591	0.4540	73.70	64.76
320	(0.653	0.4743	80.10	69.30

Heat Capacity (0°C), C_p, [cal deg^{-1} g^{-1}]   59

	Value
High density polyethylene (Marlex), annealed, 93% crystallinity	0.3739
amorphous	0.5455
Low density polyethylene 53% crystallinity	0.4755
drawn	0.4540

Viscosity-Molecular Weight Relationship*

$[\eta] = K \times M^a$. Only correlations based on measurements on fractions in thermodynamically good solvents are considered reliable (37).

Molecular Weight Range	Temp. [°C]	Solvent	K x 10^4	a	
		Linear Polyethylenes			
$3.7 \times 10^3 - 10^5$	130	tetralin	5.10	0.725	38
$1.2 \times 10^5 - 4.7 \times 10^5$	105	p-xylene	1.65	0.83	21
$10^4 - 1.8 \times 10^5$	105	p-xylene	1.76	0.83	39,40
$1.3 \times 10^5 - 4.7 \times 10^5$	105	tetralin	1.62	0.83	21
		Branched Polyethylenes (correlation with $\overline{M}_n$)			
$9 \times 10^3 - 10^5$	81	p-xylene	1.05	0.63	40

* See also Table on "Viscosity-Molecular Weight Relationships".

Table Ia: Crystallographic Data and Crystallographic
            Modifications of Polyethylene*

Polyethylene Sample Type	Crystal System	Space Group	Unit Cell Parameters [Å] a	b	c	Angles, [deg]	Monomers per Unit Cell	Calculated Density [g cc^{-1}]	Ref.
"High Pressure"	Orthorhombic	Pnam	7.40	4.93	2.534		2	1.00	1
			7.36	4.92	-		-	1.014	4
	Monoclinic	C2/m	8.09	2.53	4.79	β=107.9	2	0.997	5
"Low Pressure" polymethylenes	Triclinic		4.285	4.820	2.54	α= 90 β=110 γ=108	1	1.00	6
Single Crystal	Triclinic		7.84	5.56	~120	α= 63 β= 71 γ= 82	48	1.013	7

Table Ib: Infrared Absorption Bands of Polyethylene (34, 35, 36)

Wave Number (cm^{-1})	Polarization**	Assignments** Crystalline	Amorphous	Unsaturation, Irregularities, and Oxygen Containing Groups
720	σ_b	CH$_2$ Rocking, B$_{2u}$	CH$_2$ Rocking, t	
731	σ_a	CH$_2$ Rocking, B$_{1u}$		
888	σ			RR' C=CH$_2$
890	π			CH$_3$ Rocking
908	σ			RCH=CH$_2$
964	σ		CH$_2$ Rocking, g	trans RCH=CHR'
990	σ			RCH=CH$_2$

* See also table on "Crystallographic Data for Various Polymers".

** Notation: π = parallel to direction of stretch; σ = perpendicular to direction
   of stretch; σ_a = parallel to crystallographic a-axis; σ_b = parallel
   to crystallographic b-axis; t = trans, g = gauche conformation of the
   amorphous chain; B$_{1u}$, B$_{2u}$, B$_{3u}$ = group theoretical description
   of the normal vibration.

References page VI-51

Wave Number (cm^{-1})	Polarization*	Assignments*		
		Crystalline	Amorphous	Unsaturation, Irregularities, and Oxygen Containing Groups
1050	π	CH$_2$ Twisting, B$_{3u}$		
1065	σ		C-C Stretching	
1078	σ		C-C Stretching	
1110	π			
1131	π		C-C Stretching	
1150	π			
1170	σ		CH$_2$ Rocking (?)	
1176		CH$_2$ Wagging B$_{3u}$		
1185	σ			
1303	π		CH$_2$ Twisting, g	
1353	π		CH$_2$ Wagging, g	
1369	π		CH$_2$ Wagging, t (?),g	
1375				CH$_3$ Symmetrical bending
1436			CH$_2$ Bending	
1457				CH$_3$ Asymmetrical bending
1463	σ_b	CH$_2$ Bending B$_{2u}$	CH$_2$ Bending t,g	
1473	σ_a	CH$_2$ Bending B$_{1u}$		
1640	π			C=C Stretching
1722	σ			C=O Stretching
1737				C=O Stretching
1894	σ	1168 (Ag) + 731 (B$_{1u}$)		
2850	σ_a	CH$_2$ Symmetrical	CH$_2$ Symmetrical stretching, t,g	
2857	σ_b	CH$_2$ Symmetrical stretching B$_{2u}$		
2874				CH$_3$ Symmetrical stretching
2899	σ_b	CH$_2$ Asymmetrical stretching, B$_{2u}$		
2924	σ_a	CH$_2$ Asymmetrical stretching, B$_{1u}$	CH$_2$ Asymmetrical stretch, t,g	
2960				CH$_3$ Asymmetrical stretching

* Notation: π = parallel to direction of stretch; σ = perpendicular to direction of stretch; σ_a = parallel to crystallographic a-axis; σ_b = parallel to crystallographic b-axis; t = trans, g = gauche conformation of the amorphous chain; B$_{1u}$, B$_{2u}$, B$_{3u}$ = group theoretical description of the normal vibration.

Table Ic: Properties of A Series of Selected Polyethylene Samples*

| Sample No. | Optical Melting Point °C | Density[1] g/cm³ | Infrared Functional Groups | | | | |
| | | | per 100 C | | per 2000 C | | |
			Methyl	Vinyl	Trans-unsaturation	Vinylidene	Carbonyl
PE 1	104.2	0.9142	3.68	0.18	0.15	0.79	0.13
PE 2	112.4	0.9225	2.59	0.32	0.11	0.32	0.02
PE 3	112.2	0.9218	2.48	0.10	0.06	0.29	0.05
PE 4	113.7	0.9232	2.55	0.11	0.06	0.29	n.d.
PE 5	114.0	0.9219	2.46	0.11	0.05	0.30	0.01
PE 6	114.5	0.9228	2.31	0.06	0.05	0.26	n.d.
PE 7	113.5	0.9207	2.59	0.11	0.06	0.33	0.02
PE 8	112.0	0.9188	2.54	0.10	0.06	0.31	n.d.
PE 9	121.5	0.9334	1.40	0.04	0.02	0.11	0.87
PE 10	135.8	0.9549	0.1	1.82	0.04	0.15	<0.005
PE 11	-	0.9554	0.165	0.86		0.17	

| Sample No. | Molecular Weight | | Intrinsic Viscosity[2] dl/g | Melt Index[3] | Melt Viscosity[4] Poise | Elastic Compliance[5] cm²/dyne |
	Weight Ave.	Number Ave.				
PE 1	$510{,}000^6$	$10{,}700^{10}$	0.795	1.80	6.4	6.3
PE 2	$300{,}000^6$	$13{,}300^{10}$	0.757	1.95	3.8	4.6
PE 3	$550{,}000^6$	$19{,}100^{10}$	0.961	0.16	62.	4.6
PE 4	$225{,}000^7$	$(16{,}000)^9$	0.62	19.9	0.24	2.2
PE 5	$500{,}000^7$	$(18{,}000)^9$	0.75	3.30	1.85	3.6
PE 6	$500{,}000^7$	$(22{,}000)^9$	0.82	1.06	7.3	5.4
PE 7	$300{,}000^7$	$(45{,}000)^9$	0.77	2.94	2.3	3.1
PE 8	$800{,}000^7$	$(55{,}000)^9$	0.97	0.21	31.	5.4
PE 9	$300{,}000^7$	$(27{,}000)^9$	0.73	3.75	1.53	3.9
PE 10	$144{,}000^6$	$11{,}500^{10}$	1.16	2.92	-	-
PE 11	-	-	-	0.46	-	-

Notes:

1. Samples annealed 1 hour at about 100°C.
2. α-Chloronaphthalene, 125°C.
3. ASTM D-1238-57T
4. Newtonian melt viscosity at 150°C and 4 x 10³ dyres/cm².
5. Steady-state elastic compliance from creep recovery at 150°C and 4 x 10³ dynes/cm².
6. Light scattering after optical clarification by high temperature ultracentrifugation.
7. Preliminary value, subject to revision.
8. Measured by osmometry.
9. "Best guess." Subject to drastic revision.
10. Cryoscopy

* Data supplied through the courtesy of R. Longworth, Plastics Department, E. I. du Pont de Nemours & Co., Wilmington, Delaware.

REFERENCES

1. G. W. Bunn, Trans. Faraday Soc., 35, 482 (1939).
2. A. Charlesby, Proc. Phys. Soc. (London), 57, 496 (1945).
3. J. J. Trillat, Compt. Rend., 230, 1522 (1950).
4. E. R. Walter and F. P. Reding, J. Polymer Sci., 21, 561 (1956).
5. K. Tanaka, T. Seto, and T. Hara, J. Phys. Soc. Japan, 17, 873 (1962).
6. A. Turner-Jones, J. Polymer Sci., 62, S53 (1962).
7. W. D. Niegisch and P. R. Swan, J. Appl. Phys., 31, 1906 (1960).
8. M. Baccaredda and G. Schiavinato, J. Polymer Sci., 12, 155 (1954).
9. E. A. Cole and D. R. Holmes, J. Polymer Sci., 46, 245 (1960).
10. C. Sella, Compt. Rend., 248, 1819 (1959).
11. F. P. Reding, J. Polymer Sci., 32, 487 (1958).
12. F. C. Hahn, M. L. Macht, and D. A. Fletcher, Ind. Eng. Chem., 37, 526 (1945).
13. B. Ke, J. Polymer Sci., 42, 15 (1960).
14. R. T. Aggarwal and O. J. Sweeting, Chem. Rev., 57, 665 (1957).
15. S. Buckser and L. H. Tung, J. Phys. Chem., 63, 763 (1958).
16. G. Allen, G. Gee, and G. J. Wilson, Polymer, 1, 456 (1960).
17. K. W. Doak and A. Schrage, "Polymerization and Copolymerization Processes," in R. A. V. Raff and K. W. Doak, Ed., "Crystalline Olefin Polymers," Part I, Interscience, New York, 1965, p. 301ff.
18. K. Ziegler, Angew. Chem., 64, 323 (1952).
19. K. Ziegler, E. Holzkamp, H. Breil, and H. Martin, Angew. Chem., 67, 426, 541 (1955).
20. J. P. Hogan and R. L. Banks, U. S. Patent 2,825,721 assigned to Phillips Petroleum Company, March 4, 1958.
21. Q. A. Trementozzi, J. Polymer Sci., 36, 113 (1959).
22. P. J. Flory, A. Ciferri, and R. Chiang, J. Am. Chem. Soc., 83, 1023 (1961).
23. V. L. Lanza and D. B. Herrmann, J. Polymer Sci., 28, 622 (1958).
24. G. P. Mikhailov, S. P. Kabin, and T. A. Krylova, Zh. Tekhn. Fiz; 27, 2050 (1957).
25. H. D. Anspon, et al, "Polyethylene" in W. M. Smith, Ed., "Manufacture of Plastics," Reinhold, New York, 1964, p. 150ff.
26. K. H. Stark and C. G. Garton, Nature, 176, 1225 (1955).
27. F. A. Quinn, and L. Mandelkern, J. Am. Chem. Soc., 80, 3178 (1958).
28. H. W. Starkweather, Jr., and R. H. Boyd, J. Phys. Chem., 64, 410 (1960).
29. L. Mandelkern, "Crystallization of Polymers," McGraw-Hill, New York, 1964, p. 130.
30. G. A. Patten, Mod. Plastics, 38, (11), 119 (1961).
31. R. C. Bowers, W. C. Clinton, and W. A. Zisman, PB 111185 (Naval Research Laboratory Report 4167), May 19, 1953.
32. Reference 25, p. 160.
33. B. Wunderlich and M. Dole, J. Polymer Sci., 24, 201 (1957).
34. S. Krimm, Fortschr. Hochpolymer Forschung, 2, 51 (1960).
35. J. R. Nielsen and R. F. Holland, J, Mol. Spectr., 4, 488 (1960); 6, 394 (1961).
36. M. P. Groenewege, J. Schuyer, J. Smidt, and C. A. F. Tuijnman, "Absorption and Relaxation Spectra of Polyolefins," in R. A. V. Raff and K. W. Doak, Ed., "Crystalline Olefin Polymers," Part I, Interscience, New York, 1965, p. 762.
37. Q. A. Trementozzi and S. Newman, "Dilute Solution Properties," in R. A. V. Raff and K. W. Doak, Ed., "Crystalline Olefin Polymers," Part I, Interscience, New York, 1965, p. 406ff.
38. L. H. Tung, J. Polymer Sci., 24, 333 (1957).
39. Q. A. Trementozzi, J. Polymer Sci., 22, 187 (1956).
40. Q. A. Trementozzi, J. Polymer Sci., 23, 887 (1957).
41. R. F. Chiang and P. J. Flory, J. Am. Chem. Soc., 83, 2857 (1961).
42. M. G. Broadhurst, J. Chem. Phys., 36, 2578 (1962).
43. A. S. Michaels and H. J. Bixler, J. Polymer Sci., 50, 413 (1961).
44. A. W. Myers, V. Stannett and M. Szwarc, J. Polymer Sci., 35, 285 (1959).
45. W. M. D. Bryant, J. Polymer Sci., 2, 556 (1947).
46. J. P. Bianchi, W. G. Luetzel, and F. P. Price, J. Polymer Sci., 27, 561 (1958).
47. J. A. Faucher and F. P. Reding, "Relationship Between Structure and Fundamental Properties," in R. A. V. Raff and K. W. Doak, Ed., "Crystalline Olefin Polymers," Part I, Interscience, New York, 1965, p. 700ff.
48. F. P. Reding, J. A. Faucher, and R. D. Whitman, J. Polymer Sci., 57, 483 (1962).
49. L. H. Tung, J. Polymer Sci., 20, 495 (1956).
50. L. H. Tung, J. Polymer Sci., 24, 333 (1957).
51. P. S. Francis, R. C. Cooke, Jr., and J. H. Elliot, J. Polymer Sci., 31, 453 (1958).
52. J. E. Guillet, R. L. Combs, D. F. Slonaker, and H. W. Coover, J. Polymer Sci., 47, 307 (1960).

53. I. V. Mussa, J. Polymer Sci., 28, 587 (1958).
54. L. Nicolas, Compt. Rend., 242, 2720 (1956).
55. L. N. Cherkasova, Zh. Fiz. Khim., 33, 1928 (1959).
56. H. C. Raine, R. B. Richards, and H. Ryder, Trans. Faraday Soc., 41, 56 (1945).
57. K. Eiermann, Kunststoffe, 51, 512 (1961).
58. R. W. Warfield and M. C. Petree, Makromol. Chem., 51, 113 (1962); data used
     were from different sources: (a) I. V. Sochava, and O. N. Trapeznikova,
     Dokl. Akad. Nauk SSSR, 113, 784 (1957); (b) I. V. Sochava, Dokl. Akad. Nauk
     SSSR, 130, 126 (1960); (c) M. Dole, W. P. Hettinger, Jr., N. R. Larson, and
     J. A. Wethington, Jr., J. Chem. Phys., 20, 781 (1952).
59. M. Dole, Kolloid-Z., 165, 40 (1959).

PHYSICAL CONSTANTS OF POLYBUTADIENE

G. H. Stempel

The General Tire and Rubber Company
Akron, Ohio

The data in these tables are limited for the most part to those for reasonably homogeneous (>90%) samples of the four stereoregular homopolymers of butadiene. The percentages in parentheses indicate steric purity.

Property							Value				Ref.
Crystallographic Data									14-20,22		

Isomer	Lattice	Monomers per Unit Cell	Cell Dimension, [Å]			Cell Angles,°					
			a	b	c(chain axis)	α	β	γ			
1,4-trans- (99-100%)	Pseudo-hexagonal	1	4.54 / 4.88	4.54 / 4.88	4.9 (Mod. I) / 4.68(Mod.II)						
1,4-cis- (98-99%)	Monoclinic	4	4.60	9.50	8.6	90	109	90			
1,2-isotactic (99%)	Rhombohedral	18	17.3	17.3	6.5	90	90	120			
1,2-syndio-tactic (98%)	Orthorhombic	4	10.98	6.60	5.14	90	90	90			

*Transition temperature: 75°C

Density, [g cc^{-1}]   15

1,4-trans- (99-100%)	Modification I	0.97
	Modification II	0.93
1,4-cis- (98-99%)		1.01
1,2-isotactic (99%)		0.96
1,2-syndiotactic (98%)		0.96

Entropy of Fusion, [eu/monomer unit °K^{-1}]   21

1,4-trans- (99%)	Modification I	6.4
	Modification II	2.7
1,4-cis- (98%)		8

Entropy of Polymerization, [cal deg^{-1} mole^{-1}]

at 25°C: butadiene to cis-1,4-polybutadiene (94%)   20.12   6

First Order Transition Temperature, [°C]

1,4-trans- Modification I to Modification II		75

21

Glass Transition Temperature, [°C]

1,4-cis- ("high")		-102
1,4-cis- (98-99%)		-95
1,4-trans- (94%)		-83

26
3
6

Heat of Fusion [cal/monomer unit]   21

1,4-trans- (99%)	Modification I	2400 ± 1000
	Modification II	1100
1,4-cis- (98.5%)		2200

Property	Value	Ref.

Infrared Absorption Coefficients, $[dl\ cm^{-1}\ mg^{-1}]$ 12

		Wave Length, microns	
Isomer	10.35	10.95-10.98	13.5-13.65
1,4-trans	23.3×10^{-3}		
1,2-	0.828×10^{-3}	26.7×10^{-3}	0.231×10^{-3}
1,4-cis	0.609×10^{-3}	0.107×10^{-3}	5.73×10^{-3}

Infrared Molar Absorptivities, $[liters\ moles^{-1}\ cm^{-1}]$ 25

		Wave Length, microns	
Isomer	10.3	11.0	12-15.75
1,4-trans-	133	2.4	0.86
1,2-	6.7	184	4.7
1,4-cis-	4.4	1.9	10.1

Melting Temperature, $[°C]$ 13,15

1,4-trans- (99-100%)	145
1,4-cis- (98-99%)	2
1,2-isotactic (99%)	126
1,2-syndiotactic (98%)	156

Sedimentation Constants for 1,4-cis

Solvent	Temp.°C	% cis	s_o	
Diethyl ketone	10.3	95	$s_o = 5.30 \times 10^{-3}\ \bar{M}^{0.5}$ svedbergs	2
n-Hexane/n-Heptane,(1:1)	20		$s_o = 3.02 \times 10^{-2}\ \bar{M}^{0.48}$ svedbergs	23

Specific Refractivity, r, for Emulsion Polymers Made at T°C: 11

$r = (1/d)(n^2-1)/(n^2+2)$, where n is the index of refraction for the sodium D line, d is the density, and r is specific refractivity

				Weight Fractions		
T°C	d^{25}	n_D^{25}	r	1,4-trans-	1,2-	1,4-cis-
-10	0.8911	1.5147	0.33824	0.775	0.159	0.066
0	0.8915	1.5148	0.33814	0.730	0.179	0.091
25	0.8920	1.5149	0.33820	0.683	0.188	0.129
50	0.8920	1.5151	0.33815	0.643	0.209	0.148
75	0.8925	1.5156	0.33821	0.561	0.198	0.241
100	0.8933	1.5160	0.33816	0.545	0.201	0.245

Theta Solvents and Temperatures   T°C

	T°C	
Diethyl ketone	10.3	2
n-Hexane/n-Heptane, (1:1)	5	23
Isobutyl acetate	20.5	7
Methyl isoamyl ketone	12.6	1
Methyl n-propyl ketone	59.7	1

Viscosity-Molecular Weight Relationship, $[\eta]$ g^{-1}]

$$[\eta] = K M_v^a$$

a. Good Solvents

Solvent	Temp.	Sample	K	a	Ref.
Toluene	25°C	97% cis-	3.05×10^{-4}	0.725	4
Toluene	30°C	High trans-	2.94×10^{-4}	0.753	8
Cyclohexane	20°C	79% trans- 21% 1,2- $LiAlH_4, Cr_2O_3$	3.6×10^{-4}	0.70	24
Benzene		Butyl lithium	1.45×10^{-4}	0.76	5
Toleune	25.9%	Emulsion, 50°C 62% trans- 14.8% cis- 23.2% 1,2-	72.5×10^{-4}	0.45	10
Toluene	25.9°C	Emulsion, -20°C 79.6% trans- 19.6% 1,2-	10.6×10^{-4}	0.63	10
Cyclohexane	25°C	Alfin 70% trans- 20% 1,2- 10% cis-	1.25×10^{-4}	0.77	27

b. Theta Conditions (for 1,4-cis-)

Solvent	Theta Temp. °C	cis-Content,%	K	a	M_w/M_n	
Diethyl ketone	10.3	95 95	1.52×10^{-3} 1.81×10^{-3}	$0.5 (M_v)$ $0.5 (M_n^w)$	1.43	2 2
Methyl isoamyl ketone	12.6	95	1.5×10^{-3} 1.30×10^{-3}	$0.5 (M_n)$ $0.5 (M_w^w)$		2 9
Isobutyl acetate	20.5	98	1.85×10^{-3}	$0.5 (M_n)$	1.11	7
n-Hexane/n-Heptane,(1:1)	5	90	1.38×10^{-3}	$0.53(M_v)$		23

REFERENCES

1. M. Abe, H. Fujita, Repts. Progr. Polymer Phys. Japan 7, 42 (1964).
2. M. Abe, Y. Murakami, and H. Fujita, J. Appl. Polymer Sci. 9, 2549 (1965).
3. M. Baccaredda and E. Butta, Chim. Ind. Milan 42, 978 (1960).
4. U. Bianchi and E. Bianchi, Rubber Chem. and Tech. 38, 343 (1965).
5. W. Cooper, D. E. Eaves and G. Vaughn, J. Polymer Sci. 59, 241 (1962).
6. F. S. Dainton, D. M. Evans, F. E. Hoare and T. P. Melia, Polymer 3, 297 (1962).
7. F. Danusso, G. Moraglio and G. Gianotti, J. Polymer Sci. 51, 475 (1961).
8. R. Endo, Nippon Gomu Kyokaishi 35, 658 (1962).
9. H. Fujita, N. Takaguchi, K. Kawahara, M. Abe, H. Utiyama and K. Kajitani, 12th Polymer Symposium, Nagoya, Japan, November, 1963.
10. B. L. Johnson and R. D. Wolfangel, Ind. Eng. Chem. 41, 1580 (1949).
11. L. Mandelkern, M. Tryon and F. A. Quinn, J. Polymer Sci. 19, 81 (1956).
12. P. Morero, A. Santambrogio, L. Porri and F. Ciampelli, Chim. Ind. Milan 41, 758 (1959).
13. G. Natta, Rev. Gen. Caoutchouc 40, 786 (1963).
14. G. Natta, Rubber Plastics Age 38, 495 (1957).
15. G. Natta, Science 147, 269 (1965).
16. G. Natta and P. Corradini, Angew. Chem. 68, 615 (1956).
17. G. Natta and P. Corradini, J. Polymer Sci. 20, 251 (1956).
18. G. Natta and P. Corradini, Nuovo Cimento 15, Suppl. 1, 9 (1960).
19. G. Natta and P. Corradini, Rubber Chem. and Tech. 33, 732 (1960).
20. G. Natta, P. Corradini and L. Porri, Atti. Accad. Nazl. Lincei Rend. 20, 728 (1956).

21. G. Natta, G. Moraglio, Rubber Plastics Age 44, 42 (1963); Makromol. Chem. 66, 218 (1963).
22. G. Natta, L. Porri, P. Corradini and D. Morero, Atti. Accad. Nazl. Lincei Rend. 20, 560 (1956).
23. I. Y. Poddubnyi and V. A. Grechanovskii, Vysokomolekul. Soedin. 6, 64 (1964).
24. Ph. Ribeyrolles, A. Guyot and H. Benoit, J. Chim. Phys. 56, 383 (1959).
25. R. S. Silas, J. Yates and V. Thornton, Anal. Chem. 31, 529 (1959).
26. G. S. Trick, J. Appl. Polymer Sci. 3, 253 (1960).
27. R. L. Cleland, J. Polymer Sci. 27, 349 (1958).

PHYSICAL CONSTANTS OF DIFFERENT RUBBERS*

Lawrence A. Wood

National Bureau of Standards
Washington, D. C.

Contents

Where a range is given, there are available several observations which differ. In most cases the differences are thought to be real, arising from differences in the rubber rather than from errors of observation. Where a single value is given, it is either because no other observations are available or because there seems to be no significant disagreement among values within the errors of observation. Where no values are given, no data have been found. Where dashes are shown, either the physical measurement is impossible or the constant in question is not adequately defined under the given conditions. 50 phr means "50 parts of carbon black by weight per 100 parts of rubber."

The values are given, in most instances, in terms of the units used by the respective authors. Where the calorie has been used, it may be defined, with sufficient accuracy for the purposes of these tables, as the thermochemical calories, which is equal to 4.1840 joules. The kilogram weight is taken as 980.665 dynes (0.00980665 newton).

Values are given for 25°C and 1 bar ($=10^6$ dyne $cm^{-2}=10^5$ newton m^{-2}), equivalent to 0.986923 (=1/1.01325) normal atmosphere.

---

* This table was originally published in the Smithsonian Physical Tables (9th Edition) 1954. It was revised and extended for this Handbook in 1965.

1 - POLYISOPRENE, NATURAL RUBBER (HEVEA)

Property	Unvulcanized	Ref.	Pure-gum Vulcanizate	Ref.	Vulcanizate Containing About 33% Carbon Black (=50 phr)	Ref.	Hard Rubber (Ebonite)	Ref.
Density [g cm^{-3}]	0.913 (0.906-0.916)	10 10	0.97 (0.92-1.0)	14,34 2	1.12 (1.12-1.15)	14 2,34	1.17 (1.13-1.18)	10,33 6
Coefficient of Expansion, volume (1/V)(dV/dT) [(deg C)$^{-1}$]	67 x 10^{-5}	10	66 x 10^{-5}	10	53 x 10^{-5} (45-55 x 10^{-5})	14 5	19 x 10^{-5}	10
Thermal Glass Transition Temperature [deg C]	-72 (-74 to -69)	12 12	-63 (-72 to -61)	38 38	-65	8,19,27	+80	33
Specific Heat Cp [cal g^{-1} (deg C)$^{-1}$] dCp/dT [cal g^{-1} (deg C)$^{-2}$]	0.449 1.2 x 10^{-3}	10 10	0.437	20	0.357	20	0.331	6,10
Thermal Conductivity [cal sec^{-1} cm^{-1} (deg C)$^{-1}$]	32 x 10^{-5}	20	34-36 x 10^{-5}	3,34	68 x 10^{-5}	31	39 x 10^{-5} (38-42 x 10^{-5})	10 6,8
Heat of Combustion [cal g^{-1}]	10.8 x 10^{3}	10	10.6 x 10^{3}	10			7.9 x 10^{3}	6,10
Optical Refractive Index, n$_D$ dn$_D$/dT [(deg C)$^{-1}$]	1.5191 -37 x 10^{-5}	39 33	1.5264 -37 x 10^{-5}	10 10	---- ----		1.6	10
Electrical Dielectric Constant (1 kc)	2.37-2.45	7,10	2.68 (2.5-3.0)	7,10			2.82 (2.8-2.9)	7 6,7
Dissipation Factor (1 kc)	0.001-0.003	7	0.002-0.04	7			0.0043-0.009	6,7
Conductivity (1 min.) [mho cm^{-1}]	2-57 x 10^{-17}	7,10	2-100 x 10^{-17}	7,10			2-3000 x 10^{-17}	6,7

POLYISOPRENE (Cont'd.)

Mechanical

Property	Unvulcanized	Ref.	Pure-gum Vulcanizate	Ref.	Vulcanizate Containing About 33% Carbon Black (=50 phr)	Ref.	Hard Rubber (Ebonite)	Ref.
Compressibility B dB/dP [bar^{-1}]	51×10^{-6}		51×10^{-6}	25,33,37	41×10^{-6}	25	24×10^{-6}	33
dB/dT [bar^{-2}]	-0.021×10^{-6}		-0.024×10^{-6}	37	-0.018×10^{-6}	25	-0.0041×10^{-6}	33
dB/dT [bar^{-1} (deg C)$^{-1}$]	$+0.23 \times 10^{-6}$		$+0.21 \times 10^{-6}$	37			$+0.11 \times 10^{-6}$	33
Bulk Wave Velocity v_b [m sec^{-1}]	1580	37	1580 (1500-1580)	37, 15,21,37	1490	15		
dv_b/dT [m sec^{-1} (deg C)$^{-1}$]	-3		-3	37				
Strip (longitudinal wave) Velocity v_l (1 kc) [m sec^{-1}]			45 (35-51)	15, 8,10,15	~41	15	1540	10,24
dv_l/dT [m sec^{-1} (deg C)$^{-1}$]			-0.2	10				
Ultimate Elongation [%]	----		750-850	1,2	550-650	1,2	6 (3-8)	5, 6
Tensile Strength [kg cm^{-2}]	----		170-250	1,2	250-350	1,2	600-800	6
Initial Slope of Stress-Strain Curve Young's Modulus E (1 min) [dyne cm^{-2}]	----		13×10^6 ($10-20 \times 10^6$)	23, 2,23,38	$30-80 \times 10^6$	2	3×10^{10}	5,24
Shear Modulus G (1 min.) [dyne cm^{-2}]	----		4.3×10^6 ($3-7 \times 10^6$)	38, 29,38	$13-20 \times 10^6$	9,29	0.6×10^{10}	24
Shear Compliance J (1 min.) [cm^2 (dyne)$^{-1}$]	----		0.23×10^{-6} ($0.15-0.35 \times 10^{-6}$)	38, 29,38	$0.05-0.07 = 10^6$	9,29	1.7×10^{-10}	24
Creep $(1/J)(dJ/d \log t)$ [% (decade)$^{-1}$]	----		2 (1-3)	23,38, 23,38	8 (7-12)	8, 8		

POLYISOPRENE (Cont'd.)

Property		Unvulcanized	Ref.	Pure-gum Vulcanizate	Ref.	Vulcanizate Containing About 33% Carbon Black (=50 phr)	Ref.	Hard Rubber (Ebonite)	Ref.
Complex Dynamic Shear Modulus G* (1 cycle)			8,19,27, 32,40		8,17,18, 19,26,27, 29,32		8,17,19, 27,29		8,13, 27,32
Storage Modulus G' (Values of log G')	[dyne cm^{-2}]	6.61 (6.53-6.75)	40	6.61 (6.49-6.78)	18	7.79 (7.27-8.12)	19	10.05	27
Loss Modulus G'' (Values of log G'')	[dyne cm^{-2}]	5.46 (5.43-5.65)	40	4.80 (4.72-5.48)	18	6.83 (6.50-7.11)	19	8.65	27
Loss Tangent G''/G'		0.09 (0.07-0.13)	40	0.016 (0.01-0.05)	18	0.11 (0.10-0.17)	18	0.040	19
Resilience (rebound)	[%]	75-77	2,16	75-84	16,17	50 (45-55)	16 2,9 16,17	63-67	5

2 – POLY(BUTADIENE-CO-STYRENE), (SBR, GS-S), (ABOUT 23.5% BOUND STYRENE CONTENT)

Property	Unvulcanized	Ref.	Pure-gum Vulcanizate	Ref.	Vulcanizate Containing About 33% Carbon Black (=50 phr)	Ref.
Density $[g\ cm^{-3}]$	0.933 (0.9325-0.9335)	12 / 12	0.98 (0.94-1.00)	14 / 14	1.15	14,34
Coefficient of Expansion, volume $(1/V)(dV/dT)$ $[(deg\ C)^{-1}]$	66×10^{-5}	12	66×10^{-5} $(65\text{-}70 \times 10^{-5})$	9,14,34 / 34	53×10^{-5}	14
Thermal Glass Transition Temperature $[deg\ C]$	-64 to -59	12	-52	38	-52	38
Specific Heat Cp $[cal\ g^{-1}(deg\ C)^{-1}]$ dCp/dT $[cal\ g^{-1}(deg\ C)^{-2}]$	0.453 0.76×10^{-3}	30 / 30	0.437	20	0.358	20
Thermal Conductivity $[cal\ sec^{-1}cm^{-1}(deg\ C)^{-1}]$			$46\text{-}59 \times 10^{-5}$	8,31	72×10^{-5}	31
Heat of Combustion $[j\ (g\ of\ CO_2)^{-1}]$	13.5×10^{3}	12				
Optical Refractive Index, n_D $[(deg\ C)^{-1}]$ $\partial n_D/dT$	1.5345 (1.534-1.535) -37×10^{-5}	12 / 12 / 12				
Electrical Dielectric Constant (1 kc)	2.5	7	2.66	7		
Dissipation Factor (1 kc)	0.0009	7	0.0009	7		
Mechanical Compressibility B $[bar^{-1}]$ dB/dP $[bar^{-2}]$	53×10^{-6} -0.027×10^{-6}	25 / 25	51×10^{-6} -0.02×10^{-6}	15,25 / 25	40×10^{-6} -0.018×10^{-6}	25 / 25
Bulk Wave Velocity $[m\ sec^{-1}]$			1485	15	1510	15
Strip (longitudinal wave) Velocity v_1 (1 kc) $[m\ sec^{-1}]$ dv_1/dT $[m\ sec^{-1}\ deg^{-1}]$			73 0.2	35 / 35	161	15

References page VI-67

PHYSICAL CONSTANTS OF RUBBERS

POLY(BUTADIENE-CO-STYRENE) (Cont'd.)

Property	Unvulcanized	Ref.	Pure-gum Vulcanizate	Ref.	Vulcanizate Containing About 33% Carbon Black (=50 phr)	Ref.
Ultimate Elongation [%]	---		400-600	1,2	400-600	1,2
Tensile Strength [kg cm^{-2}]	---		14-28	1,2	170-280	1,2
Initial Slope of Stress-Strain Curve Young's Modulus E (1 min.) [dyne cm^{-2}]	---		16×10^6 $(10\text{-}20 \times 10^6)$	23,38 23	$30\text{-}60 \times 10^6$	2
Shear Modulus G (1 min.) [dyne cm^{-2}]	---		5.3×10^6 $(3\text{-}7 \times 10^6)$	38 23	20×10^6 $(20\text{-}25 \times 10^6)$	29 9,29
Shear Compliance J [cm^2 (dyne)$^{-1}$]	---		0.19×10^{-6}	38	0.05×10^{-6}	29
Creep (1/J)(dJ/d log t) [% (decade)$^{-1}$]	---		7 (3-10)	23,38 23,38	12	8
Complex Dynamic Shear Modulus G* (1 cycle)		28,40		17,19, 21,28		17,28 29,34
Storage Modulus G' (Values of log G') [dyne cm^{-2}]	6.82 (6.82-6.85)	40	6.88 (6.64-7.20)	19	7.94 (7.39-7.94)	28
Loss Modulus G'' (Values of log G'') [dyne cm^{-2}]	5.94 (5.56-5.94)	40	5.92 (5.73-6.04)	19	7.28 (6.66-7.28)	28
Loss Tangent G''/G'	0.13 (0.05-0.13)	40	0.11 (0.07-0.18)	19	0.22 (0.14-0.22)	28
Resilience (rebound) [%]			65	2,16,17	40 (40-50)	16 2,16,17

3 - POLY(ISOBUTENE-CO-ISOPRENE), (BUTYL RUBBER, IIR, GR-I)

Property	Unvulcanized	Ref.	Pure-gum Vulcanizate	Ref.	Vulcanizate Containing About 33% Carbon Black (≈50 phr)	Ref.
Density [g cm^{-3}]	0.916	14	0.97 (0.93-0.97)	14 14	1.13	14
Coefficient of Expansion, volume (1/V)(dV/dT) [(deg C)$^{-1}$]			57 x 10^{-5}	14	46 x 10^{-5}	14
Thermal						
Glass Transition Temperature [deg C]	-75 to -67	8,12	-63	18		
Specific Heat Cp [cal g^{-1}(deg C)$^{-1}$]	0.464	20	0.443	20		
Thermal Conductivity [cal sec^{-1}cm^{-1}(deg C)$^{-1}$]			31 x 10^{-5}	31	55 x 10^{-5}	31
Optical						
Refractive Index, n$_D$	1.5081	12			----	
Electrical						
Dielectric Constant (1 kc)	2.38	7	2.42	7		
Dissipation Factor (1 kc)	0.003	7	0.0054	7		
Mechanical						
Compressibility B [bar^{-1}]			54 x 10^{-6}	15	46 x 10^{-6}	15
Bulk Wave Velocity [m sec^{-1}]			1485	15	1510	15
Strip (longitudinal wave) Velocity v$_1$ (1 kc) [m sec^{-1}] dv$_1$/dT [m sec^{-1} deg^{-1}]			100 (100-111) -2.2	8,15 / 35 35 35	210	15
Ultimate Elongation [%]	----		750-950	1,2	650-850	1,2
Tensile Strength [kg cm^{-2}]	----		180-210	1,2	180-210	1,2

References page VI-67

POLY(ISOBUTENE-CO-ISOPRENE) (Cont'd.)

Property	Unvulcanized	Ref.	Pure-gum Vulcanizate	Ref.	Vulcanizate Containing About 33% Carbon Black (≈50 phr)	Ref.
Initial Slope of Stress-Strain Curve Young's Modulus E (1 min.) [dyne cm^{-2}]	----		10×10^6 $(7\text{-}15 \times 10^6)$	23,38 2,23,38	$30\text{-}40 \times 10^6$	2
Shear Modulus G (1 min.) [dyne cm^{-2}]	----		3.3×10^6 $(2\text{-}5 \times 10^6)$	38 2,23,38	18×10^6	9
Shear Compliance J (1 min.) [cm^2 (dyne)$^{-1}$]	----		0.31×10^{-6} $(0.2\text{-}0.4 \times 10^{-6})$	38 2, 28,38	0.056×10^{-6}	9
Creep (1/J)(dJ/d log t) [% (decade)$^{-1}$]	----		4 (2-8)	23,38 23,38		
Complex Dynamic Shear Modulus G* (60 cycles)						
Storage Modulus G' (Values of log G') [dyne cm^{-2}]	7.50	32	6.64	17	7.56	17
Loss Modulus G" (Values of log G") [dyne cm^{-2}]	6.98	32	6.48	17	7.21	17
Loss Tangent G"/G'	0.3	32	0.70	17	0.45	17
Resilience (rebound) [%]			13-16	2,16	14	2

4 - POLYCHLOROPRENE (CR, NEOPRENE)

Property	Unvulcanized	Ref.	Pure-gum Vulcanizate	Ref.	Vulcanizate Containing About 33% Carbon Black (≈50 phr)	Ref.
Density $[g\ cm^{-3}]$	1.23	4,12,36	1.32	14	1.42	14
Coefficient of Expansion, volume (1/V(dV/dT)) $[(deg\ C)^{-1}]$	60×10^{-5}	4,8	$61-72 \times 10^{-5}$	4,14		
Thermal						
Glass Transition Temperature $[deg\ C]$	-45	22	-44	22,33	-43	22
Specific Heat $[cal\ g^{-1}(deg\ C)^{-1}]$	0.52	4	0.49-0.52	3	0.40-0.42	4,34
Thermal Conductivity	46×10^{-5}	4	46×10^{-5}	8,34	50×10^{-5}	4
Optical						
Refractive Index n_D	1.558	11				
dn_D/dT $[(deg\ C)^{-1}]$	-36×10^{-5}	11				
Electrical						
Dielectric Constant (1 kc)			6.5-8.1	7		
Dissipation Factor (1 kc)			0.031-0.086	7		
Conductivity $[mho\ cm^{-1}]$			$3-1400 \times 10^{-14}$	7		
Mechanical						
Compressibility B $[bar^{-1}]$	48×10^{-6}	15,25	44×10^{-6}	15,25	36×10^{-6}	15,25
dB/dP $[bar^{-2}]$	-0.028×10^{-6}	25	-0.023×10^{-6}	25	-0.017×10^{-6}	25
Bulk Wave Velocity v_b $[m\ sec^{-1}]$			1420	15	1520	15
Strip (longitudinal wave) Velocity v_l (1 kc) $[m\ sec^{-1}]$			69	8,15	196	15
Ultimate Elongation $[\%]$	----		800-1000	1,2	500-600	1,2
Tensile Strength $[kg\ cm^{-2}]$	----		250-375	1,2	210-300	1,2

References page VI-67

POLYCHLOROPRENE (Cont'd.)

Property	Unvulcanized	Ref.	Pure-gum Vulcanizate	Ref.	Vulcanizate Containing About 33% Carbon Black (≈50 phr)	Ref.
Initial Slope of Stress-Strain Curve Young's Modulus E (1 min.) [dyne cm^{-2}]	----		16×10^6 ($10\text{-}30 \times 10^6$)	23,38 2,23,38	$30\text{-}50 \times 10^6$	2
Shear Modulus G (1 min.) [dyne cm^{-2}]	----		5.2×10^6 ($3\text{-}10 \times 10^6$)	38 2,23,28	14×10^6	9
Shear Compliance J (1 min.) [cm^2 (dyne)$^{-1}$]	----		0.20×10^{-6} ($0.1\text{-}0.3 \times 10^{-6}$)	38 2,23,38	0.07×10^{-6}	9
Creep (1/J)(dJ/d log t) [% (decade)$^{-1}$]	----		6 (5-10)	23,38 23,38		
Complex Dynamic Shear Modulus G* (60 cycles)						
Storage Modulus G' (Values of log G') [dyne cm^{-2}]			6.81	17	7.45	17
Loss Modulus G" (Values of log G") [dyne cm^{-2}]			6.04	17	6.75	17
Loss Tangent G"/G;			0.17	17	0.20	17
Resilience (rebound) [%]			60-65	2,16	48 (40-50)	16 2,16

5 - REFERENCES

1. J. M. Ball and G. C. Maasen, American Society for Testing Materials, Symposium on the Applications of Synthetic Rubbers, March 2, 1944, p. 27.
2. B. B. S. T. Boonstra, "Properties of Elastomers," Chapter 4 of Vol. III in R. Houwink (Ed.), "Elastomers. Their Chemistry, Physics, and Technology," Elsevier Publishing Company, New York, 1948.
3. L. C. Carwile and H. J. Hoge, "Thermal Conductivity of Soft Vulcanized Natural Rubber, Selected Values," in "Advances in Thermophysical Properties at Extreme Temperatures and Pressures," American Society of Mechanical Engineers, New York, 1965.
4. N. L. Catton, "The Neoprenes," Rubber Chemicals Division, E. I. du Pont de Nemours and Company, Wilmington, Delaware, 1953.
5. T. R. Dawson and B. D. Porritt, "Rubber Physical and Chemical Properties," Research Association of British Rubber Manufacturers, Croydon, England, 1935.
6. A. R. Kemp and F. S. Malm, "Hard Rubber (Ebonite)," Chapter XVIII in C. C. Davis and J. T. Blake (Ed.) "Chemistry and Technology of Rubber." Reinhold Publishing Corp., New York, 1937.
7. A. T. McPherson, "Electrical Properties of Elastomers and Related Polymers, Rubber Chem. Technol. (Rubber Reviews), 36, 1230 (1963).
8. A. R. Payne and J. R. Scott, "Engineering Design with Rubber," Interscience Publishers, New York, 1960.
9. I. B. Prettyman, "Physical Properties of Natural and Synthetic Rubber Stocks," Handbook of Chemistry and Physics, Chemical Rubber Pub. Co., Cleveland, Ohio, 44th Edition, 1962, p. 1564.
10. L. A. Wood, "Values of the Physical Constants of Rubber," Proceedings of the Rubber Technology Conference, (Institution of the Rubber Industry, London), 1938, p. 933; Rubber Chem. Technol., 12, 130 (1939).
11. L. A. Wood, "Synthetic Rubbers: A Review of Their Compositions, Properties, and Uses," Natl. Bur. Std. Circ., C427 (1940); Rubber Chem. Tech., 13, 861 (1940); India Rubber World, 102, No. 4, 33 (1940).
12. L. A. Wood, "Physical Chemistry of Synthetic Rubbers," Chapter 10 in C. S. Whitby (Ed.) "Synthetic Rubbers," John Wiley, Inc., New York, 1954.
13. G. W. Becker and H. Oberst, Kolloid-Z., 148 6 (1956).
14. N. Bekkedahl and F. L. Roth, National Bureau of Standards, Unpublished observations of density and expansivity, 1948.
15. W. S. Cramer and I. Silver, NAVORD Report 1778, Feb. 1951, U. S. Naval Ordinance Lab., White Oak, Md.
16. B. B. S. T. Boonstra, Rev. Gen. du Caoutchouc, 27, 409 (1950). Translated in Rubber Chem. Technol., 24, 199 (1951).
17. J. H. Dillon, I. B. Prettyman, and G. L. Hall, J. Appl. Phys., 15, 309 (1944); Rubber Chem. Technol., 17, 597 (1944).
18. J. D. Ferry, R. G. Mancke, E. Maekawa, Y. Oyanagi, and R. A. Dickie, J. Phys. Chem., 68, 3414 (1964).
19. W. P. Fletcher and A. N. Gent, British J. Appl. Phys., 8, 194 (1957).
20. W. H. Hamill, B. A. Mrowca, and R. L. Anthony, Ind. Eng. Chem., 38, 106 (1946); Rubber Chem. Technol., 19, 622 (1946).
21. D. G. Ivey, B. A. Mrowca, and E. Guth, J. Appl. Phys., 20, 486 (1949); Rubber Chem. Technol., 23, 172 (1950).
22. R. M. Kell, B. Bennett, and P. B. Stickney, J. Appl. Polymer Sci., 2, 8 (1959).
23. G. M. Martin, F. L. Roth and R. D. Stiehler, Trans. Inst. Rubber Ind., 32, 189 (1956); Rubber Chem. Technol., 30, 876 (1957).
24. G. Mikhailov and V. Kirilina, Tech. Phys. USSR 5, 842 (1938); Rubber Chem. Technol. 14, 858 (1941).
25. W. H. S. Naunton et al,"Rubber in Engineering," Ministry of Supply, London, 1945, or Chemical Publishing Co., Brooklyn, N. Y. 1946, p. 30.
26. A. W. Nolle, J. Polymer Sci., 5, 1 (1950).
27. A. R. Payne in P. Mason and N. Wookey, (Ed.) "Rheology of Elastomers," Pergamon Press, London 1958, p. 86, values tablulated in J. D. Ferry "Viscoelastic Properties of Polymers," John Wiley, New York, 1961, p. 458.
28. A. R. Payne in "The Physical Properties of Polymers," S.C.I. Monograph No. 5, Society of Chemical Industry, London and Macmillan, New York, 1959, p. 273.
29. W. Philippoff, J. Appl. Phys., 24, 685 (1953).
30. R. D. Rands, Jr., W. J. Ferguson, and J. L. Prather, J. Res. Natl. Bur. Std., 33, 63 (1944), RP 1595.
31. H. Schilling, Kautschuk und Gummi, 16, 84 (1963).
32. K. Schmieder and K. Wolf, Kolloid-Z., 134, 149 (1953).

33. A. H. Scott, J. Res. Natl. Bur. Std., 14, 99 (1935), RP 760; Rubber Chem. Technol., 8, 401 (1935).

34. A. J. Wildschut, "Technological and Physical Investigations on Natural and Synthetic Rubbers," Elsevier Publishing Company, Inc., New York, 1946.

35. R. S. Witte, B. A. Mrowca, and E. Guth, J. Appl. Phys., 20. 481 (1949); Rubber Chem. Technol., 23, 163 (1950).

36. L. A. Wood, N. Bekkedahl, and F. L. Roth, J. Res. Natl. Bur. Std., 29, 391 (1942), RP 1507; Ind. Eng. Chem., 34, 1291 (1942); Rubber Chem. Technol., 16, 244 (1943).

37. L. A. Wood and G. M. Martin, J. Res. Natl. Bur. Std., 68A, 259 (1964); Rubber Chem. Technol., 37, 850 (1964).

38. L. A. Wood and F. L. Roth, Proc. 4th Rubber Technology Conference, London, 1962, p.328, Institution of the Rubber Industry, London, 1963; Rubber Chem. Technol., 36, 611 (1963).

39. L. A. Wood and L. W. Tilton, Proc. 2nd Rubber Technology Conference, London, 1948, p.142, Institution of the Rubber Industry, London; J. Res. Natl. Bur. Std. 43, 57 (1949), RP 2004.

40. L. J. Zapas, S. L. Shufler, and T. W. de Witt, J. Polymer Sci., 18, 245 (1955); Rubber Chem. Technol., 29, 725 (1956).

PHYSICAL CONSTANTS OF POLYACRYLONITRILE

R. Chiang

Chemstrand Research Center
Durham, North Carolina

Table I:	Property	Value	Remarks		Reference
Birefringence, $n_{\parallel} - n_{\perp}$		-0.004		(e)	29-31
Coefficient of expansion					
volume, $(1/\bar{v})(d\bar{v}/dt) \times 10^4$, $[\deg^{-1}]$		3.0 above T_g; 1.4 below T_g			17
		2.8 1.6			16
		3.8	=		19
linear, $(1/\ell)(d\ell/dt) \times 10^4$, $[\deg^{-1}]$		1.6	1.0		15
		2 ± 0.4	-		20
Crystallization temperature determined in propylene carbonate, $[°C]$		95-100		(a)	4b,4c
Crystallographic Data		see Unit Cell Dimensions			
Decomposition temperature, $[°C]$		250-310		(b)	6
Density for flakes at 25°C		1.17-1.18			4a,4b
Dielectric constant, film					
10^6 c		4.2			29
10^3 c		5.5			
60 c		6.5			
Dissipation factor, film					
10^6 c		0.033			29
10^3 c		0.085			
60 c		0.113			
Dissolution temperature in propylene carbonate, $[°C]$		125-130		(a)	4b,4c
Glass transition temperature T_g, $[°C]$		87,103			15
		96.5			16
		87			17
		80			18
		104			5
		85			19,20
		87; 140			20a
Heat of polymerization, $[kcal/mole of monomeric unit]$		17.3 ± 0.5			1
Infrared spectrum		see Table Ia, Ib			
Intrinsic viscosity, $[dl\ g^{-1}]$				(c)	

Solvent	Temp., °C	Huggins' constant	$-(d\ln[\eta]/dt) \times 10^2$	Reference
N,N-Dimethylformamide	25	0.34		24
	35	0.33		25
			0.19	26
			0.14-0.19	27
N,N-Dimethylacetamide			0.27	26
Dimethyl sulfoxide			0.08	26
60% HNO_3			0.05	26
γ-Butyrolactone			0.14	26
			0.13-0.17	27
Hydroxyacetonitrile			0.07	26

Property	Value	Remarks	Reference
Melting point (estimated), [°C]	319	(d)	5
Properties of fibers	See Table Ic		
Refractive index	n_D^{25} = 1.518	(e)	16
Acrilan	$n_\perp$ = 1.524;		29
	$n_{\parallel}$ = 1.520		
Orlon	$n_\perp$ = 1.510		29
	$n_{\parallel}$ = 1.500-1.510		
$(dn/dt) \times 10^4$, $[deg^{-1}]$	-0.98 below T_g; -1.70 above T_g		16
Resistivity, [ohm-cm]	1×10^{14}		29
Solvents	N,N-dimethylformamide; dimethyl sulfoxide dimethylacetamide; ethylene carbonate propylene carbonate malononitrile; succinonitrile; adiponitrile; γ-butyrolactone; conc. sulfuric and nitric acid; conc. salt solutions: LiBr, NaCNS, $ZnCl_2$; see Tables "Solvents-Nonsolvents" in this Handbook.		11,21-23
Unit cell dimensions, [Å]	Orthorhombic: a=10.20 b=6.10 Orthorhombic: a=10.55 b=5.80 Hexagonal: a=5.99 b=5.99	(f)	1a 2 3
Viscosity-average molecular weight relationship	$[\eta]_{DMF}^{25}$ = 2.43 $\times 10^{-4} M_v^{0.75}$	(g)	28

a. The dissolution and crystallization temperatures given here are obtained from a free-radical polyacrylonitrile. They are sensitive to chain irregularities in the polymer. Samples of polyacrylonitrile obtained from different sources show marked difference in the dissolution and crystallization temperatures, although they have similar IR-spectra, x-ray diffraction patterns, and densities (4b,4c).

b. The thermal decomposition temperature determined by thermogravimetric analysis ranges from 250°C for a polyacrylonitrile prepared with an ionic catalyst, to 310°C for a commercial fiber. Pyrolysis of polyacrylonitrile carried out in the absence of oxygen at 500-800°C yields HCN and low molecular weight nitriles such as monomer, dimer, and methacrylonitrile (7), leaving a residue with a condensed ring structure (8-14).

c. The factors which convert the intrinsic viscosity in one solvent (e.g. DMF) into that in another (dimethylacetamide, dimethyl sulfone, ethylene carbonate, γ-butyrolactone) can be calculated from data given by Fujisaki and Kobayashi (26).

d. Polyacrylonitrile decomposes before melting.

e. $n_\perp$ and $n_{\parallel}$ are refractive indices measured with incident ligh having the vibration vector perpendicular and parallel to the fiber axis, respectively.

f. The reported unit cell dimensions, especially the c dimension along the chain axis, can only be regarded as estimated because of the diffuse meridian and polar reflections. For more data see Table on "Crystallographic Data for Various Polymers" in this Handbook.

g. For equations reported by other authors, see Table on "Viscosity-Molecular Weight Relationships" in this Handbook. The constants K and a change markedly with the conditions of polymerization.

Table Ia: Infrared Spectrum of Polyacrylonitrile

(Observed Data, Calculated Frequencies, and Assignements
(34,35) Additional References 32,33)

Frequency Observed (cm^{-1})			Calculated (cm^{-1})	Assignment[a]
2950	$(\perp)$	vs	2935	$\nu_a(CH_2)(B_1)(B_2)$
2930	$(\perp)$	sh	2929	$\nu(CH)(A_1)(B_1)$
2870	$(\perp)$	m	2886	$\nu_s(CH_2)(A_1)$
2810	$(\parallel)$	vw		
2237	$(\perp)$	vs	2237	$\nu(CN)(A_1)(B_1)$
1447	$(\perp)$	vs	1453	$\delta(CH_2)(63)(A_1)$
			1396	$\delta(CH)(50)-w(CH_2)(40)(B_1)$
1362	$(\perp)$	m	1362	$\delta(CH)(64)(A_1)$
1355	$(\parallel)$	m	1357	$w(CH_2)(55) + \nu_a(CC)(37)(B_2)$
1310	$(\perp)$	w	1309	$w(CH_2)(44) - \delta(CH)(33)(B_1)$
1247	$(\parallel)$	s	1189	$w(CH)(40) + w(CH_2)(29) - \nu_a(CC)(26)(B_2)$
1115	$(\perp)$	sh	1101	$\nu_s(CC)(33) - \delta(CH)(20)(A_1)$
1073	$(\perp)$	vs	1080	$\nu_s(CC)(69)(B_1)$
			1066	$r(CH_2)(47) - \delta(C-C-CN)(21)(B_1)$
1015	$(\parallel)$	sh	1018	$w(CH)(57) + \nu_a(CC)(26)(B_2)$
			999	$t(CH_2)(59)(A_1)$
865	$(\parallel)$	vw	847	$r(CH_2)(91)(B_2)$
778	$(\perp)$	m	796	$\nu(C-CN)(48) + t(CH_2)(34)(A_1)$
			764	$\nu(C-CN)(59) - r(CH_2)(28)(B_1)$
570	$(\perp)$	sh	551	$\delta(C-C-CN)(53) - \delta(C-C-N)(22)(B_1)$
537	$(\perp)$	m	518	$\delta(C-C-CN)(34) - \delta(C-C-N)(37)(A_1)$
520	$(\perp)$	sh	524	$w(C-C-CN)(45) - w(C-C-N)(40)(B_2)$
			357	$\delta(C-C-C)(65)(B_1)$
260	$(\perp)$	m	271	$\delta(C-C-N)(58) + \delta(C-C-CN)(19) - \delta(C-C-C)(19)(B_1)$
			246	$\delta(C-C-N)(63) + \delta(C-C-CN)(28)(A_1)$
			204	$w(C-C-N)(54) + w(C-C-CN)(40)(B_2)$

Symbols: ν_a: stretching; ν_s: symmetric stretching; ν_a: antisymmetric stretching;
δ: bending, or deformation perpendicular to the chain axis; w: wagging,
or deformation parallel to the chain axis; r: rocking; t: twisting. The
potential energy distribution (in percent) among the symmetry coordinates
is given in parentheses. The signs denote the phase relation of the
coupled coordinates.

For the infrared spectra of poly(α-deuteroacrylonitrile) $(-CH_2-CD(CH)-)_n$, poly(α,β,β-trideuteroacrylonitrile) $(-CD_2-CD(CN)-)_n$, and poly(β,β-dideuteroacrylonitrile),
$(-CD_2-CH(CN)-)_n$, see references 34,35.

Ib: <u>Additional Infrared Absorption Peaks Often Observed in Polyacrylonitrile</u>

Frequency, cm^{-1}	Structure	Reference
1600-1750	Impurities such as carbonyls, amides, etc.	32
1693	-C=N- in polymethacrylonitrile	14
1675	-C=N in PAN	36
2012[a]	>C=C=N in polymethacrylonitrile	14, 37-41
2030[a]	>C=C=N in PAN	36, 42-46
1420[b]	-CH$_2$CN	47

(a) Keteneimines are often produced by γ-ray, x-ray, or other high-energy radiations.

(b) Miller (47) showed that the polyacrylonitrile samples prepared with butyl-Li toluene at 0, 40, and -78°C contained cyanoethyl groups of approximately 23, 10, and 0%, respectively.

Table Ic: <u>Properties of Acrylic Fibers</u> (48,49)

Properties	Orlon	Acrilan	Zefran Zefkrome	Creslan
Breaking tenacity,[g den^{-1}]	2.2-2.6	2.0-2.7	3.3-4.2	2.0-3.0
Tensile strength, [psi]	(3.2 to 3.9) x 10^4	(3.2 to 3.9) x 10^4	(5.3 to 5.9) x 10^4	(3.0 to 4.5) x 10^4
Elongation at break, [%]	20-28	34-50	30-36	40-55
Elastic Recovery, [%]		99 at 2% 89 at 5%	94 at 1% 86 at 3% 58 at 10%	90 at 1% 55 at 3% 40 at 5%
Average stiffness,[g den^{-1}]	10	7	10.8-11.3	4.0-8.0
Average toughness	0.40	0.46	0.58-0.67	0.50-0.70
Density	1.16	1.17	1.18	1.18
Water absorption,% 21.1°C, 65% RH* 21.1°C, 95% RH	1.5 ~ 4	1.5 5	1.5-2.5 3-5	1.0-1.5 2.0-2.5
Sticking temp.,°C	230	245	210	
Effect of acids and alkalis	Good to excellent resistance to mineral acids. Fair to good resistance to weak alkalis; moderate resistance to strong, cold solutions.			
Effect of bleaches and solvents	Good resistance to bleaches and common solvents. Unaffected by dry cleaning solvents. Can be bleached with sodium chlorite.			
Resistance to mildew, aging, sunlight, abrasion	Not attacked by mildew. Good resistance to aging, sunlight, and abrasion.			

* RH = relative humidity

References page VI-73

REFERENCES

1. L. K. J. Tong and W. O. Kenyon, J. Am. Chem. Soc., 69, 2245 (1947).
1a. R. Stefani, M. Chevreton, M. Garnier, and M. C. Eyraud, Compt. Rend., 251, 2174 (1960).
2. V. F. Holland, S. B. Mitchell, W. L. Hunter, and P. H. Lindenmeyer, J. Polymer Sci., 62, 145 (1962).
3. C. Natta, G. Mazzanti, and P. Corradini, Atti. Accad. Nazl. Lincei, Mem. Classe Sci. Fis., Mat. Nat., 25, 3 (1958).
4. a. R. Chiang, J. Polymer Sci., A1, 2765 (1963); b. J. Polymer Sci., A3, 2019 (1965); c. R. Chiang, J. H. Rhodes and V. F. Holland, J. Polymer Sci., A3, 479 (1965).
5. W. R. Krigbaum and N. Tokita, J. Polymer Sci., 43, 467 (1960).
6. M. Baer, private communication, April, 1962.
7. H. Zahn and P. Schäfer, Makromol. Chem., 30, 225 (1959).
8. S. L. Madorsky and S. Straus, J. Res. Natl. Bur. Std., 63A, 261 (1959).
9. J. McCartney, "Polymer Degradation Mechanisms," Natl. Bur. Std. Circ., 525, 123 (1953).
11. R. C. Houtz, J. Textile Res. 20, 786 (1956).
12. W. J. Burland and J. L. Parsons, J. Polymer Sci., 22, 249 (1956).
13. E. M. LaCombe, J. Polymer Sci., 24, 152 (1957).
14. See, for example, N. Grassie and J. N. Hay, J. Polymer Sci., 56, 189 (1962).
15. W. H. Howard, J. Appl. Polymer Sci., 5, 303 (1961).
16. R. B. Beevers, J. Polymer Sci., A2, 5257 (1964).
17. H. J. Kolb and E. F. Izard, J. Appl. Phys., 20, 564 (1949).
18. J. J. Kearvey and E. C. Eberlin, J. Appl. Sci., 3, 47 (1960).
19. G. F. Lanzl, quoted in ref. 31.
20. C. E. Black, quoted in ref. 31.
20a. R. D. Andrews and R. M. Kimmel, J. Polymer Sci., B3, 167 (1965).
21. E. E. Walker, J. Appl. Chem., 2, 470 (1952).
22. C. E. Schildknecht, "Vinyl and Related Polymers," John Wiley & Sons, Inc., New York, 1952, p. 270-274.
23. C. H. Bamford and G. C. Eastmond, "Properties of Polymers and Copolymers of Acrylonitrile," in "Encyclopedia of Polymer Science and Technology," ed. by H. F. Mark, N. G. Gaylord, and N. M. Bikales, Interscience, New York, 1964, Vol. I, p. 407-425.
24. M. L. Miller, J. Polymer Sci., 56, 203 (1962).
25. H. Kobayashi, J. Polymer Sci., B1, 299 (1963).
26. Y. Fujisaki and H. Kobayashi, Chem. High Polymer (Japan), 19, 81 (1962).
27. R. Chiang and J. H. Rhodes, unpublished work, 1964.
28. R. L. Cleland and W. H. Stockmayer, J. Polymer Sci., 17, 473 (1955).
29. M. Harris, "Handbook of Textile Fibers," Harris Research Laboratories, 1246 Taylor St., N. W., Washington, D. C.
30. P.-A. Koch and C. J. W. Hooper, "Microscopic and Chemical Testing of Textiles," Chapman and Hall, London, 1963.
31. C. R. Bohn, J. R. Schaefgen, and W. O. Statton, J. Polymer Sci., 55, 531 (1961).
32. C. Y. Liang and S. Krimm, J. Polymer Sci., 31, 513 (1958).
33. C. Y. Liang, F. C. Pearson, and R. H. Marchessault, Spectrochim. Acta., 17, 568 (1961); C. Y. Liang, "IR Spectra: Deuteration and Polarization," Chapter II, in "Newer Methods of Polymer Characterization," ed. by B. Ke, Interscience, New York 1964, p. 47-50.
34. H. Tadokoro, S. Murahashi, R. Yamadera, and T.-I. Kamei, J. Polymer Sci., A1, 3029 (1963).
35. R. Yamadera, H. Tadokoro, and S. Murahashi, J. Chem. Phys., 41, 1233 (1964).
36. Y. Tsuda, Bull. Chem. Soc. (Japan), 34, 1046 (1961).
37. M. Talat-Erben and S. Bywater, Ricerca Sci., 25A, 11 (1955); through ref. 40.
38. N. Grassie and I. C. McNeill, J. Polymer Sci., 27, 207 (1958).
39. N. Grassie and I. C. McNeill, J. Polymer Sci., 30, 37 (1958).
40. N. Grassie and I. C. McNeill, J. Polymer Sci., 33, 171 (1958).
41. W. J. Burlant and C. R. Taylor, J. Phys. Chem., 62, 247 (1958).
42. C. S. H. Chen, N. Colthup, W. Deichert, and R. L. Webb, J. Polymer Sci., 45 247 (1960).
43. A. Bernas, R. Bensasson, I. Rossi, and P. Barchewitz, J. Chim. Phys., 59, 1442 (1962).
44. C. A. Levine and G. H. Harris, J. Polymer Sci., 62, S100 (1962).
45. C. L. Stevens, and J. C. French, J. Am. Chem. Soc., 76, 4398 (1954).
46. R. Dijkstra and H. J. Backer, Rec. Trav. Chim., 73, 575 (1954).
47. M. L. Miller, ACS Meeting, St. Louis, Polymer Preprint, 1, No. 2, 47 (1961).
48. "1964 Man-Made Fiber Chart," ed. by T. Benton Sevison, Jr., Textile World, 330 W. 42nd St., New York, N. Y.
49. R. W. Moncrieff, "Man-Made Fibers," John Wiley, New York, 1963.

PHYSICAL CONSTANTS OF POLYSTYRENE

J. F. Rudd

Physical Research Laboratory
The Dow Chemical Company
Midland, Michigan

Property	Value	Remarks	Ref.
Birefringence dispersion $\dfrac{\Delta n(\lambda)}{\Delta n(5461\ \text{Å})}$	$A + \dfrac{B}{\lambda^2} + \dfrac{C}{\lambda^4}$	$A = 0.8905$ $B = 1.869 \times 10^{-9}\ \text{Å}^2$ $C = -6.685 \times 10^{-19}\ \text{Å}^4$	21
Coefficient of expansion (linear) [deg^{-1}]	(6 to 8) x 10^{-5}	$<T_g$ (unoriented)	3
(volume) [deg^{-1}]	(1.7 to 2.1) x 10^{-4}	$<T_g$	7
	(5.1 to 6.0) x 10^{-4}	$>T_g$	7
Compressibility [bar^{-1}]	2.2 x 10^{-5}		3
Compressive modulus [dynes cm^{-2}]	3.0 x 10^{10}	(Unoriented)	18
Crystallographic Data	see Unit Cell		
Density, ρ [g cm^{-3}] amorphous	1.04-1.065		3,4
crystalline	1.111		2
	1.12		1,5
$d\rho/dt$, [g cm^{-3}deg^{-1}]	-2.65 x 10^{-4}	$<T_g$	6
	-6.05 x 10^{-4}	$>T_g$	6
Dielectric constant amorphous	2.49 to 2.55	1000 c (flat to 10^9c)	3
crystalline	2.61	"	16
Dissipation factor amorphous	15 x 10^{-4}	"	3
crystalline	3 x 10^{-4}	"	16
Glass transition temperature, T_g [deg]	80		6
	90		8
	(100)	$T_g = 373 - 10^5/M_v$ (fractions)	9
Heat of combustion [kcal/monomer unit]	-1.034 x 10^3		13
	-1.036 x 10^3		14
Heat of fusion crystalline [kcal/monomer unit]	2.00 ± 0.02		10
	2.15		2
Heat of polymerization [kcal/monomer unit]	-16.1	to solid polymer	15
	-16.7	to solid polymer	13
Heat of solution [kcal/monomer unit]	-0.86	in monomer	13
Melting point, T_m [deg]	240		10
	(250)		11

Property	Value	Remarks	Ref.

Melt viscosity-molecular
  weight relationship
  $\log \eta_T = 3.4 \log M - k$

Type	T, °C	M Range	k	
atactic	217	$\geq$ 38,000	13.40	31
isotactic	281	100,000 --600,000	14.42	32

Property	Value	Remarks	Ref.
Optical dispersion, $n_F - n_C$	1.92×10^{-2}	$\lambda = 4861.3$ Å (F) $\lambda = 6562.8$ Å (C)	3
Poisson's ratio	0.325 0.33		3 20
Refractive index, n_D	1.59-1.60	$\lambda = 5892.6$ Å (D)	3
dn_D/dt [deg^{-1}]	-1.42×10^{-4}		3
Resistivity [ohm-cm]	10^{20} to 10^{22}		17
Solvents	see tables on "Solvents-Nonsolvents" in this Handbook.		
Specific heat, [cal g^{-1}] C_p	0.283 (0.272) 0.300 (0.333) 0.439 (0.435)	0°C 50°C 100°C	3(12) 3(12) 3(12)
dC_p/dt [cal g^{-1} deg^{-1}]	9.65×10^{-4}	50°C	3
Stress-optical coefficient [brewsters]	10.1 9.5 8.3, 8.7	monofilament extruded sheet compr. molding	22 22 22
Tensile modulus [dynes cm^{-2}]	3.2×10^{10} 3.4×10^{10}	unoriented	19 18
Thermal conductivity [cal sec^{-1}cm^{-1} deg^{-1}]	2.51×10^{-4} 2.78×10^{-4} 3.06×10^{-4}	0°C 50°C 100°C	3 3 3
Unit cell [Å] a_o	21.90 22.08	rhombohedral	1 2
b_o	21.90 22.08		1 2
c_o	6.65 6.626		1 2
Velocity of sound [m sec^{-1}]	2.1×10^3		3

References page VI-78

Property	Value	Remarks	Ref.

Viscosity-molecular weight relationships for atactic polystyrene*
   $[\eta] = KM^a$

[η]		M				
Solvent	Temp. (°C)	Solvent	Method	K x 10⁴	a	
benzene	30	benzene	osmotic	0.97	0.74	23
benzene	25	toluene	osmotic	1.13	0.73	24
toluene	25	butanone	osmotic	1.34	0.71	
toluene	25	butanone	light scattering	1 7	0.69	25
toluene	30	butanone/iso-propyl alcohol	light scattering	0.923	0.72	26
benzene	30	toluene	osmotic	1.06	0.735	27
toluene	30	toluene	osmotic	1.10	0./25	
toluene	25	cyclohexane	sedimentation velocity	0.977	0.73	28

Viscosity-molecular weight relationships for isotactic polystyrene*
   $[\eta] = KM^a$

[η]		M				
Solvent	Temp. (°C)	Solvent	Method	K x 10⁴	a	
benzene	30	toluene	osmotic	1.06	0.735	27
toluene	30	toluene	osmotic	1.10	0.725	
benzene	room temp.	toluene	osmotic	0.95	0.77	29
benzene	25	toluene	osmotic	0.979	0.744	30
toluene	25	butanone	light scattering	1.7	0.69	25

* See also table on "Viscosity-Molecular Weight Relationships."

REFERENCES

1. G. Natta, Makromol. Chem., 35, 94 (1960).
2. R. L. Miller and L. E. Nielsen, J. Poly. Sci., 55, 643 (1961).
3. "Styrene, Its Polymers, Copolymers and Derivatives," Ed. R. H. Boundy and R. F. Boyer, Reinhold Publishing Corp., New York, 1952.
4. G. Natta, J. Polymer Sci., 16, 143 (1955).
5. G. Natta, P. Pino, P. Corradini, F. Danusso, E. Mantica, G. Mazzanti, and G. Moraglio, J. Am. Chem. Soc., 77, 1708 (1955).
6. W. Patnode and W. J. Scheiber, J. Am. Chem. Soc., 61, 3449 (1939).
7. R. S. Spencer and G. D. Gilmore, J. Appl. Phys., 20, 502 (1949).
8. F. P. Reding, J. A. Faucher and R. D. Whitman, J. Polymer Sci. 57, 483 (1962).
9. T. G. Fox and P. J. Flory, J. Appl. Phys., 21, 581 (1950). The effect of residual monomer, low molecular weight polymer, ethyl benzene and plasticizers being to depress T_g, the value given by these authors represents the limiting glass temperature at high molecular weights. In this connection, see also the work of Ueberreiter and Kanig, Z. Naturforsch. 6a, 551 (1951) and Ueberreiter and Asmussen, J. Polymer Sci., 23, 75 (1957).
10. R. Dedeurwaerder and J. F. M. Oth, J. Chim. Phys., 56, 940 (1959).
11. T. W. Campbell and A. C. Haven, Jr., J. Appl. Polymer Sci., 1, 73 (1959).
12. K. Ueberreiter and E. Otto-Laupenmuhlen, Z. Naturforsch. 8a, 664 (1953).
13. D. E. Roberts, W. W. Walton and R. S. Jessup, J. Polymer Sci., 2, 420 (1947).
14. J. W. Breitenbach and J. Derkosch, Monatsh, 81, 698 (1950).
15. L. K. J. Tong and W. O. Kenyon, J. Amer. Chem. Soc., 69, 1402 (1947).
16. F. L. Saunders and R. C. Mildner, The Dow Chemical Company, unpublished data.
17. P. Woodland, The Dow Chemical Company, unpublished data.
18. Dow Chemical Technical Publication "Plastics Design Data" (1965 Revision), section on "Strength and Stiffness."
19. J. F. Rudd and E. F. Gurnee, J. Appl. Phys., 28, 1096 (1957).
20. L. E. Nielsen, "Mechanical Properties of Polymers," Reinhold Publishing Corp., New York, 1962.
21. E. F. Gurnee, The Dow Chemical Company, unpublished data.
22. J. F. Rudd and R. D. Andrews, J. Appl. Phys., 31, 818 (1960).
23. R. H. Ewart and H. C. Tingey, Abstracts of 111th ACS Meeting (April, 1947) quoted in Fox and Flory, J. Amer. Chem. Soc., 73, 1915 (1951).
24. C. E. H. Bawn, R. F. J. Freeman and A. R. Kamaliddin, Trans. Faraday Soc., 46, 1107 (1950).
25. P. Outer, C. I. Carr and B. H. Zimm, J. Chem. Phys., 18, 830 (1950).
26. S. N. Chinai, P. C. Scherer, C. W. Bondurant, and D. W. Levi, J. Polymer Sci., 22, 527 (1956).
27. F. Danusso and G. Moraglio, J. Polymer Sci., 24, 161 (1957).
28. H. W. McCormick, J. Polymer Sci., 36, 341 (1959).
29. F. Ang, J. Polymer Sci., 25, 126 (1957).
30. W. R. Krigbaum, D. K. Carpenter and S. Newman, J. Phys. Chem., 62, 1586 (1958).
31. T. G. Fox and P. J. Flory, J. Polymer Sci., 14, 315 (1954).
32. J. Boon, G. Challa, and P. H. Hermans, Makromol. Chem. 74, 129 (1964).

PHYSICAL CONSTANTS OF POLY(HEXAMETHYLENE ADIPAMIDE)

O. A. Pickett, Jr.

Chemstrand Research Center
Durham, North Carolina

Property	Value	Ref.
Abrasion Resistance, [mils (24 hrs)$^{-1}$]		
wear rate, nylon-low carbon steel, 50 psi, 87.7 fpm	0.3	19
Adhesive Bond Strength, tensile, [psi]		
nylon-aluminum	9,700	32
nylon-steel	9,900	32
nylon-copper	10,900	32
Birefringence		
index of parallel refraction minus index of perpendicular refraction	0.060	30
yarn draw ratio 1	0.004	1
1.4	0.017	1
2.4	0.045	1
3.0	0.049	1
4.1	0.056	1
4.6	0.059	1
Brittleness Temperature, [°C]		
dry	-85	42
Coefficient of Friction		
nylon-nylon, static	0.42	5
nylon-nylon, kinetic	0.35	5
nylon-steel, static	0.37	5
nylon-steel, kinetic	0.34	5
Coefficient of Thermal Expansion, [°F^{-1}]	5.5×10^{-5}	19
	5.7×10^{-5}	48
	4.5×10^{-5}	13
Cohesive Energy, [cal mole^{-1}]		
methylene group	680	10
carboxyl group	5,600	10
amine group	3,100	10
amide group	8,500	10
repeat unit	23,800	10
Compressive Strength, [psi]	7,200 - 13,000	29
Crystal Structure Change, [°C]		
triclinic below, pseudohexagonal above	175	41,45
	165	49
Crystallographic Data: see Unit Cell		
Density, [g cc^{-1}]		
drawn fiber	1.14	15
	1.14 - 1.16	11
amorphous	1.09	31,43
	1.069	44
crystalline	1.24	11,31
	1.22	44

Property	Value	Ref.
Density, [g cc^{-1}] (Cont'd.)		
drawn fiber, % RH* 0	1.140	8
12	1.141	8
23	1.142	8
39	1.143	8
48	1.144	8
65	1.146	8
78	1.147	8
90	1.146	8
98	1.145	8
Dielectric Constant, ε		
1000 cycles, 18% RH*, 22°C	4.0	15
1000 cycles, wet, 22°C	20.0	15
60 cycles, dry, 33°C	3.8	15
60 cycles, dry, 90°C	7.0	15
Dielectric Strength, [v mil^{-1}]		
9 mil unrolled film, 50% RH, 21°C	1300	15
2 mil rolled film, 50% RH, 21°C	3000	15
Elastic Recovery, % in 60 seconds		
no load, 4% stretch for 100 seconds	100	15
8% stretch for 100 seconds	100	15
12% stretch for 100 seconds	91	15
0.25 gpd load,		
1% stretch for 30 seconds	38	15
2% stretch for 30 seconds	63	15
4% stretch for 30 seconds	73	15
Elongation, [%]		
at yield	25	43
ultimate	300	43
regular yarn, dry	26 - 65	46
wet	30 - 70	46
high tenacity yarn, dry	16 - 28	46
wet	18 - 32	46
Entropy of Fusion, [cal deg^{-1} mol^{-1}]		
repeat unit	20.4	2
	20.6	38
	18.7	45
repeat unit, constant volume	15.8	2
	13.9	45
Flammability, [°C]	532	15
Glass Transition Temperature, [°C]	49	6
	50	14
	47	37
Hardness		
23°C, dry	M79	42
	R118	42
23°C, 50% RH	M59	42
	R108	42
Heat Capacity, [cal g^{-1} °C^{-1}]		
-4.5°C to 28.5°C	0.343	26
20°C to 250°C	0.555	3,15
25°C	0.35	17
100°C	0.48	17
180°C	0.56	17

*RH = relative humidity

References page VI-84

Property	Value	Ref.
Heat Distortion Temperature, [°C]		
66 psi	204	19
	182	13
264 psi	66	13
Heat of Crystallization, [cal g^{-1}]	12.8	24
Heat of Fusion, [cal g^{-1}]	22	23
	20.3	25
	48.6	49
	45	16
	48	2
ribbon	29.0	49
drawn filaments	39.5	49
annealed	33.3	49
total sample	17.6	24
crystalline region	46.8	24
Heat of Wetting, [cal g^{-1}]	7.3	36
Impact Strength		
Izod, [ft lb in^{-1}]	2.0	43
	2.66	7
25°C	1.4	19
4°C	0.4	19
Tensile, [ft lb in^{-2}]	76	13
Infrared Spectra, [cm^{-1}]		
crystalline bands	936	31,44
	6536	31
amorphous bands	1139	44
	6757	31
miscellaneous bands -NH-	3310	12,28,35,47
	3300	12,28,35,47
	3100	12,28,35,47
	3075	12,28,35,47
-CH$_2$-	2930	12,28,35,47
	2925	12,28,35,47
	2860	12,28,35,47
-CONH-	1700	12,28,35,47
	1640	12,28,35,47
-CO-	1630	12,28,35,47
-CONH-	1200	12,28,35,47
	730	12,28,35,47
	688	12,28,35,47
Mechanical Loss		
[°K], dry	170,370	50
0.9% water	170,250,370	50
3.3% water	170,240,310	50
6.4% water	280	50
[% RH] for maximum loss, 35°C	70	33
Melt Index, [g (10 min)$^{-1}$], ASTM-D1238-57T		
$\bar{M}_n$, (end groups), 34,000	2	4
$\bar{M}_n$, (end groups), 18,000	5	4
Melting Point, [°C]		
air	250	15
nitrogen	265	21,38
ribbon	263	49
undrawn filaments	264	49
drawn filaments	259	49
annealed	262	49

Property	Value	Ref.
Modulus		
modulus of elasticity, [g den^{-1}]		
medium range	24	36
high range	45	36
1% stretch, % RH, 0	0.48	23
50	0.31	23
100	0.12	23
shear modulus, [dyn cm^{-2}]		
undrawn, 66% RH	3.0×10^9	1
drawn, 66% RH	3.6×10^9	1
sonic modulus, [g den^{-1}]		
unoriented	21	14
Young's modulus, [dyn cm^{-2}]		
undrawn, 66% RH	8.6×10^9	1
drawn, 66% RH	20.4×10^9	1
Moisture Regain, [% of dry]		
% RH, 10	1.1	15
20	1.4	15
30	1.7	15
40	2.3	15
50	2.8	15
60	3.4	15
70	4.1	15
80	5.0	15
90	5.7	15
97	6.2	15
Molecular Weight		
repeat unit	226.32	
non-fiber forming	6,000 or less	30
fibers, brittle and weak	6,100 - 10,000	30
optimum range	12,000 - 20,000	30
difficult to melt spin	20,000 or more	30
Nuclear Magnetic Resonance		
second moment, [gauss^2]		
77°K (liquid nitrogen)	26	39
298°K (room temperature)	18	39
temperatures, spin lattice relaxation time minima, [°C]	20, 155	27
Oligomers		
monomer, cyclic		
melting point, [°C]	248	9
	253	51
density, [g cc^{-1}]	1.171	9
molecular weight	226	9
cell structure	triclinic	9
cell dimensions, [Å] a	9.58	9
b	8.71	9
c	8.47	9
cell angles, [deg] α	110° 58'	9
β	104° 35'	9
γ	86° 17'	9
dimer, cyclic		
melting point, [°C]	237	9
	241	51
molecular weight	445	9
trimer, cyclic		
melting point, [°C]	236	51

Property	Value	Ref.
Oligomers (Cont'd.)		
x-mer cyclic		
melting point, [°C]	267	51
monomer, linear		
melting point, [°C]	190	52
dimer, linear		
melting point, [°C]	208	52
tetramer, linear		
melting point, [°C]	245	52
Power Factor, [%]		
1000 cycles, 18% RH, 22°C	5.0	15
1000 cycles, wet, 22°C	11.0	15
60 cycles, dry, 33°C	1.8	15
60 cycles, dry, 90°C	13.0	15
Refractive Index		
index of parallel refraction	1.580	30
	1.582	20
index of perpendicular refraction	1.520	30
	1.519	20
undrawn, or molded	1.53	29
principal values for single crystals		
α, calc.	1.475	11
β, calc.	1.565	11
γ, obs.	1.580	11
Resistivity, [ohm-cm]		
film, 18% RH	4×10^{14}	15
film, wet	5×10^{9}	15
Shear Stress, [psi]	9,600	19
Shrinkage		
boiling water, [%]		
unrelaxed multifilament	8.5 - 10.0	23
unrelaxed monofilament	10.3 - 11.8	23
mold shrinkage, [in. in.$^{-1}$]		
thickness: 1/32 inch	0.010	40
1/16 inch	0.012	40
1/8 inch	0.015	40
1/4 inch	0.022	40
Shrinkage Force, [g den^{-1}]		
boiling water	0.4	23
Solvents *		
acetic acid, hot, containing calcium chloride; benzyl alcohol, hot; m-cresol; formic acid, conc.; hydrochloric acid, conc.; methyl alcohol containing calcium chloride or zinc chloride; nitric acid, conc.; sulfuric acid, conc.		15
Specific Volume Change, [cc g^{-1}]		
on melting	0.116	22
Stiffness, [g den^{-1}]		
regular yarn	22	19
	5 - 23	46
high tenacity	41	19
	21 - 58	46

*Additional values in the corresponding table of this Handbook.

Property	Value	Ref.
Tensile Strength		
regular, $[g\ den^{-1}]$	3.0 - 6.0	46
high tenacity, $[g\ den^{-1}]$	5.9 - 9.2	46
regular, [psi]	44,000 - 88,000	46
high tenacity, [psi]	86,000 - 134,000	46
Thermal Conductivity, $[BTU\ hr^{-1}\ sq\ ft^{-1}\ °F^{-1}\ in^{-1}]$	1.7	13,19
Toughness, $[g\text{-}cm\ den\text{-}cm^{-1}]$		
regular	0.78 - 0.97	46
high tenacity	0.74 - 0.84	46
Unit Cell		
dimensions, $[\overset{\circ}{A}]$		
alpha, triclinic, a	4.9	11
b	5.4	11
c	17.2	11
beta, triclinic, a	4.9	11
b	8.0	11
c	17.2	11
angles , [deg.]		
alpha, triclinic, α	48½	11
β	77	11
γ	63½	11
beta, triclinic, α	90	11
β	77	11
γ	67	11
volume, [cc]		
single cell	301×10^{-24}	11
weight, [g]		
single monomer unit	373×10^{-24}	11
Wettability		
critical surface tension, $[dyn\ cm^{-1}]$	42.5 - 46.0	18
Yield Stress		
air, $[g\ den^{-1}]$	0.45	34
water, $[g\ den^{-1}]$	0.26	34
ratio, yield stress/drawing stress		
air	1.03	34
water	1.24	34
dry, 23°C, [psi]	8,100 - 11,800	42
dry, 50°C, [psi]	7,200 - 9,300	42
50% RH, 23°C, [psi]	6,700 - 8,500	42

REFERENCES

1. N. Adams, J. Textile Inst., 47, T530 (1956).
2. G. Allen, J. Appl. Chem., 14, 1 (1964).
3. Anonymous, Rayon Textile Monthly, 25, 51 (April, 1944).
4. E. C. Bernhardt, Editor,"Processing of Thermoplastic Materials", Reinhold Publishing Corp., New York, 1959.
5. R. C. Bowers, W. C. Clinton, and W. A. Zisman, Ind. Eng. Chem., 46, 2416 (1954).
6. R. F. Boyer, and R. S. Spenser, J. Appl. Phys., 15, 398 (1944).
7. C. G. Bragaw, Modern Plastics, 33, 199 (June, 1956).
8. British Nylon Spinners Technical Manual.
9. C. J. Brown, A. Hill and P. V. Youle, Nature, 177, 128 (1956).
10. C. W. Bunn, J. Polymer Sci., 16, 323 (1955).
11. C. W. Bunn, E. V. Garner, Proc. Roy. Soc. (London), A189, 39 (1947).
12. G. Caroti and J. H. Dusenbury, J. Polymer Sci., 22, 399 (1956).
13. D. D. Carswell, Machine Design, 36, 76 (Sept. 17, 1964).
14. W. H. Charch and W. W. Moseley, Jr., Textile Res. J., 29, 525 (1959).
15. Chemstrand Technical Information Manual.
16. M. Dole and B. Wunderlich, Makromol. Chem., 34, 29 (1959).
17. DuPont Technical Information Manual.
18. A. H. Ellison and W. A. Zisman, J. Phys. Chem., 58, 503 (1954).
19. D. E. Floyd, "Polyamide Resins," Reinhold Publishing Corp., New York, 1958.

20. A. N. J. Heyn, Textile Res. J., 23, 246 (1953).
21. R. Hill and E. E. Walker, J. Polymer Sci., 3, 609 (1948).
22. D. C. Hookway, J. Textile Inst., 49, P292 (1958).
23. K. H. Inderfurth, "Nylon Technology," McGraw-Hill Book Co., Inc., New York, 1953.
24. M. Inoue, J. Polymer Sci., A1, 2697 (1963).
25. B. Ke, A. W. Sisko, J. Polymer Sci., 50, 87 (1961).
26. F. C. Magne, H. J. Portas, and H. Wakeman, J. Am. Chem. Soc., 69, 1896 (1947).
27. D. W. McCall and E. W. Anderson, Polymer, 4, 93 (1963).
28. A. Miyake, J. Polymer Sci., 44, 223 (1960).
29. Modern Plastics Encyclopedia, Plastics Properties Chart, Plastics Catalogue Corp., New York, 1963.
30. R. W. Moncrieff, "Artificial Fibres," John Wiley & Sons, Inc., New York, 1950.
31. J. B. Nichols, J. Appl. Phys., 25, 840 (1954).
32. J. Pellon and W. G. Carpenter, J. Polymer Sci., A1, 863 (1963).
33. J. M. R Quistwater and B. A. Dunell, J. Polymer Sci., 28, 309 (1958).
34. R. G. Quynn, J. Appl. Polymer Sci., 4, 253 (1960),
35. R. G. Quynn and R. Steele, Nature, 173, 1240 (1954).
36. B. P. Ridge, J. Textile Inst., 44, P48 (1953).
37. P. D. Ritchie, "A Chemistry of Plastics and High Polymers," Cleaver-Hume Press Ltd., London, 1949.
38. J. R. Schaefgen, J. Polymer Sci., 38, 549 (1959).
39. W. P Slichter, J. Appl. Phys., 26, 1099 (1955).
40. Society of Plastics Industry, Inc., "Plastics Engineering Handbook," 3rd Edition, Reinhold Plublishing Corp., New York, 1960.
41. H. W. Starkweather, Jr., SPE Trans., 3, 57 (1963).
42. H. W. Starkweather, Jr. and R. E. Brooks, J. Appl. Polymer Sci., 1, 236 (1959).
43. H. W. Starkweather, Jr., G. E. Moore, J. E. Hansen, T. M. Roder, and R. E. Brooks, J. Polymer Sci., 21, 189 (1956).
44. H. W. Starkweather, Jr. and R. E. Moynihan, J. Polymer Sci., 22, 363 (1956).
45. H. W. Starkweather, Jr., J. F. Whitney, and D. R. Johnson, J. Polymer Sci., A1, 715 (1963).
46. Textile World, 1964 Man-Made-Fiber Chart, Textile World, 114, 181 (July, 1964).
47. H. W. Thompson and P. Torkington, Trans. Faraday Soc., 41, 246 (1945).
48. R. L. Wakeman, "The Chemistry of Commercial Plastics," Reinhold Publishing Corp., New York, 1947.
49. R. C. Wilhoit and M. Dole, J. Phys. Chem., 57, 14 (1953).
50. A. E. Woodward, J. M. Crissman and J. A. Sauer, J. Polymer Sci., 44, 23 (1960).
51. H. Zahn, Z. Ges. Textilind., 66, 928 (1964).
52. H. Zahn, W. Lauer, Makromol. Chem., 23, 85 (1957).

PHYSICAL CONSTANTS OF POLY(ETHYLENE TEREPHTHALATE)[*]

E. L. Ringwald

Chemstrand Research Center
Durham, North Carolina

Table I: Property	Value	Ref.
Break Elongation [%] (film)	75	5,32,33
Bursting Strength [psi] (film)	55-66	32
Coefficient of Volume Expansion [deg $^{-1}$]		
30-60°C	1.6×10^{-4}	1
90-190°C	3.7×10^{-4}	1
Conductivity for Direct Current:	see Figure III	
Crystallographic Data:	see Unit Cell	

Density [g cm^{-3}]

Form	Sample Density	Estimate of % Crystallinity by		Ref.
		Density	Infrared	
Amorphous, non-oriented	1.335	0	?	10
Partly cryst., non-oriented	1.385	42	48	10
Highly cryst., oriented	1.390	46	65	10
	1.389	45	76	10
	1.381	38	80	
Calculated, crystal	1.455			24

Dielectric Strength [v mil^{-1}] (film)		
25°C, 60 c	7,000	5,32,33
150°C, 60 c	5,000	5,32,33
Dielectric Constant (film)		
25°C, 60 c	3.25	5,32,33
150°C, 60 c	3.7	5,32,33
25°C, 1 kc	3.1	5,32,33
25°C, 1 megacycle	3.0	5,32,33
Dissipation Factor (film)		
25°C, 60 c	0.002	5,32,33
150°C, 60 c	0.006	5,32,33
25°C, 1 kc	0.005	5,32,33
150°C, 1 megacycle	0.016	5,32,33
Glass Transition Temperature, [T_g]		
amorphous	67°C	29,30
crystalline	81°C	30
crystalline and oriented	125°C	31
Heat of Fusion, latent [cal deg^{-1}]	9 - 16	1
Impact Strength [kg cm mil^{-1}] (film)	6	5,32,33
Infrared Spectra:	see Table Ia	
Insulation Resistance, [megohm mfds] (film)		
100°C	5000	5,32,33
130°C	400	5,32,33
150°C	100	5,32,33

[*]Mechanical and electrical properties are given for Mylar; properties of Terylene
can be found in refs. 2 and 6.

Property	Value	Ref.
Melting Point		
commercial PET	265°C	1
pure PET	271°C	3,4
effect of diethylene glycol content:	see Figure IV	
Moisture Absorption		
immersion in water at 25°C for 1 week	0.8%	5,32,33
Oligomers		

Structure	Melting Point [°C]	
AG	178	7
G(AG)$_1$	110	7
G(AG)$_2$	170, 160	7,8
G(AG)$_3$	202, 186	8
G(AG)$_4$	220	7
G(AG)$_{10}$ or greater	271	3,4,9

A - Terephthalic acid moiety
G - Ethylene glycol moiety

Property	Value	Ref.
Permeability (film)		
water vapor [g/100 sq m/hr]	110	5,32,33
oxygen [g/100 sq m/hr]	0.90	5,32,33
Refractive Index [n_D^{25}]	1.64	5,32,33
Resistivity, volume , [ohm cm]		
25°C	1×10^{18}	32,33
150°C	1×10^{13}	32,33

Solvents: see table "Solvents-Nonsolvents" in this Handbook

Specific Heat, C_p [cal g^{-1}(deg C)$^{-1}$]   1,11

$$C_p = A + B \times T°C$$

Condition of Polymer	A	B x 10^4	Effective Temp.,T(°C)
Molten polymer	0.3243	5.65	270 to 290
Flake	0.2502	9.40	-20 to 60
Yarn (undrawn)	0.2469	10.07	-5 to 60
Yarn (drawn)	0.2482	9.89	-10 to 55
Yarn (drawn + annealed)	0.2431	9.23	-10 to 80
	0.2502	9.31	100 to 200

Property	Value	Ref.
Stick Point Temperature	230 to 240°C	1
Tear Strength [g mil^{-1}] (film)		
propagating	12 - 15	5,32,33
initial	1000 - 1300	5,32,33
Tensile Strength [psi] (film)	25,000 - 40,000	5,32,33
Thermal Conductivity [cal cm^{-1} sec^{-1} deg^{-1}]	3.36×10^{-4}	1,32
Transition Temperatures		
from second moment (NMR) measurements on fibers		
unoriented	120°C $\pm$ 5°	27,28
oriented	140°C $\pm$ 10°	27,28

References page VI-92

Property	Value	Ref.
Unit Cell [at 291°K]		24
a	4.56	
b	5.94	
c	10.75 (fiber axis)	
α	98.5°	
β	118°	
γ	112°	
Viscosity-Molecular Weight Relationship:	see Table Ib	
Yield Stress [psi] (film)	12,000 to 22,000	32
Zero Strength Temperature (fiber)	248°C	1

Table Ia: Infrared Spectra   21,22,23

Wave Numbers [cm^{-1}]	Absorption Strength	Assignment
3546	weak	Hydroxyl end group stretching
3448	weak	Carbonyl overtone
3278	weak	Carboxyl OH stretching
3067	weak	Phenyl hydrogen stretching
2970 - 2985	strong	Aliphatic C-H stretching
2910 - 2920	strong	" "
1724 - 1729	very strong	Carbonyl stretching
1590 - 1600	medium	
1560	medium	Aromatic -C=C- stretching
1506	weak	or
1410	strong	Phenyl -C-C- (in plane)
1019	medium	
793	weak	
1470 - 1475	medium	
1445 - 1460	medium	Aliphatic C-H deformation
1370	medium	or -CH$_2$- wagging
1340	weak	-CH$_2$- deformation ⊥ to plane of CH$_2$
1266 - 1269	strong	C-O-C stretching
1227	strong	" "
1129	strong	" "
1099	strong	" "
1042	weak	
973	weak	
897	weak	-CH$_2$- group
849	weak	
1019	medium	CH phenyl (in plane)
793	weak	deformation
873	med. weak	CH phenyl (out of plane)
726	strong	deformation

Table Ib: Intrinsic Viscosity-Molecular Weight Relationships[*]

$$[\eta] = K \times M_n^{a}$$

1. Unfractionated Samples (Fig. I)

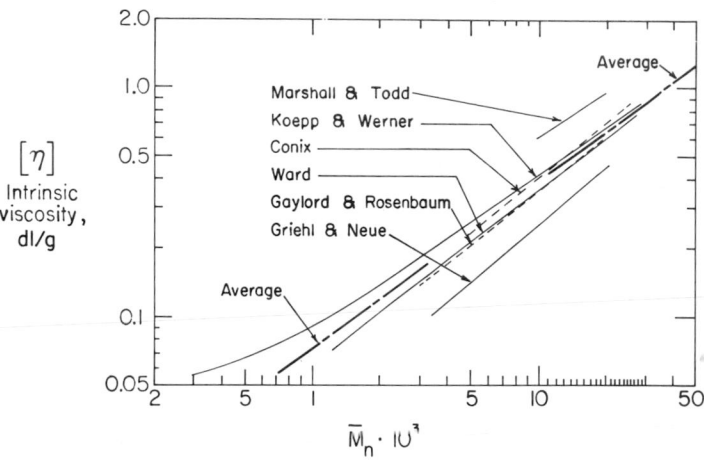

$[\eta]$
Intrinsic
viscosity,
dl/g

$\overline{M}_n \cdot 10^{\gamma}$

Solvent	Temp.[°C]	K x 10^4	a	Investigators	Ref.
phenol/tetrachloroethane	20	0.9	0.87	Griehl & Neue[*]	12
phenol/tetrachloroethane	25	2.1	0.82	Conix	14
phenol/tetrachloroethane	20	7.55	0.685	Koepp & Werner	15
o-chlorophenol	--	3.0	0.77	Ward	16
phenol	50	5.517	0.709	Marshall & Todd	19
phenol/trichlorophenol	29.8	2.88	0.775	Gaylord & Rosenbaum	17
Average		5.0	0.73		

*Griehl and Neue report

$$[\eta] = \frac{\sqrt{1 + 4\eta sp} - 1}{k'}$$ where ηsp is for c = 0.5% and
                              the Huggins constant k' = 0.35

2. Fractionated Samples (Fig. II)

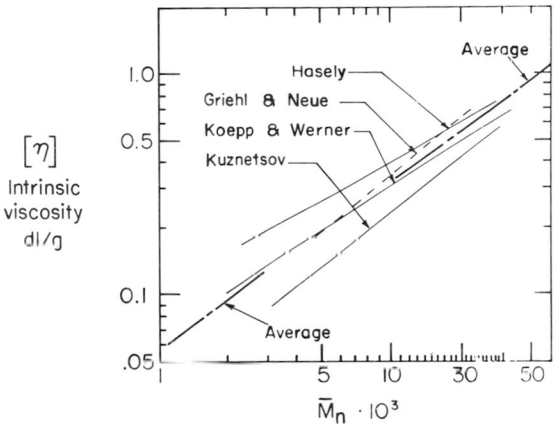

Solvent	Temp.[°C]	K x 10⁴	a	Investigators	Ref.
phenyl/trichlorophenol	?	17.96	0.59	Hasely	18
tetrachloroethane	20	1.27	0.86	Griehl & Neue	12
phenol/tetrachlorophenol	20	5.6	0.68	Koepp & Werner	15
phenol/dichloroethane	20	0.92	0.85	Kuznetsov	20
Average		2.9	0.76		

Figure III: Direct Current Conductivity at Various Temperatures and Degrees of
             Orientation and Crystallinity (28)

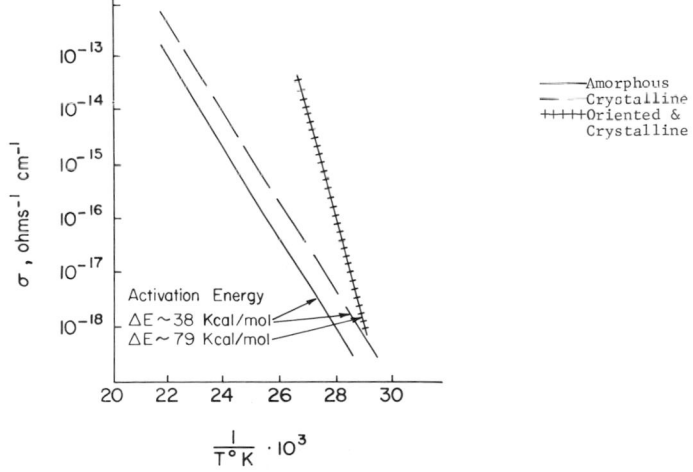

Figure IV: Effect of Diethylene Glycol (DEG) Content on Poly(ethylene terephthalate) (PET) Melting Point

Melting Point [°C] = 271 - 3 (Mol % DEG)

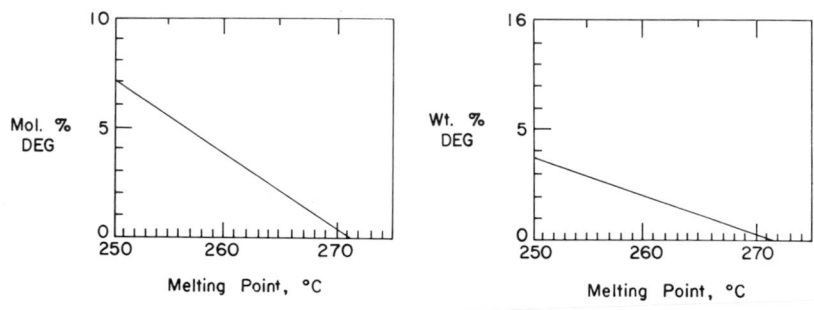

REFERENCES

1. B. V. Petukhov, "The Technology of Polyester Fibers," Macmillan Co., New York,
    N.Y., 1963, p. 32.
2. Plastics (London), 18, 17 (1953).
3. G. W. Taylor, Polymer 3, 543 (1962).
4. R. Janssen, H. Ruysschaert, and R. Vroom, Makromol. Chem. 77, 153 (1964).
5. DuPont Technical Bulletin No. 1-2-53.
6. Chemical Age, 68, 8 (1953).
7. H. Zahn and R. Krzikalla, Makromol. Chem. 23, 31 (1957).
8. H. Binder, U. S. Patent 2,855,432.
9. I. Nakamma, E. Hayashi, J. Polymer Sci. 2, 851 (1964).
10. A. B. Thompson and D. W. Woods, Nature, 176, 78 (1955).
11. C. W. Smith and M. Dole, J. Polymer Sci. 20, 37 (1956).
12. W. Griehl and S. Neue, Faserforsch. Textiltech. 5, 423 (1954).
13. W. A. Griehl, A. Gordijenko, S. Neue and H. Sieber, Faserforsch. Textiltech.
    6, 260 (1955).
14. A. Conix, Makromol. Chem. 26, 226 (1958).
15. H. M. Koepp and H. Werner, Makromol. Chem. 32, 79 (1959).
16. J. Ward, Nature 180, 141 (1957); Trans. Faraday Soc. 53, 1406 (1957).
17. N. Gaylord and S. Rosenbaum, J. Polymer Sci. 39, 549 (1959).
18. E. Haseley, J. Polymer Sci. 35, 309 (1959).
19. J. Marshall and A. Todd, Trans. Faraday Soc. 49, 67 (1953).
20. E. V. Kuznetsov, A. O. Vizel, I. M. Shermergorn and S. S. Tyulenev,
    Vysokomolekul. Soedin. 2, 205 (1960).
21. D. Grime and I. M. Ward, Trans. Faraday Soc. 54, 959 (1958).
22. W. W. Daniels and R. E. Kitson, J. Polymer Sci. 33, 161 (1958).
23. A. Miyake, J. Polymer Sci. 38, 479 (1959).
24. R. de P. Daubeny, C. W. Bunn and C. J. Brown, Proc. Roy. Soc. (London) A226,
    531 (1954).
25. R. Land, R. E. Richards, I. M. Ward, Trans. Faraday Soc. 55, 225 (1959).
26. I. M. Ward, Trans. Faraday Soc. 56, 648 (1960).
27. S. Nohara, Chem. High Polym. Japan 14, 318 (1957).
28. L. E. Amborski, J. Polymer Sci. 62, 331 (1962).
29. H. J. Kolb and E. F. Izard, J. Appl. Phys. 20, 564 (1949).
30. O. B. Edgar and R. Hill, J. Polymer Sci. 8, 1 (1952).
31. D. W. Woods, Nature 174, 753 (1954).
32. DuPont Technical Bulletin No. M-1A.
33. D. D. Lanning, Product Engineering, July, 187, (1956).

VII.
PHYSICAL DATA OF OLIGOMERS

PHYSICAL DATA OF OLIGOMERS

M. Rothe

Universität Mainz
Organisch-Chemisches Institut
Mainz, Germany

Contents*

* References follow after each subgroup.

CONTENTS (Cont'd.)   <u>Page</u>

Oligomers are defined as the low members of the polymeric-homologous series, with molecular weights up to about 1000-2000. They are easily accessible by stepwise synthesis or by separation from the polymers. Being low molecular weight materials of defined molecular weights oligomers represent ideal model substances for the polymers. Deep insight is gained into the relation between chain length and physical properties by physical studies of whole series of oligomers. In this way certain physical data of polymers could be explained for the first time. In chemical respect oligomers on principle must have the same properties as the related polymers; they are, however, much easier accessible to all studies owing to their strictly defined and comparatively simpler structure.

Homologous oligomers due to their low molecular weights differ sufficiently in their physical properties so that they can be separated into chemical individuals. Therefore they can be used for elucidating the structure of polymers and--in close relation--for the investigation of the mechanism of polymerization. Oligomers are intermediates in polycondensation and polyaddition reactions and are present in more or less significant amounts in the polymers due to the equilibrium between different chains and between chains and rings. Therefore, important conclusions on the structure of the related high polymers can be drawn from isolation and structure of oligomers along with a comparison of chemical properties of polymers and oligomers. In this way exact evidence can be gained on the type of linkage between the monomer units in the polymer and on the structure of unknown endgroups. Finally, unequivocal evidence on the mechanism of polymer formation is to be expected from the behaviour of oligomers under the conditions of polycondensation.

The following tables give the physical properties of the most important linear, cyclic, and branched oligomers which are significant for polymer chemistry. Derivatives and co-oligomers (such as co-oligopeptides, -saccharides and -nucleotides) as well as organosilicon and inorganic oligomers are not included. Only those literature references are included which indicate the best methods of synthesis and the most important properties of the oligomers concerned.

A.   OLIGOOLEFINS

1 - Oligo(methylenes) and Oligo(ethylenes)

1.1 - n-Alkanes

$H[CH_2]_n H$

n	Mol. Wt.	m. p. °C	b. p. °C/mm.	$d_4/°C$	References
1	16.0	-182.6	-161.6	0.4240/-164	21,22
2	30.1	-183.3	-88.5	0.5462/-89	21
3	44.1	-187.1	-42.2	0.5824/-45	21,22
4	58.1	-138.4	-0.5	0.6011/0	21
5	72.2	-129.7	36.1	0.6263/20	5,7,13,21
6	86.2	-94.0	68.7	0.6594/20	3,7,5,21
7	100.2	-90.5	98.4	0.6838/20	5,7,13,21,22
8	114.2	-56.8	125.7	0.7026/20	3,5,7,13,21
9	128.3	-53.5	150.8	0.7177/20	5,7,13,21
10	142.3	-29.7	174.1	0.7301/20	3,5,7,18,21
11	156.3	-25.6	195.9	0.7402/20	3,5,7,13,21
12	170.3	-9.7	216.3	0.7487/20	5,7,17,21
13	184.4	-5.4	235.5	0.7563/20	5,7,13,21
14	198.4	5.5	253.6	0.7627/20	5,7,17,21
15	212.4	10.0	270.7	0.7684/20	3,5,7,21
16	226.4	18.0	287.1	0.7733/20	3,5,7,15,16,19,21
17	240.5	22.0	302.6	0.7767/22	3,5,7,13,14,21
18	254.5	28.2	317.4	0.7768/28	3,5,7,14,15,17,19,21
19	268.5	32.0	331.6	0.7776/32	1,3-5,7,14,15,19,21
20	282.6	36.6	345.1	0.7550/70	1,3-5,7,14,15,17-19,21
21	296.6	40.4	215/15	0.7583/70	1-4,14,15,19,21,22
22	310.6	44.4	224-225/15	0.7631/70	1-4,7,14,21
23	324.6	47.5	234/15	0.7641/70	1-4,14,21
24	338.7	51.1	243/15	0.7657/70	1-4,14,17,21
25	352.7	53.5	259/15	0.7693/70	1-4,5,14,21
26	366.7	57.0	262/15	0.7704/70	1-4,7,14,21
27	380.7	60.0	270/15	0.7732/70	1-4,8,14,21
28	394.8	61.2	279-281/15	0.7750/70	1,2,4,13,14,15,17,19,21
29	408.8	64.0	286/15	0.7755/70	1-4,14,21
30	422.8	66.0	304/15	0.7795/70	1-4,7,14,18,21
31	436.9	68.4	302/15	0.7678/100	1-4,8
32	450.9	70.5	310/15	0.7645/100	1,2,4,16,19,20
33	464.9	72			1,2,4,5
34	478.9	72.8			1-4,7
35	493.0	74.6	331/15	0.7814/74	1,2,4,7,8,10,15,19
36	507.0	75.9	298.4/3	0.7783/90	1,2,4,7,10,13-15,19
37	531.0	77.7			75
38	535.0	79			75
39	549.1	80.3			12

References page VII-8

n	Mol. Wt.	m. p. °C	b. p. °C/mm.	$d_4/°C$	References
40	563.1	81.5	$150/10^{-4}$		6,7,10,17,18,21
41	577.1	81 7			75
42	591.2	82.9			76
43	605.2	85.3	332/3	0.7812/90	10,22
44	619.2	86.4			3,11,13,15,19
50	703.4	91.9-92.3	420-422/15		6,7,11,15,21
54	759.5	95			2,7
60	843.6	98.5-99.3	$250/10^{-4}$		6,7,11,21
62	871.7	100.5			2,7,11
64	899.7	102.6			2,11,22
66	927.8	103.6			9
67	941.8	104.1			9
70	983.9	105-105.5	$300/10^{-4}$		6,7,11,21
94	1320.6	114.1-114.5			15,19,20
100	1404.7	115.1-115.4			21

1.2 - Cycloalkanes

$$[\,{}^{[CH_2]}{}_n\,]$$

n	Mol. Wt.	m. p. °C	b. p. °C/mm.	$d_4/°C$	References
3	42.1	-127.5	-32.8	0.7352/-80	23,24
4	56.1	<-80	13.1/774	0.698/0	25
5	70.1	-93.9	49.3	0.745/20	26
6	84.2	6.6	80.7	0.7784/20	27-29
7	98.2	-8.0	118.1	0.8098/20	29-31
8	112.2	13.5	149/749	0.8349/20	32-34
9	126.2	9.7	69/14	0.8534/15.2	29,34
10	140.3	10.8	201	0.8577/20	29,35,36
11	154.3	-7.3	91/12	0.8591/20	29,37
12	168.3	62-63		0.861	29,38,39
13	182.4	23.5	128/20	0.861	29,34,38
14	196.4	55-55.5	131/11	0.8259/79	29,38,40,41
15	210.4	65-66	147/12	0.8240/78	29,38,40
16	224.4	62-63	170-171/20	0.819/79	38,40,41,42
17	238.5	66-67		0.8200/77	40,43,44
18	252.5	74-75		0.8201/76	40-42,45
19	266.5	81-82			40
20	280.5	61-62			18,41
21	294.6	63-64			41
22	308.6	52-53	177/0.4	0.8174/75	38,43

n	Mol. Wt.	m. p. °C	b. p. °C/mm.	$d_4/°C$	References
23	322.6	49-50	177/0.1	0.8259/64	46
24	336.6	50-51	222-228/0.6		38,40,41,45
25	350.7	53-54			47
26	364.7	44-46	218-219/0.5	0.8120/78	38,40,43
27	378.7	47-48			41
28	392.8	48	213-214/0.25	0.8243/58	38,41,48
29	406.8	47	215/1.1	0.8232/64	38
30	420.8	57-58	230/0.2	0.8233/69	18,41,42,45,48
32	448.9	59-60		0.8261/70	41,48
34	476.9	66-67	230-240/0.3	0.8229/76	48
36	505.0	70-71			41,45
40	561.1	76-77			18,41
42	589.2	75-76			45
45	631.2	80-81			41
50	701.4	87-88			18
54	757.5	90-91			41

2 - Oligo(perfluoromethylenes) and Oligo(perfluoroethylenes)

2.1 - Perfluoro-n-alkanes

$F[CF_2]_n F$

n	Mol. Wt.	m. p. °C	b. p. °C/mm.	$d_4/°C$	References
1	88.0	-183.7	-128/754	1.619/-129	49
2	138.0	-94	-78.3	1.590/-78	49,50
3	188.0	-183	-38		51,52
4	238.0		-2.0		52-54
5	288.1	-125.4	29.3	1.620	52,54-56
6	338.1	-86.3	57.2	1.6995	52,57,58
7	388.7	-78	82.2	1.7333	52,56,59
8	438.1	-65	103.3	1.776/25	52,59
9	488.1	-16	125.3	1.799/25	52,59
10	538.1	36	144.2	1.770/45	52,59
11	588.1	57	161	1.745/70	52,59
12	638.1	75	178	1.670/113.5	52,59
16	838.2	125	232		54,59

References page VII-8

2.2 - Perfluoro-cycloalkanes

$$\left[CF_2 \right]_n$$

n	Mol. Wt.	m. p. °C	b. p. °C	References
3	150.0	-80	-31.5	52,60,61
4	200.0	-38.7	-5	61-63
5	250.0	9.9-10.2	23.5-2	51,61,64,65
6	300.0	58.2		51,56,65
7	350.0		80	51

3 - Oligomers of Higher Olefins

3.1 - Oligo(isobutylenes) (References 66-74)

	Compound	Mol. Wt.	m. p. °C	b. p. °C/mm.	d_4^{20}
Monomer:	isobutylene $CH_2 = C(CH_3)_2$	56.1		-6	
Dimers:	2,2,4-trimethyl-4-pentene $CH_2=C - CH_2C(CH_3)_3$ $\quad\ CH_3$	112.2	-93.6	101.4	0.7150
	2,2,4-trimethyl-3-pentene $CH_3-C = CH-C(CH_3)_3$ $\quad\ CH_3$	112.2	-106	104.9	0.7211
	2,2,3-trimethyl-2-pentene $CH_3-CH=C - C(CH_3)_3$ $\quad\quad\ CH_3$	112.2		112.3	0.7392
	2,3,4-trimethyl-2-pentene $(CH_3)_2CH-C - C(CH_3)_2$ $\quad\quad\quad CH_3$	112.2	-113.4	116.3	0.7434
	2,3,4-trimethyl-1-pentene $CH_2=C - CH - CH(CH_3)_2$ $\quad\ CH_3\ CH_3$	112.2		108	0.729
	2,3,3-trimethyl-1-pentene $CH_2=C - C(CH_3)_2-CH_2-CH_3$ $\quad\ CH_3$	112.2	-69	108.4	0.7352
Trimers:	1,1-dineopentylethylene $CH_2=[CH_2C(CH_3)_2]_2$	168.3		85-86/40	0.7599

REFERENCES

1. F. Krafft, Ber. Deut. Chem. Ges. 15, 1687, 1711 (1882); 19, 2218 (1886); 40, 4479 (1907).
2. A. Gascard, Ann. Chim. (Paris) [9] 15, 332 (1921).
3. A. Müller, Proc. Roy. Soc. (London) Ser. A120, 437 (1928); 127, 417 (1930); 138, 514 (1932).
4. J. H. Hildebrand and A. Wachter, J. Am. Chem. Soc. 51, 2487 (1929).
5. G. S. Parks, H. M. Hoffmann, and S. B. Thomas, J. Am. Chem. Soc. 52, 1032 (1930).
6. W. H. Carothers, J. W. Hill, J. E. Kirby, and R. A. Jacobsen, J. Am. Chem. Soc. 52, 5279 (1930).
7. W. E. Garner, K. van Bitter, and A. M. King, J. Chem. Soc. 1931, 1533.
8. H. Staudinger and F. Staiger, Ber. Deut. Chem. Ges. 68, 707 (1935).
9. F. Francis, A. M. King, and J. A. V. Willis, J. Chem. Soc. 1937, 999.
10. H. J. Bacher and J. Strating, Rec. Trav. Chim. 59, 933 (1940).
11. W. F. Syer, R. F. Patterson, and J. L. Keays, J. Am. Chem. Soc. 66, 179 (1944).
12. E. Stenhagen and B. Tägtström, J. Am. Chem. Soc. 66, 846 (1944).
13. A. K. Doolittle and R. H. Peterson, J. Am. Chem. Soc. 73, 2145 (1951).
14. A. A. Schaerer, C. J. Busso, A. E. Smith, and L. B. Shinner, J. Am. Chem. Soc. 77, 2017 (1955).
15. P. R. Templin, Ind. Eng. Chem. 48, 154 (1956).
16. F. Sondheimer and Y. Amiel, J. Am. Chem. Soc. 79, 5817 (1957).
17. F. Sondheimer, Y. Amiel, and R. Wolovsky, J. Am. Chem. Soc. 79, 6263 (1957).
18. F. Sondheimer, R. Wolovsky, and D. A. Ben-Efraim, J. Am. Chem. Soc. 83, 1686 (1961).
19. A. Odajima, J. A. Sauer, and A. E. Woodward, J. Phys. Chem. 66, 718 (1962).
20. D. W. MacCall, D. C. Douglass, and E. W. Anderson, Ber. Bunsenges. Physik. Chem. 67, 336 (1963).
21. J. D. Downer, K. J. Beynon, in Rodd's "Chemistry of Carbon Compounds," Vol. I, Part A, 2nd ed., Elsevier Publ. Co., Amsterdam-London-New York, 1964, p. 367.
22. R. Simha and A. J. Havilik, J. Am. Chem. Soc. 86, 197 (1964).
23. M. Trautz and K. Winkler, J. Prakt. Chem. 104, 37 (1922).
24. R. A. Ruehrwein and T. M. Powell, J. Am. Chem. Soc. 68, 1063 (1946).
25. G. B. Heisig, J. Am. Chem. Soc. 63, 1698 (1941).
26. J. G. Aston, H. L. Fink, and S. C. Schumann, J. Am. Chem. Soc. 65, 341 (1943).
27. J. G. Aston, G. J. Szasz, and H. L. Fink, J. Am. Chem. Soc. 65, 1135 (1943).
28. R. A. Raphael, in E. R. Rodd, Ed., "Chemistry of Carbon Compounds," Vol. II, Part A, 1st ed., Elsevier, New York, 1953, p. 124.
29. L. Ruzicka, P. A. Plattner, and H. Wild, Helv. Chim. Acta 29, 1611 (1946).
30. E. P. Kohler, M. Tishler, H. Potter, and H. T. Thompson, J. Am. Chem. Soc. 61, 1057 (1939).
31. R. Willstätter and T. Kametaka, Ber. Deut. Chem. Ges. 41, 1480 (1908).
32. N. D. Zelinsky and M. G. Freimann, Ber. Deut. Chem. Ges. 63, 1485 (1930).
33. L. Ruzicka and H. A. Boekenoogen, Helv. Chim. Acta 14, 1319 (1931).
34. L. Ruzicka, P. A. Plattner, and H. Wild, Helv. Chim. Acta 28, 395 (1945).
35. P. A. Plattner and J. Hulstkamp, Helv. Chim. Acta 27, 220 (1944).
36. W. Hückel, A. Gercke, and A. Gross, Ber. Deut. Chem. Ges. 66, 563 (1933).
37. P. A. Plattner, Helv. Chim. Acta 27, 801 (1944).
38. L. Ruzicka, M. Stoll, H. W. Huyser, and H. A. Boekenoogen, Helv. Chim. Acta 13, 1152 (1930).
39. R. Wolovsky and F. Sondheimer, J. Am. Chem. Soc. 84, 2844 (1962).
40. J. Dale, A. J. Hubert, and G. S. D. King, J. Chem. Soc. 1963, 73.
41. F. Sondheimer, Y. Amiel, and R. Wolovsky, J. Am. Chem. Soc. 81, 4600 (1959).
42. L. Ruzicka, W. Brügger, C. F. Seidel, and H. Schinz, Helv. Chim. Acta 11, 496 (1928).
43. L. Ruzicka and G. Giacomello, Helv. Chim. Acta 20, 548 (1937).
44. L. Ruzicka, W. Brügger, M. Pfeiffer, H. Schinz, and M. Stoll, Helv. Chim. Acta 9, 499 (1926).
45. F. Sondheimer and R. Wolovsky, J. Am. Chem. Soc. 84, 260 (1962).
46. R. Stoll, Helv. Chim. Acta 16, 493 (1933).
47. A. J. Hubert and J. Dale, J. Chem. Soc. 1963, 86.
48. L. Ruzicka, M. Hürbin, and M. Furter, Helv. Chim. Acta 17, 78 (1934).
49. O. Ruff, Angew, Chem. 46, 739 (1939).
50. E. L. Pace and J. G. Aston, J. Am. Chem. Soc. 70, 566 (1948).
51. J. H. Simons and L. P. Block, J. Am. Chem. Soc. 61, 2962 (1939).
52. R. N. Haszeldine, J. Chem. Soc. 1953, 3761.
53. J. A. Brown and W. H. Mears, J. Phys. Chem. 62, 961 (1958).
54. W. B. Burford, R. D. Fowler, J. M. Hamilton, Jr., H. C. Anderson, C. E. Weber, and R. G. Sweet, Ind. Eng. Chem. 39, 319 (1947).
55. L. L. Burger and G. H. Cady, J. Am. Chem. Soc. 73, 4245 (1951).

56. F. L. Mohler, E. G. Bloom, J. H. Lengel, and C. E. Wise, J. Am. Chem. Soc. 71, 337 (1949).
57. V. E. Stiles and G. H. Cady, J. Am. Chem. Soc. 74, 3771 (1952).
58. R. D. Dunlap, C. J. Murphy, and R. G. Bedford, J. Am. Chem. Soc. 80, 83 (1958).
59. R. N. Haszeldine and F. Smith, J. Chem. Soc. 1950, 3617; 1951, 603.
60. B. Atkinson, J. Chem. Soc. 1952, 2684.
61. J. D. Park, A. F. Benning, F. Downing, J. F. Laucius, and R. C. McHarness, Ind. Eng. Chem. 39, 354 (1947).
62. J. R. Lacher, G. W. Tompkin, and J. D. Park, J. Am. Chem. Soc. 74, 1693 (1952).
63. G. Bier, R. Schäff, and K. H. Kahrs, Angew. Chem. 66, 285 (1954).
64. N. Fukuhara and L. A. Bigelow, J. Am. Chem. Soc. 63, 2792 (1941).
65. H. J. Christoffers, E. C. Lingafelter, and G. H. Cady, J. Am. Chem. Soc. 69, 2502 (1947).
66. F. C. Whitmore and S. N. Wren, J. Am. Chem. Soc. 53, 3136 (1931).
67. C. O. Tongberg, J. D. Pickens, M. R. Fenske, and F. C. Whitmore, J. Am. Chem. Soc. 54, 3706, 3710 (1932).
68. F. C. Whitmore and K. C. Laughlin, J. Am. Chem. Soc. 54, 4011 (1932).
69. F. C. Whitmore, K. C. Laughlin, J. F. Matuszeski, and J. D. Surmatis, J. Am. Chem. Soc. 63, 757 (1941).
70. J. A. Dixon, N. C. Cook, and F. C. Whitmore, J. Am. Chem. Soc. 70, 3363 (1948).
71. F. C. Whitmore, C. D. Wilson, J. V. Capinjola, C. O. Tongberg, G. H. Fleming, R. V. McGrew, and J. N. Cosby, J. Am. Chem. Soc. 63, 2035 (1941).
72. F. L. Howard, T. W. Mears, A. Fookson, P. Pomorantz, and D. B. Brooks, J. Res. Natl. Bur. Stand. 38, 365 (1947).
73. P. D. Bartlett, G. L. Fraser, and R. B. Woodward, J. Am. Chem. Soc. 63, 498 (1941).
74. M. J. Batujew, A. P. Meschtschorjakow, and A. D. Matwejewa, Dokl. Akad. Nauk, SSSR, 1958, 75; through C. 1960, 1870.
75. F. D. Rossini et al., "Selected Values of Physical and Thermodynamic Properties of Hydrocarbons and Related Compounds," Pittsburgh, 1953.
76. C. L. Clark and H. A. Smith, Ind. Eng. Chem., 23, 700 (1931).

B. OLIGOPHENYLENES

1 - Oligo(o-phenylenes)

1.1 - Linear Oligo(o-phenylenes)   1.2 - Cyclic Oligo(o-phenylenes)

n	Mol. Wt.	m. p. °C	b. p. °C	Ref.
3	230.3	59	332	1,2
4	306.4	119	420	1,3,4,5,6
6	458.6	217		3,5
8	610.8	320		5

n	Mol. Wt.	m. p. °C	Reference
2	152.2	111	4,7,8,9
3	228.3	196.5	10,11
4	304.4	233	4,5
6	456.6	335	5
8	608.8	425	5

2 - Oligo(m-phenylenes)

2.1 - Linear Oligo(m-phenylenes)

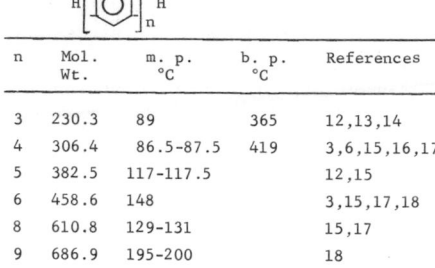

n	Mol. Wt.	m. p. °C	b. p. °C	References
3	230.3	89	365	12,13,14
4	306.4	86.5-87.5	419	3,6,15,16,17
5	382.5	117-117.5		12,15
6	458.6	148		3,15,17,18
8	610.8	129-131		15,17
9	686.9	195-200		18

2.2 - Cyclic Oligo(m-phenylenes)

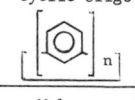

n	Mol. Wt.	m. p. °C	Reference
6	456.6	509.5-511	19

2.3 - Oligo(3-methyl-m-phenylenes)

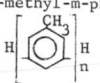

n	Mol. Wt.	m. p. °C	b. p. °C	Reference
2	182.3	9-9.5	280	20,21,22,23
3	272.4	65		12

3 - Oligo(p-phenylenes)

3.1 - Oligo(p-phenylenes)

n	Mol. Wt.	m. p. °C	b. p. °C	Solubility [g/ℓ toluene]	References
1	78.1	5.5	80.1	∞	
2	154.2	71	256	430	24
3	230.3	215	376	7.4	3,12,14,25,26
4	306.4	322	428/18	0.12	3,12,16,21,25,26
5	382.5	395		< 0.005	12,16,21,25,27,28
6	458.6	465			3,29,30,31

3.2 - Oligo(3-methyl-p-phenylenes)

n	Mol. Wt.	m. p. °C	b. p. °C	Ref.
1	92.1	-95	110.6	
2	182.3		273-274	22,23,32
3	272.4	43		33

References page VII-13

3.3 - Oligo(p-2,5-dimethylphenylenes)

n	Mol. Wt.	m. p. °C	b. p. °C	Solubility [g/ℓ toluene]	Ref.
1	106.2	13.3	138.4	∞	
2	210.3	53-54		700	20,34
3	314.5	182-183		28	34
4	418.6	264-266		1.1	34
5	522.8	307-309		0.24	34

3.4 - Oligo(2,3,5,6-tetramethyl-p-phenylenes)

n	Mol. Wt.	m. p. °C	b. p. °C	Solubility [g/ℓ toluene]	Ref.
1	134.2	79.2	196-198	∞	
2	266.4	136-137		365	34,35
3	398.6	270-272		24	34
4	530.8	270-272		3.4	34

3.5 - Oligo(2,2'-dimethyl-biphenylenes)

n	Mol. Wt.	m. p. °C	Solubility [g/ℓ toluene]	Ref.
1	182.3	24		20,23,36
2	362.5	96	490	37

3.6 - Oligo(3,3'-dimethyl-biphenylenes)

3.7 - Oligo(3,3''-dimethyl-p-terphenylenes)

n	Mol. Wt.	m. p. °C	b. p. °C	Solubility [g/ℓ toluene]	Ref.
1	182.3	9-9.5	280	∞	20,21,22 23,38
2	362.5	76.5		512	27,37
3	542.8	142		87	39
4	723.0	273		<6.5	39
5	903.3	285		~2	40
6	1083.5	298		<0.8	40

n	Mol. Wt.	m. p. °C	Solubility [g/ℓ toluene]	Ref.
1	258.4	140-141	4.9	27,37
2	514.7	258	0.4	27

3.8 - Oligo(2,5-dimethoxy-p-phenylenes)

3.9 - Oligo(3,3'-dimethoxy-biphenylenes)

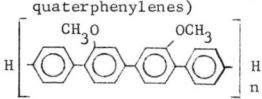

n	Mol. Wt.	m. p. °C	b. p. °C	Reference
1	138.2	56	212.6	
2	374.3	105		20,41
3	410.5	189		41
4	546.6	246		41

n	Mol. Wt.	m. p. °C	b. p. °C	Solubility [g/ℓ toluene]	Ref.
1	214.3	36	328		42
2	426.5	158		22	38,43

3.10 - Oligo(2',3''-dimethoxy-p-quaterphenylenes)

4 - Oligo(p-quinones)

n	Mol. Wt.	m. p. °C	Solubility [g/ℓ toluene]	Ref.
1	366.5	183-184	13	43
2	730.9	276-277	~0.2	43

n	Mol. Wt.	m. p. °C	Ref.
1	108.1	116.5	
2	214.2	194	41
3	320.3	>230	41
4	426.3	230-270	41

References page VII-13

5 - Oligo(thienyls) and Oligo(pyridyls)

5.1 - Oligo(2,5-thienyls)

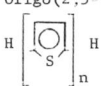

n	Mol. Wt.	m. p. °C	b. p. °C	Ref.
1	84.1	-38.4	84.1	
2	166.3	32-33.5	260	44,45
3	248.4	94-95.5		44,46
4	330.5	215-216		44,46
5	412.5	256-257		44,46
6	494.8	304		46
7	576.9	326-328		46

5.2 - Oligo(2,6-pyridyls)

n	Mol. Wt.	m. p. °C	b. p. °C	Ref.
1	79.1	-42	115.5	
2	156.2	70.1	273-275	47,48
3	233.3	88-89	370	47,48,49
4	310.4	219-220		48
5	387.5	265		48
6	464.5	350		48

5.3 - Oligo(3,5-pyridyls)

n	Mol. Wt.	m. p. °C	b. p. °C	Ref.
2	156.2	68	291-292/736	12
3	233.3	249-251		12

5.4 - Oligo(2,6-quinolyls)

n	Mol. Wt.	m. p. °C	b. p. °C	Ref.
1	129.2	-15.6	237.1	
2	256.3	144		50,51
3	383.5	267-269		51
4	510.6	348-350		51

REFERENCES

1. W. E. Bachmann and H. T. Clarke, J. Am. Chem. Soc. 49, 2089 (1927).
2. C. F. H. Allen and F. D. Pingert, J. Am. Chem. Soc. 64, 1365 (1942).
3. J. A. Cade and A. Pilbeam, Tetrahedron, 20, 519 (1964); J. A. Cade and A. Pilbeam, J. Chem. Soc. 1964, 114.
4. W. S. Rapson, R. G. Shuttleworth, and J. N. van Niekerk, J. Chem. Soc. 1943, 326.
5. G. Wittig and G. Lehmann, Chem. Ber. 90, 875 (1957).
6. S. T. Bowden, J. Chem. Soc. 1931, 1111.
7. W. Baker, M. P. V. Boarland, and J. F. W. McOmie, J. Chem. Soc. 1954, 1476.
8. W. C. Lothrop, J. Am. Chem. Soc. 63, 1187 (1941).
9. G. Wittig and W. Herwig, Chem. Ber. 87, 1511 (1954).
10. C. Mannich, Ber. Deut. Chem. Ges. 40, 159 (1907).
11. D. G. Copeland, K. E. Dean, and D. McNeil, J. Chem. Soc. 1960, 1689.
12. M. Busch and W. Weber, J. Prakt. Chem. 146, 1 (1936).
13. A. Gillam and D. H. Hey, J. Chem. Soc. 1939, 1170; H. France, J. M. Heilbron, and D. H. Hey, J. Chem. Soc. 1939, 1288; H. France, J. M. Heilbron, and D. H. Hey, J. Chem. Soc. 1938, 1364.
14. C. F. Woods and J. W. Tucker, J. Am. Chem. Soc. 70, 2174 (1948).
15. R. L. Alexander, Jr., J. Org. Chem. 21, 1464 (1956).

16. G. F. Woods and F. T. Reed, J. Am. Chem. Soc. 71, 1348 (1949).
17. M. Bennett, N. B. Sunshine, and G. F. Woods, J. Org. Chem. 28, 2514 (1963);
     W. Davey and D. H. Maass, J. Chem. Soc. 1963, 4386.
18. L. Silverman and W. Houk, Anal. Chem. 27, 1956 (1955).
19. H. A. Staab and F. Binnig, Tetrahedron Letters 1964, 319.
20. F. Ullmann, G. M. Meyer, O. Loewenthal, and E. Gilli, Liebigs. Ann. Chem. 332,
     38 (1904).
21. E. Müller and T. Töpel, Ber. Deut. Chem. Ges. 72, 273 (1939).
22. G. F. Woods, A. L. van Artsdale, and F. T. Reed, J. Am. Chem. Soc. 72, 3221
     (1950).
23. E. A. Johnson, J. Chem. Soc. 1957, 4155.
24. E. Clar, "Polycyclic Hydrocarbons," Academic Press, New York and Springer,
     Berlin, 1964.
25. O. Gerngross and M. Dunkel, Ber. Deut. Chem. Ges. 57, 739 (1924); O. Gerngross,
     C. Schachnow, and R. Jonas, ibid. 57, 747 (1924).
26. H. O. Wirth, K. H. Günner, and W. Kern, Makromol. Chem. 63, 53 (1963).
27. H. O. Wirth, K. H. Günner, R. Stück, and W. Kern, Makromol. Chem. 63, 30 (1963).
28. T. W. Campbell and R. N. McDonald, J. Org. Chem. 24, 730 (1959).
29. P. Kovacic and R. M. Lange, J. Org. Chem. 29, 2416 (1964).
30. T. Nozaki, M. Tamura, Y. Harada, and K. Saito, Bull. Chem. Soc. Japan 33, 1329
     (1960).
31. R. Pummerer and K. Bittner, Ber. Deut. Chem. Ges. 57, 84 (1924); 64, 2477 (1931);
     R. Pummerer and L. Seligsberger, Ber. Deut. Chem. Ges. 64, 2477 (1931).
32. F. Mayer and K. Freitag, Ber. Deut. Chem. Ges. 54, 347 (1921).
33. H. O. Wirth, H. Hefner, and W. Kern, unpublished results.
34. H. O. Wirth, F. U. Herrmann, and W. Kern, Makromol. Chem. 80, 120 (1964).
35. E. Marcus, W. M. Lauer, and R. T. Arnold, J. Am. Chem. Soc. 80, 3742 (1958).
36. D. M. Hall, M. S. Leslie, and E. E. Turner, J. Chem. Soc. 1950, 711.
37. W. Kern, M. Seibel, and H. O. Wirth, Makromol. Chem. 29, 164 (1959).
38. W. Schlenk and M. Brauns, Ber. Deut. Chem. Ges. 48, 661 (1914).
39. W. Kern, W. Gruber, and H. O. Wirth, Makromol. Chem. 37, 198 (1960).
40. W. Heitz, R. Ullrich, and W. Kern, unpublished results.
41. H. Erdtman, M. Granath, and G. Schultz, Acta Chem. Scand. 8, 1442 (1954).
42. N. Kornblum, Org. Synth., Coll. Vol. III, 3rd ed., Y. Wiley & Sons, Inc., New
     York, 1962, p. 295.
43. W. Kern, H. W. Ebersbach, and I. Ziegler, Makromol. Chem. 31, 154 (1959).
44. J. W. Sease and L. Zechmeister, J. Am. Chem. Soc. 69, 270 (1947).
45. W. Borsche and B. G. B. Scholten, Ber. Deut. Chem. Ges. 50, 596 (1917).
46. W. Steinkopf, R. Leitsmann, and K. H. Hoffmann, Liebigs. Ann. Chem. 546, 180
     (1941).
47. G. T. Morgan and F. H. Burstall, J. Chem. Soc. 1932, 20.
48. F. H. Burstall, J. Chem. Soc. 1938, 1662.
49. F. H. Case and W. A. Butte, J. Org. Chem. 26, 4415 (1961).
50. H. Weidel, Monatsh. Chem. 8, 120 (1887).
51. S. G. Waley, J. Chem. Soc. 1948, 2008.

C. MISCELLANEOUS OLIGOMERIC HYDROCARBONS

1 - Oligo(phenyl-oxdiazolyls)

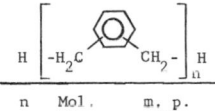

n	Mol. Wt.	m. p. °C	Ref.
2	366.4	322-322.5	1,2
4	654.6	465 (d)	2

2 - Oligo(diphenylmethanes)

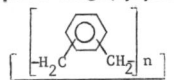

n	Mol. Wt.	m. p. °C	Ref.
1	168.2	25.1	
2	334.5	115	3,4
3	500.7	180	3
4	666.9	240	3

3 - Oligo(xylylenes)

3.1 - Linear Oligo(xylylenes)

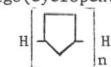

n	Mol. Wt.	m. p. °C	b. p. °C/mm	Ref.
o- 1	106.2	-25	144	
2	210.3	66.5	177-178/20	5,6,7
m- 1	106.2	-47.4	139	
2	210.3		296	7,8
p- 1	106.2	13-14	138	
2	210.3	82	178/18	7,9, 10,11,12
3	314.5	141-142		10,13

3.2 - Cyclic Oligo(xylylenes)

n	Mol. Wt.	m. p. °C	b. p. °C	Ref.
o- 2	208.3	112-112.5		5,6,14
3	312.5	184.5		5,6
4	416.6	205		15
m- 2	208.3	132-133	290	10
p- 2	208.3	285-287		8,11,12, 13,19
3	312.5	166-167		10,13
4	416.6	179-182		13

4 - Oligo(cyclopentylenes)

n	Mol. Wt.	m. p. °C	b. p. °C/mm	d_4^{20}	Ref.
1	70.1	-93.9	42.3	0.7510	
2	138.3		190	0.8646	16,17
3	206.4		293-294	0.9177	16,17
4	274.5		369-370	0.9564	16,17
6	410.7	143-146	235/0.1		16

5 - Oligo(spiranes)

R	n	Mol. Wt.	m. p. °C	b. p. °C/mm.	Ref.
-CH$_2$-	5	216.3		78/0.3	18
-(CH$_2$)$_2$-	3	244.4		84/0.05	18
	5	324.5	61		18
	7	406.6	107-108		18
-(CH$_2$)$_3$-	3	272.5	52.5	120-122/0.05	18
	5	352.6	79.5		18
	7	432.7	103-104		18
	9	512.8	138-140		18

References page VII-16

REFERENCES

1. F. N. Hayes, B. S. Rogers, and D. G. Ott, J. Am. Chem. Soc. 77, 1850 (1955).
2. J. Sauer, R. Huisgen, and H. J. Sturm. Tetrahedron 11, 241 (1960).
3. M. Busch and W. Weber, J. Prakt. Chem. 146, 1 (1936).
4. N. Wolf, Ber. Deut. Chem. Ges. 14, 2031 (1881).
5. W. Baker, R. Banks, D. R. Lyon, and F. G. Mann, J. Chem. Soc. 1945, 27.
6. A. C. Cope and S. W. Fenton, J. Am. Chem. Soc. 73, 1668 (1951).
7. G. H. Coleman, W. H. Holst, and R. D. Maxwell, J. Am. Chem. Soc. 58, 2310 (1936).
8. M. Szwarcz, J. Chem. Phys. 16, 128 (1948).
9. T. Reichstein and R. Oppenauer, Helv. Chim. Acta 16, 1373 (1933).
10. W. Baker, J. F. W. McOmie, and J. M. Norman, J. Chem. Soc. 1951, 1114.
11. C. J. Brown and A. C. Farthing, Nature (London), 164, 915 (1949); J. Chem. Soc.
    1953, 3261, 3265, 3270.
12. D. J. Cram and H. Steinberg, J. Am. Chem. Soc. 73, 5691 (1951).
13. L. A. Errede, R. S. Gregorian, and J. M. Hoyt, J. Am. Chem. Soc. 82, 5218 (1960).
14. L. A. Errede, J. Am. Chem. Soc. 83, 949 (1961).
15. E. D. Bergmann and Z. Pelchowicz, J. Am. Chem. Soc. 75, 4281 (1953).
16. J. v. Braun and J. Reitz-Kopp, Ber. Deut. Chem. Ges. 74, 1105 (1941).
17. G. E. Goheen, J. Am. Chem. Soc. 63, 744 (1941).
18. E. Buchta and K. Geibel, Liebigs Ann. Chem. 678, 53 (1964).
19. H. E. Winberg, F. S. Fawcett, W. E. Mochel, and C. W. Theobald, J. Am. Chem.
    Soc. 82, 1428 (1960).

D. PHENOL-FORMALDEHYDE AND RELATED OLIGOMERS

1 - Linear Phenol-formaldehyde Oligomers

1.1 - Phenol-formaldehyde Oligomers

n	Mol. Wt.	m. p. °C	Ref.
1	200.2	119-120	1,2,3,4
2	306.4	158-159	2,3,4,5,6
3	412.5	161-162	3,4
4	518.6	148-150	4,7
5	624.7	203-204	4
6	730.8	213-214	4

1.2 - p-Cresol-formaldehyde Oligomers

1.2.1

n	Mol. Wt.	m. p. °C	Ref.
1	228.3	126	8,9,10
2	348.4	214-215	8,9,10,11
3	468.6	173	8,9
4	588.7	130	12
5	708.9	215-217	12
6	829.1	225-230	12
7	949.2	167-170	12
8	1069.4	205-210	12
9	1189.5	175-180	12
11	1429.8	245	12

1.2.2 - p-Cresol-formaldehyde Oligomers

n	Mol. Wt.	m. p. °C	Ref.
2	256.3	148	11,13,14,15,16
3	376.5	183-184	11
4	496.7	204-205	11

1.3 - p-tert-Butylphenol-formaldehyde Oligomers

n	Mol. Wt.	m. p.	Ref.
1	312.5	156	17,18
2	474.7	218-220	17,18
3	636.9	211	17,18
4	799.2	216-217	17,18
5	961.4	250	17,18
6	1123.6	249-250	17,18
7	1285.9	253-256	18
8	1448.1	224-226	17
10	1772.6	140	17

1.4 - 2,4,6-Mesitol-formaldehyde Oligomers

n	Mol. Wt.	m. p. °C	Ref.
1	284.4	188	19
2	432.6	257	19

1.5 - p-Cresol-acetaldehyde Oligomers

R	n	Mol. Wt.	m. p. °C	Ref.
H	1	241.3	141	20,21
H	2	373.5	214-215	21
CH$_3$	1	270.4	135-135.5	22
CH$_3$	2	404.6	154-155	22a
CH$_3$	3	538.7	204-205	22a

1.6 - Oligomers with Carbonyl and Sulfonyl Bridges

1.6.1

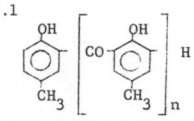

n	Mol. Wt.	m. p. °C	Ref.
1	242.3	106-107	23,24
2	376.4	147	24

1.6.2

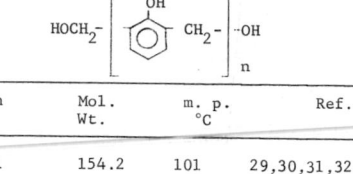

n	Mol. Wt.	m. p. °C	Ref.
1	347.2	179	25
2	517.4	238-240	25
3	687.6	246-252	25

2 - Oligomeric Phenol Alcohols

2.1 - Phenol Monoalcohols

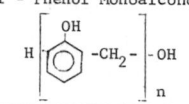

n	Mol. Wt.	m. p. °C	Ref.
1	124.1	86-87	3,26
2	230.3	121.5-123	3,27,28

2.2 - Phenol Dialcohols

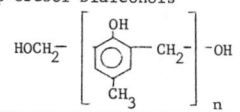

n	Mol. Wt.	m. p. °C	Ref.
1	154.2	101	29,30,31,32
2	260.3	126-127	28

2.3 - p-Cresol Monoalcohols

n	Mol Wt.	m. p. °C	Ref.
1	138.2	107	8,33,34
2	258.3	148	8,9,35
4	498.6		36

2.4 - p-Cresol Dialcohols

n	Mol. Wt.	m. p. °C	Ref.
1	168.2	133-134	13,37
2	288.3	151.5	9,35,38,39
3	408.5	203	9,39,40

References page VII-21

2.5 - p-tert-Butylphenol Dialcohols

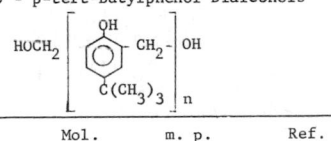

n	Mol. Wt.	m. p. °C	Ref.
1	210.3	74-75	41
2	372.5	117-118	18

2.6 - o-Hydroxydibenzyl Ethers

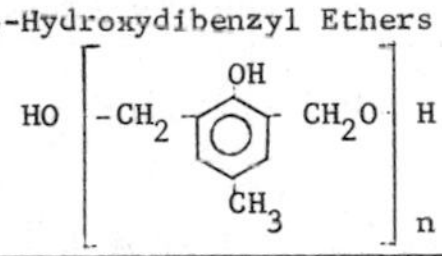

n	Mol. Wt.	m. p. °C	Ref.
2	318.4	85	42

3 - Cyclic Phenol-formaldehyde Oligomers

3.1

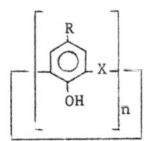

X	R	n	Mol. Wt.	m. p. °C	Ref.
-CH$_2$-	-CH$_3$	4	480.6	>300	36,43
	-C(CH$_3$)$_3$	4	648.9	>300	18,44
	-C$_6$H$_5$	4	728.9	300-360(Z)	18
	-C$_6$H$_{11}$	4	753.1	>330	18
	-CH$_2$C$_6$H$_5$	4	785.0	>330	18
	-C(CH$_3$)$_2$CH$_2$CH$_3$	4	705.0	>280	18
	-C(CH$_3$)$_2$CH$_2$C(CH$_3$)$_2$	4	813.2	~333	18
-CH$_2$OCH$_2$-	-CH$_3$	4	600.7	264-266	42
	-C(CH$_3$)$_3$	3	576.8	245	45

3.2

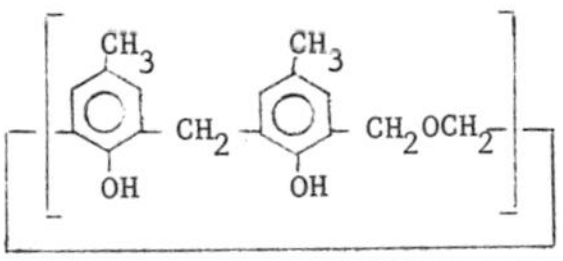

n	Mol. Wt.	m. p. °C	Ref.
2	540.7	325-330	46

3.3

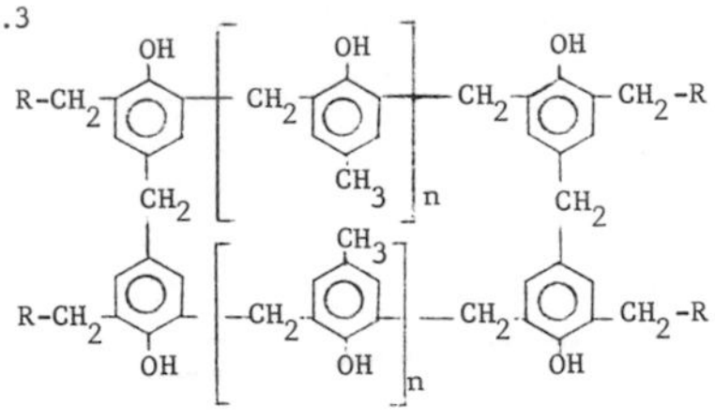

4 - Branched Phenol-formaldehyde
    Oligomers

4.1

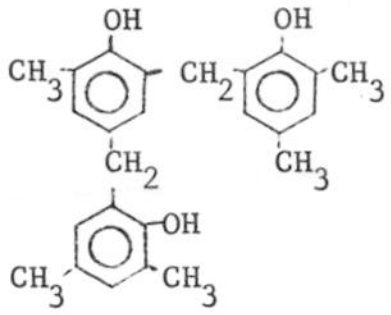

R	n	Mol. Wt.	Ref.
H	2	916.2	47
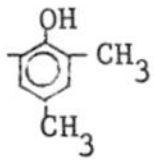 (structure: OH–CH₃, CH₃)	1	1201.5	43,47

Mol. Wt.	m. p. °C	Ref.
376.5	158	48

4.2

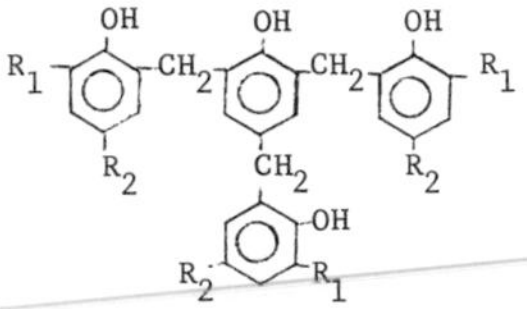

4.3

R₁	R₂	Mol. Wt.	m. p. °C	Ref.
H	H	411.5		49
H	CH₃	453.6	184-187	30,50
CH₃	CH₃	495.6	185-186	51

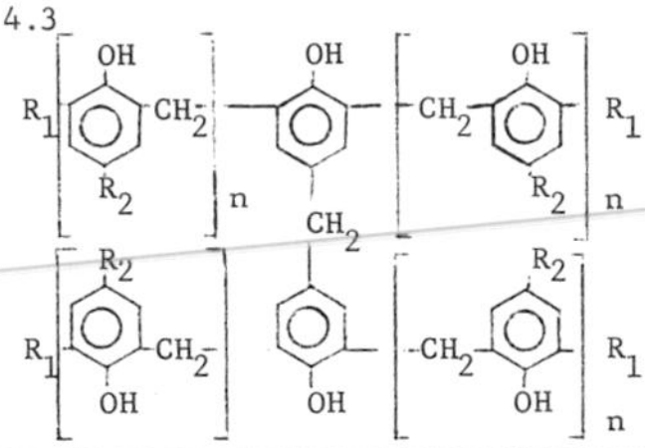

R₁	R₂	n	Mol. Wt.	m. p. °C	Ref.
H	H	1	624.7	185-187	52,53
CH₃	CH₃	1	737.0	207-208	6,53,54
CH₃	CH₃	2	1217.5	190-191	54

4.4

4.5

n	Mol. Wt.	m. p. °C	Ref.
1	730.9	160-162	52
2	1049.2	130-135	52
3	1367.6	133-137	52

R_1	R_2	Mol. Wt.	m. p. °C	Ref.
H	CH_3	574.7	266	48,55
CH_3	CH_3	630.8	217.5	48,55

REFERENCES

1. C. A. Buehler, D. E. Copper, and E. O. Scrudder, J. Org. Chem. 8, 316 (1943).
2. S. R. Finn, J. W. James, and C. J. S. Standen, J. Appl. Chem. 4, 497 (1954);
    S. R. Finn, G. Lewis, and N. J. L. Megson, J. Soc. Chem. Ind. 69, 551 (1950);
    S. R. Finn and G. Lewis, J. Appl. Chem. 1, 524 (1954).
3. D. A. Fraser, R. W. Hall, P. A. Jenkins, and A. L. Raum, J. Appl. Chem. 7, 689 (1957).
4. H. Kämmerer and H. Lenz, Makromol. Chem. 27, 162 (1958).
5. H. L. Bender, A. C. Franham, J. W. Guyer, F. N. Apel, and T. B. Gibb, Jr., Ind. Eng. Chem. 44, 1619 (1952).
6. A. C. Davis, B. T. Hayes, and R. F. Hunter, J. Appl. Chem. 3, 312 (1953).
7. S. Seto, H. Horiuchi, and A. Takahashi, J. Chem. Soc. Japan, Ind. Chem. Sect. 58, 378 (1955).
8. H. Kämmerer and W. Rausch, Makromol. Chem. 24, 152 (1957).
9. M. Koebner, Z. Angew. Chem. 46, 251 (1933).
10. N. J. L. Megson and A. A. Drummond, J. Soc. Chem. Ind. 49, 251 T (1930).
11. E. Ziegler, Monatsh. Chem. 78, 334 (1948).
12. H. Kämmerer, W. Rausch, and H. Schweikert, Makromol. Chem. 56, 123 (1962).
13. K. v. Auwers, Ber. Deut. Chem. Ges. 40, 2524 (1907).
14. K. Fries and K. Kann, Liebigs. Ann. Chem. 353, 335 (1907).
15. K. Hultzsch, Ber. Deut. Chem. Ges. 74, 898 (1941).
16. A. Zinke and E. Ziegler, Ber. Deut. Chem. Ges. 74, 541 (1941).
17. H. Kämmerer and K. Haberer, Monatsh. Chem. 95, 1589 (1964).
18. A. Zinke, R. Kretz, E. Leggewie, and K. Hüssinger, Monatsh. Chem. 83, 1213 (1952).
19. S. R. Finn and J. W. G. Musty, J. Soc. Chem. Ind. 69, Supp. No. 1, S3 (1950).
20. E. Adler, H. v. Euler, and G. J. Gie, Arkiv. Kemi 16A, Nr. 12 (1943).
21. L. M. Debing, Trans. Electrochem. Soc. 90, 277 (1946).
22. H. v. Euler, E. Adler, and J. O. Cedwall, Arkiv. Kemi 15 A, Nr. 19 (1942).
22a. H. Kämmerer and A. Kiegel, unpublished results.
23. A. v. Bayer and V. Drewsen, Liebigs Ann. Chem. 212, 344 (1882).
24. H. Kämmerer, G. Büsing, and H.-G. Haub, Makromol. Chem. 66, 82 (1963).
25. H. Kämmerer and M. Harris, Makromol. Chem. 62, 18 (1963); J. Polymer Sci. A, 2, 4003 (1964).
26. S. Lederer, J. Prakt. Chem. 50, 223 (1894).
27. S. R. Finn, J. W. James, and C. J. S. Standen, Chem. Ind. (London) 1954, 188; J. Appl. Chem. 4, 296 (1954).
28. A. T. Carpenter and R. F. Hunter, J. Appl. Chem. 3, 486 (1953).

29. S. R. Finn and J. W. G. Musty, J. Appl. Chem. 2, 88 (1952).
30. J. H. Freeman, J. Am. Chem. Soc. 74, 6257 (1952).
31. H. Kämmerer and M. Grossmann, Chem. Ber. 86, 1492 (1953).
32. J. Reese, Angew. Chem. 64, 399 (1952).
33. H. v. Euler, E. Adler, G. Eklund, and O. Törngren, Arkiv. Kemi, 15 B, Nr. 9 (1942).
34. O. Manasse, Ber. Deut. Chem. Ges. 27, 2409 (1894).
35. P. Maitland and D. C. Pepper, J. Soc. Chem. Ind. 61, 66 (1942).
36. B. T. Hayes and R. F. Hunter, J. Appl. Chem. 8, 743 (1958).
37. F. Ullmann and K. Brittner, Ber. Deut. Chem. Ges. 42, 2539 (1909).
38. E. Adler, Arkiv. Kemi 14, B, Nr. 23 (1941).
39. S. R. Finn and G. J. Lewis, J. Soc. Chem. Ind. 69, 132 (1950).
40. S. Kyrning, Arkiv Kemi 15 A, Nr. 2 (1941).
41. F. Hanus and E. Fuchs, J. Prakt. Chem. 153, 327 (1939).
42. H. Kämmerer and M. Dahm. Kunststoffe-Plastics 6, 1 (1959).
43. B. T. Hayes and R. F. Hunter, Chem. Ind. (London) 1956, 193.
44. A. Zinke and E. Ziegler, Ber. Deut. Chem. Ges. 77, 264 (1944).
45. K. Hultzsch, Kunststoffe 52, 19 (1962).
46. H. v. Euler, E. Adler and B. Bergström, Arkiv Kemi 14 B, Nr. 30 (1941).
47. R. F. Hunter and C. Turner, Chem. Ind. (London) 1957, 72.
48. E. Ziegler, Monatsh. Chem. 79, 142 (1948).
49. E. Ziegler, Oesterr. Chemiker. Ztg. 49, 92 (1948).
50. A. T. Carpenter and R. F. Hunter, J. Appl. Chem. 1, 217 (1951).
51. A. T. Carpenter and R. F. Hunter, J. Chem. Soc. 1954, 2731.
52. H. Kämmerer and H. Lenz, Kunststoffe, 51, 26 (1961).
53. A. C. Davis, B. T. Hayes and R. F. Hunter, J. Appl. Chem. 7, 521 (1957).
54. R. F. Hunter and C. Turner, J. Appl. Chem. 7, 528 (1957).
55. H. v. Euler, E. Adler, S. v. Kispeczy, and A. M. Fagerlund, Arkiv Kemi 14 A, Nr. 10 (1940).

E. VINYL OLIGOMERS

1 - Oligo(vinyl aldehydes) and Oligo(vinyl ketones)

No.	Monomer	Oligomers	Mol. Wt.	m. p. °C	b. p. °C/mm.	Ref.
1	Acrolein $CH_2=CH-CHO$	2-formyl-2,3-dihydropyran -CHO	112.1		145-148	1,2,3,4
		3-formyl-3,4-dihydropyran -CHO	112.1		77-78/12	5,6
2	α-Methylacrolein $CH_2=C - CHO$ CH_3	2-formyl-2,5-dimethyl-2,3-dihydropyran	140.2	-75	166/750	3,7
3	α-Ethylacrolein $CH_2=C - CHO$ C_2H_5	2-formyl-2,5-diethyl-2,3-dihydropyran	168.2		195	3

References page VII-28

No.	Monomer	Oligomers	Mol. Wt.	m. p. °C	b. p. °C/mm.	Ref.
4	Methyl vinyl ketone $CH_2=CH-CO-CH_3$	6-methyl-2-acetyl-2,3-dihydropyran $CH_3-\overset{\bigcirc}{O}-COCH_3$	128.2		68/13	8
5	2-Methyl-1-butene (3)-one	2,6-dimethyl-3,7-dioxo-1-octene $CH_3COCH(CH_3)CH_2-$ $-CH_2COC=CH_2$ $\quad\quad\underset{CH_3}{\mid}$	168.2		83-85/17	9

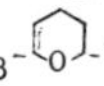

2 - Oligo(acrylonitriles)

2.1 - Saturated Oligomers

2.1.1 - $H[-CH_2CH(CN)-]_nH$

n	Mol. Wt.	b. p. °C/mm.	$n_D/°C$	Ref.
1	55.1	97.1	1.3689/15	
2	108.1	135/12	1.4312/25	10
3	161.2	195-196/2.5	1.4609/20	10,13

2.1.2 - $H[-CH_2CH(CN)-]_nCH_3$

n	Mol.	m. p. °C	b. p. °C/mm.	$d_4/°C$	$n_D/°C$	Ref.
1	69.1		107-108	0.773/60		
2	122.2	8.8[a)	106/2	0.9051/60	1.4191/60	12,13
		50[b)	94/2	0.8940/60	1.4155/60	12,13
3	175.2[c)	37-39				13
		45-46				13
		80-81				13
4	228.3[d)	130-135				13
		158				13

a) isotactic, b) syndiotactic, c) 3 isomers, d) 2 isomers.

2.1.3 - $H[-CH(CN)CH_2-]_nCH_2CN$

2.1.4 - Anionic Oligo(methacrylonitriles)

$$CH_3O\left[-CH_2\underset{CH_3}{C(CN)}-\right]_n H$$

n	Mol. Wt.	b. p. °C/mm.	n_D/°C	Ref.
1	94.1	287.4	1.4347/20	
2	147.2		1.4644/25	10,14
3	200.2	95/0.01		10,14

n	Mol. Wt.	b.p. °C	n_D	Ref.
1	99.1			
2	166.2	92	1.438	15
3	233.3	165	1.464	15
4	300.4	235	1.478	15
5	367.5	300-305	1.488	15

2.1.5 - 1,2-Dicyanocyclobutanes

$$\left[-CH_2CR(CN)-CR(CN)CH_2-\right]_n$$

R	n		Mol. Wt.	m. p. °C	b. p. °C/mm.	n_D^{25}	Ref.
H	1	cis	106.1	0	108-115/3-4	1.4628	16,17
		trans	106.1	62	140-145/3-4		16,17
CH_3	1	cis	134.2	107-108	170/25		18
		trans	134.2	90.3	120/25		18

2.2 - Unsaturated Oligomers

No.	Oligomers	Mol. Wt.	m. p. °C	b. p. °C/mm	n_D^{25}	Ref.
1	2,3-Dihydromuconitrile $NCCH_2CH=CHCH_2CN$ (trans)	106.1	76			17,19
2	1,1,4,4-Tetracyanoethyl-1,4-dicyano- trans-2-butene $(NCCH_2CH_2)_2C(CN)-CH$ $(NCCH_2CH_2)_2C(CN)-\overset{..}{C}H$	318.4	240			17
3	α-Methylene-δ-methyladiponitrile $NCCH(CH_3)CH_2CH_2C(CN)=CH_2$	134.2		148/25	1.4502	18

References page VII-28

3 - Oligo(acrylic acids)

3.1 - Saturated Oligo(acrylic acids)

$$H \left[-CH_2CH(COOR) - \right]_n CH_3$$

R	n	Mol. Wt.	Steric Structure	m. p. °C	b. p. °C/mm.	$n_D/°C$	Ref.
H	1	88.1					
	2	160.2	isotactic	128			20,21,22
			syndiotactic	141			20,21,22
	3	232.2	isotactic	162-165			22
			heterotactic	143-147			22
			syndiotactic	142-146			22
CH_3	1	102.1			91.5/742	1.3838/20	23
	2	188.2	isotactic		64/0.7	1.4258	22,23
			syndiotactic				22,23
	3	274.3	isotactic		150-160/2	1.4405	22,23
			heterotactic		120-160/2	1.4416	22,23
			syndiotactic		150-160/2	1.4433	22,23

3.2 - Unsaturated Oligo(acrylic acids)

$$CH_3OOC-C \underset{\overset{\|}{CH_2}}{} \left[-CH_2CH_2CH(COOCH_3) - \right]_n CH_3$$

n	Mol. Wt.	b. p. °C/mm.	n_D^{25}	Ref.
1	188.2	107/7	1.4445	18,24
2	276.3	173/3	1.4588	18,24

3.3 - Anionic Oligo(methacrylic acids)

$$CH_3O \left[-CH_2C(CH_3) - \atop COOR \right]_n H$$

R	n	Mol. Wt.	m. p. °C	b. p. °C/mm.	d^{20}	Ref.
CH_3	1	132.2		147	0.9749	25
	2	232.3		241	1.0540	25
	3	332.4		116/0.1	1.1045	25
	4	432.5		190/0.1	1.12	25
	6	632.8			1.1565	25
H	2	204.2	82			25
	3	290.3	160			25

4 - Oligo(styrenes)

No.	Monomer	Oligomers	Mol. Wt.	m. p. °C	b. p. °C/mm.	n_D^{20}	Ref.
1	Styrene 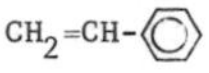 $CH_2=CH-$⟨◯⟩	3-methyl-1-phenylindane (2 stereoisomers) 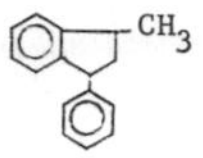	208.3 208.3	9.5 25.5	168-169/16 157/12	1.5810 1.5809	26,27,28 29,30
		1,3-diphenyl-1-butene 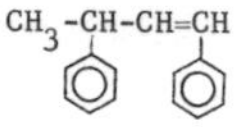 $CH_3-CH-CH=CH$	208.3 208.3		181-182/20 134-135/1	1.5930	11,26,27, 28
		1,4-diphenyl-1-butene 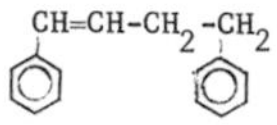 $CH=CH-CH_2-CH_2$	208.3	124			11
		1,2-diphenylcyclobutane 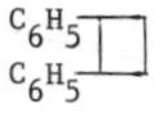 $\begin{matrix}C_6H_5\\C_6H_5\end{matrix}$⬜	208.3			1.5913	32
2	α-Methylstyrene 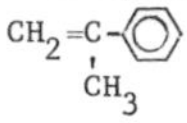 $CH_2=C-$⟨◯⟩ $\quad CH_3$	1,3,3-trimethyl-1-phenylindane 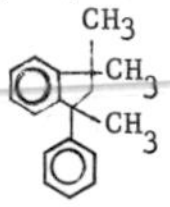	236.4	53	158-160/10		33,34,35
		4-methyl-2,4-diphenyl-2-pentene 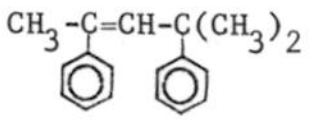 $CH_3-C=CH-C(CH_3)_2$	236.4	52	166-167/15	1.5728	31,33,36
3	α-Methyl-ρ-methoxystyrene 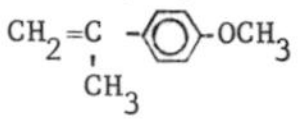 $CH_2=C$ ⟨◯⟩-OCH_3 $\quad CH_3$	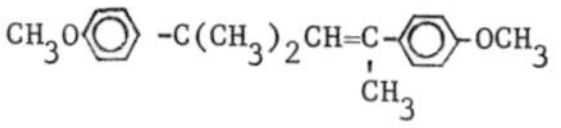 CH_3O⟨◯⟩ $-C(CH_3)_2CH=C-$⟨◯⟩$-OCH_3$ $\qquad\qquad\qquad\qquad CH_3$	296.4		237-240/18	1.5703	34,37
4	α-Methyl-p-aminostyrene 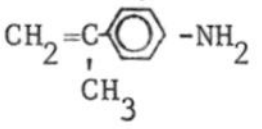 $CH_2=C$⟨◯⟩ $-NH_2$ $\quad CH_3$	1,3,3-trimethyl-4,6-diamino-phenylindane 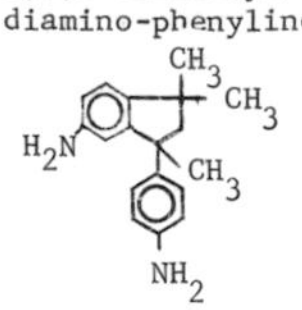	266.4	93-94			34
		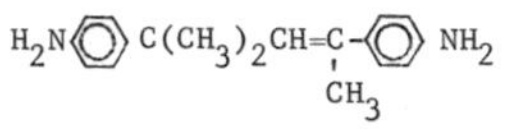 H_2N⟨◯⟩ $C(CH_3)_2CH=C-$⟨◯⟩ NH_2 $\qquad\qquad\qquad CH_3$	266.4	173			34,38

References page VII-28

No.	Monomer	Oligomers	Mol. Wt.	m. p. °C	b. p. °C/mm.	n_D^{20}	Ref.
5	α-Methyl-p-carboxystyrene 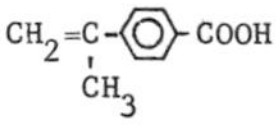	1,3,3-trimethyl-1-phenyl-indane-4',6-dicarboxylic acid 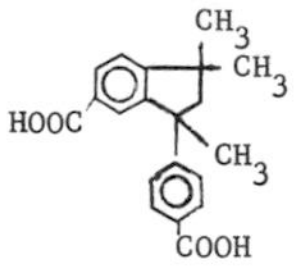	348.4	297			34,38
6	α,p-Dimethylstyrene 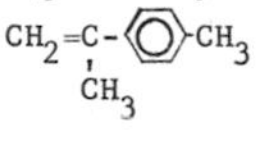	1,3,3,4,6-pentamethyl-1-phenylindane 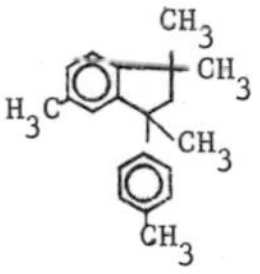	264.4	40	142-144/0.8		34,39, 40
7	α-Ethylstyrene 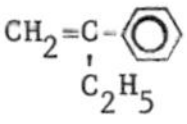	1,3-diethyl-3-methyl-1-phenylindane 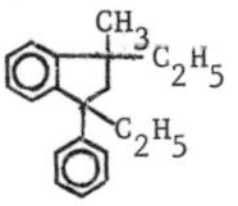	264.4		104-106/0.3	1.5642	41
		3,5-diphenyl-5-methyl-2-heptene 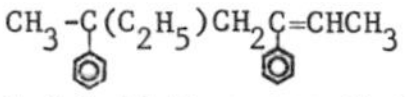	264.4		133-135/1.2	1.5434/25	41
8	α,m-Dimethyl-styrene 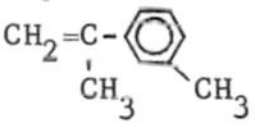	1,3,3,3',7-pentamethyl-1-phenylindane 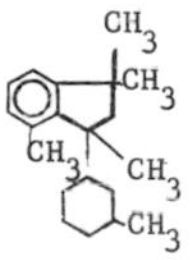	264.4	57			34
9	p-Bromostyrene 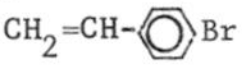	cis-1,3-di(p-bromophenyl)-1-butene 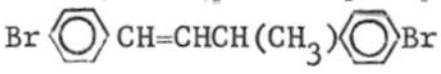	366.1	67-68			42,43
10	Stilben 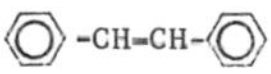	1,2,3,4-tetraphenyl-cyclobutane 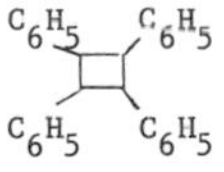	360.5	164-165			44,45, 46
		1,2-diphenyl-1-p-tolylethane 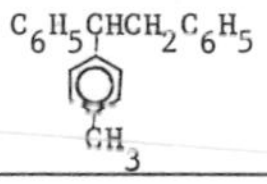	272.4	42-43			44

Monomer structures:

5: $CH_2=C(CH_3)-C_6H_4-COOH$

6: $CH_2=C(CH_3)-C_6H_4-CH_3$

7: $CH_2=C(C_2H_5)-C_6H_5$

8: $CH_2=C(CH_3)-C_6H_3(CH_3)$

9: $CH_2=CH-C_6H_4-Br$

10: $C_6H_5-CH=CH-C_6H_5$

Oligomer partial structures:

7 (heptene): $CH_3-C(C_2H_5)CH_2C=CHCH_3$ (with phenyl groups)

9: $Br-C_6H_4-CH=CHCH(CH_3)-C_6H_4-Br$

10 (cyclobutane): C_6H_5, C_6H_5 / C_6H_5, C_6H_5

10 (ethane): $C_6H_5CHCH_2C_6H_5$ (with tolyl CH_3)

5 - Oligomeric N-Vinyl Derivatives

No.	Monomer	Oligomers	Mol. Wt.	m. p. °C	Ref.
1	N-Vinylpyrrolidone	1,3-bis-[N-pyrrolidone-(2)-yl]-1-butene	212.3	75	47
2	N-Vinylpyridine	sym-tri(4-pyridyl)cyclohexane	315.4	228.5	48

REFERENCES

1. K. Alder and E. Rüden, Ber. Deut. Chem. Ges. 74, 920 (1941).
2. S. Potnis, K. Shohara, R. C. Schulz, and W. Kern, Makromol. Chem. 63, 78 (1963).
3. H. Schulz and H. Wagner, Angew. Chem. 62, 105 (1950).
4. S. M. Scherlin, A. J. Berlin, T. A. Sserebrennikowa, and F. E. Rabinowitsch, J. Gen. Chem. USSR 8, 22 (1938); through C. 1939 I, 1971.
5. R. Hall, Chem. Ind. (London) 1955, 1772.
6. G. Dumas and P. Rumpff, Compt. Rend. 242, 2574 (1956).
7. G. G. Stoner and J. S. McNulty, J. Am. Chem. Soc. 72, 1531 (1950).
8. K. Alder, H. Offermanns, and E. Rüden, Ber. Deut. Chem. Ges. 74, 905 (1941).
9. H. Staudinger and B. Ritzenthaler, Ber. Deut. Chem. Ges. 67, 1773 (1934).
10. H. Zahn and P. Schäfer, Chem. Ber. 92, 736 (1959), Makromol. Chem. 30, 225 (1959).
11. R. Fittig and E. Erdmann, Liebigs Ann. Chem. 216, 179 (1883); H. Stobbe and G. Posujak, Liebigs Ann. Chem. 371 287 (1909).
12. H. G. Clark, Makromol. Chem. 63, 69 (1963).
13. T. Takata and M. Taniyama, Chem. High Polymers Japan 16, 693 (1959); T. Takata, H. Ishii, Y. Nishiyama, and M. Taniyama, Chem. High Polymers Japan 18, 235 (1961); through C. 1964, No. 50, 729-731.
14. R. C. Houtz, Textile Res. J. 20, 786 (1950).
15. B.-A. Feit, J. Wallach, and A. Zilkha, J. Polymer Sci. A2, 4743 (1964).
16. E. C. Coyner and W. S. Hillmann, J. Am. Chem. Soc. 71, 324 (1949).
17. N. Takashima and C. C. Price, J. Am. Chem. Soc. 84, 489 (1962).
18. C. J. Albisetti, D. C. England, M. J. Hogsed, and R. M. Joyce, J. Am. Chem. Soc. 78, 472 (1956).
19. E. Reppe, et. al. Liebigs Ann. Chem. 596, 133 (1956).
20. K. Auwers and J. Thorpe, Liebigs Ann. Chem. 285, 335 (1895).
21. E. Moeller, Ber. Deut. Chem. Ges. 43, 3250 (1910).
22. H. G. Clark, Makromol. Chem., 86, 107 (1965).
23. D. Lim and O. Wichterle, J. Polymer Sci. 29, 579 (1958).
24. E. Trommsdorff, Angew. Chem. 68, 355 (1956).
25. Th. Völker, A. Neumann, and V. Baumann, Makromol. Chem. 63, 182 (1963); G. Schreyer and Th. Völker, Makromol. Chem. 63, 202 (1963).
26. P. E. Spoerri and M. J. Rosen, J. Am. Chem. Soc. 72, 4918 (1950).
27. M. J. Rosen, J. Org. Chem. 18, 1701 (1953).
28. B. B. Corson, J. Dorsky, J. E. Nickels, W. M. Kutz, and H. J. Thayer, J. Org. Chem. 19, 17 (1954)
29. M. J. Rosen, Org. Syn. 35, 83 (1955).
30. R. Stoermer and H. Kootz, Ber. Deut. Chem. Ges. 61, 2330 (1928).
31. F. S. Dainton and R. H. Tomlinson, J. Chem. Soc. 1953, 151.
32. I. S. Bengelsdorf, J. Org. Chem. 25, 1468 (1960).

33. E. Bergmann, H. Taubadel, and H. Weiss, Ber. Deut. Chem. Ges. 64, 1493 (1931).
34. J. C. Petropoulos and J. J. Fisher, J. Am. Chem. Soc. 80, 1938 (1958).
35. L. M. Adams, R. J. Lee, and F. T. Wadsworth, J. Org. Chem. 24, 1186 (1959).
36. J. M. Van der Zanden and Th. R. Rix, Rec. Trav. Chim. 75, 1343 (1956).
37. J. M. Van der Zanden and Th. R. Rix, Rec. Trav. Chim. 75, 1166 (1956).
38. J. v. Braun, E. Anton, W. Haensel, and G. Werner, Liebigs Ann. Chem. 472, 1 (1929).
39. M. Tiffenear, Ann. Chim. Phys. 10, 197 (1907).
40. V. N. Ipatieff, H. Pines, and R. C. Olberg, J. Am. Chem. Soc. 70, 2123 (1948).
41. C. G. Weiberger, E. M. Pearce, and D. Tanner, J. Am. Chem Soc. 80, 1761 (1958).
42. G. L. Goerner and J. W. Pearce, J. Am. Chem. Soc. 73, 2304 (1951).
43. J. Hukki, Acta. Chem. Scand. 3, 279 (1949).
44. D. S. Brackmann and P. H. Plesch, J. Chem. Soc. 1958, 3563; Chem. and Ind. 1955, 255.
45. M. Pailer and O. Müller, Monatsh. Chem. 79, 615 (1948).
46. Y. D. Fulton and J. D. Dunitz, Nature (London) 160, 161 (1947).
47. J. W. Breitenbach, F. Galinovsky, H. Nesvadba, and E. Wolf, Naturwissenschaften 42, 155, 440 (1955).
48. F. Longo, J. W. Bassi, F. Greco, and M. Cambini, Tetrahedron Letters 1964, 995, A. Segre, Tetrahedron Letters, 1964, 1001.

F. OLIGODIENES

1 - Oligo(butadienes)

No.	Oligomers	Mol. Wt.	m. p. °C	b. p. °C/mm.	n_D^{20}	Ref.
1	1-Vinyl-3-cyclohexene	108.2		129-130		1-7
2	cis-1,5-Cyclooctadiene trans-1,5-Cyclooctadiene	108.2	-/0.1 -62	150.8/755	1.4936	3-5, 7-10
3	1,5,9-Cyclododecatriene all-trans- trans, trans, cis- cis, cis, trans-	162.3	 34 -16.8 -9 to -8	 237.5 241.5 244	 1.5005 1.5078 1.5129	6, 10-12
4	1-Vinyl-3,7-cyclodecadiene	162.3		100-110/14		10
5	trans-3-Methyl-1,4,6-heptatriene	108.2		117-118	1.4670	13,14

2 - Oligomers of Derivatives of Butadiene

No.	Monomer	Oligomers	Mol. Wt.	m. p. °C	b. p. °C/mm.	Ref.
1	2-Chloro-1,3-butadiene $CH_2=CCl-CH=CH_2$	1,5- (or 1,6-) dichloro-1,5-cyclooctadiene	177.1		92-94/3.8	9
2	Isoprene $CH_2=C-C=CH_2$ $\quad CH_3$	dipentene (2 isomers)	136.3		163-167 167-170	15-17
		diprene	136.3		173-174	15,16
3	1,3-Diphenyl-1,3-butadiene $CH=CH-C=CH_2$ $C_6H_5 \quad C_6H_5$	1,3,4-triphenyl-4-trans-styrylcyclohexene	411.6	137-138		18,19
4	Hexafluoro-1,3-butadiene $CF_2=CF-CF=CF_2$	cyclic dimer	324.1	40 80		20,21

3 - Oligo(cyclopentadienes)

No.	Oligomer	Mol. Wt.	m. p. °C	b. p. °C/mm.	Ref.
1	Dicyclopentadiene	132.2	33	70/15	22
2	Tricyclopentadiene	198.3	68	130-145/15	22,23

4 - Oligo(allenes)

No.	Oligomers	Mol. Wt.	m. p. °C	b. p. °C/mm.	$n_D/°C$	Ref.
1	1,2-Dimethylene-cyclobutane	80.1		73-74	1.4721/20	24-27
22	2,7-Dimethylene-$\Delta^{9,10}$-octalin	160.3		107-108/13	1.5248/25	24,28

REFERENCES

1. W. E. Vaughan, J. Am. Chem. Soc. 54, 3863 (1952).
2. N. E. Duncan and G. Janz, J. Chem. Phys. 20, 1644 (1952).
3. J. C. Hillyer and J. V. Smith, Jr., Ind. Eng. Chem. 45, 1133 (1955).
4. K. Ziegler and H. Wilms, Liebigs Ann. Chem. 567, 1 (1950); K. Ziegler, H. Sauer, L. Bruns, H. Froitzheim-Kühlborn, and J. Schneider, Liebigs Ann. Chem. 589, 122 (1954).
5. G. Wilke, Angew. Chem. 69, 397 (1957); G. Wilke, E. W. Müller, and M. Kröner, Angew. Chem. 73, 33 (1961).
6. G. Wilke, Angew. Chem. 75, 10 (1963).
7. G. Pajarr, D. Fiumani, and M. Morr, Gazz. Chim. Ital. 92, 1452 (1962); through C. 1965, No. 2, 990.
8. E. Vogel, Angew. Chem. 68, 413 (1956).
9. A. E. Cope and W. J. Bailey, J. Am. Chem. Soc. 70, 2305 (1948).
10. H. W. B. Reed, J. Chem. Soc. 1954, 1931.
11. G. Wilke, J. Polymer Sci. 38, 45 (1959).
12. H. Breil, P. Heimbach, M. Kröner, H. Müller, and G. Wilke, Makromol. Chem. 69, 18 (1963).
13. S. Tanaka, K. Mabuchi, and N. Shimazaki, J. Org. Chem. 29, 1626 (1964).
14. S. Otsuka, T. Kikuchi, and T. Taketomi, J. Am. Chem. Soc. 85, 3709 (1963).
15. T. Wagner-Jauregg, Liebigs Ann. Chem. 488, 176 (1931).
16. O. Aschan, Liebigs Ann. Chem. 439, 221 (1924).
17. C. Walling and J. Peisach, J. Am. Chem. Soc. 80, 5819 (1958).
18. W. Herz and E. Lewis, J. Org. Chem. 23, 1646 (1958).
19. T. L. Jacobs and M. H. Goodrow, J. Org. Chem. 23, 1653 (1958).
20. I. L. Karle, J. Karle, T. B. Owen, R. W. Broge, A. H. Fox, and J. L. Hoard, J. Am. Chem. Soc. 86, 2523 (1964).
21. M. Prober and W. T. Miller, J. Am. Chem. Soc. 71, 598 (1949).
22. K. Alder and G. Stein, Liebigs Ann. Chem. 496, 204 (1932); 504, 216 (1933).
23. H. Staudinger and H. A. Bruson, Liebigs Ann. Chem. 447, 109 (1926).
24. S. V. Lebedev, Zh. Russ. Fiz-Khim. Obshch. 45, 1357 (1913).
25. R. N. Meinert and C. D. Hurd, J. Am. Chem. Soc. 52, 4540 (1930).
26. K. Alder and O. Ackermann, Chem. Ber. 87, 1567 (1954).
27. A. T. Blomquist and J. A. Verdol, J. Am. Chem. Soc. 78, 109 (1956).
28. B. Weinstein and A. H. Fenselau, Tetrahedron Letters 1963, 1463.

G. OLIGOOXIDES

1 - Oligo(formaldehyde)

1.1 - Oligo(formaldehyde) Dihydrates

$H[OCH_2]_n OH$

n	Mol. Wt.	m. p. °C	Ref.
4	138.1	95-105(d)	1,2
8	258.1	115-120(d)	1,2

1.2 - Oligo(formaldehyde) Diacetates

$CH_3CO-[OCH_2]_n-OCOCH_3$

n	Mol. Wt.	m. p. °C	b. p. °C	d/°C	n_D/°C	Ref.
1	132.1	-23	39-40	1.128/24	1.4025/24	2,3,4
2	162.1	-13	60-62	1.158/24	1.4124/24	3,4
3	192.2	- 3	84	1.179/24	1.4185/24	3
4	222.2	7	102-104	1.195/24	1.4233/24	2,3
5	252.2	17	124-126	1.204/24	1.4258/24	3
8	342.3	32-34		1.216/36	1.4297/36	2,3
9	372.3	40-43		1.353/15		3
10	402.4	52-53.5				3
11	432.4	65.5-67				3
12	462.4	73-75				2,5
14	522.5	84-86				3
15	552.5	90.5-92		1.364/25		3
16	582.5	93-95				2,3
17	612.6	98.5-99.5		1.370/15		3
19	672.6	107-109		1.390/15		3
20	702.6	111-112				2,3
22	762.7	116-118		1.465		3

1.3 - Oligo(formaldehyde) Dimethyl Ethers

$CH_3-[OCH_2]_n-OCH_3$

n	Mol. Wt.	m. p. °C	d/°C	Ref.
1	76.1	-105	0.8538/20	5,12,15
2	106.1	- 69.7	0.9597/25	5,13,14,15
3	136.2	- 42.5	1.0242/25	5
4	166.2	- 9.8	1.0671/25	5
5	196.2	18.3	1.1003/25	5

References page VII-35

1.4 - Oligo(formaldehyde) Dipropyl Ethers

$C_3H_7-[OCH_2]_n-OC_3H_7$

C_3H_7	n	Mol. Wt.	m. p. °C	b. p. °C/mm.	d/°C	n_D/°C	Ref.
n-	1	132.2		137.2-137.6	$0.8333_{25}/25$	1.3913/25	6,7,8
	2	162.2		67/11	$0.897_{25}/25$	1.4004/25	6,9
	3	192.2		97/11	$0.943_{25}/25$	1.4086/23	6,9
	4	222.3	-15 to -13		$0.990_{25}/25$	1.4137/26	6
	5	252.3	8-8,5		$1.014_{24}/25$	1.4181/26	6
i-	1	132.2		117-119	0.8742/20	1.3864/20	10
	2	162.2		39.5-41/23	0.8897/20	1.3971/20	10
	3	192.2		68.2-68.5/3	0.9348/20	1.4035/20	10
	4	222.3		93.5-94.5/3	0.9751/20	1.4117/20	10
	5	252.3		120-123/3	1.0275/20	1.4235/20	10
	6	282.3	23.4-24.3	159-163/3.7	1.101/26	1.4467/26	10

1.5 - Oligo(formaldehyde) Diallyl Ethers

$CH_2=CHCH_2-[OCH_2]_n-OCH_2CH=CH_2$

n	Mol. Wt.	m. p. °C	b. p. °C/mm.	d_{25}^{25}	n_D/°C	Ref.
1	128.2		138-139		1.4226°21	6,11
2	158.2		75-76.5/15	0.946	1.4280/25	6
3	188.2		58.5-64/0.3	0.992	1.4320/25	6
4	218.3	-4.3	82-87/0.3	1.027	1.4350/25	6
5	248.3	15.5	105-107/0.3	1.059	1.4377/25	6
6	278.3	22.5	144-155/0.4	1.079	1.4411/25	6

1.6 - Cyclic Oligo(formaldehydes)

$[\underline{[OCHR]}_n]$

R	n	Mol. Wt.	m. p. °C	b. p. °C	Ref.
H	3	90.1	6/-68	114.5	16,17
H	4	120.1	112		17,18,19
CH_3	3	132.2	12.6	125	20
CH_3	4	176.2	246.2 (sealed tube)	112-115 (subl.)	20,21

2. Cyclic Oligo(alkylene formals)

$$\left[OCH_2O(CH_2)_x\right]_n$$

x	n	Mol. Wt.	m. p. °C	b. p. °C/mm.	Ref.
5	1	116.2		40-44/11	22
	2	232.2	55-56		22
6	2	260.4	71-72		22
9	2	344.5	68-69		22
10	2	372.6	93-94		22
14	2	484.8	103.5-104		22

3 - Oligo(ethylene oxides)

3.1 - Linear Oligo(ethylene oxides)

$$H\left[OCH_2CH_2\right]_nOH$$

n	Mol. Wt.	m. p. °C	b. p. °C/mm.	d_{20}^{20}	n_D^{20}	Ref.
1	62.1	-12.6	197.8	1.113	1.4324	23,24,25
2	106.1	-10.1	245	1.120	1.4477	23,24,25,26
3	150.2	- 9.4	122-123/0.1	1.1274/15	1.4568	23,25,26
4	194.2	- 9.4	144-145.5/0.1	1.127	1.4604	23,24,25,26
5	238.3	- 8.7	174-176/0.14		1.4629	25,26,27
6	282.3	2.1	185-186/0.015	1.127	1.4647	23,24,25,26, 27,28
7	326.4	7.7	241-244/0.6		1.4663	25,26
8	370.4		206-209/0.015			27
10	458.6		220-223/0.01			27

3.2 - Cyclic Oligo(ethylene oxides)

$$\left[OCH_2CH_2\right]_n$$

n	Mol. Wt.	m. p. °C	b. p. °C	$d_4/°C$	Ref.
1	44.1	-111.3	10.7	0.8922/6	29
2	88.1	11.7	101.5	1.0336/20	30

REFERENCES

1. H. Staudinger and W. Kern, in "Die Hochmolekularen Organischen Verbindungen,"
    Springer, Berlin, 1960, p. 248.
2. W. Kern, Angew, Chem. 73, 177 (1961).
3. H. Staudinger, R. Signer, H. Johner, M. Lüthy, W. Kern, D. Russidis, and
    O. Schweitzer, Liebigs Ann. Chem. 474, 145 (1929).
4. M. Descudé, Ann. Chim. (Paris) 29, 502 (1903).
5. R. H. Boyd, J. Polymer Sci. 50, 133 (1961).
6. R. F. Webb, A. J. Derke, and L. S. A. Smith, J. Chem. Soc. 1962, 4307.
7. M. Ghysels, Bull. Soc. Chim. Belges 33, 57 (1924).
8. A. J. Vogel, J. Chem. Soc. 1948, 623.
9. A. Rieche and H. Gross, Chem. Ber. 93, 259 (1960).
10. E. Klein, J. K. Smith, and R. J. Eckert, Jr., J. Appl. Polymer Sci. 7, 383 (1963).
11 J. A. Trillat and R. Cambier, Bull. Soc. Chim. France 11, 757 (1894).
12. E. Fischer and G. Ciehe, Ber. Deut. Chem. Ges. 30, 3054 (1897).
13. M. Descudé, Compt. Rend. 138, 1705 (1904).
14. J. Lübering and R. Fleischmann, Ber. Deut. Chem. Ges. 70, 1680 (1937).
15. T. Uchida, Y. Kurita, and M. Kubo, J. Polymer Sci. 19, 365 (1956).
16. V. Jaacks and W. Kern, Makromol. Chem. 52, 37 (1962).
17. J. F. Walker, "Formaldehyde," 3rd ed., Reinhold Publ. Corp., New York, 1964.
18. H. Staudinger and M. Lüthy, Helv. Chim. Acta 8, 66 (1925).
19. K. Hayashi, H. Ochi, M. Nishii, Y. Miyake, and S. Okamura, J. Polymer Sci. A1,
    427 (1963).
20. A. W. Johnson, et al., in "Chemistry of Carbon Compounds", ed. E. H. Rodd, Vol.
    I, Part A, Elsevier, New York, 1951, p. 476.
21. T. S. Patterson and G. M. Holmes, J. Chem. Soc. 1935, 904.
22. J. W. Hill and W. H. Carothers, J. Am. Chem. Soc. 57, 925 (1935).
23. K. J. Rauterkus, H. G. Schimmel, and W. Kern, Makromol. Chem. 50, 166 (1961);
    K. J. Rauterkus and W. Kern, Chimia 16, 114 (1962).
24. P. Rempp, Bull. Soc. Chim. France 1957, 844.
25. Y. Kuroda and M. Kubo, J. Polymer Sci. 26, 323 (1957); T. Uchida, Y. Kurita,
    N. Koizumi, and M. Kubo, J. Polymer Sci. 21, 313 (1956).
26. A. F. Gallaugher and H. Hibbert, J. Am. Chem. Soc. 58, 813 (1936).
27. S. Perry and H. Hibbert, Can. J. Res. A14, 77 (1936), B14, 82 (1936).
28. R. Fordyce, E. L. Lovell, and H. Hibbert, J. Am. Chem. Soc. 61, 1905, 1912,
    1916 (1939).
29. A. W. Johnson, A. G. Long, and C. E. Dalgliesh, in "Chemistry of Carbon Compounds",
    ed. E. H. Rodd, Vol. I, Part A, Elsevier, New York, 1951, p. 670.
30. G. R. Ramage, E. H. Rodd, and J. K. Landquist, in "Chemistry of Carbon Compounds",
    ed. E. H. Rodd, Vol. IV, Part C, Elsevier, New York, 1951, p. 1529.

H. OLIGOIMINES

1 - Linear Oligoimines

1.1 - Linear Oligo(ethylene imines)

$H[NHCH_2CH_2]_nNH_2$

n	Mol. Wt.	m. p. °C	b. p. °C/mm.	d_{20}^{20}	n_D^{25}	Ref.
1	60.1	8.5	116.5	0.8994	1.4536	1,2
2	103.1		207.1	0.9586	1.4810	1,2,3,
3	146.2	12.0	277.9	0.9839	1.4951	1,2,3,4
4	189.3		333	0.9994	1.5015	1,2,3
7	318.5		109-110/8.5		1.5132	2,5
9	404.7		199-200/1		1.5161	2,5

References page VII-37

1.2 - Linear Oligo(alkylene imines)

$R-[NH(CH_2)_6NH(CH_2)_{10}]-R'$

R	R'	n	Mol. Wt.	m. p. °C	Ref.
H	OH	1	272.5	64-67	6
		2	526.9	70-72	6
		3	781.4	85-86	6
$(CH_2)_{10}OH$	OH	1	428.8	99-100	6
		2	683.2	90-93	6
		3	937.7	80-84	6
H	$NH(CH_2)_6NH_2$	1	370.7	70-72	6
		2	625.1	86-88	6
		3	879.6	81-85	6

2 - Cyclic Oligoimines

$[NH(CH_2)_x]_n$

x	n	Mol. Wt.	m. p. °C	b. p. °C/mm.	$d_4/°C$	Ref.
2	1	43.1		55-56	0.8321/24	2,7,8
	2	86.1	104	145-146		8,9
	4	172.3	35	$110/10^{-4}$		10
3	1	57.1		63	0.8436/20	11
	2	114.2	14-15	186-188		8,11,12,13
4	1	71.1		88	0.8520/22.5	14
	2	142.2		95/12	0.9020/18	8,13
5	1	85.2	-9	106	0.8606/20	14
	2	170.3		108-110/12	0.9195/13	8
6	1	99.2		138	0.8864/21	8,15,16
	2	198.3	72			13,17,18
	3	297.5	42			17
	4	396.7	59-60			17
	5	495.9	45			17
	6	595.1	67-68			17
7	1	113.1	-33	162	0.8895/20	16,19
	2	226.2	26		0.9012/30	19
8	1	127.2		90/24	0.9021/21	16
	2	254.5	55			20
9	1	141.3			0.8982/21	16
	2	282.5	38			19
13	1	197.4	50-51			16
	2	394.7	52			21

REFERENCES

1. A. L. Wilson, Ind. Eng. Chem. 27, 870 (1935).
2. G. D. Jones, A. Langsjoen, M. M. Ch. Neumann, and J. Zomlefer, J. Org. Chem. 9, 125 (1944).
3. H. B. Jonassen, T. B. Crumpler, and T. D. O. Brien, J. Am. Chem. Soc. 67, 1709 (1945).
4. F. G. Mann, J. Chem. Soc. 1934, 461.
5. G. S. Whitby, N. Wellman, V. W. Floutz, and L. H. Stephens, Ind. Eng. Chem. 42, 445 (1950).
6. H. Zahn and G. B. Gleitsmann, Makromol. Chem. 63, 129 (1963).
7. C. F. H. Allen, F. W. Spangler, and E. R. Webster, Org. Syn. 30, 38 (1950).
8. J. v. Braun, G. Blessing, and F. Zobel, Ber. Deut. Chem. Ges. 57, 185 (1924).
9. A. Ladenburg and J. Abel, Ber. Deut. Chem. Ges. 21, 758 (1888).
10. H. Stetter and K.-H. Mayer, Chem. Ber. 94, 1410 (1961).
11. C. C. Howard and W. Marckwald, Ber. Deut. Chem. Ges. 32, 2031, 2038 (1899).
12. E. L. Buhle, J. Am. Chem. Soc. 65, 29 (1943).
13. H. Stetter and J. Marx, Liebigs Ann. Chem. 607, 59 (1958); H. Stetter and H. Spangenberger, Chem. Ber. 91, 1982 (1958).
14. T. S. Stevens, in E. G. Rodd, Ed., "Chemistry of Carbon Compounds, Vol. IV, Part A, 1st. ed., Elsevier, New York, 1953, p. 61; N. Campbell, ibid. p. 570.
15. K. Ziegler and Ph. Orth, Ber. Deut. Chem. Ges. 66, 1867 (1933).
16. L. Ruzicka, M. Kobelt, O. Häfliger, and V. Prelog, Helv. Chim. Acta 32, 544 (1949).
17. H. Zahn and H. Spoor, Chem. Ber. 89, 1296 (1956); 92, 1375 (1959).
18. M. A. Th. Rogers, Nature 177, 128 (1956).
19. A. Müller, E. Srepel, E. Funder-Fritzsche, and F. Dicker, Monatsh. Chem. 83, 386 (1952).
20. A. Müller and L. Kindlmann, Ber. Deut. Chem. Ges. 74, 416 (1941).
21. A. Müller, Ber. Deut. Chem. Ges. 67, 295 (1934).

I. OLIGOESTERS

1 - Oligoesters of Hydroxy Acids

1.1 - Cyclic Oligoesters of α-Hydroxy Acids

$$[OCHRCO]_n$$

R	n	Config.	Mol. Wt.	m. p. °C	b. p. °C/mm.	$[\alpha]_D$ in C_6H_6	Ref.
H	2	-	116.1	86-87		-	1
CH_3	2	D	144.1	98.7	150/25	+ 281.6°(c=0.82, 16°C)	3
CH_3	2	L	144.1	98.7	150/25	- 280°(c=0.58, 18°C)	3,4
CH_3	2	DL	144.1	128	256	-	1,2,3,4, 5,6,7

1.2 - Cyclic Oligoesters of ω-Hydroxy Acids

$$\left[\mathrm{O(CH_2)_xCO}\right]_n$$

x	n	Mol. Wt.	m. p. °C	b. p. °C/mm.	Ref.
5	1	114.1	5	104-106/10	8,9,10
	2	228.3	112-113	130/0.13	8,9
	3	342.4		250/0.2	9
6	1	128.2		80-82/11	10
	2	256.3	41	135/0.25	9
	3	384.5		202/0.2	9
7	1	142.2		72-73/11	10
	2	284.4	93	152/0.13	9
8	1	156.2	31-31.5	86-87/10	9,10,11
	2	312.5	57-58	158/0.03	9,10
	3	468.7	20	240/0.1	9
9	1	170.3	6.4	100/10	9,10,11,12
	2	340.5	97	192/0.3	9,12,13,14
	3	510.8	29	270/0.3	9
10	1	184.3	3	116/10	9,10,11,12
	2	368.6	74		9,12
11	1	198.3	2	130/10	10,11,15
	2	396.6	101		9
12	1	212.3	27.5	143/10	9,10,11,12,16
	2	424.7	84		9,14
13	1	226.4	33-33.7	165/15	9,11,16
	2	452.7	107		9,12
14	1	240.4	37-37.5	169/10	9,10,11,16
	2	480.7	88		9,15
15	1	254.4	35.5-36.5	188/15	9,11,16
	2	508.8	108		9
16	1	268.4	42-43	194/15	9,11,16
	2	536.9	97		9
17	1	282.5	37	143/0.25	9
	2	564.9	114		9
22	1	348.6	36	175/0.2	9
	2	697.2	105		9

1.3 - Oligoesters of Aromatic Hydroxy Acids 1.3.2 - Cyclic Oligoesters of Salicyclic Acid

1.3.1 - Linear Oligoesters of Salicylic Acids

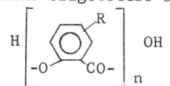

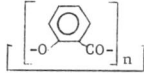

R	n	Mol. Wt.	m. p. °C	Ref.	n	Mol. Wt.	m. p. °C	Ref.
H	2	258.2	148-149	17,18,19	2	240.2	234	17,19
m-CH₃	2	286.3	162	20	3	360.3	200	17,21
p-CH₃	2	286.3	128-129	20	4	480.4	298-300	17
					6	720.7	375(d)	17

References page VII-42

1.3.3 - Cyclic Oligoesters of
       Cresotic Acids

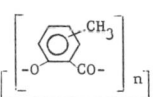

-CH₃	n	Mol. Wt.	m. p. °C	Ref.
o-	2	268.3	240(d)	20,22,23
	3	402.4	264-265	22
	4	536.5	299-300	22
m-	2	268.3	255(d)	22,23
	3	402.4	207-207.5	22
	4	536.5	305(d)	22
p-	2	268.3	235-235.5	22,23
	3	402.4	244.5-245	22
	4	536.5	347(d)	22

1.3.4 - Cyclic Oligoesters of
       Thymotic Acid

$$\left[\begin{array}{c} CH(CH_3)_2 \\ CH_3 \\ -O \quad CO- \end{array} \right]_n$$

n	Mol. Wt.	m. p. °C	Ref.
2	352.4	207	24
3	528.7	217	24

1.3.5 - Cyclic Oligoesters of
       Thiosalicylic Acid

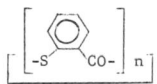

n	Mol. Wt.	m. p. °C	Ref.
2	272.3	176-177	25,26
3	408.5	257-258	25
4	544.7	288-290	25

1.3.6 - Linear Oligoesters of
       p-(β-Hydroxy)-ethoxybenzoic Acid

$$H[OCH_2CH_2O \bigcirc CO]_n OR$$

R	n	Mol. Wt.	m. p. °C	Ref.
H	1	182.2	177	27
	2	346.3	165	27
	3	510.5	183	27
	4	674.7	192	27
-CH₂CH₂OH	1	226.2	77	28
	2	390.4	144	28
	3	554.6	136	28
	4	718.7	156	28

2 - Oligoesters of Diols and Dicarboxylic Acids

2.1 - Cyclic Oligo(alkylene succinates)

$$\left[O(CH_2)_x O-CO(CH_2)_2 CO \right]_n$$

x	n	Mol. Wt.	m. p. °C	b. p. °C/mm.	Ref.
2	2	288.3	131		29,30
3	1	158.2	81	94-100/2	29
	2	316.3	138		29
4	1	172.2	42	95-96/2	29
	2	344.4	121		29
5	1	186.2	19	88-89/1	29

2.1 (Cont'd.)

x	n	Mol Wt.	m. p. °C	b. p. °C/mm.	Ref.
5	2	372.4	87		29
6	1	200.2	-15	108-110/2	29
	2	400.5	110		29
7	1	214.3	49	116-118/1-2	29
	2	428.5	86		29
8	1	228.3	71		29
	2	456.6	109		29
10	1	256.3	58	135-140/2	29
	2	512.7	109		15,29

2.2 - Cyclic Oligo(alkylene sebacates)

$$\left[O(CH_2)_x O-CO(CH_2)_8 CO \right]_n$$

x	n	Mol. Wt.	m. p. °C	Ref.
2	1	228.3	40-41	29
	2	456.6	80-81	15
3	1	242.3	14	29,31
	2	484.6	113-113.5	15,31

2.4 - Cyclic Oligo(diol carbonates)

$$\left[O(CH_2)_x O-CO \right]_n$$

x	n	Mol. Wt.	m. p. °C	Ref.
4	2	232.2	175-176	32
5	2	260.3	117-118	15
6	2	288.3	128-129	15
7	2	316.4	97-98	15
8	1	172.2	21.5-23	15
	2	344.5	116-117	15
9	1	186.3	34-35	15
	2	372.5	95-95.5	15
10	1	200.3	10-11	15
	2	400.6	105-106	15
11	1	214.3	40-41	15
	2	428.6	97-97.5	15
12	1	228.3	11-12	15
	2	456.7	93-95	15

2.3 - Cyclic Oligo(ethylene dicarboxylates)

$$\left[O(CH_2)_2 O-CO(CH_2)_x CO \right]_n$$

x	n	Mol. Wt.	m. p. °C	Ref.
7	1	214.3	52	29
	2	428.5	145	29
8	1	228.3	40-41	15
	2	456.6	80-81	15
9	1	242.3	35	15
	2	484.6	143	15
10	1	256.3	18	29
	2	512.7	95-96	15
11	1	270.4	-8	29
	2	540.7	145-146	15
12	2	568.8	102-103	15

2.5 - Cyclic Oligo(diphenol carbonates)

$$\left[O\bigcirc -A-\bigcirc -O-CO \right]_4$$

A	Mol. Wt.	m. p. °C	Ref.
>C(CH_3)_2	1017.2	375	33
-S-	977.1	320-322	33

2.6 - Cyclic Oligo(ethylene isophthalates)   2.7 - Oligo(ethylene terephthalates)

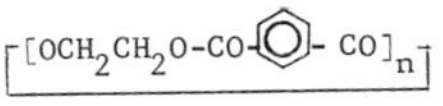

2.7.1 - Oligomeric Hydroxy Acids*

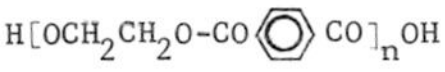

$[OCH_2CH_2O-CO-\bigcirc-CO]_n$

$H[OCH_2CH_2O-CO\bigcirc CO]_nOH$

n	Mol. Wt.	m. p. °C	Ref.
2	384.4	325-327	34

n	Mol. Wt.	m. p. °C	Ref.
1	210.2	178	35
2	402.4	200-205	36
3	594.6	219-223	36

2.7.2 - Oligomeric Diols*

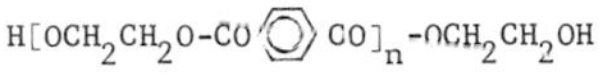

$H[OCH_2CH_2O-CO\langle\bigcirc\rangle CO]_n-OCH_2CH_2OH$

n	Mol. Wt.	m. p. °C	Ref.
1	·254.2	109-110	35,36
2	446.4	173-174	35,36
3	638.6	200-205	35,36
4	830.8	213-216	35,36
5	1023.0	218-220	36

2.7.3 - Oligomeric Dicarboxylic Acids*

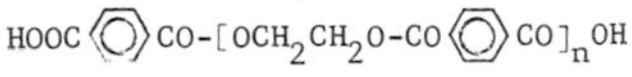

$HOOC\langle\bigcirc\rangle CO-[OCH_2CH_2O-CO\langle\bigcirc\rangle CO]_nOH$

n	Mol. Wt.	m. p. °C	Ref.
1	358.3	> 360	36,37
2	550.5	280-281	36,37
3	742.7	268-270	37
4	934.9	252-255	38
5	1127.1	233-236	38

2.7.4 - Cyclic Oligoesters

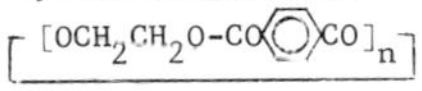

$[OCH_2CH_2O-CO\langle\bigcirc\rangle CO]_n$

n	Mol. Wt.	m. p. °C	Ref.
3	576.6	325-327	39,40
4	768.8	225-229	40
5	961.0	249-250	40

2.7.5 - Cyclic Oligoesters of Diethylene Glycol

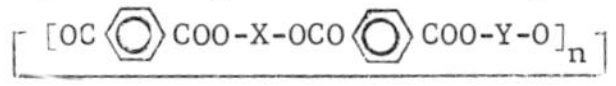

$[OC\langle\bigcirc\rangle COO-X-OCO\langle\bigcirc\rangle COO-Y-O]_n$

X	Y	n	Mol. Wt.	m. p. °C	Ref.
$-CH_2CH_2-$	$-(CH_2)_2O(CH_2)_2-$	1	428.4	165-157	40

* Taken from H. Zahn and G. B. Gleitsmann, Angew. Chem. *75*, 772 (1963).

2.8 - Oligo(1,4-cyclohexylenedimethylene terephthalates)

2.8.1 - Oligomeric Hydroxy Acids

$$H[OCH_2\langle H \rangle CH_2O-CO\langle O \rangle CO]_nOH$$

n	Config.	Mol. Wt.	m. p. °C	Ref.
1	trans	292.3	175-178	41

2.8.2 - Oligomeric Dicarboxylic Acids

$$HOOC\langle O \rangle CO-[OCH_2\langle H \rangle CH_2O-CO\langle O \rangle CO]_nOH$$

n	Config.	Mol. Wt.	m. p. °C	Ref.
1	trans	440.4	>310	41
1	cis	440.4	>300	41

2.8.3 - Cyclic Oligoesters

$$\left[OCH_2\langle H \rangle CH_2O-CO\langle O \rangle CO \right]_n$$

n	Mol. Wt.	m. p. °C	Ref.
3	823.0	288-298	42

REFERENCES

1. C. A. Bischoff and P. Walden, Liebigs Ann. Chem. 279, 45 (1893); Ber. Deut. Chem. Ges. 26, 262 (1893).
2. C. A. Bischoff and P. Walden, Liebigs Ann. Chem. 279, 71 (1893); Ber. Deut. Chem. Ges. 27, 2949 (1894).
3. E. Jungfleisch and M. Godchot, Compt. Rend. 141, 111 (1905), 142, 632 (1906), 144, 425 (1908).
4. J. Kleine and H.-H. Kleine, Makromol. Chem. 30, 23 (1959).
5. R. Dietzel and R. Krug, Ber. Beut. Chem. Ges. 58, 1307 (1925).
6. J. Wislicenus, Liebigs Ann. Chem. 167, 318 (1873).
7. R. Eder and F. Kutter, Helv. Chim. Acta 9, 557 (1926).
8. F. J. van Natta, J. W. Hill, and W. H. Carothers, J. Am. Chem. Soc. 56, 455 (1934).
9. M. Stoll and A. Rouve, Helv. Chim. Acta 18, 1087 (1935).
10. R. Huisgen and H. Ott, Tetrahedron 6, 253 (1959).
11. H. Hunsdiecker and H. Erlbach, Chem. Ber. 80, 129 (1947).
12. E. W. Spanagel and W. H. Carothers, J. Am. Chem. Soc. 58, 654 (1936).
13. W. H. Lycan and R. Adams, J. Am. Chem. Soc. 51, 3450 (1929).
14. W. H. Carothers and F. J. van Natta, J. Am. Chem. Soc. 55, 4714 (1933).
15. J. W. Hill and W. H. Carothers, J. Am. Chem. Soc. 55, 5031 (1933).
16. L. Ruzicka and M. Stoll, Helv. Chim. Acta 11, 1159 (1928).
17. W. Baker, W. D. Ollis, and T. S. Zeally, J. Chem. Soc. 1951, 201.
18. A. Einhorn, Ber. Deut. Chem. Ges. 44, 437 (1911).
19. G. Schroeter, Ber. Deut. Chem. Ges. 52, 2224 (1919).
20. R. Anschütz, Liebigs Ann. Chem. 439, 8 (1924).
21. A. Einhorn and H. Pfeiffer, Ber. Deut. Chem. Ges. 34, 2952 (1901); A. Einhorn and C. Mettler, Ber. Deut. Chem. Ges. 35, 3644 (1902).
22. W. Baker, B. Gilbert, W. D. Ollis, and T. S. Zealley, J. Chem. Soc. 1951, 209.
23. L. Anschütz and G. Gross, Ber. Deut. Chem. Ges. 77, 644 (1944).
24. W. Baker, B. Gilbert, and W. D. Ollis, J. Chem. Soc. 1952, 1443.
25. W. Baker, A. S. El-Nawary, and W. D. Ollis, J. Chem. Soc. 1952, 3163.
26. R. Anschütz and E. Rhodius, Ber. Deut. Chem. Ges. 47, 2733 (1914).
27. M. Ishibashi and M. Hirai, Chem. High Polymers, Japan 21, 231 (1964).
28. M. Ishibashi and M. Hirai, Chem. High Polymers, Japan 21, 235 (1964).
29. E. W. Spanagel and W. H. Carothers, J. Am. Chem. Soc. 57, 929 (1935).
30. W. H. Carothers and G. L. Dorough, J. Am. Chem. Soc. 52, 711 (1930).
31. M. Stoll and A. Rouve, Helv. Chim. Acta 19, 253 (1936).
32. W. H. Carthers and F. J. van Natta, J. Am. Chem. Soc. 52, 314 (1930).
33. H. Schnell and L. Bottenbruch, Makromol. Chem. 57, 1 (1962).
34. C. E. Berr, J. Polymer Sci. 40, 591 (1955).
35. H. Zahn and R. Krzikalla, Makromol. Chem. 23, 31 (1957).
36. H. Zahn, C. Borstlap and G. Valk, Makromol. Chem. 64, 18 (1963).
37. H. Zahn and B. Seidel, Makromol. Chem. 29, 70 (1959).
38. H. Zahn and B. Gleitsmann, Angew. Chem. 75, 772 (1963).
39. S. D. Ross, E. R. Coburn, W. A. Leach, and W. B. Robinson, J. Polymer Sci. 13, 406 (1954).
40. J. Goodman and B. F. Nesbitt, Polymer 1, 384 (1960); J. Polymer Sci. 48, 423 (1960).
41. H. Zahn and G. Valk, Makromol. Chem. 64, 37 (1963).
42. H. Zahn and G. Valk, Polymer Letters 1, 105 (1963).

K. OLIGOURETHANS AND OLIGOUREAS

1 - Oligo(pentamethylene urethans)

1.1 - Acetoxy-oligo(pentamethylene urethans)   **1.2 - Hydroxy-oligo(pentamethylene urethans)**

$$CH_3CO-[O(CH_2)_5NHCO]_nOCH_3$$

$$H[O(CH_2)_5-NHCO]_nOCH_3$$

n	Mol. Wt.	m. p. °C	Ref.
2	332.4	62-63.5	1
3	461.6	97-98.5	1
4	590.7	107-109	1
5	719.9	123-124.5	1
6	849.0	129.5-131	1
7	978.2	136-138	1
8	1107.4	140 143	1

n	Mol. Wt.	m. p. °C	b. p. °C	Ref.
1	161.2		131-134/0.2	1
2	290.4	74-75		1
3	419.5	99 101		1
4	548.7	112		1
5	677.8	116		1
6	807.0	122-125		1
7	936.2	131-134.5		1
8	1065.3	139-140.5		1

2 - Oligourethans of Diisocyanates and Glycols

2.1 - Oligourethans of Hexamethylene Diisocyanate and Diglycols

2.1.1 - Diol Oligourethans

$$HO[(CH_2)_2X(CH_2)_2OCONH(CH_2)_6NHCOO]_n-$$
$$-(CH_2)_2X(CH_2)_2OH$$

2.1.2 - Cyclic Oligourethans

$$-[(CH_2)_2X(CH_2)_2O-CO-NH(CH_2)_6NH-CO-O]_n-$$

X	n	Mol. Wt.	m. p. °C	Ref.
O	1	380.4	66.5-67.5	2,3
	2	654.8	103-104	2
	3	929.1	123-125	2,3
	4	1203.4	120-123	2
	5	1478.7	123-124	2,3
	7	2026.3	122-124	2,3
	15	4221.0	119-123	2,3
S	1	412.6	105-106	2
	3	993.4	132-134	2
	7	2155.5	133-135	2

X	n	Mol. Wt.	m. p. °C	Ref.
O	1	274.3	138	4
S	1	290.4	128	4

2.2 - Oligourethans of Diisocyanates and 1,4-Butanediol

2.2.1 - Diol Oligourethans*

$$HO[(CH_2)_4O-CO-NHXNH-CO-O]_n-(CH_2)_4OH$$

X	n	Mol. Wt.	m. p. °C	Ref.
$-(CH_2)_6-$	1	348.4	103-105	2,3,5,6
	2	606.8	146	2,3,5
	3	865.1	162-163	2,3,5
	4	1123.4	169-170	2,3
	5	1381.7	171-173	2,3
	6	1640.0	173-174	2,3
	7	1898.3	175-176	2,3
	9	2414.9	177-179	2,3
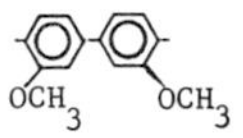 OCH₃ OCH₃	1	476.5	133.5	2,3
	2	862.9	127-128	2,3
	3	1249.4	164-166	2,3
	7	2795.0	190-195	2,3
	15	5886.3	210-215	2,3

2.2.2 - Diamine Oligourethans*

$$H[NH(CH_2)_6NH-CO-O(CH_2)_4O-CO]_n-$$
$$-NH(CH_2)_6NH_2 \cdot 2 \; HBr$$

n	Mol. Wt.	m. p. °C	Ref.
1	536.4	228	5
2	794.7	226	5
3	1053.0	218	5
4	1311.4	212	5

2.2.3 - Cyclic Oligourethans*

$$\left[\dfrac{[NH(CH_2)_6NH-CO-O(CH_2)_4O-CO]_n}{}\right]$$

n	Mol. Wt.	m. p. °C	Ref.
1	258.3	164	4,6,7
2	516.6	198	6,8

3 - Oligo(methylene ureas)

$$H[NHCONHCH_2]_nNHCONH_2$$

n	Mol. Wt.	m. p. °C	Ref.
1	132.1	218 (d)	9,10
2	204.2	227	9
3	276.3	231-233	9,10
5	420.5	236 (d)	10

4 - Oligo(methylene thioureas)

$$H[NHCSNHCH_2]_nNHCSNH_2$$

n	Mol. Wt.	m. p. °C	Ref.
1	164.3	198 (d)	11,12
2	252.4	210 (d)	11
3	340.5	215 (d)	11

* Taken from H. Zahn and B. Gleitsmann, Angew. Chem. 75, 772 (1963).

5 - Oligo(methylol thioureas)

$R[NHCSNHCH_2]_nOH$

R	n	Mol. Wt.	m. p. °C	Ref.
H	1	106.2	104-105	11,12
	2	194.3	190-192 (d)	11
-CH$_2$OH	1	136.2	92	11
	2	224.3	132	11,12

REFERENCES

1. Y. Iwakura, K. Hayashi, and K. Iwata, Makromol. Chem. 1965, in press.
2. W. Kern, H. Kalsch, K. J. Rauterkus, and H. Sutter, Makromol. Chem. 44-46, 78 (1961).
3. W. Kern, Angew. Chem. 71, 585 (1959).
4. W. Kern, K. J. Rauterkus, and W. Weber, Makromol. Chem. 43, 98 (1961).
5. H. Zahn and M. Dominik, Makromol. Chem. 44-46, 290 (1961).
6. H. Zahn and M. Dominik, Chem. Ber. 94, 125 (1961).
7. O. Bayer, Liebigs Ann. Chem. 549, 286 (1941); Angew. Chem. 59A, 257 (1947).
8. W. Kern, K. J. Rauterkus, W. Weber, and W. Heitz, Makromol. Chem. 57, 241 (1962).
9. A. A. Wanscheidt, S. K. Naumova, and J. P. Melnikowa, Zh. Obshch. Khim. 10, 1968 (1940); through C. 1941 II 184.
10. H. Kadowaki, Bull. Chem. Soc. Japan 11, 248 (1936).
11. H. J. Becher and F. Griffel, Chem. Ber. 91, 691 (1958).
12. H. Staudinger and K. Wagner, Makromol. Chem. 12, 168 (1954).

L. OLIGOPEPTIDES

1 - Oligopeptides of Glycine

1.1 - Linear Oligopeptides

$H[NHCH_2CO]_nOH$

n	Mol. Wt.	m. p. °C	Ref.
1	75.1	233-236 (d)	1
2	132.1	210-215	2
3	189.2	235 (d)	3,4
4	246.2	240 (d)	4,5
5	303.3	270 (d)	4,5
6	360.3	d	6

1.2 - Cyclic Oligopeptides

$[NHCH_2CO]_n$

n	Mol. Wt.	m. p. °C	Ref.
2	114.1	309	2,7
4	228.2	>330	8,9
5	285.3	>330	9
6	342.3	>355 (d)	8,10,11

2 - Oligopeptides of Alanine

2.1 - Linear Oligopeptides

H[NHCH(CH$_3$)CO]$_n$OH

n	Mol. Wt.	Config.	m. p. °C	$[\alpha]_D$	Specific Rotation °C	Concn.	Solvent	Ref.
1	89.1	L		+ 14.5	25	10	6 N HCl	1
2	160.2	LL	298	- 37.3	24	2	0.5 N HCl	6,12
		DD		+ 37.9	24	2	0.5 N HCl	12
		LD		+ 74.1	23	2	0.5 N HCl	12,13
		DL		- 71.1	25	2	H$_2$O	13
3	231.3	LLL	257-263	- 85.4	23	2	0.5 N HCl	14,15
		DDD		+ 85.9	23	2	0.5 N HCl	14
		LDL		+ 37.0	23	2	0.5 N HCl	14
		LLD		- 4.6	23	2	0.5 N HCl	14
		DLL		-115.2	23	2	0.5 N HCl	14
4	302.3	LLLL	269-272	-131.0	25	2	0.5 N HCl	16
		LDLL		- 14.2	21	2	0.5 N HCl	16
		LLDL		- 5.0	25	2	0.5 N HCl	16
		DLLL		-145.1	22	2	0.5 N HCl	16
5	373.4	LLLLL		-149.7	23	2	0.5 N HCl	16
6	444.5	LLLLLL		-156.6	23	0.9	0.5 N HCl	16
7	515.6	LLLLLLL	320					15

2.2 - Cyclic Oligopeptides

[NHCH(CH$_3$)CO]$_n$]

n	Mol. Wt.	Config.	m. p.	$[\alpha]_D$	Specific Rotation °C	Concn.	Solvent	Ref.
2	142.2	LL	297	- 28.8	20	2	H$_2$O	6
		DD	272	+ 29.1	20	2	ethanol	16a
6	426.5	LDDLDL	>330 (d)	- 20.8		1.4	50% ethanol	17
		LDLDDL	330	+ 22.9		1.4	50% ethanol	17

References page VII-51

3 - Oligopeptides of Valine, Leucine, and Isoleucine

3.1 - Linear Oligopeptides

H[NHCHRCO]$_n$OH

R	n	Mol. Wt.	Config.	Specific Rotation				Ref.
				$[\alpha]_D$	°C	Concn.	Solvent	
-CH(CH$_3$)$_2$	1	117.2	L	+28.8	20	3.4	6 N HCl	1
	2	216.3	LL	+10.8	25	2	H$_2$O	18,19
			DD	-10.8	25	2	H$_2$O	19,20
			LD	+59.5	25	2	H$_2$O	18,19
			DL	-62.1	25	2	H$_2$O	19,21
	3	315.4	LLL	-41.8	21	2.7	N HCl	19
			DDD	+41.3	21	2.8	N HCl	19
			LLD	+ 2.4	33	1.7	N HCl	19
			LDL	+39.9	33	3.9	N HCl	19
			LDD	+73.6	33	3.3	N HCl	19
			DDL	- 0.4	33	1.8	N HCl	19
			DLL	-71.9	33	3.6	N HCl	19
-CH$_2$CH(CH$_3$)$_2$	1	131.2	L	+13.9	25	9.075	4.5 N HCl	1
	2	244.3	LL	-13.4	23	1	N NaOH	18,22,23,24
			DD	+13.9	25	4.5	N NaOH	25
			LD	+68.9	20	9.7	N HCl	18,25
			DL	-68.0	20	9.4	N HCl	25
	3	357.5	LLL	-51.4	20	3.1	N NaOH	26
			DDD	+46.0	25	6.5	N NaOH	27
	4	470.7	LLLL	-90.0	20	7.6	N NaOH	26
-CH(CH$_3$)CH$_2$CH$_3$	1	131.2	L	+40.6	20		6 N HCl	1
	2		LL	+17.1	25	1	H$_2$O+1 eq. HCl	20

3.2 - Cyclic Oligopeptides

[[NHCHRCO]$_n$]

R	n	Mol. Wt.	Config.	m. p. °C			Specific Rotation			Ref.
					$[\alpha]_D$	°C	Concn.	Solvent		
-CH$_2$CH(CH$_3$)$_2$	2	226.3	LL		+48.7	20	8.7	CH$_3$COOH		25
			DD	277	-42.9	20	8.1	CH$_3$COOH		22

4 - Oligopeptides of Hydroxy and Mercapto Amino Acids

4.1 - Linear Oligopeptides

$\text{H[NHCHRCO]}_n\text{OH}$

R	n	Mol. Wt.	Config.	m. p. °C	$[\alpha]_D$	°C	Specific Rotation Concn.	Solvent	Ref.
$-CH_2OH$	1	105.1	L		+14.5	25	9.3	N HCl	1
	2	192.2	LL		+14.2	25	7	N HCl	28
$-CH_2C_6H_4OH$	1	181.2	L		- 7.3	25	4	6.1 N HCl	1
	2	344.4	LL		+30.1	19	4	H_2O + 1 eq. HCl	29,30
	3	507.6	LLL·$2H_2O$	181-182					31
$-CH_2SH$	1	121.1	L		+ 7.6	26	12.1	N HCl	1
	2	224.2	LL·1.5 HCl		+35	22	1	0.2 N HCl	37
$-CH_2CH_2SCH_3$	1	149.2	L		+23.4	20	5	3 N HCl	1
	2	280.4	LL		+27.0	24	2	H_2O	32,33,34
	2	280.4	LD		+75.8	25	1	H_2O	34
	3	411.6	LLL		-70.0	16	1	H_2O	33

4.2 - Cyclic Oligopeptides

[NHCHRCO]_n

R	n	Mol. Wt.	Config.	m. p. °C	$[\alpha]_D$	°C	Specific Rotation Concn.	Solvent	Ref.
$-CH_2OH$	2	174.2	LL	247	- 67.5	25	2.2	H_2O	35
$-CH_2C_6H_4OH$	2	326.4	LL	277-280	-223.8	20	2.4	NaOH	36

4.3 - Oligopeptides of Cystine

	Mol. Wt.	Config.	$[\alpha]_D$	°C	Specific Rotation Concn.	Solvent	Ref.
H-CyS-CyS-OH[+)	222.3	L	-29	25	1	N HCl	38
H-CyS-CyS-OH H-CyS-CyS-OH	444.6	LL LL	-58.7	26	1	N HCl	37,38
		LD LD	-187	26	1	N HCl	38
		DL DL	+190	26	1	N HCl	38

+) $CyS = \begin{bmatrix} CH_2S \\ -NHCHCO \end{bmatrix}$

References page VII-51

5 - Oligopeptides of Basic Amino Acids

H[NHCHRCO]$_n$OH

R	n	Mol. Wt.	Config.	R_F [+)]	Specific Rotation $[\alpha]_D$	°C	Concn.	Solvent	Ref.
-(CH$_2$)$_4$NH$_2$	1	146.2	L	0.24	+25.7	25	1.6	6 N HCl	1
	2	274.4	LL	0.17	+ 5.6	25	2	6 N HCl	39,40
	2		LD		+39.6	23	2	6 N HCl	39
	3	402.6	LLL,·3 HCl	0.12	- 2.2	24	2	0.5 N HCl	40,41
	3		LLD,·3 HCl		+54.9	22	2	0.5 N HCl	40
	3		LDD		+27.7	24	2	0.5 N HCl	40
	4	530.7	LLLL	0.09					40
	5	658.9	LLLLL	0.06					40

[+)] Solvent: n-butanol/acetic acid/water/pyridine (30/6/24/20)

6 - Oligopeptides of Acidic Amino Acids

6.1 - α- and γ-Oligopeptides of Glutamic Acid

H[NHXCO]$_n$OH

X	n	Mol. Wt.	Config.	Specific Rotation $[\alpha]_D$	°C	Concn.	Solvent	Ref.
CH$_2$CH$_2$COOH -CH-	1	147.1	L	+31.2	22.4	1	6 N HCl	1
	2	276.3	LL	+18.2	24	1-2	0.5 N HCl	42,43,44
	2		LD	+56.4	24	1-2	0.5 N HCl	44
	3	405.4	LLL	- 7.2	19	1.4	H$_2$O	45
COOH -CHCH$_2$CH$_2$-	2	276.4	LL	+ 3.8	24	1-2	0.5 N HCl	43,44,46, 47
	2		LD	+36.7	22	1-2	0.5 N HCl	44
	3	405.4	LLL	- 7.2	24	2	0.5 N HCl	48

6.2- Oligopeptides of Benzyloxycarbonyl-all-L-aspartic Acid and Glutamic Acid Esters

$C_6H_5CH_2OCO-[NHCHRCO]_{n-1}-NHCHR'COOC_2H_5$

R	R'	n	Mol. Wt.	m. p. °C	Specific Rotation $[\alpha]_D^{25}$	Concn.[+)	Ref.
$-CH_2COOCH_3$	$-CH_2COOC_2H_5$	2	452.5	80-81	+17.9	3.1	49
		3	581.6	127-128	- 1.01	3.1	49
		4	710.7	143-144	-13.1	1.1	49
		5	839.8	161-163	-19.1	0.75	49
		6	968.9	175-178	-26.6	0.7	49
		8	1227.2	207 (d)	-35.1	0.5	49
		11	1614.5	224 (d)	-42.9	0.45	49
		14	2001.9	233 (d)	-46.0	0.3	49
$-CH_2CH_2COOCH_3$	$-CH_2CH_2COOC_2H_5$	2	480.5	86	-12.4	2	50
		3	623.6	124	-18.0	2	50
		4	766.8	139	-21.3	2	50
		5	910.0	200	-22.7	2	50
		6	1053.1	250	-26.7	2	50
		7	1196.3	259	-28.7	2	50
		9	1482.5	d	-32.6	2	50
		11	1768.8	d	-35.6	2	50

[+) in $Cl_2CHCOOH$

6.3 - Cyclic Peptides

$[NHCHRCH_2CO]_n$

R	n	Mol. Wt.	m. p. °C	Ref.
$-COOC_2H_5$	2	286.3	212	51

7 - Oligopeptides of Proline

7.1 - Linear Oligopeptides

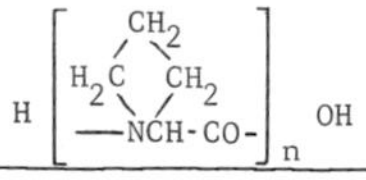

n	Mol. Wt.	Config.	m. p.	$[\alpha]_D$	°C	Specific Rotation Concn.	Solvent	Ref.
1	115.1	L	215-222(d)	-85.0	25.3	1	H_2O	1
2	212.3	LL	146(d)	-160.2	21	1	H_2O	52
3	309.4	LLL·0.5 H_2O	125-130(d)	-219.5	20	1	H_2O	53

7.2 - Cyclic Oligopeptides

$$\left[\begin{array}{c} CH_2 \\ H_2C \diagup \diagdown CH_2 \\ \left[\diagdown\diagup \right] \\ -NCH-CO- \end{array}\right]_n$$

n	Mol. Wt.	Config.	m. p. °C	Specific Rotation $[\alpha]_D$	°C	Concn.	Solvent	Ref.
2	194.2	LL	144-146	-151.2	20		H_2O	54,55
3	291.4	LLL	338	+ 48.5	25	0.48	CH_3OH	53

REFERENCES

1. J. P. Greenstein and M. Winitz, "Chemistry of the Amino Acids," Vol. III,
    J. Wiley & Sons, New York, 1961.
2. E. Fischer and E. Fourneau; Ber. Deut. Chem. Ges. 34, 2868 (1901).
3. E. Fischer, Ber. Deut. Chem. Ges. 36, 2982 (1903).
4. M. Rothe, H. Brünig, and G. Eppert, J. Prakt. Chem. 8, 323 (1959).
5. E. Fischer, Ber. Deut. Chem. Ges 37, 2468 (1904).
6. E. Fischer, Ber. Deut. Chem. Ges. 39, 453 (1906).
7. H. F. Schott, J. B. Larkin, L. B. Rockland, and M. S. Dunn, J. Org. Chem. 12
    490 (1947).
8. R. Schwyzer, B. Iselin, W. Rittel, and P. Sieber, Helv. Chim. Acta 39, 872 (1956).
9. M. Rothe and G. Lüdke, unpublished data.
10. J. C. Sheehan and W. L. Richardson, J. Am. Chem. Soc. 76, 6329 (1954);
    J. C. Sheehan, M. Goodman, and W. L. Richardson, J. Am. Chem. Soc. 77, 6391 (1955).
11. D. G. Ballard, C. H. Bamford, and F. J. Weymouth, Proc. Roy. Soc. 277A, 155 (1955).
12. B. F. Erlanger and E. Brand, J. Am. Chem. Soc. 73, 3508 (1951).
13. E. Fischer and K. Raske, Ber. Deut. Chem. Ges. 39, 3981 (1906).
14. E. Brand, B. F. Erlanger, H. Sachs, and J. Polatnik, J. Am. Chem. Soc. 73, 3510
    (1951).
15. H. Zahn and A. Meissner, Liebigs Ann. Chem. 636, 132 (1960).
16. E. Brand, B. F. Erlanger, and H. Sachs, J. Am. Chem. Soc. 74, 1849 (1952).
16a. F. B. Kipping and W. J. Pope, J. Chem. Soc. 1926, 496.
17. H. Gerlach, J. A. Owtschinnikow, and V. Prelog, Helv. Chim. Acta 47, 2294 (1964).
18. M. A. Nyman and R. M. Herbst, J. Org. Chem. 15, 108 (1950).
19. S. Shankman and Y. Schvo, J. Am. Chem. Soc. 80, 1164 (1958).
20. T. Sugimura and W. K. Paik, unpublished data.
21. E. Fischer and H. Scheibler, Liebigs Ann. Chem. 363, 136 (1908).
22. E. Fischer, Ber. Deut. Chem. Ges. 39, 2893 (1906).
23. F. H. Carpenter and D. T. Gish, J. Am. Chem. Soc. 74, 3818 (1952).
24. F. C. McKay and N. F. Albertson, J. Am. Chem. Soc. 79, 4686 (1957).
25. E. Fischer and A. H. Koelker, Liebigs Ann. Chem. 354, 39 (1907).
26. E. Abderhalden and R. Fleischmann, Fermentforsch. 9, 524 (1928).
27. P. A. Levene, R. E. Steiger, and R. E. Marker, J. Biol. Chem. 93, 605 (1931).
28. J. S. Fruton, J. Biol. Chem. 146, 463 (1942).
29. M. Bergmann, L. Zervas, L. Salzmann, and H. Schleich, Z. Physiol. Chem. 224,
    17 (1934).
30. J. L. Bailey, J. Chem. Soc. 1950, 3461.
31. A. E. Barkdoll and W. F. Ross, J. Am. Chem. Soc. 66, 951 (1944).
32. C. A. Dekker, S. P. Taylor, and J. S. Fruton, J. Biol. Chem. 180, 155 (1949).
33. M. Brenner and R. W. Pfister, Helv. Chim. Acta 34, 2085 (1951).
34. H. B. Milne and C.-H. Peng, J. Am. Chem. Soc. 79, 645 (1957).
35. E. Fischer, Ber. Deut. Chem. Ges. 40, 1501 (1907); E. Fischer and W. A. Jacobs,
    Ber. Deut. Chem. Ges. 39, 2942 (1906).
36. E. Fischer and W. Schrauth, Liebigs Ann. Chem. 354, 21 (1907).
37. J. P. Greenstein, J. Biol. Chem. 121, 9 (1937).
38. N. Izumiya and J. P. Greenstein, Arch. Biochem. Biophys. 52, 203 (1954); R. Wade
    M. Winitz, and J. P. Greenstein, J. Am. Chem. Soc. 78, 373 (1956).
39. B. F. Erlanger and E. Brand, J. Am. Chem. Soc. 73, 4025 (1951); 72, 3314 (1950).
40. S. G. Waley and J. Watson, J. Chem. Soc. 1953, 475.
41. E. Brand, B. F. Erlanger, J. Polatnik, H. Sachs, and D. Kirschenbaum, J. Am.
    Chem. Soc. 73, 4027 (1957).
42. M. Bergmann and L. Zervas, Ber. Deut. Chem. Ges. 65, 1192 (1932).
43. S. Goldschmidt and C. Jutz, Chem. Ber. 89, 518 (1956).
44. H. Sachs and E. Brand, J. Am. Chem. Soc. 75, 4608 (1953).
45. D. A. Rowlands and G. T. Young, Biochem. J. 65, 516 (1957).
46. V. Bruckner, M. Szekerke, and J. Kovacs, Z. Physiol. Chem. 309, 25 (1957).

47. W. L. Le Quesne and G. T. Young, J. Chem. Soc. 1950, 1959.
48. H. Sachs and E. Brand, J. Am. Chem. Soc. 76, 1811 (1954).
49. M. Goodman, F. Boardman, and J. Listowsky, J. Am. Chem. Soc. 85, 2483, 2491
    (1963).
50. M. Goodman, E. E. Schmitt, and D. A. Yphantis, J. Am. Chem. Soc. 84, 1283, 1288
    (1962).
51. F. Weygand and H.-J. Dietrich, Chem. Ber. 87, 482 (1954).
52. N. C. Davis and E. L. Smith, J. Biol. Chem. 200, 373 (1953).
53. M. Rothe, K.-D. Steffen, and I. Rothe, Angew. Chem. 77, 347 (1965).
54. J. Kapfhammer and A. Matthes, Z. Physiol. Chem. 223, 43 (1934).
55. E. Abderhalden and H. Nienburg, Fermentforsch. 13, 573 (1933).

M. OLIGOAMIDES

1 - Oligoamides of β-Alanine (Nylon 3)

1.1 - Linear Oligoamides

$$H[NH(CH_2)_2CO]_nOH$$

n	Mol. Wt.	m. p. °C	Ref.
1	89.1	206 (d)	1
2	160.2	212	2,4
3	231.2	>255 (d)	3,4
4	302.3	>260 (d)	4
5	373.4	>310 (d)	5
6	444.5	>320 (d)	5

1.2 - Cyclic Oligoamides

$$[NH(CH_2)_2CO]_n$$

n	Mol. Wt.	m. p. °C	Ref.
1	71.1	74-74.5	6,7
2	142.2	298-299	4,8,9
3	213.2	>350	4,10
4	284.3	>350	4,10
5	355.4	>350	5
6	426.5	>350	5

2 - Oligoamides of γ-Aminobutyric Acid (Nylon 4)

2.1 - Linear Oligoamides

$$H[NH(CH_2)_3CO]_nOH$$

n	Mol. Wt.	m. p. °C	Ref.
1	103.1	204-205	11
2	188.2	186	4,12
3	273.3	198-199	4
4	358.4	202-203	4

2.2 - Cyclic Oligoamides

$$[NH(CH_2)_3CO]_n$$

n	Mol. Wt.	m. p. °C	Ref.
1	85.1	24	13,14
2	170.2	283	4,10
3	255.3	242-243	4,10
4	340.4	255	4,10
6	510.6	295	10

References page VII-58

2.3 - Anionic Oligoamides

$$C_6H_5CO-[NH(CH_2)_3CO]_n-N\underset{OC}{\overset{}{\underset{}{\diagdown}}}(CH_2)_3$$

n	Mol. Wt.	m. p. °C	Ref.
0	189.2	92.5	15
1	274.3	121	16

3 - Oligoamides of δ-Aminovaleric Acid (Nylon 5)

3.1 - Linear Oligoamides

$$H[NH(CH_2)_4CO]_nOH$$

n	Mol. Wt.	m. p. °C	Ref.
1	117.2	160-162	17
2	216.3	178	18
3	315.4	184-185.5	18
4	414.5	196.5-198.5	18

3.2 - Cyclic Oligoamides

$$\left[\overline{[NH(CH_2)_4CO]_n}\right]$$

n	Mol. Wt.	m. p. °C	Ref.
1	98.1	39-40	14,17, 19
2	198.3	295-296	8,18
3	297.4	329-331	18
4	396.5	266-267	18

4 - Oligoamides of ε-Aminocaproic Acid (Nylon 6)

4.1 - Linear Oligoamides*

$$H[NH(CH_2)_5CO]_nOH$$

n	Mol. Wt.	m. p. °C	Ref.
1	131.2	206-208	20,21
2	244.3	198-199	22,23,24
3	357.5	203-204	23,24,25
4	470.7	206-207	23,24
5	583.8	207-208	23
6	697.0	209-210	23,24
7	810.1	209-210	23
8	923.3	210-211	23
9	1036.5	208-211	26
10	1149.6	212-213	26
11	1262.8	209-212	26
12	1375.9	211-213	26

* Taken from H. Zahn and C. D. Gleitsmann, Angew. Chem. 75, 772 (1963),

4.2 - Cyclic Oligoamides

$$\left[[NH(CH_2)_5CO]_n \right]$$

n	Mol. Wt.	m. p. °C	TCW[x]	R_F EAW[xx]		Ref.
1	113.2	69.5	0.56	0.88		14,17,27
2	226.3	348	0.48	0.81		4,24,28,29
3	339.5	244	0.34	0.77		4,24,28,29
4	452.6	256-257	0.25	0.69		4,24,28,29
5	565.8	254	0.16	0.59		4,24,29
6	678.9	260	0.10	0.49		4,24,29
7	792.1	236	0.08	0.40		29,30
8	905.3	226-230	0.04			29,30
9	1018.4	224-226	0.02			29,30

[x] Solvent: Tetrahydrofuran/cyclohexane/water (186/14/10);

[xx] Solvent: Ethyl acetate/acetone/water (10/10/2).

4.3 - Endgroup Protected Oligoamides*

$$C_2H_5CO-[NH(CH_2)_5CO]_n-NHC_3H_7$$

n	Mol. Wt.	m. p. °C	Ref.
1	228.3	106	31
2	341.5	149	31
3	454.7	172	31
4	567.8	181	31
5	681.0	191	31
6	794.2	191	31
7	907.3	197	31
8	1020.5	200	31
9	1133.6	201	31
10	1246.8	201	31
11	1360.0	204	31
12	1473.1	202	31
13	1586.3	200	31
14	1699.3	205	31
15	1812.6	206	31
16	1925.8	206	31

4.4 - Anionic Oligoamides

$$CH_3CO-[NH(CH_2)_5CO]_n-N \underset{OC}{\overset{|}{\underset{}{}}}(CH_2)_5$$

n	Mol. Wt.	b. p. °C/mm	R_F^x	Ref.
0	135.1	133-134/16		32
1	268.3		0.76	33
2	381.5		0.67	33
3	494.7		0.58	33

[x] Solvent: Tetrahydrofuran/cyclohexane/ water (186/14/10).

---

* Taken from H. Zahn and G. B. Gleitsmann, Angew. Chem. 75, 772 (1963).

References page VII-58

5 - Oligoamides of the Higher ω-Amino
    Acids (Nylon 7,8,9,10,11,12)

5.1 - Linear Oligoamides

$$H[NH(CH_2)_x CO]_n OH$$

x	n	Mol. Wt.	m. p. °C	Ref.
6	1	145.2	195	34,35
	2	272.4	205-208	36
7	1	159.2	188	4,37
	2	300.4	191-192	4,38
8	1	173.3	184	4,34
	2	328.5	184-186	4
10	1	201.3	186-187	34,38
	2	384.6	187-188	4,40
	3	567.9	191	5,40
	4	751.2	177-179	40
11	1	215.3	186-187	41
	2	412.6	192-193	31

5.2 - Cyclic Oligoamides

$$[[NH(CH_2)_x CO]_n]$$

x	n	Mol. Wt.	m. p. °C	Ref.
6	1	127.2	29-30	14,17,42
	2	254.4	236-237	4,10
7	1	141.2	72-73	13,14,34,42
	2	282.4	277	4,10
8	1	155.3	138-139	14,42
	2	310.5	201	4,10
9	1	169.3	162	14,42
	2	338.4	230	10
10	1	183.3	155	42,43
	2	366.6	188-189	4,44
	3	549.9	183-184	44
11	1	197.3	155	13,14,42,45
	2	394.6	201-202	31
	3	531.9	175	31

6 - Oligoamides of Anthranilic Acid

6.1 - Linear Oligoamides

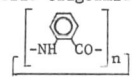

$$H[HN \quad CO]_n OH$$

n	Mol. Wt.	m. p. °C	Ref.
1	137.1	146.1	46,47,48
2	256.3	203-204 (d)	46
3	375.4	228 (d)	46
4	494.5	d	46

6.2 - Cyclic Oligoamides

$$[-NH \quad CO-]_n]$$

n	Mol. Wt.	m. p. °C	Ref.
2	238.3	330	47

7 - Cyclic Diamides of Aliphatic Dicarboxylic Acids and Diamines

$$\left[NH(CH_2)_x NH-CO(CH_2)_x CO \right]_n$$

x	n	Mol. Wt.	m. p. °C	Ref.
3	2	170.2	268	49,50
4	2	198.3	295	49,51
5	2	226.3	303	49
6	2	254.3	234	49,51
7	2	282.4	256	49
8	2	310.5	205	8,49
9	2	338.5	224	49
10	2	366.6	191	8,49

8 - Oligoamides of Adipic Acid and Hexamethylenediamine (Nylon 6,6)

8.1 - Linear Oligoamino Acids*

$$H[NH(CH_2)_6 NH-CO(CH_2)_4 CO]_n OH$$

n	Mol. Wt.	m. p. °C	Ref.
1	244.3	193	52,53
2	470.7	221-22	52,33
3	696.9	246-248	52,53
4	923.3	246-248	31
5	1149.5	247-252	31

8.2 - Cyclic Oligoamides

$$\left[NH(CH_2)_6 NH-CO(CH_2)_4 CO \right]_n$$

n	Mol.	m. p.	TCW^x	R_F	EAW^{xx}	Ref.
1	226.3	254	0.47		0.51	51,53, 54,55
2	452.6	243-244	0.28		0.38	53,54, 55
3	678.9	235	0.13		0.23	31,53, 55
4	905.3	236-239	0.06		0.16	31,53

x   Solvent: Tetrahydrofuran/cyclo-hexane/water (186/14/10);

xx Solvent: Ethyl acetate/acetone/water (10/10/2).

8.3 - Endgroup Protected Oligoamides

8.3.1 - Oligomeric Dicarboxylic Acid Dipropylamides

$$C_3H_7NH-CO(CH_2)_4CO-[NH(CH_2)_6NH-CO(CH_2)_4CO]_n-NHC_3H_7$$

n	Mol. Wt.	m. p. °C	Ref.
1	454.7	229-230	31
2	681.0	245-247	31
3	907.3	247-248	31
4	1133.6	248-250	31
5	1359.9	248-251	31

8.3.2 - Oligomeric Dipropionyl Diamines

$$C_2H_5CO-[NH(CH_2)_6NH-CO(CH_2)_4CO]_n-NH(CH_2)_6NH-COC_2H_5$$

n	Mol. Wt.	m. p. °C	Ref.
1	454.7	202-203	31
2	681.0	222-227	31
3	907.3	225-228	31

* Taken from H. Zahn and G. B. Gleitsmann, Angew. Chem. 75, 772 (1963).

References page VII-58

8.4 - Oligomeric Diamines*

$H[NH(CH_2)_6NH-CO(CH_2)_4CO]_n-NH(CH_2)_6NH_2 \cdot 2HCL$

n	Mol. Wt.	m. p. °C	Ref.
1	415.4	248-250	31
2	641.7	249-251	31
3	868.0	254-255	31
5	1320.6	236-240	31

8.5 - Oligomeric Dicarboxylic Acids*

$HOOC(CH_2)_4CO \cdot [NH(CH_2)_6NH-CO(CH_2)_4CO]_nOH$

n	Mol. Wt.	m. p. °C	Ref.
1	372.4	188-189	56
2	598.7	200-205	56,57
3	825.0	210-211	56
4	1051.3	214-219	31

9 - Oligoamides of Sebacic Acid and Hexamethylenediamine (Nylon 6,10)*

9.1 - Linear Oligoamino Acids

$H[NH(CH_2)_6NH-CO(CH_2)_8CO]_nOH$

n	Mol. Wt.	m. p. °C	Ref.
1	300.4	187-188	58
2	582.8	198-201	58
3	865.3	201-205	58

9.2 - Cyclic Oligoamides

$[\overline{[NH(CH_2)_6NH-CO(CH_2)_8CO]_n}]$

n	Mol. Wt.	m. p. °C	Ref.
1	282.4	227-228	51
2	564.8	223-225	58

9.3 - Oligomeric Diamines

$H[NH(CH_2)_6NH-CO(CH_2)_8CO]_n-NH(CH_2)_6-NH_2$

n	Mol. Wt.	m. p. °C	Ref.
1	398.6	129-131	57,58
2	681.1	177-179	58
3	963.5	203-210	58

9.4 - Oligomeric Dicarboxylic Acids

$HOOC(CH_2)_8CO-[NH(CH_2)_6NH-CO(CH_2)_8CO]_nOH$

n	Mol. Wt.	m. p. °C	Ref.
1	494.6	156-159	57,58
2	767.1	182-184	57,58
3	1049.5	181-185	58

---

* Taken from H. Zahn and G. B. Gleitsmann, Angew. Chem. 75, 772 (1963).

REFERENCES

1. J. H. Ford, Org. Syn., Coll. Vol. III, 34; T. W. J. Taylor, J. Chem. Soc. 1928, 1898.
2. H. Th. Hanson and E. L. Smith, J. Biol. Chem. 175, 883 (1948).
3. E. Adams, N. C. Davis, and E. L. Smith, J. Biol. Chem. 199, 845 (1952).
4. M. Rothe, Habilitationsschrift, Universität Halle, Germany, 1960.
5. M. Rothe unpublished data.
6. R. W. Holley and A. D. Holley, J. Am. Chem. Soc. 71, 2129 (1949).
7. S. Searles, Jr. and R. E. Wann, Chem. Ind. (London) 1964, 2097.
8. M. Rothe and R. Timler, Chem. Ber. 95, 783 (1962).
9. H. K. Hall, Jr., J. Am. Chem. Soc. 80, 6404 (1958).
10. M. Rothe, Angew. Chem. 74, 725 (1962).
11. C. C. DeWitt, Org. Syn., Coll. Vol. II, 25 (1943).
12. R. L. Evans and F. Irreverre, J. Org. Chem. 24, 863 (1959); S. Murahashi, H. Sekiguchi, and H. Yuki, Compt. Rend. 248, 1521 (1959).
13. K. Dachs and E. Schwarz, Angew. Chem. 74, 540 (1962).
14. R. Huisgen, H. Brade, H. Walz, and I. Glogger, Chem. Ber. 90, 1437 (1957).
15. S. J. Kanewskaja, Ber. Deut. Chem. Ges. 69, 266 (1936).
16. H. Sekiguchi, Bull. Soc. Chim. France 1960, 1835.
17. O. Wallach, Liebigs Ann. Chem. 312, 171 (1900); 324, 281 (1902).
18. M. Rothe and R. Hossbach, Makromol. Chem. 70, 140 (1964).
19. N. Yoda and A. Miyake, J. Polymer Sci. 43, 117 (1960).
20. S. Gabriel and A. Maass, Ber. Deut. Chem. Ges. 32, 1266 (1899).
21. J. C. Eck, Org. Syn., Coll. Vol. II 28 (1943); C. Y. Myers and L. E. Miller, Org. Syn. 32, 13 (1952).
22. G. M. van der Want and A. Staverman, Rec. Trav. Chim. 71, 379 (1952).
23. H. Zahn and D. Hildebrand, Chem. Ber. 90, 320 (1957).
24. M. Rothe and F.-W. Kunitz, Liebigs. Ann. Chem. 609, 88 (1957).
25. M. van der Want, A. Staverman, and P. Inklaar, Rec. Trav. Chim. 71, 1252 (1952).
26. H. Zahn and H. Hildebrand, Chem. Ber. 92, 1963 (1959).
27. C. S. Marvel, Org. Syn., Coll. Vol. II, 371 (1943).
28. P. H. Hermans, Rec. Trav. Chim 72, 798 (1953).
29. I. Rothe and M. Rothe, Chem. Ber. 88, 284 (1955); M. Rothe, J. Polymer Sci. 30, 227 (1958).
30. H. Zahn and J. Kunde, Liebigs Ann. Chem. 70, 189 (1958).
31. H. Zahn and G. B. Gleitsmann, Angew. Chem. 75, 772 (1963).
32. H. A. Offe, Z. Naturforsch. 2b, 183 (1947).
33. K. Gehrke, Faserforsch. Textiltech. 13, 557 (1962).
34. D. D. Coffman, N. L. Cox, E. L. Martin, W. E. Mochel, and F. J. van Natta, J. Polymer Sci. 3, 85 (1948).
35. C. F. Horn, B. T. Freure, H. Vineyard, and H. J. Decker, Angew. Chem. 74, 531 (1962).
36. M. Rothe and R. Hossbach, unpublished data.
37. A. G. Goldsobel, Ber. Deut. Chem. Ges. 27, 3121 (1894).
38. T. Gäumann and Hs. H. Günthard, Helv. Chim. Acta, 35, 53 (1952).
39. M. Genas, Angew. Chem. 74, 535 (1962).
40. H. Zahn, H. Roedel, and J. Kunde, J. Polymer Sci. 36, 539 (1959).
41. A. Neuberger, Proc. Roy. Soc. [A] 158, 84 (1937).
42. L. Ruzicka, M. Kobelt, O. Häfliger, and V. Prelog, Helv. Chim. Acta. 32, 544 (1949).
43. W. Ziegenbein and W. Lang, Angew. Chem. 74, 943 (1962).
44. H. Zahn and J. Kunde, Chem. Ber. 94, 2470 (1961).
45. G. Wilke, Angew. Chem. 75, 10 (1963).
46. H. Meyer, Liebigs Ann. Chem. 351, 267 (1907).
47. G. Schroeter and O. Eisleb, Liebigs Ann. Chem. 367, 101 (1909); Ber. Deut. Chem. Ges. 52, 2224 (1919).
48. E. Mohr, F. Köhler, and H. Ulrich, J. Prakt. Chem. 79, 281 (1909); 80, 1 (1909).
49. J. Dale and R. Coulon, J. Chem. Soc. 1964, 182.
50. G. J. Glover and H. Rapoport, J. Am. Chem. Soc. 86, 3397 (1964).
51. H. Stetter and J. Marx, Liebigs. Ann. Chem. 607, 59 (1957).
52. H. Zahn and F. Schmidt, Makromol. Chem. 36, 1 (1959).
53. I. Rothe and M. Rothe, Makromol. Chem. 68, 206 (1963).
54. H. Zahn and F. Schmidt, Chem. Ber. 92, 1381 (1959); H. Zahn, P. Miro, and F. Schmidt, Chem. Ber. 90, 1411 (1957).
55. M. Rothe, I. Rothe, H. Brünig, and K. D. Schwenke, Angew. Chem. 71, 700 (1959).
56. H. Zahn and W. Lauer, Makromol. Chem. 23, 85 (1957).
57. C. D. Cowell, Chem. Ind. (London) 1954, 577.
58. H. Zahn and G. B. Gleitsmann, Makromol. Chem. 60, 45 (1963).

N. OLIGOSACCHARIDES

1 - Oligomeric Pentoses

1.1 - Oligo(β-xylopyranoses) (Ref. 1-3)

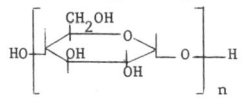

n	Mol. Wt.	m. p. °C	$[\alpha]_D^{25}$
1	150.1	153	+19.2
2	282.2	186-187	-25.6
3	414.4	215-216	-48.1
4	546.5	224-226	-61.9
5	678.6	240-242	-72.9
6	810.7	237-242	-78.5
7	942.8	240-242	-74

1.2 - Oligo(β-xylopyranose) Acetates (Ref. 1-3)

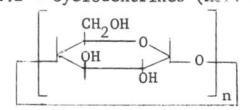

n	Mol. Wt.	m. p. °C	Specific Rotation $[\alpha]_D^{25}$	c in CHCl_3
1	318.3			
2	534.5	155.5-156.5	-74.5	0.9
3	750.7	109-110	-84.3	0.6
4	966.9	201-202	-93.7	0.8
5	1183.1	249-250	-97.5	1.1
6	1399.3	260-261	-102.0	1.5

2 - Oligomeric Hexoses

2.1 - Maltooligooses (Ref. 4-6)

n	Mol. Wt.	m. p. °C	$[\alpha]_D^{15}$ in H_2O
1	180.2	146	+ 52.6
2	342.3	160-165	+136.0
3	504.4		+160.0
4	666.6		+177.0
5	828.7		+180.3
6	990.9		+184.7
7	1153.0		+186.4

2.2 - Cyclodextrines (Ref. 4-6)

n	Mol. Wt.	$[\alpha]_D$ (c=1,H_2O)
6	972.8	149
7	1135.0	158.8
8	1297.1	170.0

2.3 - Cellooligooses (Ref. 7-14)

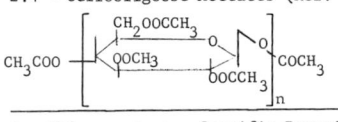

n	Mol. Wt.	m. p. °C	Specific Rotation		
			$[\alpha]_D$	°C	c in H_2O
1	180.2	150	+52.5	20	4
2	342.3	225 (d)	+34.6	20	8
3	504.4	238 (d)	+21.6	26	4
4	666.6	252-253 (d)	+16.5	23	3.4
5	828.7	266-268 (d)	+11.0	30	4.1
6	990.9	275-278 (d)	+10.0	30	1.2
7	1153.0	283-286 (d)	+ 7±3	30	0.1

2.4 - Cellooligoose Acetates (Ref. 7-14)

CH_3COO

n	Mol. Wt.	m. p. °C	Specific Rotation $[\alpha]_D^{20-25}$ in $CHCl_3$ (c>5)
1	390.4	113	+101.6
2	678.6	229.5	+ 41.0
3	966.9	223-224	+ 22.6
4	1255.1	230-234	+ 13.4
5	1543.4	240-241	+ 4.2
6	1831.6	252-255	- 0.2
7	2119.8	263-266	- 4.4

2.5 - Isomaltooligooses (Ref. 15)

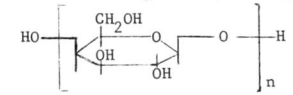

n	Mol. Wt.	m. p. °C	$[\alpha]_D$ in H_2O
1	180.2	146	+52.6
2	342.3	225 (d)	
3	504.4		
4	666.6		+153
5	828.7		+160
6	990.9		+163

2.6 - Gentiooligooses (Ref. 15)

n	Mol. Wt.	m. p. °C	$[\alpha]_D$ in H_2O
1	180.2	150	+52.5
2	342.3	190-195	+ 9.6
3	504.4		-10.5
4	666.6		-19.5

2.7 - Galaktooligooses (Ref. 15)

n	Mol. Wt.	m. p. °C	$[\alpha]_D^{25}$ in H_2O
1	180.2	167	+52.5
2	342.3	210-211	+173
3	504.4	115-120	+58
4	666.6		+53

2.8 - Mannooligooses (Ref. 16,17)   3 - Oligomeric Amino Sugars

3.1 - N-Acetyl Chitooligooses (Ref. 18,19)

n	Mol. Wt.	m. p. °C	Specific Rotation [α]$_D$ °C	c in H$_2$O
1	180.2	132		
2	342.3	193-194	- 7.7 25	0.9
3	504.4	137-137.5	-23.3 25	1.3
4	666.6	232-234	-31	1.6

n	Mol. Wt.	m. p. °C	Specific Rotation [α]$_D$	c in H$_2$O
1	221.2			
2	424.4	260-262(d)	+17.2	0.5
3	627.6	290-311(d)	+ 2.2	0.9
4	830.8	290-300(d)	- 4.1	1.0
5	1034.0	285-295(d)	- 9.1	1.0
6	1237.2		-11.4	0.8
7	1440.4		-12.6	0.3

REFERENCES

1. R. L. Whistler and C.-C. Tu, J. Am. Chem. Soc. 74, 4334 (1952).
2. R. H. Marchessault and T. E. Timell, J. Polymer Sci. 2, C, 49 (1963).
3. C. T. Bishop, Can. J. Chem. 33, 1073 (1955).
4. W. J. Whelan, J. M. Bailey, and P. J. P. Roberts, J. Chem. Soc. 1953, 1293
5. J. M. Bailey, W. J. Whelan, and S. Peart, J. Chem. Soc. 1950, 3692.
6. K. Freudenberg and F. Cramer, Chem. Ber. 83, 296 (1950).
7. E. E. Dickey and M. L. Wolfrom, J. Am. Chem. Soc. 71, 825 (1949).
8. M. L. Wolfrom and J. C. Dacons, J. Am. Chem. Soc. 74, 5331 (1952).
9. L. Zechmeister and G. Tóth, Ber. Deut. Chem. Ges. 64, 854 (1931).
10. K. Hess and K. Dziengel, Ber. Deut. Chem. Ges. 68, 1594 (1935).
11. C. S. Hudson and J. M. Johnson, J. Am. Chem. Soc. 37, 1276 (1915).
12. R. Willstätter and L. Zechmeister, Ber. Deut. Chem. Ges. 46, 2401 (1913), 62, 722 (1929).
13. K. Freudenberg and G. Blomqvist, Ber. Deut. Chem. Ges. 68, 2070 (1935).
14. H. Staudinger and E. V. Leupold, Ber. Deut. Chem. Ges. 67, 479 (1934).
15. W. Walter, in H. M. Rauen, Ed., Biochemisches Taschenbuch, Part 1, 2nd ed., Springer, Berlin-Göttingen-Heidelberg, 1964, p. 98.
16. R. L. Whistler and C. G. Smith, J. Am. Chem. Soc. 74, 3795 (1952).
17. R. L. Whistler and J. Z. Stein, J. Am. Chem. Soc. 73, 4187 (1951).
18. S. A. Barker, A. B. Foster, M. Stacey, and J. M. Webber, J. Chem. Soc. 1958, 2218.
19. H. P. Lenk, M. Wenzel, and E. Schütte, Z. Physiol. Chem. 326, 116 (1961).

VIII.
PHYSICAL PROPERTIES OF
MONOMERS AND SOLVENTS

PHYSICAL PROPERTIES OF MONOMERS

Y. P. Castille*

Research Triangle Institute
Durham, N. C.

This table contains some of the principal physical properties of monomers with carbon-carbon double bonds. The monomers were arranged alphabetically many derivatives being grouped together under the same parent compound by placing the substituting atoms or groups after the parent name. Compounds were listed under their most commonly used name in polymer chemistry. Therefore, the names used are not always in agreement with the rules of the International Union of Chemistry. No special annotations have been added to distinguish between international union and common names.

Molecular Weights are computed according to the International Atomic Weight values.

Densities are relative to water and are given in grams per milliliter at the indicated temperature. The reference temperature of the water is $4°C$, except as otherwise stated.

Melting and Boiling points are given in degrees centigrade ($°C$). The boiling points are stated at atmospheric pressure unless otherwise indicated by a superscript which shows the pressure (in mm of Hg) under which the compound boils at the given temperature.

Refractive index is determined at the stated temperature and is reported for the D line of the spectrum of sodium (n_D).

Vapor pressure is given in mm mercury at the temperature indicated by superscript.

The physical data in this table were collected from the open literature, technical information sheets and patents. Various sources sometimes gave different values which have been added in parentheses. Being aware of the incompleteness of this list, several discontinuities in the numeration have been reserved for future completion.

Abbreviations:

aa	acetic acid	o	ortho
Ac	acetone	OS	organic solvents
Alc	alcohol	p	para
Bz	benzene	polym	polymerizes
Chl	chloroform	ss	slightly soluble
calc	calculated	s	soluble
cond	concentrated	subl	sublimes
d	decomposes	unst	unstable
eth	ether	unsym	unsymmetrical
exp	explodes	vs	very soluble
frz	freezes	w	water
h	hot	<	below
i	insoluble	∞	soluble in all proportions
m	meta		

* Present address: E. I. du Pont de Nemours & Co.
Textile Fiber Department
Wilmington, Delaware

No.	Name	Synonyms and Formula	Mol. Wt.	Density
1	Acetylene	ethyne $HC\vdots CH$	26.04	0.6181^{-82}
2	--,chloro-	ethynyl chloride $HC\vdots CCl$	60.48	..
3	--,dichloro-	$ClC\vdots CCl$	94.93	..
4	--,diphenyl-	$C_6H_5C\vdots CC_6H_5$	178.24	0.9657^{100}
5	Acrolein	propenal; acrylaldehyde; acrylic aldehyde; $CH_2\vdots CHCHO$	56.06	$0.8406^{20/20}$ $0.8625^{20/0}$
6	--,1-chloro-	2-chloropropenal; $CH_2\vdots CClCHO$	90.51	1.199^{20}
7	--,1-methyl-	methacrolein; $CH_2\vdots C(CH_3)CHO$ 2-methylpropenal	70.09	0.837^{20} $0.8474^{20/20}$
8	--,2-methyl-	2-butenal; crotonaldehyde; $CH_3CH\vdots CHCHO$	70.09	0.8575^{15}
9	--,--,1-chloro-	2-chloro-2-butenal; $CH_3CH\vdots CClCHO$	104.54	1.1404^{23}
10	Acrylaldehyde	See Acrolein		
11	Acrylamide	propenamide; $CH_2\vdots CHCONH_2$	71.08	1.122^{30}
12	--,1-methyl-	methacrylamide; $CH_2\vdots C(CH_3)CONH_2$	85.10	..
13	--,2-methyl-	2-butenamide; crotonamide; $CH_3CH\vdots CHCONH_2$	85.10	..
14	Acrylates	See Acrylic acid, esters		
15	Acrylic acid	propenoic acid; $CH_2\vdots CHCO_2H$ ethylenecarboxylic acid	72.06	$1.0472^{20/20}$ 1.0511^{20}
16	--,allyl ester	$CH_2\vdots CHCO_2CH_2CH\vdots CH_2$	112.13	1.0452^{20}
17	--,benzyl ester	$CH_2\vdots CHCO_2CH_2C_6H_5$	162.18	1.068^{20}
18	--,butyl ester	$CH_2\vdots CHCO_2C_4H_9$	128.17	0.8986^{20} 0.894^{25}
19	--,2-cyanoethyl ester	$CH_2\vdots CHCO_2CH_2CH_2CN$	125.13	$1.0690^{20/20}$
20	--,cyclohexyl ester	$CH_2\vdots CHCO_2C_6H_{11}$	154.21	1.0275^{20}
21	--,ethyl ester	$CH_2\vdots CHCO_2C_2H_5$	100.11	0.924^{20} $0.9230^{20/20}$
22	--,2-ethyl hexyl ester	$CH_2\vdots CHCO_2CH_2CH(C_2H_5)C_4H_9$	184.28	$0.8869^{20/20}$
23	--,isobutyl ester	$CH_2\vdots CHCO_2CH_2CH(CH_3)_2$	128.17	0.8896^{20}
24	--,methyl ester	$CH_2\vdots CHCO_2CH_3$	86.09	0.9558^{18} 0.953^{20}
34	--,chloride	propenoyl chloride: $CH_2\vdots CHCOCl$ acrylyl chloride	90.51	1.14^{0}
35	--,1-chloro-	2-chloropropenoic acid	106.51	..
36	--,--,ethyl ester	$CH_2\vdots CClCO_2C_2H_5$	134.56	..

No.	Boiling point, °C	Melting point, °C	Refractive index	Vapor pressure	w	alc	eth	
1	-83.6; subl	-81.8	1.00051^0	..	ss	ss	.	s:Chl
2	-32	-126	..	..	d	s	.	
3	exp	-66	..	..	.	s	s	
4	-170^{19}; 300^{760}	63.5	..	..	i	ss	vs	
5	52.69 (52.5-3.5)	-86.9 (-87.7)	1.3998^{20} $(1.4013^{20}$	213.84^{20}	vs	s	s	
6	40^{30}		1.463^{20}	..	.	.	vs	vs:CCl_4
7	68.4	-81.5	1.4169^{20} (1.4191^{20})	118.9^{20}	∞	∞	∞	
8	104-5	-69;frz-74	$1.4383^{17.3}$ 1.4373^{20}	..	vs	∞	∞	∞:Bz
9	147-8	..	1.478^{23}	..	ss	s	s	s:CCl_4 s:Chl_4
10								
11	125^{25}; 116.5^{10}	84.8	..	0.14^{40}	vs	.	s	vs:Chl
12	..	110	..	..	.	s	ss	
13	..	158	..	..	ss	s	ss	s:Bz
14								
15	48.5^{15};39^{10}; 141.3	12.3	1.4224^{20}	3.1^{20}	∞	∞	∞	
16	122; 72^{27}	..	1.4390^{9}	..	ss	.	.	s:Ac
17	$113-4^{19}$;94^{6}; 228	..	1.513^{24} 1.5143^{20}	..	i	s	s	
18	39^{10}; 69^{50} 146-8(polym)	-64	1.4187^{20} 1.4156^{25}	3.3^{20}	i	s	s	
19	103^{10}	-16.9	1.4433^{20}	0.03^{20}				
20	$182-4$;88^{20}	..	1.4673^{20}	..	i	∞	∞	
21	99.6	-75	1.4054^{20}	29.5^{20}	s	∞	∞	
22	90^{10},215(polym)	-90	1.4350^{20} 1.4330^{25}	<1				
23	70^{60}	..	1.4150^{20}	..	i	∞	∞	
24	79.6-80.2	<-75	1.3984^{20} (1.4022^{20})	68.2^{20}	ss	s	s	
34	75-6	..	1.4343^{20}	..	d	.	.	vs:Chl
35	176-81(d)	65	..	..	s	s	s	
36	$51-3^{18}$	..	..	..	.	vs	vs	

No.	Name	Synonyms and Formula	Mol. Wt.	Density
	Acrylic acid			
37	--,--,methyl ester	$CH_2:CClCO_2CH_3$	120.54	1.189 [20]
38	--,--,phenyl ester	$CH_2:CClCO_2C_6H_5$	182.61	..
39	--,2-chloro- cis	3-chloropropenoic acid; $ClCH:CHCO_2H$	106.51	..
40	- trans	"　　"　　"　　"	106.51	..
41	--,1,2-dichloro-	$ClCH:CClCO_2H$	140.96	..
42	--,2,2-dichloro-	$Cl_2C:CHCO_2H$	140.96	..
43	--,2,2-difluoro-	$F_2C:CHCO_2H$	108.04	..
44	--,--,ethyl ester	$F_2C:CHCO_2C_2H_5$	136.09	..
45	--,1-fluoro-	$CH_2:CFCO_2H$	90.05	..
46	--,--,methyl ester	$CH_2:CFCO_2CH_3$	104.08	..
47	--,--,2-difluoro-	$F_2C:CFCO_2H$	126.03	..
48	--,1-methyl-	See Methacrylic acid		
49	--,2-methyl- cis	isocrotonic acid $CH_3CH:CHCO_2H$	86.09	1.0312 [15]
50	- trans	crotonic acid	86.09	1.018 [20]
51	--,1-trifluoromethyl-	$CH_2:C(CF_3)CO_2H$	140.07	....
52	--,--,methyl ester	$CH_2:C(CF_3)CO_2CH_3$	154.09	....
60	Acrylic aldehyde	See Acrolein		
61	Acrylonitrile	propenenitrile; $CH_2:CHCN$ vinyl cyanide	53.06	0.8060 [20] 0.8075 [20/20]
62	--,1-chloro- 2-difluoro-	$F_2C:CClCN$	123.48	..
63	--,1-difluoromethyl-	$CH_2:C(CHF_2)CN$	103.06	..
64	--,1-fluoro-	$CH_2:CFCN$	71.04	..
65	--,1-methyl-	methacrylonitrile $CH_2:C(CH_3)CN$	67.09	0.805 [25] 0.7998 [20]
66	--,2-methyl-	2-butenenitrile; $CH_3CH:CHCN$ propenyl cyanide	67.09	0.8239 [20] 0.826 [23]
67	--,1-trifluoromethyl-	$CH_2:C(CF_3)CN$	121.06	..
68	Acrylyl chloride	See Acrylic acid, chloride		
69	Allyl acetate	$CH_3CO_2CH_2CH:CH_2$	100.12	0.9276 [20]
70	Allylacetic acid	4-pentenoic acid; $CH_2:CHCH_2CH_2CO_2H$	100.12	0.9843 [18]
71	Allylacetonitrile	allylmethyl cyanide; 4-pentene-nitrile; $CH_2:CHCH_2CH_2CN$	81.12	1.1803 [13]

No.	Boiling point, °C	Melting point, °C	Refractive index	Vapor pressure	Solubility w	alc	eth
37	57-9 [55]	..	1.4420^{20}	..	.	.	vs
38	91-3 [8]	..	1.5808^{20}	..			
39	..	63-4	..	..	.	s	s
40	..	86	..	..	.	s	s
41	..	85-6	..	..	vs	vs	vs ss:Bz
42	subl.	76-7	..	..	ss	.	vs vs:Chl
43	..	..	..	..			
44	90.5-91.7	..	1.3869^{20}	..			
45	..	51.5-2	..	..			
46	92.5-3.5	..	1.3870^{25}	..			
47	..	35.5-6.5	..	..			
48							
49	171.9(d)	14-5	1.4457^{20}	..	vs	s	.
50	189	72	$1.4228^{79.7}$	..	vs	vs	.
51	146-8	50.2	..	..			
52	103.8-5.0	..	1.3370^{20}	..			
60							
61	77.3 (77.5-9)	-83.6 (-82)	1.393^{20} 1.3888^{25}	83^{20}	s	ω	∞
62	63	..	1.3793^{24}	..			
63	43-8	..	..	..			
64	17.7-18	..	1.3162^{10}	..			
65	90.3	-35.8 (-40)	1.4013^{30} 1.4007^{20}	16^{0}; 48.3^{20} 123^{40}	i	∞	∞
66	118-9	..	1.4242^{20}	..	i	vs	vs
67	75.9-76.2	..	1.3239^{20}	..			
68							
69	103.5	..	1.4049^{20}	..	ss	∞	∞
70	187-9	<-18	$1.4341^{7.5}$	..	ss	vs	vs
71	140	..	..	..	i	∞	∞

No.	Name	Synonyms and Formula	Mol. Wt.	Density
72	Allyl acrylate	See Acrylic acid, allyl ester		
73	Allyl alcohol	2-propen-1-ol; $CH_2:CHCH_2OH$	58.09	0.8540_{20} $0.8533^{20}/_{20}$
74	--,2-bromo-	$CH_2:CBrCH_2OH$	136.98	1.6^{15}
75	--,2-chloro-	$CH_2:CClCH_2OH$	92.53	1.162^{20}
76	--,3-chloro-	$CHCl:CHCH_2OH$	92.53	1.162
77	--,3-methyl	2-buten-1-ol; crotyl alcohol propenylcarbinol;$CH_3CH:CHCH_2OH$	72.10	0.8726_0 0.854^{20}
78	Allylaldehyde	See Acrolein		
79	Allylamine	2-propenylamine; 3-aminopropene; $CH_2:CHCH_2NH_2$	57.09	0.7627^{20}
90	Allyl bromide	3-bromoprene; $CH_2:CHCH_2Br$	120.99	1.398^{20}
91	--,1-bromo-	2,3-dibromopropene; $CH_2:CBrCH_2Br$	199.89	1.934^{20}
92	Allylcarbylamine	See Allyl isocyanide		
93	Allyl chloride	3-chloroprene; $CH_2:CHCH_2Cl$ 1-chloro-2-propene	76.53	0.938^{20} $0.9392^{20}/_{20}$
94	--,1-chloro-	2,3-dichloropropene; $CH_2:CClCH_2Cl$	110.98	1.205^{25} 1.236^0
95	Allyl cyanide	3-butenenitrile; $CH_2:CHCH_2CN$ vinylacetonitrile	67.09	0.8318_{20} $0.8359^{20}/_{20}$
96	Allyl ether	diallyl ether; $CH_2:CHCH_2OCH_2CH:CH_2$	98.15	0.8260^{20}
97	Allyl ethyl ether	3-ethoxypropene; $CH_2:CHCH_2OC_2H_5$	86.13	0.7651^{20}
98	Allyl formate	$CH_2:CHCH_2OOCH$	86.09	0.948^{18}
99	Allyl fluoride	3-fluoropropene; $CH_2:CHCH_2F$	60.07	..
100	Allyl iodide	3-iodopropene; $CH_2:CHCH_2I$	167.99	1.8454^{22} $1.848^{12}/_{15}$
101	Allyl isocyanide	allylcarbylamine; $CH_2:CHCH_2NC$	67.09	0.794^{17}
102	Allyl isopropyl ether	$CH_2:CHCH_2OC_3H_7$	100.16	0.7764^{20}
103	Allylmethyl cyanide	See Allylacetonitrile		
104	Allyl methyl ether	3-methoxypropene; $CH_2:CHCH_2OCH_3$	72.11	$0.77^{11}/_{11}$
105	Allyl phenyl ether	$CH_2:CHCH_2OC_6H_5$	134.18	0.9832^{15}
106	--,4-chloro-	$ClC_6H_4OCH_2CH:CH_2$	168.62	1.131^{15}
107	--,2,4,6-tribromo-	$Br_3C_6H_2OCH_2CH:CH_2$	370.88	..
108	Allyl propyl ether	$CH_2:CHCH_2OC_3H_7$	100.16	0.7670^{20}

No.	Boiling point, °C	Melting point, °C	Refractive index	Vapor pressure	Solubility		
					w	alc	eth
72							
73	96-7	-129	1.41345^{20}	17.2^{25}	∞	∞	∞
74	152	..	..	..			
75	136-140	..	1.4588^{20}	..	d^h	s^h	.
76	153	..	..	..	ss	.	.
77	118 (117-20)	<-30	1.4240^{20}	..	b	...	∞
78							
79	53.2	-88.2	1.41943^{22}	..	∞	∞	∞ s:Chl
90	71.3	-119.4	1.4654^{20}	..	i	∞	∞
91	140	..	..	..			
92							
93	44.96	-134.5	1.4160^{20}	294.3^{20}	i	∞	∞ ∞:Ac / ∞:Bz
94	94	..	..	..	i	∞	∞
95	118.9	-84	1.40602^{20}	..	ss	∞	∞
96	94	..	..	..			
97	66^{761}	..	1.3881^{20}	..	i	∞	∞
98	83	..	..	..	ss	s	∞
99	-10	..	..	..	ss	∞	∞
100	103.1	-99.3	1.5540^{21}	..	i	s	s
101	106	..	..	..	ss	∞	∞
102	83-4	..	1.3946^{20}	..	.	.	∞
103							
104	$42.5\text{-}3^{757}$	..	1.3803^{20}	..	i	∞	∞
105	191.7^{760}	..	1.5218^{20}	..	i	s	∞
106	$106\text{-}7^{12}; d^{760}$	..	..	..	i	s	s s:Bz
107	..	33-4	..	..			
108	90-2	..	1.3919^{20}	..	s	∞	.

No.	Name	Synonyms and Formula	Mol. Wt.	Density
109	Allyl 2-tolyl ether	$CH_2:CHCH_2OC_6H_4CH_3$	148.21	0.9698 [15]
110	Allyl 3-tolyl ether	$CH_2:CHCH_2OC_6H_4CH_3$	148.21	0.965 [15]
111	Allyl 4-tolyl ether	$CH_2:CHCH_2OC_6H_4CH_3$	148.21	0.9728 [15]/15
132	Aminoethene	See Vinylamine		
133	Biisopropenyl	See 1,3-Butadiene-,2,3-dimethyl-		
134	Bivinyl	See 1,3-Butadiene		
135	Bromoethene	See Vinyl bromide		
136	Bromoprene	See 1,3-Butadiene-,2-bromo-		
137	1,2-Butadiene	methylallene; $CH_2:C:CHCH_3$	54.09	0.676 [0]
138	--,4-bromo-	$CH_2:C:CHCH_2Br$	133.00	1.4255 [20]
139	--,4-chloro-	$CH_2:C:CHCH_2Cl$	88.54	1.9891 [20]
140	--,4-iodo-	$CH_2:C:CHCH_2I$	179.99	1.7129[20]
141	--,3-methyl-	$CH_2:C:C(CH_3)_2$	68.11	0.6833 [20]
142	1,3-Butadiene	vinylethylene; erythrene; bi-ethylene; bivinyl; $CH_2:CHCH:CH_2$	54.09	0.6211 [20] 0.650 [-6]
143	--,2-bromo-	bromoprene; $CH_2:CBrCH:CH_2$	133.00	1.397 [20]
144	--,1-chloro-	$CH_2:CHCH:CHCl$	88.54	0.9606 [20]
145	--,--,2-methyl-	$CH_2:CHC(CH_3):CHCl$	102.57	0.9710 [20]
146	--,--,3-methyl-	$CH_2:C(CH_3)CH:CHCl$	102.57	0.9543 [20]
147	--,2-chloro-	$CH_2:CHCCl:CH_2$; chloroprene	88.54	0.9583[20]/20
148	--,--,3-methyl-	$CH_2:C(CH_3)CCl:CH_2$	102.57	0.9593 [20]
149	--,1,2-dichloro-	$CH_2:CHCCl:CHCl$	122.99	1.199 [15]
150	--,2,3-dichloro-	$CH_2:CClCCl:CH_2$	122.99	1.1829 [20]
151	--,2,3-dimethyl-	biisopropenyl; $CH_2:C(CH_3)C(CH_3):CH_2$	82.14	0.7262 [20]
152	--,2-fluoro-	fluoroprene; $CH_2:CHCF:CH_2$	72.08	0.843 [4]
153	--,hexachloro-	$CCl_2:CClCCl:CCl_2$	260.79	1.6820 [20]
154	--,hexafluoro-	$CF_2:CFCF:CF_2$	162.04	1.553 [-20]
155	--,2-iodo-	iodoprene; $CH_2:CHCI:CH_2$	179.99	1.7278 [20]
166	--,2-methyl-	See Isoprene		
167	2,3-Butadien-1-ol	$CH_2:C:CHCH_2OH$	70.09	0.9164 [20]
180	2-Butenal	See Acrolein, 2-methyl-		
181	2-Butenamide	See Acrylamide, 2-methyl-		
182	1-Butene	1-butylene; ethylethylene; $CH_3CH_2CH:CH_2$	56.104	0.668 [0] 0.5951 [20]

No.	Boiling point, °C	Melting point, °C	Refractive index	Vapor pressure	Solubility		
					w	alc	eth
109	205-8;85[12]	..	1.5188[15]	..			
110	211-4	..	..	..			
111	214.5[760]	..	..	..			
132							
133							
134							
135							
136							
137	18-9	-136.3	1.4205[20]	..	i	∞	∞
138	109-111	..	1.5248[20]	..			
139	88	..	1.4775[20]	..	ss		vs:OS
140	130	..	1.5709[20]	..			
141	40.5-41.5	-120	1.4166[20]	..			
142	-4.4	-108.9	1.4292[-25]	..	i	s	. s:OS
143	42-3(165)	..	1.4393[20]	..	i	s	s
144	68	..	1.4712[20]	..	.	.	. vs:Chl
145	99-101	..	1.4792[20]	..	.	vs[h]	. s:Ac
146	99-100	..	..	..	.	.	s s:Chl
147	59.4	..	1.4583[20]	..	ss	.	. s:OS
148	93	..	1.4686[20]	..		vs	vs:Chl
149	60-5[105]	..	1.5078[15]	..			vs:CCl$_4$
150	98	..	1.4890[20]	..			vs:Chl
151	75.9	-76.01	1.437717[20]	..			
152	12	..	1.400[4]	..			
153	215;101[20]	-21	1.5542[20]	..	i	s	s
154	6	-132	1.378[-20]	..			
155	111-3	..	1.5616[20]	..			
166							
167	126-8	..	1.4759[20]	..	s	vs	vs:OS
180							
181							
182	-6.3	-185.4	1.3962[20]	63.05[37.7]	i	vs	vs

No.	Name	Synonyms and Formula	Mol. Wt.	Density
183	--,4-bromo-	$BrCH_2CH_2CH:CH_2$	135.01	1.3230 [20]
184	--,2-methyl-	$CH_3CH_2C(CH_3):CH_2$	70.14	0.6623 [20]
185	2-Butene cis	2-butylene; pseudobutylene; $CH_3CH:CHCH_3$	56.104	0.6213 [20]
186	trans	" " " " ;	56.104	0.6041 [20]
187	--,2,3-dimethyl-	tetramethylethylene; $(CH_3)_2C:C(CH_3)_2$	84.16	0.712 [20]
188	--,1,4-diol-	$HOCH_2CH:CHCH_2OH$	88.10	1.067 [20]
189	2-Butenenitrile	See Acrylonitrile, 2-methyl-		
190	3-Butenenitrile	See Allyl cyanide		
191	3-Butenoic acid	See Vinyl acetic acid		
192	2-Buten-1-ol	See Allyl alcohol, 3-methyl-		
194	Butylene	See Butene		
195	Butyric acid, --,ethenyl ester	See Vinyl butyrate		
196	Chloroethene	See Vinyl chloride		
197	Chloroprene	See 1,3-Butadiene, 2-chloro-		
198	Citraconic acid	See Maleic acid, 2-methyl-		
199	Crotonaldehyde	See Acrolein, 2-methyl-		
200	Crotonamide	See Acrylamide, 2-methyl-		
201	Crotonic acid	See Acrylic acid, 2-methyl-		
202	Crotononitrile	See Acrylonitrile, 2-methyl-		
203	Diallylamine	$(CH_2:CHCH_2)_2NH$	97.6	0.7874 [20]
204	Dibromopropene	See Allyl bromide, 1-bromo-		
205	Dimethylallene	See 1,2 Butadiene, 3-methyl-		
206	Erythrene	See 1,3-Butadiene		
207	Ethylene	Ethene; $CH_2:CH_2$	28.05	0.566 [-102]
208	--,amino-	See Vinylamine		
209	--,bromo-	See Vinyl bromide		
210	--,chloro-	See Vinyl chloride		
211	--,1-chloro-1-fluoro-	$CH_2:CClF$	80.48	..
212	--,chlorotrifluoro-	$CF_2:CFCl$	116.47	..
213	--,1,1-dibromo-	vinylidene bromide; $CH_2:CBr_2$	185.87	2.178 [21]
214	--,1,2-dibromo- cis-	acetylene dibromide; $CHBr:CHBr$	185.87	2.2464 [20]
215	-trans-	" " " " "	185.87	2.2308 [20]

No.	Boiling point, °C	Melting point, °C	Refractive index	Vapor pressure	Solubility		
					w	alc	eth
183	98.5	..	1.4622^{20}	..	i	s	s
184	38.6	-133.8	1.3874^{20}	..			
185	3.7	-138.9	1.3931^{-25}	..	i	vs	vs
186	0.9	-105.6	1.3848^{-25}	..			
187	72-73	-74.3	1.4128^{20}	..	.	s	s
188	232-5	4-7	$1.477^{\ 25}$	..			
189							
190							
191							
192							
194							
195							
196							
197							
198							
199							
200							
201							
202							
203	110.4	-88.4	..	..			
204							
205							
206							
207	-103.9	-169.4 frz -181	1.363^{-100}	..	s	ss	s
208							
209							
210							
211	-24	-169	..	..			
212	-27.9	-157.5	..	$77^{25};175^{50}$ $42^{0};500^{100}$			
213	92	..	..	..			
214	112.5	-53	1.5428^{20}	..	i	vs	vs
215	100	-6.5	1.5505^{18}	..			

No.	Name	Synonyms and formula	Mol. Wt.	Density
216	Ethylene --,1,1-dichloro-	vinylidene chloride; $CH_2:CCl_2$	96.95	1.2129^{20}_{20} (1.218^{20})
217	--,1,2-dichloro- cis-	acetylene dichloride; $\quad$ CHCl:CHCl	96.95	1.2837^{20}
218	- trans-	" " " "	96.95	1.2565^{20}
219	--,1,1-difluoro-	vinylidene fluoride; $CH_2:CF_2$	64.04	..
225	--,1,1-dimethyl-	See Propene, 2-methyl-		
226	--,1,1-diphenyl-	$(C_6H_5)_2C:CH_2$	180.24	1.0206^{22}
227	--,fluoro-	See Vinyl fluoride		
228	--,iodo-	See Vinyl iodide		
230	--,phenyl-	See Styrene		
231	--,tetrabromo-	perbromoethylene;$Br_2C:CBr_2$	343.66	..
232	--,tetrachloro-	perchloroethylene;$Cl_2C:CCl_2$	165.83	1.623^{20}
233	--,tetrafluoro-	perfluoroethylene; $F_2C:CF_2$	100.02	1.519^{20}
234	--,tetraiodo-	periodoethylene; $I_2C:CI_2$	531.64	2.983^{20}
235	--,tetramethyl-	See 2-Butene, 2,3-dimethyl-		
236	--,tribromo-	$CHBr:CBr_2$: ethynil tribromide	264.76	$2.708^{20.5}$
237	--,trichloro-	$CHCl:CCl_2$;ethynil trichloride	131.39	1.462^{20}
238	Ethylenecarboxylic acid	See Acrylic acid		
239	Ethylene sulfonic acid	vinyl sulfonic acid; $\quad CH_2:CHSO_3H$	108.10	1.3921^{25} $1.4003^{20}/20$
240	--,n-amyl ester	$CH_2:CHSO_3(CH_2)_4CH_3$	178.23	1.087^{20}
241	--,n-butyl ester	$CH_2:CHSO_3(CH_2)_3CH_3$	164.21	1.122^{20}
242	--,ethyl ester	$CH_2:CHSO_3C_2H_5$	136.16	1.1831^{25}
243	--,n-hexyl ester	$CH_2:CHSO_3C_6H_{13}$	192.26	1.050^{20}
244	--,isoamyl ester	$CH_2:CHSO_3CH_2CH_2CH(CH_3)_2$	178.23	1.082^{20}
245	--,isobutyl ester	$CH_2:CHSO_3CH_2CH(CH_3)_2$	164.21	1.1898^{25}
246	--,isopropyl ester	$CH_2:CHSO_3CH(CH_3)_2$	152.20	1.132^{20}
247	--,methyl ester	$CH_2:CHSO_3CH_3$	122.13	1.248^{20}
248	--,phenyl ester	$CH_2:CHSO_3C_6H_5$	184.20	1.1657^{25}
249	--,n-propyl ester	$CH_2:CHSO_3C_3H_7$	152.20	1.156^{20}
260	Ethylethylene	See 1-Butene		
261	Fluoropropene	See 1,3-Butadiene, 2-fluoro-		

No.	Boiling point, °C	Melting point, °C	Refractive index	Vapor pressure	Solubility		
					w	alc	eth
216	31.7	-122.1	1.4249^{20}	215.9^0 599^{25}	i		
217	60.3	-80.5	1.4490^{20}	..	ss	∞	∞
218	47.5	-50	1.4454^{20}	..	ss	.	∞
219	<-84	..	..	..	i	s	vs
225							
226	277	9	1.610^{14}	..			
227							
228							
230							
231	226-7	56.5	..	..			
232	121	-22	1.5044^{20}	..	i	∞	∞
233	-76.3	-142.5	..	..	i		
234	subl.	190	..	..	i	ss	ss
235							
236	163-4	..	1.6045^{16}	..			
237	87	-88	1.4784^{20}	..	ss	∞	∞
238							
239	$100^{0.5}_{1}$ 125^{1}	..	1.4493^{20}_{25} 1.4496^{25}	..			
240	131^{17}	..	1.4412^{20}	..			
241	117^{15}	..	1.4416^{20}	..			
242	76^{5}	..	1.4316^{25}	..			
243	146^{15}	..	1.4430^{20}	..			
244	124^{15}	..	1.4415^{20}	..			
245	$78^{5.5}$	..	1.4258^{25}	..			
246	70^{4}	..	1.4321^{20}	..			
247	91^{15}	..	1.4316^{20}	..			
248	46^{2}	..	1.4258^{25}	..			
249	110^{18}	..	1.4368^{20}	..			
260							
261							

No.	Name	Synonyms and formula	Mol. Wt.	Density
262	Fumaric acid	butenedioic acid, trans; $HO_2CCH:CHCO_2H$	116.07	1.635^{20}
263	--,di-n-amyl ester	$C_5H_{11}O_2CCH:CHCO_2C_5H_{11}$	256.33	0.9681 [20]
264	--,di-n-butyl ester	$C_4H_9O_2CCH:CHCO_2C_4H_9$	228.29	0.9869 [20]
265	--,diethyl ester	$C_2H_5O_2CCH:CHCO_2C_2H_5$	172.18	1.0521 [20]
266	--,diisoamyl ester	$C_5H_{11}O_2CCH:CHCO_2C_5H_{11}$	256.33	0.9655 [20]
267	--,diisobutyl ester	$C_4H_9O_2CCH:CHCO_2C_4H_9$	228.29	0.9760 [20]
268	--,diisopropyl ester	$C_3H_7O_2CCH:CHCO_2C_3H_7$	200.24	..
269	--,dimethyl ester	$CH_3O_2CCH:CHCO_2CH_3$	144.13	..
270	--,diphenyl ester	$C_6H_5O_2CCH:CHCO_2C_6H_5$	268.27	..
271	--,dipropyl ester	$C_3H_7O_2CCH:CHCO_2C_3H_7$	200.24	1.6120 [17] 1.0129 [20]
272	--,bromo-	$HO_2CCH:CBrCO_2H$	194.98	..
273	--,chloro-	$HO_2CCH:CClCO_2H$	150.52	..
274	--,--,diethyl ester	$C_2H_5O_2CCH:CClCO_2C_2H_5$	206.63	1.188 [20]
275	--,--,dimethyl ester	$CH_3O_2CCH:CClCO_2CH_3$	178.57	1.2899 [25]
276	--,dimethyl-	$HO_2C(CH_3)C:C(CH_3)CO_2H$	144.12	..
277	--,methyl-	mesaconic acid; $HO_2CC(CH_3):CHCO_2H$	130.10	1.466 [20]
278	--,--,diethyl ester	$C_2H_5O_2CC(CH_3):CHCO_2C_2H_5$	186.20	$1.0453^{20/20}$
279	--,--,dimethyl ester	$CH_3O_2CC(CH_3):CHCO_2CH_3$	158.76	1.1153 [20]
290	Hemiterpene	See Isoprene		
291	Iodoprene	See 1,3-Butadiene, 2-iodo-		
292	Isobutenyl chloride	See Propene,3-chloro-2-methyl-		
293	Isobutylene	See Propene, 2-methyl-		
294	Isocrotonic acid	See Acrylic acid, 2-methyl-(cis)		
295	Isocrotyl chloride	See Propene,1-chloro-2-methyl-		
296	Isoprene	2-methyl-1,3-butadiene; hemi-terpene; $CH_2:CHC(CH_3):CH_2$	68.11	0.6806 [20]
297	Maleic acid	butenedioic acid (cis); $HO_2CCH:CHCO_2H$	116.07	1.609 [20] (1.590^{20})
298	--,di-n-amyl ester	$C_5H_{11}O_2CCH:CHCO_2C_5H_{11}$	256.33	0.9741 [20]
299	--,di-n-butyl ester	$C_4H_9O_2CCH:CHCO_2C_4H_9$	228.29	0.9938 [20]
300	--,diethyl ester	$C_2H_5O_2CCH:CHCO_2C_2H_5$	172.18	1.0662 [20] 1.064 [25]
301	--,diisoamyl ester	$C_5H_{11}O_2CCH:CHCO_2C_5H_{11}$	256.33	0.9714 [20]

No.	Boiling point, °C	Melting point, °C	Refractive index	Vapor pressure	Solubility w	alc	eth
262	$165^{1.7}$subl. 290	286-7	..	..	ss	s	ss ss:Ac ss:CCl$_4$
263	162^{7}	..	1.4496^{20}	..			
264	138^{8}	..	1.4469^{20}	..			
265	214	..	1.4408^{20}	..			
266	166^{11}	..	1.4479^{20}	..			
267	170^{160}, 122^{5}	..	$1\ 4431^{20}$	...	i	s	.
268	225-6	..	..	..	.	s	s
269	192	102	..	..			
270	219^{14}	161-2	..	..	i	s^h	.
271	110^{5}	..	1.4439^{20}	..	.	s	s
272	200^{d}	185-6	..	..	s	s	.
273	subl.	191.2	..	..	vs	vs	vs ss:Bz
274	250^{d}, 136^{19}	..	$1.188\ ^{20}$	..	i	vs	vs
275	224	..	..	..	.	s	s
276	...	241	..	..	s^h	ss	. i:Bz
277	205 d	202-4	..	..	vs^h ss	vs	s ss:Bz ss:Chl
278	$229^{\ 760}$	..	$1.4488^{20/}20$	..	.	s	s s:Bz
279	203.5	..	1.4512^{20}	..	ss	s	s
290							
291							
292							
293							
294							
295							
296	34	-146	1.4194^{20}	..	i	∞	∞
297	...	130.5	..	..	vs	vs	s vs:Ac ss:Bz
298	161^{10}	..	1.4475^{20}	..			
299	147.5^{12}	-85	1.4454^{20}	..			
300	$219^{\ 225}$ 105-6	-11.2	1.4401^{20}	..	i	s	s
301	157^{13}	..	1.4459^{20}	..			

No.	Name	Synonyms and formula	Mol. Wt.	Density
302	Maleic acid --,diisobutyl ester	$C_4H_9O_2CCH:CHCO_2C_4H_9$	228.29	0.9820 [20]
303	--,dimethyl ester	$CH_3O_2CCH:CHCO_2CH_3$	144.13	1.1502 [20] (1.1606 [20])
304	--,diphenyl ester	$C_6H_5O_2CCH:CHCO_2C_6H_5$	268.27	..
305	--,di-n-propyl ester	$C_3H_7O_2CCH:CHCO_2C_3H_7$	200.24	1.0245 [20]
306	--,bromo-	$HO_2CCH:CBrCO_2H$	194.98	..
307	--,chloro-	$HO_2CCH:CClCO_2H$	150.52	..
308	--,--,diethyl ester	$C_2H_5O_2CCH:CClCO_2C_2H_5$	206.63	1.174 [20]
309	--,--,dimethyl ester	$CH_3O_2CCH:CClCO_2CH_3$	178.58	1.2775 [25]
310	--,dichloro-	$HO_2CCCl:CClCO_2H$	184.97	..
311	--,dihydroxy-	$HO_2CCOH:COHCO_2H$	148.08	..
312	--,methyl-	citraconic acid; $HO_2CCH:C(CH_3)CO_2H$	130.10	1.617 [25]
313	--,--,diethyl ester	$C_2H_5O_2CCH:C(CH_3)CO_2C_2H_5$	186.21	1.0491 [20]
314	--,--,dimethyl ester	$CH_3O_2CCH:C(CH_3)CO_2C_2H_5$	158.16	1.9491 [20]
315	Mesaconic acid	See Fumaric acid, methyl-		
320	Methacrolein	See Acrolein, 1-methyl-		
321	Methacrylamide	See Acrylamide, 1-methyl-		
322	Methacrylates	See Methacrylic acid, esters		
323	Methacrylic acid	2-methyl-propenoic acid; $CH_2:C(CH_3)CO_2H$	86.09	1.0153 [20]
324	--,allyl ester	$CH_2:C(CH_3)CO_2CH_2CH:CH_2$	126	0.935 [20]
325	--,butyl ester	$CH_2:C(CH_3)CO_2C_4H_9$	142.19	0.895 [20]
326	--,ethyl ester	$CH_2:C(CH_3)CO_2C_2H_5$	114.14	0.907 [20] 0.911 [25]
327	--,hexyl ester	$CH_2:C(CH_3)CO_2C_6H_{13}$	170.24	0.885 [25]
328	--,isobutyl ester	$CH_2:C(CH_3)CO_2CH_2CH(CH_3)_2$	142.19	0.889 [15.6/15.6]
329	--,isopropyl ester	$CH_2:C(CH_3)CO_2CH(CH_3)_2$	128.17	0.890 [20]
330	--,methyl ester	methyl methacrylate; $CH_2:C(CH_3)CO_2CH_3$	100.11	0.936 [20] 0.940 [25]
331	--,propyl ester	$CH_2:C(CH_3)CO_2C_3H_7$	128.17	0.902 [15.6/15.6]
342	Methacrylonitrile	See Acrylonitrile,1-methyl-		
343	Methoxyethene	See Vinyl methyl ether		
344	Methoxystyrene	See Vinyl methyl ether, 1-phenyl		
345	Methyl isopropenyl ketone	1-methylvinyl methyl ketone $CH_3COC(CH_3):CH_2$	84.12	0.8550 [20/20]

No.	Boiling point, °C	Melting point, °C	Refractive index	Vapor pressure	Solubility		
					w	alc	eth
302	$125.5\ ^5$	..	1.4418^{20}	..			
303	102^{17} 202	-19	1.4423^{20}	..	i	.	s
304	226^{15}	73	..	..	i	vs	vs vs:Ac
305	126^{12}	..	1.4433^{20}	..			
306	d	138-41; (128)	..	..	vs	vs	vs
307	..	108;(114)	..	..	s^h	vs	vs ss:Bz
308	$235\ d;125^{19}$	..	..	..	.	vs	.
309	106.5^{18}	..	..	..	.	vs	vs
310	..	119-20	..	..	vs	s	.
311	..	155	..	..	ss	s	ss
312	..	92-3	..	..	vs	.	ss ss:Bz ss:Chl
313	$230.3;120^{20}$	..	1.4442^{20}	..	.	s	s
314	$210.5;94\text{-}5^{11}$	..	1.4486^{20}	..	ss	s	s
315							
320							
321							
322							
323	$161;\ 60^{10}$	15.5	1.4288^{25} 1.43143^{20}	..	s	∞	∞
324	$42\text{-}3^{15}$	..	1.4365^{20}	..			
325	165-8	..	1.4215^{25} 1.426^{16}	..	i	∞	∞
326	117.5-119.5	..	1.4115^{25} 1.414^{20}	..	ss	∞	∞
327	198-240	..	$1.429\ ^{25}$	..			
328	155	..	$1.418\ ^{24}$	..			
329	127	..	$1.412\ ^{24}$	..	i	∞	∞ ∞:Bz
330	100.6-101.1	-48.2	$1.413\ ^{20}$ 1.4118^{25}	32^{20}	ss	∞	∞
331	141	..	$1.420^{15.6}$	..	i	∞	∞
342							
343							
344							
345	$98;\ 38^{85}$	~-54	1.4220^{20}	..	s		

No.	Name	Synonyms and formula	Mol. Wt.	Density
346	Methyloxirene	See Propene, 1,2-epoxy-		
347	4-Pentenenitrile	See Allylacetonitrile		
348	4-Pentenoic acid	See Allylacetic acid		
349	Perbromoethylene	See Ethylene, tetrabromo-		
350	Perfluoropropene	See Propene, hexafluoro-		
351	Propenal	See Acrolein		
352	Propenamide	See Acrylamide		
353	Propene	propylene; methylethylene; $CH_2:CHCH_3$	42.07	0.5139^{-20}
354	--,3-amino-	See Allylamine		
355	--,1-bromo-	propenyl bromide; $CHBr:CHCH_3$	120.99	1.4133^{20}
356	--,2-bromo-	isopropenyl bromide; $CH_2:CBrCH_3$	120.99	1.362^{20}
357	--,3-bromo-	See Allyl bromide		
358	--,1-chloro- cis	propenyl chloride; 1-chloropropylene;	76.53	..
359	- trans	$CHCl:CHCH_3$	76.53	..
360	--,2-chloro-	isopropenyl chloride; $CH_2:CClCH_3$	76.53	0.918^{9}
361	--,3-chloro-	See Allyl chloride		
362	--,1-chloro-2-methyl-	isocrotyl chloride; $CHCl:C(CH_3)_2$	90.55	0.925^{16}
363	--,3-chloro-2-methyl-	isobutenyl chloride; $CH_2:C(CH_3)CH_2Cl$	90.55	0.925^{20}
364	--,2,3-dibromo-	See Allyl bromide, 1-bromo-		
365	--,1,1-dichloro-	$Cl_2C:CHCH_3$	110.98	$1.1764^{19.5}/_0$
366	--,1,2-dichloro-	$CHCl:CClCH_3$	110.98	1.1818^{20}
367	--,2,3-dichloro-	See Allyl chloride; 1-chloro-		
368	--,1,2-epoxy-	allylene oxide; $CH_3C\overset{\diagdown}{\underset{O}{}}:CH$ methyloxirene;	56.06	..
369	--,3-ethoxy-	See Allyl ethyl ether		
370	--,3-fluoro-	See Allyl fluoride		
371	--,hexafluoro-	perfluoropropene; $CF_2:CFCF_3$	150.03	1.583^{-40}
372	--,3-iodo-	See Allyl iodide		
373	--,3-methoxy-	See Allyl methyl ether		
374	--,2-methyl-	isobutylene; $CH_2:C(CH_3)_2$ (unsym)-dimethylethylene	56.10	$0.6266^{-6.6}$
375	--,--,tetramer	tetraisobutylene; $(C_4H_8)_4$	224.42	0.7944^{20}
376	--,--,trimer	triisobutylene; $(C_4H_8)_3$	168.31	0.7590^{20}

No.	Boiling point, °C	Melting point, °C	Refractive index	Vapor pressure	Solubility w	alc	eth
346							
347							
348							
349							
350							
351							
352							
353	-47.8	-185.2	..	226.4^{38}	vs	vs .	vs:aa
354							
355	60.2	-116.6	1.4519^{20}	..	i	.	.
356	48.4	-124.8	1.4467^{16}	..	.	.	.
357							
358	32.8	-134.8	..	..			
359	37.4	-99	..	..			
360	23^{738}	-138.6	1.404^{6}	..			
361							
362	$68-9^{775}$	..	1.4221^{20}	..	.	∞	∞
363	71.5-2.5	..	1.427^{20}	..	.	∞	∞
364							
365	78	..	..	..	i	.	. s:CHl
366	77.0^{757}	..	1.4471^{20}	..	i	vs	vs:CCl$_4$
367							
368	63	..	..	..	ss	∞	∞
369							
370							
371	-29.4	-156.2	..	..			
372							
373							
374	-6.6	-141	1.3814^{-25}	10^{-82}; 700-9	i	vs	vs
375	109.5^{15}	..	1.4482^{20}	..			
376	179-81	-76	1.4314^{20}	..			

No.	Name	Synonyms and formula	Mol. Wt.	Density
	Propene			
377	--,2-phenyl-	See Styrene, 1-methyl-		
378	--,1,1,2-trichloro-	$CCl_2:CClCH_3$	145.43	1.387 [14]/[14]
379	--,1,2,3-trichloro-	$CHCl:CClCH_2Cl$	145.43	1.414 [20]/[20]
380	--,3,3,3-trichloro-	$CH_2:CHCCl_3$	145.43	1.369 [20]/[20]
391	Propenenitrile	See Acrylonitrile		
392	Propenoic acid	See Acrylic acid		
393	2-Propen-1-ol	See Allyl alcohol		
394	Propenyl carbinol	See Allyl alcohol, 3-methyl-		
395	Propionic acid, --, ethenyl ester	See Vinyl propionate		
396	Propenyl cyanide	See Acrylonitrile, 2-methyl-		
397	Propylene	See Propene		
398	Propylene aldehyde	See Acrolein, 2-methyl-		
399	Styrene	ethenylbenzene; vinylbenzene; phenylethylene; $C_6H_5CH:CH_2$	104.14	0.9090 [20] 0.9075 [20]/[20]
400	--,o-amino-	$C_6H_4NO_2CH:CH_2$	149.15	..
401	--,p-amino-	$NO_2C_6H_4CH:CH_2$	149.15	..
402	--,1-bromo-	$C_6H_5CBr:CH_2$	183.05	1.4025 [23]
403	--,2-bromo-	$C_6H_5CH:CHBr$	183.05	1.4269 [16] 1.0984 [25]
404	--,m-bromo-	$C_6H_4BrCH:CH_2$	183.06	1.4160 [20]
405	--,o-bromo-	$C_6H_4BrCH:CH_2$	183.06	1.4059 [20]
406	--,p-bromo-	$BrC_6H_4CH:CH_2$	183.06	1.400 [20]
407	--,1-chloro-	$C_6H_5CCl:CH_2$	138.59	1.1016 [18] 1.0984 [25]
408	--,2-chloro-	$C_6H_5CH:CHCl$	138.59	1.1095 [15]
409	--,m-chloro-	$C_6H_4ClCH:CH_2$	138.59	1.090 [20]
410	--,o-chloro-	$C_6H_4ClCH:CH_2$	138.59	1.100 [20]
411	--,p-chloro-	$ClC_6H_4CH:CH_2$	138.59	1.1554 [20]
412	--,o-cyano-	$C_6H_4(CN)CH:CH_2$	129.16	..
413	--,m-cyano-	$C_6H_4(CN)CH:CH_2$	129.16	..
414	--,p-cyano-	$NCC_6H_4CH:CH_2$	129.16	..
415	--,1,2-difluoro-	$C_6H_5CF:CF_2$	141.08	..
416	--,m-fluoro-	$C_6H_4FCH:CH_2$	122.14	1.025 [20]

No.	Boiling point, °C	Melting point, °C	Refractive index	Vapor pressure	Solubility		
					w	alc	eth
377							
378	$118; 41^{52}$	..	1.4827^{20}	..			s:Chl
379	142	..	..	..	i	vs	vs
380	$114\text{-}5;5/^{103}$	-30	1.4827^{20}	..			s:Chl
391							
392							
393							
394							
395							
396							
397							
398							
399	145.2	-30.6	1.54682^{20}	5^{20}	i	s	s s:CS$_2$
400	104^{12}	..	1.608^{15}	..			
401	$81^{2.5}$	..	1.6070^{25}	..			
402	$160^{75};86\text{-}7^{14}$	-43.5	$1.5881^{19.5}$	..			
403	$107^{23};71^{6}$ 219 sl.d.	-7 (-8)	1.5990^{22} $1.6094^{20.5}$	..	i	∞	∞
404	$75^{3};90\text{-}4^{20}$	..	1.5855^{20} 1.5903^{20}	..			
405	$206.2; 65^{3}$	frz-52.8	1.5927^{20} 1.5914^{20}	..			
406	$88^{12};89^{16}$	4.5	1.5933^{20} 1.5950^{20}	..	i	.	. vs:Chl
407	$199; 76^{17}$	-23	1.5612^{20} 1.523^{17}	..	i	s	s
408	199	..	1.5736^{25}	..	i	s	s
409	$62\text{-}3^{6}; 57^{3}$	..	1.5619^{20}	..	i	s	s
410	$188.7;60\text{-}1^{4}$	-63.15	1.5648^{20}	..	.	s	s s:Ac
411	$53\text{-}4^{3}; 74^{12}$	..	1.5658^{20}	..	i	s	s
412	$53^{0.15}$	..	1.5756^{20}	..			
413	$83^{3.5}$	..	1.5630^{20}	..			
414	$90^{1.5}$	-15	1.5750^{25}	..			
415	$86.2\text{-}90.2^{60}$	..	1.5061^{20}	..			
416	$30\text{-}1^{4};32^{0.2}$	..	1.5173^{20}	..	i	s	s

No.	Name	Synonyms and formula	Mol. Wt.	Density
	Styrene			
417	--,o-fluoro-	$C_6H_4FCH:CH_2$	122.14	1.030 [20]
418	--,p-fluoro-	$FC_6H_4CH:CH_2$	122.14	1.024 [20]
419	--,m-hydroxy-	vinylphenol; $C_6H_4OHCH:CH_2$	120.14	1.0468 [35]
420	--,o-hydroxy-	vinylphenol; $C_6H_4OHCH:CH_2$	120.14	1.061 [19.2]
421	--,p-hydroxy-	vinylphenol; $HOC_6H_4CH:CH_2$	120.14	..
422	--,m-iodo-	$C_6H_4ICH:CH_2$	233.05	..
423	--,m-methoxy-	m-vinylanisole; $CH_2:CHC_6H_4OCH_3$	134.18	0.999 [16]
424	--,o-methoxy-	o-vinylanisole; $CH_2:CHC_6H_4OCH_3$	134.18	1.0609 [19]
425	--,p-methoxy-	p-vinylanisole; $CH_2:CHC_6H_4OCH_3$	134.18	1.0001 [13]
426	--,1-methyl-	2-phenyl-1-propene; $C_6H_5C(CH_3):CH_2$	118.17	0.9165 [10]
427	--,m-methyl-	$C_6H_4(CH_3)CH:CH_2$	118.17	0.9164[15.5/15.5]
428	--,o-methyl-	$C_6H_4(CH_3)CH:CH_2$	118.17	0.9165[15.5/15.5]
429	--,p-methyl-	$C_6H_4(CH_3)CH:CH_2$	118.17	0.9261[15.5/15.5]
430	--,2-nitro-	1,2-nitrovinylbenzene $C_6H_5CH:CHNO_2$	149.14	..
431	--,m-nitro-	$NO_2C_6H_4CH:CH_2$	149.14	..
432	--,o-nitro-	$C_6H_4NO_2CH:CH_2$	149.14	..
433	--,p-nitro-	$NO_2C_6H_4CH:CH_2$	149.14	..
434	--,m-trifluoromethyl-	$C_6H_4(CF_3)CH:CH_2$	172.14	..
455	Tetraisobutylene	See Propene, 2-methyl-,tetramer		
456	Tetramethylethylene	See 2-Butene, 2,3-dimethyl-		
457	Triallylamine	$(CH_2:CHCH_2)_3N$	137.22	0.800 [20]
458	Triisobutylene	See Propene, 2-methyl-, trimer		
459	Vinyl acetate	acetic acid, ethenyl ester; $CH_3CO_2CH:CH_2$	86.09	0.9338 [20/20]
460	Vinyl acetic acid	3-butenoic acid; $CH_2:CHCH_2CO_2H$	86.09	1.0091 [20]
461	Vinylacetonitrile	See Allyl cyanide		
462	Vinyl alcohol	ethenol; vinol; $CH_2:CHOH$	44.05	..
463	Vinylamine	ethenylamine; aminoethene; $CH_2:CHNH_2$	43.07	0.8321 [20]
464	Vinylanisole	See Styrene, methoxy-		
465	Vinylbenzene	See Styrene		
466	Vinyl bromide	bromoethene; $CH_2:CHBr$	106.96	1.5167 [14]

No.	Boiling point, °C	Melting point, °C	Refractive index	Vapor pressure	Solubility w	alc	eth
417	32-4[3];46[32]	..	1.5179[20] 1.5201[20]	..	i	s	s
418	296; 30[14];67[50]	-34.5	1.5158[20]	..	i	s	s
419	114-6[16]	..	..	..			
420	108[15]	29	1.577[35] 1.5783[27]	..	s	vs	vs
421	..	73.5	..	..			
422	73[3]	..	1.6390[20]	..			
423	114 6[17];89[14]	..	1.555[16]	..	i	s	s
424	195-9; 84[12]	29	1.5388[20]	..	i	s	s
425	204-5; 96[16]	..	1.5642[13]	..	i	s	s
426	72 30 163.4	-23.2	1.5386[20] 1.5358[25]	19[20]	i	s	s s:MeOH s:CS$_2$
427	171-2;51[3]	..	1.5411[20]	..			
428	170;52[9]	..	1.5437[20]	..			
429	173;66[18]	..	1.5420[20] 1.5402[25]	..			
430	250;150[14]	58	..	..	i	s	vs vs:Chl vs;CS$_2$
431	100[3]	-5	1.5818[20]	..			
432	..	13.5	..	..			
433	d	29[21]	..	..	.	vs[h]	vs
434	55[17]	..	1.4655[20]	..			
455							
456							
457	149.5	<-70	..	..			
458							
459	72.5	-100.2	1.3953[20]	88.7[20]	i	∞	.
460	169	-3.9	1.4252[20]	..	s	∞	∞
461							
462	unst.	..	..	..			
463	55-6	..	..	..	∞	s	∞
464							
465							
466	15.8	-137.8	1.4462[20]	..	i	i	i

No.	Name	Synonyms and formula	Mol. Wt.	Density
467	Vinyl butyl ether	butoxyethene; $CH_2:CHOC_4H_9$	100.16	0.7742^{25} $0.7803^{20/20}$
468	Vinyl butyl sulfide	$CH_2:CHSC_4H_9$;	116.21	0.9174^{15}
469	Vinyl butyrate	butyric acid, ethenyl ester $CH_2:CHO_2CC_3H_7$	114.14	$0.9022^{20/20}$ $(0.8994^{20/20})$
470	Vinyl chloride	chloroethene; $CH_2:CHCl$	62.50	0.99176^{-15}
471	Vinyl 2-chloro- ethyl ether	$CH_2:CHOCH_2CH_2Cl$	106.55	$1.0493^{20/20}$
472	Vinyl crotonate	2-butenoic acid, ethenyl ester $CH_3CH:CHCO_2CH:CH_2$	112.12	$0.9439^{20/20}$ $(0.941^{20/20})$
473	Vinyl cyanide	See Acrylonitrile		
474	Vinyl ether	divinyl ether; $CH_2:CHOCH:CH_2$ ethenyloxyethene	70.09	0.773^{20} $0.774^{20/20}$
475	--,hexachloro-	$Cl_2C:CClOCCl:CCl_2$	276.76	1.654^{21}
476	Vinylethylene	See 1,3-Butadiene		
477	Vinyl ethyl ether	$C_2H_5OCH:CH_2$	72.11	0.7589^{20} $0.7541^{20/20}$
478	--,1-chloro-	$C_2H_5OCCl:CH_2$	106.55	1.02^{22}
479	--,2'-chloro-	$ClCH_2CH_2OCH:CH_2$	106.55	1.0475^{20}
480	--,1,2-dichloro-	$C_2H_5OCCl:CHCl$	141.00	1.1972^{25}
481	--,1-ethyl-	$C_2H_5OC(C_2H_5):CH_2$	100.162	..
482	--,1-methyl-	$C_2H_5OC(CH_3):CH_2$	86.135	..
483	--,1-phenyl-	$C_2H_5OC(C_6H_5):CH_2$	148.206	..
484	Vinyl ethyl ketone	$CH_2:CHCOC_2H_5$	84.12	0.8468^{20}
485	Vinyl ethyl sulfide	$C_2H_5SCH:CH_2$	88.16	..
490	Vinyl 2-ethyl hexoate	$C_4H_9CH(C_2H_5)CO_2CH:CH_2$	170.24	$0.8751^{20/20}$
491	Vinyl 2-ethylhexyl ether	$C_4H_9CH(C_2H_5)CH_2OCH:CH_2$	156.27	$0.8102^{20/20}$
492	Vinyl fluoride	fluoroethene; $CH_2:CHF$	46.04	..
493	Vinyl formate	$HCO_2CH:CH_2$	72.06	$0.9651^{20/20}$
494	Vinyl heptafluoro- butyrate	$C_3F_7CO_2CH:CH_2$	300.09	..
495	Vinylidene bromide Vinylidene chloride	See Ethylene, 1,1-dibromo- See Ethylene, 1,1-dichloro-		
496	Vinyl iodide	iodoethene; $CH_2:CHI$	153.96	2.08^{0} 2.037^{20}
497	Vinyl isoamyl ether	$(CH_3)_2CHCH_2CH_2OCH:CH_2$	114.19	0.7826^{20}
498	Vinyl isobutyl ether	$(CH_3)_2CHCH_2OCH:CH_2$	100.16	0.7645^{20} $0.7692^{20/20}$

No.	Boiling point, °C	Melting point, °C	Refractive index	Vapor pressure	Solubility		
					w	alc	eth
467	94.3	-112.7 (-92)	1.3997^{25} 1.4017^{20}	42^{20}	i	.	. ∞:OS
468	86	..	..	...			
469	116.5	..	1.411^{20}	14.5^{20}			
470	-13.37	-153.79	1.398^{15} calc	$100^{-55.8}$	ss	s	vs
471	109 1	-69.7	1.4378^{20}	18^{20}	.	vs	vs
472	133.7	..	1.450^{20}	0.5^{20}	s		
473							
474	39;(28.3)	..	1.3989^{20}	..	,	∞	∞ ∞:Ac ∞:Chl
475	210	..	...	...			
476							
477	35-6	-115.3	1.3767^{20} 1.3739^{25}	426^{20}	ss	s	∞
478	122-3	..	...	..			
479	108^{760}	..	1.4378^{20}	..	.	vs	vs
480	128	..	1.4558^{17}	..	s		
481	87	..	1.4018^{20}	..			
482	62	..	1.3927^{20}	..			
483	$211;96^{12.5}$	..	...	..			
484	$102^{740};38^{60}$	..	1.4192^{20}	..	s		
485	91.5	..	1.4631^{25}	..			
490	185.5	..	...	0.3^{20}			
491	174	-100	1.4247^{25}	..			
492	-51	-161	...	..	i	s	s:Ac
493	46.6	..	...	270^{20}			
494	$78-9^{745}$	..	1.3086^{20}	..			
495							
496	56	..	1.5385^{20}	..	i	∞	∞
497	$112-3^{760}$	..	1.4072^{20}	..	.	s	vs
498	83	-132.3	1.3966^{20} 1.3938^{25}	57^{20}	ss		

No.	Name	Synonyms and formula	Mol. Wt.	Density
499	Vinyl isopropyl ether	$(CH_3)_2CHOCH:CH_2$	86.13	0.7534 [20]
510	Vinyl 2-methoxy-ethyl ether	$CH_3OCH_2CH_2OCH:CH_2$	86.29	0.8967 [20/20]
511	Vinyl methyl ether	methoxyethene; $CH_3OCH:CH_2$	58.08	0.7725 [0] 0.7500 [20/20]
512	--,1-amyl-	$CH_3OC(C_5H_{11}):CH_2$	128.23	..
513	--,1-methyl-	$CH_3OC(CH_3):CH_2$	72.11	..
514	--,1-phenyl-	1-methoxystyrene; $CH_3OC(C_6H_5):CH_2$	134.18	..
515	Vinyl methyl ketone	$CH_2:CHCOCH_3$	69.08	0.8636 [20] 0.8393 [25]
516	Vinyl methyl sulfide	$CH_2:CHSCH_3$	74.13	..
517	Vinyl pentafluoro-propionate	$C_2F_5CO_2CH:CH_2$	194.07	..
518	Vinyl phenyl ether	$C_6H_5OCH:CH_2$	120.15	0.9770 [20]
519	--,1-bromo-	$C_6H_5OCBr:CH_2$	199.06	..
520	--,1-chloro-	$C_6H_5OCCl:CH_2$	154.60	..
521	--,1-methyl-	$C_6H_5OC(CH_3):CH_2$	134.18	..
522	--,1-phenyl-	$C_6H_5OC(C_6H_5):CH_2$	196.25	..
523	Vinyl phenyl sulfide	$C_6H_5SCH:CH_2$	136.20	..
524	Vinyl propionate	$C_2H_5CO_2CH:CH_2$	100.11	0.9173 [20/20]
525	Vinyl propyl ether	$C_3H_7OCH:CH_2$	86.13	..
526	2-Vinylpyridine	$CH_2:CHC_5H_4N$	105.13	0.9985 [0]
527	3-Vinylpyridine	$CH_2:CHC_5H_4N$	105.13	..
528	4-Vinylpyridine	$CH_2:CHC_5H_4N$	105.13	..
530	1-Vinyl-2-pyrrolidone	$CH_2CH_2CH_2CONCH:CH_2$	111	1.04 [25]
531	Vinyl sulfide	ethenylthioethene; divinyl sulfide; $CH_2:CHSCH:CH_2$	86.15	0.9125 [20]
532	Vinylsulfonic acid	See Ethylene sulfonic acid		
533	Vinyl thioethers	See Vinyl corresponding sulfides		
534	Vinyl trifluoro-acetate	$CF_3CO_2CH:CH_2$	140.06	..

No.	Boiling point, °C	Melting point, °C	Refractive index	Vapor pressure	Solubility		
					w	alc	eth
499	55.6	-140	1.3840^{20} 1.3830^{25}	..	.	vs	vs
510	109	-83	1.4072^{25}	..			
511	8	-122	1.3730^{0} 1.3947^{-25}	..			
512	144.5	..	$1.4284^{13.5}$	..			
513	38	..	1.3816^{20}	..			
514	196	..	1.5422^{20}	..			
515	32^{120} 81.4	..	1.4084^{25} 1.4086^{20}	..			
516	66.8	..	1.4835^{20}	..			
517	58^{745}	..	1.3095^{20}	..			
518	155-6	..	1.5224^{20}	..			
519	121^{13}	..	1.5700^{20}	..			
520	106^{20}	..	1.5511^{20}	..			
521	169	..	1.5172^{23}	..			
522	151^{14}	..	1.1073^{20}	..			
523	$201;78^{4}$	..	1.5883^{20}	..			
524	94.9	..	...	35^{20}			
525	65.5	..	1.3908^{20}	..			
526	$79-82^{29}$; $158-9$ d	..	1.5494^{20}	..	ss	vs	vs vs:Chl
527	68^{18}	..	1.5530^{20}	..			
528	$59^{12};65^{15}$	..	1.5499^{20}	..	s^{h}	s^{h}	ss
530	$94-6^{13-4}$	..	1.5120^{25}	..			
531	101;(86)	..	0.9174^{15}	..	ss	w	m
532							
533							
534	39.5^{747}	..	1.3106^{25}	..			

ISOREFRACTIVE AND ISOPYCNIC SOLVENT PAIRS

H.-G. Elias and F. W. Ibrahim

Dept. of Industrial and Engineering Chemistry
Swiss Federal Institute of Technology, Zurich, Switzerland

Isorefractive solvents are solvents having the same refractive index, and isopycnic solvents, those which have the same density.

The determination of molecular weights in mixed solvents by non-colligative methods, such as light scattering and ultracentrifugation will lead only to apparent molecular weights, if non-isorefractive solvent components are used. The observed apparent increase or decrease of molecular weights depends in sign and magnitude on preferential solvation as well as on the refractive index increment of solvent component 2 in solvent component 1 at a fixed polymer concentration. The effect will disappear, if isorefractive solvent pairs are used.

A similar effect may be observed in ultracentrifugal experiments with nonisopycnic solvent pairs. To suppress these effects, isopycnic/isorefractive solvent pairs should be used. A table of isorefractive and isopycnic solvent pairs was prepared (for 25°C), starting with 392 commonly used solvents (1). A solvent pair was classified as isorefractive and isopycnic if the deviations between the respective components were not higher as ± 0.002 in refractive index and ± 0.015 g/ml in density. No check on compatibility of the components was made.

---

(1) H.-G. Elias and F.W. Ibrahim, Makromol. Chem. 65, 127 (1963).

Solvent 1	Solvent 2	Refractive Index 1	2	Density 1	2
Acetone	ethanol	1.357	1.359	0.788	0.786
Ethyl formate	methyl acetate	1.358	1.360	0.916	0.935
Ethanol	propionitrile	1.359	1.363	0.786	0.777
2,2-Dimethylbutane	2-methylpentane	1.366	1.369	0.644	0.649
2-Methylpentane	n-hexane	1.369	1.372	0.649	0.655
	2,3-dimethylbutane	1.369	1.372	0.649	0.657
	3-methylpentane	1.369	1.374	0.649	0.660
2,3-Dimethylbutane	n-hexane	1.372	1.372	0.657	0.655
	3-methylpentane	1.372	1.374	0.657	0.660
n-Hexane	3-methylpentane	1.372	1.374	0.655	0.660
Isopropyl acetate	2-chloropropane	1.375	1.376	0.868	0.865
2-Butanone	butyraldehyde	1.377	1.378	0.801	0.799
Butyraldehyde	butyronitrile	1.378	1.382	0.799	0.786
Propylether	butyl ethyl ether	1.379	1.380	0.753	0.746
2,4-Dimethylpentane	2-methylhexane	1.379	1.382	0.799	0.786
Acetaldehyde-diethyl acetal	butyl ethyl ether	1.379	1.380	0.753	0.746
Propyl acetate	ethyl propionate	1.382	1.382	0.883	0.888
	isobutyl formate	1.382	1.383	0.883	0.881
	1-chloropropane	1.382	1.386	0.883	0.890
Butyronitrile	tert-butanol	1.382	1.385	0.786	0.781
ethyl propionate	isobutyl formate	1.382	1.383	0.888	0.881
	1-chloropropane	1.382	1.386	0.888	0.890
2-Methylhexane	n-heptane	1.382	1.385	0.674	0.680
	3-methylhexane	1.382	1.386	0.674	0.683
Propanol	3-methyl-2-butanone	1.383	1.386	0.806	0.807
	2-pentanone	1.383	1.387	0.806	0.804
Isobutyl formate	1-chloropropane	1.383	1.386	0.881	0.890
	sec-butyl acetate	1.383	1.387	0.881	0.868
	butyl formate	1.383	1.387	0.881	0.888
Diethylamine	n-propylamine	1.384	1.386	0.702	0.713
n-Heptane	3-methylhexane	1.385	1.386	0.680	0.683
	2,3,3-trimethylbutane	1.385	1.387	0.680	0.686
	2,2,4-trimethylpentane	1.385	1.389	0.680	0.687
	2,3-dimethylpentane	1.385	1.389	0.680	0.691
3-Methylhexane	2,3,3-trimethylbutane	1.386	1.387	0.683	0.686
	2,2,4-trimethylpentane	1.386	1.389	0.683	0.687
	2,3-dimethylpentane	1.386	1.389	0.683	0.691
1-Chloropropane	butyl formate	1.386	1.387	0.890	0.888
3-Methyl-2-butanone	2-pentanone	1.386	1.390	0.807	0.802
	3-pentanone	1.386	1.390	0.807	0.810
n-Propylamine	diisopropylamine	1.386	1.390	0.713	0.712
	sec-butylamine	1.386	1.390	0.713	0.720
2,3,3-Trimethylbutane	2,2,4-trimethylpentane	1.387	1.389	0.686	0.683
	2,3-dimethylpentane	1.387	1.389	0.686	0.691

Solvent 1	Solvent 2	Refractive Index 1	2	Density 1	2
sec-Butyl acetate	methyl butyrate	1.387	1.391	0.868	0.875
Butyl formate	n-dodecane	1.387	1.391	0.808	0.775
Isobutyl acetate	methyl butyrate	1.388	1.391	0.871	0.875
	butyl acetate	1.388	1.392	0.871	0.877
2,2,4-Trimethylpentane	2,3-dimethylpentane	1.389	1.389	0.687	0.691
Diisopropylamine	sec-butylamine	1.390	1.390	0.712	0.720
2-Pentanone	3-pentanone	1.390	1.390	0.802	0.810
	4-methyl-2-pentanone	1.390	1.394	0.802	0.797
	2-methyl-1-propanol	1.390	1.394	0.802	0.798
3-Pentanone	4-methyl-2-pentanone	1.390	1.394	0.810	0.797
	2-methyl-1-propanol	1.390	1.394	0.810	0.798
Methyl butyrate	butyl acetate	1.391	1.392	0.875	0.877
	2-chlorobutane	1.391	1.395	0.875	0.868
2-Chloro-2-methylpropane	2-chlorobutane	1.392	1.395	0.872	0.868
Butyl acetate	2-chlorobutane	1.392	1.395	0.877	0.868
4-Methyl-2-pentanone	2-methyl-1-propanol	1.394	1.394	0.797	0.798
	valeronitrile	1.394	1.395	0.797	0.795
	2-butanol	1.394	1.395	0.797	0.803
	2-hexanone	1.394	1.395	0.797	0.810
	1-butanol	1.394	1.397	0.797	0.812
	methacrylonitrile	1.394	1.398	0.797	0.795
	3-methyl-2-pentanone	1.394	1.398	0.797	0.808
2-Methyl-1-propanol	valeronitrile	1.394	1.395	0.798	0.795
	2-butanol	1.394	1.395	0.798	0.803
	2-hexanone	1.394	1.395	0.798	0.810
	butanol	1.394	1.397	0.798	0.812
	methacrylonitrile	1.394	1.398	0.798	0.795
	3-methyl-2-pentanone	1.394	1.398	0.798	0.808
Octane	2,2,5-trimethylhexane	1.395	1.397	0.698	0.703
2-Butanol	butanol	1.395	1.397	0.803	0.812
	methacrylonitrile	1.395	1.398	0.803	0.795
	3-methyl-2-pentanone	1.395	1.398	0.803	0.808
	2,4-dimethyl-3-pentanone	1.395	1.399	0.803	0.805
2-Hexanone	butanol	1.395	1.397	0.810	0.812
	methacrylonitrile	1.395	1.398	0.810	0.795
	3-methyl-2-pentanone	1.395	1.398	0.810	0.808
	2,4-dimethyl-3-pentanone	1.395	1.399	0.810	0.805
Valeronitrile	methacrylonitrile	1.395	1.398	0.795	0.795
	3-methyl-2-pentanone	1.395	1.398	0.795	0.808
	2,4-dimethyl-3-pentanone	1.395	1.399	0.795	0.805
2-Hexanone	3-methyl-2-pentanone	1.395	1.398	0.810	0.808
Isobutylamine	triethylamine	1.395	1.399	0.729	0.723
	n-butylamine	1.395	1.399	0.729	0.736
2-Chlorobutane	isobutyl n-butyrate	1.395	1.399	0.868	0.860

Solvent 1	Solvent 2	Refractive Index 1	2	Density 1	2
Butyric acid	2-methoxy-ethanol	1.396	1.400	0.955	0.960
Butanol	3-methyl-2-pentanone	1.397	1.398	0.812	0.808
	2,4-dimethyl-3-pentanone	1.397	1.399	0.812	0.805
1-Chloro-2-methylpropane	isobutyl n-butyrate	1.397	1.399	0.872	0.860
	amyl acetate	1.397	1.400	0.872	0.871
	1-chlorobutane	1.397	1.400	0.872	0.881
2,5,5-Trimethylhexane	2,2,3-trimethylpentane	1.397	1.401	0.703	0.712
Methyl methacrylate	3-methyl-2-pentanone	1.398	1.398	0.795	0.808
Methacrylonitrile	2,4-dimethyl-3-pentanone	1.398	1.399	0.795	0.805
	2-methyl-2-butanol	1.398	1.404	0.795	0.805
3-Methyl-2-pentanone	2,4-dimethyl-3-pentanone	1.398	1.399	0.808	0.805
Triethylamine	n-butylamine	1.399	1.399	0.723	0.736
	2,2,3-trimethylpentane	1.399	1.401	0.723	0.712
	n-nonane	1.399	1.401	0.723	0.714
Triethylamine	dipropylamine	1.399	1.401	0.723	0.736
n-Butylamine	n-dodecane	1.399	1.400	0.736	0.746
Isobutyl n-butyrate	amyl acetate	1.399	1.400	0.860	0.871
	isoamyl acetate	1.399	1.403	0.860	0.868
	1-chlorobutane	1.399	1.401	0.860	0.875
1-Nitropropane	propionic anhydride	1.399	1.400	0.995	1.007
Amyl acetate	1-chlorobutane	1.400	1.400	0.871	0.881
	tetrahydrofuran	1.400	1.404	0.871	0.885
n-Dodecane	dipropylamine	1.400	1.403	0.746	0.736
	cyclopentane	1.400	1.404	0.746	0.740
1-Chlorobutane	tetrahydrofuran	1.400	1.404	0.871	0.885
2,2,3-Trimethylpentane	n-nonane	1.401	1.403	0.712	0.714
Isovaleric acid	2-ethoxyethanol	1.402	1.405	0.923	0.926
	valeric acid	1.402	1.406	0.923	0.936
Dipropylamine	cyclopentane	1.403	1.404	0.736	0.740
	methylcyclopentane	1.403	1.407	0.736	0.744
n-Nonane	2,2,4-trimethyl-1-pentene	1.403	1.407	0.714	0.712
Isoamyl acetate	tributyl borate	1.403	1.407	0.868	0.854
2-Pentanol	2-methyl-2-butanol	1.404	1.404	0.804	0.805
	3-methyl-1-butanol	1.404	1.404	0.804	0.805
	4-heptanone	1.404	1.405	0.804	0.813
	2-heptanone	1.404	1.406	0.804	0.811
2-Methylbutanol	3-methyl-1-butanol	1.404	1.404	0.805	0.805
	capronitrile	1.404	1.405	0.805	0.801
	4-heptanone	1.404	1.405	0.805	0.813
	2-heptanone	1.404	1.406	0.805	0.811
	pentanol	1.404	1.408	0.805	0.810
	3-methyl-2-butanol	1.404	1.408	0.805	0.815
3-Methyl-1-butanol	capronitrile	1.404	1.405	0.805	0.801
	4-heptanone	1.404	1.405	0.805	0.813

Solvent 1	Solvent 2	Refractive Index 1	2	Density 1	2
3-Methyl-1-butanol	2-heptanone	1.404	1.406	0.805	0.811
	pentanol	1.404	1.408	0.805	0.810
	3-methyl-2-butanol	1.404	1.408	0.805	0.815
Cyclopentane	methylcyclopentane	1.404	1.407	0.740	0.744
Capronitrile	4-heptanone	1.405	1.405	0.801	0.813
	2-heptanone	1.405	1.406	0.801	0.811
	2-pentanol	1.405	1.407	0.801	0.804
	pentanol	1.405	1.408	0.801	0.810
	3-methyl-2-butanol	1.405	1.408	0.801	0.815
	4-methyl-2-pentanol	1.405	1.409	0.801	0.802
	3-isopropyl-2-pentanone	1.405	1.409	0.801	0.808
	2-methyl-1-butanol	1.405	1.409	0.801	0.815
4-Heptanone	2-heptanone	1.405	1.406	0.813	0.811
	pentanol	1.405	1.408	0.813	0.810
	3-methyl-2-butanol	1.405	1.408	0.813	0.815
	4-methyl-2-pentanol	1.405	1.409	0.813	0.802
	3-isopropyl-2-pentanone	1.405	1.409	0.813	0.808
	2-methyl-1-butanol	1.405	1.409	0.813	0.815
2-Ethoxy-ethanol	valeric acid	1.405	1.406	0.926	0.936
2-Heptanone	pentanol	1.406	1.408	0.811	0.810
	3-methyl-2-butanol	1.406	1.408	0.811	0.815
	4-methyl-2-pentanol	1.406	1.409	0.811	0.802
	3-isopropyl-2-pentanone	1.406	1.409	0.811	0.808
	2-ethoxy-ethanol	1.406	1.409	0.811	0.815
	2-methyl-1-butanol	1.406	1.409	0.811	0.815
	amyl ether	1.406	1.410	0.811	0.799
2-Pentanol	pentanol	1.407	1.408	0.804	0.810
	3-methyl-2-butanol	1.407	1.408	0.804	0.815
	4-methyl-2-pentanol	1.407	1.409	0.804	0.802
	3-isopropyl-2-pentanone	1.407	1.409	0.804	0.808
	2-methyl-1-butanol	1.407	1.409	0.804	0.815
	amyl ether	1.407	1.410	0.804	0.799
2,2,4-Trimethyl-1-pentene	n-decane	1.407	1.409	0.712	0.726
Tributyl borate	isoamyl isovalerate	1.407	1.410	0.854	0.853
	allyl alcohol	1.407	1.411	0.854	0.847
Pentanol	3-methyl-2-butanol	1.408	1.408	0.810	0.815
	4-methyl-2-pentanol	1.408	1.409	0.810	0.802
	3-isopropyl-2-pentanone	1.408	1.409	0.810	0.808
	2-methyl-1-butanol	1.408	1.409	0.810	0.815
	amyl ether	1.408	1.410	0.810	0.799
3-Methyl-2-butanol	4-methyl-2-pentanol	1.408	1.409	0.815	0.802
	3-isopropyl-2-pentanone	1.408	1.409	0.815	0.808
	2-methyl-1-butanol	1.408	1.409	0.815	0.815
	amyl ether	1.408	1.410	0.815	0.799

Solvent 1	Solvent 2	Refractive Index 1	2	Density 1	2
4-Methyl-2-pentanol	3-isopropyl-2-pentanone	1.409	1.409	0.802	0.808
	2-methyl-1-butanol	1.409	1.409	0.802	0.815
	amyl ether	1.409	1.410	0.802	0.799
3-Isopropyl-2-pentanone	2-methyl-1-butanol	1.409	1.409	0.808	0.815
	amyl ether	1.409	1.410	0.808	0.799
2-Methyl-1-butanol	amyl ether	1.409	1.410	0.815	0.799
Isoamyl isovalerate	allyl alcohol	1.410	1.411	0.853	0.847
Amyl ether	2-octanone	1.410	1.414	0.799	0.814
2,4-Dimethyldioxane	allyl chloride	1.412	1.413	0.935	0.932
	caproic acid	1.412	1.415	0.935	0.923
Diethyl malonate	ethyl cyanoacetate	1.412	1.415	1.051	1.056
Allyl chloride	capric acid	1.413	1.415	0.932	0.923
2-Octanone	3-methyl-2-heptanone	1.414	1.415	0.814	0.818
	hexanol	1.414	1.416	0.814	0.814
	2-pentanol	1.414	1.416	0.814	0.826
	caprylonitrile	1.414	1.418	0.814	0.810
	2-heptanol	1.414	1.418	0.814	0.818
3-Octanone	3-methyl-2-heptanone	1.414	1.415	0.830	0.818
	2-pentanol	1.414	1.416	0.830	0.826
3-Methyl-2-heptanone	hexanol	1.415	1.416	0.818	0.814
	2-pentanol	1.415	1.416	0.818	0.826
	caprylonitrile	1.415	1.418	0.818	0.810
	2-heptanol	1.415	1.418	0.818	0.818
Hexanol	2-pentanol	1.416	1.416	0.814	0.826
	caprylonitrile	1.416	1.418	0.814	0.810
	2-heptanol	1.416	1.418	0.814	0.818
	3-methyl-2-pentanol	1.416	1.420	0.814	0.823
	2-ethyl-1-butanol	1.416	1.420	0.814	0.829
2-Pentanol	2-heptanol	1.416	1.418	0.826	0.818
	3-methyl-2-pentanol	1.416	1.420	0.826	0.823
	2-ethyl-1-butanol	1.416	1.420	0.826	0.829
Dibutylamine	allylamine	1.416	1.419	0.756	0.758
Caprylonitrile	2-heptanol	1.418	1.418	0.810	0.818
	3-methyl-2-pentanol	1.418	1.420	0.810	0.823
	heptanol	1.418	1.422	0.810	0.818
2-Heptanol	3-methyl-2-pentanol	1.418	1.420	0.818	0.823
	2-ethyl-1-butanol	1.418	1.420	0.818	0.829
	heptanol	1.418	1.422	0.818	0.818
	3-isopropyl-2-heptanone	1.418	1.423	0.818	0.815
Allylamine	methylcyclohexane	1.419	1.421	0.758	0.765
3-Methyl-2-pentanol	2-ethyl-1-butanol	1.420	1.420	0.823	0.829
	heptanol	1.420	1.422	0.823	0.818
	3-isopropyl-2-heptanone	1.420	1.423	0.815	0.815
2-Ethyl-1-butanol	heptanol	1.420	1.422	0.829	0.818
	3-isopropyl-2-heptanone	1.420	1.423	0.829	0.815

Solvent 1	Solvent 2	Refractive Index		Density	
		1	2	1	2
Methylcyclohexane	cyclohexane	1.421	1.424	0.765	0.774
Heptanol	3-isopropyl-2-heptanone	1.422	1.423	0.818	0.815
3-Isopropyl-2-heptanone	octanol	1.423	1.427	0.815	0.821
	3-methyl-2-pentanol	1.423	1.427	0.815	0.824
3-Chloro-2-methyl-1-propene	caprylic acid	1.425	1.426	0.917	0.905
Caprylic acid	N-methyl-alaninenitrile	1.426	1.429	0.905	0.895
Octanol	3-methyl-2-pentanol	1.427	1.427	0.821	0.824
1-Chlorooctane	1-chloro-2-ethylhexane	1.428	1.430	0.867	0.872
2-Methyl-7-ethylnonane	2-methyl-7-ethyl-4-undecanone	1.433	1.435	0.830	0.832
Butyrolactone	chloro-tert-butanol	1.434	1.436	1.051	1.059
	1,3-propanediol	1.434	1.438	1.051	1.049
	diethyl maleate	1.434	1.438	1.051	1.064
4-n-Propyl-5-ethyldioxane	N-methyl-morpholine	1.435	1.436	0.927	0.924
2-Methyl-7-ethyl-4-undecanone	2-methyl-7-ethyl-4-nonanol	1.435	1.438	0.832	0.829
2-Methyl-7-ethyl-4-undecanone	6-ethyl-2-nonanol	1.435	1.438	0.832	0.836
6-ethyl-3-octanol	5-ethyl-2-nonanol	1.435	1.438	0.832	0.830
Chloro-tert-butanol	1,3-propanediol	1.436	1.438	1.059	1.049
	diethyl maleate	1.436	1.438	1.059	1.064
N-Methyl-morpholine	dibutyl sebacate	1.436	1.440	0.924	0.932
2-Methyl-7-ethyl-4-nonanol	5-ethyl-2-nonanol	1.438	1.438	0.829	0.830
	6-ethyl-3-octanol	1.438	1.438	0.829	0.836
	butanethiol	1.438	1.440	0.829	0.837
	2-methyl-7-ethyl-4-undecanol	1.438	1.442	0.829	0.829
	ethyl sulfide	1.438	1.442	0.829	0.831
	6-ethyl-3-decanol	1.438	1.441	0.829	0.838
5-Ethyl-2-nonanol	6-ethyl-3-octanol	1.438	1.438	0.830	0.836
	butanethiol	1.438	1.440	0.830	0.837
	2-methyl-7-ethyl-4-undecanol	1.438	1.442	0.830	0.829
	ethyl sulfide	1.438	1.442	0.830	0.831
	6-ethyl-3-decanol	1.438	1.441	0.830	0.838
1,3-Propanediol	diethyl maleate	1.438	1.438	1.049	1.064
Methyl salicylate	2-methyl-7-ethyl-1-undecanol	1.438	1.442	0.836	0.829
	ethyl sulfide	1.438	1.442	0.836	0.831
	butanethiol	1.438	1.442	0.836	0.837
6-Ethyl-3-octanol	6-ethyl-3-decanol	1.438	1.441	0.836	0.838
Butanethiol	6-ethyl-3-decanol	1.440	1.441	0.837	0.838
	2-methyl-7-ethyl-4-undecanol	1.440	1.442	0.837	0.829
	ethyl sulfide	1.440	1.442	0.837	0.831

Solvent 1	Solvent 2	Refractive Index 1	Refractive Index 2	Density 1	Density 2
Butanethiol	mesityl oxide	1.440	1.442	0.837	0.850
6-Ethyl-3-decanol	2-methyl-7-ethyl-4-undecanol	1.441	1.442	0.838	0.829
	ethyl sulfide	1.441	1.442	0.838	0.831
	mesityl oxide	1.441	1.442	0.838	0.850
1-Chlorododecane (techn.)	mesityl oxide	1.441	1.442	0.862	0.850
	butyl stearate	1.441	1.442	0.862	0.854
	1-chlorotetradecane (techn.)	1.441	1.445	0.862	0.858
2-Methyl-7-ethyl-4-undecanol	ethyl sulfide	1.442	1.442	0.829	0.831
	2-butyloctyl-3-aminopropyl ether	1.442	1.446	0.829	0.842
Mesityl oxide	butyl stearate	1.442	1.442	0.850	0.854
	1-chlorotetradecane techn.	1.442	1.445	0.850	0.858
	2-butyloctyl-3-aminopropyl ether	1.442	1.446	0.850	0.842
Butyl stearate	1-chlorotetradecane techn.	1.442	1.445	0.850	0.858
	2-butyloctyl-3-aminopropyl ether	1.442	1.446	0.854	0.842
Ethyl sulfide	2-butyloctyl-3-aminopropyl ether	1.442	1.446	0.831	0.842
1,3-Butanediol sulfite	1,2-dichloroethane	1.444	1.444	1.231	1.245
	trans-1,2-dichloroethylene	1.444	1.444	1.231	1.257
1,2-Dichloroethane	trans-1,2-dichloroethylene	1.444	1.444	1.231	1.257
1-Chlorotetradecane (techn.)	2-butyloctyl-3-aminopropyl ether	1.445	1.446	0.857	0.842
	1-chlorohexadecane (techn.)	1.445	1.448	0.857	0.859
Diethylene glycol	formamide	1.445	1.446	1.128	1.129
	ethylene glycol diglycidyl ether	1.445	1.447	1.128	1.134
2-Butyloctyl-3-aminopropyl ether	3-lauroxy-1-propylamine	1.446	1.447	0.842	0.840
Formamide	ethylene glycol diglycidyl ether	1.446	1.447	1.129	1.134
2-Methylmorpholine	cyclohexanone	1.446	1.448	0.951	0.943
	1-amino-2-propanol	1.446	1.448	0.951	0.961
Dipropyleneglycol-mono-ethyl ether	tetrahydrofurfuryl alcohol	1.446	1.450	1.043	1.050
1-Amino-2-methyl-2-pentanol	2-butylcyclohexanone	1.449	1.453	0.904	0.901
Tetrahydrofurfurylalcohol	dipropyleneglycol-monoethyl ether	1.450	1.452	1.050	1.047
3-Methyl-5-ethyl-2,4-heptanediol	2-propylcyclohexanone	1.452	1.452	0.922	0.923
	4-methylcyclohexanone	1.452	1.454	0.922	0.908
	3-methylcyclohexanol	1.452	1.455	0.922	0.913
	2,2'-dimethyl-2,2'-dipropyl-diethanolamine	1.452	1.456	0.922	0.922
2-Propylcyclohexanone	4-methylcyclohexanol	1.452	1.454	0.923	0.908

Solvent 1	Solvent 2	Refractive Index 1	Refractive Index 2	Density 1	Density 2
2-Propylcyclohexanone	3-methylcyclohexanol	1.452	1.455	0.923	0.913
	2,2'-dimethyl-2,2'-dipropyl-diethanolamine	1.452	1.456	0.923	0.922
	1,8-cineole	1.452	1.456	0.923	0.921
4-Methylcyclohexanol	2,2'-dimethyl-2,2'-dipropyl-diethanolamine	1.454	1.456	0.908	0.922
3-Methylcyclohexanol	2,2'-dimethyl-2,2'-dipropyl-diethanolamine	1.455	1.456	0.913	0.922
Cyclohexylamine	1-chloroeicosane (techn.)	1.456	1.459	0.862	0.872
1-Chloroeicosane (techn.)	oleic acid	1.459	1.459	0.872	0.887
Oleic acid	2-(β-ethyl)butylcyclohexanone	1.459	1.461	0.887	0.892
	2-butylcyclohexanol	1.459	1.462	0.887	0.898
	2-(β-ethyl)-hexylcyclohexanone	1.459	1.463	0.887	0.892
(1,1',2,2'-Tetramethyl)-diethanolamine	1-aminopropanol	1.459	1.459	0.973	0.965
	N-(n-butyl)-diethanolamine	1.459	1.461	0.973	0.965
Carbon tetrachloride	4,5-dichloro-1,3-dioxolane 2-one	1.459	1.461	1.584	1.591
2-(β-Ethyl)-butylcyclohexanone	2,4-bis-(α-phenylethyl)-phenylmethyl ether	1.461	1.462	0.892	0.898
	2-(β-ethyl)-hexylcyclohexanone	1.461	1.463	0.892	0.892
N-(n-Butyl)-diethanolamine	Cyclohexanol	1.461	1.465	0.965	0.968
2-Butylcyclohexanol	2-(β-ethyl)-hexylcyclohexanone	1.462	1.463	0.898	0.892
	2-ethylcyclohexanol	1.462	1.463	0.898	0.908
N-β-Oxypropyl-morpholine	fluorobenzene	1.462	1.463	1.013	1.020
Fluorobenzene	N(2-hydroxyethyl)-2-hydroxy-butylamine	1.463	1.467	1.020	1.027
d-α-Pinene	1-α-pinene	1.464	1.465	0.855	0.855
	trans-decahydronaphthalene	1.464	1.468	0.855	0.867
m-Fluorotoluene	p-fluorotoluene	1.465	1.467	0.994	0.994
	o-fluorotoluene	1.465	1.468	0.994	0.995
1-α-Pinene	trans-decahydronaphthalene	1.465	1.468	0.855	0.867
p-Fluorotoluene	o-fluorotoluene	1.467	1.468	0.994	0.995
N-(2-hydroxyethyl)-2-hydroxy-butylamine	N-(2-hydroxyethyl)-2-hydroxy-propylamine	1.467	1.468	1.027	1.042
	3-allyloxy-2-hydroxy-propylamine	1.467	1.469	1.027	1.017
	di-(2-hydroxybutyl)-ethanolamine	1.467	1.469	1.027	1.018
	di-(2-hydroxypropyl)-ethanolamine	1.467	1.469	1.027	1.042
	di-(2-hydroxypropyl) ethanolamine	1.468	1.469	1.042	1.042
3-Allyloxy-2-hydroxy-propylamine	di-(2-hydroxybutyl)-ethanolamine	1.469	1.469	1.017	1.018

Solvent 1	Solvent 2	Refractive Index 1	Refractive Index 2	Density 1	Density 2
cis-Decahydronaphthalene	1-methoxy-1-butene-3-yn	1.479	1.480	0.893	0.902
	n-dodecyl-4-tert-butyl-phenyl ether	1.479	1.482	0.893	0.881
	n-dodecylphenyl ether	1.479	1.482	0.893	0.891
	4-dodecyl-4-methylphenyl-ether	1.479	1.483	0.893	0.889
1-Methoxy-1-butene-3-yn	n-dodecylphenyl ether	1.480	1.482	0.902	0.891
	n-dodecyl-4-methylphenyl-ether	1.480	1.483	0.902	0.889
n-Dodecyl-4-tert-butyl-phenyl ether	n-dodecylphenyl ether	1.482	1.482	0.881	0.891
	n-dodecyl-4-methylphenyl ether	1.482	1.483	0.881	0.889
n-Dodecylphenyl ether	n-dodecyl-4-methylphenyl ether	1.482	1.483	0.891	0.889
Butylbenzene	dioctylbenzene (90% p.; 10% m.)	1.487	1.487	0.856	0.856
	p-cymene	1.487	1.488	0.856	0.853
	isopropylbenzene	1.487	1.489	0.856	0.857
	tert-butylcumene(80% p.; 15% m.)	1.487	1.490	0.856	0.856
	n-propylbenzene	1.487	1.490	0.856	0.856
	sec-butylbenzene	1.487	1.490	0.856	0.856
	hexyl-m-xylene	1.487	1.490	0.856	0.860
	tert-butylbenzene	1.487	1.490	0.856	0.862
	isopropylethylbenzene (35% p.; 60% m.)	1.487	1.491	0.856	0.856
p-Cymene	isopropylbenzene	1.488	1.489	0.853	0.857
	tert-butylcumene(80% p.; 15% m.)	1.488	1.490	0.853	0.856
	n-propylbenzene	1.488	1.490	0.853	0.858
	sec-butylbenzene	1.488	1.490	0.853	0.858
	hexyl-m-xylene (mainly 1,3,5-)	1.488	1.490	0.853	0.860
	tert-butylbenzene	1.488	1.490	0.853	0.862
	isopropylethylbenzene (35% p.; 60% m.)	1.488	1.491	0.853	0.856
	tert-butyltoluene (85% p.; 10% m.)	1.488	1.491	0.853	0.858
	hexylcumene (90% p.; 5% m.)	1.488	1.492	0.853	0.863
	octyltoluene (96% p.; 2% m.)	1.488	1.492	0.853	0.866
Isopropylbenzene	tert-butylcumene (80% p.; 15% m.)	1.489	1.490	0.857	0.856
	n-propylbenzene	1.489	1.490	0.857	0.858
	sec-butylbenzene	1.489	1.490	0.857	0.858
	hexyl-m-xylene (mainly 1,3,5-)	1.489	1.490	0.857	0.860
	tert-butylbenzene	1.489	1.490	0.857	0.862
	isopropylethylbenzene (35% p.; 60% m.)	1.489	1.491	0.857	0.856

Solvent 1	Solvent 2	Refractive Index		Density	
		1	2	1	2
Isopropylbenzene	tert-butyltoluene (80% p.; 15% m.)	1.489	1.491	0.857	0.858
tert-Butylcumene (80% p.; 15% m.)	n-propylbenzene	1.490	1.490	0.856	0.858
	sec-butylbenzene	1.490	1.490	0.856	0.858
	hexyl-m-xylene (mainly 1,3,5-)	1.490	1.490	0.856	0.860
	tert-butylbenzene	1.490	1.490	0.856	0.862
	isopropylethylbenzene 35% p.; 60% m.)	1.490	1.491	0.856	0.856
	tert-butyltoluene 80% p.; 15% m.)	1.490	1.491	0.856	0.858
	hexylcumene (90% p.; 5% m.)	1.490	1.492	0.856	0.863
	octyltoluene (96% p.; 2% m.)	1.490	1.492	0.856	0.866
	octylcumene (90% p.; 4% m.)	1.490	1.492	0.856	0.869
	dihexylbenzene	1.490	1.492	0.856	0.870
	p-xylene	1.490	1.493	0.856	0.857
	1.3-diethylbenzene	1.490	1.493	0.586	0.860
	tert-butyl-m-xylene (mainly 1,3,5-)	1.490	1.493	0.856	0.862
	ethylbenzene	1.490	1.493	0.856	0.863
	octylethylbenzene (80-90% p.; 10% m.)	1.490	1.493	0.856	0.866
	isopropyl-m-xylene (mainly 1,3,5-)	1.490	1.494	0.856	0.860
	toluene	1.490	1.494	0.856	0.862
n-Propylbenzene	sec-butylbenzene	1.490	1.490	0.858	0.858
	hexyl-m-xylene (mainly 1,3,5-)	1.490	1.490	0.858	0.860
	tert-butylbenzene	1.490	1.490	0.858	0.862
	isopropylethylbenzene (35% p.; 60% m.)	1.490	1.491	0.858	0.856
	tert-butyltoluene (80% p.; 15% m.)	1.490	1.491	0.858	0.858
	hexylcumene (90% p.; 5% m.)	1.490	1.492	0.858	0.863
	octyltoluene (96% p.; 2% m.)	1.490	1.492	0.858	0.866
	octylcumene (90% p.; 4% m.)	1.490	1.492	0.858	0.869
	dihexylbenzene (85% p.; 10% m.)	1.490	1.492	0.858	0.870
	p-xylene	1.490	1.493	0.858	0.857
	1.3-diethylbenzene	1.490	1.493	0.858	0.860
	tert-butyl-m-xylene (mainly 1,3,5-)	1.490	1.493	0.858	0.862
	ethylbenzene	1.490	1.493	0.858	0.862
	octylethylbenzene (80-90% p.; 10% m.)	1.490	1.493	0.858	0.866
	isopropyl-m-xylene (mainly 1,3,5-)	1.490	1.494	0.858	0.860
	toluene	1.490	1.494	0.858	0.860

Solvent 1	Solvent 2	Refractive Index 1	2	Density 1	2
sec-Butylbenzene	hexyl-m-xylene (mainly 1,3,5-)	1.490	1.490	0.858	0.860
	tert-butylbenzene	1.490	1.490	0.858	0.862
	isopropylethylbenzene 35% p.; 60% m.)	1.490	1.491	0.858	0.856
	tert-butyltoluene (80% p.; 15% m.)	1.490	1.491	0.858	0.858
	hexylcumene (90% p.; 5% m.)	1.490	1.492	0.858	0.863
	octyltoluene (96% p.; 2% m.)	1.490	1.492	0.858	0.866
	octylcumene (90% p.; 4% m.)	1.490	1.492	0.858	0.869
	dihexylbenzene (85% p.; 10% m.)	1.490	1.492	0.858	0.870
	p-xylene	1.490	1.493	0.858	0.857
	1,3-diethylbenzene	1.490	1.493	0.858	0.860
	tert-butyl-m-xylene (mainly 1,3,5-)	1.490	1.493	0.858	0.862
	ethylbenzene	1.490	1.493	0.858	0.863
	octylethylbenzene (80-90% p.; 10% m.)	1.490	1.493	0.858	0.866
	isopropyl-m-xylene (mainly 1,3,5-)	1.490	1.494	0.858	0.860
	toluene	1.490	1.494	0.858	0.862
Hexyl-m-xylene (mainly 1,3,5-)	tert-butylbenzene	1.490	1.490	0.860	0.862
	isopropylethylbenzene (35% p.; 60% m.)	1.490	1.491	0.860	0.856
	tert-butyltoluene (85% p.; 10% m.)	1.490	1.491	0.860	0.858
	hexylcumene (90% p.; 5% m.)	1.490	1.492	0.860	0.863
	octyltoluene (96% p.; 2% m.)	1.490	1.492	0.860	0.866
	octylcumene (90% p.; 4% m.)	1.490	1.492	0.860	0.869
	dihexylbenzene (85% p.; 10% m.)	1.490	1.492	0.860	0.870
	p-xylene	1.490	1.493	0.860	0.857
	1.3-diethylbenzene	1.490	1.493	0.860	0.860
	tert-butyl-m-xylene (mainly 1,3,5-)	1.490	1.493	0.860	0.862
	ethylbenzene	1.490	1.493	0.860	0.863
	octylethylbenzene (80-90% p.; 10% m.)	1.490	1.493	0.860	0.866
	isopropyl-m-xylene (mainly 1,3,5-)	1.490	1.494	0.860	0.860
	toluene	1.490	1.494	0.860	0.862
tert-Butylbenzene	isopropylethylbenzene (35% p.; 60% m.)	1.490	1.491	0.862	0.856
	tert-butyltoluene (80% p.; 15% m.)	1.490	1.491	0.862	0.858
	hexylcumene (90% p.; 5% m.)	1.490	1.492	0.862	0.863
	octyltoluene (96% p.; 2% m.)	1.490	1.492	0.862	0.866

Solvent 1	Solvent 2	Refractive Index		Density	
		1	2	1	2
tert-Butylbenzene	octylcumene (90% p.; 4% m.)	1.490	1.492	0.862	0.869
	dihexylbenzene (85% p.; 10% m.)	1.490	1.492	0.862	0.870
	p-xylene	1.490	1.493	0.862	0.857
	1.3-diethylbenzene	1.490	1.493	0.862	0.860
	tert-butyl-m-xylene (mainly 1,3,5-)	1.490	1.493	0.862	0.862
	ethylbenzene	1.490	1.493	0.862	0.863
	octylethylbenzene (80-90% p.; 10% m.)	1.490	1.493	0.862	0.866
	isopropyl-m-xylene (mainly 1,3,5-)	1.490	1.494	0.862	0.860
	toluene	1.490	1.494	0.862	0.862
Isopropylethylbenzene (35% p.; 60% m.)	tert-butyltoluene (80% p.; 15% m.)	1.491	1.491	0.856	0.858
	hexylcumene (90% p.; 5% m.)	1.491	1.492	0.856	0.863
	octyltoluene (96% p.; 2% m.)	1.491	1.492	0.856	0.866
	octylcumene (90% p.; 4% m.)	1.491	1.492	0.856	0.869
	dihexylbenzene (85% p.; 10 % m.)	1.491	1.492	0.856	0.870
	p-xylene	1.491	1.493	0.856	0.857
	1.3-diethylbenzene	1.491	1.493	0.856	0.860
	tert-butyl-m-xylene (mainly 1,3,5-)	1.491	1.493	0.856	0.862
	ethylbenzene	1.491	1.493	0.856	0.863
	octylethylbenzene (80-90% p.; 10% m.)	1.491	1.493	0.856	0.866
	isopropyl-m-xylene (mainly 1,3,5-)	1.491	1.494	0.856	0.860
	toluene	1.491	1.494	0.856	0.862
	tert-butyl ethylbenzene (70 % p.; 25% m.)	1.491	1.495	0.856	0.854
	m-xylene	1.491	1.495	0.856	0.860
	hexylethylbenzene (70 % p.; 25% m.)	1.491	1.495	0.856	0.868
tert-Butyltoluene (85% p.; 10% m.)	hexylcumene (90% p.; 5% m.)	1.491	1.492	0.858	0.863
	octyltoluene (96% p.; 2% m.)	1.491	1.492	0.858	0.866
	octylcumene (90% p.; 4% m.)	1.491	1.492	0.858	0.869
	dihexylbenzene (85% p.; 10% m.)	1.491	1.492	0.858	0.870
	p-xylene	1.491	1.493	0.858	0.857
	1,3-diethylbenzene	1.491	1.493	0.858	0.860
	tert-butyl-m-xylene (mainly 1,3,5-)	1.491	1.493	0.858	0.862
	ethylbenzene	1.491	1.493	0.858	0.863
	octylethylbenzene (80-90% p.; 10% m.)	1.491	1.493	0.858	0.866
	isopropyl-m-xylene (mainly 1,3,5-)	1.491	1.494	0.858	0.860

Solvent 1	Solvent 2	Refractive Index		Density	
		1	2	1	2
tert-Butyltoluene (85% p.; 10% m.)	toluene	1.491	1.494	0.858	0.862
	tert-butylethylbenzene (70% p.; 25% m.)	1.491	1.495	0.858	0.854
	m-xylene	1.491	1.495	0.858	0.860
	hexylethylbenzene (70% p.; 25% m.)	1.491	1.495	0.858	0.868
1-Phenyl-1-hydroxy-phenyl ether	1,3-dimorpholyl-2-propanol	1.491	1.493	1.081	1.094
Hexylcumene (90% p.; 5% m.)	octyltoluene (96% p.; 2% m.)	1.492	1.492	0.863	0.866
	octylcumene (90% p.; 4% m.)	1.492	1.492	0.863	0.869
	dihexylbenzene (85% p.; 10% m.)	1.492	1.492	0.863	0.870
	p-xylene	1.492	1.493	0.863	0.857
	1,3-diethylbenzene	1.492	1.493	0.863	0.860
	tert-butyl-m-xylene (mainly 1,3,5-)	1.492	1.493	0.863	0.862
	ethylbenzene	1.492	1.493	0.863	0.863
	octylethylbenzene (80-90% p.; 10% m.)	1.492	1.493	0.863	0.866
	isopropyl-m-xylene (mainly 1,3,5-)	1.492	1.494	0.863	0.860
	toluene	1.492	1.494	0.863	0.862
	tert-butylethylbenzene (70% p.; 25% m.)	1.492	1.495	0.863	0.854
	m-xylene	1.492	1.495	0.863	0.860
	hexylethylbenzene (70% p.; 25% m.)	1.492	1.495	0.863	0.868
	1,4-diethylbenzene	1.492	1.496	0.863	0.858
	isopropylbenzene	1.492	1.498	0.863	0.857
Dihexylbenzene (85% p.; 10% m.)	octylcumene (90% p.; 4% m.)	1.492	1.492	0.870	0.869
	p-xylene	1.492	1.493	0.870	0.857
	1,3-diethylbenzene	1.492	1.493	0.870	0.860
	tert-butyl-m-xylene (mainly 1,3,5-)	1.492	1.493	0.870	0.862
	ethylbenzene	1.492	1.493	0.870	0.863
	octylethylbenzene (80-90% p.; 10% m.)	1.492	1.493	0.860	0.866
	isopropyl-m-xylene (mainly 1,3,5-)	1.492	1.494	0.870	0.860
	toluene	1.492	1.494	0.870	0.862
	m-xylene	1.492	1.495	0.870	0.860
	hexylethylbenzene (70% p.; 25% m.)	1.492	1.495	0.870	0.868
	1,4-diethylbenzene	1.492	1.496	0.870	0.858
	isopropylbenzene	1.492	1.498	0.870	0.857

Solvent 1	Solvent 2	Refractive Index		Density	
		1	2	1	2
Octyltoluene (96% p.; 2% m.)	octylcumene (90% p.; 4% m.)	1.492	1.492	0.866	0.869
	dihexylbenzene (85% p.; 10% m.)	1.492	1.492	0.866	0.870
	p-xylene	1.492	1.493	0.866	0.857
	tert-butyl-m-xylene (mainly 1,3,5-)	1.492	1.493	0.866	0.862
	ethylbenzene	1.492	1.493	0.866	0.863
	octylethylbenzene (80-90% p.; 10% m.)	1.492	1.493	0.866	0.866
	isopropyl-m-xylene (mainly 1,3,5-)	1.492	1.494	0.866	0.860
	toluene	1.492	1.494	0.866	0.862
	tert-butylethylbenzene (70% p.; 25% m.)	1.492	1.495	0.866	0.854
	m-xylene	1.492	1.495	0.866	0.860
	hexylethylbenzene (70% p.; 25% m.)	1.492	1.495	0.866	0.868
	1,4-diethylbenzene	1.492	1.496	0.866	0.858
	isopropylbenzene	1.492	1.498	0.866	0.857
Octylcumene (90% p.; 4% m.)	p-xylene	1.492	1.493	0.866	0.857
	1,3-diethylbenzene	1.492	1.493	0.866	0.860
	tert-butyl-m-xylene (mainly 1,3,5-)	1.492	1.493	0.866	0.862
	ethylbenzene	1.492	1.493	0.866	0.863
	octylethylbenzene (80-90% p.; 10% m.)	1.492	1.493	0.866	0.866
	isopropyl-m-xylene (mainly 1,3,5-)	1.492	1.494	0.866	0.860
	toluene	1.492	1.494	0.866	0.862
	tert-butylethylbenzene 70% p.; 25% m.)	1.492	1.495	0.866	0.854
	m-xylene	1.492	1.495	0.866	0.860
	hexylethylbenzene (70% p.; 25% m.)	1.492	1.495	0.866	0.868
	1,4-diethylbenzene	1.492	1.496	0.866	0.858
	isopropylbenzene	1.492	1.498	0.866	0.857
p-Xylene	1,3-diethylbenzene	1.493	1.493	0.857	0.860
	tert-butyl-m-xylene (mainly 1,3,5-)	1.493	1.493	0.857	0.862
	ethylbenzene	1.493	1.493	0.857	0.863
	octylethylbenzene (80-90% p.; 10% m.)	1.493	1.493	0.857	0.866
	isopropyl-m-xylene (mainly 1,3,5-)	1.493	1.494	0.857	0.860
	toluene	1.493	1.494	0.857	0.854
	tert-butylethylbenzene (70% p.; 25% m.)	1.493	1.495	0.857	0.854
	m-xylene	1.493	1.495	0.857	0.860

Solvent 1	Solvent 2	Refractive Index		Density	
		1	2	1	2
p-Xylene	hexylethylbenzene (70% p.; 25% m.)	1.493	1.495	0.857	0.868
	1,4-diethylbenzene	1.493	1.496	0.857	0.858
	mesitylene	1.493	1.497	0.857	0.861
	hexyltoluene (70% p.; 25% m.)	1.493	1.497	0.857	0.870
	isopropylbenzene	1.493	1.498	0.857	0.857
1,3-Diethylbenzene	tert-butyl-m-xylene (mainly 1,3,5-)	1.493	1.493	0.860	0.862
	ethylbenzene	1.493	1.493	0.860	0.863
	octyltoluene (96% p.; 2% m.)	1.493	1.493	0.860	0.866
	octylethylbenzene (80-90% p.; 10% m.)	1.493	1.493	0.860	0.866
	isopropyl-m-xylene (mainly 1,3,5-)	1.493	1.494	0.860	0.860
	toluene	1.493	1.494	0.860	0.860
	tert-butyl-ethylbenzene (70% p.; 15% m.)	1.493	1.495	0.860	0.854
	m-xylene	1.493	1.495	0.860	0.860
	1,4-diethylbenzene	1.493	1.496	0.860	0.858
	mesitylene	1.493	1.497	0.860	0.861
	hexyltoluene (70% p.; 25% m.)	1.493	1.497	0.860	0.870
	isopropylbenzene	1.493	1.498	0.860	0.857
tert-Butyl-m-xylene (mainly 1,3,5-)	ethylbenzene	1.493	1.493	0.862	0.863
	octylethylbenzene (80-90% p.; 10% m.)	1.493	1.493	0.862	0.866
	isopropyl-m-xylene (mainly 1,3,5-)	1.493	1.494	0.862	0.860
	toluene	1.493	1.494	0.862	0.862
	tert-butyl-ethylbenzene (70% p.; 25% m.)	1.493	1.495	0.862	0.854
	m-xylene	1.493	1.495	0.861	0.860
	hexylethylbenzene 70% p.; 25% m.)	1.493	1.495	0.862	0.868
	1,4-diethylbenzene	1.493	1.496	0.862	0.858
	mesitylene	1.493	1.497	0.862	0.861
	hexyltoluene (70% p.; 25% m.)	1.493	1.497	0.862	0.870
	isopropylbenzene	1.493	1.498	0.862	0.857
Ethylbenzene	octylethylbenzene (80-90% p.; 10% m.)	1.493	1.493	0.863	0.866
	isopropyl-m-xylene (mainly 1,3,5-)	1.493	1.494	0.863	0.860
	toluene	1.493	1.494	0.863	0.862
	tert-butyl-ethylbenzene (70% p.; 25% m.)	1.493	1.495	0.863	0.854
	m-xylene	1.493	1.495	0.863	0.860

Solvent 1	Solvent 2	Refractive Index 1	Refractive Index 2	Density 1	Density 2
Ethylbenzene	hexylethylbenzene (70% p.; 25% m.)	1.493	1.495	0.863	0.868
	1,4-diethylbenzene	1.493	1.496	0.863	0.858
	mesitylene	1.493	1.497	0.863	0.861
	hexyltoluene (70% p.; 25% m.)	1.493	1.497	0.863	0.870
	isopropylbenzene	1.493	1.498	0.863	0.857
Octylethylbenzene (80-90% p.; 10% m.)	isopropyl-m-xylene (mainly 1,3,5-)	1.493	1.494	0.866	0.860
	toluene	1.493	1.494	0.866	0.860
	tert-butyl-ethylbenzene (70% p.; 25% m.)	1.493	1.495	0.866	0.854
	m-xylene	1.493	1.495	0.866	0.860
	hexylethylbenzene (70% p.; 25% m.)	1.493	1.495	0.866	0.868
	1,4-diethylbenzene	1.493	1.496	0.866	0.858
	mesitylene	1.493	1.497	0.866	0.861
	hexyltoluene (70% p.; 25% m.)	1.493	1.497	0.866	0.870
	isopropylbenzene	1.493	1.498	0.866	0.857
isopropyl-m-xylene (mainly 1,3,5-)	toluene	1.494	1.494	0.860	0.862
	tert-butyl-ethylbenzene (70% p.; 25% m.)	1.494	1.495	0.860	0.854
	m-xylene	1.494	1.495	0.860	0.860
	hexylethylbenzene (70% p.; 25% m.)	1.494	1.495	0.860	0.868
	1,4-diethylbenzene	1.494	1.496	0.860	0.858
	mesitylene	1.494	1.497	0.860	0.861
	hexyltoluene (70% p.; 25% m.)	1.494	1.497	0.860	0.870
	benzene	1.494	1.498	0.860	0.874
Toluene	tert-butylethylbenzene (70% p.; 25% m.)	1.494	1.495	0.862	0.854
	m-xylene	1.494	1.495	0.862	0.854
	hexylethylbenzene (70% p.; 25% m.)	1.494	1.495	0.862	0.868
	1,4-diethylbenzene	1.494	1.496	0.862	0.858
	mesitylene	1.494	1.497	0.862	0.861
	hexyltoluene (70% p.; 25% m.)	1.494	1.497	0.862	0.870
	benzene	1.494	1.498	0.862	0.874
tert-Butylethylbenzene (70% p.; 25% m.)	m-xylene	1.495	1.495	0.854	0.860
	1,4-diethylbenzene	1.495	1.496	0.854	0.858
	mesitylene	1.495	1.497	0.854	0.861
m-Xylene	hexylethylbenzene (70% p.; 25% m.)	1.495	1.495	0.860	0.868
	1,4-diethylbenzene	1.495	1.496	0.860	0.858

Solvent 1	Solvent 2	Refractive Index 1	Refractive Index 2	Density 1	Density 2
m-Xylene	mesitylene	1.495	1.497	0.860	0.861
	benzene	1.495	1.498	0.860	0.874
Hexylethylbenzene (70% p.; 25% m.)	1,4-diethylbenzene	1.495	1.496	0.868	0.858
	mesitylene	1.495	1.497	0.868	0.861
	hexyltoluene (70% p.; 25% m.)	1.495	1.497	0.868	0.870
	benzene	1.495	1.497	0.868	0.874
1,4-Diethylbenzene	mesitylene	1.496	1.497	0.858	0.861
	hexyltoluene (70% p.; 25% m.)	1.496	1.498	0.858	0.870
Mesitylene	ethylbenzene	1.497	1.497	0.861	0.870
Hexyltoluene (70% p.; 25% m.)	benzene	1.497	1.498	0.870	0.874
	1,2-diethylbenzene	1.497	1.501	0.870	0.876
Benzene	mesitylene	1.498	1.498	0.874	0.874
	1,2-diethylbenzene	1.498	1.501	0.874	0.876
Mesitylene	1,2-diethylbenzene	1.498	1.501	0.874	0.876
1,2-Diethylbenzene	o-xylene	1.501	1.503	0.867	0.876
β-Picoline	phenetole	1.504	1.505	0.953	0.961
Phenetole	pyridine	1.505	1.507	0.961	0.978
Cyclohexylcumene (50% p.; 20% m.)	cyclohexylethylbenzene (60% p.; 20% m.)	1.516	1.520	0.917	0.923
Benzyl acetate	chloro-tert-butylbenzene	1.518	1.521	1.051	1.039
Cyclohexylethylbenzene (60% p.; 20% m.)	cyclohexyltoluene	1.520	1.523	0.923	0.923
2-Furfurol	thiophene	1.524	1.526	1.057	1.059
Benzyl alcohol	m-cresol	1.538	1.542	1.041	1.037
m-Cresol	benzaldehyde	1.542	1.544	1.037	1.041
m-Toluidine	o-toluidine	1.566	1.570	0.985	0.994

REFRACTIVE INDICES OF COMMON SOLVENTS

H.-G. Elias and F. W. Ibrahim

Dept. of Industrial and Engineering Chemistry,
Swiss Federal Institute of Technology, Zurich, Switzerland

Measurements which depend upon the difference in refractive index between the polymer and the solvent will, in general, give greater accuracy as the refractive index increment between polymer and solvent is increased. The magnitude of the increment may be either positive or negative. Systems involving refractive index increments are those of light scattering and ultracentrifugation when either schlieren or interference optics are used. A table of commonly used solvents, arranged according to increasing refractive index, will be useful in practical work with many different polymers.

Solvents arranged according to increasing refractive index

Trifluoroacetic acid	1.283	2,3-Dimethylbutane	1.372
Trifluoroethanol	1.290	3-Methylpentane	1.374
Octafluoro-1-pentanol	1.316	2-Propanol	1.375
Dodecafluoro-1-heptanol	1.316	Isopropyl acetate	1.375
Methanol	1.326	Propyl formate	1.375
Acetonitrile	1.342	2-Chloropropane	1.376
Ethyl ether	1.352	2-Butanone	1.377
Acetone	1.357	Butyraldehyde	1.378
Ethyl formate	1.358	2,4-Dimethylpentane	1.379
Ethanol	1.359	Propyl ether	1.379
Methyl acetate	1.360	Acetaldehyde diethyl acetal	1.379
Propionitrile	1.363	Butyl ethyl ether	1.380
2,2-Dimethylbutane	1.366	Nitromethane	1.380
Isopropyl ether	1.367	Trifluoropropanol	1.381
2-Methylpentane	1.369	2-Methylhexane	1.382
Formic acid	1.369	Butyronitrile	1.382
Ethyl acetate	1.370	Propyl acetate	1.382
Acetic acid	1.370	Ethyl propionate	1.382
Propionaldehyde	1.371	2-Methyl-2-propanol	1.383
n-Hexane	1.372	Propanol	1.383

Isobutyl formate	1.383	1-Chlorobutane	1.400
Diethyl carbonate	1.383	2-Methoxyethanol	1.400
Heptane	1.385	Propionic anhydride	1.400
tert-Butanol	1.385	2,2,3-Trimethylpentane	1.401
Propionic acid	1.385	1-Chlorobutane	1.401
3-Methylhexane	1.386	β-Methoxypropionitrile	1.401
Propylamine	1.386	Isovaleric acid	1.402
3-Methyl-2-butanone	1.386	Nonane	1.403
1-Chloropropane	1.386	Dipropylamine	1.403
2,2,3-Trimethylbutane	1.387	Isoamyl acetate	1.403
sec-Butyl acetate	1.387	Cyclopentane	1.404
Butyl formate	1.387	2-Methyl-2-butanol	1.404
Isobutyl acetate	1.388	3-Methyl-1-butanol	1.404
2,2,4-Trimethylpentane	1.389	Tetrahydrofuran	1.404
2,3-Dimethylpentane	1.389	Capronitrile	1.405
Acetic anhydride	1.389	4-Heptanone	1.405
Diisopropylamine	1.390	2-Ethoxyethanol	1.405
2-Butylamine	1.390	2-Heptanone	1.406
2-Pentanone	1.390	Valeric acid	1.406
3-Pentanone	1.390	Diisobutylene	1.407
Nitroethane	1.390	Methylcyclopentane	1.407
Methyl n-butyrate	1.391	Isoamyl ether	1.407
Butyl acetate	1.392	2-Pentanol	1.407
2-Nitropropane	1.392	Tributyl borate	1.407
4-Methyl-2-pentanone	1.394	Pentanol	1.408
2-Methyl-1-propanol	1.394	3-Methyl-2-butanol	1.408
Octane	1.395	Diethyl oxalate	1.408
Isobutylamine	1.395	Decane	1.409
Valeronitrile	1.395	4-Methyl-2-pentanol	1.409
2-Butanol	1.395	3-Isopropyl-2-pentanone	1.409
2-Hexanone	1.395	2-Methyl-1-butanol	1.409
2-Chlorobutane	1.395	Butyric anhydride	1.409
Butyric acid	1.396	Amyl ether	1.410
2,2,5-Trimethylhexane	1.397	Isoamyl isovalerate	1.410
Dibutyl ether	1.397	1-Chloropentane	1.410
Butanol	1.397	Allyl alcohol	1.411
Acrolein	1.397	2,4-Dimethyldioxane	1.412
1-Chloro-2-methylpropane	1.397	Ethyl lactate	1.412
Methacrylonitrile	1.398	Diethyl malonate	1.412
3-Methyl-2-pentanone	1.398	3-Chloropropene	1.413
Triethylamine	1.399	Ethyleneglycol diacetate	1.413
Butylamine	1.399	2-Octanone	1.414
2,4-Dimethyl-3-pentanone	1.399	3-Octanone	1.414
Isobutyl n-butyrate	1.399	3-Methyl-2-heptanone	1.415
1-Nitropropane	1.399	Caproic acid	1.415
Dodecane	1.400	4-Methyldioxane	1.415
Amyl acetate	1.400	1,2-Propyleneglycol-1-monobutyl ether	1.415

Ethyl cyanoacetate	1.415	Triethyleneglycol monobutyl ether	1.437
Dibutylamine	1.416	2-Methyl-7-ethyl-4-nonanol	1.438
Hexanol	1.416	5-Ethyl-2-nonanol	1.438
2-Pentanol	1.416	6-Ethyl-3-octanol	1.438
1,1-Dichloroethane	1.416	1,3-Propanediol	1.438
Heptachlorodiethyl ether	1.416	Diethyl maleate	1.438
3-Methoxy-propylamine	1.417	Butanethiol	1.440
Caprylonitrile	1.418	Dibutyl sebacate	1.440
2-Heptanol	1.418	2-Chloroethanol	1.440
Allylamine	1.419	6-Ethyl-3-decanol	1.441
1,2-Propyleneglycol carbonate	1.419	1-Chlorododecane (techn.)	1.441
2-Heptanol	1.420	3-Methyl-2,4-pentanediol	1.441
3-Methyl-2-pentanol	1.420	Dimethyl maleate	1.441
2-Ethyl-1-butanol	1.420	2-Methyl-7-ethyl-4-undecanol	1.442
1-Chloro-2-methyl-1-propene	1.420	Ethyl sulfide	1.442
p-Dioxane	1.420	Mesityl oxide	1.442
Methylcyclohexane	1.421	Butyl stearate	1.442
4-Hydroxy-4-methyl-2-pentanone	1.421	Cyclohexene	1.443
Heptanol	1.422	Lauryl glycidyl ether	1.443
3-Isopropyl-2-heptanone	1.423	Dibutyl maleate	1.444
Cyclohexane	1.424	1,3-Butyleneglycol sulfite	1.444
2-Bromopropane	1.424	1,2-Dichloroethane	1.444
3-Chloro-2-methyl-1-propene	1.425	Glycol sulfite	1.444
Caprylic acid	1.426	Chloroform	1.444
Ethylene carbonate	1.426	1-Chlorotetradecane (techn.)	1.445
Octanol	1.427	Diethylene glycol	1.445
3-Methyl-2-heptanol	1.427	cis-1,2-Dichloroethylene	1.445
N,N-Dimethylformamide	1.427	2-Butyloctyl-3-aminopropyl ether	1.446
Sulfuric acid	1.427	2-Methyl-morpholine	1.446
1-Chlorooctane	1.428	Formamide	1.446
Triisobutylene	1.429	3-Lauryl-1-hydroxypropylamine	1.447
N-Methyl-alaninnitrile	1.429	Ethylene glycol diglycidyl ether	1.447
1,2-Ethanediol	1.429	1-Chlorohexadecane (techn.)	1.448
1-Chloro-2-ethylhexane	1.430	Cyclohexanone	1.448
Ethylcyclohexane	1.431	1-Amino-2-propanol	1.448
1,2-Propanediol	1.431	Diethyleneglycol mono-β-hydroxy isopropylether	1.448
1-Bromopropane	1.431		
2-Methyl-7-ethyl-4-nonanone	1.433	1-Amino-2-methyl-2-pentanol	1.449
Ethyleneglycol monoallyl ether	1.434	Tetrahydrofurfuryl alcohol	1.450
Butyrolactone	1.434	2-Propylcyclohexanone	1.452
2-Methyl-7-ethyl-undecanone	1.435	2-Aminoethanol	1.452
4-n-Propyl-5-ethyldioxane	1.435	1,4-Butanediol glycidyl ether	1.452
1,2-Dichloroisobutane	1.435	4-Chloro-1,3-dioxolane-2-one	1.452
1,2-Propyleneglycol sulfite	1.435	1-Chlorooctadecane (techn.)	1.453
N-Methyl-morpholine	1.436	2-Butylcyclohexanone	1.453
Chloro-tert-butanol	1.436	Ethylenediamine	1.454
Epichlorohydrin	1.436	2-(β-Methyl) propylcyclohexanone	1.454

4-Methylcyclohexanol	1.454
3-Methylcyclohexanol	1.455
Bis(2-chloroethyl) ether	1.455
Cyclohexyl	1.456
1,8-Cineole	1.456
2,2'-Dimethyl-2,2'-dipropyl diethanolamine	1.456
1,3-Butanediol glycidyl ether	1.456
1-Chloroeicosane (techn.)	1.459
Oleic acid	1.459
(1,1',2,2'-Tetramethyl)-diethanol-amine	1.459
3-Aminopropanol	1.459
Carbon tetrachloride	1.459
3-Methyl-5-ethyl-2,4-heptanediol	1.459
2-(β-Ethyl)-butylcyclohexanone	1.461
2-Methylcyclohexanol	1.461
N-(n-Butyl)-diethanolamine	1.461
4,5-Dichloro-1,3-dioxolane-2-one	1.462
2-Butylcyclohexanol	1.462
N-β-Hydroxypropyl-morpholine	1.462
2-(β-Ethyl)-hexylcyclohexanone	1.463
2-Ethylcyclohexanol	1.463
Fluorobenzene	1.463
d-α-Pinene	1.464
l-α-Pinene	1.465
Cyclohexanol	1.465
m-Fluorotoluene	1.465
p-Fluorotoluene	1.467
N-(2-Hydroxyethyl)-2-hydroxybutyl-amine	1.467
4-Chloromethyl-1,3-dioxolane-2-one	1.467
trans-Decahydronaphthalene	1.468
o-Fluorotoluene	1.468
N-(2-Hydroxyethyl)-2-hydroxy-propylamine	1.468
3-Allyloxy 2-hydroxypropylamine	1.469
Di-(2-hydroxybutyl)-ethanolamine	1.469
Di-(2-hydroxypropyl)-ethanolamine	1.469
d-Limonene	1.471
2-(α-Hydroxybutyl)-cyclohexanol	1.473
1,2,3-Trichloroisobutane	1.473
Decahydronaphthalene	1.474
1,2,3-Propanetriol	1.474
Trichloroethylene	1.475
N(β-Hydroxyethyl)-morpholine	1.476
Dimethyl sulfoxide	1.476
cis-Decahydronaphthalene	1.479
2-(α-Hydroxyethyl)-cyclohexanol	1.479
1-Methoxy-1-butene-3-yn	1.480
2-Butylidenecyclohexanone	1.481
N(β-Chloroallyl)-morpholine	1.481
n-Dodecyl-4-tert-butyl phenylether	1.482
n-Dodecyl phenyl ether	1.482
n-Dodecyl 4-methylphenyl ether	1.483
N-Hydroxyethyl-1,3-propanediamine	1.483
Morpholyl N-(ethylhydroxy) ethylamine	1.485
2-Ethylidenecyclohexanone	1.486
Butylbenzene	1.487
Dioctylbenzene (90% p.; 10% m.)	1.487
p-Cymene	1.488
Isopropylbenzene	1.489
Furfurylalcohol	1.489
tert-Butylcumene (80% p.; 15% m.)	1.490
n-Propylbenzene	1.490
sec-Butylbenzene	1.490
Hexyl-m-xylene (mainly 1,3,5-)	1.490
tert-Butylbenzene	1.490
Dibutyl phthalate	1.490
Isopropylethylbenzene (35% p.; 60% m.)	1.491
tert-Butyltoluene (85% p.; 10% m.)	1.491
1-Phenyl-1-hydroxyphenylethane	1.491
Hexylcumene (90% p.; 5% m.)	1.492
Octyltoluene (96% p.; 2% m.)	1.492
Octylcumene (90% p.; 4% m.)	1.492
Dihexylbenzene (85% p.; 10% m.)	1.492
p-Xylene	1.493
1,3-Diethylbenzene	1.493
tert-Butyl-m-xylene (mainly 1,3,5-)	1.493
Ethylbenzene	1.493
Octylethylbenzene (80-90% p.; 10% m.)	1.493
1,3-Dimorpholyl-2-propanol	1.493
1,1,2,2-Tetrachloroethane	1.493
Isopropyl-m-xylene (mainly 1,3,5-)	1.494
Toluene	1.494
Benzyl ethyl ether	1.494
tert-Butylethylbenzene (70% p.; 25% m.)	1.495
m-Xylene	1.495
Hexylethylbenzene (70% p.; 25% m.)	1.495
1,4-Diethylbenzene	1.496
2,3-Dichlorodioxane	1.496

Mesitylene	1.497	Styrene	1.545
Hexyltoluene (90% p.; 5% m.)	1.497	Nitrobenzene	1.550
2-Iodopropane	1.497	o-Dichlorobenzene	1.551
Benzene	1.498	Bromobenzene	1.557
Propyl benzoate	1.498	o-Nitroanisole	1.560
α-Picoline	1.499	m-Toluidine	1.566
1,2-Diethylbenzene	1.501	Benzyl benzoate	1.568
Pentachloroethane	1.501	o-Toluidine	1.570
1-Jodopropane	1.502	1-Methoxyphenyl-1-phenylethane	1.571
o-Xylene	1.503	Aniline	1.583
Ethyl benzoate	1.503	o-Chloroaniline	1.586
β-Picoline	1.504	Bromoform	1.587
Tetrachloroethylene	1.504	Thiophenol	1.588
Phenetole	1.505	2,4-Bis-(α-phenylethyl) phenyl- methyl ether	1.590
Pyridine	1.507		
Iodoethane	1.512	Carbon disulfide	1.628
Phenyl methallyl ether	1.514	1,1,2,2-Tetrabromoethane	1.633
Anisole	1.515	Methylene iodide	1.749
Methyl benzoate	1.515		
Cyclohexylcumene (60% p.; 25% m.)	1.516		
Diallyl phthalate	1.517		
Benzyl acetate	1.518		
Cyclohexylethylbenzene (60% p.; 20% m.)	1.520		
2-Methyl-4-tert-butyl-phenol	1.521		
Phenyl acetonitrile	1.521		
(Chloro-tert-butyl)benzene	1.521		
Methyl salicylate	1.522		
Cyclohexyltoluene (50% p.; 20% m.)	1.523		
Chlorobenzene	1.523		
Furfural	1.524		
Octachlorodiethyl ether	1.524		
Benzonitrile	1.526		
Thiophene	1.526		
Nonachlorodiethyl ether	1.529		
Iodomethane	1.530		
4-Phenyldioxane	1.530		
3-Phenyl-1-propanol	1.532		
Acetophenone	1.532		
Benzyl alcohol	1.538		
1,2-Dibromoethane	1.538		
1,2,3,4-Tetrahydronaphthalene	1.539		
m-Cresol	1.542		
β,β'-Di(butylxanthogenic acid) diethylester	1.543		
m-Dichlorobenzene	1.543		
Benzaldehyde	1.544		

PHYSICAL CONSTANTS OF THE MOST COMMON SOLVENTS

Solvent	b.p.,(°C)	m.p.,(°C)	Density at Various Temperatures (°C) [g/ml]			Viscosity at Various Temp.,(°C), [centistokes]			n_D at Various Temp.,(°C)	
			20	25	30	20	25	30	20	25
Acetic acid	117.72	16.63	1.04923	1.04365	1.03802	1.314*(15°)		1.040	1.37160	1.36995
Acetone	56.24	-95.35	0.7908	0.7851	0.77933*	0.337-*(15°)	0.3075	0.2954	1.35880	1.35609
Benzene	80.10	5.533	0.87368	0.86845	0.86836*	0.649*	0.6028	0.569*	1.50110	1.49790
Benzyl alcohol	205.45	-15.3	1.04535*	1.04127	1.03765	2.996*		4.650	1.54033	1.5371
Eityl acetate	126.11	-73.5	0.3813	0.87636		0.734	0.688		1.39406	
n-Butyl alcohol	117.73	-89.53	0.80961*	0.8057*	0.80206	3.379*(15°)		2.271	1.39922	1.3970*
Carbon tetrachloride	76.75	-22.99	1.5940*	1.5842	1.5748	0.965	0.8876*	0.843	1.46030	1.45759
m-Cresol	202.70	-11.95	1.0341*		1.02598			9.807	1.5438	
Chloroform	61.15	-63.55	1.4892		1.4706	0.568*		0.514	1.4455*	
Cyclohexane	80.74	6.554	0.77855	0.77389*	0.76928	1.056*(15°)	0.838	0.820*	1.42623	1.42354
Cyclohexanone	155.65	-16.40	0.9462*		0.93761	2.453*(15°)		1.803	1.45097	
Decalin	191.7	-124	0.8865	0.8789			2.415		1.4758	
Dimethylformamide	153.0			0.9445						1.4269
Dioxane	101.32	11.80	1.03375	1.02687	1.0223*	1.439*(15°)		1.087	1.42241	1.42025
Ethyl acetate	77.11	-83.97	0.90063	0.89455	0.88851		0.426	0.400*	1.37239	1.36979
Ethyl alcohol	78.33	-114.5	0.78934	0.78506	0.78079*		1.078	0.991	1.36159	1.35941
Ethyl ether	34.48	-116.3	0.71352*	0.70778	0.70205	0.242	0.224*		1.35272	
Formic acid	100.70	8.25	1.21961	1.21328	1.20775*		1.366	1.443	1.37140	1.36938
n-Heptane	98.43	-90.6	0.6836*	0.67951	0.6751*	0.411*	0.3903	0.364*	1.38765	1.38512
n-Hexane	68.7	-95.3	0.65937	0.65482	0.6505*	0.318*	0.2923	0.278*	1.37436	1.37226
Methanol	64.51	-97.49	0.7915*	0.78675	0.7319*	0.5506	0.5445	0.510	1.32863	1.32663
Methyl ethyl ketone	79.50	-87.30	0.30473	0.79945	0.79452*	0.423*(15°)		0.365	1.37850	1.37612
n-Octane	125.67	-56.8	0.70252	0.69849	0.6942*	0.5458	0.5136	0.472	1.39743	1.39505
n-Propyl alcohol	97.15	-126.2	0.8035*	0.79950	0.7960*	2.522*(15°)		1.722*	1.38556	1.3835

Solvent	b.p.,(°C)	m.p.,(°C)	Density at Various Temperatures (°C) [g/ml]			Viscosity at Various Temp.,(°C), [centistokes]			n_D at Various Temp.,(°C)	
			20	25	30	20	25	30	20	25
Tetrahydrofuran	64-65	-65	0.8898	0.8811					1.4091	1.4040
Tetralin	207.6	-35.80	0.9702	0.9662		2.202	2.003		1.54135	1.53919
Toluene	110.62	-94.991	0.8669*	0.86231	0.85769		0.5516	0.526*	1.49693	1.49413
Water	100	0	0.99823	0.99707	0.99567	1.0050	0.8937	0.8007	1.33299	
Xylene	138.35	13.26	0.86105	0.85669	0.8523*	0.644	0.605	0.568*	1.49581	1.49325

* In this table, the constants for water and tetrahydrofuran are taken from "Handbook of Chemistry and Physics," 1955-1956. Asterisks following figures indicate constants taken from J. Timmermans, "Physiochemical Constants of Pure Organic Compounds," Elsevier, 1950. The remaining constants have been taken from Weissberger, "Organic Solvents," Wiley, New York, 1958.

IX.
CONTEMPORARY THERMOPLASTIC MATERIALS

CONTEMPORARY THERMOPLASTIC MATERIALS, PROPERTY AND PRICE CHART

Resin Material	Impact Strength, Notched Izod (ft.lb/in., ½" bar) (psi x 10^-3 bar)	Tensile Strength (psi x 10^-3)	Tensile Modulus (psi x 10^-3)	Elongation (%)	Flexural Strength (psi x 10^-3)	Compressive Strength (psi x 10^-3)	Compressive Modulus (psi x 10^-3)	Heat Distortion Temp. (°F, 264 psi)	Heat Resistance (con't. °F)
Polyethylene low density	no break	1 -2.4	14-38	20-800	...	...	...	...	140-175
Polyethylene medium density	no break	1.7-2.8	55-85	80-600	...	...	...	...	150-180
Polyethylene high density	0.5-23	2.5-4	75-160	10-800	2-3	...	50-110	110-125	180-250
Polypropylene	0.5-11	3.5-5	150-250	10-700	4.5-6	8.5-10	...	140-160	250
Acrylic resins	0.4-0.5	7 -10.5	350-450	2-10	14-16	14 -17	350-450	150-210	140-205
High impact acrylic resins	0.5-4.5	5.5-8	225-380	15-50	8.5-12	7-12	250-390	169-190	140-195
Polystyrene	0.25-0.65	5-9	400-500	1-2.5	7-15	11.5-16	300-560	167-203	150-180
Polystyrene high impact resin	0.7-1.5	3.5-8	300-400	10-40	5.5-12.5	8-16	...	150-196	120-170
Poly(styrene-co acrylonitrile)	0.3-55	10-12	500	1-3.2	17	15-17.5	650	200-208	...
Polystyrene A.B.S. resins	1.5-9.5	3.5-10.5	200-450	10-100	2-19	6-11	200-450	170-230	160-235
Poly(vinyl chloride) (rigid)	0.4-15	6-9	200-600	5-40	8-15	10-11	300-400	140-175	160-165
Poly(vinyl chloride)	varied	1-4	...	100-450	...	...	...	...	...
Poly(vinylidene chloride)(rigid)	0.8-6.3	7.5-8.8	348-450	65	14.2-17	...	...	212-220	185
Chlorinated polyether	0.4	6	160	60-160	5	...	130	185-210	250-275
Poly(chlorotri-fluoroethylene)	3.5	6	150-190	60-190	8-10	6-12	130	170-200	390
Fluorinated poly(ethylene-co-propylene) FEP-resins	no break	2-3.2	60-80	350	...	...	70	124	400

Resin Material	Impact Strength, Notched Izod (ft.lb/in.,½" bar)	Tensile Strength (psi x 10^-3)	Tensile Modulus (psi x 10^-3)	Elongation (%)	Flexural Strength (psi x 10^-3)	Compressive Strength (psi x 10^-3)	Compressive Modulus (psi x 10^-3)	Heat Distortion Temp. (°F, 264 psi)	Heat Resistance (cont'd. °F)
Poly(tetra-fluoroethylene)	no break	2-2.5	58	75-100	...	0.4-1.2	70-90	132	550
Nylon 66	0.9-2	9-12	210-410	25-100	14.6	5-13	...	200	250
Nylon 6	0.9-2.5	9.5-11.7	200-450	25-250	9-16.6	4-11	347	150-175	230
Acetal resins	1.2-3	8.8-10	400-410	12-75	13-14	18	410	212-230	185-250
Polycarbonate resins	2-3	8.5-10.5	320	75-120	11-13	12.5	240	270	250-275
Polyurethan resins	no break	4.5-8	...	100-600	0.7-1	20	...	...	180-230
Cellulose acetate	0.5-5.6	2.3-8.1	...	10-73	2.2-11.5	2.2-10.9	...	111-195	140-175
Cellulose acetate butyrate	0.8-6.3	2.6-6.9	...	40-83	1.8-9.3	2.1-9.4	...	113-202	140-175
Cellulose propionate	0.9-10.2	1.8-7.3	...	30-100	2.8-11	3-9.6	...	121-228	140-175
Ethyl cellulose	1.7-6	2.3-6.5	...	10-45	3-6.7	...	...	150-200	140-180

Resin Material	Coefficient Thermal Expansion (in/°C x 10^5)	Thermal Conductivity (cal/cm^2/sec/ °C/cm x 10^4)	Volume Resistivity (ohm-cm)	Dielectric Constant (60 cycles)	Dielectric Strength, ST 1/8" thickness (volts/mil)	Power Factor (60 cycles)	Arc Resistance (sec.)	Water Absorption 24 hrs. (%)	Rockwell Hardness
Polyethylene low density	10-20	8	10^{15}-10^{18}	2.28	450-1000	0.0002-0.0005	melts	<0.02	R10
Polyethylene medium density	10-20	8	10^{15}-10^{18}	2.3	450-1000	0.0002-0.0005	melts	<0.02	R15
Polyethylene high density	10-20	8	6×10^{15}-10^{18}	2.3	450-1000	0.0002-0.0005	melts	<0.01	R30-60
Polypropylene	2-20	2.8	6.5-10^{16}	2.1-2.27	450-990	0.0025	13-185	<0.01	R65-99
Acrylic resins	5-3.5	4-6	>10^{14}	3.5-4.5	450-500	0.04-0.05	no failure	0.2-0.4	M85-105
High impact acrylic resins	8.5-10.5	3.8-5	10^{16}-10^{17}	3.2-3.8	400-500	3.5%-5%	no tracking	0.2-0.3	M20-67
Polystyrene	6-8	1.9-3.3	10^{17}-10^{21}	2.5-2.65	500-700	0.0001-0.0005	60-100	0.03-0.05	M65-80
Polystyrene high impact resin	6.5-8.5	1-3	10^{13}-10^{17}	2.5-3.5	500	0.003-0.005	60-90	0.05-0.10	M25-M69
Poly(styrene-co acrylonitrile)	7	3	10^{15}	2.8-3	400-500	...	...	0.23-0.28	M30-M83
Polystyrene A.B.S. resins	5.7-13	5-7	10^{12}-10^{17}	2.9-4.9	300-450	0.005-0.007	45-90	0.2-0.4	R50-R120
Poly(vinyl chloride) (rigid)	5-10	3-5	10^{12}-10^{16}	3-4	425-1400	0.01-0.02	...	0.07-0.40	R100-120
Poly(vinyl chloride)	7-25	3-4	10^{11}-10^{15}	5-9	300-1000	0.08-0.15	...	0.15-0.75	...
Poly(vinylidene chloride)(rigid)	7-8	...	...	...	...	...	...	0.11	R118
Chlorinated polyether	8	3.13	1.5×10^{16}	3	400	0.01	...	0.01	R100
Poly(chlorotri-fluoroethylene)	7	6	10^{18}	2.65	450	0.015	>360	nil	R85-112
Fluorinated poly(ethylene-co-propylene) FEP-resins	8.3-10.5	5.9	>10^{18}	2.1	500	0.0002	>165	<0.01	...

Resin Material	Coefficient Thermal Expansion (in/°C x 10^5)	Thermal Conductivity (cal/cm^2/sec/°C/cm x 10^4)	Volume Resistivity (ohm-cm)	Dielectric Constant (60 cycles)	Dielectric Strength, ST 1/8" thickness (volts/mil)	Power Factor (60 cycles)	Arc Resistance (sec.)	Water Absorption 24 hrs. (%)	Rockwell Hardness
Poly(tetra-fluoroethylene)	5.5(25-60°C)	6	10^{18}	2.1	400	0.0002	>200	0.01	R58
Nylon 66	10	5.8	4.5×10^{12}	3.9-7.6	300-400	0.01-0.09	140	1.5	R108-118
Nylon 6	8.3	5.9	3.3^{13}-4.5^{13}	6.1	300-400	0.1-0.6	140	1.5	R107-119
Acetal resins	8.1-8.5	1.6-5.5	1-10^{13}	3.7-3.8	500	0.004-0.005	129	0.12-0.25	M94,R120
Polycarbonate resins	7	4.6	1.7×10^7	3.17	400	0.0009	10-11	0.15	M78,R118
Polyurethan resins	10-20	5	2×10^{11}	6.7-7.5	450-550	0.050-0.060	...	0.60-0.80	M28-R60
Cellulose acetate	8-16	4-8	10^{10}-10^{12}	3.5-7.5	290-600	0.01-0.06	50-310	2.1-4.2	R35-118
Cellulose acetate butyrate	11-17	4.8	10^{10}-10^{12}	3.5-6.4	250-400	0.01-0.04	...	0.9-2.2	R31-116
Cellulose propionate	11-16	4-8	10^{10}-10^{16}	3.4-4.2	300-450	0.01-0.04	170-190	1.2-2.8	R15-R120
Ethyl cellulose	10-20	3.8-7	...	...	...	...	...	1.3-1.5	R50-110

Resin Material	Flammability (in/min)	Specific Gravity	Mold Shrinkage (in/in)	Clarity	Average Minimum Price per lb. (Jan. 1965)	Representative Trade Names
Polyethylene low density	slow burning	0.90-0.925	0.02-0.04	transparent to opaque	$0.205	Alathon(9), Bakelite(32),Dylan(21), Petrothene(30),Catalin(5), Terite(11), Marlex(26), Poly-eth(29), Monsanto(25),Dow(10), Fortiflex(6), Grace(17)
Polyethylene medium density	slow burning	C.926-0.940	0.02-0.04	transparent to opaque	$0.215	Tenite(11), Dylan(21), Marlex(26), Po-yeth(29), Petrothene(30),Dow(10), Fortiflex(6), Grace(17), Bakelite(32), Alathon(9), Monsanto(25)
Polyethylene high density	slow burning	0.94-0.98	0.02-0.04	translucent to opaque	$0.265	Super Dylan(21), Marlex(26), Fortiflex(6), Petrothene(30), Hi-Fax(20), Catalin(5), Grex(17), Bakelite(32), Tenite(11),Dow(10), Alathon(9), Monsanto(25)
Polypropylene	slow burning	0.90-0.908	0.01-0.03	translucent to opaque	$0.30	Moplen(7), Profax(19), Catalin(5), Polypro(29), Escon(12), Tenite(11), Avisun(4),Dow(10), Pro-Fax(20), Olemer(4), Marlex(26)
Acrylic resins	0.5-1.1	1.18-1.19	0.002-0.006	transparent	$0.505	Lucite(9), Plexiglas(27), Acrylite(3)
High impact acrylic resins	0.8-1.2	1.08-1.18	0.004-0.008	semi-transparent to opaque	$0.46	Implex(27)
Polystyrene	0.5-2.5	1.05-1.06	0.002-0.006	transparent	$0.145	Styron(10), Lustrex(23), Bakelite(32), Dylene(21), Solar (23), Catalin(5), Fostarene(15), Cosden(8), Grace(17)
Polystyrene high impact resins	0.5-2.5	1.04-1.06	0.003-0.005	translucent to opaque	$0.222	Lustrex(25), Bakelite(32), Dylene(21), Styron(10), Solar (28), Catalin(5), Grace(17), Marbon(22), Fosta Tuflex(15)
Poly(styrene-co acrylonitrile)	0.4-0.7	1.07-1.08	0.003-0.004	transparent	$0.30	Tyril(10, Bakelite(32), Catalin(5), Lustran A(25),Kralac(31)
Polystyrene A.B.S. resins	1.0-2	1.01-1.07	0.003-C.007	opaque	$0.335	Kralastic(31), Abson(18), Cycolac(22), Lustran(25)

Resin Material	Flammability	Specific Gravity	Mold Shrinkage	Clarity	Average Minimum Price per lb. (Jan. 1965)	Representative Trade Names
Poly(vinyl chloride) rigid	self exting.	1.36-1.58	...	transparent	$0.16	Exon(14), Geon(18), Dow(10), Marvinol(31), Vipla(7), Bakelite(32), Opalon(25), Escambia (13), Pliovic(19), Vyram(25)
Poly(vinyl chloride)	self-exting.	1.15-1.80	0.002	transparent to opaque	$0.175	Pliovic(19), Escambia(13), Ultron(25), Geon(18), Exon(14)
Poly(vinylidene chloride)(rigid)	self-exting.	1.50-1.54	...	transparent to opaque	$0.50	Hi-Temp Geon(18)
Chlorinated polyether	self-exting.	1.4	0.004-0.006	semi-translucent to opaque	$2.50	Penton(20)
Poly(chlorotri-fluoroethylene)	nil	2.11-2.14	0.005-0.010	transparent to opaque	$6.50	Kel-F(22), Polyfluoron(1)
Fluorinated poly-(ethylene-co-pro-pylene)FEP-resins	non-flam.	2.14	0.03	transparent to opaque	$9.60	Teflon 100(9)
Poly(tetra-fluoroethylene)	non-flam.	2.13	0.06	transparent to opaque	$3.25	Teflon(9)
Nylon 66	self-exting.	1.13-1.15	<0.015	translucent to opaque	$0.98	Zytel(9), Catalin(5)
Nylon 6	self-exting.	1.13-1.14	0.007-0.011	transparent to opaque	$0.92	Fosta(15), Spencer(29), Plaskon(2), Catalin(5), Zytel (9), Firestone(14)
Acetal resins	1.1	1.410-1.425	0.20	translucent to opaque	$0.65	Delrin(9), Celcon(6)
Polycarbonate resins	self-exting.	1.2	0.005-0.007	transparent	$1.175	Lexan(16), Merlon(24)
Polyurethan resins	slow burning	1.20-1.26	0.008-0.009	translucent to opaque	$1.40	Estane(18), Texin(24)
Cellulose acetate	0.5-2	1.23-1.34	0.001-0.007	transparent	$0.40	Tenite(11), Celanese(6), Vuepak(25)
Cellulose acetate butyrate	0.5-1.5	1.15-1.22	0.001-0.005	transparent	$0.62	Tenite(11)
Cellulose propionate	1.16-1.23	0.001-0.003		transparent	$0.62	Tenite(11), Forticel(6),
Ethyl cellulose	1.11-1.13	...		transparent to opaque	$0.67	Ethocel(10)

Material Manufacturers:

1. Acme Resin Corp., 2. Allied Chemical Corp., 3. American Cyanamid Co., 4. Avisun Corp., 5. Catalin Corp., 6. Celanese Polymer Corp., 7. Chemore Corp., 8. Cosden Petroleum Corp., 9. E. I. duPont de Nemours & Co., 10. Dow Chemical Co., 11. Eastman Chemical Products, 12. Enjay Chemical Co., 13. Escambia Chemical Corp., 14. Firestone Plastics Co., 15. Foster Grant Co., 16. General Electric Co., Chemical Materials Dept., 17. W. R. Grace & Co., 18. B. F. Goodrich Chemical Co., 19. Goodyear Tire & Rubber Co., 20. Hercules Powder Co., 21. Koppers Co., Inc., 22. Marbon Chemical Div., Borg-Warner Corp., 23. Minnesota Mining & Mfg. Co., 24. Mobay Chemical Co., 25. Monsanto Co., 26. Phillips Petroleum Co., 27. Rohm & Haas Co., 28. Solar Chemical Corp., 29. Spencer Chemical Co., 30. U. S. Industrial Chemicals Co., 31. U. S. Rubber Co., Naugatuck Chemical Div., 32. Union Carbide Plastics Co.

SUBJECT INDEX

This index only contains physical constants of polymers, while the names of polymers may be found in the table of the corresponding constant. Often polymers of Section VI are individually listed in this index. The page numbers given for them do not represent the only place of reference. Additional data for these polymers may be found in the appropriate table section of the particular constant concerned.

A

B

C

D

G

H

I

N

O

P

Q

R

S

W

X

Y

Z

Polymer	Solvent	T°C	$s_o \times 10^{13}$	k_s	$D_o \times 10^7$	k_D	f/f_o	$\bar{v}_2$	$M \times 10^{-4}$	Remarks	Ref.
Myosin (Cont'd.) crystallized	phosphate buffer pH 7.6 & 7.0		7.2								256
Notatin (from penicillium notatum)	phosphate buffer pH 5.6	20	7.91		5.56		1.11	0.75	13.8	a;	51
					5.10						46
					5.13						47
Ovalbumin crystalline	water	25						0.7479			161
	acetate buffer pH 4.7	20			7.67				3.45	c=4 g/1	158
	pH 4.57				7.76					D_σ	67
4x recrystallized	pH 4.4		3.55		7.76			0.749	4.38	s_t; D_σ; $M_{t,w}$ c=1.3 g/1	168
			3.54							c=1.3 g/1	38
Pepsin	acetate buffer pH 4.6	20			8.81					D_σ; different buffers and conditions given in ref.; c=5 g/1	67
r-Phycocyan	different buffers	20	11.3						20.9		113
c-Phycocyan			11.5						20.8		
Phycocyan from geranium rubrum	different buffers	20	11.4		4.05				27.2	s_t; $M_{t,D}$	157, 158
			6.2		4.58				13.1		
	acetate buffer pH 5.4	20	1.5		4.15			0.75	26.9	D_σ; c=2.0 g/1	67
	pH 7.5		6.2		4.58			0.75	13.1		
Phycoerythrin	phosphate buffer	20	12.0		4.06			0.75	28.6	D_σ; c=4 g/1	67
different sources	different buffers		11.3-12.4						19.6	s_t; $M_{t,D}$	113
			12		4-6						157, 158
Pomelin from orange seed	buffer, see ref.	20	2.2							component 1	77
			11.38							2	
			16.75							3	